P9-DWU-858

Neil Jespersen
Department of Chemistry
University of Texas

D. O. Jones
David O. Jones Company
Chelan, Washington

Charles H. Lochmüller
Department of Chemistry
Duke University

J. West Loveland
Applied Physics Laboratory
Sun Oil Company

Ronald E. Majors
Instrument Division
Varian

Harry B. Mark, Jr.
Department of Chemistry
University of Cincinnati

S. P. Perone
Department of Chemistry
Purdue University

J. W. Prather II
Department of Chemistry
University of Missouri—Kansas City

George H. Schenk
Department of Chemistry
Wayne State University

S. Sternhell
Department of Organic Chemistry
University of Sydney

John R. Wasson
Department of Chemistry
University of North Carolina

Lo I Yin
Astrochemistry Branch
Laboratory for Extraterrestrial Physics
NASA Goddard Space Flight Center

Instrumental Analysis

This book is part of

The Allyn and Bacon Chemistry Series

and was developed under the co-consulting editorship of

DARYLE H. BUSCH AND HARRISON SHULL

Instrumental Analysis

Editors	HENRY H. BAUER *University of Kentucky*
	GARY D. CHRISTIAN *University of Washington*
	JAMES E. O'REILLY *University of Kentucky*

Allyn and Bacon, Inc.
Boston,   London,   Sydney,   Toronto

Copyright © 1978 by Allyn and Bacon, Inc.
470 Atlantic Avenue, Boston, Massachusetts 02210.
All rights reserved. Printed in the United States of America.
No part of the material protected by this copyright notice
may be reproduced or utilized in any form or by any means,
electronic or mechanical, including photocopying, recording,
or by any information storage and retrieval system, without
written permission from the copyright owner.

Library of Congress Cataloging in Publication Data

Main entry under title:
Instrumental analysis.

    (Allyn and Bacon chemistry series)
    Includes index.
    1. Instrumental analysis. I. Bauer, Henry H.
II. Christian, Gary D. III. O'Reilly, James E., 1945–
QD79.I5I5   543'.08   77-12051

ISBN 0-205-05922-8

ISBN 0-205-06556-2 (*International*)

Printing number and year (last digits):
10 9 8 7 6 5 4   85 84 83 82 81 80

Contents

Preface

The editors embarked on the venture of editing a textbook dealing with instrumental methods in chemical analysis for several reasons. None of the available texts seemed to us to be as well suited to the types of courses generally given in this area as we would like: coverage of the various types of techniques was uneven in depth, emphasis, and modernity; and in particular there seemed to be insufficient attention to applications of the techniques in practice. We felt that these shortcomings might be minimized if we could have each method discussed by people active in that particular field.

The individual authors were asked to make the theoretical background of each method as brief and qualitative as possible consistent with clarity and accuracy, to limit discussion of instrumentation to general principles as far as possible (i.e., no details of the operation of commercially available apparatus), and to emphasize the utility and actual applications of each method.

Some cynics, particularly in academia, maintain that the last thing ever successfully accomplished by committee was the King James version of the Bible. In a sense, this text has also been composed by a committee. As editors, we have tried to keep the depth of presentation more or less even, consistent with our feelings as to the importance of a particular method for quantitative applications; and to provide the continuity of thought and mode of expression so important in a text. We happily allot to the authors whatever credit may accrue for the quality of the individual parts and, as editors, assume responsibility for the shortcomings of the whole.

We thank the authors for their efforts, for the quality of their presentations, for their patience with the various changes and requests made during several drafts of the manuscript, and in particular for their benign attitude to the liberties we have taken with their style and mode of expression.

It is appropriate at this point to elaborate a few of the things we have chosen to do and not do. We have chosen to concentrate particularly on those applications and methods that are, in our opinion, most useful for quantitative analytical measurements—not because these are intrinsically more important than measurements that are more physically oriented, but simply because of the limitations of space. Thus, for example, we have no discussion of optical rotatory dispersion, certainly an important instrumental technique, because it presently has no practical usage as a quantitative method.

The text does not have a description of basic and advanced electronics, except for some discussion of digital electronics in the chapter on computers. There are perhaps two distinct approaches to instrumental analysis: one is in terms of *instrumentation* and instrument design, the second in terms of *instrumental methods* of analysis. We have chosen the latter approach because, first, we believe this to be the more profitable approach for the majority of students in a course of this nature, and second, because there is simply too much material in modern scientific electronics and instrumental methods to cover both comfortably in one semester and do justice to either. There are several excellent texts devoted to scientific electronics and several packages of electronics experiments on the market today; and many universities and colleges now offer separate courses in this area. We have chosen to leave the subject of electronics to these, and to the discretion of the individual instructor.

We have also not included an accompanying set of laboratory experiments. There are several excellent compendia of instrumental analysis experiments available, and a number of quantitative analytical experiments, particularly those involving analysis of "real" samples, appear in the *Journal of Chemical Education* monthly. Moreover, because of the cost and complexity of modern instrumentation, many instructors face a very limited array of instruments, and are forced to drastically redesign experiments for their particular instrument or model anyway. We have chosen to leave the instrumental laboratory to the ingenuity of the individual instructor.

A number of people have helped us in various ways, and we wish to thank them all, while mentioning specifically only a few—Petr Zuman for sharing with us his unmatched experience in the practice of polarographic techniques; Stan Smith for a complete set of NMR problems; Regina Palomo and Ellen Swank for patiently typing, retyping, and reretyping the entire manuscript; and our colleagues for putting up with us through the entire production stage. One of us (JEO) makes Acknowledgement to the Donors of The Petroleum Research Fund, administered by the American Chemical Society, for partial support of this research.

We genuinely hope that instructors will find this book a useful pedagogical aid, and we would appreciate comments concerning shortcomings and errors that we could attempt to rectify should there be the occasion for a later edition.

It is our fondest hope that students will read this text, and feel good about it. We have tried to express things as though we were talking to students, and not with an eye toward impressing an instructor with the depth of coverage or sophistication of the discussion. We hope that, at the end of a semester, the student can emerge with an idea of what the various instrumental methods are capable of doing in order to solve a problem or make a measurement. We hope to impart the overview of the true analytical chemist—selecting the right tool for the job at hand. Perhaps this can be expressed with a quotation from the Bible:

> *Thou shalt not have in thine bag divers weights, a great and a small.*
> *Thou shalt not have in thine house divers measures, a great and a small. But*
> *thou shalt have a perfect and just weight, a perfect and just measure shalt*
> *thou have . . .*
>
> —DEUTERONOMY 25: 13–15

Instrumental Analysis

1

Introduction to Electrochemical Methods

HENRY H. BAUER
JAMES E. O'REILLY

Electrochemistry is a scientific discipline with a well developed system of theories and quantitative relationships. It has many applications and uses in both fundamental and applied areas of chemistry—in the study of corrosion phenomena, for example, for the study of the mechanisms and kinetics of electrochemical reactions, as a tool for the electrosynthesis of organic and inorganic compounds, and in the solution of quantitative analytical problems. This last area will be emphasized in the next four chapters.

1.1 GENERALITIES OF ELECTROCHEMICAL METHODS

It can be said with some degree of accuracy that, with the exception of the nearly universal use of the potentiometric pH-meter, electrochemical methods in general are not as widely used as are spectrochemical or chromatographic methods for quantitative analytical applications. A recent informal readers' survey conducted by *Research/Development* [1] indicated that about 75% of the laboratories responding used pH meters, ranking them approximately fifth in usage behind analytical balances, hot plates, fume hoods, and laboratory ovens. Yet where about half of the respondents used visible, ultraviolet, and infrared spectrophotometers and about 30% used atomic absorption spectrophotometers, only about 12% used what were termed polarographic analyzers and 30% used ion-selective electrodes. In general, there is a more widespread usage of electrochemical methods in Europe and Japan than in the United States.

There are probably several reasons why electrochemical methods are not as "popular" as chromatographic or optical methods. One is that electrochemistry and electrochemical methods are not emphasized in typical college curricula. One can cite the nearly universal disappearance of fundamental electrochemistry from beginning general and physical-chemistry courses, whereas the interaction of electromagnetic radiation with matter and the energy levels concerned is covered in many first-year courses. Electrochemical theory is really no more complex or abstruse, but probably not so well unified at present, as spectrochemical theory.

A second reason is that spectrochemical methods appear somewhat more amenable to automation or mechanization than electrochemical methods. An extreme example of this can be seen in the clinical analysis laboratory. In 1971, for instance, one particular hospital performed nearly a half-million chemical tests, 91% of which were done with spectrochemical methods and instruments [2]. This, of course, was due to its use of automated clinical analyzers, which are primarily optical in approach.

There are, however, many times when electrochemical methods can provide essentially the same information as other methods, thus offering an alternative approach, and other times when only electrochemistry will provide the answer or will provide the best answer to the problem at hand.

Advantages of Electrochemical Methods

Although it is very difficult to consider electrochemical methods *in general* versus other methods *in general*, electrochemical methods do have certain advantages. First of all, electrochemical instrumentation is comparatively inexpensive. The most expensive piece of routine electrochemical instrumentation costs about $15,000, with most commercial instrumentation under about $3000. By contrast, some sophisticated nonelectrochemical equipment, such as nuclear-magnetic-resonance or mass spectrometers, may run over a quarter of a million dollars.

Secondly, elemental electrochemical analysis is generally *specific for a particular chemical form* of an element. For example, with a mixture of Fe^{2+} and Fe^{3+}, electrochemical analysis can reveal the amount of each form present, where most elemental spectrochemical or radiochemical methods simply give the total amount of iron present almost regardless of its chemical form. Depending on the analytical problem at hand or the question to be answered, one particular method may be "better." For example, mercury is a serious environmental pollutant. Elemental or inorganic forms of mercury [Hg^0, Hg^{2+}, Hg_2Cl_2, $\cdots$] are bad, but organic mercury [CH_3Hg^+, $(CH_3)_2Hg$, $\cdots$] is much worse. Perhaps, in a given situation, it is important to know both the total mercury level and the forms it takes.

Another advantage (or disadvantage, depending on the problem at hand) of many electrochemical methods is that they respond to the *activity* of a chemical species rather than to the *concentration*. An example where this may be of importance is the calcium level in serum. Ion-selective electrodes respond to free, aquated Ca^{2+} ions, whereas the usual clinical method for serum calcium is flame photometry, which measures the total calcium present including a large amount tied up as protein-bound calcium. The more important physiological parameter, the measure of the *effective* level of calcium actually available for participation in various enzymatic reactions, may be the free Ca^{2+} level. For another example, lead is a cumulatively toxic substance; plants grown in lead-laden soils can accumulate high levels of lead. If these plants are then eaten by humans, toxic levels of lead may be reached. Lead in heavy clay soils is, however, much less available for absorption by plants than is lead in more sandy soil. Perhaps the more useful measure of the arability of trace-metal-contaminated land is the metal-ion activity, rather than the total metal concentration.

It can be safely said that in recent years there has been a renaissance of interest in quantitative electrochemical methods. This has been brought about primarily by two factors: the development of ion-selective potentiometric electrodes, which can quantitatively monitor most of the common ionic species in solution (Chap. 2); and the introduction of a new generation of inexpensive commercial voltammetric instrumentation based on pulse methods (Chap. 3), which has increased the sensitivity of electrochemical methods by several orders of magnitude.

Classification of Electrochemical Methods

For the present purpose, an electrochemical method can be defined as one in which the electrical response of a chemical system or sample is measured. The experimental system can be divided as follows: the electrolyte, a chemical system capable of conducting current; the measuring or external circuit, used to apply and to measure electrical signals (currents, voltages); and the electrodes, conductors that serve as contacts between the measuring system and the electrolyte.

Electrodes are classed as *anodes* and *cathodes*. At the anode, *oxidation* occurs—electrons are abstracted from the electrolyte and pass into the measuring circuit; at the cathode, *reduction* occurs—electrons flow from the cathode into the electrolyte. Furthermore, one speaks of *working* or *indicator electrodes*—those at which a reaction being studied is taking place; of *reference electrodes*, which maintain a constant potential irrespective of changes in current; and of *counter electrodes*, which serve to allow current to flow through the electrolyte but whose characteristics do not influence the measured behavior—the latter depends on what happens at the working electrode.

When current flows in an electrochemical system, the current is determined by the total resistance of the whole circuit. Good experimental design ensures that the magnitude of the current is not influenced by the measuring circuit. That done, one can distinguish two types of methods: those in which the resistance of the electrodes is made negligible, so that one measures the conductance of the electrolyte (see Chap. 5); and those in which the resistance of the electrolyte is made negligible, and one studies phenomena occurring at the electrodes (Chaps. 3 and 4).

A multitude of electrochemical techniques based on electrode processes exist; however, only a comparatively small number are of real importance to the analytical chemist. Some of the chief features of these techniques are shown in Table 1.1.

Electrochemical methods can be divided into two classes: those involving no net current flow ("potentiometric"), and all others. In potentiometry, one measures the equilibrium thermodynamic potential of a system essentially without causing electrolysis or current drain on the system—because this would affect the existing equilibrium. In all other methods, a voltage or current is applied to an electrode

TABLE 1.1. *Analytically Useful Electrochemical Techniques*

Technique	Controlled Electrical Variable	Response Measured	Relative Time-Scale for Analysis
Potentiometry	$i(=0)$	E	short
Potentiometric titration	$i(=0)$	E vs. volume of reagent	long
Voltammetry	E	i vs. E	
Polarography	↓	↓	medium
Linear-sweep or cyclic voltammetry			short
Pulse methods			medium
Stripping analysis	E	i vs. E	medium
Electrogravimetry	i or E	weight of deposit	long
Coulometry	i or E	charge consumed (integrated current)	long
Coulometric titration	i	time	medium
Conductivity	V (AC)	i (AC)	short

and the resultant current flow through, or voltage change of, the system is monitored. The applied waveform is often quite complex. Although this approach may be more complicated than is the case in potentiometry, there are advantages in that we are not forced to deal with the particular equilibrium characteristics of the system. By forcing the system to respond electrochemically to a stimulus, we can gain a good deal of analytical control over it.

1.2 ELECTROCHEMICAL DEFINITIONS AND TERMINOLOGY

As in all other disciplines, electrochemistry has its own terminology with which one needs to be familiar before studying specific electrochemical methods.

Faradaic and Nonfaradaic Processes

$$\oint E \, dl = \frac{d\phi_s}{dt}$$

Two types of processes occur at electrodes. One kind includes those in which charge (e.g., electrons) is transferred across the electrode-solution interface. In these processes, actual *oxidation or reduction occurs*; they are governed by Faraday's laws, and are called *faradaic* processes.

Under some conditions an electrode may be in a potential region where charge-transfer reactions do not occur because they are either thermodynamically or kinetically unfavorable. However, such processes as adsorption can occur, and the structure of the electrode-solution interface can change, causing transitory changes in current and/or potential. These processes are called *nonfaradaic* processes.

Charging Current. An important example of a nonfaradaic process is that of the *charging* of an electrode (see Fig. 1.1). At some potential E_A (Fig. 1.1A) there is a

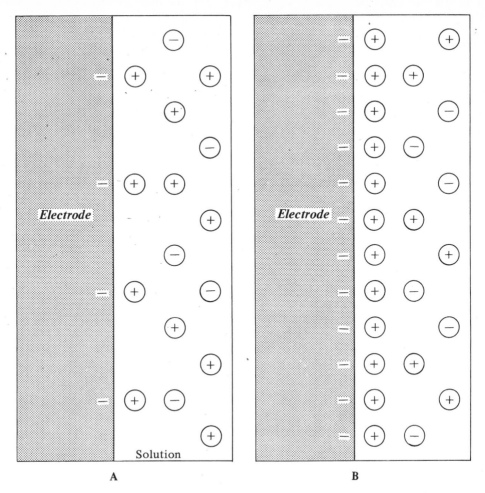

FIGURE 1.1. *Arrangement of charge at the electrode-solution interface. In case B, the electrode is at a more negative potential than in A; hence the greater amount of negative charge at the electrode surface in B.*

certain charge per unit area in the metal electrode, with an equal amount of charge of opposite sign present in the solution immediately adjacent to the electrode (forming what is called the *electrical double-layer*). If the potential is now changed to E_B, where the charge per unit area is greater, current must flow to bring these extra charges to the interface. This is the *charging current*, and it is a transient current, flowing only until the new charge equilibrium is attained. Then the current stops, since there is no mechanism to cause current to flow *across* the interface, in the absence of redox reactions. So the charging process is nonfaradaic, and the charging current is a nonfaradaic current.

An electrode at which no charge-transfer occurs across the electrode-solution interface, regardless of the potential imposed from an outside source of voltage, is called an *ideally polarized electrode*. No real electrode, of course, can behave in this manner at all potentials; but certain systems approach this behavior over a limited range of potentials. For example, a mercury electrode in contact with a (deoxygenated) NaCl solution acts as an ideally polarized electrode over a range of nearly 2 volts. The two *faradaic* processes that can occur—the reduction of Na^+ to sodium amalgam, and the oxidation of the electrode to Hg_2Cl_2—occur at potentials that differ by about 2 volts.

Only nonfaradaic processes occur at an ideally polarized electrode.

Capacitance of an Electrode. Since charge cannot cross the interface at an ideally polarized electrode when the potential is changed, the behavior of this interface is similar to that of a capacitor (Fig. 1.1). When a potential is applied across a capacitor, it will charge until it satisfies the relation

$$C = q/V \qquad (1.1)$$

where C = the capacitance in farads
          q = the charge in coulombs
          V = the voltage across the capacitor in volts

The time during which the charging or condenser current flows is directly proportional to the capacity of the electrode and the resistance of the solution; for electrodes of constant area immersed in solutions of fairly low resistance, the time during which the charging current is appreciable is very short, small fractions of a second. With electrodes whose area expands with time, e.g., at the dropping mercury electrode, the charging current dies down more slowly—it is essentially proportional to the rate of exposure of fresh surface. In terms of analytical applications, the charging current is often a distinct liability, as it often is the limiting factor in the sensitivity of an electrochemical method. One must use special techniques to distinguish between the current flow due to charging of the double layer and the current flow due to the faradaic reactions of the substance of interest. In general, this is done by using the fact that charging current decreases rapidly with time, whereas faradaic current changes with time much more slowly in typical experiments.

Faradaic Processes. Consider an ideally polarized electrode; only nonfaradaic processes occur, no charges cross the interface, and no continuous current can flow. Upon addition of a substance that can be oxidized or reduced at the particular potential difference, current now flows—the electrode is *depolarized*, and the substance responsible is called a *depolarizer*.

The faradaic process may proceed at various rates, within a wide range of possible rates. If the process is so rapid that the oxidized and reduced species are in equilibrium, then the reaction is termed *reversible* and the Nernst equation (1.3) applies.

Reversibility, so defined, actually depends on the relative rates of the electrode process and of the rapidity of the electrochemical measurement: a particular system may behave reversibly when measurements are made slowly, but irreversibly if the measurement involves short times (pulses of current or voltage, or high frequencies of an alternating electrical signal). Consequently, in modern usage, one prefers to talk about electrode processes as *being* fast or slow, and as *behaving* reversibly or irreversibly (rather than the classical usage in which systems were talked of as *being* reversible or irreversible).

Once faradaic current flows, the equilibrium between oxidized and reduced species is disturbed, and can be continually reestablished only if all the steps involved in the electrode process are rapid enough. (These steps include charge transfer, movement of depolarizer to the electrode and of product away from it (mass transport), and possibly adsorption or chemical reactions.) If there is a lag, then the electrode potential changes from its equilibrium value, the magnitude of the change being the *overpotential* or *overvoltage*.

Most systems can show overvoltages; i.e., they can become *polarized*. At a polarized electrode, current flows—but the magnitude of the current is less than if the system were behaving reversibly. The current is limited by the rate of one (or more) of the steps in the electrode process. If charge transfer is the slow (limiting) step, the effect is called *activation polarization*; if slow movement of depolarizer or product is responsible, one speaks of *concentration polarization*.

If the electrode process were infinitely fast, then current could be drawn without producing an overvoltage; this would be a *nonpolarizable electrode*. In practice, there are some electrode systems that permit appreciable currents to flow with negligible overpotentials, and such systems are used in reference electrodes.

Sign Conventions and the Nernst Equation

The sign conventions of electrochemistry have caused students and researchers a great deal of difficulty and misunderstanding over the years. All electrochemical cells are considered as a combination of two half-cells—one for the reduction reaction, one for the oxidation reaction. To have current flow in *any* electrochemical system, both an oxidation and a reduction reaction must occur; electrons must have someplace to go, they simply do not appear and disappear.

Any half-cell reaction can be written as either an oxidation or a reduction; by convention, they are written as reductions.

$$\text{Ox} + ne^- \;\rightleftharpoons\; \text{Red} \tag{1.2}$$

where Ox = general symbol for the *ox*idized form of the balanced half-reaction
Red = general symbol for the *red*uced form of the balanced half-reaction
n = the number of electrons involved in the half-reaction.

By use of a table of electromotive forces or standard reduction potentials (E^0 values) for half-reactions, the potential of each half-cell can be calculated by means of the Nernst equation

$$E = E^0 - \frac{RT}{nF} \ln \frac{(\text{Red})}{(\text{Ox})} \tag{1.3}$$

where R = the molar gas constant (8.314 J/mole-K)
T = the absolute temperature in K
F = the faraday constant (96,487 coulombs/mole)
(Red) = *activity* of the reduced chemical species
(Ox) = *activity* of the oxidized chemical species

If the ln term is converted to $\log_{10}$ basis, the value of the constant term 2.303 RT/nF becomes $0.05916/n$ V at 25°C. The logarithmic term (Red)/(Ox) is simply the thermodynamic equilibrium expression for the electrochemical reaction, *written as a reduction*, and will be affected by changes in concentration of the various chemical species in the same manner as any other equilibrium expression. Further details on the Nernst equation and its use are contained in Chapter 2.

Modes of Electrochemical Mass Transport

In general, chemical species are transported in solution by one or more, conceptually distinct, processes: *migration*, *convection*, and *diffusion*.

Migration. Electrical migration is the movement of charged substances in an *electrical gradient*, a result of the force exerted on charged particles by an electric field; this can be viewed as a result of simple coulombic attraction of, for example, a positively charged ion to a negatively charged electrode surface or, alternatively, repulsion from a positively charged electrode. In almost all electrochemical methods of analysis, migration effects serve no useful purpose; they are usually swamped out by the addition of a relatively large amount (perhaps 0.1 or 1 M) of "background" (or "inert" or "indifferent") electrolyte such as KCl or HNO_3. Current can then flow as a result of migration of, for instance, K^+ or Cl^- ions, with negligible migration of the electroactive species, which then moves as a result of concentration differences only (diffusion, see below).

Convection. Convection means, essentially, the mass transport of electroactive material to the electrode by *gross physical movement*—fluid or hydrodynamic flow—of the solution. Generally, fluid flow occurs because of natural convection (caused by density gradients) or forced convection (usually caused by *stirring* of some sort).

Diffusion. Mass transfer by diffusion is the natural transport or movement of a substance under the influence of a *gradient of chemical potential*, that is, due to the *concentration gradient*; substances move from regions of high concentration to regions of low concentration in order to minimize or eliminate concentration differences. Diffusion is perhaps the most widely studied means of mass transport.

The rate of diffusion is given by

$$\text{Rate} = D \frac{dc}{dx} \tag{1.4}$$

where D = the *diffusion coefficient* (in cm^2/sec) of the substance
dc/dx = the concentration gradient

This expression is often approximated by

$$D \frac{\Delta c}{\delta} \tag{1.5}$$

where Δc = the difference in concentration across the region where diffusion occurs (the *diffusion layer*)
δ = the thickness of the diffusion layer (Fig. 1.2)

The diffusion coefficient, D, is a constant for a given substance under a specified set of solution conditions (temperature, electrolyte nature, and concentration). Since a concentration gradient is established as soon as any electrolysis is begun, diffusion is a part of every practical electrode reaction.

Faradaic current reflects the rate of the electrode process. If the latter is a

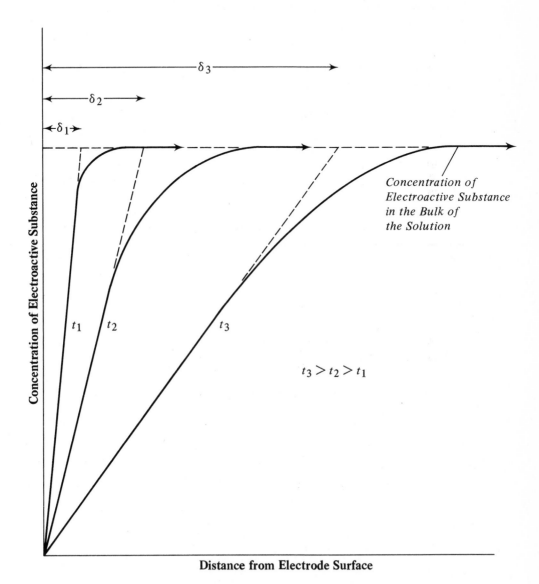

FIGURE 1.2. *Concentration-distance profiles for diffusion of an electroactive substance to an electrode surface at different times. At zero time, a voltage large enough to cause the electrode reaction to occur is suddenly applied to the electrode. Note that with increasing time ($t_3 > t_2 > t_1$), the* concentration gradient—*the slope of the concentration-distance curve—becomes less steep, and the diffusion layer thickness, δ, becomes larger.*

multi-step reaction, then each step has its own inherent rate and the faradaic current reflects the rate of the slowest process in the sequence of steps. That might be an adsorption process, or some chemical reaction in solution involving the oxidant or the reductant, or the charge-transfer process itself, or the rate at which the electroactive species diffuses to the electrode from the bulk of the solution. When a supporting electrolyte is present, in the simplest cases, the movement of the electroactive species is limited by diffusion; therefore, the solution of the equations governing diffusion is relevant to many electrochemical techniques.

Consider an electrode of fixed area immersed in a solution containing an electroactive species and a supporting electrolyte. Initially, the composition of the solution is uniform throughout. When a potential large enough to cause a faradaic reaction to occur is applied, those particles of the electroactive species in the immediate vicinity of the electrode undergo reaction. Then the rate of the reaction, and consequently the magnitude of the current, depends on the rate at which the electroactive species diffuses to the electrode surface. The concentration gradient is steep at first, and the layer of depleted solution (the diffusion layer δ) is thin (see Fig. 1.2); as time goes by, the thickness of the diffusion layer increases, the concentration gradient becomes less steep, and the rate of diffusion decreases. As a result, a large current flows when the potential is first applied, and then the magnitude of the current decreases with time. Solution of the equations for diffusion leads to the relation

$$i(t) = \frac{nFAD^{1/2}c}{\pi^{1/2}t^{1/2}} \tag{1.6}$$

where $i(t)$ = current at time t
  n = number of electrons involved in the electrochemical process
  A = area of the electrode
  c = the concentration of the electroactive species

That is to say, the current decreases in proportion to the square root of time from the instant at which electrolysis starts.

We can now proceed, in the following chapters, to consider details of the analytical applications of four classes of electrochemical techniques: in Chapter 2, measurements of electrode potentials in the absence of current flow; in Chapter 3, measurements of current flow as potential is varied; in Chapter 4, measurements of the amount of charge required for complete electrolysis (or deposition) of the substance concerned; and in Chapter 5, measurements of the conductances of solutions under conditions where processes at the electrodes themselves are not of concern.

SELECTED BIBLIOGRAPHY

BAUER, H. H. *Electronics: Modern Ideas Concerning Electrode Reactions.* Stuttgart: Thieme, 1972.

BOCKRIS, J. O'M., and REDDY, A. K. N. *Modern Electrochemistry*, vols. 1 and 2. New York: Plenum Press, 1970. *A* thorough treatment of electrochemical fundamentals.

MURRAY, R. W., and REILLEY, C. N. In *Treatise on Analytical Chemistry*, I. M. Kolthoff and P. J. Elving, eds., part I, vol. 4. New York: John Wiley, 1963, pp 2109–

2232. *Fundamentals of electrode processes and introduction to electrochemical techniques.*

SAWYER, D. T., and ROBERTS, J. L., JR. *Experimental Electrochemistry for Chemists.* New York: John Wiley, 1974. *A good introduction to the more popular electrochemical methods; details of cell constructions, instrumentation, purification of solvents and electrolytes.*

REFERENCES

1. "Trends in Analytical Instruments and Equipment," *Res./Dev.*, *26*(*2*), 20 (1975).
2. G. N. BOWERS, JR., in *Analytical Chemistry: Key to Progress on National Problems,* W. W. Meinke and J. K. Taylor, eds., NBS Special Publication 351, U.S. Government Printing Office, Washington, D.C., 1972, pp 77–157.

2

Potentiometry

James E. O'Reilly

Potentiometry—the measurement of electric potentials in electrochemical cells—is probably one of the oldest methods of chemical analysis still in wide use. The early, essentially qualitative, work of Luigi Galvani (1737–1798) and Count Alessandro Volta (1745–1827) had its first fruit in the work of J. Willard Gibbs (1839–1903) and Walther Nernst (1864–1941), who laid the foundations for the treatment of electro-chemical equilibria and electrode potentials. The early analytical applications of potentiometry were essentially to detect the endpoints of titrations. More extensive use of direct potentiometric methods came after Haber developed the glass electrode for pH measurements in 1909. In recent years, several new classes of ion-selective sensors have been introduced, beginning with glass electrodes more or less selectively responsive to other univalent cations (Na^+, NH_4^+, etc.). Now, solid-state crystalline electrodes for ions such as F^-, Ag^+, and sulfide, and liquid ion-exchange membrane electrodes responsive to many simple and complex ions—Ca^{2+}, BF_4^-, ClO_4^-—provide the chemist with electrochemical probes responsive to a wide variety of ionic species.

2.1 ELECTROCHEMICAL CELLS

An electrochemical cell can be defined as two conductors or electrodes, usually metallic, immersed in the same electrolyte solution, or in two different electrolyte solutions which are in electrical contact. Electrochemical cells are classed into two groups. A *galvanic* (sometimes, *voltaic*) cell is one in which electrochemical reactions occur spontaneously when the two electrodes are connected by a conductor. These cells are often employed to convert chemical energy into electrical energy. Many types are of commercial importance, such as the lead-acid battery, flashlight batteries, and various fuel cells. An *electrolytic* cell is one in which chemical reactions are caused to occur by the imposition of an external voltage greater than the reversible (galvanic) voltage of the cell. Essentially, these cells are used to carry out chemical reactions at the expense of electrical energy. Some important commercial uses of electrolytic cells involve synthesizing processes, such as the preparation of chlorine gas and caustic soda from brines, and electroplating procedures.

A simple galvanic electrochemical cell (shown in Fig. 2.1) consists of a strip of zinc and a strip of copper immersed in solutions of a zinc and a copper salt, respec-

FIGURE 2.1. *Schematic diagram of a simple galvanic electrochemical cell.* V *is a voltmeter or other voltage-measuring device. The arrows indicate the direction of the spontaneous flow of electrons. The + and − indicate the* polarity *of the cell as measured by a voltmeter.*

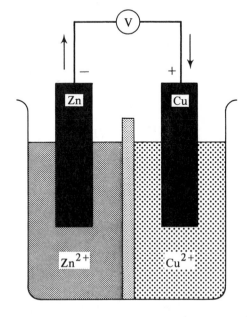

tively. If the Zn^{2+} and Cu^{2+} concentrations are approximately equal, the spontaneous reactions correspond to the *oxidation* of zinc metal (at the anode) and the *reduction* of copper ions (at the cathode):

$$Zn \rightleftharpoons Zn^{2+} + 2e^- \tag{2.1}$$

$$Cu^{2+} + 2e^- \rightleftharpoons Cu \tag{2.2}$$

Both reaction 2.1 and reaction 2.2 represent a *half-cell* reaction. If the strips of copper and zinc are connected by a wire so that electrolysis proceeds, the solution in the zinc compartment shows an increase in zinc-ion concentration, while the solution in the copper compartment is depleted in cupric ions. It is the purpose of the porous barrier separating the two compartments to allow the migration of ions between the two compartments so that there is no buildup of charge inhomogeneity, but without the gross mixing of solutions.

Schematic Representation of Cells

In order to simplify the description of cells, a type of electrochemical shorthand has evolved, which allows an easier depiction of cells and cell components. For example, for the cell in Figure 2.1, one would write

$$- \quad Zn/Zn^{2+}(c_{Zn^{2+}})//Cu^{2+}(c_{Cu^{2+}})/Cu \quad + \tag{2.3}$$

Slant lines, vertical lines, or sometimes a semicolon, indicate phase boundaries across which there arise potential differences that are included in the measured potential of the entire cell. Conventionally, a double slant or vertical line signifies a liquid junction—the zone of contact between two electrolyte solutions. Physically, this may be a porous membrane as in Figure 2.1, or a salt bridge of some sort. The anode is written to the left, the cathode on the right. If there are several components in one electrolyte solution, the components are separated by a comma. For example, for a cell (without liquid junction) composed of a silver/silver-chloride half-cell and a hydrogen gas electrode, one could write for one set of conditions

$$- \quad Pt, H_2 \text{ (0.5 atm)/HCl (0.1 } M), AgCl/Ag \quad + \qquad (2.4)$$

A comma is usually used to separate different chemical species occurring in the same phase.

Cell Potentials

The *electromotive force* (emf) of cell 2.3 is the algebraic sum of the potentials developed across the two electrode-solution interfaces, and the liquid-junction potential, E_{lj}. If the electrode reactions are *written* as reductions, and the electrode potentials are calculated according to the Nernst equation using *reduction potentials*, as in the present convention [1], the cell potential can be written as

$$E_{cell} = E_{Cu^{2+}, Cu} + E_{lj} - E_{Zn^{2+}, Zn} \qquad (2.5)$$

More generally, E_{cell} is the potential of the right-hand electrode (cathode) minus the potential of the left-hand electrode (anode)

$$E_{cell} = E_{cathode} + E_{lj} - E_{anode} \qquad (2.6)$$

If all the substances participating in the *reversible* operation of a cell are in their standard states (unit activities), the potential of an individual electrode is simply its respective *standard potential*, E^0. The free energy change for the cell reaction is therefore

$$\Delta G^0_{cell} = -nFE^0_{cell} \qquad (2.7)$$

where n = number of electrons transferred in the cell reaction
F = the faraday (96,487 coulombs/mole)

No valid method exists for determining the *absolute* potential of an electrode. All potential measurements require a second electrode, and are therefore *relative* potentials. It is then necessary to choose one particular electrode to be arbitrarily assigned the zero position on the potential scale. By convention, the standard hydrogen electrode (SHE) is defined to have a potential of exactly 0 V, and is the reference point from which the potentials of all other electrodes are stated (Sec. 2.3). The electromotive force of a cell is the potential difference between two electrodes and is independent of the particular reference-electrode scale used.

Liquid-Junction Potentials. At the boundary between two dissimilar solutions, a junction potential is always set up. The solvents, the nature of the electrolytes, and the concentration of a given electrolyte can all differ, and therefore the mobilities of positive and negative ions diffusing across the boundary will not be equal. Thus a slight charge separation arises, which results in the junction potential. Junction potentials can become rather large (50 mV or more), particularly when one of the electrolyte ions, such as H^+ or OH^-, has a very high mobility.

Almost all electrochemical cells contain at least a small liquid-junction potential, generally of unknown magnitude. Only in a few special cases can it be calculated or measured. Experimentally, the usual approach is to minimize the junction potential by use of a concentrated *salt bridge* between dissimilar solutions. Because the mobilities of potassium and chloride ions are nearly equal, the usual choice for the electrolyte in a salt bridge is saturated KCl. When potassium or chloride ions are undesirable for chemical reasons, such as in trace Cl^- determinations, saturated KNO_3 or K_2SO_4 or $5 M$ lithium trichloroacetate can be used. Various styles of electrolyte junctions or salt bridges have been designed such as a ground glass joint or a wick of asbestos sealed into glass (Fig. 2.3), an agar gelatin bridge containing an electrolyte (Fig. 3.9), a porous glass or ceramic plug, or a fine capillary drip.

2.2 THE NERNST EQUATION

For the generalized half-cell reaction, *written as a reduction*

$$Ox + ne^- \rightleftharpoons Red \tag{2.8}$$

the potential is given by the generalized form of the Nernst equation

$$E = E^0 - \frac{RT}{nF} \ln \frac{(Red)}{(Ox)} = E^0 - \frac{RT}{nF} \ln \frac{a_{Red}}{a_{Ox}} = E^0 - \frac{2.303 \, RT}{nF} \log \frac{a_{Red}}{a_{Ox}} \tag{2.9}$$

where $E^0 = $ *standard* electrode potential
$R = $ molar gas constant (8.314 joule/K-mole)
$T = $ absolute temperature
(Red) or $a_{Red} = $ *activity* of reduced form
(Ox) or $a_{Ox} = $ *activity* of the oxidized form

If numerical values are inserted for the constants and the temperature is 25°C, the Nernst equation becomes

$$E = E^0 - \frac{0.05916}{n} \log \frac{a_{Red}}{a_{Ox}} \tag{2.10}$$

A change of one unit in the logarithmic term changes the value of the electrode potential by $59.16/n$ mV. If the copper electrode of cell 2.3 is dipped into a solution of copper ion at $a = 0.001 \, M$, the electrode potential is

$$E_{Cu^{2+}, \, Cu} = E^0_{Cu^{2+}, \, Cu} - \frac{0.05916}{2} \log \frac{(Cu)}{(Cu^{2+})} \tag{2.11}$$

Since the activity of a solid-phase, such as the copper metal, is unity,

$$E_{Cu^{2+}, \, Cu} = E^0_{Cu^{2+}, \, Cu} + \frac{0.05916}{2} \log (Cu^{2+}) \tag{2.12}$$

$$= +0.337 + \frac{0.05916}{2} \log (0.001 \, M)$$

$$= +0.248 \text{ V}$$

relative to the standard hydrogen electrode.

Effect of Concentration—Activity Coefficients

If the Nernst equation (2.9) is written in terms of *concentrations* and *activity coefficients*, it becomes

$$E = E^0 - \frac{RT}{nF} \ln \frac{f_{Red}[Red]}{f_{Ox}[Ox]} = E^0 - \frac{RT}{nF} \ln \frac{f_{Red}}{f_{Ox}} - \frac{RT}{nF} \ln \frac{[Red]}{[Ox]}$$

$$= E^{0\prime} - \frac{RT}{nF} \ln \frac{c_{Red}}{c_{Ox}} \tag{2.13}$$

where $E^{0\prime}$ = *formal electrode potential*
f_{Red} = the activity coefficient of the reduced species
f_{Ox} = activity coefficient of the oxidized species
c (or brackets) stand for *concentration* units

The formal potential, which is somewhat like a standard potential under a given set of experimental conditions, lacks the fundamental thermodynamic significance of the standard potential; but it is often experimentally useful; and can often be directly measured.

There are several ways in which activity coefficients can be calculated or estimated [2]; the simplest of these is known as the Debye-Hückel Limiting Law. The *ionic strength, I*, of any electrolyte medium is given by

$$I = \frac{1}{2} \sum c_i z_i^2 \tag{2.14}$$

where c_i = concentration of ionic species i
z_i = charge on that ion

For aqueous solution at 25°C, the activity coefficient of an ion, f_i, is then given approximately by

$$-\log f_i = 0.5 z_i^2 I^{1/2} \tag{2.15}$$

This illustrates the fact that as the total electrolyte concentration increases, the *activity* coefficients decrease. For example, the activity of Ca^{2+} in a solution containing only 0.01 M $CaCl_2$ is 0.0045 M; whereas if 0.1 M NaCl is also present, the Ca^{2+} activity is only 0.0019 M.

Effect of Complexation on Electrode Potentials

As mentioned previously, electrodes respond directly to the activity of ionic species, the "free" or "effective" concentration. For example, if a complexing reagent is also present that reacts with a metal ion, the metal ion is then no longer as free to react with the electrode; its "effective concentration" has been decreased. The simplest case that can be considered is that of a single ionic species formed over a range of concentrations of complexing agent. For example, let us again consider the copper electrode of cell 2.3, where EDTA (ethylenediaminetetraacetic acid) has also been added to the Cu^{2+} solution. The formation of the copper-EDTA complex can be represented by the equilibrium

$$Cu^{2+} + EDTA^{4-} \rightleftharpoons CuEDTA^{2-} \tag{2.16}$$

(where $EDTA^{4-}$ is the basic form of the tetra-acid) for which the formation constant is written as

$$K_f = \frac{(CuEDTA^{2-})}{(Cu^{2+})(EDTA^{4-})} = 6.17 \times 10^{18} \tag{2.17}$$

For the half-reaction involving copper ions and copper, Equation 2.2, the Nernst equation is expressed by Equation 2.12. Combining Equation 2.17 with 2.12 yields the potential of a copper electrode in aqueous $EDTA^{4-}$ systems

$$E_{Cu^{2+}, Cu} = E^0_{Cu^{2+}, Cu} + \frac{RT}{nF} \ln \frac{1}{K_f(EDTA^{4-})} + \frac{RT}{nF} \ln (CuEDTA^{2-}) \tag{2.18}$$

At 25°C, for 0.001 M Cu^{2+} and 0.10 M $EDTA^{4-}$, the potential would then be -0.278 V (neglecting activity coefficients), since for a strong complexing agent like EDTA it can be assumed that nearly 100% of the copper is present as $CuEDTA^{2-}$; that is, $(CuEDTA^{2-}) \approx 0.001$ M and $(EDTA^{4-}) \approx 0.10$ M.

The shift in electrode potential caused by the complexing agent is contained in the second term of Equation 2.18. In this case, it amounts to a shift of -0.526 V. The important practical consequences of chelation and complexation will be discussed in more detail later. For example, one can determine copper ion by direct potentiometry using a copper-ion-selective electrode, or via a potentiometric titration with EDTA using the electrode as an endpoint detector.

2.3 REFERENCE ELECTRODES

In most practical situations involving potentiometry, one uses a reference electrode (in conjunction with a sensing or indicator electrode) whose potential is invariant with respect to solution composition, and unchanging with the passage of the small amount of current (10^{-9} A or less) required to "drive" the measuring instrument— an electrometer, pH meter, or high-impedance voltmeter. Furthermore, one strives to make all liquid-junction potentials either constant or negligible. Ideally, therefore, the reference electrode is of known and constant potential, with negligible variation in the liquid-junction potential from one test or standard solution to another. In this case, the cell potential of the overall system, Equation 2.6, can be expressed as

$$E_{cell} = E_{constant} + E_{ind} \tag{2.19}$$

where $E_{constant} =$ some constant potential
            $E_{ind} =$ the potential (varying with the solution composition) of the indicator or sensing electrode

Under these conditions, the indicator electrode can provide unambiguous information about ionic activities in the cell solution. In most analytical work, it is not necessary to know the actual value of the reference electrode potential—as long as it is constant—because $E_{constant}$ is determined using known standard solutions.

Hydrogen Gas Electrode

The hydrogen electrode is the ultimate standard electrode not only for the determination of (relative) potentials, but also for the determination of pH values. Owing to the experimental difficulties associated with it, however, it is seldom used for routine measurements, but rather for the evaluation of secondary reference and pH electrodes such as the calomel reference electrode and the glass pH electrode.

The hydrogen electrode consists essentially of a piece of platinum foil, electroplated ("platinized") with a thin layer of finely divided platinum. This provides a catalytic surface on which the half-cell reaction

$$2H^+ + 2e^- \rightleftharpoons H_2 \tag{2.20}$$

can proceed reversibly. The electrode is immersed in the test solution, and high-purity hydrogen gas is bubbled through the solution and over the electrode surface so that both will be saturated with hydrogen gas. The construction of a typical hydrogen electrode is illustrated in Figure 2.2.

FIGURE 2.2. *Typical hydrogen-gas electrode assembly.*

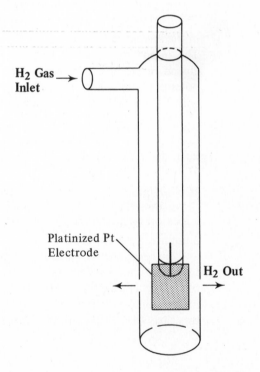

H₂ Gas Inlet

Platinized Pt Electrode

H₂ Out

The primary disadvantage of the hydrogen gas electrode is that it is rather difficult to prepare properly and inconvenient to use. Another disadvantage is that its potential is sensitive to oxidants and reductants in solution—anything that will oxidize H_2 or reduce H^+. Also, the catalytic Pt surface is poisoned by a variety of substances including As, CN^-, H_2S, and Hg, and is coated by high-molecular-weight substances, such as proteins, and other surface-active compounds. Nevertheless, the hydrogen gas electrode, at least the hypothetical [3] standard hydrogen electrode (SHE), is used as the ultimate standard for potential and pH.

Calomel Electrodes

Perhaps the most widely used reference electrode for electrochemical measurements is one form or other of the calomel electrode. This electrode consists of mercury, mercurous chloride (calomel), and a chloride-ion solution:

$$Hg/Hg_2Cl_2 \text{ (satd.)}, Cl^- \text{ (X } M) \tag{2.21}$$

The half-cell reaction is

$$Hg_2Cl_2 + 2e^- \rightleftharpoons 2Hg + 2Cl^- \qquad E^0 = +0.2676 \text{ V} \tag{2.22}$$

Since the activities of solid Hg_2Cl_2 and Hg are unity, the potential of this electrode is governed entirely by the activity of the chloride ion. The most common type of calomel electrode is the saturated (with KCl) calomel electrode (SCE). It is easily made and maintained, and its potential is quite reproducible. A great variety of commercial calomel electrodes is available; two of these are illustrated in Figure 2.3.

Perhaps the major disadvantages of the SCE are that its potential varies strongly with temperature, owing to the change in solubility of KCl; that there is a perceptible hysteresis effect following temperature changes, partly owing to the time required for solubility equilibrium to be established; and that it can only be used at temperatures less than about 80°C, probably owing to the disproportionation of mercurous ion to form mercury and mercuric ion.

For accurate work, 0.1 M or 1 M KCl calomel electrodes may be used because they reach their equilibrium potential more rapidly, and have less temperature-dependence. Calomel electrodes with NaCl electrolyte have also found use. Table 2.1 gives the potentials of several common reference electrodes at selected temperatures.

Silver/Silver-Chloride Electrodes

A silver/silver-chloride reference electrode is prepared by plating a layer of silver chloride onto a metallic silver wire or sheet. The electrode is immersed in a chloride solution (usually KCl) of known concentration, which is also saturated with AgCl.

TABLE 2.1. *Potentials of Some Reference Electrodes in Volts versus the Standard Hydrogen Electrode as a Function of Temperature*

Temperature °C	Calomel[a] (0.1 M KCl)	Calomel[a] (Satd. KCl)	Ag/AgCl[a] (Satd. KCl)
10	0.3362	0.2543	0.2138
20	0.3359	0.2479	0.2040
25	0.3356	0.2444	0.1989
30	0.3351	0.2411	0.1939
40	0.3336	0.2340	0.1835

Source: Reprinted from R. G. Bates, *Determination of pH*, 2nd ed., pp 325–35, by permission of the author and John Wiley and Sons. Copyright © 1973 by John Wiley and Sons.
a. Liquid-junction potential included.

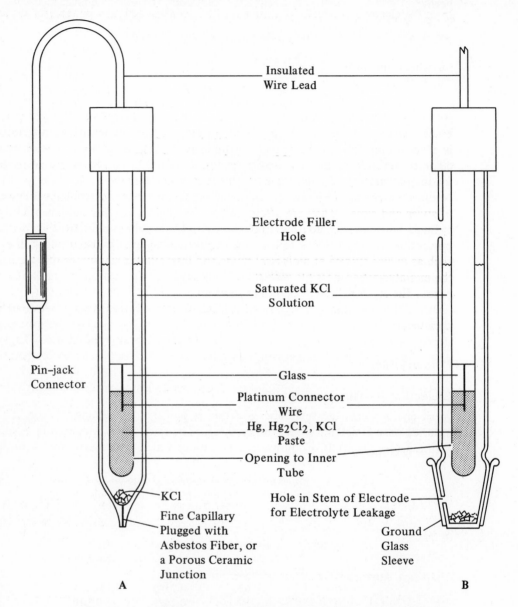

Insulated Wire Lead

Electrode Filler Hole

Saturated KCl Solution

Pin–jack Connector

Glass

Platinum Connector Wire

Hg, Hg$_2$Cl$_2$, KCl Paste

Opening to Inner Tube

KCl

Fine Capillary Plugged with Asbestos Fiber, or a Porous Ceramic Junction

Hole in Stem of Electrode for Electrolyte Leakage

Ground Glass Sleeve

A

B

FIGURE 2.3. *Schematic cross-section representation of the construction of some typical commercial calomel electrodes: (A) fiber or porous-ceramic junction type and (B) ground glass–sleeve type. The electrolyte leak rate of the fiber or porous-ceramic junction type is quite low, typically 1–10 μl/hr; that for the sleeve type around 100 μl/hr.*

Since AgCl is appreciably soluble in concentrated chloride media, solid AgCl is usually added to the solution to insure saturation and prevent dissolution of AgCl from the electrode surface. The half-cell thus constructed may be represented as

$$\text{Ag/AgCl (satd.), Cl}^- \text{ (X } M\text{)} \tag{2.23}$$

for which the half-reaction is

$$\text{AgCl} + e^- \rightleftharpoons \text{Ag} + \text{Cl}^- \qquad E^0 = +0.2223 \text{ V} \tag{2.24}$$

As in the calomel electrode, the potential is governed by the chloride ion activity. Useful silver-chloride electrodes can be prepared by simply anodizing a silver wire in chloride media, but the apparent equilibrium potential of these electrodes may differ by several millivolts from one electrode to another. More care is necessary for the preparation of highly stable and reproducible electrodes [4].

Commercial silver/silver-chloride reference electrodes are available in a variety of styles and sizes. They are often used as the internal reference electrodes in glass pH and other ion-selective electrodes. Ag/AgCl microelectrodes formed from very thin silver wire have found extensive use, for example, in biomedical applications such as *in vivo* studies of biological fluids and intracellular measurements, because of the miniaturization possible with these electrodes.

The Ag/AgCl electrode is also sufficiently stable for use at temperatures up to about 275°C, making it a useful alternative to calomel electrodes at elevated temperatures.

Mercury/Mercurous-Sulfate Electrodes

When leakage of chloride ion through the reference electrode into the test solution is not permissible (as in titrations involving Ag^+), a mercury/mercurous-sulfate reference electrode may be used instead of calomel or silver-chloride electrodes. This consists of a mercury electrode in contact with a sulfate electrolyte saturated with excess mercurous sulfate:

$$\text{Hg/Hg}_2\text{SO}_4 \text{ (satd.), SO}_4{}^{2-} \text{ (X } M\text{)} \tag{2.25}$$

Electrolytes commonly used are saturated K_2SO_4 ($E = +0.64$ V vs. SHE) or 0.5 M H_2SO_4 ($E = +0.68$ V vs. SHE). The electrode potential is quite stable and reproducible.

Thallium-Amalgam/Thallous-Chloride Electrodes

The Tl(Hg)/Tl^+ reference electrode (Thalamid®) is said to be superior to either calomel or silver-chloride electrodes when measurements are made over a range of temperatures, because it attains its equilibrium potential very rapidly after changes in temperature. The half-cell can be written as

$$\text{Tl (40\% amalgam)/TlCl (satd.), KCl (satd.)}$$

Some commercial glass pH electrodes use Thalamid® electrodes as internal reference electrodes.

2.4 pH—DEFINITION AND MEASUREMENT

Perhaps the earliest definition of pH was given by Sørensen [5], who defined it as the negative logarithm of hydrogen-ion concentration,

$$pH \equiv pcH = -\log [H^+] \qquad (2.26)$$

Because of deficiencies in the theoretical assumptions made, this early definition was a measure of neither concentration nor activity. When the concept of thermodynamic activity became established, primarily through the efforts of Lewis and Randall, Sørensen and Linderstrøm-Lang defined pH as the negative logarithm of the hydrogen-ion activity

$$pH \equiv paH = -\log a_{H^+} = -\log [H^+] f_{H^+} \qquad (2.27)$$

Unfortunately, since individual ionic activity coefficients cannot be evaluated without extrathermodynamic assumptions, the theoretical thermodynamic elegance and desirability of this pH definition cannot be rigorously related to experimental quantities. For this reason, the modern *operational* NBS (National Bureau of Standards) scale of acidity has been developed.

Operational Definition of pH

For the analytical chemist, an experimentally useful scale of acidity should allow the interpretation of the most important and common measurements as, for example, those with a glass electrode and saturated calomel reference electrode. The operational definition of pH of an aqueous solution is

$$pH = pH_s + \frac{(E - E_s)F}{RT \ln 10} \qquad (2.28)$$

where E = the electromotive force of a cell containing the unknown solution
E_s = the electromotive force of a cell containing a standard reference buffer solution of known or defined pH, that is, pH_s

This definition has been endorsed by standardizing groups in many countries and has been recommended by the International Union of Pure and Applied Chemistry.

In actual practice, the NBS pH standards were assigned pH_s values from measurements of a hydrogen gas–silver/silver-chloride cell without liquid junction,

$$Pt/H_2, \text{ Buffer Solution, } Cl^-, \text{ AgCl/Ag} \qquad (2.29)$$

while making reasonable assumptions about activity coefficients in such a way as to make pH_s represent as nearly as possible $-\log a_{H^+}$.

Since every practical pH electrode can be regarded only as a somewhat imperfect tool that functions more or less unevenly over the whole pH range, and every practical pH reading involves a (possibly variable) liquid-junction potential, the NBS has adopted a series of six primary standard pH buffer solutions (Table 2.2). The pH of the standards is temperature dependent, primarily because of the variation of the K_a of the buffer system with temperature.

The primary standards cover the pH range from about 3.5 to 10.5, and were chosen for their reproducibility, stability, buffer capacity, and ease of preparation.

TABLE 2.2. *pH$_s$ Values of NBS Primary Standards*

Temp. °C	KH Tartrate[a]	KH Phthalate[b]	Phosphate[c] (Equimolal)	Phosphate[d] (3.5:1)	Borax[e]	Carbonate[f]
0	——	4.003	6.982	7.534	9.460	10.321
10	——	3.996	6.921	7.472	9.331	10.181
20	——	3.999	6.878	7.430	9.227	10.064
25	3.557	4.004	6.863	7.415	9.183	10.014
30	3.552	4.011	6.851	7.403	9.143	9.968
40	3.547	4.030	6.836	7.388	9.074	9.891
50	3.549	4.055	6.831	7.384	9.017	9.831

a. Saturated at 25°C; NBS Certificate 188
b. 0.05 m KHC$_8$H$_4$O$_4$; NBS Certificate 185e; m = molality (mole/kg)
c. 0.025 m KH$_2$PO$_4$, 0.025 m Na$_2$HPO$_4$; NBS Certificates 186-I-c and 186-II-c
d. 0.008695 m KH$_2$PO$_4$, 0.03043 m Na$_2$HPO$_4$; NBS Certificates 186-I-c and 186-II-c
e. 0.01 m Na$_2$B$_4$O$_7 \cdot$10H$_2$O; NBS Certificate 187b
f. 0.025 m NaHCO$_3$, 0.025 m Na$_2$CO$_3$; NBS Certificates 191 and 192

From studies of the internal consistency of the six primary standards, it appears that the total uncertainty of the pH$_s$ values is within ± 0.006 pH. This means that the pH determined by a practical cell like

$$\text{Pt/H}_2,\ \text{Solution/Saturated KCl/Reference Electrode} \qquad \textbf{(2.30)}$$

with properly designed liquid junction will be the same regardless of which of the six buffers is chosen as a standard. The same is true if a glass electrode with perfect pH response is substituted for the hydrogen electrode.

With regard to the significance of pH values, it can be said that they are at best an *estimate* of $-\log a_{\text{H}^+}$, depending on how accurately the liquid-junction potential remains constant for the measurement of standard and unknown. For many dilute solutions (less than 0.1 M) between pH 2 and 12, the pH may be considered to correspond to the true hydrogen-ion activity to within about ± 0.02 pH. This is equivalent to ± 1.2 mV in the potential reading, and about a $\pm 5\%$ uncertainty in a_{H^+}.

Secondary Standards. In addition to the six primary standards, the NBS has designated two secondary standards, one on the acidic and one on the basic end of the intermediate pH region, in order to affirm the proper functioning of the glass electrode (Table 2.3). Furthermore, a great number and variety of "secondary" pH standard solutions have been collected in various treatises and compendia [4, 6, 7]. A secondary standard may often prove convenient because it may be more easily prepared or more stable than the primary standards, or matches more closely the composition and pH of a group of unknowns on which many measurements are to be made over a period of time. Particularly in process-control applications with, for example, very concentrated electrolyte solutions, reproducibility may be the most important concern.

TABLE 2.3. *pH of NBS Secondary Standards*

Temp. °C	K Tetroxalate[a]	Ca(OH)$_2$[b]
0	1.666	13.423
10	1.670	13.003
20	1.675	12.627
25	1.679	12.454
30	1.683	12.289
40	1.694	11.984

Source: V. E. Bower, R. G. Bates, and E. R. Smith, *J. Res. Natl. Bur. Stand.*, *51*, 189 (1953); R. G. Bates, V. E. Bower, and E. R. Smith, *J. Res. Natl. Bur. Stand.*, *56*, 305 (1956).
a. 0.05 *m* KH$_3$(C$_2$O$_4$)$_2$·2H$_2$O; NBS Certificate 189
b. Saturated at 25°C

pH Electrodes

The premier pH electrode, from both a historical and a fundamental point of view, is the H$_2$ gas electrode. As was mentioned in Section 2.3, however, this electrode is difficult to prepare and use, and has been replaced almost universally by the modern glass electrode except for specialized applications.

Glass Electrode. The glass pH electrode is composed of (a), a thin, H$^+$-ion-responsive glass membrane sealed to a stem of high-resistance, nonresponsive glass, and (b), an internal reference electrode with a constant internal hydrogen-ion concentration. The internal electrode may be either Ag/AgCl in HCl or Hg/Hg$_2$Cl$_2$ in HCl. The entire cell requires an external reference electrode for operation. The complete cell may be diagrammed schematically as

$$
\left.\begin{array}{c}\text{Internal}\\\text{Reference}\\\text{Electrode}\end{array}\right/ \left.\begin{array}{c}\text{Internal}\\\text{Electrolyte}\end{array}\right/ \left.\begin{array}{c}\text{H}^+\text{-responsive}\\\text{Glass}\\\text{Membrane}\end{array}\right/ \left.\begin{array}{c}\text{External}\\\text{Solution}\end{array}\right/\!\!\left/ \begin{array}{c}\text{External}\\\text{Reference}\\\text{Electrode}\end{array}\right. \qquad (2.31)
$$

Glass is an irregular three-dimensional arrangement of silicate tetrahedra in which each oxygen atom is shared by two silicate groups. With one type of pH-responsive glass, Na$^+$ and Ca^{2+} cations are located in this array. Modern glass pH electrodes contain Li$^+$ and Ba^{2+} to varying degrees, in place of Na$^+$ and Ca^{2+}, to make the electrode more selective to H$^+$. When immersed in aqueous solution, cations from the surface of the glass are leached out and replaced by protons to form a hydrated silica-rich layer about 500 Å thick, depending on the hygroscopic nature of the glass. The external part of this hydrated gel layer can act as a cation exchange membrane which has a particularly high degree of selectivity among the various cations. By variation of the glass composition, glass electrodes can be made responsive to a variety of monovalent cations (Sec. 2.5). When a thin membrane of glass is interposed between two solutions, an electrical potential difference is developed across the membrane that depends on the activities and nature of the ions present in the two solutions, the composition of the glass, and other factors. Although the mechanism by which cations affect the potential developed across the glass membrane is not completely understood, the most generally accepted theory is based on an ion-exchange equilibrium occurring at the solution-glass boundary [8].

It is a fact that glass electrodes give a Nernstian response to hydrogen-ion activity, at least over a large portion of the pH range.

Because of their convenience and wide use, a great variety of glass pH electrodes is commercially available in various sizes, shapes, temperature ranges, and so forth. Figure 2.4 illustrates the construction of a common type of glass electrode.

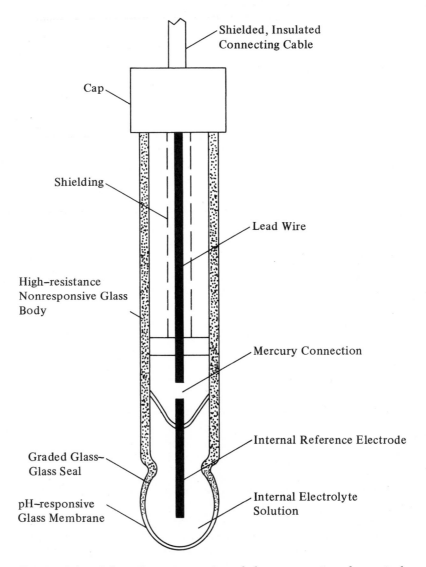

FIGURE 2.4. *Schematic representation of the construction of a typical glass pH electrode.*

A major advantage of glass electrodes is that there is no formal *electron* exchange involved in their functioning; thus they are completely uninfluenced by oxidizing and reducing agents in solution, unlike all other pH electrodes. Their major disadvantage is that they have a very high impedance (1 to 500 megohms, typically) thus necessitating the use of a voltmeter with very high input impedance or an electrometer. Glass electrodes must also be calibrated fairly often, preferably with buffers within about a pH unit of the pH to be measured; they also cannot be used in acidic fluoride media, and exhibit "acid" and "alkaline" errors. In highly acidic media, glass electrodes exhibit a negative "acid" error which is thought to be due to the migration of the anions of the acid into the gel layer and/or a change in activity of water in the gel layer, thereby affecting the hydrogen-ion activity. In highly basic media, glass electrodes exhibit a positive "alkaline" error owing to the partial exchange of cations other than H^+ (notably Na^+) between the pH-sensitive surface layer and the basic solution.

Quinhydrone Electrode. The quinhydrone electrode is an important hydrogen-ion electrode, and is perhaps typical of a whole class of such electrodes which function as pH sensors owing to a reversible organic oxidation-reduction pair involving protons. Quinhydrone (an equimolar compound of benzoquinone and hydroquinone) is only slightly soluble in water. The reversible oxidation-reduction couple

$$+ 2e^- + 2H^+ \rightleftharpoons \tag{2.32}$$

Quinone, Q   Hydroquinone, H_2Q

involving H^+ will fix the potential of an "inert" electrode, usually gold or platinum, immersed in a solution, as given by

$$E_{Q, H_2Q} = E^0_{Q, H_2Q} + \frac{RT}{2F} \ln \frac{(Q)(H^+)^2}{(H_2Q)} \tag{2.33}$$

The quinhydrone electrode, therefore, responds directly to hydrogen-ion activity in a Nernstian manner as long as the ratio of activities of Q and H_2Q remains constant. The electrode is simple to construct, reaches equilibrium fairly rapidly, and is less disturbed by poisons and by oxidizing and reducing agents than is the hydrogen-gas electrode. It functions well in many nonaqueous and partially aqueous media, and has a relatively low impedance. Its chief disadvantage is that it cannot be used in solutions of pH greater than about 8 owing to the air oxidation of hydroquinone to quinone and the acidic dissociation of hydroquinone, both of which cause the ratio $(Q)/(H_2Q)$ to increase and the apparent pH to be too low.

Antimony Electrode. The antimony electrode is perhaps the best representative of a whole class of metal/metal-oxide redox electrodes that respond to pH. The potential is probably developed as a result of an oxidation-reduction reaction involving antimony and a skin of antimony(III) oxide which forms on the surface of the metal:

$$Sb_2O_3 + 6H^+ + 6e^- \rightleftharpoons 2Sb + 3H_2O \tag{2.34}$$

Since antimony and the oxide are both solids, and can be regarded as being in their standard states of unit activity, the potential of the electrode can be expressed as

$$E_{Sb_2O_3, Sb} = E^0_{Sb_2O_3, Sb} + \frac{RT}{F} \ln (H^+) \qquad (2.35)$$

if the activity of liquid water is unity, as would be expected for dilute solutions.

In actual practice, the antimony electrode does not give highly accurate results. The previous history, preparation, and surface characteristics of each antimony billet used affect the response. Each electrode must be carefully calibrated over the pH range to be used; and factors such as dissolved oxygen and the composition of the buffer solution affect response. Nevertheless, the ruggedness, simplicity, very low resistance, and low cost of the antimony electrode have made it useful, for example, in continuous industrial-process monitoring when high precision and accuracy is not required.

2.5 ION-SELECTIVE ELECTRODES

Within about the last 10 years a wide variety of commercial and homemade ion-selective electrodes (ISEs) has become available; they respond more or less selectively to a wide range of ions in solution.

Properties of Ion-Selective Electrodes

One of the more interesting intrinsic properties of ion-selective electrodes is that they respond *logarithmically* to the *activity* of an ion of interest; that is, in the case where the reference-electrode and liquid-junction potentials are constant, for a cation electrode

$$E_{cell} = E_{constant} + E_{ISE} = E'_{constant} + \frac{RT}{nF} \ln a_i \qquad (2.36)$$

One interesting result of this property is that the relative concentration error for direct potentiometric measurements is theoretically independent of the actual concentration. Unfortunately, the error is rather large—approximately $\pm 4n\%$ per mV uncertainty in measurement, perhaps the most serious limitation of ISEs. Since potential measurements are seldom better than ± 0.1 mV total uncertainty, the best measurements for monovalent ions under near-ideal conditions are limited to about $\pm 0.5\%$ relative concentration error. For divalent ions, this error would be doubled; and in particularly bad cases where, for example, liquid-junction potentials may vary by ± 5 to 10 mV (as in high or variable ionic-strength solutions), the relative concentration error may be as high as 50%. This limitation may be overcome, however, by using ISEs as endpoint indicators in potentiometric titrations (Sec. 2.6). At the cost of some extra time, accuracies and precisions on the order of 0.1% or better are possible.

Another intrinsic property of ISEs is that they measure activities—the thermodynamic "free" concentration of an ion—although they can be made to determine concentrations by appropriate calibration procedures. Activity measurements may be more valuable in certain cases because activities or "free" concentrations determine rates of reactions and equilibria. Therefore, ISEs can be used to study such phenomena as complexation or chelation, activity coefficients, and so forth.

Interferences. Broadly speaking, interferences may be classed into two general categories: chemical interferences in solution, such as complexation, and electrode interferences due to less than perfect electrode specificity. An ion-selective electrode will respond, more or less strongly, to ions other than the one for which it is nominally designed.

Consider Figure 2.5, for example, which shows a typical calibration curve that might be obtained with a calcium ion–selective electrode. Note that the elec-

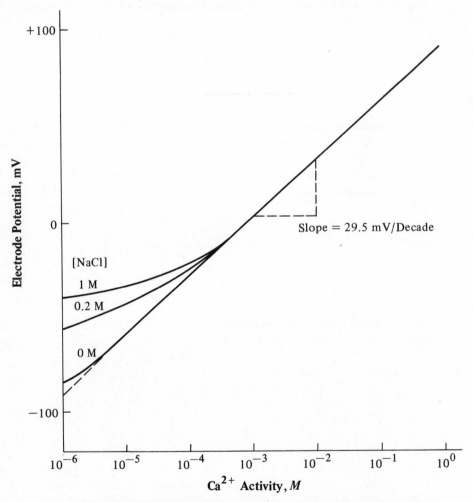

FIGURE 2.5. *The response of a calcium ion–selective electrode to pure CaCl₂ solutions, and to CaCl₂ solutions with 0.2 or 1 M NaCl also present. Redrawn from J. W. Ross, Jr., in* Ion-Selective Electrodes, *R. A. Durst, ed., N.B.S. Special Publication 314, chap. 2, Washington, D.C.: U.S. Government Printing Office, 1969, by permission of the author and the National Bureau of Standards.*

trode response is linear with the logarithm of the calcium activity and has a Nernstian slope. In pure Ca^{2+} solutions, there is departure from the theoretically linear slope at about 6×10^{-6} M, as the electrode nears its detection limit—that concentration below which the electrode output is constant, regardless of the Ca^{2+} activity. The calcium electrode, however, also responds somewhat to Na^+ ion. The curve obtained with Ca^{2+} solutions of varying activity, but also containing 1 M NaCl, exhibits a departure from the theoretical linear portion at about 3×10^{-4} M Ca^{2+} activity—a much higher concentration than with the pure Ca^{2+} solutions. In this region, the calcium electrode is responding appreciably to the Na^+ ion present.

In the case where an electrode is responding to more than one ion, the response can be approximated by a modification of Equation 2.36 above, namely

$$E_{cell} = E'_{constant} + \frac{RT}{nF} \ln (a_i + k_{1j}a_j^{n/z}) \tag{2.37}$$

where $\quad a_j$ = the activity of the interferent ion of charge z
$\quad\quad\quad k_{1j}$ = the *selectivity coefficient*

Selectivity coefficients can vary from about zero for no interference to about 10^3 for different electrodes and different interfering ions. For example, the sodium-ion glass electrode actually responds about 350 times more strongly to Ag^+ ($k_{1j} = 350$) and about 10^4 times less strongly to Cs^+ ($k_{1j} = 0.0001$) than to Na^+. As the selectivity coefficient is written in Equation 2.37, *small* values of k_{1j} mean a more selective electrode, one less affected by interferences. Selectivity coefficients can really be regarded as only approximations, perhaps accurate to within an order of magnitude depending on experimental conditions and solution composition. Most selectivity coefficients, for example, show a dependence on total concentration as well as on the ratio of the interfering ion to the ion of interest.

Types of Ion-Selective Electrodes

In recent years, most of the significant electrode discoveries have involved materials for electrodes of the membrane type—that is, electrodes whose potential originates at two interfaces and the intervening bulk membrane. At present, ion-selective electrodes, including the pH glass electrode, imply membrane electrodes.

There are various ways of classifying ion-selective electrodes; for example, by the type of mechanism that produces the electrode response. The approach taken here will be to subdivide the description of electrodes according to the composition of the membrane sensor.

Glass Electrodes. By varying the chemical composition of the thin, ion-sensitive glass membrane, glass electrodes can be prepared that are differentially responsive to (primarily monovalent) cations. The pH glass electrode already discussed is one member of this class; its general construction and mechanism of operation also holds for other glass electrodes. Table 2.4 shows the typical properties of some commercial glass electrodes. These electrodes show very little response to divalent cations.

TABLE 2.4. *Typical Properties of Commercial Glass Ion-Selective Electrodes*

Type of Electrode	Concentration Range M	Glass Composition	Relative Electrode Response
H^+	10^0–10^{-13} (with corrections)	Li_2O–BaO–La_2O_3–SiO_2 or Na_2O–CaO–SiO_2 (21%) (6%) (72%)	$H^+ \gg Li^+, Na^+ > K^+$
Na^+	10^0–10^{-6}	Li_2O–Al_2O_3–SiO_2 or Na_2O–Al_2O_3–SiO_2 (11%) (18%) (71%)	Ag^+ (350) > H^+ (100) > Na^+ (1) $\gg Li^+, K^+,$ Cs^+ (0.001) > $NR_4^+,$ Tl^+ (0.0003) > $Rb^+,$ NH_4^+ (0.00003)
General Cation (monovalent)	10^0–10^{-5}	Na_2O–Al_2O_3–SiO_2 (27%) (4%) (69%)	K^+ (33), Rb^+ (17), NH_4^+ (11), Na^+ (4), H^+ (3), Li^+ (2), Cs (1), $Tl^+,$ Cu^+, R_4N^+

Solid-State Crystalline and Pressed-Pellet Electrodes. There are two basic types of crystalline-based electrodes. The first is exemplified by the fluoride electrode, with a europium-doped LaF_3 single crystal as the sensor. The LaF_3 crystal is sealed into the end of a rigid, cylindrical electrode body made of plastic; an internal electrolyte solution, typically NaF and NaCl, and an internal reference electrode complete the construction (Fig. 2.6). At room temperature, LaF_3 is a pure F^--ion conductor,

FIGURE 2.6. *Schematic representation of the construction of a crystal-sensor ion-selective electrode.*

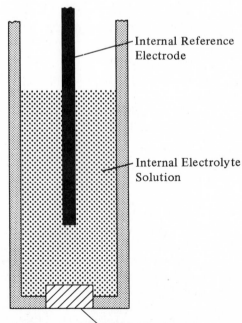

Internal Reference Electrode

Internal Electrolyte Solution

Single–crystal, Polycrystalline, or Pressed–pellet Sensor

thus remarkably free from interferences, an almost "specific" electrode. Virtually the only interferences encountered with the electrode are at low pH, where fluoride ion forms HF ($pK_a \approx 3$), and at pHs greater than about 8, where OH^- interferes—probably by some chemical modification of the LaF_3 crystal. The fluoride electrode was the first to really capture the minds of chemists; and there are probably several hundred publications dealing with the analytical determination of fluoride in such samples as municipal drinking and waste waters, seawater, air particulates, bone, minerals, organic materials, plant tissues, biological fluids, soils, toothpastes, and so forth.

The second class of crystalline sensors is based on the easily fabricated, low-resistance, selectively permeable cast-disk and pressed-pellet membranes based on Ag_2S. Silver sulfide is an ionic conductor in which silver ions are the mobile species. By itself, it can be used to detect silver ions or to measure sulfide-ion levels. The potential-determining mechanism in an Ag_2S electrode is due to the very low solubility product of Ag_2S [$K_{sp} = 10^{-51}$]. The silver-ion activity

$$Ag_2S \rightleftharpoons 2Ag^+ + S^{2-} \tag{2.38}$$

of the test solution on one side of the membrane and the (constant) silver-ion activity of the inner filling solution (Fig. 2.6) establish an electrochemical half-cell that responds to the Ag^+ activity of the test solution.

$$E = E_{constant} + \frac{RT}{F} \ln (Ag^+) \tag{2.39}$$

($E_{constant}$ contains such factors as E^0 for the electrode and a term containing the silver-ion activity of the inner solution.)

By making mixed pellets containing AgX-Ag_2S, where X = Cl, Br, I, or SCN, one has an electrode responsive to one of these particular anions. The silver-ion activity at the surface of the electrode is controlled by the activity of X^- in solution via its solubility equilibrium

$$AgX \rightleftharpoons Ag^+ + X^- \tag{2.40}$$

This in turn controls the electrode potential by being coupled with the Ag_2S solubility equilibrium. By substituting into Equation 2.39,

$$E = E_{constant} + \frac{RT}{F} \ln (Ag^+) = E_{constant} + \frac{RT}{F} \ln \frac{K_{sp}}{(X^-)} = E'_{constant} - \frac{RT}{F} \ln (X^-) \tag{2.41}$$

These electrodes, of course, are also responsive to Ag^+ or S^{2-} ions.

In an entirely similar manner, electrodes responsive to Cu^{2+}, Cd^{2+}, and Pb^{2+} cations (M^{2+}), which form insoluble metal sulfides, can be made by mixing the appropriate metal sulfide with Ag_2S. In this case, the M^{2+} activity controls the sulfide-ion activity in solution, which in turn controls the Ag^+ activity and the electrode response.

The selectivity and properties of these various electrodes are basically a function of the solubility products involved. Anything with a lower solubility product than the ion being determined will interfere. For this reason, AgCl membranes are subject to greater interference than AgBr, and so on. Iodide and bromide must be reduced to levels less than 5×10^{-7} and 2×10^{-3} times the lowest chloride activity anticipated when using an AgCl membrane.

Cast pellets of silver halides alone can also serve as membranes for the respective halide-selective electrode, but function less well than the mixed crystalline sensors. A CN^- electrode can be made with an AgI/Ag_2S membrane. The typical properties of some commercial crystalline-sensor ion-selective electrodes are listed in Table 2.5. Although most of the electrodes cannot be used at total concentrations below about 10^{-6} to $10^{-7} M$, this lower limit is generally too high to be caused by the solubility of the membrane, and reflects instead the experimental difficulty of accurately preparing very dilute solutions. With solutions of higher concentrations, it is quite possible to obtain accurate measurements of very low activities of the free ions—for example, free sulfide ion activities can be measured in acid solutions down to about $10^{-19} M$. In such equilibrium systems, the parent compound is at high enough total concentration that losses of the free ion by adsorption on the container walls, and so forth, are negligible and are compensated by equilibrium shifts.

The Ag_2S-based electrodes can be fabricated with a solid-state internal connection—a silver wire attached directly to the membrane. This eliminates the problems associated with internal filling solutions.

Another variation of the polycrystalline-type electrode is the Pungor design [9], which involves incorporation of the membrane material in a matrix such as sili-

TABLE 2.5. *Typical Properties of Commercial Crystalline Solid-State Electrodes*

Electrode	Concentration Range (M)	Activity Limit $C > 10^{-6} M$	Interferences
F^-	10^0–10^{-6}		$OH^- < 0.1\ F^-$
Ag^+ or S^{2-}	10^0–10^{-7}	10^{-20}	$Hg^{2+} < 10^{-7}\ M$
Cl^-	10^0–5×10^{-5}	10^{-6}	$S^{2-} < 10^{-7}\ M$; trace Br^-, I^-, CN^- permitted
Br^-	10^0–5×10^{-6}	10^{-7}	$S^{2-} < 10^{-7}\ M$; $I^- < 2 \times 10^{-4}\ Br^-$
I^-	10^0–2×10^{-7}	10^{-10}	$S^{2-} < 10^{-7}\ M$
CN^-	10^{-2}–10^{-6}		$S^{2-} < 10^{-7}\ M$; $I^- < 0.1\ CN^-$; $Br^- < 5 \times 10^3\ CN^-$
SCN^-	10^0–5×10^{-6}		I^-, $S^{2-} < 10^{-7}\ M$; $Br^- < 3 \times 10^{-3}\ SCN^-$; CN^-, $S_2O_3^{2-} < 10^{-2}\ SCN^-$; $NH_3 < 0.1\ SCN^-$; $OH^- < SCN^-$; $Cl^- < 20\ SCN^-$
Cd^{2+}	10^0–10^{-7}	10^{-10}	Ag^+, Hg^{2+}, $Cu^{2+} < 10^{-7}\ M$
Cu^{2+}	10^0–10^{-8}	10^{-10}	S^{2-}, Ag^+, $Hg^{2+} < 10^{-7}\ M$
Pb^{2+}	10^0–10^{-7}	10^{-10}	Ag^+, Hg^{2+}, $Cu^{2+} < 10^{-7}\ M$

Source: Selected values have been taken from data supplied through the courtesy of Orion Research, Incorporated.

cone rubber. The proportion of material imbedded in the matrix must be high enough to produce physical contact between particles.

Liquid-Membrane Ion-Exchange Electrodes. One design of a liquid-membrane ion-exchange electrode consists of two concentric cylindrical tubes constructed of inert plastic (Fig. 2.7). The inner tube holds the internal reference electrode and an aqueous

FIGURE 2.7. *Schematic representation of the construction of a liquid-liquid ion-exchange electrode.*

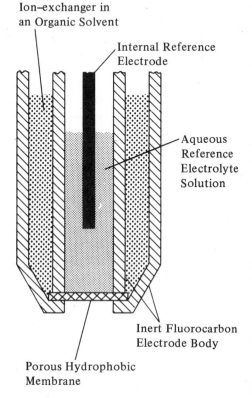

Ion–exchanger in an Organic Solvent

Internal Reference Electrode

Aqueous Reference Electrolyte Solution

Inert Fluorocarbon Electrode Body

Porous Hydrophobic Membrane

electrolyte solution containing the ion of interest. The outer compartment contains a charged or neutral organic ion-exchanger dissolved in an organic solvent that wicks into a thin hydrophobic membrane; this now forms a thin organic-membrane phase separating two aqueous solutions. The membrane may be, for example, a cellulose-acetate Millipore® filter. An ion-exchange equilibrium is set up at both the inner and outer surfaces of the membrane, and the difference in activity of the ion of interest in the inner electrolyte and outer test solutions gives rise to the potential response of the electrode.

The selectivity and sensitivity of these electrodes is determined primarily by the selectivity of the particular organic ion-exchanger for the ion of interest and, secondarily, by the organic solvent used to dissolve the exchanger. The extent of interference is related to the stability of the complex formed between the ion and the ion-exchanger in the membrane, and the mobility of the complexes within the membrane. One of the consequences of this selectivity is that the electrodes are occasionally more sensitive to an interferant ion than to the ion for which the electrode was nominally designed. Thus, by soaking a Ca^{2+} electrode in Zn^{2+} or Fe^{2+} solution, or better, by preparing the electrode with zinc or ferrous ion in the internal solution instead of calcium, an electrode for Zn^{2+} or Fe^{2+} is obtained.

Phosphate diesters $((RO)_2PO_2^-$, with R groups in the C_8–C_{16} range) dissolved in a relatively polar solvent such as dioctylphenylphosphonate show good selectivity for Ca^{2+} in the presence of Na^+, as well as for Ca^{2+} in the presence of other alkaline-earth ions. Less polar solvents such as decanol produce electrodes that give virtually identical response to all the alkaline-earth ions; electrodes of this type are useful for the determination of water hardness.

Ion-exchangers of the form $R–S–CH_2COO^-$ (in which the sulfur and carboxylate groups can readily form a 5-member chelate ring with a heavy-metal ion) show good selectivity for Cu^{2+} and for Pb^{2+}.

Certain positively charged ion-exchangers can be used for anion-selective electrodes. Charged metal salts of appropriately substituted orthophenanthrolines—$M(o\text{-phen})_3^{2+}$—result in good electrodes for nitrate, fluoroborate, or perchlorate by forming ion-association complexes with these anions. The ClO_4^- electrode, in particular, has few interferences; and perchlorate is a difficult ion to measure by almost any other method. A dimethyl-distearyl-ammonium ion, R_4N^+, can be used as an ion-exchanger in an electrode that has fair selectivity for chloride.

The organic ion-exchanger used need not be charged. Neutral organic ligands, typically dissolved in a low-dielectric liquid such as decane, can show good selectivity for certain cations. These lipid-soluble molecules usually contain a ring-arrangement of oxygen atoms that can replace the aqueous hydration shell around cations and thus extract them into organic solvents. This provides a mechanism for transport of the cations across the membrane and, thereby, an electrode response to the cation. The antibiotics valinomycin and the macrotetrolides such as nonactin and monactin are highly selective natural products that can be used for the measurement of K^+ or NH_4^+. The valinomycin electrode, in particular, shows excellent selectivity for K^+ over Na^+ (4000:1), H^+ (20,000:1), and divalent metal ions (ca. 5000:1), which is much better than the best potassium-sensitive glass electrode. The actin-based membranes are about four times more responsive to NH_4^+ than to K^+. Synthetic cyclic polyethers ("crown" compounds) can be used as ion exchangers for univalent and for some alkaline-earth cations, although they generally show much less specificity than the above natural compounds.

The lower limit of detection for liquid ion-exchange electrodes is determined primarily by the solubility of the ion exchanger in aqueous media. As with crystalline solid-state electrodes, Nernstian response is obtained until the activity of the solution is within a factor of about 100 of the solubility of the membrane salt. Then the response deviates and levels off at a constant potential reflecting this solubility.

Typical characteristics of some commercially available liquid ion-exchange electrodes are presented in Table 2.6.

Liquid-membrane electrodes are more sensitive to the solution environment than are solid-state electrodes. Their usable temperature range, generally 0–50°C, is more restricted than that of solid-state electrodes so that water will not permeate the membrane, nor membrane liquids bleed excessively into the aqueous solution. Normally, it is best to restrict use of the electrodes to purely aqueous media so the

TABLE 2.6. *Typical Properties of Selected Commercial Liquid-Liquid Ion-Exchange Electrodes*

Electrode	Concentration Range (M)	Interferences (approximate k_{1j})
Ca^{2+}	10^0–10^{-5}	Zn^{2+} (50); Pb^{2+} (20); Fe^{2+}, Cu^{2+} (1); Mg^{2+}, Sr^{2+} (0.01); Ba^{2+} (0.003); Ni^{2+} (0.002); Na^+ (0.001)
Cl^-	10^0–10^{-5}	ClO_4^- (20); I^- (10); NO_3^-, Br^- (3); OH^- (1); HCO_3^-, OAc^- (0.3); F^- (0.1); SO_4^{2-} (0.02)
Divalent Cation	10^0–10^{-5}	Zn^{2+}, Cu^{2+} (3); Fe^{2+} (2); Ni^{2+}, Ca^{2+}, Mg^{2+} (1); Sr^{2+} (0.25); Ba^{2+} (0.2); Na^+ (0.1)
BF_4^-	10^{-1}–10^{-5}	NO_3^- (0.005); Br^-, OAc^-, HCO_3^-, OH^-, Cl^- (0.0005); SO_4^{2-} (0.0002)
NO_3^-	10^{-1}–10^{-5}	ClO_4^- (1000); I^- (10); ClO_3^- (1); Br^- (0.1); NO_2^- (0.05); HS^-, CN^- (0.02); Cl^-, HCO_3^- (0.002); OAc^- (0.001)
ClO_4^-	10^{-1}–10^{-5}	I^- (0.05); NO_3^-, OH^-, Br^- (0.002)
K^+	10^0–10^{-5}	Cs^+ (1); NH_4^+ (0.03); Tl^+, H^+ (0.01); Ag^+ (0.001); Na^+ (0.0002)

Source: Selected values have been taken from data supplied through the courtesy of Orion Research, Incorporated.

membrane or ion exchanger will not dissolve in the test solution. The electrodes must be recharged every few weeks with new ion exchanger and internal electrolyte. Otherwise they are handled much as glass or solid-state electrodes are.

Enzyme-Substrate Electrodes. Electrodes that can respond to a variety of organic and biological compounds are constructed by coating the surface of an appropriate ion-selective electrode with an enzyme immobilized in some matrix. Perhaps the most well-known of these is the urea electrode [10], which makes use of the enzyme urease to hydrolyze urea (the "substrate"):

$$\text{urea} + H_2O \xrightarrow{\text{urease}} HCO_3^- + NH_4^+ \tag{2.42}$$

In this case, the urease is physically entrapped in a polyacrylamide matrix polymerized on the surface of an ammonium-ion glass electrode. The enzyme-gel matrix is supported on the electrode by a sheer dacron or nylon gauze, about the thickness of a nylon stocking, or it is held by a thin semipermeable cellophane sheet. The urea diffuses to the urease-gel membrane, where it is hydrolyzed to produce ammonium ion. Some of the ammonium ion diffuses through the thin membrane to the electrode surface, where it is monitored by the ammonium-sensitive electrode. The urea electrode is fairly stable, sensitive, specific for urea, has a usable lifetime of 2–3 weeks before a new gel layer must be prepared, and has a fairly fast response time (< 120 sec). The output of the electrode is linear from about 10^{-4} to 10^{-2} M urea.

There are literally thousands of enzyme-substrate combinations that yield products which could theoretically be measured with ion-selective electrodes. The high sensitivity of the electrodes and the specificity of enzymes can thus be coupled to produce sensors of value in many biomedical applications. Electrodes responsive to the following substrates have already been described in the literature: urea,

L-amino acids, D-amino acids, asparagine, glutamine, amygdalin, creatinine, penicillin, and others.

With some modifications, an electrode system can be made responsive to *enzyme* levels in test solution by surrounding the ion-sensitive membrane with *substrate* molecules. For example, an electrode that will measure the enzyme activity of cholinesterases in blood fractions has been described. Generally, such electrodes must be designed to replenish the substrate since it is consumed in the reaction.

Gas-Sensing Electrodes. There are several gas-sensing electrodes available, which function by interposing a thin, highly gas-permeable membrane between the test solution and an appropriate sensing element. The dissolved gas passes through the membrane into a small volume of internal filling solution, where a chemical equilibrium is established between the gas dissolved in the test solution and the internal electrolyte. The internal sensor monitors the changes in this equilibrium, and thus produces an output proportional to this concentration of dissolved gas. Potentiometric electrodes for ammonia (ammonium), sulfur dioxide (sulfite), nitrogen oxide (nitrite), and carbon dioxide (carbonate) are available.

The operation of gas-sensing electrodes can be illustrated by considering the sulfur-dioxide electrode, which responds directly to dissolved SO_2. Sulfite (SO_3^{2-}) and bisulfite (HSO_3^-) are measured by acidifying the sample to convert these species to SO_2. Dissolved SO_2 diffuses through the gas-permeable membrane until an equilibrium is established in the internal filling solution by the reaction of SO_2 with water

$$SO_2 + H_2O \rightleftharpoons HSO_3^- + H^+ \tag{2.43}$$

The hydrogen-ion level is then sensed by the internal sensing element (a conventional glass pH electrode), and is directly proportional to the level of SO_2 in the sample. The electrode has a usable range of 10^{-6} to 10^{-2} M SO_2, and has very few interferences, essentially only volatile weak acids such as acetic acid and HF.

The SO_2 level of stack gases can be measured by drawing a known volume of gas through an absorbing solution, acidifying an aliquot, and measuring SO_2 directly. The sulfite level of pulping liquors can be determined directly after acidification.

Ion-Selective Microelectrodes. Ion-selective electrodes can be fabricated in microassemblies for use in such applications as measuring ion activities in microsamples (10^{-3} ml) and as direct probes in tissues, tubules, capillaries, or even within individual cells. Microelectrodes can be fabricated with sensors made of glass, liquid ion-exchanger, or solid-state crystals [11, 13].

Closed-tip glass microelectrodes are fabricated by fusing a very small active tip onto a body of insulating glass or by coating the electrode stem with insulation, leaving only the tip exposed. Tip diameters of less than 1.5 μm exposed to a length of 3 to 5 μm can be achieved. Electrodes of this type have been used successfully to measure alkali-metal-ion activities in frog skeletal muscle. On a somewhat larger scale, miniaturized glass electrodes have been built within a small hypodermic syringe needle, intended for continuous monitoring of fetal blood pH during birth.

Open-tip liquid ion-exchange microelectrodes can be fabricated by pulling borosilicate glass capillary tubing to an appropriate tip diameter (0.5 to 1 μm), rendering the interior of the tip hydrophobic by coating the surface with an organic silicone compound, and filling the tip with an ion exchanger appropriate for the ion of interest (K^+, Cl^-, Ca^{2+}, and so on). The internal circuit is completed with an electrolyte solution and an Ag/AgCl reference electrode. Such electrodes can measure ion activities in single *aplasia* neurons (0.5 μl total volume).

An interesting approach to miniature electrodes is the coating of a fine platinum wire with a mixture of a liquid ion-exchanger and poly(vinyl chloride) or poly(methyl methacrylate) [14]. Although the mechanism by which these electrodes function is not known (there is no internal reference electrode), they do appear to function almost as well as the larger commercial varieties.

pH Meters

Other than the appropriate electrodes, the only major piece of instrumentation needed to perform pH and ion-electrode measurements is a pH meter. This is a very-high-impedance electronic voltmeter that draws negligible current from the reference-indicator electrode pair; thus no error arises from the voltage drop across the inherent (usually high) resistance of the electrochemical cell. A great variety of pH meters is commercially available, with an even greater variety of features. In general, pH meters can be divided into four classes based on price and "accuracy," although there is considerable overlap between classes: *utility* (portable), *general-purpose*, *expanded-scale*, and *research* grades.

Utility-grade pH meters usually cost about $100–300. Most are battery operated, and thus portable; generally they offer enough sensitivity to be used in many quality-control applications and out in the field. Their relative accuracy is about ±0.1 pH unit, and they have taut-band meter movements. General-purpose pH meters are more often line operated, and cost about $300–700. For the extra cost, they usually offer better stability and accuracy (±0.05 pH or ±3 mV), larger taut-band scales, and extra features such as a recorder output, mV scales, and a constant-current jack for performing polarized electrode measurements or dead-stop titrations such as the Karl Fischer titration for water determination.

For increased accuracy, expanded-scale pH meters (retailing for about $400–900, depending on features) generally offer accuracy of about ±0.01 pH unit. Usually any 1.0 pH unit or 100 mV range is expandable to full scale; many types that fall into this class have digital (4-digit) displays. For the most demanding applications, research-grade pH meters offer a relative accuracy of about 0.002 pH or ±0.1 mV (readability to 0.001 pH) for about $700–1200. Most of these have digital (5-digit) displays, full-range expanded-scale operation, recorder outputs, and highly adaptable slope and calibration controls.

Since there is such a wide variety of specialized features available on specific pH meters, manufacturers' literature must be consulted to select the best possible unit for the intended use.

Applications of Ion-Selective Electrodes

Ion-selective electrodes are used extensively as quantitative analytical probes in such diverse areas as air and water pollution, fundamental biomedical research, oceanography, geology, agriculture, and clinical analysis. Only a few representative examples of specific applications will be considered in detail.

Direct Potentiometry: Determination of Hydrogen Chloride Gas. A system has been described for the continuous monitoring of the HCl levels in gases or aerosols using a chloride-ion–selective electrode [15]. This arose from a study on the loss of volatile decomposition products from poly(vinyl chloride) (PVC) and other chlorocarbon polymers in simulated fires. The method works well because of the excellent solubility of HCl in water, and the fact that the chloride electrode senses only free Cl^- ion. Thus, other volatile chloride compounds will not be sensed.

The detection limit is about 20 ppm HCl in the original gaseous sample, and the accuracy of the method is within 5% from 20–6000 ppm HCl, as determined from analyses of standard gaseous samples.

The use of direct potentiometry for determination of ionic activities is quite popular, probably owing to its simplicity. The nitrate content of potatoes, for example, can be determined directly in the slurry resulting from peeling, dicing, and blending potatoes with water. The Ca^{2+} content of soils can be determined directly by diluting the supernatant from a pH 8.2 sodium-acetate extraction of dry soil. Orion Research, Incorporated, manufactures a complete system, incorporating a flow-through calcium electrode, for anaerobic ionized-calcium measurements on serum and other biological fluids. The sample volume is quite small, about 200 μl, and results are available in about two minutes. Bromide, chloride, and fluoride in rain and snow samples can be determined directly with the appropriate ion-selective electrode. Cupric ion in acid-plating baths can be determined directly after 100:1 dilution.

Ionic-Strength Buffering: Fluoride in Natural Waters. The fluoride electrode has found many uses in the determination of fluoride in various materials, primarily because of its applicability to a wide concentration range (10^0–10^{-6} M) and its simplicity and ease of use—particularly when compared with other methods for fluoride, which usually involve a time-consuming distillation step.

Because the ionic strength of natural waters may vary markedly, and thus affect activity coefficients, both samples and standards are usually diluted 1:1 with a Total Ionic Strength Adjustment Buffer (TISAB). By treating the unknown and standards in the same manner, and swamping out the ionic strength of the test solution, one calibration curve serves to determine the *concentration* of a given ion regardless of its original environment. The fluoride TISAB contains a 1 M acetic-acid/sodium-acetate buffer of pH 5.0 to buffer the solution in the middle of the electrode's pH range—thus avoiding erroneous results from HF formation or OH^- interference; about 10^{-3} M sodium citrate to preferentially complex metal ions such as iron and aluminum, which have some affinity for F^-; and 1 M NaCl to further increase the ionic strength.

A calibration curve for the determination of F^- in municipal waters is illustrated in Figure 2.8. The 40 mV difference in electrode response to two different water supplies, one with and the other without added fluoride, is easily measured. This measurement system can be readily automated for continuous monitoring of fluoride levels.

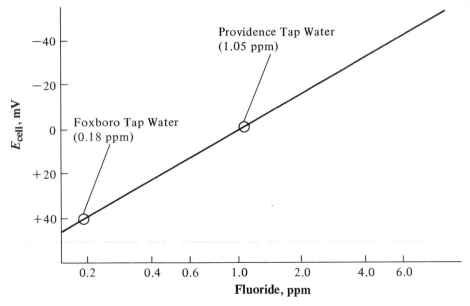

FIGURE 2.8. *Determination of fluoride in municipal water supplies by the calibration curve method using ionic-strength buffering. Redrawn from T. S. Light, in* Ion-Selective Electrodes, *R. A. Durst, ed., N.B.S. Special Publication 314, chap. 10, Washington, D.C.: U.S. Government Printing Office, 1969, by permission of the author and the National Bureau of Standards.*

The fluoride content of fluoridated toothpastes (typically about 0.09%) can be determined in an analogous manner [16].

The practice of ionic-strength buffering to fix activity coefficients (with possible use of a pH buffer and complexing agents to minimize interferences) is a fairly common practice when using ion-selective electrodes. Low levels (10–150 ppb) of Ag^+ can be determined accurately after ionic-strength adjustment with solid $NaNO_3$ [17].

Running standards and samples through the same digestion and separation procedures, for example, is another way of insuring that solution compositions and ionic strengths are similar in all test solutions.

Method of Standard Additions: Determination of Ammonia in Aquaria and Sea Water. The method of standard addition, or the known increment (or decrement) method, is a way of measuring analyte concentration, particularly for samples with high but unknown total ionic strength or for samples with highly variable solution components. This approach does not require the preparation of a calibration curve, although it is necessary to know the experimental electrode response slope (theoretically RT/nF) in the region of interest.

The initial potential reading is taken on a sample of concentration c

$$E_1 = E_{const} + \frac{RT}{nF} \ln fc \qquad (2.44)$$

where f = the activity coefficient

Next, a known amount of the ion of interest is added to the test solution so that the concentration is changed by a known amount Δc, and the potential is read again.

$$E_2 = E_{\text{const}} + \frac{RT}{nF} \ln f(c + \Delta c) \qquad (2.45)$$

Usually, the standard addition is a small volume of a concentrated solution, so that the total solution volume and ionic strength does not change appreciably. The above two equations can be combined to give

$$\Delta E = E_2 - E_1 = \frac{RT}{nF} \ln \left(\frac{c + \Delta c}{c} \right) \qquad (2.46)$$

Equation 2.46 is solved for c by rearranging and taking antilogs.

Usually, the most accurate determinations are made when Δc is such that the total concentration is approximately doubled. The only requirement is that the electrode be in a linear portion of its calibration curve over the concentration range of interest. The slope of the calibration need not be precisely equal to the Nernst factor, RT/nF; if it is not, the empirically determined slope S of the calibration curve can be substituted.

By the technique of adding several small increments and measuring the potential after each addition, concentrations can be determined with better precision than by a single standard-addition measurement. Potential is plotted against concentration on special graph paper (semi-antilogarithmic) to yield a Gran's plot [18]. The straight line obtained is extrapolated back to the horizontal axis, and the concentration corresponding to this intercept value is the sought-for concentration.

An example of the use of the standard-addition method is the determination of ammonia in aquaria and sea water [19] using an ammonia-gas electrode. To a 100 ml sample is added a sufficient number of NaOH pellets to raise the pH above 11 (to convert all ammonium ion to ammonia). The equilibrium potential is read, then a sufficient volume of standard NH_4Cl solution to approximately double the concentration is added, and the new equilibrium potential is read. The effective detection limit for this method is approximately 1 ppb NH_3; but below about 10 ppb considerable time is required for the electrode to stabilize, making the method somewhat impractical at the 1–10 ppb level. Results compare favorably with the phenol-hypochlorite spectrophotometric method for ammonia.

Calcium in beer can be determined by filtering the sample, adjusting the pH to 6, and employing a known addition of Ca^{2+}. The copper-ion content of tap water can be determined with a solid-state crystalline copper electrode using a multiple standard-addition procedure [20]. Tap water is mixed 1:1 with a complexing anti-oxidant buffer (sodium acetate, acetic acid, sodium fluoride, and formaldehyde) to buffer the pH at 4.8, to complex the Cu^{2+} uniformly with acetate, and to complex the Fe^{3+} interferant with fluoride. Copper in tap water can be determined down to about 9 ppm with a standard deviation of about $\pm 8\%$. The recovery of Cu^{2+} added to natural waters, an indication of the accuracy of the method, averaged 103% for samples in the range of 3 to 60 ppm Cu.

Only a few specific applications have been mentioned above. A great many more are contained in the scientific literature and manufacturers' literature, particularly Orion Research's *Analytical Methods Guide* [21].

Advantages and Disadvantages of Ion-Selective Electrodes

After this discussion of the types and applications of ion-selective electrodes, it is well to consider and review the general advantages and disadvantages of ion-selective electrodes as analytical tools. As mentioned previously, a unique characteristic of these electrodes is that they measure activity directly, not concentration. Another uncommon characteristic is their logarithmic response, which results in a constant, albeit rather large, error over the concentration range where the Nernst relation holds. The linear working range of many electrodes is quite large, generally from 4 to 6 orders of magnitude or more. Electrodes will function well in colored or turbid samples, where spectral methods generally will not.

In most cases, electrode measurements are reasonably rapid—equilibrium being reached in less than a minute; but in some cases, usually in very dilute solutions, slow electrode response may require fifteen minutes to an hour for equilibrium. The normally rapid response of ion-selective electrodes make them suitable in kinetic studies and for monitoring changes in flowing process streams. The equipment used is simple, quite inexpensive, and can be made portable for field operations. The method is virtually nondestructive of the sample (once it is in the liquid state), and can be used with very small samples (< 1 ml).

Perhaps the most decided disadvantage of ion-selective electrodes is that they are subject to a rather large number of interferences. The electrodes themselves respond more or less strongly to several ions; and various chemical interferences are possible, including chelation, complexation, and ionic-strength effects. Generally, fairly frequent calibration is necessary. Ion-selective electrodes are not ultra-trace level sensors; some electrodes, for example, are good only down to about $10^{-4}\,M$ and most are not usable below about $10^{-6}\,M$ concentration level—although this does correspond to perhaps 0.1 ppm.

An advantage or disadvantage, depending on the situation, is that ion-selective electrodes are responsive to a particular chemical form of an element. For example, an iodide electrode responds only to I^-, not to the total iodine content which could include IO_3^- or organically bound iodine.

2.6 POTENTIOMETRIC TITRATIONS

Many different types of ion-selective electrodes can be used as endpoint indicators in potentiometric titrations. For example, an acid-base titration can be performed with a glass pH electrode as an endpoint detector, rather than with a phenolphthalein indicator; or calcium can be titrated with EDTA using a calcium ion–selective electrode. During such a titration, the *change* in potential of a suitable indicator electrode is observed as a function of the volume added of a titrant of precisely known concentration. Since it is the change in potential rather than the absolute potential that is of interest, liquid-junction potentials and activity coefficients have little or no effect. Perhaps the primary advantage of potentiometric titrations is that (with the addition of classical titration procedures) they generally offer a large increase in accuracy and precision; $\pm 0.1\%$ levels are not uncommon. (We should note, however, certain disadvantages: the increase in analysis time and operator attention required, and the difficulties associated with the preparation, standardization, and storage of standard titrant solutions.)

Another advantage of potentiometric titrations is that substances to which the electrode does not respond can be determined, if the electrode responds to the titrant or to some low level of an indicator substance that has been added to the solution. For example, low levels of Al^{3+} can be determined by titration with standard fluoride solution, using a fluoride electrode [22]. EDTA and other chelates can be determined by titration with standard calcium or copper solution. Manganese(II), vanadium(II), or cobalt(II) can be determined via EDTA titration if a small amount of CuEDTA indicator is added to the solution and a copper electrode is used. The electrode responds directly to the Cu^{2+} activity which, however, is dependent on the activities of the EDTA and the other metal ion in solution.

The experimental apparatus for a potentiometric titration can be quite simple: only a pH or millivolt meter, a beaker and magnetic stirrer, reference and indicator electrodes, and a burette for titrant delivery are really needed for manual titrations and point-by-point plotting. Automatic titrators are available that can deliver the titrant at a constant rate or in small incremental steps and stop delivery at a preset endpoint. The instrument delivers titrant until the potential difference between the reference and indicator electrodes reaches a value predetermined by the analyst to be at, or very near, the equivalence point of the reaction. Alternatively, titrant can be delivered beyond the endpoint and the entire titration curve traced. Another approach to automatic potentiometric titration is to measure the amount of titrant required to maintain the indicator electrode at a constant potential. The titration curve is then a plot of volume of standard titrant added versus time, and is very useful, for example, for kinetic studies. The most extensive use of this approach has been in the biochemical area with so-called *pH-stats*—a combination of pH meter, electrodes, and automatic titrating equipment designed to maintain a constant pH. Many enzymes consume or release protons during an enzymatic reaction; therefore, a plot of the volume of standard base (or acid) required to maintain a constant pH is a measure of the *enzyme activity*, the amount of enzyme present.

Since potentiometric titrations are an old and well-known technique, particularly in regard to acid-base and oxidation-reduction titrations, only a few selected examples will be presented here. For more detailed treatments, the student is urged to consult the bibliography at the end of the chapter. It will be assumed that the student is already familiar with titration curves and their calculation from ionic equilibria and other pertinent data.

Acid-Base Titrations

Acid-base titrations can be performed with a glass indicator electrode and a suitable reference electrode. Titrations of strong acids and bases with suitable strong titrants are relatively simple, since there is a relatively large and abrupt change in pH at the endpoint. Calculated titration curves for the titration of various acids (0.1 M concentration) with 0.1 M sodium hydroxide are shown in Figure 2.9. Note that as the acid titrated becomes weaker, pK_a increases, and the sharpness and magnitude of the endpoint break decreases. A somewhat similar situation occurs when the concentration of the substance titrated (and the titrant) is decreased. As a rough rule of thumb, for the titration of a strong acid (or base) with strong titrant, the

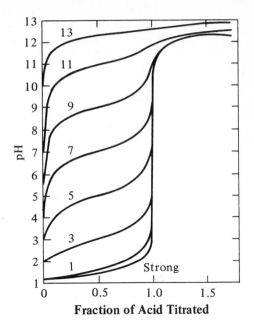

FIGURE 2.9. *Theoretical potentiometric titration curves for the neutralization titration of 0.1 M solutions of various acids with 0.1 M NaOH. The number beside each curve is the pK_a value for that acid.*

concentration of the substance titrated should be greater than about $3 \times 10^{-4} \, M$ for a 0.1% accuracy. If a 1% accuracy is sufficient, the concentration can be decreased an order of magnitude. For titration of a weak acid with strong base, the product of the acid concentration and its dissociation constant, K_a, should be greater than about 10^{-7} for a 0.1% accuracy, 10^{-9} for a 1% accuracy.

The acetic-acid content of household vinegar can be determined by potentiometric titration with sodium hydroxide. Mixtures of carbonate and bicarbonate can be analyzed by titration with HCl.

Acid-Base Titrations in Nonaqueous Solvents. It is a fact that the apparent acidity or basicity of a compound is strongly dependent on the acid-base properties of the solvent. For example, very strong acids such as HCl and HNO_3 cannot be individually titrated in water because water is sufficiently basic that these acids appear to be totally ionized. Very weak bases, such as amines, cannot be successfully titrated with strong acid in water. Many acids or bases that are too weak for titration in an aqueous medium, however, become amenable to titration in appropriate nonaqueous solvents. As a consequence, there are now many neutralization methods that call for solvents other than water [23–25].

The earliest advantages recognized arose from the use of *amphiprotic* solvents, those that have both acidic and basic properties. The prototype is water. Significant differences in acid-base properties are seen in the case of either protogenic solvents (more acidic than water), for example acetic acid, or protophilic solvents (more basic than water), for example ethylenediamine. In the protogenic cases it was found that bases too weak to be titrated in water could be successfully titrated with a strong acid dissolved in the same solvent. For example, primary, secondary, and tertiary amines can be titrated in acetic acid with perchloric acid in acetic acid as titrant. Medicinal sulfonamides, which have a primary amino group, can be titrated successfully in this manner, as can most of the common alkaloids, and purine compounds—including caffeine and theobromine.

On the other hand, acids too weak to be titrated with strong base in water appear much stronger in a protophilic solvent and can be titrated with a strong base such as sodium methoxide dissolved in the basic solvent or a compatible solvent. 2-Naphthol can be titrated in this manner. Many enols and imides can be titrated in either dimethylformamide or ethylenediamine.

A second type of very useful behavior occurs in *aprotic* (or sometimes "inert") solvents, which usually exhibit very weak acid properties. Examples are dimethylformamide, dimethylsulfoxide, dioxane, ether, various nitriles, methyl isobutyl ketone, hydrocarbons, carbon tetrachloride. These solvents often permit differentiation (or stepwise titration) of a series of acidic or basic species which, in water, either titrate together or not at all. For example, perchloric, hydrochloric, salicylic, and acetic acids and phenol can be titrated stepwise in methyl isobutyl ketone solvent to obtain discernible endpoints for each compound, using tetrabutyl ammonium hydroxide in isopropyl alcohol as titrant.

In most nonaqueous solvents, precise explanation or prediction of the shape of a potentiometric titration curve, or the possible utility of a specific titration, is usually not possible because of the lack of complete thermodynamic equilibrium constants for the numerous possible processes. In general, the shapes of curves must be determined experimentally, and the behavior of substances in diverse solvents must be considered empirically.

Oxidation-Reduction Reactions

Potentiometric titrations of oxidizing or reducing agents can be performed by making the titrated sample one-half of an electrochemical cell. Typically, the indicator electrode is an "inert" electrode such as a platinum foil or wire which is used to monitor the solution potential; the cell is completed with the addition of a suitable reference electrode such as an SCE.

Thus, in titrating a reducing substance such as Fe^{2+} with a standard solution of an oxidizing substance such as MnO_4^- or Ce^{4+}, the solution potential at equilibrium is given *either* by the formal potential of the titrant couple and the ratio of activities of its oxidized and reduced forms, *or* by the formal potential of the substance titrated and the ratio of its oxidized and reduced forms. For an analytically useful titration, the system of titrant and substance titrated reacts rapidly, and at least one of the electrode couples is reversible at the indicator electrode.

Typical examples of applications include the titration of ferrous ion with permanganate; the titration of arsenic(III) with bromate; the determination of ascorbic acid with iodine; and the determination of organic compounds such as azo, nitro, and nitroso compounds and quinones with chromous ion.

Precipitation and Complexation Reactions

Given the wide variety of ion-selective electrodes already commercially available and the many more specialized ones that can be fabricated, titrations involving the precipitation or complexation of ions are widely used. Halides, cyanide, thiocyanate, sulfide, chromate, and thiols can be titrated with silver nitrate, using the appropriate silver sulfide–based electrode; silver ion can be titrated with sodium iodide. Many metal ions can be titrated with standard EDTA, using the appropriate electrode, and possibly with the addition of an indicator reagent. Molybdate, selenide, sulfate, telluride, and tungstate can be titrated with lead perchlorate and a lead electrode. Aluminum, lithium, phosphate, various rare earths, and zirconate can be titrated with fluoride.

Generally, the sensitivity for determination is between 10^{-3} and 10^{-4} M.

SELECTED BIBLIOGRAPHY

BATES, R. G. *Determination of pH: Theory and Practice*, 2nd ed. New York: John Wiley, 1973. *Probably the definitive monograph on the fundamentals of pH.*

DURST, R. A. "Ion-Selective Electrodes in Science, Medicine, and Technology," *Amer. Sci.*, *59*, 353 (1971). *A short, easily readable article on the theory, functioning, and applications of ion-selective electrodes.*

DURST, R. A., ed. *Ion-Selective Electrodes*, N.B.S. Special Publication 314, Washington, D.C.: U.S. Government Printing Office, 1969.

IVES, D. J. G., and JANZ, G. J. *Reference Electrodes.* New York: Academic Press, 1961.

LINGANE, J. J. *Electroanalytical Chemistry*, 2nd ed., chaps. 2–8. New York: Interscience, 1958. *The fundamentals of potentiometry and many applications of potentiometric titrations.*

WEISSBERGER, A., and ROSSITER, B. W., eds. *Physical Methods of Chemistry*, vol. 1, part IIA. New York: Interscience, 1971.

REFERENCES

1. T. S. LICHT and A. J. DeBÉTHUNE, *J. Chem. Educ.*, *34*, 433 (1957).

2. H. A. LAITINEN and W. E. HARRIS, *Chemical Analysis*, 2nd ed. New York: McGraw-Hill Book Company, 1975, pp 5–17.

3. T. BIEGLER and R. WOODS, *J. Chem. Educ.*, *50*, 604 (1974).

4. R. G. BATES, *Determination of pH*, 2nd ed. New York: John Wiley, 1973, pp 328–35.

5. S. P. L. SØRENSEN, *Biochem. Z.*, *21*, 131 (1909); ibid., p 201.

6. R. A. ROBINSON and R. H. STOKES, *Electrolyte Solutions*, 2nd ed. New York: Academic Press, Inc., 1959.

7. D. D. PERRIN and B. DEMPSEY, *Buffers for pH and Metal Ion Control.* New York: Halsted Press, 1974.

8. R. A. DURST, *J. Chem. Educ.*, *44*, 175 (1967).

9. E. PUNGOR, *Anal. Chem.*, *39*(13), 28A (1967).

10. G. G. GUILBAULT, *Pure. Appl. Chem.*, *25*, 727 (1971).

11. G. A. RECHNITZ, *Chem. Eng. News*, January 27, 1975, p 29.

12. J. L. WALKER, JR., *Anal. Chem.*, *43*(3), 89A (1971).

13. G. A. RECHNITZ, *Res./Dev.*, *25*(8), 18, August, 1973.

14. R. W. CATTRALL and H. FREISER, *Anal. Chem.*, *43*, 1905 (1971).

15. T. G. LEE, *Anal. Chem.*, *41*, 391 (1969).

16. T. S. LIGHT and C. C. CAPPUCCINO, *J. Chem. Educ.*, *52*, 247 (1975).

17. D. C. MÜLLER, P. W. WEST, and R. H. MÜLLER, *Anal. Chem.*, *41*, 2038 (1969).

18. G. GRAN, *Analyst*, *77*, 661 (1952); F. J. C. ROSSOTTI and H. ROSSOTTI, *J. Chem. Educ.*, *42*, 375 (1965).

19. T. R. GILBERT and A. M. CLAY, *Anal. Chem.*, *45*, 1757 (1973); R. F. THOMAS and R. L. BOOTH, *Environ. Sci. Technol.*, 7, 523 (1973).

20. M. J. SMITH and S. E. MANAHAN, *Anal. Chem.*, *45*, 836 (1973).

21. *Analytical Methods Guide*, Orion Research, Incorporated, Cambridge, Mass., 7th ed., May, 1975.

22. B. JASELKIS and M. K. BANDEMER, *Anal. Chem.*, **41**, 855 (1969); E. W. BAUMANN, *Anal. Chem.*, **42**, 110 (1970).

23. A. H. BECKETT and E. H. TINLEY, *Titra-tions in Non-Aqueous Solvents*, 3rd ed. Pook, England: British Drug Houses, Ltd., 1962.

24. J. S. FRITZ, *Acid-Base Titrations in Non-aqueous Solvents*. Boston, Mass.: Allyn and Bacon, 1973.

25. J. J. LAGOWSKI, *Anal. Chem.*, **42**, 305R (1970).

PROBLEMS

1. Beginning with the Nernst equation for a cation electrode

$$E = E_{\text{constant}} + \frac{RT}{nF} \ln a_1$$

and differentiating, show that the *relative* concentration error incurred in the measurement of a_1 by *direct potentiometry* ($\Delta a_1/a_1$) is about $\pm 4n$ % per mV uncertainty in the measurement of E.

2. Why should one always calibrate a pH meter with a standard solution that is within 2 pH units of that of the test solution(s) to be measured?

3. Calculate the ionic strength of the following electrolyte solutions, assuming complete dissociation into ions: (a) 0.01 M $CaCl_2$, (b) 0.05 M KCl, (c) 0.1 M Na_2SO_4, (d) 0.001 M $AlCl_3$.

4. Using the simple form of the Debye-Hückel limiting law, calculate the individual activity coefficients for the ions in the following electrolyte solutions: (a) 0.002 M $MgCl_2$, (b) 0.002 M $MgCl_2$ + 0.01 M KCl, (c) 0.002 M $MgCl_2$ + 0.1 M KCl.

5. Using the simple form of the Debye-Hückel law, calculate the pH of a solution which is 0.03 M in the acid, 0.02 M in its conjugate base, and 0.1 M in KCl for the systems: (a) CH_3COOH + CH_3COONa ($K_a = 1.75 \times 10^{-5}$), (b) $CH_3NH_3{}^+Cl^-$ + CH_3NH_2 ($K_a = 2.0 \times 10^{-11}$).

6. Calculate the theoretical potential of a half-cell composed of a silver wire dipped into a solution of $10^{-3} M$ $AgNO_3$ versus the standard hydrogen electrode (SHE) and versus the saturated calomel electrode (SCE). Assume activity coefficients are unity and the temperature is 25°C.

7. Calculate the theoretical potential of the following cell at 25°C. Assume activity coefficients are unity; K_{sp} (AgI) = 8.3 × 10^{-17}.

Ag/$AgNO_3$ (1 M)//KI (1 M),

AgI (satd.)/Ag

8. A 0.6079 g sample of a purified organic acid was dissolved in 45.67 ml of a NaOH solution, and the excess base was titrated with 3.25 ml of 0.1200 N HCl. In a second titration, it was established that 39.33 ml of the base was equivalent to 31.69 ml of the HCl. Calculate the equivalent weight of the unknown acid.

9. Suppose that you are considering the application of a previously unreported potentiometric titration to a routine analysis involving hundreds of titrations daily by several analysts under one skilled supervisor. Outline the steps you would take, as a research chemist, to develop the method (a) under conditions of minimum expenditure for equipment, and (b) under conditions of minimum analyst time per sample.

10. Calculate the relative error incurred in the direct potentiometric determination of the calcium concentration of sea water due to magnesium ion interference. A typical magnesium level is 1300 parts per million (ppm), and calcium level is 400 ppm. The selectivity coefficient of the calcium electrode for magnesium is 0.014.

11. What is the maximum concentration of interfering ions that can be tolerated for a 1% interference level when measuring $10^{-4} M$ Ca^{2+} with a calcium-sensitive liquid ion-exchange electrode? For a 10% interference level? The interfering ions and

their selectivity coefficients are: Zn^{2+}, 3.2; Fe^{2+}, 0.80; Pb^{2+}, 0.63; Mg^{2+}, 0.014; Na^+, 0.003.

12. A 0.200 g sample of toothpaste was suspended in 50 ml of fluoride ionic-strength buffering medium (TISAB), and boiled briefly to extract the fluoride. The mixture was cooled, transferred quantitatively to a 100 ml volumetric flask, and diluted to volume with deionized water. A 25.00 ml aliquot was transferred to a beaker, a fluoride ISE and reference electrode inserted, and a potential of -155.3 mV was obtained after equilibration. A 0.10 ml spike of 0.5 mg/ml fluoride stock solution was added after which the potential was -176.2 mV. Calculate the percentage of F^- by weight in the original toothpaste sample.

13. A sample of skim milk is to be analyzed for its iodide content by the method of multiple standard additions. A 50.0-ml aliquot of milk is pipetted into a 100-ml beaker, 1.0 ml of 5 M $NaNO_3$ is added to increase the ionic strength, and the resultant solution is allowed to equilibrate to room temperature (25°C). A double-junction reference electrode and an iodide ion–selective electrode are inserted, and the solution is magnetically stirred. After equilibrium is reached, the voltage reading, E, is -50.3 mV. Then 100-, 100-, 200-, and 200-μl aliquots of 2.00 mM KI are added sequentially. After each addition, the equilibrium potential is measured: -64.9, -74.1, -86.0, and -94.2 mV respectively. Given that the slope, S, of the iodide calibration curve in this concentration range is 59.2 mV/decade, calculate the original I^- concentration of the milk in μg/ml. [Hint: Plot $10^{\Delta E/S}$ as a function of the total μg of I^- added, and extrapolate the straight line back to the x-axis.]

14. One way to estimate selectivity coefficients for ion-selective electrodes is to first equilibrate the electrode in a pure solution of the test ion and measure the potential

$$E_1 = E_{constant} + \frac{RT}{nF} \ln a_1$$

(for a cation-selective electrode). Then, small aliquots of an interferant ion are added, and the potential is measured each time

$$E_2 = E_{constant} + \frac{RT}{nF} \ln (a_1 + k_{1j}a_j).$$

Solve and rearrange these two equations to obtain a single linear equation of the form $y = mx + b$ which can then be used to determine k_{1j}. [Hint: Review the derivation of Equation 2.46, and the suggestion for taking antilogs.]

15. The selectivity coefficient of an iodide ion–selective electrode for bromide ion is to be determined using the equation derived in problem 14, above. An iodide ion–selective electrode and an appropriate reference electrode are equilibrated in 50.0 ml of 1.00×10^{-4} M KI at 25°C. The equilibrium potential is -130.2 mV. Then, 0.50-, 1.00-, 2.00-, and 2.00-ml aliquots of 1.00 M KBr are added sequentially. After each addition, the equilibrium potential is measured: -131.5, -133.9, -137.5, and -140.8 mV, respectively. Determine the selectivity coefficient for bromide ion if the slope of the calibration curve for iodide is 59.2 mV/decade. What assumptions have been made in this approach?

16. More precise location of the endpoint (i.e., inflection point) of a potentiometric titration curve can frequently be obtained from a first ($\Delta E/\Delta$ml vs. ml) or second ($\Delta^2 E/\Delta$ml^2 vs. ml) derivative plot. The following data were collected near the endpoint of a titration. Plot the first and second derivatives of the titration curve near the endpoint and compare the endpoint values.

Ml	Potential, mV
47.60	372
47.70	384
47.80	401
47.90	512
48.00	732
48.10	748
48.20	756

17. One way of experimentally estimating selectivity coefficients for ion-selective electrodes is to record the equilibrium potential of the

electrode for a series of solutions of interferant ions of (constant) known concentration. The equilibrium potentials at 25°C for a calcium ion–selective electrode in $10^{-2}\,M$ Ca^{2+} solution and in $10^{-2}\,M$ solutions of various ions were measured below. Neglecting activity coefficients, calculate selectivity coefficients for the interferant ions, assuming that the Nernst equation is valid, that the E^0 for the electrode does not change, and that liquid-junction potentials are constant.

Ion	E	Ion	E
Ca^{2+}	+63.3 mV	H^+	+92.9 mV
Zn^{2+}	+113.6	Na^+	−70.4
Pb^{2+}	+101.8	K^+	−84.6
Mg^{2+}	+4.2		

Pulse Methods Increase Sensivity Of Electro Chemical Method 10^2

3

Polarography and Voltammetry

Henry H. Bauer
James E. O'Reilly

In Chapter 2, the one electrochemical method involving no net current flow—potentiometry—was discussed. In Chapter 3, two methods will be studied—voltammetry and polarography—in which a voltage is applied to an electrode and the resulting current flow is measured.

For various reasons, classical polarographic techniques became less widely used for routine analytical purposes for some years. Particularly with the advent of flame spectroscopic methods (Chap. 10) for the analysis of metals and metalloids, polarography became primarily a tool for more fundamental studies: corrosion processes, electrode mechanisms, and kinetics. However, with the advent of low-cost commercial instrumentation and the introduction of some modern variants of the polarographic method—pulse polarography, stripping analysis, and so forth—the use of voltammetric methods for quantitative analytical measurements is again increasing. The newer variations of the method can permit selective, parts-per-billion, analyses of a variety of organic and inorganic species. The areas of application include environmental and toxicological studies, biochemistry and pharmacy, geology, and routine industrial quality control.

3.1 INTRODUCTION AND THEORETICAL BASIS

Principles

In *voltammetry*, current-versus-voltage curves are recorded when a gradually changing voltage is applied to a cell containing (a) the solution of interest, (b) a stable reference electrode, and (c) a small-area working or indicator electrode (Fig. 3.1). Usually, the voltage is increased linearly with time. Such curves are generically called *voltammo-*

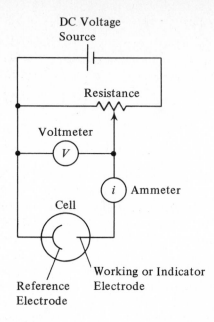

FIGURE 3.1. *Schematic diagram of a simple two-electrode voltammetric apparatus.*

grams. In the special case where the indicator electrode is the *dropping mercury electrode* (DME), introduced by J. Heyrovský in 1922, the technique is known as *polarography*, and the current-versus-voltage curves are called *polarograms*.

The DME consists of a glass capillary attached to a mercury reservoir. Drops of mercury fall from the orifice of this capillary at a constant rate, usually between 5 and 30 drops per minute (Fig. 3.2). Each drop is the electrode while attached to the column of mercury in the capillary. At the slow rate of voltage scanning generally used in polarography—about 50–200 mV/min—the change of potential of the DME during the life (usually between 2 and 12 sec) of a single drop can be neglected; thus, the current measured on each drop can be considered to be obtained under practically potentiostatic conditions (i.e., at constant potential). To distinguish this method from modern variants, it is sometimes called "conventional" or "DC" (direct-current) polarography.

The current-versus-voltage curves obtained with the DME are very reproducible, since the surface of every new mercury drop is fresh, clean, and practically unaffected by electrolysis at earlier drops. The total amount of electrolysis is very small because of the small area of the electrode and the small currents involved; for example, with 20 ml of a typical solution, 100 polarograms can be recorded without noticeable change in the curve. The small size of the DME permits the analysis of small volumes of solutions; if necessary, less than 0.01 ml can be used.

Mercury is chemically inert in most aqueous solutions, and hydrogen is evolved on it only at quite negative potentials; consequently, the reduction of many chemical species can be studied at mercury electrodes, but not at electrodes made of most other materials. However, the anodic dissolution of mercury makes it impossible to study reactions at potentials more positive than about $+0.4$ V versus the saturated calomel electrode (SCE).

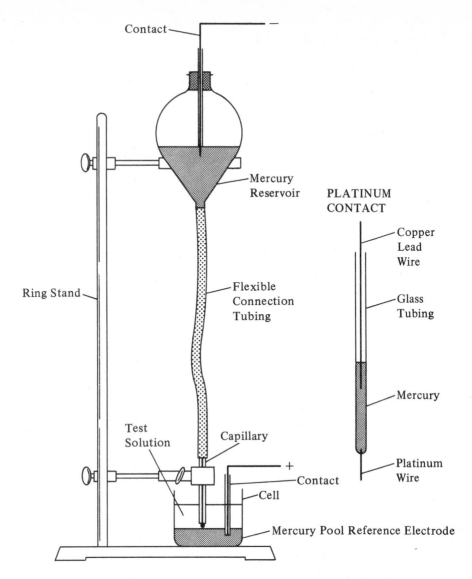

FIGURE 3.2. *Illustration of a dropping mercury electrode (DME) and a simple polarographic cell for reductions.*

Supporting electrolytes are commonly used in polarography to decrease the resistance of the solution and to ensure that the electroactive species moves by diffusion and not by electrical migration in the voltage field across the cell. The supporting electrolyte is often chosen also to provide optimum conditions for the particular analysis: e.g., buffering at a preferred pH value and elimination of interferences by selective complexation of some species. Solutions of strong acids (e.g., hydrochloric, sulfuric), strong bases (sodium or lithium hydroxide), or neutral salts (e.g., chlorides, perchlorates, sulfates of alkali metals, or tetraalkylammonium ions) are frequently used, as are buffer solutions or solutions of complexing agents (e.g., tartrates, citrates, cyanides, fluorides, or amines, including ammonia and EDTA). The total concentration of electrolyte is usually between 0.1 and 1.0 M.

A typical polarogram is shown in Figure 3.3. Only a small current flows at the most positive potentials. This nonfaradaic current is often practically identical with the current obtained in the same potential range with the supporting electrolyte alone and is called the *residual, charging,* or *condenser current*. This part of the curve is followed by a potential range where the current increases steeply: this is called a *polarographic wave* or *step*. Then follows a range of potential in which the current remains practically constant, and is often virtually parallel to the charging current; this is the plateau of the wave. The difference between the charging current and the current at the plateau is the *limiting current* (i_1 in Figure 3.3) or the *wave height*. The limiting current is usually proportional to the concentration of a polarographically active substance in the examined solution, and its measurement forms the basis of quantitative applications of polarography.

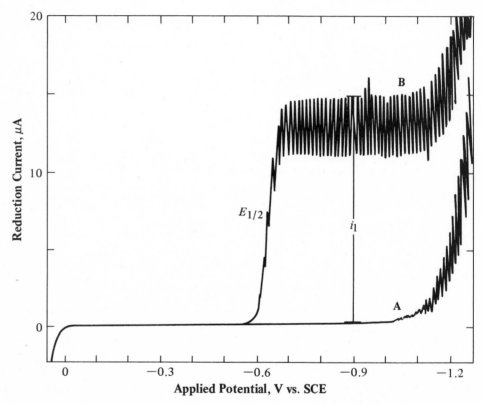

FIGURE 3.3. *Typical polarogram. Curve A: Background, residual current, or supporting electrolyte curve (1 M HCl). Curve B: Polarogram of 0.5 mM Cd²⁺ in 1 M HCl. $E_{1/2}$ is the half-wave potential and i_1 is the limiting current of the polarogram. Adapted from D. T. Sawyer and J. L. Roberts, Jr.*, Experimental Electrochemistry for Electrochemists, *New York: Wiley-Interscience, 1974, by permission of John Wiley and Sons. Copyright © 1974 by John Wiley and Sons.*

Note the oscillations in current as the mercury drop grows and falls. As the current increases, the magnitude of the oscillations increases in direct proportion. The recorded current does not fall to zero at the instant the drop falls because of the slow response of the current-recording device.

When one polarographic wave is preceded by another, the limiting current is measured as the difference between the two plateaus, which are usually parallel to one another; the wave heights are almost always additive.

The potential at which the current reaches half the magnitude of the limiting current is called the *half-wave potential* (denoted as $E_{1/2}$ in Figure 3.3). In most instances, the half-wave potential is practically independent of the concentration of the particular compound; it characterizes the oxidation-reduction properties of the studied substance and can be used as a qualitative identification of the electroactive species present. The $E_{1/2}$ is of fundamental importance and can be related to the standard oxidation-reduction potential (E^0) of the electrochemical reaction involved.

Removal of Oxygen. One difficulty encountered in voltammetric or polarographic analyses is that dissolved oxygen interferes severely and must be removed from test solutions before analysis. This is because oxygen is electrochemically reducible, producing large reduction currents, and it or its oxidation-reduction products react chemically with many solutions. Oxygen is reduced in two steps: a two-electron reduction to H_2O_2, and then a second two-electron reduction to H_2O. The $E_{1/2}$'s are at about 0 and -1 V versus SCE at pH 7. Air-saturated aqueous solutions have about a 4 mM O_2 level, and produce a total of about 5 μA diffusion current at the DME. The usual procedure for removing O_2 from solutions is to bubble them for 5 to 20 min with high-purity nitrogen or argon, or with electrolytically generated hydrogen. Compressed nitrogen in tanks often contains enough residual oxygen to be detected polarographically; it is usually further purified before use by first bubbling it through acidic V^{2+} or Cr^{2+} or passing it over hot copper turnings, to remove O_2; and then passing it through a bubbler filled with background electrolyte to further wash the gas and presaturate it with water vapor. The length of time required for complete deaeration may be greatly reduced by using a medium- or coarse-porosity fritted-glass dispersion tube in the test-solution compartment.

The Ilkovic Equation. The current that flows through the polarographic cell depends on the rate of the electrode reaction and on the rate of transport of the electroactive species to the electrode surface. At sufficiently negative potentials (that is, where the limiting current is observed) the rate of the electrode process is so fast that the rate of transport of the species to the surface becomes the limiting factor.

In the absence of migration (eliminated by addition of supporting electrolyte) and convection (prevented by keeping the electrolyzed solution unstirred), diffusion is the only mode of transport involved. Therefore, the limiting current is proportional to the rate of diffusion, and

$$i_l = nFAD\left(\frac{\partial c}{\partial x}\right)_{x=0} \tag{3.1}$$

where A = the area of the electrode

D = the diffusion coefficient of the electroactive species

$(\partial c/\partial x)_{x=0}$ = the concentration gradient of the latter at the electrode surface

The DME is virtually spherical; its volume can be calculated from the rate of flow of mercury m (mg/sec), the time t (sec) measured from the beginning of drop growth, and the density of mercury. This gives the radius of the drop, from which the surface area, A in mm², is

$$A = 0.851(mt)^{2/3} \qquad (3.2)$$

Solution of the equations for diffusion to a spherical drop then gives the Ilkovic equation

$$i_d = 708nc\,D^{1/2}m^{2/3}t^{1/6} \qquad (3.3)$$

where i_d = diffusion current in microamperes
   c = concentration in millimoles per liter of solution (mM)
   D = diffusion coefficient in cm² sec^{-1}

The subscript "d" signifies that a current limited by the rate of diffusion is considered.

When $t = t_d$, the lifetime of each drop, Equation 3.3 becomes the expression for the maximum current observed at the end of each drop, i.e., the highest value of the current recorded on the oscillating curve (Fig. 3.3). Modern strip-chart and x-y recorders have a sufficiently fast response to ensure that the recorded maximum current can be equated to the theoretical one. In the earlier literature, when fast-response recorders were not common, average currents rather than maximum currents were frequently measured; the theoretical average current is 6/7 of the maximum current, that is, the value of the constant in Equation 3.3 equals 607. Even today, many people prefer to use heavy damping when recording polarographic curves, and thus measure average currents.

It is evident from Equation 3.3 that the measured maximum current on the plateau of the wave can serve for quantitative analysis, since it is linearly proportional to the concentration of the substance being reduced. Moreover, when c is known and when the electrode reaction is known (i.e., the value of n), measurements of i_d can be used to obtain the diffusion coefficient. In other cases, where the electrochemical reaction is not yet known, one can postulate a plausible value for D and use i_d to calculate n; since the latter must be an integer, it is not necessary that D be known with accuracy.

Currents Controlled by Factors other than Diffusion

The electrochemical reaction may involve, in addition to diffusion and charge transfer, chemical reactions in which the oxidant or reductant is involved and/or adsorption of the electroactive species. Sometimes the magnitude of the current is limited by the rate of a chemical reaction or an adsorption process.

Kinetic Currents. Polarographic currents whose magnitudes are controlled by the rates of chemical reactions are called *kinetic* currents. For instance, one may have a reaction sequence

$$A + B \xrightarrow{k_1} Ox + ne^- \rightleftharpoons Red \qquad (3.4)$$

in which k_1 limits the overall rate. A is the species to be determined, and it reacts with another substance B to form the reducible species Ox. It can be shown that the magnitude of the limiting current is linearly proportional to the concentration of A provided that the concentration of B is constant (or B is present in large excess). Thus, polarography can be used to determine substances that are not reducible or oxidizable but which can be reacted in situ to give an electroactive species. In some cases when dealing with kinetic currents, the conditions for polarographic electrolysis (e.g., pH of the solution and temperature) need to be closely controlled.

Catalytic Currents. Another type of polarographic current is governed by catalytic processes. Such *catalytic currents* are of two types: either the substance undergoing electrolysis is regenerated in the vicinity of the electrode by a chemical reaction, or the electroreduction of a species is shifted to more positive potentials than would occur in the absence of the catalyst. An example of the former case is the reduction of Fe(III) to Fe(II)—the electrogenerated ferrous ion can be reoxidized back to ferric ion if hydrogen peroxide is present in solution. An example of the second case is the catalytic reduction of hydrogen ions—many substances, proteins for example, catalyze this reduction and shift the corresponding wave to more positive potential.

In both cases, the current is a nonlinear function of concentration (or a linear function only over a certain concentration range) and a calibration curve must be used for analytical determinations.

Adsorption Currents. If either the oxidized or the reduced species is adsorbed at the electrode, the magnitude of the current may be limited by the available surface area of the electrode: surface covered by the adsorbed species may not be available for charge-transfer at that particular electrode potential. A system in which adsorption is significant often has a polarogram like that shown in Figure 3.4.

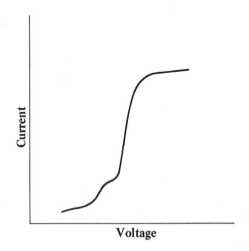

FIGURE 3.4. *Polarographic curve of methylene blue (0.4 mM), showing the adsorption prewave.*

The reduced species remains adsorbed at the electrode surface, "inactivating" the surface, and current flows only at the rate at which fresh surface is exposed to the solution. The height of the *adsorption prewave* increases with increasing concentration of the depolarizer up to a particular concentration and thereafter remains constant. However, a second wave then appears, at a potential where the reduced species is no longer adsorbed, and this second wave is usually diffusion-controlled. The combined wave heights are often linearly related to concentration and quantitative analysis can be carried out.

If it is the oxidized, rather than the reduced, species that is strongly adsorbed, the adsorption wave typically appears as a "postwave" on the plateau of the diffusion-controlled "main" wave.

In general, it is preferable to deal with diffusion-controlled currents because they are generally much less affected by experimental variables and usually result in linear current-versus-concentration calibration curves.

Polarographic Maxima

Sometimes polarograms show currents that are, over certain ranges of potential, considerably higher than diffusion currents—higher by as much as 2 orders of magnitude. These *polarographic maxima* may be sharp or rounded, and may cover only small regions of potential or quite wide ones (Fig. 3.5). These large currents arise because of spontaneous stirring of the solution near the mercury electrode (maxima are observed at hanging mercury drops and at mercury-pool electrodes as well as at dropping mercury electrodes).

There are several mechanisms that can lead to movement of the solution and the appearance of maxima. The subject is too complicated to be satisfactorily discussed here; the origins of maxima are discussed fully in Reference [1], and methods of dealing with them to permit quantitative analysis are given in the general texts on polarography listed at the end of the chapter. One can, however, make the following generalizations:

Maxima are least likely to be encountered if one uses a low rate of mercury flow ($m < 0.5$ mg/sec), a concentrated supporting electrolyte, and a low concentration of the electroactive species ($< 10^{-3}$ M). Maxima can sometimes be avoided by altering the chemical nature of the supporting electrolyte. If need be, the maxima can usually be suppressed by adding to the solution a small amount of a surface-active substance, such as Triton X-100. One should add just enough to eliminate the maximum (determining the amount by trial and error), since even a moderate excess can distort the polarographic wave.

For quantitative analytical purposes, it is almost invariably desirable to eliminate maxima because of the distortion of the polarographic wave involved, and the resultant difficulty in measuring wave heights.

Tests for Current-Limiting Processes

Criteria used to distinguish among diffusion, kinetic, adsorption, and catalytic currents include changes in the wave height (limiting current) with (1) concentration of the electroactive species, (2) mercury pressure, (3) pH, (4) buffer concentration, and (5) temperature. (Peak-shaped current maxima (Fig. 3.5A) caused by increased transport of electroactive species by convection in the vicinity of the electrode can usually be easily recognized.)

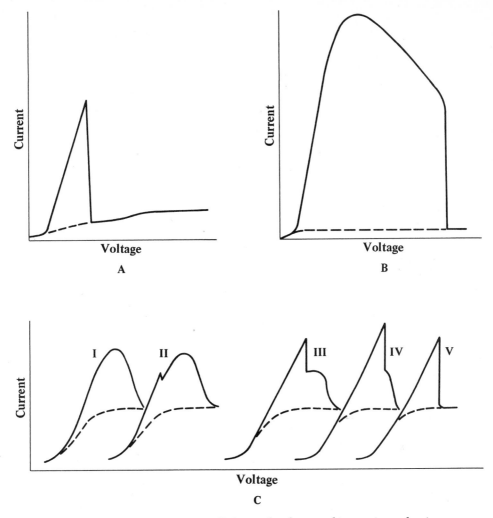

FIGURE 3.5. *Various types of observed polarographic maxima, showing actual currents (solid lines) and diffusion currents (dashed lines). A: Oxygen in 10^{-3} M KCl. B: 8 mM Cu^{2+} in 0.1 M Na_2SO_4. C: Oxygen in 0.01 M KCl; the mercury-column height is decreasing from I through V.*

Linear dependence of the limiting current on concentration as illustrated in Figure 3.6A is observed for diffusion currents, for the majority of kinetic currents, and for some catalytic currents (e.g., those involving regeneration of a reducible metal ion). Limiting dependences (Fig. 3.6, curves B, C) are observed for adsorption currents and for some catalytic currents.

Varying the height of the mercury column (h) above the orifice of the capillary provides a useful criterion for distinguishing among the various possible current-limiting processes. Diffusion currents are linearly proportional to $h^{1/2}$; kinetic currents are independent of h; and adsorption currents are linearly proportional to h (Fig. 3.7). The dependence of adsorption currents (i_a) on h should be measured at

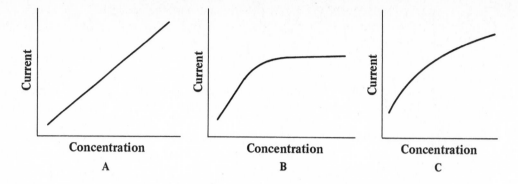

FIGURE 3.6. *Relation of limiting current to concentration. Curve A: Linear dependence observed for diffusion currents and for some kinetic and catalytic currents. Curves B and C: Limiting dependencies observed for adsorption and some catalytic currents.*

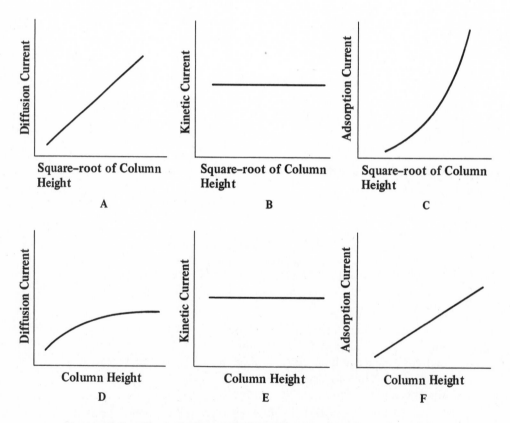

FIGURE 3.7. *The variation of the limiting current with mercury-column height for various types of polarographic currents. Curves A and D: Variation of diffusion current, i_d. Curves B and E: Variation of kinetic current, i_k. Curves C and F: Variation of adsorption current, i_a.*

concentrations where the current is concentration-independent; kinetic currents (i_k) are independent of h provided that measurements are carried out under conditions (e.g., pH) where i_k is less than 0.2 i_d.

The variation of current with time during the life of a single drop can be a most valuable criterion for determining the current-limiting process. With fast pen-recorders, one can obtain a moderately accurate measure of current-versus-time behavior by expansion of the time axis, but oscilloscopic observations are much to be preferred.

Equation 3.3 showed that diffusion-limited currents vary with time as $t^{1/6}$. This dependence is understandable from the combined effects of the increase in thickness of the diffusion layer with time, and the increase in area of the mercury drop. The first factor leads to a current proportional to $t^{-1/2}$ (Eqn. 1.6), the second to a current proportional to $t^{2/3}$ (Eqn. 3.2), and the combined effect ($t^{-1/2} \times t^{2/3}$) is $t^{1/6}$.

The rates of the homogeneous reactions responsible for kinetic and catalytic currents depend on the volume of solution in which the reactions occur. Since the reactions of interest occur near the electrode, the relevant volume is proportional to the area of the electrode, i.e., to $(mt)^{2/3}$, and thus kinetic and catalytic currents usually are proportional to $t^{2/3}$.

Adsorption-limited currents are proportional to the rate at which fresh mercury surface appears, that is, to the rate of change of the area of the electrode:

$$i_a \propto \frac{d}{dt}(mt)^{2/3} \propto t^{-1/3} \tag{3.5}$$

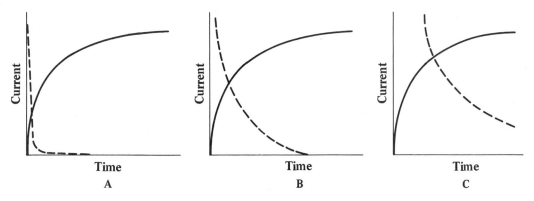

FIGURE 3.8. *Illustration of the relative importance of faradaic and charging current as the concentration of the electroactive species is reduced during the life of a single mercury drop. Solid lines: faradaic current; dashed lines: charging current. Curve A: for a 1 mM solution the contribution of the charging current is small and can be neglected. Curve B: for a 0.2 mM solution the contribution of the charging current is still small but not negligible and should be corrected for. Curve C: for 0.03 mM solution the charging current becomes larger than the faradaic and the separation of the two currents becomes necessary. The y-axes on the three curves have been normalized so that the faradaic current curves (solid lines) are the same size.*

Table 3.1. *Characteristics of Polarographic Currents*

Nature of Current	Symbol	Variation with					
		c	h	pH	Buffer Concentration	Temperature	Time
Diffusion	i_d	kc	$kh^{1/2}$	independent	independent	$+1.3\%/°C$	$t^{1/6}$
Kinetic	i_k	kc	independent	dependent	dependent	$+5\text{--}20\%/°C$	$t^{2/3}$
Adsorption	i_a	lim	kh	usually independent	independent	different	$t^{-1/3}$
Catalytic	i_c	lim	varies	strongly dependent	strongly dependent	——	$t^{2/3}$

The residual or charging current is also limited by the rate at which fresh electrode surface is formed, and hence is proportional to $t^{-1/3}$. This fact is of considerable significance in understanding variations of polarographic methods aimed at increasing sensitivity. Since diffusion currents increase with time (as $t^{1/6}$), and charging current decreases (as $t^{-1/3}$), measurement of the current late in the life of the drop gives a better sensitivity ("signal/noise") than measurements of average currents, or of currents early in the drop-life (see Fig. 3.8).

Here, only the currents (or wave heights) have been discussed, since these are the important measure for the quantitative analytical applications of polarography. When information concerning mechanisms and kinetics of reactions is sought, the shape of the rising portion of the polarographic wave is analyzed. Further, information on details of the electrode process can be obtained from measurements of half-wave potentials and their changes with the structure of the electroactive species as well as with the composition of the solution (for instance, pH and the concentration of complexing agents).

Whereas diffusion and adsorption currents are usually pH-independent, most kinetic and catalytic currents (in particular catalytic currents due to hydrogen evolution) change markedly with pH. Catalytic currents are frequently characterized by strong dependence on buffer concentration and kinetic currents sometimes show great changes with increasing temperature (Table 3.1).

3.2 INSTRUMENTATION AND APPARATUS

The apparatus for voltammetric analysis consists of a suitable cell, electrodes, a potentiostat or polarograph, and a system for removing oxygen from the solution.

Cells

Frequently, a stoppered lipless beaker is quite suitable as a polarographic cell; the stopper should have holes to accommodate the DME, reference electrode, counter electrode (when used), and gas-inlet and -outlet tubes for bubbling gas (usually purified nitrogen) through the solution to remove dissolved oxygen.

A "remote" or "isolated" reference electrode, separated from the cell by means of salt bridges, is sometimes used to prevent contamination of the sample solution by ions from the reference electrode.

Usually the gas used to remove oxygen is purified with a gas-washing train. It may be necessary (with volatile solvents or solutes) to pass the gas through a solution identical to that of the sample to avoid changes of concentration during deaeration. There may also be provision for passing gas *over* the sample solution after deaeration, if the analysis takes an appreciable time.

The cell may be immersed in a constant-temperature bath, or may have a jacket through which water from such a bath is circulated (diffusion-controlled currents increase by about 1.3% for each degree Celsius of rise in temperature).

Perhaps the most commonly used polarographic cell is the H-cell (Fig. 3.9), which has one compartment for the solution to be analyzed and a second compartment containing the reference electrode. Mixing of the solutions in the two compartments is prevented by the use of a porous glass frit (plug) and an agar-KCl salt bridge. Often, as illustrated in the figure, the reference electrode is a saturated calomel electrode constructed directly in the second compartment.

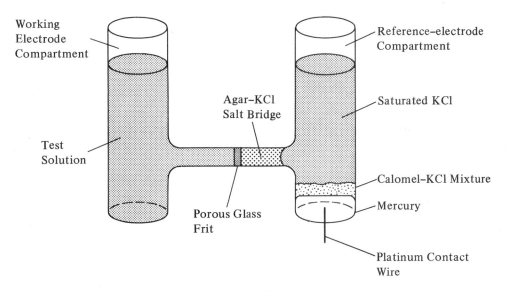

FIGURE 3.9. *Diagram of a common H-cell for polarographic analysis.*

A very large number of designs for polarographic cells have been described in the literature as being suitable for particular applications. For example, cells with reproducible liquid junctions that eliminate the use of glass frits or agar salt bridges (Fig. 3.10); very simple, easily assembled, and easily cleaned cells for routine analysis of large numbers of samples; microcells for use with test-solution volumes of a milliliter or less; and many others.

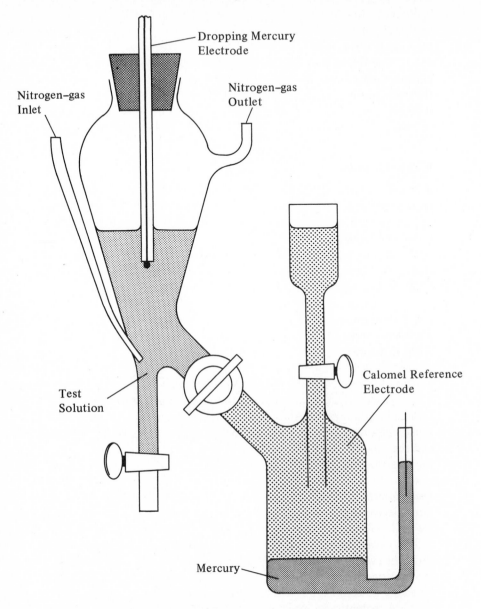

FIGURE 3.10. *Diagram of a polarographic cell designed for maintenance of a reproducible liquid junction.*

Electrodes

The DME can be made most economically by using suitable lengths (8 to 30 cm) of marine-barometer tubing (available from Corning Glass Works; 0.05 to 0.07 mm i.d.). The capillary is joined by plastic tubing to a mercury reservoir whose level can be adjusted to produce a suitable drop-time. (The drop-time is inversely proportional to the height of the mercury column, and directly proportional to the length of the capillary.) Mechanical devices to obtain a constant drop-life (drop-time) by tapping the capillary have been described in the literature, and are commercially available (Metrohm, Princeton Applied Research Corporation).

The reference electrode most commonly used is a saturated calomel, a mercurous sulfate, or silver/silver-chloride electrode. When accurate measurement of the potential is not required, a mercury pool or a platinum wire, foil, or gauze can be used. In nonaqueous solutions, various other reference electrodes may be more suitable.

Instrumentation

A simple polarograph can be constructed from a potentiometer and a sensitive current-measuring instrument according to the scheme in Figure 3.1. Manual recording of polarographic curves with such an apparatus is, however, very time consuming and cannot be recommended for practical analyses.

A number of reliable, low-cost ($2000–5000), recording DC polarographs are commercially available such as the Princeton Applied Research Model 174, Sargent XVI, Tacussel PRGS, and Beckman Electroscan.

Some of these instruments offer other applications in addition to recording DC polarographic curves. These polarographs principally consist of a source of gradually increasing voltage, a voltage-range selector, and a current-range selector. Some instruments permit a partial compensation of the charging current by a counter current linearly proportional to the applied voltage; some allow large shifts of the position for zero current, to shift unwanted waves outside the recording zone.

A wide variety of recording polarographs or potentiostats capable of simple DC polarography and linear-sweep voltammetry can be built from modern operational amplifiers for as little as about $100, depending on the number of extra features and the quality of the amplifiers desired. All that is needed in addition is a suitable *x-y* or strip-chart recorder.

Potentiostats. Most modern voltammetric instrumentation involves the use of the three-electrode potentiostatic polarograph as shown in Figure 3.11. Although simple DC polarography and slow-scan linear-sweep voltammetry can be performed with a two-electrode system in high-conductivity (low-resistance) systems, a three-electrode system (which automatically compensates for solution resistance) is necessary for investigation of nonaqueous systems of low conductivity and for investigations involving pulse-polarographic or rapid-scan techniques.

A potentiostat functions in the following manner: The reference electrode, used to measure the potential of the working electrode, is isolated by the voltage-follower amplifier so that very little current is drained from it. The output of the voltage follower (that is, the working-electrode potential measured by the reference electrode) is fed into the control or scan amplifier along with the various input voltages. If the potential measured by the reference electrode is different from the sum of the other input voltages (implying that the potential of the working electrode differs from the desired value), the control amplifier will supply a corrective voltage at the counter electrode to compensate for this. The current flow in the cell is essentially

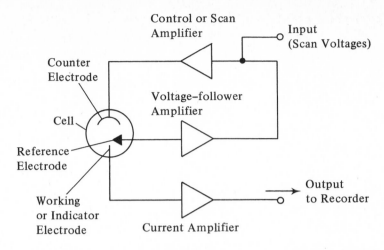

FIGURE 3.11. *Schematic diagram of a modern, three-electrode potentiostat.*

between the counter and working electrodes. Finally, the current amplifier takes the current flowing to (or from) the working electrode, converts it to a voltage that is proportional to the magnitude of the current, and amplifies the voltage for presentation to a recorder.

3.3 APPLICATIONS

Measurement of Voltammetric and Polarographic Curves

Although polarography may be occasionally used for qualitative analysis, the typical application is in quantitative analysis. To determine concentrations, the polarographic limiting current is measured.

Numerous methods of measuring the wave height are described in the literature and a choice amongst these might seem to be a difficult task. However, most of the methods used give essentially equivalent results, provided that the measurements are carried out with sufficient care and accuracy and that the wave height is measured in the same way for all waves to be compared—that is, for the samples themselves and for the standards used in calibration.

In the measurement of wave heights, corrections for the residual or capacity current must be made. This can be done either by recording the residual current separately in a solution containing all the components with the exception of the electroactive species under study, or by extrapolation. The graphical subtraction of residual current is generally considered more reliable, particularly for inorganic species and at lower concentrations. For larger organic compounds the basic assumption involved—i.e., identity of the residual current in the sample solution and in the blank—is not generally fulfilled: adsorption of the organic compound results in a change in the capacity current. In such cases, the extrapolation of portions of the polarographic curves, as shown in Figure 3.12, seems to be the most accurate approach.

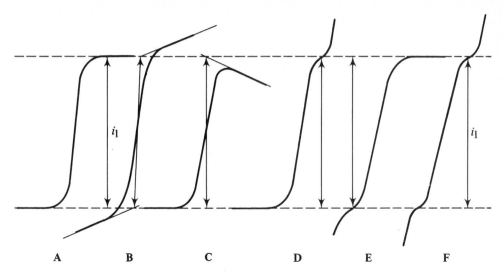

FIGURE 3.12. *Illustration of several methods for measuring the wave height of variously shaped polarographic waves. Curves A–C illustrate the technique of extrapolating the linear portions of the waves before and after the current rise. Curves D–F illustrate the technique of estimating current magnitudes for ill shaped waves.*

The exact method of measurement depends on the shape of the polarographic wave. Some examples are shown in Figure 3.12.

The maximum value of the oscillating current is the magnitude commonly measured and used in calculations. In the earlier literature, when fast-response recorders were not available, measurement of the average of the oscillations was recommended.

Determination of Concentration

Once the height of the wave has been obtained, it remains to relate this to the concentration of the studied solution. As with the majority of physical methods used in analytical chemistry, such evaluation is based on comparison with a standard.

The two methods of comparison most frequently used are that of employing a calibration curve and that of standard addition.

Calibration Curves. The calibration curve is constructed by successively adding increasing amounts of the substance to be studied to a solution of supporting electrolyte, which is prepared using all the other components present in the sample solution. The polarographic curves are recorded and measured, and the wave height is plotted as a function of concentration.

Next, curves are recorded for solutions containing samples to be analyzed in the same supporting electrolyte as was used for the construction of the calibration curve. It is essential that the curves for the sample analysis be recorded under *exactly* the same conditions as those used in the construction of the calibration curve. In particular, one uses the same capillary, the same pressure of mercury, the same sensitivity (current range) of the recording instrument, and the same temperature. The wave height obtained with the sample is then measured, compared with the calibration curve, and the concentration read off.

The pressure of mercury is kept constant by maintaining the mercury in the reservoir at a constant level. Somewhat more difficult to guarantee is the use of the same capillary. This implies that when a capillary is broken, or behaves erratically (commonly, as a result of penetration of impurities into the bore), a new calibration curve must be constructed. If the highest accuracy is aimed at, the temperature of the electrolytic cell must also be controlled by using a water-jacket or by immersing the cell in a thermostatted bath.

The most difficult condition to meet is making the solutions used for constructing calibration curves identical to those used for sample analysis. Frequently the calibration curves are recorded in solutions containing only the studied compound and supporting electrolyte; however, the preparation of the sample solution often introduces other substances. It can usually be assumed that these substances will have a negligible effect on the waves of the compound to be determined, but sometimes such electro-inactive components of the sample can affect the height of the measured wave.

If such an effect of electro-inactive components cannot be neglected, an attempt can be made to prepare synthetic sample solutions that would contain all components with the exception of the studied substance. Such synthetic samples are then added to all solutions used in the preparation of the calibration curve.

Serious difficulty with this approach can result from insufficient knowledge of the sample composition. Alternatively, it is sometimes impossible to obtain or prepare samples that would not contain any of the component to be determined. For example, in the analysis of biological material for a common trace metal or widely distributed organic compound (e.g., pyruvic acid), it is practically impossible to obtain biological material that contains a negligible concentration of the substance to be determined.

One possible solution is to use a sample with a small concentration of the investigated compound as the starting point instead of pure supporting electrolyte. Curves recorded for solutions containing successively increasing concentrations of the compound added are then corrected for the small wave in the original sample before the wave height is plotted.

Standard-Addition Method. An alternative possibility is the use of the standard-addition method. When this method is used, the condition of identical composition of compared solutions is most closely fulfilled. Moreover, because the curve of the sample and the curve obtained after addition of the standard are usually recorded within a short time interval, the temperature of the two solutions is sufficiently similar even without thermostatic control. This method assumes a direct linearity between the wave height and concentration, $i = kc$.

In the method of standard addition, a curve of the sample solution is recorded first. Then a known amount of a standard stock solution is added to the sample solution and another curve recorded. The principle of evaluation of these curves is best demonstrated with an example (Fig. 3.13). In this case, a sample of steel was dissolved in acidic solution and two aliquots taken. To one, a known volume of a standard dichromate solution was added; then a solution of hydrogen peroxide and an excess of sodium hydroxide was added to both. After removing the unreacted hydrogen peroxide by boiling, cooling, and adjusting the volume to a known value, oxygen was removed and both curves recorded (Fig. 3.13). The height, i, of the wave obtained with the steel sample was measured similarly as the height, i', of the wave obtained after addition of amount a of chromium (as metal) to the steel sample. Calculation of the weight of chromium present in the aliquot (x) is possible by means of

$$x = a \frac{i}{i' - i} \tag{3.6}$$

Knowing the weight of steel sample originally taken and the fraction of the total sample contained in the aliquot analyzed, the percentage of chromium in the steel sample can be determined.

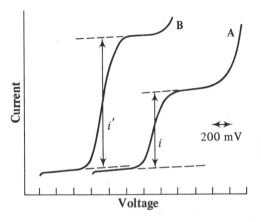

FIGURE 3.13. *Illustration of the determination of concentration by the method of standard additions. Curve A: Polarogram of chromate ion reduction from the chromium in an aliquot of a digested steel sample. Curve B: A polarogram of a similar aliquot to which has been added a known volume of a standard chromium solution.*

This approach, based on addition of the standard prior to any chemical operation and sample handling, is usually the most reliable, since it can be assumed that all losses affecting the determined component in the sample are proportional to losses in the added standard. However, it is necessary to handle two solutions in all operations.

To simplify the handling and thus to gain time, it is possible to modify the proposed procedure in cases where the dissolution of the sample is complete, the resulting solution is homogeneous, and no source of losses is known. In this modification, only one solution of the sample is prepared and handled. All separations and chemical reactions are carried out with this solution and supporting electrolyte is added. An aliquot (of volume V) of the final solution (c_{unk}) is transferred into the polarographic cell and the polarographic curve recorded (the height of which is denoted i). Then volume v of a standard stock solution of concentration c_{std} is added and a second curve (height i') is recorded. The concentration of the sample solution can then be calculated using

$$c_{\text{unk}} = c_{\text{std}} \frac{i}{i' + (i' - i)\dfrac{V}{v}} \tag{3.7}$$

If the volume of the standard addition or "spike," v, is very much smaller than the original solution volume V (1% or less), then any volume change can be ignored and Equation 3.7 simplifies somewhat to

$$c_{\text{unk}} = c_{\text{std}} \frac{iv}{(i' - i)V} \qquad (3.8)$$

Pilot-Ion Method. Another method, known as the "quotient of two waves" or "pilot-ion" method, is less frequently used, but offers some advantages. (This is known more generally as an "internal standard" method.) A known quantity of a standard "pilot" substance is added to each investigated solution. This pilot substance must be polarographically active and give a wave or waves in a potential region (preferably at more positive potentials) sufficiently different from that of the compound to be determined.

The ratio of the wave height of the unknown to that of the pilot can be assumed to be independent of capillary characteristics, viscosity of the solution, temperature, etc. Hence, a new measurement of this ratio is not needed whenever the capillary is replaced, and the temperature need not be controlled. The calibration curves are constructed by plotting the ratio of the heights of the two waves against the concentration of the substance to be determined, keeping the concentration of the pilot species constant. Such calibration curves can be used for evaluation of sample solutions (to which the same concentration of the pilot substance has been added) in the same way as the simple calibration curves mentioned above.

Intercomparison of Methods. The speed of analysis where only one curve of the sample is recorded at the time of the analysis makes the calibration-curve method preferable in serial analysis of a large number of samples of similar composition. When precise results are required, temperature control is necessary, and when the capillary is blocked or broken, additional work for construction of a new calibration curve is necessary. The calibration-curve method is always used when the relation between the measured current and concentration is nonlinear (e.g., when catalytic or adsorption currents are dealt with).

The method of "quotient of two waves" can be applied in cases similar to those in which the simple calibration curve is used. Temperature control is unnecessary, but construction of several calibration curves for different concentrations of the "pilot" substance is usually necessary.

The method of standard addition is useful when analysis of only a limited number of samples is required. In such instances the construction of a calibration curve would be too time consuming. The apparatus is simplified by the fact that temperature control is unnecessary. On the other hand, because two curves (with and without addition of the standard) have to be recorded for each sample, the time spent on a single analysis is somewhat longer.

The accuracy of the standard-addition method is somewhat lower than the procedure based on the use of calibration curves. This is because, in calculating concentrations using Equations 3.6 to 3.8, a direct proportionality is assumed between the measured current and concentration. This corresponds to a linear calibration curve passing through the origin where current and concentration equal zero. This assumption may be approximately valid at concentrations larger than about

10^{-4} M, but is rarely fulfilled in trace analysis. Nevertheless, the method of standard addition remains a first choice in cases where sample components might affect the wave height of the component analyzed, and yet it is difficult to obtain a sample with zero content of this component (e.g., biological material).

The relative methods mentioned above, based on comparison with standards, are to be preferred over so-called "absolute methods" where concentrations are calculated using predetermined and tabulated "diffusion-current constants" or diffusion coefficients, both known to be dependent on experimental conditions.

Scope of Applications

Electroactive Species. Inorganic cations, anions, and molecules can be determined polarographically. Among cations, the transition metals are most profitably determined polarographically, but some alkaline-earth and rare-earth ions also offer useful analytic curves. Strongly hydrolyzed metals (e.g., aluminum, thorium, zirconium) present difficulties (which can be circumvented by using nonaqueous solvents); so do some elements that form predominantly covalent bonds (e.g., silicon; however, some germanium complexes are reducible). Typical ions frequently determined are those of Cu(II), Cu(I), Tl(I), Pb(II), Cd(II), Zn(II), Fe(II), Fe(III), Ni(II), Co(II), Bi(III), Sb(III), Sb(V), Sn(II), Sn(IV), and Eu(III); and Mo, W, V, Mn, Cr, Ti, N, and Pt in a number of oxidation states. Even when it is possible to determine alkali metals polarographically, flame photometry or some other spectral technique is usually superior.

Anions of the halides, as well as sulfides, selenides, and tellurides, can be determined by means of anodic waves due to mercury-salt formation. Among the oxygen-containing anions—in addition to those of the metals mentioned above—cathodic reduction waves can be used for determination of bromates, iodates, periodates, sulfites, polythionates, etc.

Finally, among inorganic molecules, polarography can be used to determine oxygen, hydrogen peroxide, elemental sulfur, some sulfur oxides, and oxides of nitrogen, as well as some undissociated acids.

A great number and variety of organic compounds can be quantitatively determined by reduction at the DME. Only highly polarizable single bonds between carbon and heteroatoms are reducible in the available potential range, e.g., C–Cl, C–Br, or C–I bonds. Other single bonds, e.g., C–O, C–S, or C–N, require the presence of an adjacent activating group such as a carbonyl group or a pyridine ring.

Some single bonds between heteroatoms, such as those in peroxides and disulfides, as well as N–N, N–O, S–O, and similar bonds are also easily reducible.

Double and triple bonds are frequently reducible, in particular when the reduced bond is a part of a conjugated system; for example, unsaturated conjugated or aromatic hydrocarbons, carbonyl compounds and their nitrogen analogues, and nitro-, nitroso- and azo-compounds.

Because of the relatively easy oxidation of mercury, anodic waves are observed with the DME only for the strongest reducing agents such as hydroquinones, enediols (e.g., ascorbic acid), phenylhydroxylamine derivatives, and certain aldehydes. Numerous organic substances nevertheless yield anodic waves corresponding to mercury-salt formation, e.g., thiols and other derivatives of bivalent sulfur, amines, and some heterocycles. The organic compounds, in these cases, are not oxidized, but only make the oxidation of mercury easier (the amount being directly related to the concentration of the compound). The more stable the mercury salt, the more easily the oxidation occurs, i.e., the more negative the wave appears on the potential axis.

Nature of the Sample. Since electrolysis is almost invariably carried out in solution, it is necessary first to convert any sample into a solution. The sample itself can be a solid, liquid, or gas. In the last two cases the dissolution is usually straightforward; for solid samples, procedures used in other wet analytical procedures are followed, with the exception that the use of nitric acid is usually avoided because of the possibility of generating electroactive nitrogen oxides.

Typical examples of samples range from metals, alloys, slags, ores, minerals, and fertilizers to a variety of organic materials such as polymers, petroleum and its products, fibres and textile materials, pesticides, insecticides, herbicides, food and food products, including beverages (beer and wine), biological materials, pharmaceuticals, plants, and soils. Examples of liquid samples subjected to polarographic analysis are body fluids such as blood and urine, natural and industrial water, and seawater. Polluted atmosphere and industrial gases represent samples of gaseous nature. In particular, the ability to determine oxygen in the presence of practically all other gases is often utilized.

Detection Limits, Accuracy and Precision, Selectivity. The detection limit in DC polarography is usually between 1 and $5 \times 10^{-6} M$. Other polarographic techniques (see Sec. 3.4) offer lower detection limits: $10^{-8} M$ with differential-pulse polarography, and even lower when preconcentration is used, as in stripping voltammetry. In the last case, metals that form amalgams and anions that form insoluble mercury salts can be determined down to $10^{-9} M$ and even $10^{-10} M$. The typical range for stripping analysis, however, is 10^{-6} to $10^{-9} M$, with an absolute sample size of about 0.1 ng of the element analyzed. With care, the precision is about ± 10–20% at the $10^{-10} M$ level, and about ± 2–5% for concentrations greater than about $10^{-9} M$.

Considerably lower detection limits (than $10^{-6} M$) in DC polarography are observed for some catalytic currents. For example, cobalamine in buffers and iron in sodium hydroxide can be detected even with DC polarography down to about $10^{-8} M$.

The final volume of the solution for polarographic analysis is usually of the order of 5 to 20 ml; decrease of the volume down to 0.1 ml does not present any difficulties apart from the need to use special cells. If necessary, polarographic electrolysis can be carried out in as little as 0.01 ml. However, the handling of small volumes requires considerable skill and is much more time consuming than operation on the milliliter level (as is usually the case with microchemical operations, regardless of the particular analytical method used).

The accuracy and reproducibility of the results depend considerably on the shape of the wave under study. For well developed waves or well separated peaks, the limiting current (wave height) can be measured with an error of ± 1–2%. Considering the required constancy of the various experimental factors controlling the limiting current and inaccuracies in the preparation of the sample, an overall error of about $\pm 3\%$ can be said to be typical for polarographic determinations. In high-precision serial analyses, the error can be improved to 1% when all factors are strictly controlled.

The accuracy and precision decrease for ill-shaped waves. If, moreover, the composition of the sample with respect to electro-inactive materials that affect the shape of polarographic curves varies from sample to sample (e.g., in samples of biological materials), the error may increase to $\pm 5\%$ or even to $\pm 20\%$. However, even this level is often sufficient for clinical analysis, studies of natural products, or other biochemical applications.

For the whole concentration range from 10^{-3} M to about one order of magnitude above the detection limit of the particular polarographic technique, the *relative* error of polarographic determinations usually remains practically unchanged. This means that, from an absolute point of view, the accuracy is good or sufficient at low concentration levels but poorer at higher concentrations. This in turn means that polarography is relatively well suited for trace analysis, is suitable for determination of samples containing 30% or more of the active component only when high precision is not required, and is unsuitable for *accurate* determination of the main component when the sample consists of 90% or more of this component.

In addition to sensitivity, the main advantage of polarographic methods is their selectivity. Current-versus-voltage curves often reveal the presence of interfering substances—not the case in optical methods, especially when measurements are carried out at only one wavelength. The selectivity of polarographic methods is particularly great when the analysis is carried out in more than one supporting electrolyte.

All the characteristics of polarographic methods as analytical tools indicate that they are particularly useful for trace analysis. Components can be determined in the ppm to ppb range with accuracy sufficient for most practical analyses. The amount of sample needed for analysis varies between a few micrograms and about 50 mg. Larger samples are used only when an average composition is aimed at.

Interferences. Two types of interference may be encountered in polarographic analysis. The first is identical with problems encountered with other analytical methods in the presence of two or more species that give signals too similar to be distinguished. When two species give waves whose potentials differ by less than about 100 mV in DC polarography (and by less than about 50 mV in single-sweep voltammetry and differential-pulse polarography, Sec. 3.4), such waves or peaks overlap and prevent the determination of the individual components.

In addition, DC polarography has a more specific limitation. Measurement of a more positive wave in the presence of an excess of material reduced at more negative potentials (wave A in Fig. 3.14) can be carried out with maximum accuracy; but when the trace material to be determined is reduced at more negative potentials (wave B′ in Fig. 3.14)—that is, when a small wave follows a large one—measurement of the small, more negative, wave can be carried out only when the concentration ratio between the excess component and the analyzed species is less than about 10:1. At larger excess the accuracy of the determination of the trace component decreases considerably.

FIGURE 3.14. *Polarograms of mixtures of electroactive substances in different ratios. Curve 1: Reduction of a small amount of a more easily reduced substance in the presence of a larger amount of a substance reduced at a more negative potential. Curve 2: Reduction of a small amount of a substance in the presence of a large amount of a substance reduced at more positive potential.*

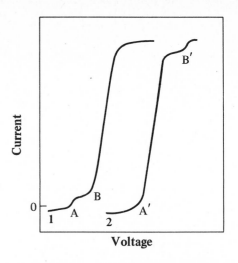

Separation of overlapping waves or peaks is frequently possible by changing the composition of the supporting electrolyte. Differences in complexing properties are made use of primarily in inorganic analysis, while differences in acid-base properties are used in organic analysis. Alternatively, a change in solvent may result in separation of overlapping curves, owing to differences in solvation of the electroactive species.

An example of separation of overlapping waves is the analysis of mixtures of lead(II) and thallium(I). A mixture of these two ions in neutral media gives a wave that cannot be resolved into the individual waves of Pb^{2+} and Tl^+; the half-wave potentials differ by only about 60 mV. When excess sodium hydroxide is added, the wave for thallium(I) remains at virtually the same potential as in neutral media (as thallium does not form hydroxo complexes), whereas the wave of lead(II) is shifted to more negative potential by about 300 mV, due to formation of plumbate (Fig. 3.15). Generally, when a metal cation forms a complex, its reduction potential is made more negative—it is more difficult to reduce.

Selectivity depends very much on the system studied, and may be either better or worse than in ultraviolet spectrophotometry. This can be illustrated for the simple alkaline cleavage of α,β-unsaturated carbonyl compounds. When cleavage of chalcone ($C_6H_5COCH{=}CHC_6H_5$) is followed, polarography permits determination of the parent compound, of benzaldehyde, and of the sum of acetophenone and the intermediate ketol $C_6H_5COCH_2CH(OH)C_6H_5$ in the mixture. Because the concentrations of benzaldehyde and acetophenone as final products must be equal, the concentrations of all four components in the mixture can be determined polarographically. Ultraviolet spectra of the intermediates and products overlap, however, and only the concentration of the starting material can be determined spectrophotometrically without interference.

On the other hand, when the products of the alkaline cleavage of cinnamaldehyde ($C_6H_5CH{=}CHCHO$) are investigated, the polarographic waves of the aldol intermediate and of benzaldehyde overlap, and the acetaldehyde waves are ill-developed. Ultraviolet spectra, on the other hand, allow the determination of cinnamaldehyde and of the aldol [$C_6H_5CH(OH)CH_2CHO$] in the presence of benzaldehyde.

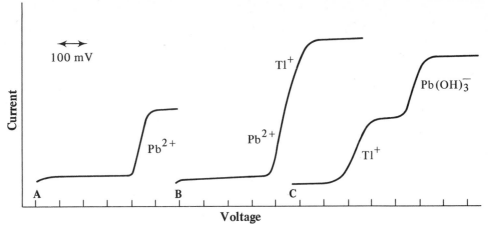

FIGURE 3.15. *Polarographic waves of Pb^{2+} and Tl^+, illustrating the shift of waves with change in background electrolyte. Curve A: Lead reduction in neutral media. Curve B: Merged waves for the reduction of lead and thallium in neutral media. Curve C: Separate waves for the reduction of lead and thallium in excess hydroxide.*

Polarographic and optical methods are thus frequently complementary rather than competitive.

Examples of Practical Applications

Since the invention of polarography in 1922, more than 30,000 papers dealing with this technique have been published. Since more than 90% of those papers deal with practical applications, any choice of examples cannot be more than an indication of the possibilities the method offers. The following selection, which is necessarily subjective, was made with the aim of showing applications in a variety of fields.

Manganese and Iron in Ores. In alkaline triethanolamine solution, manganese(III) gives a reduction wave at -0.3 V whereas the iron(III) wave is at -1.0 V. Since copper, lead, and nickel interfere, the ore is dissolved in hydrochloric acid and the resulting solution is first reduced with powdered zinc. After addition of triethanolamine and concentrated sodium hydroxide solutions, the mixture is vigorously shaken for about half a minute to ensure oxidation of the manganese and iron complexes to the trivalent state by atmospheric oxygen. The current-versus-voltage curves are recorded after removal of oxygen.

Iron in iron ores can, of course, also be analyzed by the classical redox titration with standard dichromate solution using a diphenylamine sulfonate indicator. Trace manganese in ores can also be determined using colorimetric methods or atomic absorption spectroscopy. An atomic absorption spectrophotometer, however, will cost a minimum of about $4500 and requires the periodic replacement of expensive hollow-cathode lamps. The point is that one usually has some choice of analytical methods, each with its particular advantages and disadvantages for the problem at hand.

Copper and Other Impurities in Lead. Lead (that used in storage batteries, for instance) is dissolved in nitric acid and the greater part of the lead precipitated by adding sulfuric acid. The supernatant is treated with citric acid and the pH adjusted to about 6 with ammonia. The polarograms show waves of copper at -0.2 V, bismuth at -0.5 V, and lead (the unprecipitated remainder) at -0.4 V. The wave of iron(III), if present, coincides with that of copper(II).

To another portion of the supernatant, evaporated to a small volume, ammonia–ammonium chloride buffer is added. The curve recorded in this solution shows waves of copper at -0.25 and -0.5 V, nickel at -1.1 V, zinc at -1.3 V, and manganese at -1.6 V. Cobalt, if present, gives a wave that overlaps that of zinc.

If antimony is present, it can be detected by recording the current-versus-voltage curve in the original acidic solution, where its wave follows a combined wave of copper, iron, and bismuth.

Lead in Tinned Food. The sample, digested with sulfuric and nitric acids, is treated with hydrogen peroxide to remove the oxides of nitrogen. Treating the sample with sodium thiosulfate and nitric acid precipitates stannic acid. Any iron present is reduced by metallic magnesium, and the polarogram of lead is recorded after adding tartaric acid and adjusting the pH to about 5 with base.

Morphine. Morphine can be determined in pharmaceutical preparations after reacting it with nitrite to form a nitro compound. The procedure can also be used to analyze blood or other biological fluids for morphine after separating the fluid into its constituents by paper or thin-layer chromatography. The sample is dissolved in hydrochloric acid, potassium nitrite is added, and the sample is allowed to stand for 5 min at 20°C. After adding an excess of potassium hydroxide and removing oxygen, the polarogram is recorded.

When nitration is carried out under the described conditions, the presence of narcotine, papaverine, or codeine does not interfere. Heroin can be determined after acid hydrolysis of the acetyl group.

DDT. The insecticide DDT (p,p'-dichlorodiphenyltrichloroethane) gives a well developed wave at -0.9 V in 96% ethanol containing lithium and tetraalkylammonium salts.

A mixture of the biologically active p,p'-dichlorodiphenyl derivative and the inactive o,p'-isomer can be analyzed. Polarography is useful for residue analysis of a number of insecticides, both chlorinated (e.g., hexachlorocyclohexane) and non-chlorinated (e.g., dithiocarbamates, pyrethrins, rotenone, etc.).

Ascorbic Acid in Fruit and Vegetables. Anodic waves corresponding to the oxidation of ascorbic acid (vitamin C) can be used for analysis of fruit and vegetables. Soft and juicy fruits (e.g., citrus fruit, currants, melons, gooseberries) and vegetables (e.g., tomatoes) can simply be squeezed, the collected juice mixed with deoxygenated (to prevent oxidation of ascorbic acid) pH 4.7 acetate buffer and the anodic waves recorded. For hard fruit and vegetables, prior homogenization is necessary.

Biological thiols such as glutathione, which interfere with or complicate titrimetric methods, do not interfere with the polarographic determination.

Carbon Disulfide in the Atmosphere. The pulp and paper industry often causes pollution of the atmosphere with carbon disulfide. To determine CS_2 in the atmosphere, a gaseous sample from a chimney, for instance, is drawn into a vessel containing diethylamine solution in 96% ethanol which converts the carbon disulfide into diethyldithiocarbamate while still at the site. The solution does not deteriorate with time, so the sample vessel can be left in place for several days to enrich the sample in CS_2. In the laboratory, the sample is diluted with a lithium-chloride solution and a polarogram recorded.

The method is unaffected by a fivefold excess of hydrogen sulfide and of most mercaptans (phenylmercaptan, however, interferes). If carbon oxysulfide is present, the method must be modified.

Dissolved Oxygen: The "Oxygen Electrode." Compact portable units are available for the determination of dissolved O_2 gas in aqueous solutions. The "oxygen electrode" or sensor probe is really an electrochemical cell composed of a gold or platinum cathode and a suitable reference anode—usually some type of silver electrode. A constant potential of about 0.8 V is applied between the two electrodes. The cell is separated from the test solution by a gas-permeable membrane, typically cellophane, polyethylene, or Teflon. Oxygen diffuses from the test solution through the membrane and is reduced at the cathode; the resulting current is proportional to the oxygen level of the test solution. The entire system must be calibrated with one or more solutions of known oxygen content.

Complete benchtop units are used routinely for monitoring dissolved oxygen in biological fluids and systems. Portable pressure- and temperature-compensated oxygen-electrode systems are available for monitoring oxygen levels in oceans, lakes, and rivers and in effluents and wastewaters at depths down to about 30 m.

3.4 VARIATIONS OF THE CONVENTIONAL POLAROGRAPHIC METHOD

Many modifications of polarography have been proposed for a number of specific purposes: to investigate mechanisms of electrode reactions, to decrease the time needed for examination of a given sample, to increase sensitivity (usually by decreasing the residual or charging current), and so on. Here, those modifications that have found significant applications in analytical work will be briefly described.

Pulse Polarography

One approach that minimizes the effect of charging current is *pulse polarography*. In this technique, instead of applying a continuously increasing voltage, a single rectangular voltage pulse is applied to the electrode during the last portion of its life. In this way, the period at the beginning of the drop-life, when changes in charging current are greatest, is avoided. Moreover, the current is measured over a very short time, and appreciably later than the sudden change in voltage, so that the charging current has decreased more than the faradaic current has at the time the current is measured.

In pulse polarography, two main variants can be distinguished: techniques using gradually increasing amplitude of the voltage pulse (pulse polarography) and those in which the voltage pulse used has a constant amplitude, superimposed on a slowly increasing voltage (differential-pulse polarography).

In *pulse polarography*, a square-wave voltage pulse of about 40 msec duration is applied to the electrode during the last quarter of the drop-life (Fig. 3.16A). At the instant the voltage pulse is applied, the charging current is very large, but it decays rather rapidly (exponentially). The current is then measured during the 20 msec of the second half of the pulse (Fig. 3.16B) when the charging current is quite small. The amplitude of the applied voltage pulses increases linearly with time. When the current response is recorded as a function of voltage, the shape of the resulting curve resembles waves in DC polarography (Fig. 3.16C), except that it has a "staircase" appearance because the current is sampled once during each drop-life and stored until the next sample period.

In *differential-pulse polarography* the duration of pulses is similar to that used in the previous technique (i.e., 40–60 msec), the pulses are also applied during the last quarter of the drop-life (when the surface area of the dropping electrode changes little with the time), but the pulses used have a constant amplitude (usually 5 to 100 mV) and are superimposed on a slowly increasing linear voltage ramp (Fig. 3.16D). Two measuring periods are used, one immediately preceding the pulse, the other very near the end of the pulse. The overall response plotted is the difference in the two currents sampled: one at point b in Figure 3.16E, corresponding to the polarographic current that would be measured at the given potential in the absence of a voltage pulse, and one at point d in Figure 3.16E, which is the sum of the current at b and the current resulting from the application of the additional voltage. The plot of this difference (Δi) as a function of potential is peak-shaped (Fig. 3.16F).

By measuring the difference in current before the application of the voltage pulse and towards the end of the pulse, the charging current contribution is further reduced in magnitude.

The peak shape of differential-pulse polarograms results from the relation

FIGURE 3.16. *Waveforms for pulse and differential-pulse polarography. Curves A and D: Excitation signal applied to the working electrode. Curves B and E: Instantaneous current observed at a single drop as a function of time. Curves C and F: The resulting current-versus-voltage curves. In pulse polarography, square-wave voltage pulses of 40-msec duration are applied to the mercury drop, of drop-life mechanically controlled at 2.5 sec (A); $t_d, t_d', t_d'', \ldots$ represent successive drops. The overall rate of increase of the amplitude of the voltage pulses is about 0.1 V/min. The instantaneous current at a single drop (B) shows the decay of current, primarily capacitive, during the first 20 msec after the application of the pulse, and the amount of the current flowing during the latter 20 msec of the pulse duration. The response (C) of the system has the familiar sigmoidal shape of an ordinary polarogram. In differential-pulse polarography, constant-amplitude pulses between about 5 and 100 mV are superimposed on a linearly increasing DC voltage ramp (D). The instantaneous current response at a single drop is similar to that for pulse polarography, except that the current is sampled at two places (E). The response is now peak shaped (F).*

POLAROGRAPHY

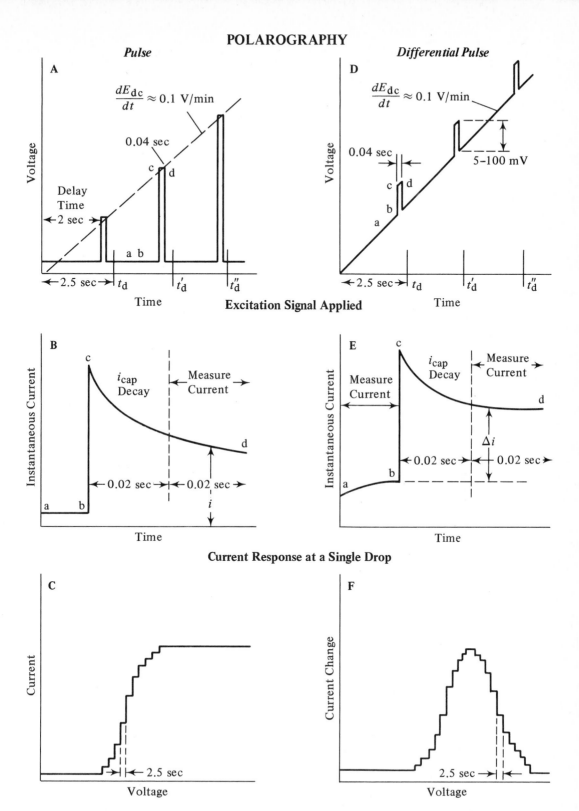

Pulse

A

$$\frac{dE_{dc}}{dt} \approx 0.1 \text{ V/min}$$

0.04 sec

c d

Delay Time
← 2 sec →

Voltage

a b

← 2.5 sec → t_d t'_d t''_d

Time

Differential Pulse

D

$$\frac{dE_{dc}}{dt} \approx 0.1 \text{ V/min}$$

0.04 sec

c d

b

a

5–100 mV

Voltage

← 2.5 sec → t_d t'_d t''_d

Time

Excitation Signal Applied

B

c

i_{cap} Decay

Measure Current

d

a b

← 0.02 sec → ← 0.02 sec →

i

Instantaneous Current

Time

E

c

i_{cap} Decay

Measure Current

Measure Current

d

a

b

← 0.02 sec → ← 0.02 sec →

Δi

Instantaneous Current

Time

Current Response at a Single Drop

C

Current

← 2.5 sec →

Voltage

F

Current Change

2.5 sec →

Voltage

Resultant Current–Voltage Curve

between the potentials applied during the two sampling periods. When potentials of both sampling periods are either at more positive or at more negative potentials than the rising portion of the DC polarographic wave, the faradaic currents flowing at both potentials are practically the same and hence Δi approaches zero value (or is generally small). However, when at least one of the sampling periods corresponds to a potential on the rising portion of the polarographic wave, the difference between the currents flowing during the two sampling periods is different from zero, and Δi increases. The difference between the two currents is largest in the vicinity of the half-wave potential, where the slope of the DC polarographic wave is usually largest. The position of the peak on the Δi-versus-E curve depends on the amplitude of the pulse.

Both pulse techniques involve synchronization of the drop-time of the DME with the frequency of the applied pulses. This is achieved by mechanical drop-control using a magnetically controlled "hammer" knocking the capillary and causing detachment of drops from the capillary. The frequency of knocking, and hence the drop-time, can be electronically controlled and synchronized with the application of voltage pulses. It has proven useful to synchronize the detachment of the mercury drop with the power-line frequency to minimize electrical noise picked up by the electrodes and metal supporting stands from the surroundings.

Both techniques produce signals that are a linear function of concentration provided that the characteristics of the capillary electrode and the pattern of pulses remain constant. The use of differential pulse assumes constant amplitude of the pulse as well as constant frequency, pulse duration, and location of sampling periods.

The detection limit for pulse polarography is typically about $10^{-7}\,M$, and about $10^{-8}\,M$ for the differential-pulse method—although, of course, detection limits do depend on the electrochemical properties of the substance analyzed, interferences, and other experimental variables. The detection limit for arsenic(III) by differential-pulse polarography, for example, has been reported to be $4 \times 10^{-9}\,M$ (0.3 ppb), with a linear calibration curve up to $8 \times 10^{-4}\,M$.

Linear-Sweep Voltammetry

Principles. Instead of working under essentially potentiostatic conditions with a DME as in DC and pulse polarography, it is possible to carry out the whole potential scan (e.g., from 0 V to −2.0 V or over any other similar potential range) on a more or less constant electrode surface.

This can be achieved in two different ways. In the first, a slow scan, comparable to that used in DC polarography, is carried out using an electrode with a constant, unchanging surface such as a mercury pool, a hanging mercury drop, or a solid electrode. The electrode can be stationary and the solution stationary or stirred; or the electrode can be periodically displaced in the solution by rotation, vibration, etc.

Alternatively, an electrode with a periodically renewed surface (dropping or streaming mercury electrodes) can be used. To accomplish the voltage scan during the life of a single drop, the rate of scanning must then be much faster than with stationary electrodes, and the scanning speed must be even greater if the area of the electrode is to remain virtually constant during the scan.

Recording of current-versus-voltage curves using electrodes with unchanged surface and slow rate of scanning has not found wide analytical application, with the

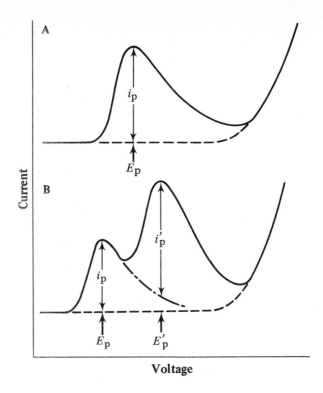

FIGURE 3.17. *Typical linear-scan voltammograms for reductions. Curve A: Reduction of a single species. The peak potential (E_p), and the magnitude of the peak current (i_p) are marked. The dashed line represents the "background" current obtained in the absence of the electroactive species. Curve B: Reduction of two species, with some overlap of peaks. Note that the peak current for the second wave, i_p', is measured from the (extrapolated) current due to the first peak.*

exception of some uses of graphite and platinum electrodes, and those are generally used in oxidations. On the other hand, the use of fast voltage scanning for analytical purposes seems promising for some applications. The current-versus-voltage curves obtained under such conditions show a peak (Fig. 3.17A).

For qualitative interpretation of the shape of such curves, it is useful to consider two potential regions. At potentials more positive than that of the peak, the increase in current with increasing voltage is caused by the same factors as the rise of the wave in DC polarography, namely, the increased rate of the electrolytic process with increasing potential. On the other hand, at potentials more negative than that of the maximum current (E_p), the depletion of the electroactive species in the vicinity of the electrode surface becomes of importance. At the high voltage-scan rates employed, diffusion of the electroactive species from the bulk of the solution is not fast enough to replenish that removed at the electrode surface; hence, the concentration at the surface, and thus the current, decreases with time. This appears also as a decrease with increasing potential, since the voltage is linearly proportional to time.

Theory. For a reversible oxidation-reduction system where both oxidized and reduced forms are soluble, it can be shown that the current under these conditions depends on potential in such a way as to pass through a maximum. For the potential of a peak obtained with a planar electrode it can be shown that

$$(E_\mathrm{p})_\mathrm{planar} = E_{1/2} - 1.1 \frac{RT}{nF} \tag{3.9}$$

The potential of the peak corresponding to a reduction process is thus more negative than the half-wave potential by $28/n$ mV. Similarly, it is possible to show that for anodic peaks corresponding to the reversible oxidation of the reduced form of the couple, the potential of the peak is more positive than the half-wave potential by $28/n$ mV.

The current (with both spherical and planar electrodes) is a linear function of concentration and can be used for analytical purposes. For reversible systems the peak current (i_p) obtained with a linear sweep at a planar electrode of area A is given by

$$i_\mathrm{p} = k n^{3/2} A D^{1/2} c v^{1/2} \tag{3.10}$$

where k = the Randles-Sevcik constant
            v = the scanning rate

The current thus depends on the area of the electrode, on the concentration of the electroactive species, and on its diffusion coefficient. Apart from the difference in the value of the proportionality constant k, the peak current i_p shows a dependence on the number of electrons transferred (n) different from that observed in polarography: in DC polarography, the diffusion current is directly proportional to n, whereas in linear-sweep voltammetry the peak current is proportional to $n^{3/2}$. Finally, the essential difference between the currents obtained by the two techniques is in the dependence of the peak currents on the rate of scanning, v, which becomes an important variable, whereas polarographic diffusion currents are not dependent on v.

For irreversible electrode processes, the peak current is often lower than that for a reversible one. Peaks for irreversible processes are also less sharp, and the whole curve is more drawn out; but the peak potential E_p is independent of the concentration of the oxidized form and the current is a linear function of concentration.

Measurement of Peak Current. Measurement of the peak current is usually carried out by extrapolating the current before the peak and measuring the difference between this extrapolated baseline and the peak (Fig. 3.17A). This presents no problems provided that there is only one peak on the current-versus-voltage curve or, if there is more than one peak, that the individual peaks are separated by several hundred mV.

In the presence of several peaks that differ by 100–200 mV or less, measuring the most positive peak (in reductions) is still relatively simple. Measuring peak currents corresponding to successive processes is more difficult, since extrapolating the decreasing current of the more positive peak is always somewhat arbitrary (see Fig. 3.17B).

Stripping Voltammetry

For cations of amalgam-forming metals and for anions forming slightly soluble compounds with mercury, the sensitivity of polarographic techniques can be increased by accumulating the material within the electrode (as an amalgam) or at the surface

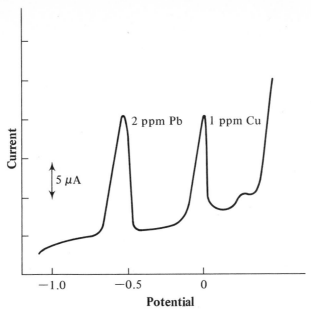

FIGURE 3.18. *Linear-sweep anodic-stripping voltammogram, 2 ppm Pb and 1 ppm Cu in* 0.1 *M* HNO_3. *Conditions: 5-min plating time at* −1.10 *V; 15-sec rest time; a thin-mercury-film electrode on glassy carbon; and a voltage scan rate of* 1 *V/min for the stripping step.*

of the electrode by preelectrolysis. This electrolysis, carried out at a controlled potential usually corresponding to the limiting current of the investigated species, is essentially an electrochemical preconcentration step wherein the electroactive material is concentrated from the relatively large solution volume, perhaps 5 to 20 cm³, into the much smaller electrode "volume," perhaps 10^{-3} to 10^{-4} cm³. Typical increases in concentration are of the order of 10- to 500-fold. This is followed by a voltage sweep from negative to positive potentials (when metal amalgam was formed by reduction) or from positive to negative potential (when mercury salts were anodically formed). Resulting curves (Fig. 3.18) correspond to the anodic dissolution of the amalgam or to the cathodic reduction of mercury from the mercury salts, the current signals being a measure of the amount of amalgam or mercury salt formed.

Mercury electrodes, particularly the hanging mercury drop electrode (HMDE) and mercury-coated platinum or graphite electrodes, are frequently used. A HMDE can be made by collecting two or three drops from a DME in a small glass or teflon spoon and attaching the resulting drop to the tip of a platinum wire that has been sealed into soft glass tubing. Another method is to use a capillary attached to a small mercury reservoir into which extends a micrometer-driven plunger. The micrometer is turned an appropriate number of divisions, and a mercury drop is extruded at the capillary orifice. Electrical contact is made to the mercury reservoir and, thus, to the mercury drop. Mercury film electrodes can be prepared by plating a thin (10–100 μm) mercury film onto a small platinum wire or onto the surface of a carbon or graphite rod, the sides of which have been suitably insulated. A recent innovation involves the simultaneous plating of mercury and metal ion during the preelectrolysis step: all solutions are made about 10^{-4} *M* in mercuric ion, the mercury film is formed and the amalgam generated during preelectrolysis at negative potential, and then the trace metal and mercury film are sequentially stripped off during the anodic reoxidation step. The mercury, since it is present in much larger concentration, gives a very large peak at about $+0.1$ V.

The types of elements that can be determined by cathodic deposition at mercury electrodes are the amalgam-formers—Cu, Pb, Cd, Bi, Sn, Zn, Tl, and so forth. Using anodic deposition, halides and various sulfides can be determined at mercury electrodes, iodide at silver electrodes, and lead (as PbO_2) and iron (as Fe_2O_3) at various solid electrodes.

The overall sensitivity of the stripping technique depends on the amount formed in preelectrolysis, which in turn depends on (a) the concentration of the substance in the solution; (b) the geometry of the electrode and the current density in the course of the preelectrolysis; (c) transport from the bulk of the solution (diffusion in unstirred solutions, convection and diffusion in stirred solutions); (d) the duration of electrolysis; and (e) the particular electrochemical technique used in the stripping step. Usually either linear-sweep voltammetry or differential-pulse voltammetry is used for the stripping of the accumulated material. Sensitivities can be truly spectacular, rivalling even those of neutron activation analysis. In fact, sensitivities are usually limited by the trace contaminants in the reagents used for digestions or for background electrolytes. For example, 0.1 M analytical reagent KCl with 0.0002% Pb (approximately the maximum impurity limit) has about 10^{-7} M Pb; and stripping analysis is normally used for the 10^{-6} to 10^{-9} M level. One way around this is to purify large volumes of the reagent solutions to be used by long-term controlled-potential electrolysis over large mercury-pool cathodes.

Signals obtained with linear-sweep voltammetry are less sensitive than those obtained with the differential-pulse technique. Therefore, the time needed for accumulating a sufficient amount of the preelectrolysis product is typically 10–60 min for the linear-sweep technique as opposed to 30 sec to 5 min for the differential-pulse mode. Since it is more difficult to control the conditions of the electrolysis over a prolonged period of time, the results obtained with differential-pulse voltammetry are usually more reproducible than those obtained with linear-sweep stripping voltammetry.

Instrumentation

Instrumentation for pulse polarography is quite complex. For differential-pulse polarography, the instrumentation requires various timing and sampling circuits, low-drift analog memories to allow storage and subtraction of two sampled currents, and good differential amplifiers to allow the amplification of Δi, etc. Early instruments used tube circuits of limited reliability. Recent instruments (Princeton Applied Research 170, 171, and 174, and the Tacussel PRG4), employing stable integrated-circuit amplifiers and high-impedance field-effect transistors, are reliable and not overly expensive ($2500–15,000).

For stripping analysis, only a special electrode (HMDE, mercury-coated carbon electrode, or another solid electrode) is needed. Any instrument generating a slow linear voltage sweep and recording the resulting current-versus-voltage curves can be used for linear-sweep stripping voltammetry. Preferably the instrument allows curve-recording both from positive to negative potentials and vice versa. For differential-pulse stripping voltammetry, any pulse polarograph can be used.

The measurement of peaks in linear-sweep voltammetry and pulse polarography is usually done by measuring the current at a chosen potential (usually that of the peak) and comparing it to the current at the same potential obtained with a blank. Such measurements are sufficiently accurate when the measured peak is not preceded by any other peak. Measuring a second peak at more negative potentials presents all the problems encountered with overlapping spectrophotometric absorption bands or chromatographic elution peaks. An empirical extrapolation of the tailing of the first peak is often used; computer-based analysis of such curves is possible.

Separation of adjacent peaks in differential-pulse polarography, where the symmetry of the peak can also be made use of, is usually easier than that of consecutive peaks in linear-sweep voltammetry. As is the case in conventional polarography, more positive peaks that interfere can sometimes be shifted to more negative potentials and the sequence of peaks inverted by change in supporting electrolyte.

In linear-sweep voltammetry and differential-pulse polarography, the problem of an excess of a species reduced at more positive potentials is of considerably smaller consequence than in conventional polarography. When the current peaks of the species present in excess and that of the components to be determined are separated by more than about 0.3 V in the former and about 0.2 V in the latter technique, the presence of the more positive peak has almost no influence.

Applications

Once again, only a few examples are presented from a very large number of actual reported analyses.

Differential-Pulse Stripping Analysis of Water. The water to be analyzed is deaerated and a voltage of -1.2 V is applied to a hanging mercury drop electrode and a platinum counter electrode for 60 sec while the solution is gently stirred by a magnetic stirrer. The stirring must be constant and reproducible. After 60 sec the stirrer is turned off, and after 15 sec the stripping curve is recorded using a differential-pulse technique. The peak for zinc appears at -1.0 V, that for lead at -0.5 V, and that for copper at -0.1 V. Typical concentrations in tapwater might be 2 ppb for Pb and 10–600 ppb for Zn and Cu [2].

This method was devised for tapwater analysis. When lower metal-ion concentrations are to be determined (e.g., in distilled or deionized water) the pre-electrolysis period can be prolonged.

Cu, Pb, Cd, and Zn have been determined in seawater by pulsed stripping analysis. A similar analysis of the metallic content of fish, seaweed, and oysters inhabiting this water indicates that there are biological concentration factors of 10^2 to 10^5 for these trace metals.

Stripping analysis has been used to determine 10^{-9} M Ag levels in rain and snow samples from clouds seeded with AgI. Precisions are about $\pm 20\%$ at the 0.2 nM level, and $\pm 4\%$ at concentrations above 1 nM.

Differential-Pulse Stripping Determination of Lead in Blood. The blood sample (typically 50 μl) is digested with a mixture of sulfuric and perchloric acids, transferred into the electrolytic cell and, after removal of oxygen, preelectrolyzed at -0.7 V for about 5 min using a hanging mercury drop electrode in a stirred solution (the period of deposition chosen depends on the electrode used). The differential-pulse stripping curve shows a peak for lead at -0.4 V. A typical "normal" level of 200–300 ppb of lead in blood will give a large signal, well above background, unless the acids are contaminated [3].

Barbital, Phenobarbital, Pentothal. Barbital can be determined in a borate buffer of pH 9.3 by means of an anodic wave that corresponds to mercury-salt formation. Since the wave height is governed by adsorption at higher concentrations, it is necessary to keep the concentration of barbital below 1×10^{-4} M.

When DC polarography is applied to phenobarbital, the wave is indistinct. However, when differential-pulse polarography is used, easily measurable peaks corresponding to mercury-salt formation are obtained, the total height of which is a linear function of concentration. This procedure has been successfully applied to the determination of phenobarbital in the presence of a number of other drugs in studies of drug metabolism.

Pentothal [ethyl(1-methylbutyl)thiobarbiturate] can be easily determined by simply dissolving the sample in 0.1 M sodium hydroxide and recording the well developed anodic wave.

Linear-Sweep Voltammetry of Tocopherols and Antioxidants in Oils and Fats. Phenolic antioxidants are added to many food products to enhance their stability. In addition, certain foods, particularly vegetable oils, contain significant quantities of natural phenolic materials, the most prominent of which are the various tocopherols (vitamin E group). Linear-sweep voltammetric oxidation of vegetable oils dissolved in 2:1 ethanol/benzene solvent (0.12 M sulfuric acid) is a rapid method for estimating the tocopherol content of oils and fats. (Almost all other methods involve considerable sample preparation, such as saponification and extraction, before chromatographic separation and measurement.) The reproducibility of the voltammetric method is good; for a typical α-tocopherol content of 0.3 mg/g of oil, the standard deviation is ± 0.02 mg/g. Quantitation is achieved by the method of standard additions, and a glassy carbon electrode is used [4].

Differential-Pulse Polarography of Arsenic. The determination of metallic elements by polarographic methods generally faces stiff competition from atomic absorption spectroscopy (Chap. 11), which is often the method of choice. Atomic absorption, however, is comparatively insensitive to arsenic. In acidic media, As(III) gives two well developed polarographic peaks; the first (-0.5 V) is due to its three-electron reduction to As, and the second (-0.8 V) to its further reduction to AsH_3. In 1 M HCl, the detection limit for arsenic determination is about 0.3 ppb (4×10^{-9} M), with a linear current-versus-concentration response up to 60 ppm [5], a linear range of five decades of concentration. The relative standard deviation is about $\pm 16\%$ at 2 ppb and $\pm 2\%$ at 20 ppb. The inorganic ions that interfere seriously are Pb^{2+}, Sn^{2+}, Sn^{4+}, Tl^+, and Tl^{3+}. One interesting aspect of the pulse-polarographic method is that As(V) is polarographically inactive, so that this method can be used to study the oxidation state of arsenic in various samples. Total arsenic can be determined by prior chemical reduction of As(V) with suitable reducing agents such as hydrazine salts or acidic KI. With the possible exception of neutron-activation analysis (Chap. 19), differential-pulse polarography is probably the most sensitive method presently available for arsenic assay.

3.5 AMPEROMETRIC TITRATIONS

A titration in which measurement of the current flowing at a voltammetric indicator electrode is used for detection of the equivalence point is termed an *amperometric titration*. The current measured is almost always a limiting current which is proportional to concentration, and can be due to the substance titrated, to the titrant itself, to a product of the reaction, or to any two of these—depending on the potential of the electrode and the electrochemical characteristics of the chemical substances involved. The titration curve is a plot of the limiting current, corrected for dilution by the reagent and, if necessary, for any residual current, as a function of the volume of titrant. Ideally, the titration curve consists of two linear segments which intersect at the equivalence point.

Amperometric titrations can be classified into two groups: those using one polarized (indicator) electrode plus a reference electrode, and those using two polarized or indicator electrodes.

One Polarized or Indicator Electrode

Many of the principles of amperometric titrations can be understood by considering an example: the titration of Pb^{2+} with standard sodium sulfate solution. Figure 3.19 illustrates the current-versus-voltage curves for lead ion that could be obtained during the course of an amperometric titration, and the resulting amperometric titration. Under the experimental conditions employed, lead ion is reducible, with an $E_{1/2}$ at about -0.4 V, and the sulfate ion is nonreducible. A constant voltage which may have any value on the diffusion-current plateau is applied to the indicator electrode; in this case, -1.0 V is applied to a dropping mercury electrode.

At the start of the titration, a polarogram of the test solution would have the appearance of curve a in Figure 3.19A (after sufficient deaeration to remove the dissolved oxygen). Therefore, the current measured at -1.0 V would have the value i_0. Increments of titrant precipitate $PbSO_4$ and remove some of the Pb^{2+} from solution; since the titrant does not produce a reduction current at the applied voltage, the current decreases with successive additions to i_1, i_2, and so on. When the lead ions have been completely removed from solution, the only current flowing is the residual current, i_R, caused by the supporting electrolyte. A plot of current as a function of titrant volume will have the L-shaped appearance shown in Figure 3.19B.

Normally, there will be some rounding in the vicinity of the equivalence point because of equilibrium effects—the more dilute the solutions employed and the more the position of equilibrium favors the reactants, the more pronounced

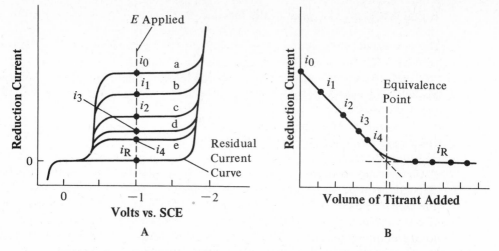

FIGURE 3.19. *Current-versus-voltage curves and amperometric titration curve for the titration of* Pb^{2+} *with* Na_2SO_4 *solution.* A: *Successive current-versus-voltage curves for the reduction of* Pb^{2+} *ion at a mercury electrode, made after increments of* SO_4^{2-} *were added.* B: *The resulting amperometric titration curve for currents* ($i_0, i_1, i_2, \ldots$) *measured at an applied potential of* -1 *V versus SCE.*

the rounding. In the example, the finite solubility of $PbSO_4$ will result in some Pb^{2+} ions being still in solution at the equivalence point, and an excess of titrant is necessary to drive the lead-ion concentration to a sufficiently low level that the lead-ion diffusion current is insignificant compared to the residual current.

One advantage of amperometric titrations is that the substance titrated does not have to be electroactive if an appropriate titrant with electrolytic properties is used. For example, sulfate ion can be determined by titration with Pb^{2+}. In this case, an essentially constant residual current flows until there is *excess* titrant in the test solution. After the endpoint a linearly increasing current appears which is proportional to the concentration of the excess titrant. The amperometric titration curve will have a shape the reverse of that shown in Figure 3.19B: ⟋-shaped, or "reverse L-shaped."

When both the substance titrated and the titrant undergo electrochemical reactions at the voltage selected, the current will decrease (linearly) up to the equivalence point, then increase again with addition of excess titrant, resulting in a V-shaped titration curve. An example of this is the titration of Pb^{2+} with potassium dichromate in a weakly acidic supporting electrolyte. Dichromate ion is reduced to Cr^{3+} at the DME with $E_{1/2} \approx 0$ V versus SCE. If -1.0 V is applied to the indicator electrode, both Pb^{2+} and $Cr_2O_7^{2-}$ are reducible, and a V-shaped titration curve will result. If, on the other hand, the applied voltage is -0.2 V, only dichromate ion is reducible, and a reverse L-shaped titration curve results.

In general, the best way to predict the shape of amperometric titration curves is to look at or construct the current-versus-voltage curves of the test solution during the course of the electrolysis.

Two Polarized or Indicator Electrodes

The apparatus used for titrations with one polarized electrode, described above, includes a reference electrode whose potential remains fixed during the course of the titration. A second approach involves applying a small, fixed, potential difference (20–250 mV) across two identical indicator electrodes; this is often called a *bi-amperometric* titration.

Again the principles underlying this type of titration can best be understood by considering an example, in this case the titration of ferrous ion (Fe^{2+}) in acidic medium with standard cerate (Ce^{4+}) solution—two reversible redox couples. Figure 3.20 illustrates the current-versus-voltage curves expected during the titration. At the start (Fig. 3.20A), the only electrochemical processes that occur are the oxidation of Fe^{2+} to Fe^{3+} at about $+0.5$ V and the two background processes—reduction of protons to hydrogen gas and oxidation of water to oxygen. The small, fixed, potential difference (ΔE) applied to the indicator electrodes shifts along the potential axis until it stops at that place on the current-versus-voltage curve where the current due to the reduction taking place at the cathode is equal to the current due to the oxidation taking place at the anode. This is at the voltage where the residual current curve crosses the $i = 0$ axis; and the actual current flowing is very close to zero.

Once some Ce^{4+} is added, Fe^{3+} and Ce^{3+} are generated by the chemical redox reaction, and the current-versus-voltage curves for the test solution now have components reflecting the reduction of Fe^{3+} and oxidation of Ce^{3+}, as shown in Figure 3.20B. The ΔE shifts along the current-versus-voltage curve to the point where the

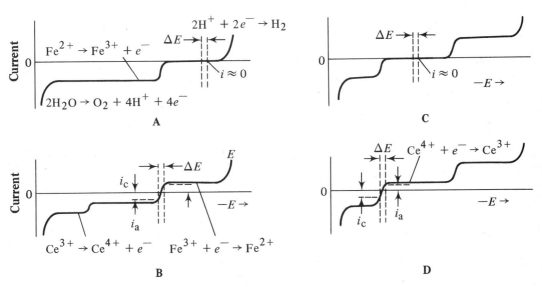

FIGURE 3.20. *Theoretical current-versus-voltage curves at a platinum electrode during an amperometric titration of Fe²⁺ with Ce⁴⁺ with two polarized or indicator electrodes. ΔE is the constant voltage applied to the two indicator electrodes. A: At the start of the titration. B: At the midpoint of the titration. C: At the equivalence point. D: After the equivalence point.*

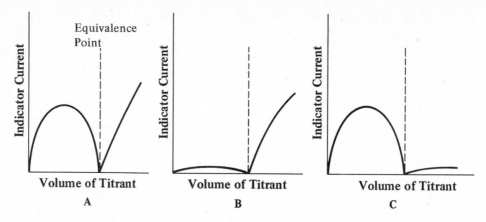

FIGURE 3.21. *Titration curves for amperometric titrations with two polarized or indicator electrodes. A: Both the titrant and the substance titrated have reversible voltammetric curves. B: The substance titrated displays irreversibility, and the titrant reversibility. C: The substance titrated displays reversibility, and the titrant irreversibility.*

anodic and cathodic indicator currents, i_a and i_c, are equal; they are due to the reversible Fe^{2+}/Fe^{3+} oxidation-reduction couple. Prior to the equivalence point, the indicator current, $i = i_a = i_c$, increases until about halfway to the equivalence point and then decreases back to 0 at the equivalence point—Figure 3.20C—where the current is once again due to only the small residual current. The voltage applied is insufficient to cause appreciable oxidation of Ce^{3+} and reduction of Fe^{3+}. After the equivalence point, there is some excess Ce^{4+} in solution, ΔE shifts to the potential of the reversible Ce^{3+}/Ce^{4+} couple at about $+1.4$ V, and the indicator current again begins to increase.

The shape of the amperometric titration curve in this case, where both the titrant and the substance titrated undergo reversible redox reactions, is illustrated in Figure 3.21A. In the case where the substance titrated does not have a reversible voltammetric wave, the titration curve will have the shape illustrated in Figure 3.21B. Prior to the equivalence point, the applied voltage is too small to cause both oxidation and reduction of the redox couple of the substance titrated. If the titrant has an irreversible wave, the titration curve will look like that in Figure 3.21C. This type of titration is commonly called a "dead-stop" titration, because the indicator current falls to zero at the equivalence point.

Applications of Amperometric Titrations

If the stoichiometry of the titration reaction is known and reproducible, amperometric titrations are intrinsically more accurate and precise than direct voltammetric analyses. Precision and accuracy of a few tenths of a percent are commonly attainable with sufficiently concentrated solutions, about 10^{-4} M or greater. Precision and accuracy are limited primarily by the errors involved in standardizing the titrant and measuring the volume delivered, and by the abruptness of change in indicator current at the equivalence point. High accuracies require, of course, minimization of or correction for any volume change during the titration. The apparatus for amperometric titrations is quite simple, and requires no prior calibration. Their primary disadvantages, as with potentiometric titrations, are the time required to perform a titration as opposed to a single measurement, and the effort involved in the preparation and storage of standard solutions.

There are numerous examples of the application of amperometric titrations in the literature [6, 7]. One popular titrant is the silver ion, in the form of a silver-nitrate solution, coupled with a rotating platinum indicator electrode. Ions such as cyanide, tetraphenylborate, various sulfides, and (singly or mixed) chloride, bromide and iodide can be titrated. For example, anywhere from 8 μM to 0.1 M cyanide in 0.1 M sodium hydroxide can be titrated amperometrically with silver-nitrate solution with good accuracy and precision. Again, the total chlorine in insecticides decomposed with sodium and xylene has been titrated at silver electrodes using biamperometric endpoint detection. A very important application is the determination of sulfhydryl groups, especially in proteins and other natural materials. The method is based on the reaction of silver ion—and some other heavy-metal ions such as Hg^{2+}—with sulfhydryl compounds to form highly undissociated mercaptides. For example, SH groups in cysteine, glutathione, certain proteins, and dialyzed human sera can be determined. Under appropriate conditions, as little as about 10 nmoles of protein can be titrated reproducibly.

Another important amperometric titrant is bromine solution, which undergoes stoichiometric oxidation-reduction reactions with many substances such as As(III), Sb(III), ammonium salts, and others. Often the titration involves adding an excess of KBr to an acidified solution of the substance to be oxidized and then titrating it with potassium bromate solution. Bromine is thereby generated in situ.

$$BrO_3^- + 5Br^- + 6H^+ \rightleftharpoons 3H_2O + 3Br_2 \tag{3.11}$$

This avoids the problems involved in storing unstable Br_2 solutions. Bromine can be used to titrate a wide variety of oxidizible organic compounds such as phenols, hydrazines, and anilines. The "bromine numbers" of olefinic hydrocarbons—a measure of the total unsaturation present—are often determined by titrating the hydrocarbon with acidified potassium bromate, or by generating Br_2 electrolytically from an acetic-acid/methanol/water solvent containing KBr. Olefinic hydrocarbons generally display no electrochemical properties under the experimental conditions employed; however, at the equivalence point, the presence of a small excess of bromine increases the current through the indicator electrode pair. Chapter 4 discusses a number of other reagents that can be electrolytically generated in situ in order to perform an amperometric titration.

SELECTED BIBLIOGRAPHY

ADAMS, R. N. *Electrochemistry at Solid Electrodes.* New York: Marcel Dekker, 1969.

BARD, A. J., ed. *Electroanalytical Chemistry,* vols. I–VII. New York: Marcel Dekker, 1966–1974.

BREYER, B., and BAUER, H. H. *Alternating Current Polarography and Tensammetry.* New York: John Wiley, 1963.

BREZINA, M., and ZUMAN, P. *Polarography in Medicine, Biochemistry, and Pharmacy.* New York: Interscience, 1958.

HEYROVSKY, J., and KUTA, J. *Principles of*

Polarography. New York: Academic Press, 1965.

KOLTHOFF, I. M., and LINGANE, J. *Polarography*, 2nd ed, vols. I and II. New York: Interscience, 1952.

MEITES, L. *Polarographic Techniques*, 2nd ed. New York: John Wiley, 1965.

SCHMIDT, H., and VON STACKELBERG, M.

Modern Polarographic Methods. New York: Academic Press, 1963.

SCHMITZ, C. L.; EWEN, E. F.; and DODD, S. P. *Bibliography of Polarographic Literature 1922–1967.* Skokie, Ill.: Sargent-Welch Scientific Co., 1969.

ZUMAN, P. *Organic Polarographic Analysis.* Oxford: Pergamon Press, 1964.

REFERENCES

1. H. H. BAUER, in *Electroanalytical Chemistry*, A. J. Bard, ed., vol. 8, New York: Marcel Dekker, 1965, pp 169–279.

2. H. SIEGERMAN and G. O'DOM, *Amer. Lab.*, *5*(6), 48 (1972).

3. Application Note AN-16, Princeton Applied Research Corporation, Princeton, New Jersey, 1972.

4. H. D. MCBRIDE and D. H. EVANS, *Anal. Chem.*, *45*, 446 (1973).

5. D. J. MYERS and J. OSTERYOUNG, *Anal. Chem.*, *45*, 267 (1973).

6. J. T. STOCK, *Amperometric Titrations*, New York: Interscience Publishers, 1965.

7. J. T. STOCK, *Anal. Chem.*, *48*, 1R (1976).

PROBLEMS

1. Brass contains about 65% copper and 30% zinc. Would you suggest polarography as a method for determining the main components? When and why? The alloy contains also 1% or less of lead and cadmium. Is polarography useful for those metals? Explain why or why not.

2. Deionized water contains ppb levels of heavy metals, mostly zinc, copper, and lead. Which method would you suggest for determining these levels? All common chemicals contain metal ions at the same concentration level or greater. How would you choose your supporting electrolyte? (Suggestion: Gases usually do not contain metal ions as impurities.)

3. Reaction of *p*-cyanoacetophenone with hydroxylamine is being investigated. An analytical method is needed to follow concentration changes in *p*-cyanoacetophenone. Assuming that *p*-cyanoacetophenone has not been studied polarographically before, how would you carry out preliminary experiments to elucidate the electrode process? Find a description of the electroreduction in the literature and

propose conditions for the kinetic study, keeping in mind that only the unprotonated form of hydroxylamine ($pK_a = 6.0$) reacts.

4. You have to determine: (a) formaldehyde and acetaldehyde in 50 samples of white wine per day; (b) 2,4,6-trinitrotoluene in white powder samples which might be potential material in making bombs—3 to 5 samples per month; (c) copper content in a rare Etruscan vase; (d) a toxic keto compound in an antibiotic, the analysis being done in a production-line quality-control laboratory in a pharmaceutical company. In which cases and why would you use a standard-addition method and when would you use a calibration curve for evaluating current-versus-voltage curves?

5. Explain differences (with the help of the literature) between pulse polarography, differential-pulse polarography, and AC polarography.

6. List advantages and limitations of linear-sweep voltammetry. Suggest examples of when this technique can be used in practical analysis.

7. Why do we speak about "diffusion current"? Describe how you would check equations for diffusion currents. What can cause a difference between theoretical values and experimental data?

8. The *diffusion current constant* I_d is used to correct polarographic diffusion currents for differences in capillary characteristics. For average currents

$$I_d = \frac{i_d}{cm^{2/3}t^{1/6}} = 607nD^{1/2}$$

For a given electroactive substance under a given set of experimental conditions (temperature, supporting electrolyte, potential of the DME, etc.), I_d should actually be a constant according to the Ilkovic equation; it should be independent of the capillary characteristics and reproducible in different laboratories or in the same laboratory with different capillaries. Cadmium ion exhibits a reversible two-electron reduction wave at -0.64 V in $1\ M$ HCl. A $0.50\ \text{m}M$ Cd^{2+} solution gave a wave with average $i_d = 3.96\ \mu$A at the $E_{1/2}$; the capillary characteristics were $m = 2.50$ mg/sec, $t = 3.02$ sec. (a) Calculate I_d for Cd^{2+}. (b) Calculate the diffusion coefficient for Cd^{2+} in $1\ M$ HCl.

9. A typical value for the mercury flow-rate m for a DME is 2.5 mg/sec and a typical drop-time is 3.0 sec. What is the maximum area of the mercury drop under these conditions?

10. The oxygen content of aqueous solutions can be estimated by simply measuring the height of its polarographic reduction wave, and inserting a known value of the diffusion coefficient D (2.12×10^{-5} cm²/sec) into the Ilkovic equation. A sample of tap water was taken, sufficient solid KCl was added to make a $0.10\ M$ solution, and the solution was analyzed polarographically. The average current for the first two-electron oxygen-reduction wave at $E_{1/2} = -0.05$ V was $1.81\ \mu$A. If the capillary used had $m = 2.00$ mg/sec and $t = 5.00$ sec at -0.05 V, what was the oxygen level of the tap water in mM? In ppm?

11. With the experimental system described in problem 8 above, the average residual (charging) current was $0.32\ \mu$A at the plateau of the wave due to the reduction of Cd^{2+} ions. Assuming that the limit of detectability corresponds to a diffusion current whose magnitude is one-half of the residual current, what is the lowest concentration of Cd^{2+} that could be detected?

12. It is often said that one can run polarograms many times with the same solution because the amount of material electrolyzed under polarographic conditions is so small. With the system described in problem 8, for how long could one electrolyze at the plateau of the wave before the diffusion current changes by 1%? Assume that the volume of solution in the polarographic cell is 50 ml.

13. In studying the mechanisms of reduction of organic compounds, one vital parameter is the number of electrons transferred per molecule. An estimate of this parameter can be obtained by assuming a value for the diffusion coefficient. (a) For a particular ketone, we wish to decide whether n is 1 or 2. A millimolar solution yields a (maximum) diffusion current of 7.2 μA at a DME with $m = 2$ mg/sec at $t = 5$ sec. A reasonable value for the diffusion coefficient is 5×10^{-6} cm²/sec. What is the value of n? (b) Suggest another way of determining n with the polarograph—a way that does not depend on knowledge of the diffusion coefficient and does not presuppose that the reduction is reversible.

14. The following voltammograms were recorded in a suitable supporting electrolyte at a silver electrode versus the SCE: (a) Solution of silver ion; (b) Solution of chloride ion.

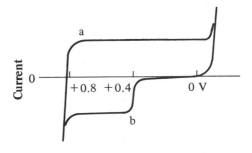

A titration of 10 ml of 0.001 M silver

nitrate with 0.001 M sodium chloride was performed, and the endpoint was detected biamperometrically with two silver-wire electrodes. Sketch the biamperometric titration curve for the titration with (a) an applied potential difference of 100 mV, and (b) with an applied potential difference of 600 mV. Assume no Ag^+ nor Cl^- can be detected in a saturated AgCl solution. (c) Specify the anodic and the cathodic reaction occurring in each segment of the titration curves.

4

Electrogravimetry and Coulometry

DONALD G. DAVIS

In this chapter, we shall consider those electroanalytical methods characterized by the fact that some reaction goes to completion in an electrochemical cell. The amount of the material analyzed is found either by weighing an insoluble compound (usually a metal) deposited on an electrode, or by measuring the number of coulombs necessary to complete the reaction. In the latter type of experiment, use is made of Faraday's law, which states that the quantity of chemical change produced at the electrodes of a cell is directly proportional to the quantity of electricity passed through the cell. To produce one equivalent of chemical change, one *faraday* is required. Very accurate determinations of a variety of substances can be made by these methods because of the relative ease with which electrical quantities (and weights) can be measured. The value of the faraday (96484.56 ± 0.27 coulombs) is known to within about 3 ppm at present; and atomic weights are often known to the same accuracy or better. Many coulometric methods are more time consuming than polarography, direct potentiometry, or other methods, but the high accuracy and precision attainable (often 0.1% or better) may well be worth the extra time and effort.

4.1 ELECTROGRAVIMETRY

The technique of electrogravimetry consists of electroplating a metal (usually) onto a previously weighed electrode, and then reweighing to determine the amount of metal initially present in solution. Sufficient voltage is applied to the electrochemical cell for long enough to remove the metal quantitatively from solution.

Many of the principles involved in electrogravimetry can be illustrated by considering the determination of copper. A simplified version of the apparatus used for electrogravimetry is shown in Figure 4.1. Instruments using 60 Hz line voltage (rectified to DC) rather than batteries and incorporating all components in a single case are commercially available. Before the experiment starts, the platinum gauze is cleaned with nitric acid, rinsed, dried, and carefully weighed. It is then immersed in the copper solution. The potential across the cell is increased until appreciable current flows, as indicated by ammeter A. At this point the copper will start to plate on the cathode and oxygen will be liberated at the anode.

The total voltage, E_{app}, applied across the cell is given by

$$E_{app} = (E_a + \eta_a) - (E_c + \eta_c) + iR \tag{4.1}$$

where
$E_a =$ the reversible anode potential
$\eta_a =$ the anodic overpotential
$E_c =$ the reversible cathode potential
$\eta_c =$ the cathodic overpotential
$i =$ the current through the cell
$R =$ the resistance of the cell

The reversible potentials can be calculated from the appropriate Nernst equation. For instance, for copper at 25°C

$$E_c = E^0_{Cu^{2+}, Cu} + \frac{0.059}{2} \log [Cu^{2+}] \tag{4.2}$$

This equation neglects activity coefficients—not a very good approximation under normal experimental conditions—but this is usually compensated for by simply applying a greater voltage than calculated. Equation 4.2 can be used to decide what potential the cathode must attain to eventually reduce the concentration of copper remaining in solution to an acceptable value. For instance, if the initial solution was $10^{-2} M$ in Cu^{2+} and it was desired to plate 99.9% of the copper, the following calculation would pertain: At the start of the electrolysis the cathode potential would be

$$E_c = 0.34 + \frac{0.059}{2} \log [10^{-2}] = 0.28 \text{ V} \tag{4.3}$$

To achieve the 1 ppt accuracy, the copper concentration must be reduced to $10^{-5} M$. Thus,

$$E_c = 0.34 + \frac{0.059}{2} \log [10^{-5}] = 0.19 \text{ V} \tag{4.4}$$

Therefore, a cathode potential of 0.15 V more reducing than E^0 would have to be attained to achieve the required analysis.

The overpotentials (ηs) are composed of two parts. One is termed the *concentration overpotential* and results from the fact that the concentration of, for instance, copper ions *at the electrode surface* is depleted relative to the rest of the solution during the passage of any appreciable current. Efficient stirring helps to keep this term to a minimum, but nevertheless, extra voltage must be applied to compensate. At the anode, concentration overpotential is caused by the accumulation of hydrogen ion as oxygen is evolved.

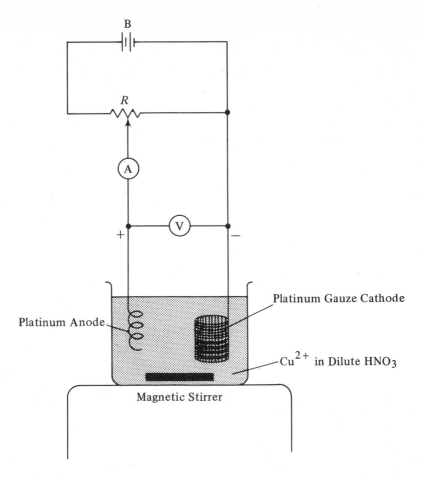

FIGURE 4.1. *Apparatus for electrogravimetry. B is a battery or other source of stable DC voltage, R is a resistor with a sliding contact used to vary the voltage applied to the cell, A is an ammeter that measures the current passing through the cell, and V is a voltmeter which measures the voltage applied to the cell.*

The other part of the overpotential term is the *activation overpotential.* The magnitude of the activation overpotential depends on the inherent rate of the electrode reaction. The activation overpotential is always such that it discourages reactions—that is, it is negative for a reduction. The activation overpotential is characteristic of the reaction under consideration, and is also influenced by the electrode material. For example, the activation overpotential for the generation of hydrogen approaches one volt on mercury, but is negligible on platinum. In our present example, however, the overpotential for O_2 generation on platinum can be as much as 1 V at fairly high current densities.

The last term in Equation 4.1 is the iR drop that develops when a current passes through the cell. The magnitude of this, in volts, is the product of the current in amperes and the resistance in ohms. Most of the iR drop occurs between the electrodes in the cell and can be minimized by adding a high concentration of an inert electrolyte to decrease the resistance of the solution.

It is not possible to calculate all of the terms in Equation 4.1 exactly, so in practice enough voltage is applied to cause considerable current (a few amperes) to flow, and electrolysis is allowed to continue with occasional adjustment of the voltage until deposition is complete. However, it is clear from the discussion that a potential larger than two volts will be required. Completeness can be tested with an appropriate spot test on a small drop of solution, or by lowering the cathode to expose more platinum to the solution and seeing if more metal plates.

Frequently, a "depolarizer" of one sort or another is added that undergoes a particular (neutral) electrode reaction more easily than an unwanted one, thus "preempting" the latter. For instance, the deposition of copper is usually carried out in nitric acid media because nitrate ion is reduced to ammonium ion at a copper surface:

$$NO_3^- + 10H^+ + 8e^- = NH_4^+ + 3H_2O \tag{4.5}$$

Thus, hydrogen is not evolved as copper is deposited. (Hydrogen evolution should be avoided because it makes the copper deposit spongy and of poor quality.) Also, metals more difficult to reduce, such as nickel, cannot deposit along with the copper because of the excess nitric acid.

Again, difficulties sometimes arise in chloride media because chlorine is generated at the anode and some platinum may dissolve. Both cause difficulties at the cathode, the first by reoxidizing copper and the second by depositing platinum; so hydrazine is often added as an anodic depolarizer since it is easily oxidized to nitrogen:

$$N_2H_4 \longrightarrow N_2 + 4H^+ + 4e^- \tag{4.6}$$

In any case, once the deposition is complete the cathode is removed from solution *with the voltage still on* and washed at the same time. It is important that the voltage not be turned off before the electrode is removed from solution, because the spontaneous cell reaction is the reverse of what we have forced to occur by applying an appropriate potential. In the copper example, the *electrolytic cell* reaction is

$$Cu^{2+} + H_2O \longrightarrow Cu + 1/2\, O_2 + 2H^+ \tag{4.7}$$

But if we look at the relative potentials of the two half-reactions involved ($Cu^{2+} + 2e^- = Cu$ at the cathode and $1/2\, O_2 + 2H^+ + 2e^- = H_2O$ at the anode), we note that Cu is a better reducing agent than H_2O; or conversely, O_2 is a better oxidizing agent than Cu^{2+}. In other words, in a *galvanic cell* (battery), the above reaction (4.7) will spontaneously go in the opposite direction. We make it go as written by supplying the appropriate energy or back emf, plus overvoltages and iR drop, as calculated from Equation 4.1.

Washing is usually accomplished by directing a gentle stream of distilled water from a wash bottle over the electrode as it is being removed from the solution. The electrode may then be dipped in alcohol (to speed drying), dried for a short time in a drying oven, cooled, and weighed. The drying time should be short in order to minimize oxide formation. Hopefully, the deposit will not flake off in the process.

The probability of obtaining good deposits is enhanced by efficient stirring, low current-density, and proper depolarizers. For some determinations (e.g., silver), adding complexing agents such as cyanide will improve the deposit, as will adding small amounts of surface-active agents.

Electrogravimetric procedures have been devised for a large number of elements. Relatively noble metals such as copper and silver are frequently determined this way since there are few interferences. The more electronegative metals like cadmium, cobalt, iron, nickel, tin, and zinc can be electrodeposited from alkaline solutions. Under these conditions the potential for hydrogen evolution is more negative because of the decreased hydrogen ion concentration. Often, complexing agents such as ammonia or cyanide are added to prevent the metal hydroxide from precipitating and to improve the nature of the deposit. Lead is often determined at the anode in nitric acid solution as PbO_2. This can be done simultaneously with the cathodic deposition of copper. Procedures exist for most common metals and a number of nonmetals [1]. Mixtures of metals can sometimes be analyzed by changing solution conditions, but most mixtures are better handled by controlled-potential electrolysis.

4.2 ELECTROLYSIS AT CONTROLLED POTENTIAL

In order to achieve separation of metals, or to assure that one and only one electrode reaction occurs, it is usually necessary to maintain the potential of the cathode (or anode) working electrode at some prescribed value. Thus, if copper is to be determined gravimetrically in the presence of tin, the cathode potential must be held at a value reducing enough to deposit copper but not reducing enough to plate out tin. In addition to gravimetric determinations of this type, controlled-potential electrolysis can be effectively used for coulometric determinations (Sec. 4.4), for separating easily reduced metals from ones reduced with more difficulty, and in synthesizing organic and inorganic chemicals. In the last case, side reactions may be avoided by careful potential control.

Figure 4.2 shows the main features of apparatus for controlled-potential electrolysis. The potential of the working electrode (cathode in the case shown) is measured versus a reference electrode, such as a saturated calomel electrode, by a potential-measuring device. The desired potential, found by calculation (Equations 4.3 and 4.4) can be set on the potentiostat. If the cathode potential varies from the desired one, a mechanical or electronic linkage is activated that causes more or less voltage to be applied to the cell by the voltage source. In its simplest form, the potential-measuring device is a pH meter, the linkage a human being, and the voltage source a variable power-supply. Because many adjustments are necessary over a period of time because of changes in concentration and iR-drop as the electrolysis proceeds, the job is tedious. Thus, amplifier-servomotor combinations and, finally, completely electronic devices were designed. Potentiostats, as these instruments are called, are now often based on operational amplifiers and resemble the three-electrode polarograph (see Chap. 3), except that a certain potential is set and maintained throughout the experiment. Potentiostats are now available that can control an electrode potential to ± 1 mV or better, which is sufficient for most analytical

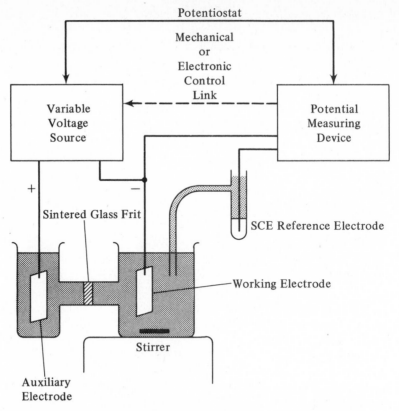

FIGURE 4.2. *Basic apparatus for controlled-potential electrolysis.*

purposes. Some of these are designed with very short rise times (a few nanoseconds) for kinetic studies, and some have current capacities up to 25 A for preparative-scale experiments.

The potential at which the electrode is energized is often selected by examining a voltammogram of the sample solution, made using an electrode of the material to be used for the controlled-potential electrolysis—a rotating platinum electrode if platinum is to be used, or a dropping mercury electrode if a mercury-pool cathode* is to be used. The desired potential is usually set just at the top of the limiting-current plateau. Here the reaction will be relatively rapid and complete, but a minimum danger of plating other metals will be encountered.

In the simplest case, the current flowing during a controlled-potential electrolysis is limited by the amount of the reducible species arriving at the electrode, and is proportional to its concentration; both the concentration and the current will decrease exponentially as the electrolysis proceeds [2]:

$$\frac{c_t}{c_0} = \frac{i_t}{i_0} = e^{-(DA/V\delta)t} = 10^{-0.43(DA/V\delta)t} \tag{4.8}$$

---

* Because of the large hydrogen overvoltage on mercury, mercury-pool cathodes are especially useful for electrodeposition of metals that are difficult to reduce. They are not used for gravimetry, however, owing to their high weight and liquid form.

where c_t = concentration at time t
i_t = current at time t
c_0 = the concentration at time zero (the start of the electrolysis)
i_0 = the current at time zero
V = the volume of the solution

The diffusion-layer thickness, δ, depends primarily on the rate of stirring. Usually, Equation 4.8 is written more simply as

$$\frac{c_t}{c_0} = e^{-kt} \qquad k = \frac{mA}{V} \tag{4.9}$$

where m = a *mass-transfer coefficient* equal to D/δ

In this form, it is obvious that the expression is simply that for a first-order chemical reaction.

Equation 4.8 indicates that, provided the electrode reaction is mass-transfer limited and uncomplicated by coupled chemical reactions, the electrolysis time may be reduced by making the electrode large and the volume small, and by stirring the solution as fast as possible to decrease the diffusion-layer thickness. In a well designed cell it is possible to carry an electrolysis to 99.9% completion in about 10 to 20 min, although times down to 1 min can be achieved by proper cell design.

In cases where a metal plated on a platinum cathode is to be quantitatively determined by weighing, the deposit may not adhere well to the cathode because of the high initial current-densities. Hence, it may be desirable to begin the electrolysis at a potential less negative than that required to reach the limiting-current plateau. The potential is later shifted to a more negative value to complete the electrolysis.

4.3 ELECTROLYTIC SEPARATIONS

Controlled-potential electrolysis can at times be useful for separating large amounts of easily reduced metals from small amounts of less easily reduced materials. This method has the advantage over precipitation in that, with adequate potential control, no coprecipitation occurs and no extraneous reagents need to be added to the solution. For example, it is possible to remove copper from solutions of copper alloys using a platinum cathode, leaving behind tin, lead, nickel, and zinc. Bismuth and antimony will be removed with the copper at a controlled potential of -0.35 V versus SCE from hydrochloric-acid solution. The minor elements can now be subjected to polarographic analysis, which would have failed before because of the large current from copper reduction preceding the smaller currents from the metals of interest. Mercury cathodes can also be successfully applied to a variety of separations. In one application, copper, lead, and cadmium have been concentrated from uranium solutions into a mercury electrode. The mercury is subsequently distilled, leaving behind the concentrated metals.

Controlled-potential electrolysis at a mercury-pool cathode to remove traces of metallic impurities is useful in preparing very pure electrolytes for use in polarography or for such applications as the "total" removal of heavy-metal ions from

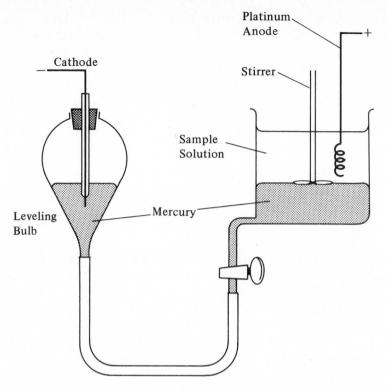

FIGURE 4.3. *Apparatus for electrolysis at a mercury-pool cathode.*

solutions to be used in enzyme work (even traces of certain metal ions will deactivate some enzymes). The apparatus shown in Figure 4.3 is suitable for accomplishing this. Furthermore, there are several commercially available units designed specifically for the purification of electrolyte solutions.

4.4 CONTROLLED-POTENTIAL COULOMETRY

Faraday's law of electrolysis states that a given amount of chemical change caused by electrolysis is directly proportional to the amount of electricity passed through the cell:

$$w = \frac{QM}{nF} \qquad (4.10)$$

where w = the weight of substance oxidized or reduced
   M = the formula weight of the substance
   Q = the number of coulombs passing through the cell

This law may be applied to the quantitative analysis of a variety of substances, provided conditions are such that the reaction proceeds with 100% current efficiency (no side reactions). One approach to 100% current efficiency is to hold the potential of the working electrode at such a value that only one reaction will occur, as can be done with the apparatus shown in Figure 4.2. The auxiliary electrode must be isolated for 100% current efficiency, otherwise its electrolysis products will migrate to the working electrode and be electrolyzed. This done, a way of measuring Q is all that is needed. Actually the integral $\int idt$, where i is the current at any instant and t is the time in seconds, is what is generally measured. The integration can be done graphically by measuring the area under a current-versus-time curve recorded on a strip-chart recorder that monitors the current passing through the cell. However, various electrochemical, mechanical, or electronic integrators are usually used.

Coulometers

Some of the first methods of measuring quantities of electricity involved the use of chemical coulometers. To do this, an electrolytic cell is placed in series with the sample electrolysis cell so that the same current passes through both. A typical coulometer cell consists of a platinum crucible containing a silver-nitrate solution and a silver anode. Silver metal is deposited on the preweighed platinum crucible and the latter reweighed to determine the amount of electricity passed; Q is calculated from Equation 4.10.

Another, more convenient, coulometer is the hydrogen-oxygen coulometer, which consists of a gas burette into the bottom of which are sealed two platinum electrodes. The burette is initially filled with an electrolyte solution. Again, this device is connected in series with the cell of interest. The volume of the gas mixture generated by the passage of current is measured, and after correcting this figure for temperature, pressure, and the partial pressure of water vapor, the quantity of electricity passed may be calculated (see Prob. 6). Accuracies of 0.1% have been obtained with this device. For best results, the electrolyte must be presaturated with hydrogen and oxygen. Oxidizable and reducible impurities may cause considerable errors.

A similar gas coulometer that uses hydrazine sulfate as an electrolyte is more accurate at low currents. In this case the hydrazine is oxidized to nitrogen at the anode (see Eqn. 4.6) so the gas mixture consists of nitrogen and hydrogen.

Several electromechanical integrators have been described. The ball-and-disk integrator, often attached to recorders on gas chromatographs, can be used; but the accuracy of these devices is about 1%, which is not really good enough for most electrochemical work. A fixed-field DC motor attached to a counter can be used as an integrator, since the speed of such motors is proportional to the voltage applied to the armature. The current to be integrated is passed through a resistor and the iR drop across this resistor is applied to the motor terminals. If compensated for electrical and mechanical losses, these motor integrators are capable of 0.1% accuracy over a 200 to 1 range [3].

In most present-day work, integrations are performed electronically. One of the best electronic integrators makes use of an operational amplifier fitted with a feedback capacitor. Another popular type of electronic integrator is a voltage-to-frequency converter, which measures the voltage drop across a standard resistor and feeds the output to a scaler, from which the current-time integral is obtained as a number of counts. Electronic integrators can be extremely accurate (to $\pm 0.01\%$) and can measure even very small amounts of charge.

Applications

Controlled-potential coulometry may be applied to the analysis of a wide variety of substances. Clearly, metals like copper could be deposited and determined without the necessity of weighing the electrode. More importantly, mercury electrodes can be used and thus most of the metals more difficult to reduce can be determined. Also, it is possible to apply coulometry to systems in which both oxidized and reduced forms are soluble, such as determining iron by reducing iron(III) to iron(II). Anions such as chloride or bromide may be converted to AgCl or AgBr by deposition on a silver anode.

Controlled-potential coulometric analysis is most often used to determine quantities from about 10 meq to about 1 μeq. The detection limit for coulometry using electronic integrators is about 0.1 μeq under normal conditions, which corresponds to the passage of about 10 μA for 15 min. This lower limit depends primarily on the precision with which the steady, final, background current can be subtracted from the total current flowing during the electrolysis. A special case occurs in surface or "stripping" analysis—for example, in determining the thickness of a metal plating on a conductive substrate. In this case, the absolute lower detection limit is of the order of about 10 μA-sec, which is as little as a few nanograms of material. Here, the limit is determined primarily by the precision with which the quantity of electricity consumed in charging the electrical double-layer can be measured.

Controlled-potential coulometry has also found some use in the study of basic electrochemistry. It is not always obvious how many electrons are involved in a newly studied electrochemical reaction, e.g., in polarography. Thus, coulometry at controlled potential, in which a known quantity of the substance is electrolyzed and Q is measured, is often used to determine values for n and thereby help elucidate electrode mechanisms for a wide variety of compounds, both organic and inorganic. Very slow chemical reactions coupled with the electrochemical reaction may also be studied by controlled-potential coulometry [4]; other electrochemical techniques usually are suitable only for much faster chemical reactions, with time scales of μsec to sec.

4.5 COULOMETRIC TITRATIONS

Coulometric titrations make use of an electrically generated titrant rather than a previously standardized solution. Usually, though not always, the reagent is generated by passing a known and constant current through a cell containing the unknown and an appropriate generating electrolyte. Since the current is constant, the number of coulombs passed can be measured by carefully measuring the length of time that the current flows (the time of generation required to reach the endpoint of the titration). Both current and time can be measured easily and accurately, so this approach has a distinct advantage over the integrators described in the previous section.

Suppose it is desired to titrate ceric ion with ferrous ion according to the reaction

$$Ce^{4+} + Fe^{2+} = Ce^{3+} + Fe^{3+} \qquad (4.11)$$

by coulometric titration. This can be done in an electrochemical cell using a platinum cathode as a generator electrode, and an isolated anode. The original solution consists of the Ce^{4+} sample and 0.6 M ferric ammonium sulfate in 2 M sulfuric acid. If a current-versus-potential curve of this solution were taken (analogous to a polarogram but using the platinum generator electrode and a stirred solution instead of a DME), the solid curve in Figure 4.4 would result. The first plateau (A) is the limiting current for the reduction of Ce^{4+} to Ce^{3+} and the second plateau (B) is the limiting current for the reduction of Fe^{3+} to Fe^{2+}. Beyond this plateau, the current rises again owing to the production of hydrogen gas.

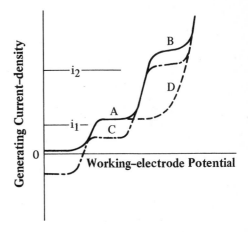

FIGURE 4.4. *Current-versus-potential working curves for the coulometric titration of ferrous ion with cerate.*

Exactly what happens in the cell depends on the magnitude of the constant current selected. Suppose that current at level i_1 was chosen. When the current is first turned on, all of the current would go to the reduction of Ce^{4+} to Ce^{3+}. As this reaction lowers the concentration of Ce^{4+}, the limiting current also goes down, eventually to the point where it is less than i_1. When this occurs, the current-versus-potential curve looks like curve C. Now part of the current i_1 must be used for another reaction, since not enough Ce^{4+} remains in solution to carry this amount of current. In other words, the potential of the generating electrode shifts to a more reducing value. This is analogous to what happens in controlled-current electrogravimetry as the electrolysis proceeds, and is one of the primary reasons a depolarizer is added in electrogravimetry to prevent the potential from shifting to a point at which undesired reactions may occur, such as deposition of another metal.

The next most easily reduced material is Fe^{3+}, which is reduced to Fe^{2+}. The Fe^{2+} is stirred out into the bulk of the solution where it reacts with the remaining Ce^{4+}. If a higher current (i_2) were originally selected, then the current divides from the beginning between the reduction of Ce^{4+} and Fe^{3+}. The net result is the same, however, since all of the Ce^{4+} eventually is reduced, either directly at the electrode or indirectly by Fe^{2+}. If the ferric ammonium sulfate were not added, the current-versus-potential curve would have the original plateau (A) but then would follow the dashed curve D. In this case, either at the start of the titration (level i_2), or sometime during the titration (level i_1), hydrogen would be produced and be lost from solution. Under these conditions the titration efficiency would be less than

100% and the results would be greatly in error; the error would be positive since current would have to be passed for a longer period of time to reduce all the Ce^{4+}.

It is obvious from the above discussion and Figure 4.4 that there will be a limiting current-density which must be exceeded for 100% current efficiency. Although it will vary from case to case (and should be checked empirically), the current density as a rule of thumb should not exceed about 0.05 mA/(cm²-mN). For example, with an electrode area of 2 cm² and a 0.1 N concentration of generating electrolyte (100 mN), the current should not exceed 10 mA. A high concentration of generating electrolyte is generally used to increase the current-density range. Obviously, the current can also be increased if the electrode area is increased. For the generation of acids and bases from electrolysis of water, a very large current density can theoretically be used, since essentially an infinite supply of water is available.

A major contribution to decreased current efficiency is the presence of electroactive impurities in the sample. This can be a particular problem with acid-base titrations. In such cases, it may be necessary to generate the titrant *externally* (in the absence of sample), and then add it to the sample in increments. A suitable arrangement is illustrated in Figure 4.5. By the use of stopcocks the titrant can be generated and flushed into the cell in increments.

FIGURE 4.5. *Apparatus for the external generation of titrant for coulometric titrations.*

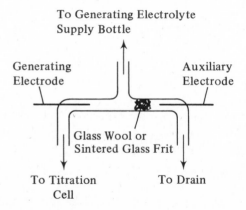

The apparatus for coulometric titrations is shown in Figure 4.6. The counter electrode is isolated in a tube terminating with a sintered glass disk to prevent products from this electrode from reacting with components of the sample solution. Provision is often made for removing air with a stream of nitrogen, if oxygen-sensitive reagents are to be generated.

The constant-current supply could be high-voltage batteries connected through a large resistance or, more likely, an electronic device. Various types of the latter are available from a number of manufacturers. Typical generating currents might be in the range of 1–200 mA. The current supply includes an on-off switch or push button which may be manipulated by the operator in an analogous way to a burette stopcock. Current supplies also have counters or timers that run only when the current is turned on. Currents are usually known to 0.1% or better and time is measured to the nearest 0.1 sec. Therefore, four-significant-figure accuracy is achieved if titrations exceed 100 seconds; this is for typical microequivalent samples.

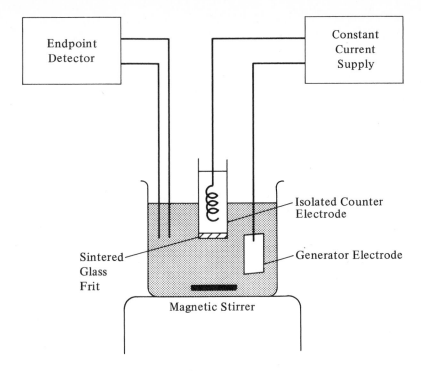

FIGURE 4.6. *Coulometric titration apparatus.*

Commercially available instruments usually read directly in microequivalents. This is accomplished by setting the current in some multiple of the Faraday constant so that the microequivalents are simply equal to some decimal fraction or multiple of the seconds of generation (see Prob. 4).

Suppose the solution of unknown Ce^{4+} was coulometrically titrated with a constant current of 75.00 mA and required 650.0 sec to complete. Then,

$$650.0 \text{ sec} \times 75.00 \text{ mA} = 48,750 \text{ millicoulombs}$$
$$\text{or } 48.75 \text{ coulombs}$$

were used. From Faraday's law it is known that there are 96,485 coulombs per equivalent and it is also known that the cerium underwent a one-electron change. Thus

$$\frac{48.75 \text{ coulombs}}{96,485 \text{ coulombs/mole}} \times 140.12 \text{ g/mole} = 0.07080 \text{ g}$$

of Ce were present in the original sample.

Naturally, some means of detecting the endpoint of the titration must be available. Indicators can be used (although their sensitivity is not good at the low levels usually investigated), as well as essentially any other method available for regular titrations. Potentiometry (Chap. 2) or amperometry with two similar electrodes is often used because of increased sensitivity over visual indicators.

Table 4.1 lists a number of titrants that have been successfully used, along with the appropriate electrodes and generating solutions. It should be noted that

TABLE 4.1. *Methods for Coulometric Generation of Titrant*

Substance Generated	Typical Solution Conditions	Working Electrode	Typical Substances Titrated
Br_2	0.1 M H_2SO_4 0.2 M NaBr	Pt	Sb(III), I^-, Tl(I), U(IV), various organic compounds
I_2	0.1 M KI 0.1 M phosphate buffer pH = 8	Pt	As(III), Sb(III), $S_2O_3^{2-}$, S^{2-}
Cl_2	2 M HCl	Pt	I^-, As(III), fatty acids
Ce(IV)	0.1 M cerous sulfate 1.5 M H_2SO_4	Pt	Fe(II), $Fe(CN)_6^{4-}$
Mn(III)	0.45 M $MnSO_4$ 1.8 M H_2SO_4	Pt	Oxalic acid, Fe(II), As(III)
Ag(II)	0.1 M $AgNO_3$ 5 M HNO_3	Au	As(III), V(IV), Ce(III), oxalic acid
$Fe(CN)_6^{4-}$	0.2 M potassium ferricyanide pH = 2	Pt	Zn(II)
Cu(I)	0.02 M $CuSO_4$	Pt	Cr(VI), V(V), IO_3^-
Fe(II)	0.6 M ferric ammonium sulfate 2 M H_2SO_4	Pt	Cr(VI), V(V), MnO_4^-
Ti(III)	0.6 M titanic sulfate 6 M H_2SO_4	Pt (Hg also used)	Fe(III), V, U(VI), Ce(IV)
Ag(I)	0.5 M $HClO_4$	Ag anode	Cl^-, Br^-, I^-
EDTA (Y^{4-})	0.02 M $HgNH_3Y^{2-}$ 0.1 M NH_4NO_3 pH = 8.3; O_2 removed	Hg	Ca(II), Zn(II), Pb(II), etc.
H^+ or OH^-	Various electrolytes	Pt	OH^- or H^+ Organic acids or bases

certain unstable titrants such as Br_2, Cl_2, and Ag(II) can be generated with 100% current efficiency, even though standard solutions of these compounds cannot be made. This is one of the important advantages of coulometric titrations, and results from the fact that the titrant reacts with the sample as it is formed.

Under proper conditions, coulometric titrations can be performed with typical accuracies of 0.1% or better, even with small quantities of compounds. (Work in the microgram range may, however, have errors on the order of 1%.) If special precautions are taken, accuracies can be obtained that are difficult to achieve by any other method. Taylor and coworkers, for example, have titrated milligram quantities of substances with precisions of 0.005% or better [5, 6]. For these titrations, series resistors in a constant-temperature oil bath are used to control and measure the current from a 48 V storage battery; the oil bath dissipates heat and thus stabilizes the resistance. The current is determined by measuring the iR drop across a precision resistor with a very sensitive potentiometer and comparing it with a standard Weston cell maintained at 1.017875 V $\pm$ 0.8 μV by careful thermostatic control. The titration time is measured with a quartz-crystal-controlled time-interval meter capable of an accuracy of 1 ppm. The meter is compared with NBS standard time signals to check its performance.

One difficulty often encountered, especially with small amounts of sample, is the effect of impurities in the supporting electrolyte. Even small percentages of impurities in the relatively large concentrations of electrolytes used may cause spurious results. These must be corrected for by performing a blank titration on a separate aliquot of the generating solution. Another way of circumventing this problem is by a pretitration during which reagent is generated until the endpoint potential, current, or whatever, has been reached or exceeded. The sample is then added and reagent generated until the endpoint detection device is in the same state as when the sample was added.

Assuming impurities can be satisfactorily pretitrated, the lower limit of the amount of sample that can be titrated is governed primarily by the sensitivity of the available endpoint detection system. Very small currents, such as 0.1 μA, can be measured accurately (actually, currents smaller than 60 electrons per second have been measured!) and the time of electrogeneration can be measured accurately. With conventional amperometric and potentiometric endpoint indication, coulometric titrations in typical solution volumes cannot be accurately made at generating currents of less than about 100 μA.

A few highly sensitive endpoint detection systems have been described. A zero-current potentiometric method using an extremely sensitive galvanometer allows the titration of 3 ng of manganese as permanganate (2.5×10^{-10} eq) with electrogenerated iron(II) in a volume of 7 ml [7]; actually, the measurement is done in an amperometric mode by setting the endpoint potential and generating titrant until the off-null galvanometer returns to zero current. The error is only 9%. A constant-current potentiometric method has been used to titrate as little as 0.8 ng of bromide in a volume of 0.5 ml (20 nM) with silver ion electrogenerated at 0.1 μA [8]; submicromole quantities of acids have also been titrated with precisions of ±2% [9]. An indirect procedure for amperometric [10] and biamperometric [11] titration using a very sensitive current-recorder has been used to titrate as little as 9 ng of arsenic(III) (0.24 neq) in a volume of 35 ml with generated bromine. A sufficient excess of bromine is electrogenerated, the sample is then added and the decrease in the detector current is measured. The "titration time" is calculated to the nearest 0.01 sec from the slope of the detector current-versus-time curve. An accuracy of better than 4% is obtained.

Coulometric titrations are easily automated—more easily, in fact, than titrations using a standard solution. This is because the addition of titrant (in effect, the electron) is so easily controlled and its rate of addition is so constant. Generally, the endpoint potential or current of the indicating electrode activates a relay which shuts off the generating current and timer at the end of the titration.

Also, there are a number of continuous coulometric analyzers that record the current magnitude required to maintain a constant solution composition while a chemical reaction removing the electrogenerated reagent is occurring. For instance, chlorinated hydrocarbons can be detected coming off a gas chromatography column (see Chap. 22) with a coulometric detector which generates Ag^+. The chlorinated compounds are burnt in a small furnace at the end of the gas chromatography column, producing HCl among the products. The HCl is carried into an electrolytic cell where it precipitates as AgCl. A potentiometric indicator electrode senses the loss of Ag^+ and causes more to be generated. The generating current is proportional to the amount of silver that has reacted, and its magnitude is recorded as a function of time to give the characteristic chromatographic peaks.

This general approach, which requires the combustion of the sample and the introduction of its gaseous products into a microcoulometric cell, has now been applied to the analysis of nitrogen, halogens, sulfur, carbon, hydrogen, phosphorus, and water. These determinations may or may not involve previous gas chromatographic separation. Sulfur is converted to H_2S which precipitates Ag_2S, while phosphorus gives PH_3 which reacts with silver to give Ag_2PH. Nitrogen-containing compounds are determined by passing them over a nickel catalyst to convert the nitrogen to NH_3, which is absorbed in an acid solution and titrated with coulometrically generated H^+ at a platinum anode. Sulfur can be determined in the presence of halides by burning it in oxygen, producing SO_2 which is absorbed in an iodine solution and titrated with electrogenerated iodine.

A wide variety of samples can be handled, including petroleum, minerals, and air and water (pollution analysis). Amounts of materials approaching the nanogram range can be handled, although, of course, the accuracy drops into the percent range rather than the ppt range usual for coulometric work.

Coulometers for this type of work typically cost about $3000, which is roughly the price of a good potentiostat and integrator. Sampling systems, however, may double the price. These costs may be contrasted with the few hundred dollars needed for a constant-current supply for simple coulometric titrations (although some sort of endpoint detecting device is also usually needed).

One final advantage not yet mentioned is that coulometry is an *absolute* technique needing no calibration with standard solutions—the electron is the standard. This minimizes error and eliminates the preparation and storage—and problems—of standard solutions; in fact, the electron has been proposed as a permanent, nondestructible standard for the analysis of materials.

All in all, with their simplicity, accuracy, relative low cost, and wide applicability, coulometric techniques deserve serious consideration by the analyst.

SELECTED BIBLIOGRAPHY

DAVIS, D. G. *Anal. Chem.*, *44*(5), 79R (1972); *46*(5), 21R (1974).

LINGANE, J. J. *Electroanalytical Chemistry*, 2nd ed. New York: Wiley-Interscience, 1958.

MILNER, G. W. C. *Coulometry in Analytical Chemistry*. Oxford: Pergamon Press, 1967.

RECHNITZ, G. A. *Controlled Potential Analysis*. Oxford: Pergamon Press, 1963.

REFERENCES

1. J. A. PAGE, in *Handbook of Analytical Chemistry*, L. Meites, ed., New York: McGraw-Hill Book Co., 1963, pp 5–170 to 5–186.

2. J. J. LINGANE, *Electroanalytical Chemistry*, 2nd ed., New York: Wiley-Interscience, 1958, pp 222–28.

3. J. J. Lingane, *Anal. Chim. Acta*, 44, 199 (1969).

4. A. J. Bard and K. S. V. Santhanam, in *Electroanalytical Chemistry*, A. J. Bard, ed., vol. 4, New York: Marcel Dekker, Inc., 1970, pp 215–315.

5. J. K. Taylor and S. W. Smith, *J. Res. Natl. Bur. Stand.*, 63A, 153 (1959).

6. G. Marienko and J. K. Taylor, *J. Res. Natl. Bur. Stand.*, 67A, 31 (1963).

7. W. D. Cooke, C. N. Reilley, and N. H. Furman, *Anal. Chem.*, 24, 205 (1952).

8. E. Bishop and R. G. Dhaneshwar, *Anal. Chem.*, 36, 726 (1964).

9. E. Bishop and G. D. Short, *Analyst*, 89, 587 (1964).

10. G. D. Christian and F. D. Feldman, *Anal. Chim. Acta*, 34, 115 (1966).

11. G. D. Christian, *Microchem. J.*, 9, 484 (1964).

PROBLEMS

1. In order to deposit 99.99% of a 10^{-2} M lead solution as PbO_2, what would be the required anode potential, neglecting overvoltage?

2. A sample (100 ml) of a 1.00×10^{-3} M solution of lead ion is electrolyzed at a mercury cathode of 5.0 cm^2 at a potential of -0.68 V versus SCE. The solution is also 0.1 M in $HClO_4$. Stirring is such that the diffusion layer is 0.02 mm thick. The diffusion coefficient of lead is about 1×10^{-5} cm^2/sec. Plot the current-versus-time curve for this electrolysis and calculate the time necessary to reduce the lead concentration to 0.1% of its original value.

3. The iron in a 0.1000 g sample was converted to Fe^{3+} and titrated coulometrically with electrogenerated titanous ion (Ti^{3+}). A current of 1.567 mA was used and the time to reach the endpoint was found to be 123.0 seconds. Calculate the percentage of iron in the sample.

4. In constant-current coulometry, what current would be required so that the time in seconds would be equal to the number of microequivalents?

5. An air sample, polluted with SO_2, is passed through a continuous coulometric cell which automatically maintains a small concentration of I_2 by electrogenerating it from acidic potassium iodide. The SO_2 is oxidized to SO_3 by the iodine. If the air sample flow rate is 5 l/min, and the coulometer averaged an output of 1.40 mA to maintain the I_2 concentration for 10 min, what is the concentration of SO_2 in ppm? The density of air may be taken as 1.2 g/l.

6. A constant-potential coulometric determination of copper is being done using a mercury-pool cathode and a water coulometer. A volume of 32.14 ml of hydrogen-oxygen mixture is obtained. The temperature of the gas is 24.0°C and the barometric pressure in the room is 752.0 mm of mercury. The water vapor pressure above the 0.1 M sodium sulfate solution in the coulometer is as follows:

T (°C)	P_{H_2O}, mm Hg
20	17.5
21	18.6
22	19.2
23	21.0
24	22.3
25	23.7

Using the experimental value of 0.1739 ml of hydrogen-oxygen mixture per coulomb for standard conditions, calculate the quantity of copper in the cell. Compare the 0.1739 ml/coul with the theoretical value.

7. The thickness of a pure silver plate on a base metal is to be determined by controlled-potential coulometry. The metal sheet is masked except for a circular area 0.50 cm in diameter; electrical connection is made to the metal, the sheet is clamped in a cell so that the unmasked area is covered with electrolyte, and the silver plate is anodically stripped. Calculate the average thickness of the silver

plating in μm, if the stripping required 0.600 coulombs and if the density of silver is 10.50 g/cm^3.

8. What is the minimum working electrode potential versus SCE required for quantitative (99.9%) electrodeposition of silver from 0.001 M solution?

9. A protein sample is analyzed by digesting it with sulfuric acid to convert protein nitrogen to ammonium sulfate (Kjeldahl digestion). The digested sample is diluted to 100.0 ml, a 1.00-ml aliquot is adjusted to pH 8.6, and the ammonia produced is titrated coulometrically with electrogenerated hypobromite:

$$Br^- + 2OH^- \longrightarrow OBr^- + H_2O + 2e^-$$
$$2NH_3 + 3OBr^- \longrightarrow N_2 + 3Br^- + 3H_2O.$$

The titration is performed at 10.00 mA current and the endpoint occurs at 159.2 sec. How many milligrams of nitrogen was present in the sample?

5

Conductance and Oscillometry

J. WEST LOVELAND

Electrical conductance occurs in many different materials—either by the flow of electrons (as in metals) or by the movement of other charged species (as in electrolytes or semiconductors). Electrolytic conductance involves the transport of anions to the anode and cations to the cathode while electrons are transferred to and from the ions at the electrode surfaces to complete the current path. Fused salts and colloidal charged particles behave in a similar fashion. Solid semiconductors carry current by the movement of positive or negative ions into vacated "hole" structures in the lattice network. Increasing the temperature of electrolytic solutions or solids improves the mobility of the charged species and hence increases the conductance; on the other hand, metallic conduction decreases with increasing temperature because of the increased vibrational-energy barriers created and a consequent loss of mobility or free energy bands of the electrons. A specialized form of conductance is that observed in the gaseous state (often called a "plasma"), where both ions and electrons conduct electricity when a potential is applied between two electrodes. A simple example of this is a fluorescent light or bunsen burner flame.

For electrolytic solutions of ions, the magnitude of the electric current depends on the number and types of ions present, their mobility, the type of solvent, and the voltage applied. The number of ions depends on the concentration, but for weak electrolytes it also depends on the degree of ionization, as well as on the temperature.

Ohm's law applies to both metallic conductors and electrolyte solutions. However, anomalies occur under special conditions such as high voltages or very high frequencies. Our emphasis will be to explore electrolytic conductance for analytical uses under the more ideal conditions of low voltage (1 to 100 V) and low frequencies (0 to 5000 Hz). We will also introduce the technique of oscillometry, which is an electrodeless method (using high frequencies) that gives results similar to conductance but is influenced to a large degree by the capacitive and dielectric properties of the system.

5.1 DEFINITIONS AND UNITS

Ohm's law states that the current i (in amperes) flowing in a conductor is directly proportional to the applied voltage E (in volts) and inversely proportional to the resistance R (in ohms, Ω) of the conductor. The familiar equation results:

$$i = E/R, \quad \text{or} \quad R = E/i \qquad (5.1)$$

For a conductor of uniform composition and cross-section, the resistance is proportional to the length, l, and inversely proportional to the area, A. The standard unit of resistance for both metallic and electrolytic conductors is called the *specific resistance* ρ (in ohm-cm) which is the resistance of a 1-centimeter cube of the material. The resistance expressed in ohms is

$$R = \rho \times l/A \qquad (5.2)$$

The reciprocal of Equation 5.2 is the *conductance* and $1/\rho$ is generally called the specific conductance, κ, with units of ohm^{-1} cm^{-1} or mho/cm. Conductance G now can be written as

$$1/R = G = \kappa \times A/l \text{ (mho or ohm}^{-1}) \qquad (5.3)$$

The specific conductances of several different types of materials are given in Table 5.1.

Equivalent Conductance

The specific conductance of electrolytic solutions depends on the concentration of the ionic species present. It becomes useful, therefore, to define the conductance of electrolytes on a basis that takes into account the concentration. This is chosen as the conductance of a hypothetical solution containing one gram-equivalent of solute between two parallel electrodes 1 cm apart. The gram-equivalent weight is equal to the gram-formula (or atomic) weight divided by the charge on the ion. Hence, the number of gram equivalents is the number of gram-formula weights (moles) multiplied by the charge, and the normality is the molarity multiplied by the charge. A $1 \, N$ solution requires 1000 cm^3, and by reference to Equation 5.3, the *equivalent conductance* Λ becomes

$$\Lambda = \kappa \frac{1000}{N} \text{ cm}^2/(\text{eq-ohm}) \qquad (5.4)$$

As a hypothetical example, a 0.1 N solution requires 10^4 cm^3 of solution for one gram-equivalent, or by Equation 5.3, 10^4 cm^2 of area for each of two electrodes spaced 1 cm apart.

TABLE 5.1. *Specific Conductance of Various Materials*

Material	Temp. °C	Specific Conductance[a] κ, mho/cm
Silver	20°	(6.18×10^5)
Copper	20°	(5.81×10^5)
Aluminum	20°	(3.55×10^5)
Iron	20°	(1.03×10^5)
Mercury	0°	(1.06×10^4)
Fused NaCl	850°	3.5
1 N HCl	25°	3.33×10^{-1}
0.1 N NaCl	25°	1.07×10^{-2}
Conc. H_2SO_4	25°	1×10^{-2}
1 N Acetic Acid	18°	1.32×10^{-3}
0.001 N HCl	25°	4.21×10^{-4}
0.001 N Acetic Acid	18°	4.10×10^{-5}
Bunsen Flame	1725°	(2.5×10^{-6})
Water[b]	18°	0.8×10^{-6}
Acetone	25°	6×10^{-8}
Acetic Acid	25°	1.12×10^{-8}
Ethyl Alcohol	25°	1.35×10^{-9}
Hexane	18°	$(\sim 1 \times 10^{-18})$

a. Values in parentheses calculated from ρ when κ not available from critical tables or handbooks.
b. "Equilibrium water" resulting from dissolution of the CO_2 present in air.

Cell Constant

Obviously, the use of very large platinum electrodes to make conductance measurements is both awkward and expensive. In actual practice, it is not necessary to fabricate a cell where two platinum electrodes are spaced exactly 1 cm apart to obtain either the specific conductance or the equivalent conductance. Moreover, the potential field between such large electrodes so far apart usually arches outward between them, and errors will occur in measuring the specific conductance. It is more feasible, therefore, to approximate the cell configuration with smaller electrodes and to determine a *cell factor* using solutions of known specific conductance. KCl solutions are generally used, since their specific conductances have been determined with high precision. Table 5.2 gives values of κ for several solutions of KCl. More generally, the specific conductance of any aqueous solution of KCl at 25°C can be calculated from the data of Lind, Zwolenik, and Fuoss [1].

The cell factor or cell constant, K, is related to the measured resistance, R, and κ of the solution by the relationship

$$K = \kappa R \text{ cm}^{-1} \tag{5.5}$$

Thus if $K = 1$, the observed resistance is equal numerically to the reciprocal of the specific conductance of the solution used. Once K has been determined for a

	Specific Conductance, κ, mho/cm		
Normality	18°C	20°C	25°C
1.000[a]	0.09822	0.1021	0.1118
0.1000	0.01119	0.01167	0.01288
0.01000	0.001225	0.001278	0.001413
0.001000	0.0001271	0.0001326	0.0001469

a. Dissolve 74.555 g KCl (weighed in air) and dilute to 1 liter.

cell, then the measurement of the resistance of any other solution will provide values of Λ or κ using Equations 5.4 and 5.5 respectively.

Example 5.1. A conductance cell was filled with a KCl solution that has a specific conductance of 0.01288 mho/cm. The measured resistance at 25°C was 48.3 ohms. (a) What is the cell factor, K? When the same cell was filled with 0.100 N CdCl$_2$, a resistance of 123.7 ohms was obtained. (b) What is the equivalent conductance of the CdCl$_2$ solution?

Solution: (a) $K = \kappa R = (0.01288 \text{ ohm}^{-1} \text{ cm}^{-1} \times 48.3 \text{ ohm}) = 0.622 \text{ cm}^{-1}$

(b) $\Lambda = \dfrac{1000}{N} \left(\dfrac{K}{R} \right) = \dfrac{1000}{0.100} \times \dfrac{0.622}{123.7} = 50.3 \text{ cm}^2/(\text{eq-ohm})$

5.2 THEORY

The conductivity of electrolyte solutions is equal to the sum of the conductivities of each type of ion present. For a single dissolved salt, the equivalent conductance can be expressed as

$$\Lambda = \lambda_+ + \lambda_- \tag{5.6}$$

where λ_+ = the equivalent conductance of the cation
λ_- = the equivalent conductance of the anion

For mixtures, Λ would be equal to the sum of all the individual ionic λ_+'s and λ_-'s. The equivalent conductance of salts or ions increases as the concentration decreases. This phenomenon is directly related to the interionic forces present in solution; a given cation, for example, will have more anions in its vicinity than expected from a purely random distribution. This "ionic atmosphere" has two effects, *electrophoretic* and *time of relaxation*, both of which tend to decrease the ion's mobility. In the former effect, the solvent molecules associated with the ionic atmosphere are moving in a direction opposite to that of the central ion. In the latter, the ionic atmosphere moves slower than the central ion, causing a charge separation (electrostatic retarding force) on the central ion.

As solutions become more dilute, the ionic atmosphere becomes weaker, with the result that both the electrophoretic and time-of-relaxation influences decrease approximately with the square root of the ionic strength of the solution. At infinite dilution there are no disturbing effects on the mobilities of the ions other than variations in solvent and temperature, and the equivalent conductance reaches its maximum value. Equation 5.6 may be written

$$\Lambda^0 = \lambda_+^0 + \lambda_-^0 \tag{5.7}$$

where Λ^0 = the equivalent conductance of the electrolyte at infinite dilution
  λ_+^0 = the limiting ionic equivalent conductances of the cation at infinite dilution
  λ_-^0 = the limiting ionic equivalent conductance of the anion at infinite dilution

Onsager [2] has shown that Λ (at finite concentrations) and Λ^0 can be related to the equation

$$\Lambda = \Lambda^0 - (A + B\Lambda^0)\sqrt{c} \tag{5.8}$$

where A = a factor accounting for the electrophoretic effect
  B = a factor accounting for the time-of-relaxation effect

Table 5.3 gives the limiting equivalent conductances for several ions. Figure 5.1 shows graphically the equivalent conductance of several electrolytes in water at 25°C over the concentration range of 0 to 0.1 N.

TABLE 5.3. *Limiting Equivalent Conductance of Ions in Water at 25°C*

Cations	λ_+^0	Anions	λ_-^0
H^+	349.8	OH^-	198.6
Li^+	38.6	F^-	55.4
Na^+	50.1	Cl^-	76.4
K^+	73.5	Br^-	78.1
Rb^+	77.8	I^-	76.8
Ag^+	61.9	NO_3^-	71.5
NH_4^+	73.3	ClO_3^-	64.6
$(CH_3)_2NH_2^+$	51.8	ClO_4^-	67.4
Hg^{2+}	53.0	IO_4^-	54.5
Mg^{2+}	53.1	———	———
Ca^{2+}	59.5	Formate	54.6
Ba^{2+}	63.6	Acetate	40.9
Cu^{2+}	53.6	Benzoate	32.4
Zn^{2+}	52.8	SO_4^{2-}	80.0
La^{3+}	69.7	CO_3^{2-}	69.3
Ce^{3+}	69.8	$Fe(CN)_6^{4-}$	111.0

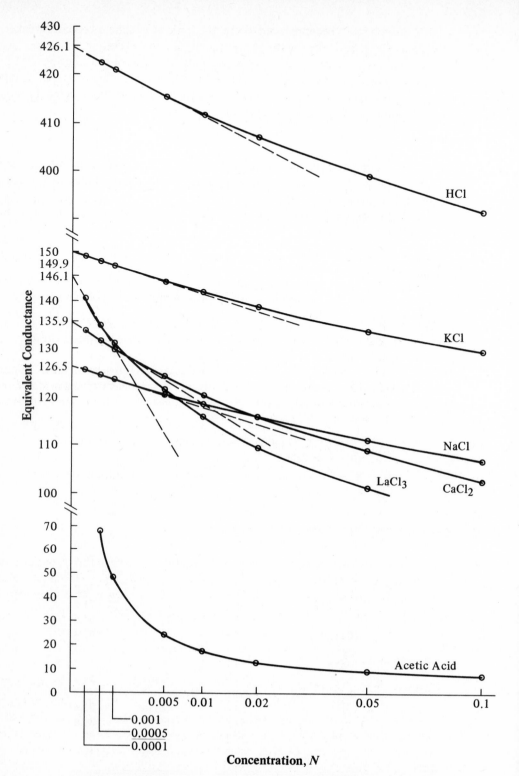

FIGURE 5.1. *Equivalent conductance versus concentration for several electrolytes at 25°C.*

Conductance Ratio: Weak Electrolytes

One of the early uses of limiting conductances was to determine the degree of dissociation of weak electrolytes. Arrhenius suggested that, at any given concentration, the measured equivalent conductance (when compared to the limiting equivalent conductance where all ions are dissociated) should be a measure of the degree of dissociation, α. This can be expressed as

$$\alpha = \Lambda/\Lambda^0 \tag{5.9}$$

To a first approximation, this equation gives values that vary only slightly from the true values. Any variation is due mainly to the fact that activity coefficients and the effect of concentration on the ionic conductances have been neglected. Acetic acid, HOAc, dissociates according to the reaction

$$HOAc \rightleftharpoons H^+ + OAc^-$$

The ionization constant K_i is expressed as

$$K_i = \frac{[H^+][OAc^-]}{[HOAc]} = \frac{\alpha[HOAc] \times \alpha[HOAc]}{[HOAc](1 - \alpha)} = \frac{\alpha^2[HOAc]}{(1 - \alpha)} \tag{5.10}$$

Using the data from Table 5.3, the limiting equivalent conductance of acetic acid is $\Lambda^0_{HOAc} = \lambda_{H^+}^0 + \lambda_{OAc^-}^0 = 349.8 + 40.9 = 390.7 \text{ cm}^2/\text{(eq-ohm)}$.

> **Example 5.2.** The equivalent conductance of a 0.0125 N acetic-acid solution was determined at 25°C to be 14.4. Calculate both the degree of dissociation and the ionization constant.

Solution: $\alpha = \Lambda/\Lambda^0 = 14.4/390.7 = 0.0369$

$$K_i = \frac{\alpha^2 c}{(1 - \alpha)} = \frac{(0.0369)^2 \times 0.0125}{0.9631} = 1.77 \times 10^{-5}$$

5.3 CONDUCTOMETRIC INSTRUMENTATION

The apparatus required for making conductance measurements and performing conductance titrations is generally inexpensive and basically simple in detail. For these reasons, the measurement of conductance finds wide acceptance in industry as an analytical tool, both in the laboratory and in process control.

Conductivity Cells

Various types of conductance cells are used depending upon the application. The most popular type uses platinum electrodes about 1 cm² in area, preferably oriented in a vertical position so that solids do not collect on the surface. The electrodes, welded to heavy platinum wire, must be sealed rigidly in Pyrex or some other rigid nonconducting medium so that no movement of the electrodes takes place during stirring. Figure 5.2 depicts three cells: (a) a cell used for exact conductance

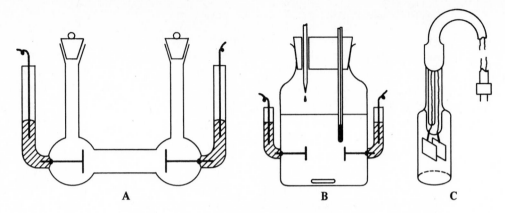

FIGURE 5.2. *Three types of conductance cells, A: Precision conductance cell. B: Conductometric titration cell. C: Concentration dip cell.*

measurement, (b) one used for conductometric titration, and (c) a concentration dip-cell for process or laboratory application.

Preparation of the electrode surfaces is very important. The electrodes should be cleaned in an acid cleaning solution, rinsed thoroughly with distilled water, and immersed in a platinizing solution. DC voltage is adjusted to give a moderate evolution of gas for about 20 seconds, after which the polarity is reversed. The reversal process is repeated until a gray (not black) deposit of platinum has formed on the surface. Too heavy a deposit should be avoided because spongy platinum will absorb unwanted chemical species.

The electrodes are washed with distilled water, immersed in $1 N$ H_2SO_4, electrolyzed with DC voltage using repeated polarity reversal to remove impurities, and finally washed and stored in distilled water. Platinizing solutions as well as cells may be purchased from a number of supply houses. More detailed discussion and exact procedures of platinization are available in an article by Jones and Bollinger [3].

Measuring Circuitry

AC Circuits. The Wheatstone bridge is used most often for determining the resistance or conductivity of an electrolyte solution. In Figure 5.3, R_c is the resistance of the electrolyte solution and R_1 is the resistance of an adjustable resistance box containing 3 or 4 decades of resistances. R_2 and R_3 may be fixed known resistors, two halves of a resistance slide-wire, or two separate decade-boxes of resistors.

The signal generator may be a 60-Hz transformer, a 1000-Hz oscillator, or a variable-frequency oscillator. If earphones are used as a null, the 1000-Hz oscillator is preferred. The null indicator can also be a sensitive microammeter or more elaborate null-point indicators.

Alternating currents are preferred to direct current because little or no polarization of platinized electrodes takes place. During electrolysis the platinum black

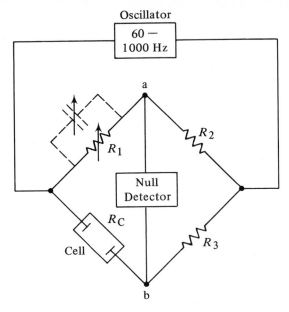

FIGURE 5.3. *Basic Wheatstone AC bridge circuit for measuring conductance.*

adsorbs gases and catalyzes their electrochemical reaction. The alternating current prevents any buildup of material on a given electrode.

In practice, one should attempt to keep R_2 and R_3 in the same range of values. If this is done, then R_1 will have to be adjusted to a range near that of the cell resistance, R_c. This requires that the size and spacing of the electrode be considered in selecting a cell to use in making the conductance measurement. For concentrated electrolyte solutions, small electrodes and long path-lengths (high cell-constant) are used, while for dilute or weak electrolytes, cells with large electrodes and short spacing (low cell-constant) should be employed.

When making the measurement, the resistance R_1 is adjusted until a null is observed. (For maximum accuracy, R_2 and R_3 may also be altered—but see previous paragraph.) Under this condition, there is no potential difference between points a and b of Figure 5.3 and therefore $E_c = E_1$ and $E_2 = E_3$, where the various Es are the voltage drops across the appropriate resistors; from Ohm's law

$$i_c R_c = i_1 R_1 \quad \text{and} \quad i_2 R_2 = i_3 R_3 \tag{5.11}$$

and

$$\frac{R_c i_c}{R_3 i_3} = \frac{R_1 i_1}{R_2 i_2} \tag{5.12}$$

Since the current passing through resistances R_1 and R_2 is the same and the current passing through the cell and R_3 is the same (there is no net current flow through the detector at null), the currents cancel and Equation 5.12 can be solved for R_c:

$$R_c = \frac{R_1 R_3}{R_2} \tag{5.13}$$

This is the basic relationship for Wheatstone bridges at balance.

Note that in Figure 5.3 a variable capacitor shunts R_1. This is to balance out any phase shifts in the alternating signal caused by the capacity effects present at the electrode surfaces. It is adjusted to give the sharpest minimum in the null signal. For conductometric titrations it is generally not needed.

DC Circuits. Measurements of conductance can also be made with direct current, and in some respects this is simpler than with the AC Wheatstone bridge arrangement. Figure 5.4 shows a simplified DC circuit for measuring conductance. With switch A closed, the current flowing through the solution is determined by the 500-V

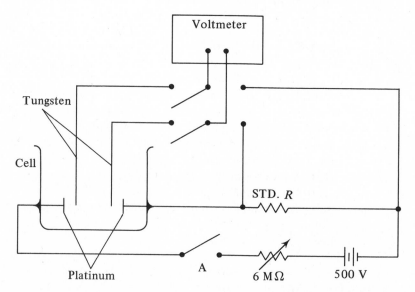

FIGURE 5.4. *Direct-current circuit for measuring conductance.*

source and the 6-MΩ variable resistor, and is measured across the standard resistor. This assumes that the resistance of the solution between the platinum electrodes is several orders of magnitude less than that of 6 MΩ plus the standard resistor. The two immersed tungsten electrodes will be at potentials that depend on the iR drop across the solution. Knowing the current and measuring the voltage between the tungsten electrodes, the resistance of the solution can be calculated from Ohm's law. The meter used to measure the voltage should be of high impedance to prevent polarization of the probe electrodes.

In order to minimize the consumption of electrodes or the introduction of new ions, small currents are employed and only for a short length of time to measure the potential drop. If the working electrodes show signs of polarization from too much current flow, then reversible working electrodes, such as Ag/AgCl should be used.

In low-conductance nonaqueous solutions, where resistances of the order of 10^8 to 10^{10} Ω are observed, a single pair of electrodes may be used with a large known external resistance of about 10^8 Ω and a 1.5 V battery; iR drops across the external resistor are measured with an electrometer. Nonaqueous conductometric titrations can be followed in solvents of low dielectric constant by this arrangement.

5.4 CONDUCTANCE TITRATIONS AND OTHER APPLICATIONS

One of the most frequent uses of conductance is in quantitative titrations of systems in which the conductance of the solution varies in such a manner (prior to and after the endpoint) that two intersecting lines can be drawn to indicate the endpoint. The actual shape of the curve depends on the sample, the titrant, and the reactions occurring. To maximize accuracy in all titration work, corrections to the measured resistance may have to be made for dilution by the titrant. To minimize this correction, titrants should be at least 10, and preferably 100, times stronger than the solute. While the term conductance implies that titrations require that conductance be measured, it should be pointed out that the reciprocal of resistance can be plotted and values need only be relative and not absolute.

Volume corrections for the added titrant are made according to the equation

$$R_s = \frac{V}{V + v} R_0 \tag{5.14}$$

where R_0 = the measured resistance
   R_s = the corrected solution resistance
   V = the original volume of solution
   v = the amount of titrant added at the time of reading R_0

In general, four to six points are taken prior to the end point and a similar number of points after the end point.

Acid-Base Titrations

Many applications of conductance titrations involve acid-base titrations.

Strong Acids and Bases. Because of the high mobilities of H^+ and OH^-, the sharpest and most accurate endpoints are obtained when strong acids are titrated with strong bases and vice versa. Referring to Table 5.3, it is seen that the equivalent conductance (or mobility) of H^+ is about 5 times that of the other cations, and that of OH^- is about 3 times greater than that of other anions.

A typical example is the titration of 100 ml of 0.001 N HCl with 0.1 N NaOH:

$$(H^+ + Cl^-) + (Na^+ + OH^-) \longrightarrow (Na^+ + Cl^-) + H_2O \tag{5.15}$$

The relative or even exact resistance values during the titration can be calculated and the shape of the curve predetermined. We will make a calculation for this

Ml Titrant	Specific Conductance $\times$ 10^4, mho/cm (25°C)					
	H^+	Cl^-	Na^+	OH^-	NaCl	Total
0.00	3.50	0.76	0.00	0.00	0.00	4.26
0.20	2.80	0.76	0.10	0.00	0.25	3.66
0.50	1.75	0.76	0.25	0.00	0.63	2.76
0.75	0.87	0.76	0.38	0.00	0.95	2.01
1.00	0.00	0.76	0.50	0.00	1.26	1.26
1.25	0.00	0.76	0.63	0.50	1.26	1.89
1.50	0.00	0.76	0.75	0.99	1.26	2.50
1.75	0.00	0.76	0.88	1.49	1.26	3.13
2.00	0.00	0.76	1.00	1.99	1.26	3.75

Note: Specific conductances have not been corrected for volume dilution.

simple titration as an example to use in approaching the more complicated titrations discussed later.

For the reaction of Equation 5.15, the total conductance is the sum of the conductances due to each of the four types of ions present:

$$G = \frac{1}{R} = \frac{1}{R_{H^+}} + \frac{1}{R_{Cl^-}} + \frac{1}{R_{Na^+}} + \frac{1}{R_{OH^-}} = \frac{\lambda_{H^+}\, {}^0c_{H^+}}{1000\,K} + \cdots \tag{5.16}$$

To simplify the calculations, it will be assumed that the cell constant K is unity and that the λ^0's of the four ions are sufficiently close to those of the 0.001 N solutions to be used without affecting the result. Under these conditions, the specific conductances of each ion and the total specific conductance of the titrated solution are given in Table 5.4.

When these data are plotted, as shown in Figure 5.5, it is seen that the conductance at first decreases rapidly owing to neutralization of H^+ and then, after the endpoint, increases rapidly as excess OH^- ions are added. The dashed line represents the conductance contribution of the salt (NaCl) formed during the neutralization. This dashed line is significant in the titration of weak and very weak acids or bases—up to the endpoint the conductance generally follows this line closely. If salts are already present in solution, the curve of Figure 5.5 is pushed upward and the relative change (as measured by the conductance bridge) decreases. When salt concentrations are very high, the relatively small change in conductance produces inaccuracy, and better results would be obtained by potentiometric titration.

In the absence of excess salts, accurate measurements can be made equally well on both very dilute and very concentrated solutions. Very dilute solutions, of course, must be protected from contamination by acidic or basic gases in the atmosphere.

Weak Acids and Bases. The titration of weak acids and bases does not result in as sharp an endpoint as is obtained with strong acids and bases.

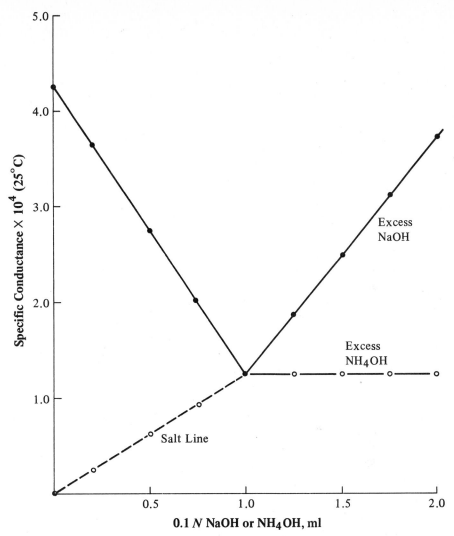

FIGURE 5.5. *Titration curve for the neutralization of 0.001 N HCl with (a) 0.1 N NaOH and (b) 0.1 N NH₄OH (the actual salt line and excess NH₄OH line have slightly higher values than shown).*

During the titration of weak acids, the law of mass action applies and, in the case of acetic acid titrated with NaOH, the common ion OAc^- causes a decrease in the hydrogen-ion concentration over and above that due to stoichiometric neutralization. Since the increase in conductance due to the production of Na^+ and OAc^- is less than the decrease due to the loss of hydrogen ions, the net conductance decreases during the early stages of the titration. At some point, depending on the concentration of the weak acid being titrated and its pK_a value, the concentration of H^+ becomes negligible and the conductance of Na^+ and the weak-acid anions follows the salt line indicated in Figure 5.5. However, owing to hydrolysis of the sodium acetate, near the endpoint a very slight rounding will take place. Figure 5.6A shows

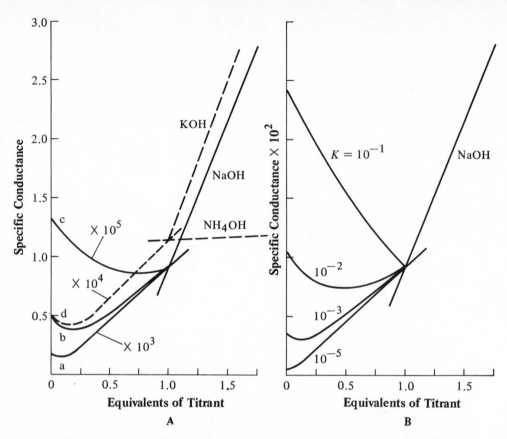

FIGURE 5.6. *A: Titration of various strengths of acetic acid—(a) 0.01 N;
(b) 0.001 N; and (c) 0.0001 N (titrated with NaOH) and (d) 0.001 N acetic
acid (titrated with NH₄OH or KOH). B: Various moderately weak acids
with NaOH.*

the titration curves of different concentrations of acetic acid with NaOH and also
with the weak base NH_4OH at about 0.001 N. Figure 5.6B shows the effect of the
ionization constant of acids at concentrations of 0.1 N on the shape of the titration
curves.

Curve c of Figure 5.6A indicates that the very dilute solution of 0.0001 N
acetic acid is dissociated to such an extent that no straight-line portion can be obtained—as in curve a—to provide a useful endpoint calculation. Even for the 0.001 N
solution (curve b), only about the last 20% of the neutralization is linear and some
care must be taken if one is to obtain accurate endpoints.

When NH_4OH is the base (curve d), a slightly sharper endpoint is obtained.
In this particular case, the titration up to the endpoint will proceed as if a strong
base were being used. However, after the endpoint, owing to the common-ion effect
of NH_4^+ on the ionization of NH_4OH, the conductance remains essentially constant
since NH_4OH remains mostly in the un-ionized state. Also, since the conductance
of NH_4^+ ($\lambda^0 = 73$) is greater than that of Na^+ ($\lambda^0 = 50$), the conductance prior to
the endpoint increases slightly faster, thereby enhancing the angle at the endpoint.

Figure 5.6B indicates that a moderately strong acid ($K_a = 10^{-1}$) at a concentration of 0.1 N can be titrated if several points are taken between the 50 and 100% neutralization points; a nearly V-shaped curve is obtained, although there is a slight curvature. The situation deteriorates rapidly, however, as slightly weaker acids are titrated; for example, for an acid with a pK_a of 2, no linear portion is available during the neutralization to obtain an endpoint.

Dilution of moderately strong acids will often provide better titration curves. For example, the 0.1 N solution of an acid with a pK_a of 2 will ionize to a much greater extent (~62% vs. 27%) when diluted 10-fold, resulting in a titration curve similar to that of an acid with a pK_a of 1 at 0.1 N. Further dilution will provide still better V-shaped curves, at least up to a point.

A general rule for obtaining useful curves is that moderately strong acids (and bases) can be titrated as strong acids if their concentration is about 100 times smaller than their ionization constant. Alternatively, they may be titrated as weak acids when their concentration is at least 150 times larger than the ionization constant. For example, the last 25% of the salt line will be followed for an acid with a pK_a of 3 if its concentration is 0.15 N or greater.

A technique for obtaining good endpoints when single titrations give poorly defined curves is to titrate equal portions of the unknown weak acid with equal concentrations of KOH and NH_4OH on two equal aliquots. The curves obtained prior to the endpoint should be identical, but after the endpoint will diverge along the weak- and strong-base lines. The intersection of the two lines formed by the excess bases gives the endpoint. The important point to observe in this technique is that the cations of the two base titrants have essentially identical equivalent conductances (NH_4^+, $\lambda^0 = 73$ and K^+, $\lambda^0 = 74$). If NaOH were the strong base, an incorrect endpoint would be determined, as can be deduced from a comparison of the three base curves of Figure 5.6A.

When no linear region prior to the endpoint can be easily obtained, one can add alcohol or some other water-soluble organic compound to reduce the dissociation of the acid so that it behaves more like a very weak acid. This often may be the easiest approach for titrating weak and moderately weak acids. If these techniques fail, then potentiometric methods should be tried.

Very Weak Acids and Bases. These compounds may be considered to have pK_a's or pK_b's in the range of 7 to 10. Since they are very weakly ionized, the initial conductance is very low. With a strong base as titrant, the curve follows the salt line from the start of the titration. Rounding of the curve in the vicinity of the endpoint takes place because of the release of OH^- ions by the hydrolysis of the anion formed. The weaker the acid, the more pronounced this effect. After the endpoint, the conductance increases rapidly because of the excess OH^- ions. The endpoint is determined by extrapolating the first straight portion of the neutralization curve and the latter portion of the excess hydroxide curve.

A marked improvement with very weak acids can be accomplished by adding an excess amount of weak base such as NH_4OH, pyridine, or ethylamine. Addition of such bases causes an increase in the dissociation of the very weak acids according to the equation

$$HA + B \longrightarrow HB^+ + A^- \tag{5.17}$$

Therefore, the following reaction occurs during titration:

$$HB^+ + Na^+ + OH^- \longrightarrow Na^+ + B + H_2O \qquad (5.18)$$

In effect, the titration becomes one of replacing the HB^+ cation by the Na^+ of the titrant up to the endpoint. After the endpoint, the excess OH^- causes the conductance to rise rapidly. An additional advantage of the use of a weak base is its ability to solubilize many slightly soluble weak acids that otherwise require non-aqueous solvents, in which generally poorer endpoints are obtained. Figure 5.7 compares titrations of a very weak acid, such as phenol, with and without the addition of NH_4OH.

FIGURE 5.7. *Titration of a very weak acid with (A) NaOH only, and (B) excess NH_4OH and NaOH titrant.*

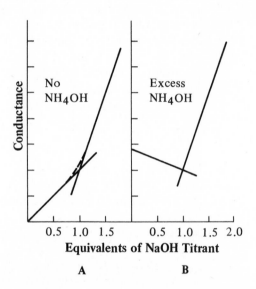

By referring to the ionic-equivalent conductances (Table 5.3), it can be deduced that LiOH should give a more acute angle for endpoint determination than NaOH or KOH. In many cases, titrations of alkaloids and their salts are more accurately followed by conductometry than by potentiometry or by using phenolphthalein as indicator.

A general guideline is that, if it is desired to have 50% of the neutralization follow the initial salt line, the K_a value should be greater than $5 \times 10^{-12}/c$, where c is the molar concentration of the weak acid.

Mixtures of Strong and Weak Acids. Where mixtures of strong and weak acids are titrated, the conductance method often may be preferred to other techniques such as potentiometry. Figure 5.8 shows the relative conductivity changes occurring when a mixture of hydrochloric and acetic acids is titrated with either (*a*) NaOH or (*b*) NH_4OH.

When a mixture of a very weak acid and a strong acid is titrated, a strong base must be used. The use of a weak base leads to large hydrolysis effects and indistinct curves at the weak-acid endpoint, although the first endpoint will give the amount of strong acid.

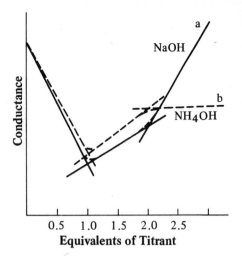

FIGURE 5.8. *Titration of a mixture of a strong and a weak acid with (a) NaOH and (b) NH₄OH.*

Salts of Weak Acids or Bases. Salts of weak acids can be titrated with a strong acid, since they are themselves Bronsted bases—that is, proton acceptors. A typical example is the titration of sodium acetate with hydrochloric acid:

$$H^+ + Cl^- + Na^+ + OAc^- \longrightarrow Na^+ + Cl^- + HOAc \qquad (5.19)$$

As sodium acetate is titrated, the acetate ion is replaced by the chloride ion, which, owing to its slightly higher ionic-equivalent conductance, causes a slight increase in conductivity up to the endpoint. Beyond the endpoint, excess hydrochloric acid causes large increases. Such titrations are useful where the ionization constant of the liberated weak acid or base, when divided by the salt's concentration, does not exceed 5×10^{-3}. If a difunctional acid is formed, then the two ionization constants should differ by about 10^{-5} if two endpoints are to be observed; Na_2S is an example of this type. Figure 5.9 shows typical replacement titration curves.

FIGURE 5.9. *Replacement reactions: Titration of (a) Na₂S with HCl titrant and (b) NH₄Cl with NaOH titrants.*

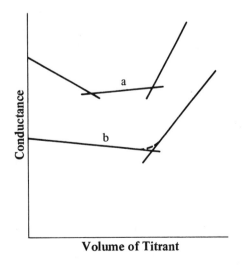

Replacement titrations are useful for titrating such salts as oxalates, phosphates, benzoates, etc.

Precipitation and Complexation Reactions

Whenever a reaction between two compounds or salts produces a change in the conductivities of the ions present before and after the endpoint, conductometry can be considered as a possible analytical method. Precipitation reactions, for instance, involve replacing one ion with another. Silver in $AgNO_3$ solution may be determined by titrating it with the chlorides of sodium, potassium, or lithium. From the ionic-equivalent conductances of the cations involved ($\lambda^0_{Li^+} = 39$, $\lambda^0_{Na^+} = 50$, $\lambda^0_{Ag^+} = 62$, and $\lambda_{K^+}^0 = 74$), lithium will give the sharpest endpoint. Since Li^+ is replacing Ag^+, the conductance decreases during the precipitation of silver chloride, but since the amount of NO_3^- remains constant, the conductivity will increase again after the endpoint because of the excess Cl^-.

The concentrations of the salts and the solubility product of the precipitate play an important role in determining whether satisfactory linear portions are obtained prior to and after the endpoint. High solubility of the precipitate causes rounding of the conductance curve at the endpoint; good curves will be obtained if no more than 1% of the precipitate exists in the ionized form. A few typical precipitation-titration curves are shown in Figure 5.10. A general rule is that the solubility product, when divided by the concentration of the titrant, should not be greater than about 5×10^{-6}. For example, the concentration of $AgNO_3$ with Cl^- titrant should be at least 0.3×10^{-4} N, since AgCl has a K_{sp} of 1.7×10^{-10}.

FIGURE 5.10. *Precipitation reactions: Titration of $AgNO_3$ with (a) KCl and (b) LiCl titrant.*

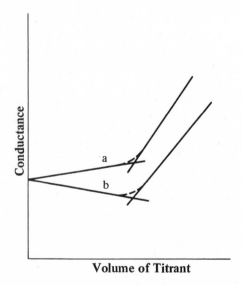

Conductance

Volume of Titrant

Errors in locating true endpoints during precipitation reactions can be caused by several factors: contamination of the electrodes by the adhering precipitate, occlusion of ions by the precipitate, and incomplete or slow precipitation reaction.

Complexometric reactions require that stable complexes be formed. A typical example is the formation of the cyanide complex of Hg^{2+} according to the reaction

$$Hg^{2+} + 2NO_3^- + 2K^+ + 2CN^- \longrightarrow Hg(CN)_2 + 2K^+ + 2NO_3^- \qquad (5.20)$$

A number of metal ions, M^{2+}, can be titrated conductometrically with the disodium salt of ethylenediaminetetraacetic acid, Na$_2$H$_2$EDTA, in buffered solutions [4].

Titrations in Nonaqueous Solutions

In nonaqueous media such as alcohols, not only Arrhenius acids and bases but also Lewis acids and bases can be titrated. (Lewis acids and bases cannot be titrated in aqueous solutions.) Interpreting the curves obtained, however, is more complex than in aqueous solution. One factor that needs to be considered is the suppression or enhancement of the ionization of the acids or bases by the solvent; another is the viscosity of the solvent (as viscosity increases, the ionic mobility decreases). In Lewis acid-base reactions, factors such as ion-pair formation, hydrogen bonding, and solute-solvent and solute-solute interactions must also be taken into account.

A few examples showing the versatility of nonaqueous titrations are the following:

1. In glacial acetic acid, sulfuric acid gives two endpoints when titrated with a strong base or sodium acetate, since the ionization of the second hydrogen is sufficiently reduced that HSO$_4^-$ acts as a weak acid. When hydrochloric acid is present, three endpoints are observed and both acids may be determined.
2. Phenols in low-dielectric solvents often give sharper endpoints than in aqueous solutions; for instance, when 2,3,5-trimethylphenol is titrated with tetrabutyl-ammonium hydroxide in toluene solvent [Fig. 5.11A], as opposed to water. Simi-

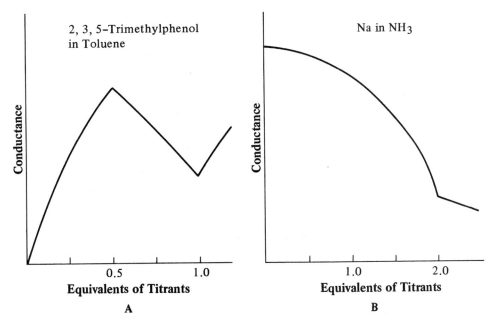

FIGURE 5.11. *Titration curves in nonaqueous solvents: A: Titration of 2,3,5-trimethylphenol with tetrabutylammonium hydroxide in toluene. B: Titration of Na in NH$_3$ with dimethyl sulfide.*

lar results are observed in pyridine solvent when sodium isopropoxide is the titrant.

3. New molecular species can be deduced or at least the molar ratios of complexes can be ascertained. In liquid ammonia ($-33°C$), elemental sodium titrated with dimethyl sulfide indicates that 2 moles of sodium react with the dialkyl sulfide (Fig. 5.11B).

In general, nonaqueous conductance titration is superior to other electrochemical methods for analyzing difficult systems. The major difficulty is the developmental work needed to establish suitable endpoints for the particular solvents and titrants required.

Single (Batch) and Continuous Measurements of Conductance

Determination of Solubilities. We have mentioned the use of single measurements of conductance in determining the ionization constants of weak acids and bases. In addition, the solubilities of many weakly soluble salts and oxides have been determined by conductance measurements. When the solubility product is less than 10^{-8}, a correction must be made for the specific conductance of water.

Water Purity: Salt Content and Moisture Content. Pure water has a specific conductance of slightly less than 1×10^{-6} mho/cm. Water purity is, of course, important in the laboratory where a few parts per million of dissolved salts may mask the component being looked for. It is also important in industry, particularly in power plants (where dissolved salts left behind in flash-boiler pipes may clog them) and in plants where water rinsing is employed. In most cases, it is the total salt content that is of importance. Compact and inexpensive instruments are available with special cells in which direct readout in specific conductance, or parts per million, or grams per gallon is provided. Sensors are of the insertion, flow, and submersion variety. Automated continuous devices are used to control the flow of raw and treated water in demineralizers (ion-exchange beds), to reroute off-test condensate, to control blowdown of boiler water, and for similar operations.

Extensive use of conductometry is now made for controlling pollution in our streams, rivers, and lakes, and for detecting sources of contaminants. Work in oceanography uses portable batch or continuous conductivity analyzers which quite often are scaled to read directly in percent salinity.

In the metal industry, the acid strength of pickling, caustic degreasing, anodizing, and rinse baths are monitored by conductance measurements.

Some automatic analyzers use conductance to indicate the concentration of some specific component. For example, ambient concentrations of SO_2 in air as low as 0.01 ppm can be recorded continuously. Sulfur dioxide is oxidized to sulfuric acid, after which the increase in conductance due to the hydrogen and sulfate ions is directly proportional to the SO_2 concentration. The moisture content of wood and soil has been measured with special electrodes.

Other analytical uses will undoubtedly be made of conductance instruments in the future because of their simplicity, ease of operation, inexpensiveness, and portability and because they can be used for both single (batch) measurement and continuous measurement.

5.5 OSCILLOMETRY OR HIGH-FREQUENCY TITRATIONS

Oscillometry differs from conductometry in several respects.

1. Electrodes are not in direct contact with the solution, but are usually separated from it by the glass walls of the container.
2. Frequencies used are of the order of 10^6 to 10^7 Hz compared with 10^3 Hz for conductance.
3. Instrument response is generally to a combination of resistance and capacitance.

In conductance, the ions absorb energy which is translated into heat and motion. In oscillometry, we have not only this aspect, but also the capacitance effect in which molecules absorb and return energy each frequency cycle owing to the induced polarization and alignment of electrically unsymmetrical molecules.

Generally, if one is working with solutions of high dielectric constant but low conductivity, the response will be primarily capacitive in nature; where the solution has a low dielectric constant and contains salts, the response will be mainly due to the conductance of the ions present.

The end result is that high-frequency titrations give a variety of responses, including the usual V-shaped curves, nonlinear intersecting curves, and inverted V-shaped curves. The shape of a curve may vary with frequency, or at a given frequency a change in dielectric constant or salt content can change the response.

Equivalent Circuit

Cells. Figure 5.12A, a drawing of a high-frequency cell, shows the essential parts affecting cell response in high-frequency titrations. Figure 5.12B is the equivalent circuit, where C_s and C_g are the capacitances and R_s and R_g the resistances of the solution and the glass walls, respectively. Figure 5.12C is a reasonable approximation, since R_g is much larger than R_s, and R_s controls the response due to resistance changes.

Oscillators. The parallel-tuned oscillator circuit is the most commonly used in high-frequency titration work; its circuit is shown in Figure 5.13. The resonance frequency, f_r, of an oscillator is given by

$$f_r = \frac{1}{2\pi\sqrt{LC}} \tag{5.21}$$

where L = the inductance in henries
C = the capacitance in farads

Both L and C display *reactance*: they resist changes in the alternating signal. The capacitive reactance X_C is equal to $1/(2\pi f C)$ and the inductive reactance X_L is $2\pi f L$

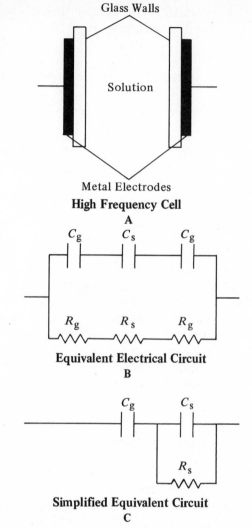

FIGURE 5.12. *Physical and equivalent circuit of high-frequency titration cell. A: High-frequency cell: solution, glass cell, and metal electrode arrangement. B: Equivalent electrical circuit of cell. C: Simplified equivalent circuit.*

where f is the frequency. Both are 90° out of phase with ohmic resistance, and at the resonance frequency are equal in magnitude and opposite in sign.

Assume for the moment that all the resistance is due to the coil resistance, R_L. The total impedance, Z, across the oscillator circuit is

$$Z = \frac{L}{C\sqrt{R_L{}^2 + (X_L - X_C)^2}} \tag{5.22}$$

and at resonance $Z = L/CR_L$. When the oscillator is at resonance, the current i_L is at a minimum since Z is at its maximum. The current i_0 in the LC oscillator is larger than i_L, by a factor of X_L/R_L. The latter is referred to as the Q of the circuit and is a measure of the power-loss factor.

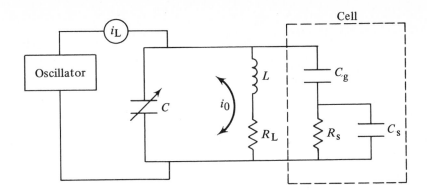

FIGURE 5.13.   *Parallel-tuned oscillator circuit for high-frequency titrations (with cell addition in dashed-line section).*

Relationship Between Low- and High-Frequency Conductance

When the parallel-oscillator circuit is loaded by the cell, the predominant factors affecting response are (a) capacitors C_g and C_s (Fig. 5.13), which change the total C in Equation 5.21, and hence the resonance frequency; and (b) R_s, which changes the resistive load in parallel with R_L and reduces the Q of the circuit. As a result, i_0 is reduced while i_L is increased. Reilley [5] has determined that the conductance term $1/R_s$ in the high-frequency method as related to the low-frequency specific conductance κ is:

$$1/R_s = \frac{\kappa 2\pi f C_g{}^2}{\kappa^2 + (2\pi f)^2(C_g + C_s)^2} \tag{5.23}$$

This implies the following points:

1. When the cell capacitance C_g increases due to larger areas or thinner walls, $1/R_s$ increases.
2. As the frequency increases, $1/R_s$ increases, and as the frequency approaches zero, $1/R_s$ approaches zero.
3. When κ is either very large or very small, $1/R_s$ approaches zero, and at some intermediate value of κ, $1/R_s$ shows a peak response.

Figure 5.14 shows how the high-frequency conductance varies with the low-frequency conductance at several different frequencies.

Instruments. A few instruments are commercially available. Response detection generally takes one of three forms: (a) a calibrated dial to increase or decrease capacity to maintain f_r; (b) a meter to record the change in current i_L (Fig. 5.13) or some other related parameter; and (c) a beat-frequency oscillator where the difference between reference frequency and the working frequency is measured using a frequency-discriminator output signal. One requirement is that the oscillator have good frequency stability.

   Cells should be made of glass or some other nonconducting material, and the electrodes should be affixed firmly to the walls either mechanically or with an

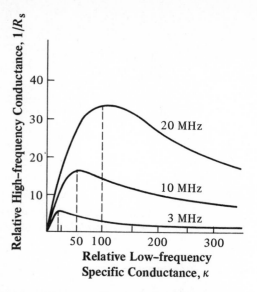

FIGURE 5.14. *High-frequency conductance response versus low-frequency specific conductance response.*

adhesive. The electrode material should be a metal to which leads can be easily soldered. The diameter of the cell and the salt concentration of the solution will determine the loading of the oscillator. If the oscillator cannot sustain oscillations, then smaller diameter cells and lower salt concentrations should be used.

Analytical Use

Titration Curves. Generally it can be expected that if a low-frequency conductance titration can be performed, a high-frequency one can also. However, the cell size, ionic strength of the solution, and frequency needed to give a good endpoint are variables that must be determined by trial and error. Even after the best conditions are found, the curves obtained may be nonlinear and show little response. However, if an endpoint *can* be found, there is a definite advantage to a method in which no

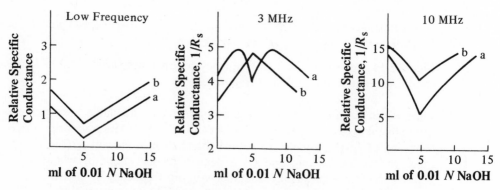

FIGURE 5.15. *Comparison of low- and high-frequency titration curves: A: Low frequency ~ 1000 Hz; B: 3 MHz; and C: 10 MHz. (a) 5 ml of 0.01 N HCl + 55 ml of water. (b) 5 ml of 0.01 N HCl + 55 ml of 0.001 N KCl.*

direct contact is necessary between solution and electrodes, particularly with precipitation titrations, since the electrodes will not be contaminated (for example, by adsorption of precipitates) or affected by electrolysis that could produce polarization.

Figure 5.15 shows a comparison of a low-frequency acid-base titration at two different ionic strengths with high-frequency titrations conducted at 3 and 10 MHz. In each case, 50 milliequivalents of HCl is titrated with 0.01 N NaOH. Obviously 10 MHz is the best frequency to use, but because of the curvature several additional titration points need to be taken to increase the precision of the endpoint determination. The M-shaped curve resulting at 3 MHz could lead to misinterpretation and an incorrect endpoint.

Dielectric Constant: Measurement of Binary Mixtures. When the conductance term κ of Equation 5.23 becomes very small, the response of the oscillator depends primarily on the values of C_g and C_s. The parallel equivalent capacity, C_p, is given by

$$C_p = \frac{C_g C_s}{C_g + C_s} \tag{5.24}$$

If C_g is relatively large compared to C_s, then the response of C_p will be dependent mainly on C_s. C_g can be increased by decreasing wall thickness and C_s decreased by increasing the distance between the walls of the cell. Since the dielectric constant of the sample will alter C_s, the instrument response will follow the dielectric constant. Figure 5.16 indicates the type of nonlinear, but smooth, response obtained with a commercially available oscillometer for compounds of varying dielectric constant.

Table 5.5 gives the dielectric constants for several of the more common liquids. The very large value for water compared to benzene, for example, makes it possible to detect trace amounts of water or some other highly polar material in benzene.

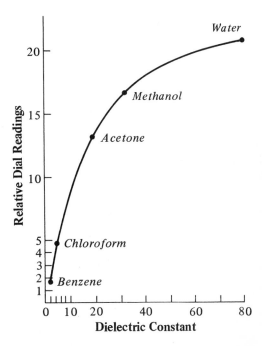

FIGURE 5.16. *Response of high-frequency readings to dielectric constant of some liquids.*

TABLE 5.5. *Dielectric Constants of Several Common Liquids*

Formamide	109 (20°C)	Phenol	9.78 (60°C)
Water	78.5	Acetic acid	6.15 (20°C)
Formic acid	58.5 (16°C)	Ethyl acetate	6.02
Methanol	32.6	Chloroform	4.81 (20°C)
Ethanol	24.3	Benzene	2.27
Acetone	20.7	Carbon tetrachloride	2.23
Isopropanol	18.3	*n*-Octane	1.95 (20°C)

Note: Values at 25°C unless otherwise specified.

Standard curves for each binary mixture have to be prepared at a given temperature. Some examples of binary systems that can be analyzed are hexane–benzene and acetone–water, as well as various lower-molecular-weight alcohols in water.

Moisture in solids such as wood, foods, and textiles can be measured. However, such determinations are more often made by instruments designed to directly measure the dielectric changes between two parallel plates of a condenser.

Reaction Rates. A fascinating application of high-frequency conductance is determining rates of reactions. The response must be related directly to the change in the composition of the solution. Thus, for example, the rapid rates of hydrolysis of esters have been determined, as well as the rates of some polymerization reactions.

Liquid Chromatograph Detector. By placing the electrodes on the outside of chromatographic columns, changes in the composition of the eluates can be followed; or by moving these electrodes up and down the column, zones or chromatographic bands can be located.

SELECTED BIBLIOGRAPHY

Conductance

FUOSS, R. M., and ACCASCINA, F. *Electrolytic Conductance.* New York: Interscience Publishers, 1959.

GLASSTONE, S. *Introduction to Electrochemistry.* New York: Van Nostrand, 1942.

KOLTHOFF, I. M., and ELVING, P. J. *Treatise on Analytical Chemistry*, part I, vol. 4, chap. 51. New York: Interscience Publishers, 1963.

ROBINSON, R. A., and STOKES, R. H. *Electrolyte Solutions.* New York: Academic Press, 1959.

WEISSBERGER, A. *Physical Methods of Organic Chemistry*, volume 1, part IV, 3rd ed., chap. XLV. New York: Interscience Publishers, 1960.

Oscillometry

BLAEDEL, W. J., and PETITJEAN, D. L. "High-Frequency Method of Chemical Analysis." In W. C. Berl, ed., *Physical Methods in Chemical Analysis*, vol. III, pp 108–34. New York: Academic Press Inc., 1956.

REILLEY, C. N., "High-Frequency Methods." In P. Delahay, ed., *New Instrumental Methods in Electrochemistry*, pp 319–45. New York: Interscience Publishers, 1954.

REFERENCES

1. J. E. LIND, JR., J. J. ZWOLENIK, and R. M. FUOSS, *J. Amer. Chem. Soc.*, *81*, 1557 (1959).
2. L. ONSAGER, *Phys. Z.*, *28*, 277 (1927).
3. G. JONES and D. M. BOLLINGER, *J. Amer. Chem. Soc.*, *57*, 280 (1935).
4. J. L. HALL, J. A. GIBSON, JR., P. R. WILKINSON, and H. O. PHILLIPS, *Anal. Chem.*, *26*, 1484 (1954).
5. C. N. REILLEY and W. H. MCCURDY, JR., *Anal. Chem.*, *25*, 86 (1953).

PROBLEMS

1. The concentrations of three dilute solutions of sodium acetate were measured in a conductance cell in which the parallel electrodes were 1 cm² in area and 0.25 cm apart. Resistances of 274,700, 91,000 and 18,320 ohms were determined for the three solutions. Calculate the normality of each solution. $T = 25°C$.

2. A conductance measurement was made of brackish water containing equimolar concentrations of $MgCl_2$ and $NaCl$, with traces of other salts that can be ignored. What is the concentration of chloride ion in ppm when a cell with a cell constant of 5.0 gives a resistance of 1549 ohms? Use the limiting equivalent conductances for the calculation.

3. In a chemical process, an aqueous solution of sodium hydroxide is to be maintained in the range 9 to 14% by weight. This corresponds to roughly 2.5 and 4.0 N solutions with equivalent conductances of 117 and 85, respectively. The commercial conductivity bridge available covers conductance ranges of 0 to 100, 0 to 10,000, and 0 to 100,000 micromhos. The midpoint of each range on the logarithmic scale is a factor of 10 lower in micromhos. (a) Should the cell constant of the conductivity cell be 0.01, 1.0, or 25 cm⁻¹, and (b) what range is most suitable for monitoring the solution?

4. A special conductance bridge reads directly over the range of 1 to 12% H_2SO_4. The recommended cell constant is 50. Extrapolating from data in handbooks and critical tables, calculate the approximate resistance and micromho range involved at 18°C.

5. 2.4425 grams of benzoic acid is dissolved in one liter of pure water at 25°C. When placed in a conductance cell having a constant of 0.150, a resistance value of 1114 ohms is obtained. Calculate the equivalent conductance of the solution, the degree of ionization, and the ionization constant.

6. The solubility product of calcium fluoride at 25°C is 3.9×10^{-11}. What was the resistance reading when the cell constant was 0.100 cm⁻¹? Ignore the conductance contribution of the water.

7. In the titration of 100 ml of acetic acid with 1.0 N NaOH, the following relative conductance readings were observed for the corresponding burette readings. What is the concentration of the acid?

0.00 ml = 0.22	1.60 ml = 1.47
0.10 ml = 0.19	1.80 ml = 1.73
0.20 ml = 0.23	2.00 ml = 2.21
0.40 ml = 0.39	2.20 ml = 2.71
0.60 ml = 0.56	2.40 ml = 3.21
0.80 ml = 0.74	2.60 ml = 3.70
1.00 ml = 0.92	3.00 ml = 4.70
1.20 ml = 1.10	3.40 ml = 5.69
1.40 ml = 1.28	

8. Using the conductance values of Table 5.3, draw the shape of the relative conductance curves for the following titrations: (a) sodium benzoate with hydrochloric acid; (b) silver acetate with lithium chloride; (c) sulfuric acid in glacial acetic acid with sodium hydroxide; (d) mercuric nitrate with potassium chloride; (e) mixture of hydrochloric acid and acetic acid with ammonium hydroxide and with sodium hydroxide; (f) ammonium chloride with potassium hydroxide; and (g) sodium carbonate with calcium nitrate (check the effect of intermediate product formation).

9. In an experiment to determine the solubility of silver chloride, the specific conductance of the demineralized water used

was 0.81×10^{-6} mho/cm at 25°C. When solid silver chloride was equilibrated in the same water at 25°C, the specific conductance was 2.62×10^{-6} mho/cm. Determine the solubility product, assuming that the limiting equivalent conductance of silver chloride is 138.3 mho/cm.

10. An oscillometer was used to determine the amount of ethylene glycol in a hydrocarbon layer and of hydrocarbon in the glycol layer. The following calibration curves were established.

0% Glycol	115	95% Glycol	1298
1% Glycol	300	96% Glycol	1324
2% Glycol	436	97% Glycol	1348
3% Glycol	551	98% Glycol	1369
4% Glycol	652	99% Glycol	1386
5% Glycol	743	100% Glycol	1399

The reading observed for the hydrocarbon layer was 371 and for the glycol layer, 1361. Draw the curves and determine the percentage of hydrocarbon in glycol and the percentage of glycol in hydrocarbon.

6

Introduction to Spectroscopic Methods

Eugene B. Bradley

The word spectroscopy is widely used to mean the separation, detection, and recording of energy changes (resonance peaks) involving nuclei, atoms, or molecules. These changes are due to the emission, absorption, or scattering of electromagnetic radiation or particles. Spectrometry is that branch of physical science that treats the measurement of spectra.

The experimental applications of spectroscopic methods in chemical problems are diverse, but all have in common the interaction of electromagnetic radiation with the quantized energy states of matter. A chemist may wish to determine a molecular structure or the value of an electric dipole moment. He may wish to make an elemental analysis or to verify the presence of a chemical bond. In order to solve such problems, the chemist chooses a particular spectroscopic method, using his knowledge of the possible energy states of matter in particular configurations and the particular wavelengths of electromagnetic radiation that interact with these states.

This chapter is meant to serve as a very general overview of spectroscopic methods; many of the topics will be covered later in greater detail, particularly in Chapters 7–9.

6.1 THEORY

The theoretical basis for the interaction between radiation and the energy states of matter is the quantized nature of energy transfer from the radiation field to matter and vice versa. Matter, composed of "particles" like protons, neutrons, and electrons, sometimes behaves like a wave; radiation, a self-propagating "wave" of crossed

139

electric and magnetic fields, sometimes behaves like a particle. This seeming paradox is reconciled in quantum theory, which is used to calculate quantized energy states. The wavelike properties of matter are illustrated in the double-slit experiment [1], in which the wave property of *diffraction* is exhibited by an electron beam passing through a double slit. The quantized, particle-like nature of electromagnetic radiation is shown by the photoelectric effect [2], in which the number of electrons emitted by an electrode is shown to be dependent on the number of incoming "packets" of radiation at a certain minimum energy, or frequency—one electron per packet. (This particular effect is useful for some types of detectors discussed later.)

The wavelike character of radiation can be described by its *wavelength*, λ; by the *wavenumber* $\bar{\nu}$, which represents the number of waves per unit of distance (the reciprocal of the wavelength); by the speed at which the wave front advances, the *velocity*, V; and by the number of waves passing a given point in unit time, the frequency, ν. The relationship among these properties is given by

$$\bar{\nu} = \frac{1}{\lambda} = \frac{\nu}{V} \tag{6.1}$$

The velocity of electromagnetic waves in a vacuum is c (the speed of light), which is about 3×10^{10} cm/sec; the velocity in any other medium is lower.

The following units are in common use for measurement of electromagnetic spectra:

$$\mu\text{m (micrometer)} = 10^{-6} \text{ meters} = 10^{-4} \text{ centimeters}$$
$$\text{nm (nanometer)} = 10^{-9} \text{ meters} = 10^{-7} \text{ centimeters}$$
$$\text{Å (angstrom)} = 10^{-10} \text{ meters} = 10^{-8} \text{ centimeters}$$

In recent years, the nanometer (nm) unit has replaced the older unit, millimicron (mμ), and micrometer (μm) has replaced micron (μ).

The terms for wavelength that are customarily used depend on the spectral region being described. The Å is commonly used to describe x-ray radiation, nm for ultraviolet and visible wavelength, and μm for infrared wavelengths.

Electromagnetic radiation is an alternating electrical and magnetic field in space. Its wave properties can be explained in terms of mutually perpendicular electric and magnetic vectors, both perpendicular to the direction of wave propagation and each maintaining the other. A continuously propagating wave motion does not appear subdivisible into discrete units having an independent existence, and could be considered a continuous stream of energy; but when radiation interacts with matter, its properties are those of particles, not waves. A quantitative description of many interactions between radiation and matter is possible by considering radiation as discrete quanta of energy called *photons*. The energy of a photon is proportional to the frequency of radiation. These dual views of radiation as waves and particles are not mutually exclusive. Indeed this duality is useful for the quantitative description of other phenomena, such as the behavior of electrons or other elementary particles.

The wave nature of radiation is familiarly illustrated by refraction effects in material media, diffraction, and interference phenomena. Discrete and band spectra are evidences of quantized energy states in matter and of quantized energy transfer between radiation and matter. The amount of energy transferred per photon is given by the Einstein-Planck relation

$$E = h\nu = \frac{hc}{\lambda} = hc\bar{\nu} \tag{6.2}$$

where E = the energy in joules
h = Planck's constant (6.62×10^{-34} joule-sec)
ν = the frequency of the radiation in hertz

Although it may seem strange at first, wavenumbers are easier for most spectroscopists to use. (Frequencies are a factor of 10^{10} greater.) Note that $1 \ \mu m = 10^{-4}$ cm $= 10^{-6}$ m. Thus

$$\lambda(\mu m) = \frac{10^4}{\nu(cm^{-1})}$$

To convert wavenumbers to electron volts

$$E(eV) = \frac{12399}{\lambda(\text{Å})} \qquad \nu = \frac{c}{\lambda}$$

Table 6.1 presents some conversion factors useful in spectroscopy.

The Einstein-Planck relation indicates that the energy of a photon of *monochromatic* (single-frequency) radiation depends only on its wavelength or frequency. A beam of radiation is more or less intense depending on the quantity of photons per unit time and per unit area, but the quantum energy (E) per photon is always the same for a given frequency of the radiation.

Planck explained correctly the energy *distribution with frequency* of a black body by assuming the atomic oscillators in the body to be quantized according to Equation 6.2. Bohr, in 1914, laid the foundation for the correct interpretation of spectra of atoms and molecules with these postulates:

1. Atomic systems exist in stable states without radiating electromagnetic energy.
2. Absorption or emission of electromagnetic energy occurs when an atomic system changes from one energy state to another.
3. The absorption or emission process corresponds to a photon of radiant energy $h\nu = E' - E''$, where $E' - E''$ is the difference in energy between two states of an atomic system.

TABLE 6.1. *Conversion Factors Useful in Spectroscopy*

Unit	ergs/molecule	cm^{-1}	cal/mole	eV/molecule
1 eV/molecule =	1.602×10^{-12}	8065.5	23,060	1
1 cal/mole =	6.948×10^{-17}	0.34975	1	4.336×10^{-5}
1 cm^{-1} =	1.986×10^{-16}	1	2.8591	1.240×10^{-4}
1 erg/molecule =	1	5.034×10^{15}	1.439×10^{16}	6.241×10^{11}

Source: Adapted from C. E. Meloan, *Elementary Infrared Spectroscopy*, New York: Macmillan, 1963, p 5.

TABLE 6.2. *Interaction of Radiation with Matter*

Radiation Absorbed	Energy Changes Involved
Visible, ultraviolet, or x-ray	Electronic transitions, vibrational or rotational changes
Infrared	Molecular vibrational changes with superimposed rotational changes
Far-infrared; microwave	Rotational changes
Radio-frequency	Too weak to be observed except under an intense magnetic field (see Chaps. 12 and 13).

The absorption or emission of radiant energy by matter is one of the most important fingerprints furnished by nature. When a beam of radiation is passed through an absorbing substance, the intensity of the incident radiation (I_0) will be greater than that (I) of the emergent radiation. (I_0 and I are sometimes symbolized by P_0 and P, since the intensity to which we refer has units of energy per unit time, or power.) Part of the radiation that passes into a substance, instead of being absorbed, may be scattered or reflected when emerging from the substance, or re-emitted at the same wavelength or at a different wavelength. In other cases, the radiation may undergo changes in orientation or polarization. The absorption of radiation at various wavelengths is summarized in Table 6.2.

Those portions of the electromagnetic spectrum useful to chemists are shown in Figure 6.1. The spectrum is divided according to frequency (energy), and corresponding spectroscopic methods are shown in the appropriate frequency ranges. For clarity, these methods and the corresponding energy states of matter are listed in Table 6.3. Notice that the various energy states and basic phenomena are diverse, and so there are different methods and techniques. These methods and techniques are not difficult to learn, however, and one need not be an expert to obtain many extremely important and useful results.

TABLE 6.3. *Spectroscopic Methods and Corresponding Energy States of Matter or Basis of Phenomenon*

Method	Basis
Nuclear Magnetic Resonance	Nuclear spin coupling with an applied magnetic field
Microwave Spectroscopy	Rotation of molecules
Electron Spin Resonance	Spin coupling of unpaired electrons with an applied magnetic field
Infrared and Raman Spectroscopy	Rotation of molecules
	Vibration of molecules
	Rotation/vibration of molecules
	Electronic transitions (some large molecules only)
Ultraviolet-visible Spectroscopy	Electronic energy
	Impinging monoenergetic electrons causing valence-electron excitations
x-Ray Spectroscopy	Electronic transitions
	Diffraction and reflection of x-ray radiation from atomic layers

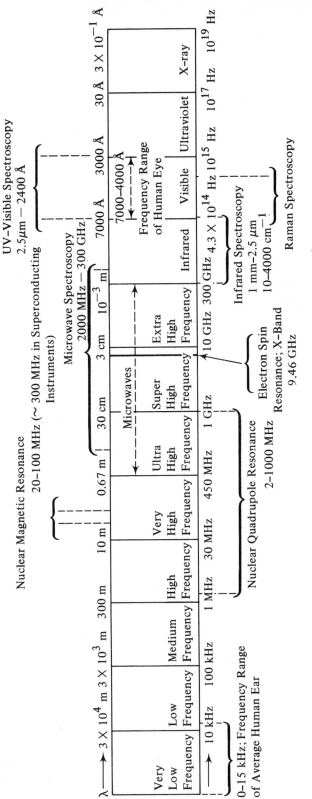

FIGURE 6.1. *The electromagnetic spectrum from DC to x-ray; frequency ranges are shown for different spectroscopic methods.*

6.2 APPLICATION OF QUANTUM THEORY TO SPECTROSCOPY

The laws of classical mechanics, which apply to the energies of objects of ordinary size, such as Ping-Pong balls, cannot be used to understand the behavior of microscopic bodies such as atoms, electrons, and molecules. For example, a Ping-Pong ball can spin (rotate) and bounce with any speed depending on how it is hit; that is, the rotational energy and the bouncing velocity of a Ping-Pong ball can assume any value on a continuous scale. However, a molecule cannot rotate or vibrate freely with any particular energy; it is subject to what are called quantum restrictions, and is limited to only certain discrete values of velocities and energies. The significance of quantum restrictions on a particular motion of a microscopic body depends on the space available for such a motion: if there is a large space for a motion, that motion is less subject to quantum restrictions on its energy.

We learn from quantum mechanics that allowed energy states exist in which a molecule or an atom may spend long or short periods of time. A molecule or atom can exist in intermediate energy states for only a transient time when it is ascending or descending from one level (or state) to another.

Monoatomic substances normally exist in the gaseous state and absorb radiation only through an increase in their electronic energy. It should be remembered that electrons in a given atom occupy discrete energy levels and are thus quantized. These quantized levels take the form of the various subshells illustrated in Figure 6.2. Therefore electronic absorption of radiation can take place only if the impinging photon has an energy that is equal to the energy difference, ΔE, between two quantized energy levels.

FIGURE 6.2. *Energy levels for the electrons in a polyelectron atom.*

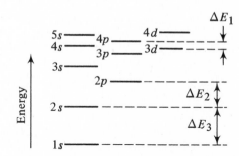

For a polyelectron atom, a multiplicity of absorptions is permissible. The energy required to produce a $3d \rightarrow 4p$ transition (ΔE_1) corresponds to visible radiation; $2s \rightarrow 2p$ (ΔE_2) requires far-ultraviolet radiation; and $1s \rightarrow 2s$ (ΔE_3) requires x-ray radiation.

For polyatomic molecules, electronic transitions involve molecular orbitals; such transitions require energy in the ultraviolet region and are of vital importance in ultraviolet spectroscopy.

Effect of Structure on Absorption

The spectrum is a function of the whole structure of a molecule rather than of specific bonds. Photons of low energy (far infrared, microwave) can produce changes of rotational energy. More energetic photons change the energy of molecular vibration as well as rotation (near-infrared). With visible and ultraviolet light, valence-shell electrons are excited, and these electronic transitions are usually accompanied by changes in vibration and rotation. In the far ultraviolet, the energies of the photons may even break bonds.

6.3 INSTRUMENTATION

A *spectrograph* is an "instrument with an entrance slit and a dispersing device that uses photography to obtain a record of spectral range. The radiant power passing through the optical system is integrated over time, and the quantity recorded is a function of radiant energy." An *optical spectrometer* has "an entrance slit, a dispersing device, and one or more slit exits, with which measurements are made at selected wavelengths within the spectral range, or by scanning over the range. The quantity detected is a function of radiant power." A *spectrophotometer* "furnishes the ratio, or a function of the ratio, of the radiant power of two beams as a function of spectral wavelength. These two beams may be separated in time, space, or both." [3]

Figure 6.3 shows the block diagram of a basic spectrometer which may be used for the study of various energy states of matter; typical components are listed in each block.

Commercial spectroscopic instruments are readily available; some of these are very sophisticated, for use in exacting research studies that require high precision. Many studies do not require such precision; for these, simple, less expensive, models are also available. In some cases, part or all of such instruments may be built by the investigator at a considerable saving.

Usually the building blocks are the same for any spectrometer, i.e., a source of electromagnetic energy, a sample to be investigated, an analyzer to sort out energies that are modified by the sample in some manner, a detector of these energies, and a recorder (which may include an electronic amplifier to boost the power level of the detected energy).

One of the simplest "spectroscopic"—more properly "optical"—methods is termed "colorimetric." In this technique, white light is passed through a sample and the percentage of energy absorbed is recorded and related to sample properties. If some type of dispersing device such as a prism or grating is used to restrict the white light to a narrow band of frequencies, the method resembles the monochromatic method in which only a single frequency, or very narrow band of frequencies, is viewed at any instant of time.

However, monochromatic methods are used more extensively because of the frequent need to extract more detailed information from a sample. The method may involve emission, absorption, or scattering of electromagnetic energy, or *fluorescence* (radiation is absorbed and reemitted).

Source

The source of electromagnetic radiation is chosen according to the spectral range to be studied, i.e., according to energy requirements (source intensity is usually less important than source energy). The typical sources listed in Figure 6.3 span the

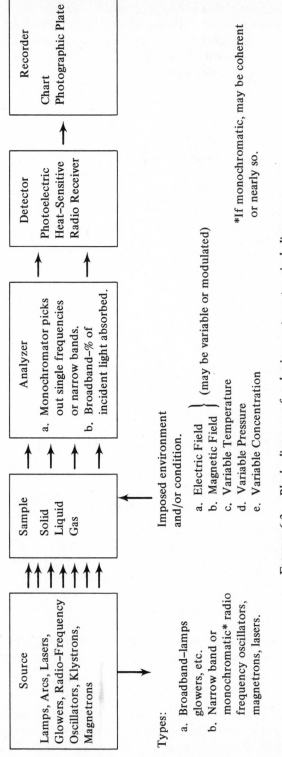

Figure 6.3. *Block diagram of a basic spectrometer, including some typical devices and conditions.*

electromagnetic spectrum from radio frequencies to x-rays. Some sources such as lasers and klystrons emit nearly monochromatic, nearly phase-coherent radiation, while other sources such as lamps and glowers emit a broad spectrum of phase-incoherent frequencies.

Sample

The sample may be a solid, a liquid, or a gas. A certain physical arrangement or enclosure of a sample is usually necessary for successful spectroscopic results; often, environmental conditions are imposed upon the sample to create either a necessary set of conditions for a recordable effect, or a perturbation of some type that produces additional energy states for study. Standard sampling techniques and apparatus suffice for the majority of compounds, but occasionally the chemical nature of the sample is troublesome and the usual techniques fail. A troublesome sample may be a highly corrosive gas, an easily decomposed compound, or a hygroscopic compound; it may be explosive, highly toxic, deeply colored, radioactive, or viscous. In cases like these, the chemist must develop a new sampling technique for his particular problem, and the integrity of the data may depend upon his ingenuity and finesse in developing it.

Experiments require that energy be absorbed or transmitted by a sample, while at the same time gases, liquids, hygroscopic materials, and other sensitive or dangerous compounds must be contained. Therefore, it is often necessary to enclose the sample in a cell of some sort. Each cell must have windows that transmit a particular band of wavelengths and resist particular forms of chemical degradation. As an example, suppose one wished to obtain the pure-rotational energies of the HF molecule (see the application section of this chapter for some reasons for wanting such information). Hydrogen fluoride is highly corrosive, and the temperature of the sample must be above room temperature to avoid dimerization. The pure-rotation energy absorption of HF occurs in the far infrared (50 μm–1000 μm wavelength) region, so one must choose a window for a low-pressure gas cell that will withstand atmospheric pressure from the outside, be highly resistant to chemical attack, transmit the desired wavelengths, and not decompose when the sample cell is heated. Polyethylene satisfies these requirements.

Monochromators

Monochromators are frequency (energy) analyzers. The analysis is usually accomplished by varying the incidence angle of prism(s) or grating(s) with respect to the incident radiation. The spectral range scanned is determined by the apex angle of the prism or by the spacing of grating lines. Filters may also be used to pass or reject specific frequencies.

Prisms. A prism is constructed to take advantage of Snell's law. Recall that for a light ray this law relates angle of incidence to angle of refraction by

$$n \sin \phi = n' \sin \phi' \qquad (6.3)$$

where ϕ = the angle of incidence
          ϕ' = the angle of refraction
          n = the refractive index of the medium of incidence
          n' = the refractive index of the medium in which refraction occurs

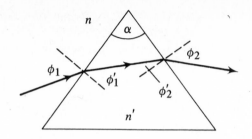

FIGURE 6.4. *Refraction of a light ray by a prism.*

In a prism, two plane surfaces are inclined at some apex angle, α, such that the deviation produced by the first surface is increased by the second surface (see Fig. 6.4). The refraction obeys Snell's law, so that

$$\frac{\sin \phi_1}{\sin \phi_1'} = \frac{n'}{n} = \frac{\sin \phi_2}{\sin \phi_2'} \tag{6.4}$$

The refractive index of the prism material depends upon the wavelength of the incident light, so the angle of deviation ϕ becomes a function of wavelength

$$\frac{d\phi}{d\lambda} = \frac{d\phi}{dn}\frac{dn}{d\lambda} \tag{6.5}$$

The factor $d\phi/dn$ is determined by geometrical considerations, but the factor $dn/d\lambda$ is characteristic of the prism material and it is called the *dispersion*. Typical prism materials are quartz glass, NaCl, KBr, or CsI. Quartz is used in the ultraviolet region, glass is used in the visible region, and the other three materials are used in the medium infrared region.

If many wavelengths strike the prism simultaneously, each wavelength emerges from the prism at a different angle. In practice, the prism is rotated about an axis perpendicular to the triangular cross-section. A radiation detector is placed at a fixed distance from the prism, so that as the prism rotates, successive wavelengths fall upon the detector.

Diffraction Gratings. The diffraction grating was invented by Joseph von Fraunhofer (1787–1826). The word *diffraction* implies effects produced by cutting off portions of wave fronts. A diffraction grating may be used either in transmission or reflection, but the dispersion of incident wavelengths depends upon the geometry of the grating.

A grating is a parallel array of equidistant grooves, closely spaced. The spacing between these grooves is called d. A transmission grating is made by ruling parallel grooves on glass with a diamond edge. Reflection gratings are made by ruling parallel grooves on a metal mirror. The great majority of spectroscopic applications of gratings use reflecting optics. In these applications, the reflection gratings are replicated from a master grating.

The reflection of incident light by a grating is shown in Figure 6.5. A portion of the collimated light beam incident at angle i is reflected at angle θ. The angle i does not have to equal the angle θ as in reflection. The path difference for incoming rays 1 and 2 is $AB = d \sin i$, and the path difference for outgoing rays 3 and 4 is

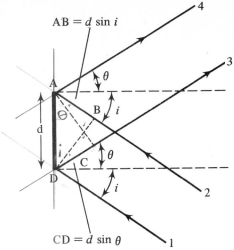

FIGURE 6.5. *Diffraction of incident light by a reflection grating having a groove spacing of d.*

$AB = d \sin i$

$CD = d \sin \theta$

$CD = d \sin \theta$. The total path difference for an incident and reflected ray is $d \sin i - d \sin \theta$. When this difference is equal to one or more wavelengths, no interference occurs and a bright image is seen. In general

$$n\lambda = d(\sin i \pm \sin \theta), \tag{6.6}$$

where n (an integer) = the *order* of the grating

The path differences are added when both light rays are on the same side of the normal to the grating surface.

    Assume that angles i and θ remain constant, and that values of n (> 1) and smaller values of λ are chosen so that the product, $n\lambda$, remains constant. It is seen that shorter wavelengths may be reflected at the same angle, θ, as were the longer wavelengths corresponding to $n = 1$. These shorter wavelengths are called *higher orders*. To disperse incident light of many wavelengths, the grating is rotated so that the angle i changes. Assuming $n = 1$, different wavelengths will be reflected at the same angle, θ. Higher-order wavelengths will also be reflected at this same angle and these wavelengths will have to be filtered out before they reach the detector.

    The dispersion of the grating, $d\theta/d\lambda$, may be calculated by assuming the angle i is a constant. Then

$$\frac{d\theta}{d\lambda} = \frac{n}{d \cos \theta} \qquad n\,d\lambda = d\cos\theta\,d\theta \tag{6.7}$$

The dispersion equals the order divided by the product of the grating spacing and the cosine of the angle of reflection. The *resolving power* of a grating is the product of the number of rulings and the order. Hence the resolving power of a large grating (more area) is greater than that of one with smaller area.

Filters. Optical filters are used extensively in spectroscopy to pass or reject certain frequencies or bands of frequencies. These filters are of three main types: (a) cut-in (or cut-off), (b) bandpass, and (c) band-rejection. The nomenclature is illustrated by the graph in Figure 6.6. Filter A is a cut-in filter if one reads from left to right along the frequency axis. The cut-in frequency is usually defined as f_0, the frequency at which the transmission begins to be approximately constant. Notice that the rate of cut-in ($\% \, T$ vs. f) may vary depending upon the construction of the filter. Filter **B** (a bandpass filter) rejects all frequencies except those between f_1 and f_2. Practically speaking, the useful frequency range of the filter is between those frequencies where the transmission is greater than 30%. Filter C (a band-rejection filter) passes all frequencies except those in the range f_3 to f_4. This filter is most useful in the region of high attenuation (small-percentage transmission). The shapes and widths of the transmission regions of these various filters may be varied considerably, depending upon the application.

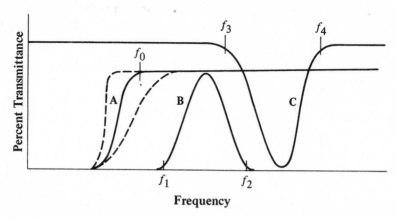

FIGURE 6.6. *Frequency versus percentage transmission for three types of optical filters. A: cut-in or cut-off. B: bandpass. C: band-rejection.*

A fourth type of filter, not shown in Figure 6.6, is called a *restrahlen* filter. This type of filter is used in reflection only, and it reflects a relatively narrow range of frequencies—all other frequencies are absorbed. Restrahlen filters are useful, for example, in suppressing unwanted orders from a grating.

It is also possible to use a prism or a grating as a selective filter. The selective transmission or reflection of electromagnetic energy is a function of the incidence angle. For example, a prism may be used in transmission to restrict the number of frequencies incident upon a grating, making it unnecessary to use additional filters to eliminate higher orders of the grating. Such a prism is called a *fore-prism*.

Resolution

The resolution (ability to separate frequencies) of a spectrometer is determined by various factors such as the dimensions of the dispersing element, the arrangement of the associated optics, and the spectral limits imposed by a mechanical slit of some sort.

The mechanical slit is placed before the detector to limit further the number of frequencies that impinge simultaneously upon it. Transfer optics may differ from one type of monochromator to another and yield different spatial spreads of the frequencies that arrive at the mechanical slit. An adjustment of the slit width effects a mechanical control of the bandwidth of radiation seen by the detector. The real measure of the radiation seen by the detector is called the *spectral slit width* (in cm^{-1}) which is a measure of the frequency spread seen by the detector. The spectral slit width is a function of the optical geometry, the instrument's dispersion, and the mechanical width of the slit.

If the source is monochromatic or nearly so, or if the source is monochromatic and tunable, then very high resolution is possible, providing the frequency stability of the source is good. Tunable sources have been available for some time in the radio-frequency and microwave regions of the spectrum, but it is only recently that tunable lasers have become available in the infrared and visible regions.

An important criterion for a monochromator is the amount of stray radiation reflected and transmitted through the system to the detector. Such extraneous radiation produces signal errors at the detector. Roughly speaking, stray light decreases as the resolution improves. Two monochromators may be coupled optically into a double monochromator to decrease stray light markedly. Also, a monochromator may be a double-pass or a single-pass type, depending upon the number of times the radiation is dispersed.

Detectors

Research has continued over the years to develop sensitive, noise-free detectors. There are inherent quantum-imposed limits on detectors, which we do not expect to exceed, but in recent years many significant breakthroughs in detector technology have occurred. Detectors are classified into two general groups, selective and nonselective. The response of a selective detector varies with the frequency of the incident radiation whereas the response of a nonselective detector does not. A listing of typical detectors is shown in Figure 6.3, but each spectroscopic method imposes its special requirements for a detector. Photoelectric detectors, photographic plates, and photoconductive cells are selective detectors, whereas thermocouples, bolometers, pneumatic cells, and square-law crystals have responses (at infrared and microwave frequencies) that are *relatively* insensitive to wavelength and thus can be classified as nonselective.

Photoelectric detectors are useful in the ultraviolet-visible region of the spectrum. When coupled with the appropriate electronic circuitry, these detectors are capable of counting as little as one photon per second. Specific types of photoelectric detectors have frequency (energy) responses that peak in different subregions of the ultraviolet-visible region. Photoelectric detectors are often cooled to reduce random tube noise ("shot" noise).

Photographic plates are extremely sensitive photon detectors in this same region. The speed of data acquisition is, of course, much lower owing to the processing time required for the plate. Most photographic plates are insensitive in the infrared region, but infrared phosphors extend their range somewhat into the infrared.

A photoconductive cell is an important selective detector. Such cells show an increase in conductivity when illuminated with infrared light, and they have high sensitivity with fast response. These cells are used extensively in the spectral region 0.5–3.5 μm (5000 Å–35,000 Å). The range may be extended slightly by cooling the cell with liquid hydrogen.

In a thermocouple—used for measuring infrared radiation—a junction of two dissimilar metals is blackened to increase absorption of incident radiation. The temperature rise at the junction relative to a "cold junction" on which infrared radiation does not fall increases the potential across the junction; this potential is amplified to a usable voltage. Thermocouples have a relatively slow response (thermal lag) and if the infrared radiation is time-varying, it must not vary too rapidly.

Bolometers have a faster response than do thermocouples, and they are useful in the infrared and microwave regions. Metal bolometers have a small thermal capacity that permits a quicker response than thermistor bolometers. Incident radiation falls upon an element that forms one arm of a Wheatstone bridge. The resistance of the arm changes with temperature and the bridge goes unbalanced, producing an error signal which is amplified. Some types of bolometers are useful in the microwave region at frequencies up to about 60 GHz. Commercial thermistor bolometers are matched pairs of "flakes" that have similar electrical and thermal properties. One of the flakes serves as a compensatory element to eliminate the effect of background radiation.

Pneumatic cells are very sensitive devices, useful from the near-infrared region to the 300–150 GHz microwave range (1 GHz = 1 Gigahertz = 10^9 Hertz). In a pneumatic cell, incident radiation heats a confined gas, which expands, moving a curved diaphragm with a mirror surface. A light beam reflected from this surface to a photocell varies in intensity with the movement of the diaphragm.

6.4 APPLICATIONS

The applications of modern spectroscopic methods are legion! They are used in such widely diverse fields as controlling pollution and detecting art forgeries. A few general applications will be discussed here for each spectroscopic method listed in Table 6.3.

Nuclear magnetic resonance (NMR) is the spectroscopic method used to study proton resonances. Electromagnetic radiation causes the magnetic moment of protons to "flip" in the presence of an external applied magnetic field. Proton chemical shifts are usually measured with respect to an arbitrary reference compound such as tetramethysilane. Proton resonances of different functional groupings occur at characteristic values called "τ-values," which depend upon the chemical and magnetic environment in which the group occurs. NMR of fluorine, phosphorus, boron, and some other elements with a nuclear magnetic moment is also used extensively. Undoubtedly, the single most important application of NMR has been in the qualitative identification of organic compounds and the elucidation of their structure. NMR, gas-liquid chromatography, and infrared spectroscopy are probably the three most important tools available today for the organic chemist.

Microwave spectroscopy is used to measure dipole moments and moments of inertia of simple molecules in the gas phase. The chemical composition of the molecule and the masses of its atoms are usually known, so one uses moments of inertia to help determine the structure of a molecule, perhaps the most important application of microwave spectroscopy. Sometimes it is necessary to use x-ray data also to supplement the microwave data. From the pattern of the rotational spectrum it is possible to determine the symmetry of the molecular configuration, i.e., whether planar, linear, or polar. The technique is very sensitive to sample concentration and pressure, and it is used in some important air-pollution measurements.

Electron-spin resonance is used to map unpaired-electron distributions in molecules and molecular fragments. The method is versatile and may be used to detect free radicals in cancer tissue, for example, or for routine monitoring of vanadium in crude petroleum. Because the effect depends simply upon the presence of unpaired electrons, there are many other analytical and practical applications.

Infrared and Raman spectroscopy are complementary methods used, for instance, to study molecular structure, identify compounds and functional groups, determine interatomic forces and bond-stretching distances, perform quantitative and qualitative analyses, and determine thermodynamic properties. The three states of matter may be studied by these methods over wide ranges of temperature and pressure. Selection rules for different molecular structures determine which spectral lines are allowed, and these rules differ for the infrared and Raman methods. This difference is used to advantage in studies of molecular structure, because two types of information are brought to bear on the same problem.

The ultraviolet-visible method is useful for the study of electronic transitions in molecules and atoms. Although various forms of ultraviolet-visible spectroscopy can be used to study a myriad of important chemical and physical properties, we will be most concerned with its use in quantitative analysis. It is probably the single most frequently used analytical method, with the possible exception of the analytical balance. For example, a single clinical analysis laboratory in a major hospital may perform a million chemical analyses a year, primarily on serum and urine, and about 70% of these tests are done by ultraviolet-visible absorption spectroscopy. Atomic absorption and emission spectroscopy (Chaps. 10 and 11) is used primarily to analyze for metallic elements in a variety of matrices—serum, natural waters, tissues, and so forth.

X-ray spectroscopy rivals visible spectroscopy as a tool for elemental analysis. Because the energies of x-rays are much higher than those of visible radiation, however, x-rays usually cause transitions of inner-shell electrons rather than of valence-shell electrons. There are many advantages of this method in spectrochemical analysis. A quantitative analysis of a mixture of rare-earth oxides may be performed or a crystal structure may be determined. A specimen that contains two elements widely separated in atomic number may be studied, or the thickness of a very thin layer of tin plating may be measured. The most widespread use of x-rays has been in the field of metallurgy, but x-rays may also be used to analyze metals, minerals, liquids, glasses, ceramics, or plastics.

REFERENCES

1. R. B. LEIGHTON, *Principles of Modern Physics*, New York: McGraw-Hill, 1959, p 81.

2. R. B. LEIGHTON, *Principles of Modern Physics*, New York: McGraw-Hill, 1959, p 67.

3. "Spectrometry Nomenclature," *Anal. Chem.*, **46**, 2257 (1974).

7

Ultraviolet and Visible Absorption Spectroscopy

K. L. CHENG
J. W. PRATHER II

Photometric methods are perhaps the most frequently used of all spectroscopic methods, and are important in quantitative analysis. The amount of visible light or other radiant energy absorbed by a solution is measured; since it depends on the concentration of the absorbing substance, it is possible to determine quantitatively the amount present.

Colorimetry refers to the determination of a substance from its ability to absorb visible light. Visual colorimetric methods are based on the comparison of a colored solution of unknown concentration with one or more colored solutions of known concentration. In spectrophotometric methods, the ratio of the intensities of the incident and the transmitted beams of light is measured at a specific wavelength by means of a detector such as a photocell.

The absorption spectrum also provides a "fingerprint" for qualitatively identifying the absorbing substance.

7.1 MOLECULAR ABSORPTION OF RADIATION: ELECTRONIC SPECTRA

Molecular absorption in the ultraviolet and visible region depends on the electronic structure of the molecule. Energy is absorbed in quanta, elevating electrons from orbitals in a lower-energy (ground) state to orbitals in a higher-energy (excited) state. Since (for quantum-mechanical reasons) only certain states are possible in any mole-

TABLE 7.1. *Absorption of Visible Light and Color*

Absorbed Wavelength nm	Color (Absorbed)	Color Observed (Transmitted) or Complementary Hue
< 380	Ultraviolet	
380–435	Violet	Yellowish-Green
435–480	Blue	Yellow
480–490	Greenish-Blue	Orange
490–560	Bluish-Green	Red
500–560	Green	Purple
560–580	Yellowish-Green	Violet
580–595	Yellow	Blue
595–650	Orange	Greenish-Blue
650–780	Red	Bluish-Green
> 780	Near Infrared	

cule and the energy difference between any ground and excited state must equal the energy added by the quantum, only certain frequencies can be absorbed. In many electronic structures, absorption does not occur in the readily accessible part of the ultraviolet region, so that, in practice, ultraviolet spectrophotometry is mostly confined to conjugated systems.

When a beam of radiation is passed through an absorbing substance, the intensity of the incident radiation (I_0) will be greater than that of the emergent radiation (I). The absorption of visible (Table 7.1), ultraviolet, and x-ray radiation usually results in electronic transitions in matter, with accompanying vibrational and rotational changes in the case of molecular substances. In general, the excited atoms and molecules resulting from absorption of radiation return to the ground state very rapidly, either by losing energy in the form of heat to the surroundings or by re-emitting electromagnetic radiation (luminescence or fluorescence).

The absorption of electromagnetic radiation by molecules is far more complex than absorption by individual atoms, which have no vibrational or rotational energy levels. The total energy may be considered as a sum of contributions from electronic, rotational, and vibrational energies:

$$E_{total} = E_{el} + E_{rot} + E_{vib} \tag{7.1}$$

where E_{el} = the electronic energy of the molecule
   E_{rot} = the energy associated with the rotation of the molecule around its center of gravity
   E_{vib} = the energy of the molecule due to interatomic vibrations

For each electronic energy state of the molecule, there normally are several possible vibrational states and for each of these, in turn, numerous rotational states (Fig. 7.1). Consequently, the number of possible energy levels for a molecule is much larger than for an atomic particle.

The electronic energy is generally larger than the other two (E_{rot} and E_{vib}), and electronic transitions ordinarily involve energies corresponding to ultraviolet

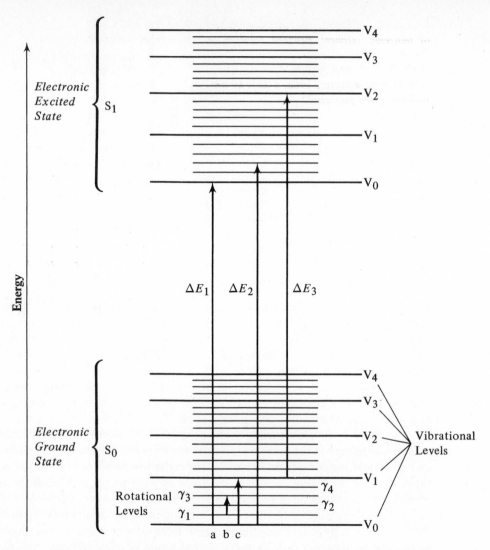

FIGURE 7.1. *Molecular energy levels and (a) electronic, (b) rotational, and (c) vibrational transitions.*

or visible radiation. Pure vibrational transitions are caused by the less energetic infrared radiation (1 to 15 μm); rotational transitions require even less energy (10 to 10,000 μm). Furthermore, changes in vibrational and rotational levels invariably accompany electronic excitation of a molecule. A molecule may jump from any of the vibrational and rotational levels in the ground state to any of a large number of possible vibrational and rotational levels in a given excited state. Because a photon of slightly different energy corresponds to each of the many possible jumps, visible and UV molecular absorption spectra consist of hundreds or thousands of lines so closely spaced that they appear as continuous absorption bands, in contrast to the sharp lines that characterize atomic spectra or rotational spectra in the far-infrared region.

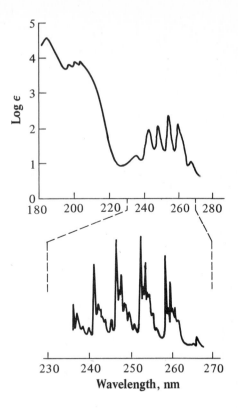

FIGURE 7.2. *Ultraviolet absorption spectra of benzene. Upper: Benzene solution in ethanol solvent. Lower: Benzene vapor. From R. E. Dodd,* Chemical Spectroscopy, *Amsterdam: Elsevier, 1962, p 227, by permission of the publisher.*

Collisions between neighboring molecules in solution cause slight modifications of the various energy levels and lead to further broadening and merging of absorption bands. A dramatic illustration of the effects due to changing from a gaseous state to a liquid state is given in Figure 7.2. The many sharp absorption peaks are an example of vibrational fine structure superimposed on the electronic absorption band; the much broader bands show that a substantial portion of the fine structure is lost because of molecular interaction and collision.

Selection Rules

In addition to matching the energy of a photon with the energy difference between two levels, a second requirement must be met for the absorption of radiation by matter: the energy transition in the molecule must be accompanied by a change in the electrical center of the molecule so that electric work can be carried out on the molecule by the electromagnetic radiation. Requirements for the absorption of radiation by matter are summarized in quantum-mechanical "selection" rules, which determine which transitions may take place. These rules, based on considerations of the symmetry of the system in the upper and lower states, point out that some transitions are more probable than others.

The first selection rule is related to all molecules with centers of symmetry and deals with the *parity-forbidden* transitions. The second rule states that singlet-triplet transitions are forbidden. The third rule applies to forbidden transitions that arise from the symmetry of states—for instance, the long-wavelength bands of C=O, C=S, some chromophores, and the 260-nm band of benzene. In addition to these three types of forbidden transitions, there are also many other *weak energy* transitions with low intensities.

However, forbidden transitions are still observed in many molecules, because intramolecular or intermolecular perturbations cause the rules to relax considerably. Singlet-triplet transitions, for instance, occur with increased intensity in the presence of paramagnetic substances such as O_2 or NO or in solvents such as C_2H_5I that contain heavy atoms.

Franck and Condon have suggested an important rule for understanding the nature of electronic transitions. Their principle states that movement of the nuclei is negligible during the time taken by an electronic transition because these transitions are so fast (about 10^{-15} sec) that the positions and velocities of nuclei have no time to change. The idea is obviously closely related to the Born-Oppenheimer approximation in which the various motions of a molecule are considered to be separable. The Franck-Condon principle indicates that electronic transitions will occur only when the internuclear distances are not significantly different in the two states and when the nuclei have little or no velocity.

Nomenclature

Unfortunately, the terms used in spectrophotometry and spectroscopy are confusing. The recommendation of the American Society for Testing Material, endorsed by *Analytical Chemistry* [1], is now widely accepted. The recommended terms, symbols, and definitions used in this chapter are given in Table 7.2. The Commission

TABLE 7.2. *Spectrophotometry Nomenclature*

Name	Symbol	Definition	Name Not Recommended
Absorbance	A	$-\log T$	Optical density (O.D.), extinction, absorbancy
Absorptivity	a	$= A/bc$*	Absorbancy index, absorbing index
Path length	b	Internal cell or sample length, in cm	l or d
Molar absorptivity	ε	$= A/bc$†	Molar absorbancy index, molar extinction coefficient, molar absorption coefficient
Transmittance	T	I/I_0‡	Transmittancy
Wavelength unit	nm	10^{-9} meter	mμ (millimicron)
	μm	10^{-6} meter	μ (micron)
Absorption maximum	$\lambda_{\max}$	Wavelength at which a maximum absorption occurs	——

* The concentration is in grams per liter.
† The concentration is in moles per liter.
‡ The ratio of radiant power transmitted to radiant power incident.

on Nomenclature, Division of Analytical Chemistry of the International Union of Pure and Applied Chemistry (IUPAC), has made recommendations to standardize the terms used in spectrometry. The following guidelines are suggested:

1. Single words are preferred, e.g., "wavelength" instead of "wave length" and "absorbance" instead of "optical density."
2. The commonly accepted metric system is preferred. The IUPAC has recommended the SI system and the U.S. National Bureau of Standards has strongly recommended the SI system.
3. The expression of absorption spectra by plotting the molar absorptivity as a function of wavelength, instead of simply plotting absorbance versus wavelength, is preferred. In addition to showing the maximum absorptions, it also gives information about sensitivity for analysis.

7.2 EFFECT OF STRUCTURE ON ABSORPTION

Spectroscopic characteristics are held in common by molecules with some of the same chemical features. It may then be reasonable to expect that the correlation can be extended, and that the presence of a certain chemical feature may be implied by the presence of a certain spectral characteristic.

Determination of molecular structure and the identification of specific functional groups are extremely important to modern chemistry. Since the interaction of ultraviolet and visible radiation with molecules is governed by the electronic structure of the molecule, these regions of the spectrum are of particular interest to the chemist. At present, most of the reported work has been on the absorption spectra (from 200 to 1000 nm) of organic molecules in dilute solutions [2–4]. In the future the trend may be to employ greater dispersion and to extend the range of wavelengths investigated.

Electronic Transitions

Electronic transitions in organic molecules are characterized by the promotion of electrons in ground-state bonding or nonbonding molecular orbitals to excited-state antibonding molecular orbitals. If molecular structure is the dominant factor in determining the electronic energies of the ground and excited states, then the photon energy required for $n \rightarrow \pi^*$, $\pi \rightarrow \pi^*$, and $n \rightarrow \sigma^*$ transitions will vary from molecule to molecule, depending on structural and environmental variations. When radiation of a frequency corresponding to one of the fundamental frequencies of a molecule interacts with that molecule, the radiant energy is absorbed to increase the energy content of the molecule by an amount equal to the energy of the quantum absorbed, in accordance with the relation

$$\Delta E = h\nu = hc/\lambda = 2.86 \times 10^5/\lambda \tag{7.2}$$

where ν = the frequency in Hz
   h = Planck's constant (6.626×10^{-27} erg/sec)
   λ = the wavelength in cm
   c = the speed of light in vacuum (2.998×10^{10} cm/sec)

The most common types of electronic transitions are illustrated in Table 7.3.

TABLE 7.3. *Electronic Energy Levels and Transitions*

Transition	Region of Electronic Spectra	Example
$\sigma \rightarrow \sigma^*$	Vacuum ultraviolet	CH_4 at 125 nm
$n \rightarrow \sigma^*$	Far ultraviolet, sometimes near ultraviolet	Acetone at 190 nm
		Methylamine at 213 nm
$\pi \rightarrow \pi^*$	Ultraviolet	Saturated aldehydes at 180 nm
$n \rightarrow \pi^*$	Near ultraviolet and visible	Acetone at 277 nm
		Nitrobutane at 665 nm

The $\sigma \rightarrow \sigma^*$ transitions are very energetic and are found only below 200 nm, in the far-ultraviolet region. This is often termed the "vacuum ultraviolet" region because the normal constituents of air, N_2 and O_2, also absorb strongly below about 160 and 200 nm, respectively; and spectra of other substances must be obtained in a "vacuum." The $n \rightarrow \sigma^*$ transitions are also high-energy transitions and generally appear at the shorter ultraviolet wavelengths; for example, absorption by alkyl halides (where the nonbonding electrons are supplied by the halogen) shows a λ_{max} that increases in the order $Cl < Br < I$, as the electrons are successively easier to excite. The most common examples of $\pi \rightarrow \pi^*$ transitions are found in conjugated polyenes, in which the energy required for the transition decreases with increasing length of the conjugated systems and correspondingly, λ_{max} increases. The $\pi \rightarrow \pi^*$ transitions are usually the least energetic, which results in their appearance at longer wavelengths.

The molar absorptivity (ε) of a compound is a function of the cross-sectional area (θ) of the absorbing species and of the transition probability (P):

$$\varepsilon = 9 \times 10^{19} P\theta \tag{7.3}$$

Using this relation, a molar absorptivity of the order of 10^5 has been calculated for the average organic molecule with an assumed cross-section of about 10^{-15} cm^2 and a unit transition probability. The highest values known for ε are a few hundred thousand; any value above 10,000 is considered high, and one under 1000 low.

By examining the locations, distribution patterns, and intensities of absorption spectra, one can gain information helpful in the identification of compounds. Unfortunately, interpretation of electronic (ultraviolet-visible) spectra is usually less certain than that of vibrational (infrared) spectra because of the broad overlapping bands that characterize electronic absorption. Even so, a great deal of research effort has been expended in hopes that the structural changes of a molecule and the shifts observed in their electronic absorption spectra can be correlated. On the other hand, absorptivities in the infrared are much lower than at shorter wavelengths, rarely exceeding 1000. As a consequence, electronic (ultraviolet-visible) spectrophotometry is sensitive to a much smaller amount of sample and is quite useful for dilute solutions.

Chromophores

It is a long-recognized fact that colored substances owe their color to absorption of light by one or more unsaturated linkages. Such linkages or groups were named

TABLE 7.4. *Representative Chromophores and Their Approximate ε_{max} and λ_{max} Values*

Chromophore	λ_{max} (nm)	ε_{max}
$C{=}C$	185	8000
$-C{\equiv}C-$	175	6000
$C{=}O$	188	900
$-NH_2$	195	2500
$-CHO$	210	20
$-COOR$	205	50
$-COOH$	205	60
$-N{=}N-$	252	8000
	371	14
$-N{=}O$	300	100
	665	20
$-NO_2$	270	14
$-Br$	205	400

chromophores by Witt in 1876. Certain groups which by themselves do not confer color to a substance but which increase the coloring power of a chromophore were called auxochromes.

Ultraviolet radiation is usually absorbed by a chromophore rather than by the molecule as a whole. Chromophores are, in most cases, covalent unsaturated groups such as those given in Table 7.4; they are functional groups that usually absorb in the near ultraviolet or visible region when they are bonded to a non-absorbing, saturated, residue that possesses no unshared or nonbonded electrons (e.g., a hydrocarbon chain). Auxochromes contain functional groups that have nonbonded valence electrons and exhibit no absorption at wavelengths above 220 nm. They do, however, absorb strongly in the far-ultraviolet region ($n \rightarrow \sigma^*$). If an auxochrome and a chromophore are combined in the same molecule, the chromophore absorption will typically shift to a longer wavelength and show an increase in intensity. Shifts to longer wavelengths are called bathochromic shifts; changes to shorter wavelengths, hypsochromic shifts. Increases in intensity of an absorption band are called hyperchromic effects, while a decrease in intensity is termed a hypochromic effect.

In general, molecules containing two or more chromophores show absorption that is the sum of all the chromophores present, provided they are separated by two or more single bonds. If two chromophores are conjugated, they exhibit a much enhanced absorption with an increase in both λ_{max} and ε_{max}; three conjugated chromophores result in a still further increase in λ_{max} and ε_{max}. Such bathochromic shifts are attributed to the formation of a new chromophore from the conjugated systems; the π electrons associated with each chromophore of the conjugated system are able to move with increased freedom throughout the new structure. Systems that show bathochromic shifts with an increase in ε_{max} are shown in Table 7.5. This

TABLE 7.5. *Effect of Structure on the Sensitivity of Reagent for Iron(II)*

Compound	Structure	$\lambda_{max, (nm)}$	ε_{max} ($\times 10^{-3}$)
A. Pyridines			
2,2'-Pyridyl		522	8.0
2,2',2'' Terpyridyl		522	11.1
2,6-Bis(4-phenyl-2-pyridyl)-4-phenylpyridine		583	30.2
B. Phenanthrolines			
1,10-Phenanthroline		508	11.1
Bathophenanthroline		533	22.3
C. Triazines			
2,4,6-Tripyridyl-*S*-triazine		595	24.1
3-(4-Phenyl-2-pyridyl)-5,6-diphenyl-1,2,4-triazine		561	28.7
3-(2-Pyridyl)-5,6-diphenyl-1,2,4-triazine-*p,p'*-disulfonic acid disodium salt		562	27.8

Source: From K. L. Cheng in J. D. Winefordner, ed., *Spectrochemical Methods of Analysis*, New York: John Wiley, 1971, p 358, by permission of the editor and John Wiley and Sons.

demonstrates an excellent application of chromophoric principles to the synthesis of new, selective, and sensitive analytical reagents.

Single Bonds and Saturated Compounds

Saturated hydrocarbons contain only single bonds with σ electrons; thus the only transitions available to these compounds are transitions of $\sigma \rightarrow \sigma^*$ type, which occur at the very short wavelengths of the vacuum ultraviolet. For example, methane and ethane are saturated hydrocarbons with all electrons involved in σ bonds. Electronic transitions are accordingly of the same type as those in the hydrogen molecule, and the separation of the levels is of the same order. Therefore, the first electronic absorption bands for methane and ethane are at 125 nm and 135 nm, respectively; this band continues to move to longer wavelengths in the larger hydrocarbons, suggesting that the C–C bond is involved.

Because of the excitation of electrons in nonbonded orbitals, saturated molecules that contain atoms with lone pairs of electrons exhibit electronic transitions at longer wavelengths than the corresponding saturated hydrocarbons. Thus, alkyl iodides and monosulfides containing the C–S–C linkage give $n \rightarrow \sigma^*$ transitions near 260 and 215 nm, respectively.

The $n \rightarrow \pi^*$ transitions associated with carbonyl groups are observed in the 270–290 nm region and are quite useful in the identification of aldehydes and ketones. For example, acetone exhibits three bands—a weak band at 280 nm ($n \rightarrow \pi^*$), a more intense band near 190 nm ($n \rightarrow \sigma^*$), and a still more intense band near 150 nm ($\pi \rightarrow \pi^*$). For these compounds, the $n \rightarrow \pi^*$ transition of the carbonyl group varies with the substituents R_1 and R_2 in the molecule:

$$\begin{matrix} R_1 \\ \\ R_2 \end{matrix} \!\!> C = O$$

Substituting a hydroxyl, amino, or halogen group (auxochromes) for hydrogen shifts the transition to higher energy, because these groups donate electron density by a resonance interaction and raise the energy of the excited state with respect to the ground state. In addition, these groups give rise to an inductive effect that withdraws electron density from the carbonyl group, thus lowering the ground state relative to the excited state.

Conjugated Chromophores

As stated above, a molecule that contains more than one chromophore has an absorption band that may be the sum of the separate chromophores, or it may be the result of an interaction between the chromophores. If the two chromophores are separated by a single bond, however, conjugation occurs and the electronic absorption spectra show dramatic changes from the bands due only to the isolated chromophores. One of the simplest examples is 1,3-butadiene, $CH_2=CH-CH=CH_2$, where the two C=C double bonds separated by a single bond give rise to an absorption spectrum that is shifted to lower energy by conjugation. In conjugated systems, the π electrons are delocalized over a minimum of four atoms; this causes a decrease in the $\pi \rightarrow \pi^*$ transition energy and the molar absorptivity increases as the result of a higher probability for the transition. The effect of conjugation on $\pi \rightarrow \pi^*$ transitions is considerable. Thus, for the series: ethylene (193 nm), 1,3-butadiene (217 nm), hexatriene (258 nm), octatetraene (300 nm), a bathochromic shift accompanied by an increase in molar absorptivity is observed as an additional $C=C$ double bond is added to each compound in progressing along the series.

Electronic absorption bands for conjugated alkynes are also shifted to lower energy; however, the molar absorptivity is much lower than for the conjugated alkenes. As an example, vinylacetylene, $CH_2=CH-C\equiv CH$, exhibits an absorption band near that of 1,3-butadiene ($\lambda_{max} = 219$ nm); however, its molar absorptivity is only 6500 compared to 21,000 for 1,3-butadiene.

An important feature of ultraviolet absorption spectra is that chromophores that are not conjugated give, not $\pi \rightarrow \pi^*$ bands, but a summation of $n \rightarrow \pi^*$ bands. A $-CH_2-$ group is sufficient to isolate two chromophores, but $-O-$, $-S-$, or $-NH-$ is not. An example of this effect is seen for hexacene, a green compound, and 6,15-dihydrohexacene, a colorless compound whose absorption spectrum is essentially the sum of the spectra of anthracene and naphthalene:

| Hexacene | 6,15-Dihydrohexacene |

Aromatic Hydrocarbons

Benzene, a cyclic conjugated polyene, absorbs at 260, 200, and 180 nm. All of these bands are associated with the π-electron system of benzene. The intense bands at 200 and 180 nm are assigned to transitions to dipolar excited states, and the weak band at 260 nm is ascribed to a forbidden transition to a homopolar excited state.

Electronic transitions in "linear" polycyclic aromatics, such as benzene, naphthalene, and anthracene, exhibit a regular shift toward lower energy with increasing size of the molecule. Figure 7.3 shows that the larger compounds absorb in the same region as benzene, but the bands are more intense. Other compounds in this class, such as phenanthrene, benzanthracene, and pyrene, show absorption spectra similar to those of the "linear" ring system but with a more complex pattern.

Resolution of the fine structure of the bands in the spectrum of benzene is highly dependent on two parameters: solvent polarity and ring substitution. Polar solvents tend to merge the bands into a broad hump while nonpolar solvents give very good resolution into narrow, separate, peaks. Electronic spectra of benzene in the vapor state exhibit excellent resolution (Fig. 7.2). Upon substitution on the benzene ring, fine structure is diminished considerably and all three bands in benzene are affected markedly.

The effects of substitution on aromatic nuclei have been studied and detailed in the literature [5–7]. Usually, but not always, the absorption maxima shift to

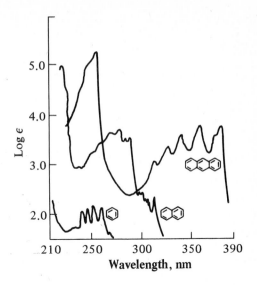

FIGURE 7.3. *Ultraviolet absorption spectra of benzene, naphthalene, and anthracene in ethanol. From K. L. Cheng, "Absorptiometry," in J. D. Winefordner, ed.,* Spectrochemical Methods of Analysis, *New York: Wiley-Interscience, 1971, chap. 6, by permission of the editor and John Wiley and Sons.*

longer wavelengths and the intensity of the absorption changes. The effects of substitution on the 200-nm band in benzene have been studied in great detail by Doub and Vanderbelt [8]. The authors found that the ratio of the wavelength of the 260-nm band to that of the 200-nm band is about 1.25 for most homo-substituted benzenes.

It is well known that resonance and induction have a marked effect on orientation in aromatic substitution. A correlation between orientation in substitution and electronic absorption spectra of benzene derivatives would be expected. Table 7.6 shows data for the position of the 200-nm benzene band [8, 9] as compared with the percentage of the meta isomer produced in nitration.

TABLE 7.6. *Variation in Position of the 200-nm Benzene Band with Percentage of the Meta Isomer Produced in Nitration*

Substituent	Meta in Nitration (percent)	λ_{max} (nm) of 200-nm benzene band
OH	2	210
Cl	0.2	210
Br	0.2	210
CH_3	4	207
CH_2Cl	16	207
$CHCl_2$	34	207
$COCH_3$	55	246
COOH	80	230
CN	81	224
NO_2	93	260

Sources: L. Doub and J. M. Vanderbelt, *J. Amer. Chem. Soc., 69,* 2714 (1947); *71,* 2414 (1949). J. R. Platt, *J. Chem. Phys., 19,* 263 (1951).

Azo Compounds

Straight-chain compounds that contain the –N=N– linkage give rise to low-intensity bands in the near-ultraviolet and visible regions. The long-wavelength bands are thought to arise from $n \rightarrow \pi^*$ transitions. For aliphatic azides, the low-energy band at 285 nm is assigned to a $\pi \rightarrow \pi^*$ electronic transition, whereas the 215-nm band is considered to arise from a s-p $\rightarrow \pi^*$ transition.

For aromatic azides, the –N=N– linkage may be conjugated with the ring π system. In azobenzene, the azo linkage is conjugated with two benzene rings and the π orbitals extend over the whole molecule. The levels are brought closer together and the $\pi \rightarrow \pi^*$ transition occurs at 445 nm. This absorption is responsible for the orange-red color of azobenzene.

Solvent Effects

Since there is electrostatic interaction between polar solvents and polar chromophores, such as the carbonyl group, these solvents tend to stabilize both the nonbonding electronic ground states and the π^* excited states. This interaction causes the $n \rightarrow \pi^*$ transitions, which usually occur at lower energy than the $\pi \rightarrow \pi^*$ transitions, to move to higher energy and $\pi \rightarrow \pi^*$ transitions to move to lower energy. Thus the $\pi \rightarrow \pi^*$ and $n \rightarrow \pi^*$ absorptions of polar chromophores move closer to each other with increasing polarity of the solvent. An example of this phenomenon is the solvent shift of the $n \rightarrow \pi^*$ transition to lower energy in the ultraviolet spectrum of N-nitroso-dimethylamine. For various solvents, the order for decreasing $n \rightarrow \pi^*$ energy is given by cyclohexane > dioxane > ethanol > water. For a series of hydrocarbon solvents, the effect on λ_{max} and ε_{max} is slight and can usually be neglected.

Steric Effects

Electronic interactions may be increased or decreased by steric effects and in certain cases totally new interactions may result. Extended conjugation of π orbitals requires coplanarity of the atoms involved in the π-cloud delocalization for maximal resonance interaction. If large bulky groups are in positions that cause perturbation of the coplanarity of the π system, λ_{max} is usually shifted to shorter wavelengths and ε_{max} also decreases. For example, diphenyl ($\lambda_{max} = 246$ nm, $\varepsilon_{max} = 20,000$) has coplanar rings and shows higher molar absorptivity than its derivative, o,o'-dialkyl-diphenyl which has nonplanar rings ($\lambda_{max} = 250$ nm, $\varepsilon_{max} = 2000$).

Molar absorptivity increases with conjugation as a result of increased transition-moment length, and reaches its maximum for a displacement of 0.1–0.3 nm, corresponding to $\varepsilon_{max} = 10^5$. This length is very sensitive to structural changes; in most cases this effect is more noticeable in the *trans*- rather than the *cis*-isomers. If conjugation is in an open-chain system rather than a constrained ring system, the effect is also greater. The isomeric absorption difference is clearly demonstrated by comparing the ultraviolet absorption spectra of *cis*- and *trans*-azobenzene [2].

Qualitative Identification

In principle, any organic molecule that contains a chromophore will probably give rise to a characteristic electronic spectrum. This provides a method for identifying structural components in such molecules. In addition to characteristic λ_{max} values, the molar absorptivities are also important in both qualitative and structural applications because this information can sometimes differentiate two chromophores that absorb at the same wavelength. Great care must be taken in suggesting relations from an observed electronic absorption spectrum without fully exploring all possibilities. It can usually be assumed that absorption at a particular wavelength is indicative of a given group, and intensity measurements may lend support to this assumption; however, a small amount of impurity from a substance with high molar absorptivity may result in misleading conclusions.

Studies of electronic absorption in the ultraviolet and visible regions find many applications. For a better appreciation of the variety of problems studied, the book by Gillam and Stern [10] should be consulted.

7.3 MAGNITUDE OF ABSORPTION OF RADIATION

Radiant power (P) is defined as the radiant energy impinging on unit area in unit time. Since the color of a solution is due to the partial absorption of visible light, the power of a beam of light will be reduced as it passes through a colored solution. The changes in radiant power that occur as monochromatic radiation passes through an absorption cell are illustrated in Figure 7.4. P_1 is the radiant power of incident radiation, P_0 is the radiant power after passing through one cell wall, P is the radiant power after passing through the absorbing solution or medium, and P_2 is the radiant power after the beam has traversed the last cell wall. An important quantity (see Table 7.2) is the transmittance, T, defined as

$$T = \frac{I}{I_0} = \frac{P_2}{P_1} \tag{7.4}$$

which is the quantity that is usually measured in spectrophotometers. T_i is the *internal* transmittance of the system,

$$T_i = \frac{P}{P_0} \tag{7.5}$$

FIGURE 7.4. *Radiation impinging on an absorption cell whose optical path length is b. From K. L. Cheng, "Absorptiometry," in J. D. Winefordner, ed.,* Spectrochemical Methods of Analysis, *New York: Wiley-Interscience, 1971, chap. 6, by permission of the editor and John Wiley and Sons.*

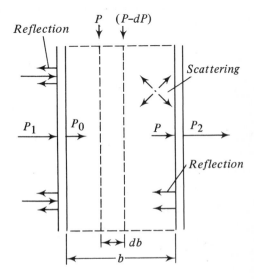

Usually, the quantities T and T_1 are nearly the same because cells are made of materials that will not appreciably absorb or scatter the radiation used. Any slight difference can be minimized by using matched cells, one containing the sample and the other the reagent blank (a solution containing all the components except the compound of interest). If T is set at 100% for the blank, a measurement of T for the sample gives T_1.

Beer's Law

Bouguer, and later Lambert, observed that the fraction of the energy, or intensity, of radiation absorbed in a thin layer of material depends on the absorbing substance and on the frequency of the incident radiation, and is proportional to the thickness of the layer. At a given concentration of the absorbing substance, summation over a series of thin layers, or integration over a finite thickness, leads to an exponential relationship between transmitted intensity and thickness. This is generally called Lambert's law. Beer showed that, at a given thickness, the absorption coefficient introduced by Lambert was directly proportional to the concentration of the absorbing substance in a solution. Combination of these results gives the relationship now commonly known as Beer's law. This law states that the amount of radiation absorbed or transmitted by a solution or medium is an exponential function of the concentration of absorbing substance present and of the length of the path of the radiation through the sample.

Beer's law can be derived as follows (see Fig. 7.4). For a layer of infinitesimal thickness, db, the decrease in radiant power $(-dP)$ is given by

$$-\frac{dP}{P} = kcdb \tag{7.6}$$

where k = a proportionality constant

Integration over the entire absorbing cell length, b,

$$\int_{P_0}^{P} \frac{dP}{P} = -k \int_0^b cdb \tag{7.7}$$

results in

$$\ln (P/P_0) = -kbc = 2.303 \log (P/P_0) \tag{7.8}$$

This gives (Table 7.2)

$$-\log (P/P_0) = -\log T = A = \varepsilon bc \tag{7.9}$$

where $\varepsilon = k/2.303$

The constant ε is called the *molar absorptivity* when the concentration c is in moles per liter and b is in cm. The value of ε is characteristic of the absorbing substance at a particular wavelength in a particular solvent and is independent of the concentration and of the path length, b. Equation 7.9 is a fundamental law on which colorimetric and spectrophotometric methods are based. It is known variously as the Bouguer-Beer, Lambert-Beer, or more simply, Beer's law. When other concentration units are used, such as grams per liter, the symbol a (for absorptivity, Table 7.3) instead of ε is used.

> **Example 7.1.** Palladium reacts with Thio-Michler's ketone, forming a colored 1:4 complex. A 0.20 ppm Pd sample gave an absorbance of 0.390 at 520 nm using a 1.00-cm cell. Calculate the molar absorptivity (ε) for the palladium Thio-Michler's ketone complex.
>
> *Solution:* $0.20 \text{ ppm Pd} = \dfrac{2.0 \times 10^{-4} \text{ g/l}}{106.4} = 1.9 \times 10^{-6} \, M$
>
> In a 1.00-cm cell for $A = 0.390$, the molar absorptivity is calculated from Beer's law:
>
> $$A = \varepsilon b c$$
> $$0.390 = (\varepsilon)(1.00)(1.9 \times 10^{-6})$$
> $$\varepsilon = \frac{0.390}{1.9 \times 10^{-6}} = 2.1 \times 10^5 \text{ l/mole-cm}$$

Beer's law assumes that (a) the incident radiation is monochromatic, (b) the absorption occurs in a volume of uniform cross-section, and (c) the absorbing substances behave independently of each other in the absorption process. Thus, when Beer's law applies to a multicomponent system in which there is no interaction among the various species, the total absorbance may be expressed as

$$A_{\text{total}} = \varepsilon_1 b c_1 + \varepsilon_2 b c_2 + \cdots + \varepsilon_i b c_i \qquad (7.10)$$

where ε_i = the molar absorptivity for the i-th absorbing species
          c_i = its molar concentration

This equation is the basis of quantitative methods for determining mixtures of absorbing substances.

Deviation from Beer's Law

Beer's law states that a plot of absorbance versus concentration should give a straight line passing through the origin with a slope equal to εb. However, deviations from direct proportionality between absorbance and concentration are sometimes encountered. In these cases, a nonlinear working curve may be prepared with solutions of known concentration, and the concentration of the unknown solution found from the absorbance obtained under the same experimental conditions.

Deviations from Beer's law may be due to instrumental factors or to chemical factors. These deviations may result in an upward curvature (positive deviation) or in a downward curvature (negative deviation), as shown in Figure 7.5. A check on instrumental factors can be made by plotting absorbance versus cell length at a constant concentration; this plot will be linear if the instrument is performing satisfactorily. Deviations arising from chemical factors are observed only when concentrations are changed.

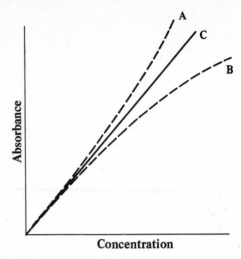

FIGURE 7.5. *Deviations from Beer's law.* *A: positive deviation; B: negative deviation;* *C: no deviation.*

Instrumental Factors. Unsatisfactory performance of an instrument may be caused by fluctuations in the power-supply voltage, an unstable light-source, or a nonlinear response of the detector-amplifier system. A double-beam system helps to minimize deviations due to these factors. In addition, the following instrumental sources of possible deviations should be understood:

1. *Polychromatic radiation.* Strict conformity of an absorbing system to Beer's law requires that the radiation be monochromatic. However, one always works with a band of wavelengths and not with a single sharp line (laser light sources are available, but there is as yet no tunable laser incorporated into a spectrophotometer).

Let us consider the effect of polychromatic radiation on the relationship between concentration and absorbance. When the radiation consists of two wavelengths, λ and λ', and assuming that Beer's law applies at each of these individually, the absorbance at λ is given by

$$\log (P_0/P) = A = \epsilon bc \tag{7.11}$$

or

$$P_0/P = 10^{\epsilon bc} \tag{7.12}$$

Similarly, at λ',

$$P_0'/P' = 10^{\epsilon' bc} \tag{7.13}$$

The radiant power of two wavelengths passing through the solvent is given by $P_0 + P_0'$, and that passing through the solution containing absorbing species by $P + P'$. The combined absorbance is

$$A_c = \log \frac{(P_0 + P_0')}{P + P'} \tag{7.14}$$

Substituting for P and P', we obtain

$$A_c = \log \frac{(P_0 + P_0')}{P_0 10^{-\epsilon bc} + P_0' 10^{-\epsilon' bc}} \tag{7.15}$$

In the very special case where $\epsilon = \epsilon'$, Equation 7.15 simply reduces to Beer's law.

However, in the general case where $\varepsilon \neq \varepsilon'$, the relationship between A_c and c will be nonlinear; therefore, departures from linearity will be greater as the difference between ε and ε' becomes greater. Further, when $\varepsilon > \varepsilon'$, the measured absorbance A_c is lower than the true "monochromatic" absorbance at wavelength λ, resulting in negative deviation, and when $\varepsilon < \varepsilon'$, the measured absorbance A_c is higher, resulting in a positive deviation (Fig. 7.5).

When a broader bandwidth (see below) is used, the lower absorbances toward the edges of the finite band contribute greater total intensities of transmitted light than the higher absorbances at the center of the band, and the summed, "average," absorbance includes those over the bandwidth. It is further noted that the steeper the absorption curve included within the bandwidth, the greater the error. From the same principle, as the concentration is increased the absorption peak becomes narrower, so the error is greater.

2. *Slit width.* The ability of a spectrophotometer to distinguish between two frequencies differing only slightly from each other depends upon the widths of the images produced (relative to the separation of two images). The width of the image produced is thus an important measure of the quality of performance of a spectrophotometer. The spread of the image along the frequency, wave number, or wavelength scale is defined as the "spectral slit width" or "spectral bandwidth." It is very closely proportional to the actual width of the slit (the mechanical slit width). The effect of slit width on absorbance is illustrated in Figure 7.6.

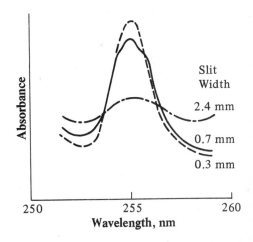

FIGURE 7.6. *Effect of slit width on absorbance. From K. L. Cheng, "Absorptiometry," in J. D. Winefordner, ed.,* Spectrochemical Methods of Analysis, *New York: Wiley-Interscience, 1971, chap. 6, by permission of the editor and John Wiley and Sons.*

The spectral bandwidth of an ultraviolet spectrophotometer is typically of the order of 1 nm. In general, molecular absorption bands are smooth and much broader than 1 nm, so that the effect of spectral bandwidth is practically negligible, especially when the absorbance is measured at the maximum absorption. If the absorption band is sharp, or if measurements are made on a steep slope of the spectral band, the absorptivity may be different over the spectral bandwidth, and deviations from the Beer's law will be noticed. Figure 7.7 shows the effect of spectral bandwidth: with increasing slit width (also increasing spectral bandwidth), the recorded bands gradually merge together.

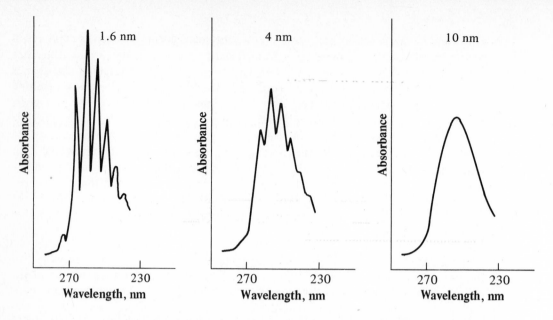

FIGURE 7.7. *Effect of spectral bandwidth on the absorption spectrum of benzene in cyclohexane.*

3. *Stray light.* Stray light that strikes the detector is a potential source of error; the apparent absorbance is decreased as a result:

$$A_m = \log \left(\frac{P_0 + P_s}{P + P_s} \right) \qquad (7.16)$$

where P_s = the radiant power of the stray light
       A_m = the measured absorbance

When P diminishes owing to increasing concentration and becomes small in comparison with P_s, $P + P_s \approx P_s$; and Equation 7.16 becomes

$$A_m = \log \frac{P_0 + P_s}{P_s} \qquad (7.17)$$

Thus, there is a negative deviation from Beer's law. Errors due to stray light are more commonly found near the wavelength limits of the instrument components. Many reports of spectra in the UV region below 220 nm should be carefully checked, since false peaks have been reported. Visible radiation usually presents the most serious stray-light problem for ultraviolet-visible spectrophotometers, because both the spectral radiance of most visible sources and the spectral response of most detectors to visible radiation are high.

Chemical Factors. Apparent deviations from Beer's law are often due to chemical effects such as dissociation, association, complex formation, polymerization, or solvolysis.

Association and polymerization are examples of the process of self-interaction, and their effects are important in both ultraviolet and visible spectroscopy. Benzoic acid exists as a mixture of the ionized and un-ionized forms, and in dilute aqueous solution it dissociates

$$C_6H_5COOH + H_2O \rightleftharpoons C_6H_5COO^- + H_3O^+ \qquad (7.18)$$

$(\lambda_{max} = 273 \text{ nm}, \varepsilon = 970)$ $\qquad$ $(\lambda_{max} = 268 \text{ nm}, \varepsilon = 560)$

The effective molar absorptivity at 273 nm will thus decrease with increased dilution or at high pH.

Another example is observed with unbuffered $K_2Cr_2O_7$ solutions. In pure water, the dichromate and chromate ions are in equilibrium

$$Cr_2O_7^{2-} + H_2O \rightleftharpoons 2CrO_4^{2-} + 2H^+ \qquad (7.19)$$

$(\lambda_{max} = 350, 450 \text{ nm})$ $\qquad$ $(\lambda_{max} = 372 \text{ nm})$

The equilibrium constant may be expressed as

$$\frac{[CrO_4^{2-}]^2[H^+]^2}{[Cr_2O_7^{2-}]} = K \qquad (7.20)$$

Obviously, there are deviations from Beer's law when aqueous solutions of chromate or dichromate are diluted with water, and the pH will affect the concentrations of $Cr_2O_7^{2-}$ and CrO_4^{2-}. The effect can be controlled by buffering dichromate with a strong acid or chromate with a strong base.

Occasionally, the absorbance is measured at an isosbestic point (or isoabsorptive wavelength)—that is, a wavelength at which the two absorbing species in equilibrium have a common value of ε; then, Beer's law holds even though there is a shift of equilibrium. Isosbestic points are often taken as criteria for the existence of two interconvertible absorbing species of a compound, the total quantity of which is constant, though points of common ε value occur also in some irreversible decomposition reactions giving two products.

1. *Solvent.* Dissolution may shift the spectrum of an absorbing substance to longer wavelength (with respect to the spectrum of the gas). This so-called "red shift" or bathochromic effect is greater in solvents of high dielectric constant because the charge displacement for the upper energy state requires less energy in a dielectric solvent than in a vacuum. A "blue shift" (to shorter wavelengths) is generally believed to be associated with a $n \rightarrow \pi^*$ transition involving a nonbonding orbital in the ground state. Dissolution generally causes larger effects on infrared spectra than on ultraviolet spectra, but may cause significant errors even in ultraviolet quantitative work. The greatest effect occurs after mixing dipolar solvated molecules (dissolved in nonpolar solvents) with polar solvents or additives. Many carbonyl compounds are sensitive to changes in solvent media.

2. *Temperature.* Changes in temperature may shift ionic equilibria. In addition, an increase in temperature exerts a bathochromic effect on ions in solution—for instance, the color of a hydrochloric acid solution of ferric chloride changes from yellow to reddish brown on heating. However, temperature is ordinarily not considered an important factor in simple systems, within limits of say $\pm 5°$.

3. *Photo effects.* Fluorescence resulting from frequencies of ultraviolet radiation in a certain range may cause an apparent increase in transmittance with

fluorescing substances. Light scattering is found in colloidal systems, the extent depending upon the particle size and shape and the wavelength region used. Photo effects in many organic compounds or indicator solutions may cause dichroism—different colors are produced by thick and thin layers. For a polymer or crystal, pleochroism may be observed; unpolarized radiation becomes partially polarized on passing through an ordered absorbing substance. Photochemical reactions or photodecomposition, of course, cause a deviation from Beer's law. The effect is usually of little significance unless high-intensity radiation is used close to the sample solution or the sample is highly photosensitive, such as the silver thio-Michler's ketone complex.

7.4 QUANTITATIVE ABSORPTION SPECTROSCOPY

Methods based on the absorption of radiation are powerful and useful tools for the analytical chemist. The ultraviolet region is particularly important for the qualitative and quantitative determination of many organic compounds. In the visible region, spectrophotometric methods are widely used for the quantitative determination of many trace substances, especially inorganic elements.

The basic principle of quantitative absorption spectroscopy lies in comparing the extent of absorption of a sample solution with that of a set of standards under radiation at a selected wavelength.

Visual Colorimetric Methods

In its simplest form, colorimetry consists of visual matching of the color of the sample with that of a series of standards. A colored compound is first formed by suitably reacting the constituent to be determined, then the colored solutions are racked side-by-side in Nessler tubes* for viewing from the top. The approximate concentration of the unknown is estimated by finding which standard most closely matches the unknown in color. Visual colorimetry suffers from poor precision since the eye is not as sensitive to small differences in absorbance as is a photoelectric device. The use of a Duboscq colorimeter constitutes a more refined method of analysis for color comparison. This is equipped with an eyepiece with a split field that permits the ready comparison of beams passing through sample and standard.

Photometric Methods

Photometers equipped with filters are suitable for many routine methods that do not involve complex spectra. Spectrophotometers can provide narrow bandwidths of radiation for accurate work and can handle absorption spectra in the ultraviolet region.

Choice of Wavelength. When filter photometers are employed, a suitable filter is selected in preparing an analytical curve for the unknown substance. With a spectrophotometer, the spectrum of the absorbing substance is determined, and a suitable

---

* Nessler tubes are essentially large, uniform, flat-bottomed test tubes, about 30 cm in length and perhaps 2.5 cm in diameter.

wavelength is chosen. Generally, a wavelength close to that of maximum absorption is chosen, for maximum sensitivity; but the wavelength chosen should also fall in a region where the absorbance does not change rapidly with change in wavelength.

Unfortunately, use of the wavelength of maximum absorption is not always feasible because the color-forming reagents often also absorb significantly at the wavelength of maximum absorption of the species being measured. The spectra of 3,3′-diaminobenzidine (DAB) and its monoselenium compound, shown in Figure 7.8, both have absorption maxima at 340 and 420 nm. At 340 nm, the reagent also absorbs strongly. Although it is possible to select 340 nm and subtract the absorbance contributed by the excess reagent, it is difficult to know the amount of excess reagent precisely, and errors increase with increasing absorption by the reagent itself. A better approach is to use a wavelength at which the absorbing substance absorbs rather strongly but at which the absorbance contribution by the excess reagent is minimal, 420 nm in this case.

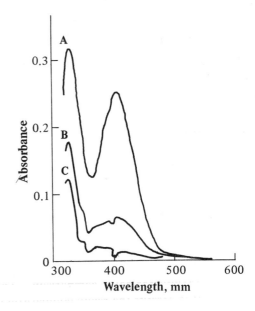

FIGURE 7.8. *Absorbance curves of toluene solution of 3,3′-diaminobenzidine and its monoselenium compound with* λ_{max} *at 340 and 420 nm. A: 25 mg Se in 10 ml of toluene. B: 5 mg Se in 10 ml of toluene. C: Diaminobenzidine in toluene. Toluene as blank. From K. L. Cheng, Anal. Chem., 28, 1738 (1956), by permission of the publishers. Copyright © 1956 by the American Chemical Society.*

For systems that are sensitive to pH, and for which an isosbestic point can be located, measurements at the wavelength of the latter are preferred if the pH cannot be readily controlled.

Separation and Formation of Absorbing Compounds. In general, more than one method is available for the spectrophotometric determination of a given substance, and selecting a suitable method plays an important role in successfully analyzing the sample. It is often necessary to separate the absorbing substance before the absorbance measurement; for instance, chromatographic separation of vitamins in natural products is made before the actual spectrophotometric determination. In many instances, the sample compound does not absorb radiation appreciably in the wavelength regions provided; it is then necessary to form an absorbing substance by reacting the compound in question with other reagents. The reagents should be selective in their reactions and should not form interfering absorbing species with foreign substances likely to be present.

Some common and important factors involved in the formation of absorbing compounds are:

1. *pH*. Since pH plays a very important role in complex formation, proper adjustment of pH or the use of a buffer often eliminates certain interfering reactions. For instance, methylthymol blue and xylenol orange (analogues of EDTA) react with many metal ions. Their selectivity for certain metals is much improved in highly acidic media. For example, zirconium may be determined in the presence of hafnium in 1 N perchloric acid [11].

2. *Reagent concentration*. The amount of reagent required is dictated by the composition of the absorbing complex formed. An optimum concentration of reagents should be determined, since either not enough reagent or too much reagent can cause deviation from Beer's law.

3. *Time*. Formation of the absorbing complex may be slow, in some cases requiring several minutes or a few hours. For example, the phosphomolybdate blue method—a very common analytical method for phosphate determinations—requires about fifteen minutes standing time for full color development after addition of the reagents.

4. *Temperature*. The optimum temperature should be established in the procedure. Certain reactions require elevated temperature to decrease the time necessary for complete color development.

5. *Order of mixing reagents*. Frequently it is important to add the reagents in a specified sequence, otherwise full color development will not be possible or interfering reactions may occur. For instance, the highly selective color reaction of cobaltic NTA (nitrilotriacetate) in the presence of hydrogen peroxide must be preceded by the formation of the cobaltous NTA complex [12].

6. *Stability*. If the absorbing complex formed is not very stable, the absorbance measurement should be made as soon as possible. If the absorbing complex is photosensitive, precautions should be taken in order to avoid its photodecomposition. Certain reagents may sometimes be added to help stabilize the absorbing complex.

7. *Masking*. Very few reactions are truly specific. However, highly selective reactions may be developed through the sophisticated use of *masking*. The term masking refers to the addition of a complexing agent to form a metal complex of such stability that, in this case, color-forming reactions with another reagent do not occur to any appreciable extent. For example, in the presence of excess EDTA, ferric ion does not form the colored $FeSCN^{2+}$ complex with thiocyanate ion.

8. *Organic solvent*. Many organic reagents or complexes are only slightly soluble in water. In such cases, it is necessary to add a water-miscible organic solvent to avoid precipitation or to aid color development. In other cases, solvent extraction might be employed, for example, to separate the colored compound from excess reagent or from interfering substances.

9. *Salt concentration*. High concentrations of electrolyte often influence the absorption spectrum of a compound. This effect may be due to the formation of

ion-association complexes that cause a shift in the maximum absorption. This is a type of masking effect and usually causes a decrease in the absorption.

Photometric Errors. Because of the logarithmic relationship between transmittance and concentration, small errors in measuring the transmittance cause large relative errors in the calculated concentration at low and at high transmittances. The concentration of a sample solution or the path length or both should be so adjusted that the absorbance will be within the range of approximately 0.2 to 0.7 (i.e., transmittance in the range of 20 to 60%). As shown in Figure 7.9, an absorbance of 0.434 (36.8% transmittance) is considered optimum, but in practice there is little difference in relative error between 0.2 and 0.7 absorbance. The relative error curve shown in Figure 7.9 is approximately correct, in practice, only for relatively simple instruments with phototube detectors. With photomultiplier detectors, and in most of the more sophisticated commercial spectrophotometers, the usable transmittance range of "minimum" error is extended to improve the electronic signal-to-noise ratio.

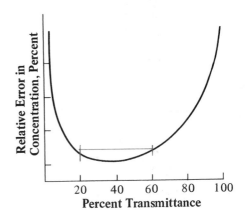

FIGURE 7.9. *Relative concentration error as a function of transmittance. From K. L. Cheng, "Absorptiometry," in J. D. Winefordner, ed.,* Spectrochemical Methods of Analysis, *New York: Wiley-Interscience, 1971, chap. 6, by permission of the editor and John Wiley and Sons.*

7.5 SPECTROPHOTOMETRIC APPLICATIONS

Analysis of Mixtures

Beer's law states that absorbance is an additive property of all the absorbing molecules present in a mixture (see Eqn. 7.10). In principle, n absorbance measurements at n different wavelengths are needed to determine the concentrations of n components in a mixture; this procedure gives n independent simultaneous equations in n unknowns. The molar absorptivities must be known or determined for each individual absorbing species, 1, 2, etc., at each wavelength. If, in a two-component mixture, the values are ε_1, ε_2 at wavelength λ, and ε_1', ε_2' at a second wavelength, λ', and the absorbance of the mixture is A at λ and A' at λ', for a path length b and unknown concentrations c_1, c_2, then Equation 7.10 becomes

$$A = A_1 + A_2 = \varepsilon_1 b c_1 + \varepsilon_2 b c_2 \qquad (7.21)$$

$$A' = A_1' + A_2' = \varepsilon_1' b c_1 + \varepsilon_2' b c_2 \qquad (7.22)$$

Thus, the two unknown concentrations are calculated by solving these two simultaneous equations, which are obtained by measuring the absorbance of the mixture at two different wavelengths. Since these equations depend upon the use of correct molar absorptivities, large errors may occur in systems where there are deviations from the laws of absorption.

Isosbestic Point. For a two-component system where the two components are in equilibrium with each other and contribute all the absorption, it can be shown that there is at least one point in the spectrum at which the absorbance is independent of the ratio of the concentrations of the two components. If the bands overlap, there is a wavelength at which the two absorbing species in equilibrium have the same ε value. This wavelength (at which the absorbance depends only on the total number of "equivalents" of the two absorbing species) is called the isosbestic point, or isobestic point, or isoabsorptive wavelength. All curves intersect at this point. The existence of such a point is not proof of the presence of only two components; there may be a third component with $\varepsilon = 0$ at this particular wavelength. The absence of an isosbestic point, however, is definite proof of the presence of a third component, providing the possibility of a deviation from Beer's law in the two-component system can be discounted. In one respect, then, the isosbestic point is a unique wavelength for quantitative determination of the total amount of two absorbing substances in mutual equilibrium.

Determination of Stoichiometry

The spectrophotometric method is particularly valuable for studying complexes of low stability. Consider the formation of a complex M_nL_p, where M is a metal ion and L is a ligand:

$$nM + pL \rightleftharpoons M_nL_p \qquad (7.23)$$

The molar ratio of the two components of a complex is important. In a quantitative determination, an excess of ligand should be added in order to force the equilibrium toward completion.

Molar-Ratio Method. In this method, the concentration of one component is kept fixed and that of the other varied to give a series of [L]/[M] ratios. The absorbances of these solutions, measured at an absorption maximum for the complex M_nL_p, increase linearly up to the molar ratio of the complex, at which virtually the whole amount of both components is complexed (assuming little dissociation). Further addition of component L cannot increase the absorbance, and the line becomes horizontal, or shows a break if component L absorbs at the same wavelength (Fig. 7.10). In rare cases, an excess component L may cause a decrease in absorbance owing to the stepwise formation of higher-order complexes that have smaller ε values at this wavelength. The composition of molybdogermanic acid has been studied by the molar-ratio method [13] showing a ratio of 36 molybdate:1 germanate.

Continuous-Variation Method. The molar ratios may also be varied by changing the concentrations of both components while the total number of moles of both com-

FIGURE 7.10. *Molar-ratio method, showing different curves.* (a) *Component L does not absorb at the wavelength of maximum absorption for the complex, e.g., Fe(III)-Tiron.* (b) *Component L absorbs slightly at the wavelength of maximum absorption for the complex, e.g., Zn-Pan.* (c) *An excess of component L causes a decrease in absorbance of the complex, e.g., Bi-xylenol orange.* From K. L. Cheng, *"Absorptiometry,"* in *J. D. Winefordner,* ed., Spectrochemical Methods of Analysis, *New York: Wiley-Interscience, 1971, chap. 6, by permission of the editor and John Wiley and Sons.*

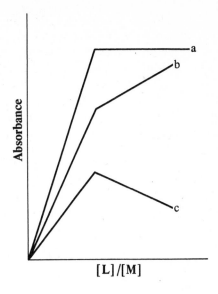

ponents are kept constant; this is termed the method of continuous variation, or Job's method [14, 15]. The mole fraction of one of the components is plotted on the abscissa scale; the ordinate scale is usually a difference in absorbance, ΔA, representing the difference between the observed absorbance and the summed absorbances of the independent (noncomplexed) components. When the curvature is pronounced and the maximum is not apparent, the apex may be obtained by drawing tangents. The results may be verified by repeating the process at other wavelengths or total concentrations, since the position of the maximum is independent of wavelength and concentration.

These methods are also applicable at the absorption wavelengths of one of the components—that is, when breaks occur at minimum instead of maximum values of ΔA. The results in Figure 7.11 show the predominant 1 Pd : 4 TMK (thio-Michler's

FIGURE 7.11. *Job curves of thio-Michler's ketone (TMK) complexes of mercury (○) and of palladium (●). From K. L. Cheng, "Absorptiometry," in J. D. Winefordner, ed.,* Spectrochemical Methods of Analysis, *New York: Wiley-Interscience, 1971, chap. 6, by permission of the editor and John Wiley and Sons.*

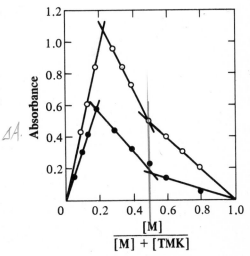

ketone) complex and the 1 Hg:3 TMK complex maxima, but they also indicate the formation of 1:1 complex for both Pd and Hg when TMK is not in large excess (the minima coming at 0.5 on the x-axis). The molar-ratio curves for the same complexes give no indication of the existence of a 1:1 complex; in general, Job's method of continuous variation is somewhat more accurate and may provide more information about complex formation. Deviations from Beer's law will result in errors in the direction of larger dissociation constants with either of these methods. The effects may be isolated by varying the path length and concentrations independently or by varying the total concentration of reactants for a given ratio of concentrations. The selection will depend in part on the nature of the deviation from Beer's law. It should be mentioned that these methods are, however, not reliable if the complexes are weak or when several complexes are simultaneously formed in solution.

Vosburgh and his associates [14] have extended Job's method, particularly in dealing with the formation of more than one complex. They investigated the o-phenanthroline (o-phen) complexes of Ni(II) in a range of wavelengths between 500 and 650 nm. The absorption by [Ni(o-phen)]$^{2+}$ at 620 nm, [Ni(o-phen)$_2$]$^{2+}$ at 580 nm, and [Ni(o-phen)$_3$]$^{2+}$ at 528 nm were shown with three linear plots.

Bjerrum Method. In the method of Bjerrum, one plots $\varepsilon/[M]_t$ versus $[L]_t$ for various constant values of $[M]_t$, where t denotes *total* concentration of the designated form. A line drawn horizontally on the graph intersects the experimental curves at points whose coordinates show the composition of the so-called "corresponding solutions" which have a given value of $\varepsilon/[M]_t$. For complexes of the type ML_n ($n = 1, 2, 3, \ldots$), the solutions also have the same value of $\bar{n}$. The value of $\bar{n}$ (an average number of ligands bonded to the central group) may be obtained at various concentrations of L when the total concentrations of such solutions are known. For detailed description, see references [16, 17].

Studies of Chemical Equilibria

Spectrophotometry can be used to assess chemical equilibria, provided the participating species absorb at markedly different wavelengths.

Determination of Acid-Base Equilibria. Since the absorption spectra of organic molecules with acidic or basic functional groups depend upon the pH of the medium, the absorption maxima and intensities vary with the hydrogen-ion concentration. The dissociation constant of an acid or a base may be determined spectrophotometrically as a result of such changes. For a weak acid in water

$$HA + H_2O \rightleftharpoons H_3O^+ + A^- \tag{7.24}$$

$$K_a = \frac{[H_3O^+][A^-]}{[HA]}$$

where K_a = the dissociation constant of acid HA

Equation 7.24 may be expressed as

$$-\log K_a = -\log [H_3O^+] - \log [A^-]/[HA]$$
$$pK_a = pH + \log [HA]/[A^-] \tag{7.25}$$

If the pH and the concentrations of HA (acid form) and A^- (basic form) are known, pK_a can be easily calculated. <u>The ratio of [HA] to [A^-] may be found spectrophoto-metrically if ε_{HA} and ε_{A^-} are known.</u> These latter values can be determined after converting completely to A^- or HA by adding excess acid or base. As an example, the dissociation constants of several weak acids and bases have been determined photometrically [18]; the base strengths of pyridine derivatives have been determined using a similar procedure [19].

According to Equation 7.25, when [HA] = [A^-], $pK_a = pH$. The pH at this point may be called $pH_{1/2}$, as it occurs at the midpoint of a photometric titration curve, namely, 50% of the titration of acid HA.

This point can be used to calculate K_a: one plots the absorbance at a particular wavelength, say λ_{max}, against the pH of the solution and obtains the midpoint graphically to find $pH_{1/2}$.

King and Hirt [20] have described an instrument called a Spectrotitrimeter, which offers a rapid and accurate determination of dissociation constants. A titration flask combined with a pH meter and a spectrometer with an automatic pump as described by Rehm et al. [21] will serve the same purpose.

The pK_a of bromophenol blue has been determined spectrophotometrically [22]. The color change may be followed spectrophotometrically as in Figure 7.12, which shows the absorption spectrum of bromophenol blue in solutions of pH from 3.0 to 5.4. Usually photometric titration gives a sigmoid curve; if the curve fails to flatten out at the ends, the midpoint is determined by a graphic method commonly used in polarography for locating $E_{1/2}$ (see Chap. 3). The spectra in Figure 7.12 suggest that the peak at 590 nm is due solely to the conjugate base, A^-, of bromophenol blue (since the peak intensity is reduced by decreasing the pH) and the HA absorption evidently occurs somewhere below 450 nm. There is no problem of overlap in this example. Hence, we may write the equation

$$[A^-] = A/\varepsilon b \tag{7.26}$$

where A = the absorbance at the maximum
  ε = the absorptivity at the maximum

For a total concentration of bromophenol blue of c, [HA] = $c -$ [A^-] and

$$[H_3O^+] = K_a\left(\frac{c}{[A^-]} - 1\right) = K_a\left(\frac{c \cdot \varepsilon b}{A} - 1\right) \tag{7.27}$$

$$pH = pK_a - \log\left(\frac{c \cdot \varepsilon b}{A} - 1\right) \tag{7.28}$$

This gives the sigmoid curve shown in Figure 7.12. Such a curve can be obtained experimentally without prior knowledge of K_a or ε by measuring the absorbance of HA in various buffer solutions.

Conversely, this experiment offers information about the nature of the indicator conjugate pair itself. Equation 7.27 can be fitted to the plot of A against pH to obtain ε and K_a. In that equation $A \neq \varepsilon bc$, because c refers to the total concentration, [HA] + [A^-]. If the pH is made sufficiently large so that practically all the indicator exists as A^-, then $c =$ [A^-] and $A = \varepsilon bc$, and hence ε is obtained. At the value of A corresponding to (εbc)/2, pH = pK_a.

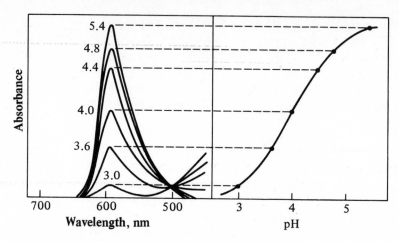

FIGURE 7.12. *The absorption spectrum of bromophenol blue at various pH values (left). The variation of A_{max} with pH (right).*

Kambe et al. [23] determined the dissociation constants of some furfurylidene-*p*-nitrophenylhydrazones by plotting appropriate absorbance values versus pH. The pK_1 and pK_2 of *p*-hydroxybenzoic acid have been found to be 4.61 and 9.31 by a spectrophotometric method [24]. Since the equations employ concentration instead of activity, the experimental results for pK values are approximate unless corrected for activity.

Equilibrium Constants. Job [15] has pointed out that, when the formula is known for a complex in solution, its equilibrium constant can be calculated through a relation between concentration and absorptivity. As a part of his continuous-variation studies, Job determined spectrophotometrically the equilibrium constants of many complexes.

Cheng [25] applied Job's method to the determination of the apparent formation constant of the Hf-xylenol orange (XO) complex using the method of mixtures of equimolar solutions. This is a rapid, though probably not too accurate, method of estimating the formation constant of a colored complex with the mole ratio 1 to 1. Application of this method gave a value of $K = 1.6 \times 10^4$ for the Hf-XO complex formational constant in 0.8 N HClO$_4$. The formation constants of the cerium, titanium, cadmium, and UO$_2{}^{2+}$ [26] complexes have also been reported.

The determination of formation constants may involve the photometric measurement of the complex formed in the presence of a large excess of one of the reagents, so that the formation of the complex may be considered to be essentially complete; this is known as the method of mixtures of nonequimolar solutions. This method is based on Job's general equation [27, 28] for systems involving mixtures. The method has been applied to the determination of the dissociation constant of Fe(III)-sulfosalicyclic acid mixtures in a pH 5.3 buffer, using sulfosalicyclic acid solutions 3, 5, and 8 times as concentrated as the ferric perchlorate. The best results were obtained by assuming that a 1:1 complex is formed, and K_d was calculated to be 2×10^{-5}.

Spectrophotometric methods of determining stability constants are generally unreliable when the complexes are rather weak, or when several complexes are formed in solution. These methods are most suitable for a situation where only one or two complexes are concerned in the equilibrium and when absorption by the free ligand is negligible at the wavelength used. Reviews of spectrophotometric methods for determining equilibrium constants are available [17, 29].

Molecular-Weight Determinations

If an unknown compound can be treated to form a derivative in which a chromophore of known ε value is incorporated, the molar concentration of the chromophore may be obtained spectrophotometrically. This provides a simple method for determining molecular weights. Although the molar absorptivity of the absorption band remains constant in all the derivatives, the absorbance (A) will depend upon the molar concentration and hence on the molecular weight of the molecule of interest. The molecular weight (M) may be determined spectrophotometrically from the relation

$$M = \varepsilon w b / A \qquad (7.29)$$

where w = the weight of the compound in grams per liter
   b = the thickness of the medium

It is assumed in this method that ε is not affected by intra- or intermolecular forces, and that no interfering bands exist.

Picric acid and the picrate salts of amines absorb at 380 nm with a molar absorptivity of 13,400. An accuracy of $\pm 2\%$ was obtained for the spectrophotometric determination of molecular weights of amines [30]. Molecular-weight determinations have been reported of sugars from the absorption spectra of their osazones [31], of aldehydes and ketones from the absorption spectra of their 2,4-dinitrophenylhydrazones [21, 32, 33], and of saturated alcohols from the absorption of their β-2,4-dinitrophenylpropionyl esters [34].

Reaction-Rate Determinations

The concentration dependence of absorbance has an obvious analytical application in the study of reaction rates. If the absorption spectra of the reactants and products are quite different, we may follow spectrophotometrically changes in concentration of either the reactants or the products during the reaction. For slow reactions, samples can be withdrawn and analyzed at leisure. Absorption spectrometry may play its part in such analysis, but no new features are involved. For fast reactions, spectrophotometry offers advantages, particularly in following the concentration changes of the reactants in situ. Chapter 18 discusses the determination of reaction rates in detail.

Purification and Trace Analysis

Trace impurities in a "pure" organic compound may be easily detected or estimated if they have fairly intense absorption bands. As when carrying out a crystallization of a solid compound to a constant (maximum) melting point, the purification should be continued until the molar absorptivity reaches a constant (minimum) value. For example, commercial absolute ethanol commonly contains benzene as an impurity, and the latter is easily detected by spectrophotometric means. The presence of CS_2 in CCl_4 can be detected spectrophotometrically at 318 nm. The absorption data can be taken as truly characteristic of a compound only when its purity has been verified by attainment of constant minimum absorption intensity after repeated fractional purifications. Absorption data have been commonly cited for the purity specifications of some therapeutic solutions of vitamins A, C, and D. Absorption spectra are often used to indicate the purity of unstable biological compounds such as nucleotides or enzymes, because this is often the most convenient, or perhaps the only, way to do so.

7.6 APPARATUS AND INSTRUMENTS

The instruments used in the ultraviolet-visible region of the electromagnetic spectrum fall into three categories, distinguished by complexity of design. Colorimeters generally are the simple visual and photoelectric devices used in the visible region. Photometers include colorimeters, but are more flexible in design so as to include ultraviolet and infrared as well as the visible region. Spectrophotometers are more complex and versatile than either of the others in that they include a monochromator, which provides a narrow band of continuously variable wavelength. A wide variety of spectrophotometers are commercially available.

The choice of source, optical materials, monochromator, and detector depends on the spectral region of interest. This usually imposes a limit on the range of a given instrument. The four ranges for which instruments are presently available are: (1) the visible region (400 to 700 nm); (2) the near ultraviolet, visible, and very near infrared (190 to 1,000 nm), using quartz optics; (3) the vacuum ultraviolet (below 190 nm), requiring an evacuated instrument; and (4) the nitrogen ultraviolet region (200 to 160 nm) requiring instruments purged with N_2.

The Components of a Spectrophotometer

There are several light sources available for use in the ultraviolet-visible region. *Mercury-vapor* lamps have been used but, owing to the heat evolved by these lamps, thermal insulation or cooling is required. More commonly used for the visible and near-infrared region are *tungsten-filament* "incandescent" lamps. These are thermal or "blackbody" sources in which the radiation is the result of high temperature of the solid filament material, with only a small dependence on its actual chemical nature. These sources provide continuous radiation from about 320 to 3000 nm—most of it, unfortunately, in the near-infrared. At the usual operating temperature of about 3000 K, only about 15% of the total radiant energy falls in the visible region, and at 2000 K, only 1%. Increasing the operating temperature above 3000 K greatly increases the total energy output and shifts the wavelength of maximum intensity to shorter wavelengths, but the lifetime of the lamp is drastically shortened. Inconveniently high temperatures are required for the production of much radiation in the ultraviolet. The lifetime of a tungsten filament lamp can be greatly increased by the presence of a low pressure of iodine or bromine vapor within the lamp; with the addition of a fused silica lamp envelope, these are now called *quartz-halogen* lamps— a popular source at present. Most work in the ultraviolet region is done with *hydrogen* or *deuterium* electrical-discharge lamps typically operated under low-pressure DC conditions (about 40 V with 5 mm gas pressure). These lamps provide a continuum emission down to about 160 nm, but the window material generally limits the

FIGURE 7.13. *Schematic diagram of three common detectors used in the ultraviolet-visible region. A: The barrier-layer or photovoltaic cell. B: A vacuum phototube. C: The vacuum photomultiplier.*

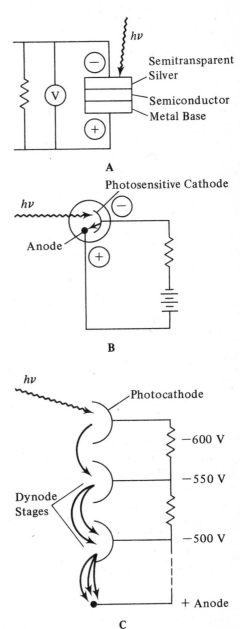

transmission at short wavelengths (about 200 nm with quartz and 185 nm with fused silica). Above about 360 nm, hydrogen emission lines are superimposed on the continuum, so incandescent sources are generally used for measurements at longer wavelengths. Deuterium lamps are more expensive, but have about 2 to 5 times greater spectral intensity and lifetime than a hydrogen lamp of comparable design and wattage.

The continuous radiation from the sources listed above is dispersed by means of monochromators (see Chap. 6).

There are three main types of detectors presently in use. The *barrier-layer* or *photovoltaic* type is illustrated in Figure 7.13A. This device measures the intensity of photons by means of the voltage developed across the semiconductor layer. Electrons, ejected by photons from the semiconductor, are collected by the silver layer. The potential depends on the number of photons hitting the detector. A second type is the photodetector or *phototube* shown in Figure 7.13B. This detector is a vacuum tube with a cesium-coated photocathode. Photons of sufficiently high energy hitting the cathode can dislodge electrons which are collected at the anode. Photon flux is measured by the current flow in the system. The vacuum-phototube type of detector needs further (external) amplification to function properly. The last type of commonly used detector is schematically illustrated in Figure 7.13C. This detector consists of a photoemissive cathode coupled with a series of electron-multiplying dynode stages, and is usually called a *photomultiplier*. The primary electrons ejected from the photocathode are accelerated by an electric field so as to strike a small area on the first dynode. The impinging electrons strike with enough energy to eject two to five *secondary electrons*, which are accelerated to the second dynode to eject still more electrons. This cascading effect takes place until the electrons are collected at the anode. Typically, a photomultiplier may have 9 to 16 stages, and an overall gain of 10^6 to perhaps 10^9 electrons per incident photon.

Single- and Double-Beam Spectrometers

The measurement of absorption of ultraviolet-visible radiation is of a relative nature. One must continually compare the absorption of the sample with that of an analytical reference or blank to insure the reliability of the measurement. The rate at which the sample and reference are compared depends on the design of the instrument. In *single-beam* instruments there is only one light beam or optical path from the source through to the detector. This usually means that one must remove the sample from the light beam and replace it with the reference after each reading. Thus, there is usually an interval of several seconds between measurements.

Alternatively, the sample and reference may be compared many times a second, as in *double-beam* instruments. The light from the source, after passing through the monochromator, is split into two separate beams—one for the sample and the other for the reference. Figure 7.14 shows two types of double-beam spectrophotometers. The measurement of sample and reference absorption may be separated in space, as in Figure 7.14A; this, however, requires two detectors which must be perfectly matched. Alternatively, the sample and reference measurement may be separated in time as in Figure 7.14B; this technique makes use of a rapidly rotating mirror or

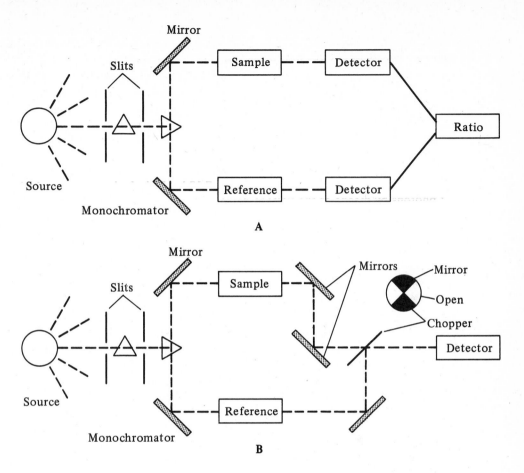

FIGURE 7.14. *Schematic diagram of two types of double-beam spectrophotometers. A: The double-beam-in-space configuration. B: The double-beam-in-time configuration.*

"chopper" to switch the beam that comes from sample and reference very rapidly. The latter method requires only one detector and is probably the better of the two methods.

There are two main advantages of double-beam operation over single-beam operation. Very rapid monitoring of sample and reference helps to eliminate errors due to drift in source intensity, electronic instability, and any changes in the optical system. Also, double-beam operation lends itself to automation—the spectra can be recorded by a strip-chart recorder.

Derivative Spectrophotometers

Derivative spectroscopy was introduced by Griese and French [35] in 1955. These authors achieved better resolution by electronically obtaining first and second derivatives of absorption spectra. More recently, Hager [36] has reported a means of obtaining derivative spectra optically rather than electronically. This is important, as derivatives taken electronically sense changes in intensity with time as well as wavelength, whereas those obtained optically do not. Changes in intensity with respect to time are considered noise; thus, by taking derivatives of these fluctuations the spectrum actually becomes "noisier." If the technique senses only changes of intensity with wavelength, time fluctuations will not be sensed and noise is minimized.

One important feature of derivative spectra is that peak heights are usually directly proportional to concentration. This is more desirable than the logarithmic relationship in direct absorption spectroscopy. Another important feature is that the sensitivity to concentration depends on the rate of change in molar absorptivity at a particular wavelength, $d\varepsilon/d\lambda$, rather than on the absolute magnitude of ε itself. Thus, very sensitive analyses are possible for compounds that have sharp absorption peaks. Since absorption spectra are broadened in condensed phases, derivative spectroscopy finds particular application in gas analysis where absorption peaks are much sharper.

Typical second-derivative spectra are shown in Figure 7.15. The derivative spectra obtained for a given sample can be analyzed for both composition and concentration. Component gases may be identified from the location of their second-derivative peaks, which occur at wavelengths characteristic of the compound. The

TABLE 7.7. *Detection Limits of Some Compounds by Use of a Second-Derivative Gas Analyzer*

Compound	Concentration (ppb)
Ammonia	1
Nitric oxide	5
Nitrogen dioxide	40
Ozone	40
Sulfur dioxide	1
Mercury vapor	0.5
Benzene	25
Toluene	50
Xylene	100
Styrene	100
Formaldehyde	200
Benzaldehyde	100
Acetaldehyde	400

Source: From R. N. Hager, Jr., *Anal. Chem.*, 45, 1131A (1973), by permission of the author and publisher. Copyright © 1973 by the American Chemical Society.
Note: Signal-to-noise ratio of two.

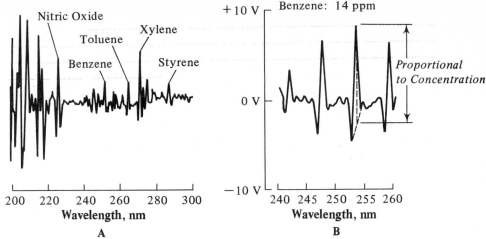

FIGURE 7.15. *Typical second-derivative absorption spectra of gaseous samples. A: Spectrum of an automobile exhaust. B: Spectrum of 14 ppm benzene. Spectra courtesy of Lear Siegler Inc., Environmental Technology Division, Englewood, Colorado.*

concentration of each species is determined directly from the peak height. Table 7.7 shows the sensitivity of the technique to various gases.

Rapid-Scan Spectrophotometers

Rapid-scanning spectroscopy (RSS) is a method in which a selected portion of the ultraviolet, visible, or near-infrared spectrum is scanned on a time scale ranging from several sec to a few μsec. The applications of this technique to systems in which short-lived transient species exist or large reaction rates are encountered are numerous [37]. Examples include studies of enzyme-substrate complexes [38], mixed complexes in ligand exchange reactions [39], and flash photolysis [40] or electrochemical reactions [41].

The instrumentation for rapid-scanning spectroscopy is divided into two groups: dispersion or multiplex. The more common is the *dispersion* method in which the light emerging from the sample is dispersed by a prism or grating into narrow bands of wavelength which are monitored independently. *Multiplex* methods use mathematical techniques, Fourier or Hadamard transforms, to resolve the spectral bands. Dispersion methods are the faster of the two groups, but have lower signal-to-noise ratios. Multiplex methods have their best application in the infrared region.

Several detectors are used in RSS. At present the one that most closely approaches the ideal is the Vidicon camera tube, Figure 7.16. This detector consists of an array of photodiodes spaced about 15 μm apart. The diodes are biased in sequence by an electron beam that repetitively scans the array in the Vidicon tube. Once the

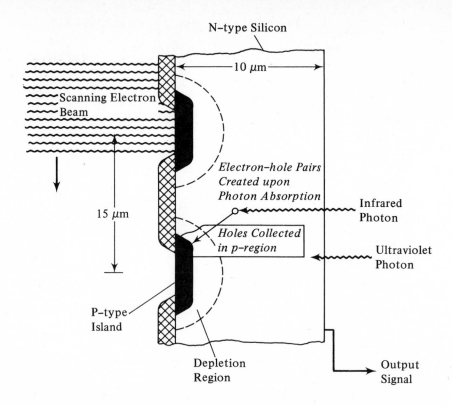

N–type Silicon

10 μm

Scanning Electron Beam

15 μm

Electron–hole Pairs Created upon Photon Absorption

Infrared Photon

Holes Collected in p–region

Ultraviolet Photon

P–type Island

Depletion Region

Output Signal

FIGURE 7.16. *Schematic diagram of a silicon Vidicon camera tube. An array of photosensitive diodes are grown on a silicon wafer about 15 μm apart. From P. Burke,* Research/Development, *24(4), 24 (1973), by permission of the publisher. Copyright © 1973 by Technical Publishing Company.*

diodes are biased they are nonconducting and no signal is recovered from the array. The diodes are discharged by photon-generated electron-hole pairs or by leakage. Once discharged, the diodes are conducting, and current flows through the diode. This current is the Vidicon signal and is directly proportional to the number of photons hitting the array. Other high-speed detectors are being refined. Two that show promise are the electrooptic type, which have the fastest scan times, 5 μsec, and the charged coupled devices (CCD) which give the best resolution.

Figure 7.17 shows time-resolved spectra of the reaction of $CuCyDTA^{2-}$ (copper cyclohexanediaminetetraacetate) with ethylenediamine (en). This reaction involves a mixed complex [39] as represented in the following equations:

$$Cu(CyDTA)^{2-} + en \longrightarrow Cu(CyDTA)en^{2-} \qquad (7.30)$$

$$Cu(CyDTA)en^{2-} + en \longrightarrow Cuen_2^{2+} + CyDTA^{4-} \qquad (7.31)$$

This example shows the value of RSS for the study of intermediates in relatively slow reactions. Faster reactions may be studied by using stopped-flow techniques.

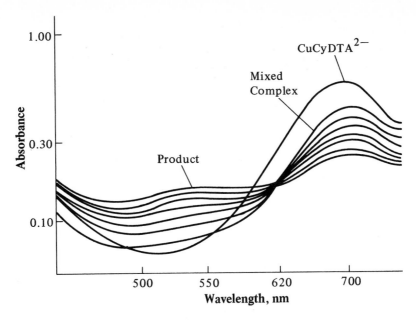

FIGURE 7.17. *Time-resolved spectra of the reaction of CuCyDTA with ethylenediamine. The scan time for one spectrum was 20 msec; spectra were taken every 2 sec. (CyDTA = cyclohexanediaminetetraacetate). Reprinted with permission from R. E. Santini, M. J. Milano, and H. L. Pardue,* Anal. Chem., **45**, 915A (1973), *by permission of the authors and publisher. Copyright © 1973 by the American Chemical Society.*

Tuned Lasers in Spectrophotometry

Laser light sources have both a high degree of monochromaticity and very high intensity. For molecular absorption measurements, it is desirable to be able to scan the spectrum, and an ideal source for such absorption measurements would be a tunable laser, one whose wavelength could be varied continuously over the spectral range of interest.

A digital scanning, tunable, dye laser has been constructed for use in the 358–641 nm range [42]. The range can be extended to both longer and shorter wavelengths by selecting other dyes, and the tunable range of laser radiation now available is from about 265 to 800 nm. Spectrophotometers using laser radiation as the source routinely exhibit resolution of about 1 nm.

The tuning action of the laser is accomplished by exciting various organic dyes with a pulsed nitrogen laser. The dyes presently available are only tunable over a 60–70 nm range (essentially, the width of their absorption bands), and thus one must use several dyes to cover a wide wavelength range. The major limitation at present is the 15% deviation in quantitative studies, owing mainly to instabilities in the laser. A further limitation is that the calibration of a particular laser is dependent upon operating conditions.

Reflectance Spectrometers

In reflectance spectroscopy, one measures the amount of radiant energy reflected from a sample surface. These data are generally reported as percent reflectance

$$\%R = I/I_0 \times 100 \qquad (7.32)$$

where I = the intensity of reflected radiation

I_0 = the intensity of radiation reflected from some "standard" reflecting surface.

For a discussion of reflectance spectroscopy, two types of reflectance must be defined, specular and diffuse. *Specular reflectance* is simply mirrorlike reflectance from a surface and is sometimes called regular reflectance; it has a well-defined reflectance angle. *Diffuse reflectance* is defined as reflected radiant energy that has been partially absorbed and partially scattered by a surface with no defined angle of reflectance. The diffuse reflectance technique is widely used today for industrial applications involving textiles, plastics, paints, dyestuffs, inks, paper, food, and building materials. In the area of basic research, diffuse reflectance spectroscopy has been used in studies of solid-solid reactions, of species absorbed on metal surfaces, of radiation transfer, and of slightly soluble species.

A common design feature of all commercial diffuse-reflectance instruments is the integrating sphere, which permits the collection of reflected light. Many of the

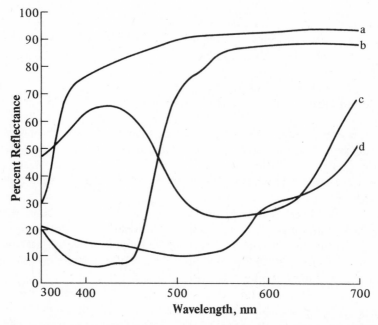

FIGURE 7.18. *Diffuse reflectance spectra of colored papers: (a) off-white, (b) yellow, (c) purple, and (d) maroon. The reference material was $MgCO_3$. From T. Surles, J. O. Erickson, and D. Priesner,* Amer. Lab., 7(3), 55 (1975), *by permission of International Scientific Communications, Inc., copyright holder.*

commercial ultraviolet-visible spectrophotometers offer this mode of operation as an accessory. The integrating sphere is usually coated with barium sulfate, which is a highly diffuse-reflecting material and serves to "homogenize" the energy being reflected from the sample surface. The intensity of reflected light at any given point in the sphere should be independent of spatial distribution and therefore directly proportional to the diffuse reflectance of the sample. A design feature of some instruments, for example, the Cary 1711, allows for exclusion of specular reflectance or, alternatively, inclusion of both types of reflectance to give total reflectance.

An example of an industrial application of reflectance is presented in Figure 7.18. This figure shows spectra taken from various colored papers. In the paper industry, diffuse reflectance is often used to monitor color, whiteness, brightness, and gloss of papers. The degree of whiteness is an important parameter that requires a system capable of detecting small variations in reflectance. As little as 0.05% R in the paper's reflectance has a perceptible effect on the whiteness observed by the human eye.

In the area of basic research, the surface properties of plastics are of continuing interest. Figure 7.19 shows the total reflectance of a clear piece of plastic on an expanded scale. An interference pattern is observed (the ripples on the curve) and the thickness of the surface film can be calculated from these data.

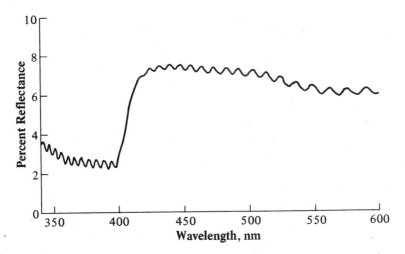

FIGURE 7.19. *A total reflectance spectrum of clear plastic. The reference material is MgCO₃. From T. Surles, J. O. Erickson, and D. Priesner, Amer. Lab., 7(3), 55 (1975), by permission of International Scientific Communications, Inc., copyright holder.*

Accessories

Matched Absorption Cells. For routine investigations in the ultraviolet and visible regions, absorption cells of silica or glass are commercially available. Commercial products offered are (1) quartz cells usable in the ultraviolet, visible, and near-infrared range between 220 and 2400 nm; and (2) fused-silica cells with extremely high ultraviolet transmission in the region from 160 nm to 2400 nm. Cells used in quantitative ultraviolet work must be matched with respect to cell width and transmission properties. Silica cells must also be fluorescence-free if accurate quantitative data are needed.

Volumetric Absorption Cells. Often the amount of sample available for trace analysis is rather limited; also, it is often desirable to make the final volume as small as possible, so that absorbance is maximized. This may be accomplished by calibrating an absorption cell to a definite volume by putting a mark on the side and using it as a "volumetric flask." Color development may be carried out in the cell, in order to keep the final volume at a minimum. If pH adjustment is required, a glass microelectrode may be used. For an ordinary 1-cm cell, volumes of about 3 ml may be used.

Long-Path and Multiple-Path Absorption Cells. For sensitive trace analysis, reactions catalyzed by the trace component are often used (see Chap. 18). One thus can resort to rate measurements for quantitative analysis of trace materials or materials that have low molar absorptivities. Another solution to this problem is to use long path length cells. According to the Beer-Lambert law, absorbance is proportional to the length of the light path. Thus, absorbance cells with long path length—5–10 cm— are commercially available for measuring solutions of low concentration or weakly absorbing species. Another approach to this problem is to use, instead of a long cell, a small cell through which the light beam may be passed many times. This should produce the same effect as cells of longer path length. Two simple designs are shown in Figure 7.20. Example A shows a cell to which two mirrors with good reflection characteristics have been attached (or deposited); the radiation beam is adjusted at an angle that will bounce it out to the detector after several passes through the sample. The number of passes is controlled by the incident angle of the light beam. If a light beam perpendicular to the wall is desired, the more complicated design shown in Figure 7.20B may be used. These designs offer increased absorption without the increased cell dimensions needed for single-pass experiments.

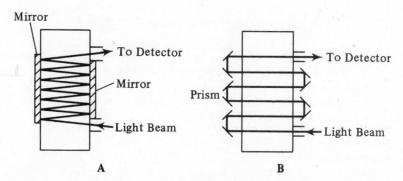

FIGURE 7.20. *Multiple-path absorption cells. From K. L. Cheng,* "*Absorptiometry,*" *in J. D. Winefordner, ed.,* Spectrochemical Methods of Analysis, *New York: Wiley-Interscience, 1971, chap. 6, by permission of the editor and John Wiley and Sons.*

Curve Resolvers. Many diverse analytical techniques, such as chromatography, electrophoresis, and spectroscopy give rise to graphs consisting of unresolved (overlapping) peaks or distribution functions. The overlap makes it necessary to reduce the experimental curve into its component parts before complete interpretation is possible. One commercial curve-resolver, for example, permits one to synthesize complex overlapped curves that are sums of up to 50 component peaks. Each of its function-generator channels yields a peak shape corresponding to Gaussian, Lorentzian, exponential, or other distributions. The parameters of width, height, and horizontal position of each peak may be varied independently until the resulting summation curve exactly matches the experimental curve. Each peak can then be presented separately on an oscilloscope or an x–y plotter for readout. The instrument also integrates the peak areas with about 15% accuracy.

7.7 OTHER DEVELOPMENTS IN SPECTROPHOTOMETRY

Charge-Transfer Spectra

The classical molecular-orbital picture of antibonding orbitals gives rise to the term *charge-transfer spectra* for transitions which take an electron from a bonding orbital to an antibonding orbital. These transitions can also be called $\sigma \rightarrow \sigma$ and $\pi \rightarrow \pi$ (or $\sigma \rightarrow \sigma^*$ and $\pi \rightarrow \pi^*$) if individual electrons and orbitals are the focus of interest, rather than the energy state of the entire molecule.

Many systems exhibit spectra generally considered to be charge-transfer spectra. Absorptions of this type are characterized by high intensity (large ε_{max}), and are fully allowed transitions. Charge-transfer transitions involve an intramolecular or an interionic redistribution of charge whereby an electron or a fraction of an electron is transferred from one ion or molecule to another ion or molecule in the same species. A complex, DA, is formed between a donor species, D, and an acceptor species, A. This type of complex can exist in two energy states, the difference in energy between these two states being equal to the energy of a quantum at the maximum of the electronic absorption band.

One of the earliest examples classified as a charge transfer is in the spectra of alkali halides [43, 44]. Frequently, a definite (and sometimes pronounced) color change is produced on mixing two compounds which would not be expected to react chemically. For example, aromatic nitro compounds mixed with aromatic hydrocarbons yield intense colors, and, in addition, stable complexes that can be isolated. In solution, however, the complexes are usually considerably dissociated. The electronic-absorption maxima of these complexes are often shifted some hundreds of nanometers to the long-wavelength side of the nearest absorption band of either component. Absorptions of this type usually result in very broad bands that lack fine structure. Charge-transfer complexes are normally formed between one member with a low ionization potential and a partner with a high electron affinity. Sensitive methods of determining amino acids with chloranil base from the charge-transfer reactions have been reported.

Charge-transfer complex formation is not limited to organic species. Mixing I_2 with benzene, naphthalene, or diphenyl produces complexes with electric dipole moments of 1.8, 2.6, and 2.9 debyes, respectively. This observation demonstrates that a definite transfer of electric charge must be taking place upon complex formation, because neither I_2 nor the aromatic hydrocarbon alone has a dipole moment. Spectrophotometric methods have established charge-transfer complex formation between various aromatic compounds and the halogens.

Precision Spectrophotometry

Precision spectrophotometry (differential spectrophotometry) is a technique that involves comparing an unknown solution with a reference. The reference scale is set at zero using a solution of a highly colored (radiation-adsorbing) species in place of a reagent blank. Concentrations of the unknown higher than the reference are then measured against this zero in the usual way.

Reilley and Crawford [45] described a precision spectrophotometric method that involves the use of two standard solutions to set the 0% and 100% T readings of the photometer. By this means, the full scale can be used for a concentration range much narrower than usual, and precision is thus increased. This method generally requires two standard solutions and several other standard solutions of intermediate concentration to construct a calibration curve, since the measured absorbance is often not a linear function of concentration (deviation from Beer's law at higher concentrations).

A method described by Ramaley and Enke [46] replaces the two-standard and calibration-curve procedure with one standard and isomation. This method involves a titration in which the absorbance of the unknown determines the endpoint. A known amount of solvent is placed in an absorption cell. A standard solution of the sample substance is then added to the cell until the absorbance, and hence the concentration, is identical to that of the unknown solution. To obtain the maximum accuracy, the cell lengths are calibrated as follows: at the endpoint

$$\frac{c_u}{c_s} = \frac{b_s}{b_u} \qquad (7.33)$$

where
c_s = the concentration of the standard
c_u = the concentration of the sample
b_s = the standard cell length
b_u = the sample cell length

The ratio of the cell lengths may be obtained by using standard solution in both cells and adjusting their concentration until the absorbance is the same for both. The ratio is calculated from Equation 7.33. With knowledge of the cell-length ratio and the concentration of the standard solution, the unknown concentration may be readily determined. With this method, species with molar absorptivity of 10^4 may be determined in the 10^{-6} M concentration range with ± 2 ppt accuracy.

Photon Counting in Spectrophotometry

Light is a source of discrete photons. When light is measured with a detector such as a photomultiplier, the photons are converted to current pulses which may not be completely resolved in time from each other. Usually these pulses are smoothed to a continuous or continuously varying signal and recorded by a readout device such as a meter. However, the number of photons per unit time reaching the detector can be decreased to a point where the individual current pulses from the photo-multiplier tube become resolvable. This can be done by decreasing the light intensity, by isolating a particular wavelength region with a monochromator, and by stopping down the optical aperture of the light beam. If the rate of photoelectron ejection and the frequency response of the measurement system are such that individual current pulses can be resolved, then the number of pulses per unit time can be counted. Because the count rate is a measure of the rate at which photons are striking the photocathode, the measurement technique is appropriately called *photon counting*. In both single- and double-beam instruments, a number proportional to the radiant power of the sample beam is obtained by counting the photoelectric pulses of the sample beam during a precisely controlled time interval [47].

Recently, photon counting has become an important technique in spectro-photometric methods where the radiation is so low in intensity that it is difficult to obtain measurements by conventional means. The ability to deal with low radiation levels with a satisfactory signal-to-noise ratio is of course one of the important factors in the photon-counting method. Improvements in precision, resolution, signal-to-noise ratio, and readout are obtainable by photon counting, and this method should be applicable to all spectrophotometric procedures (absorption, emission, reflection, fluorescence, and light scattering) in which a photomultiplier is used.

SELECTED BIBLIOGRAPHY

BAUMAN, R. P. *Absorption Spectroscopy.* New York: Wiley, 1962.

BOLTZ, D. F., and SCHENK, G. H. "Visible and Ultraviolet Spectroscopy." In L. Meites, ed., *Handbook of Analytical Chemistry.* New York: McGraw-Hill, 1963.

DODD, R. E. *Chemical Spectroscopy.* Amsterdam: Elsevier, 1962.

DONHROW, M. *Instrumental Methods in Analytical Chemistry: Their Principles and Practices*, vol. II, *Optical Methods.* New York: Pitman, 1967.

KOLTHOFF, I. M., and ELVING, P. J., eds. *Treatise on Analytical Chemistry*, part I, vol. 5. New York: Interscience, 1964.

WALKER, S., and STRAW, H. *Spectroscopy*, vol. II. London: Chapman and Hall, 1967.

REFERENCES

1. H. K. HUGHES, *Anal. Chem.*, 24, 1349 (1952); 40, 2271 (1968).

2. H. H. JAFFE and M. ORCHIN, *Theory and Applications of Ultraviolet Spectroscopy*, New York: Wiley, 1962.

3. J. R. DYER, *Applications of Absorption Spectroscopy of Organic Compounds*, Englewood Cliffs, N.J.: Prentice-Hall, 1965.

4. R. M. SILVERSTEIN and G. C. BASSLER, *Spectrometric Identification of Organic Compounds*, 2nd ed., New York: Wiley, 1967.

5. E. A. BRAUDE, *Determination of Organic Structures by Physical Methods*, New York: Academic Press, 1955.

6. C. N. R. RAO, *Ultraviolet and Visible Spectroscopy*, 2nd ed., London: Plenum, 1967.

7. S. F. Mason, *Quart. Rev.* (London), *287* (1961).

8. L. Doub and J. M. Vanderbelt, *J. Amer. Chem. Soc.*, *69*, 2714 (1947); *71*, 2414 (1949).

9. J. R. Platt, *J. Chem. Phys.*, *19*, 263 (1951).

10. A. E. Gillam and E. S. Stern, *An Introduction to Electronic Absorption Spectroscopy in Organic Chemistry*, London: Edward Arnold, 1954.

11. K. L. Cheng, *Anal. Chim. Acta*, *28*, 41 (1963).

12. K. L. Cheng, *Anal. Chem.*, *30*, 1035 (1958).

13. R. Jakubiec and D. F. Boltz, *Anal. Chem.*, *41*, 78 (1969).

14. W. C. Vosburgh and G. R. Cooper, *J. Amer. Chem. Soc.*, *53*, 435 (1941).

15. P. Job, *Anal. Chim.*, *9*, 113 (1928).

16. J. Bjerrum, *Kgl. Danske Videnskab. Selskab, Mat-Fys. Medd.*, *21*(4) (1944); H. Olerup, Thesis, "Jarn Kloridernas Komplexitet," Lund, 1944.

17. F. J. C. Rossotti and H. Rossotti, *The Determination of Stability Constants*, McGraw-Hill, New York, 1961; S. D. Christian, *J. Chem. Educ.*, *45*, 713 (1968).

18. L. A. Flexser, L. P. Hammet, and A. Dingwall, *J. Amer. Chem. Soc.*, *57*, 2103 (1935).

19. H. C. Brown and D. H. McDaniel, *J. Amer. Chem. Soc.*, *77*, 3752 (1955).

20. F. T. King and R. C. Hirt, *Appl. Spectrosc.*, *7*, 164 (1953).

21. C. Rehm, J. I. Bodin, K. A. Connors, and T. Higuchi, *Anal. Chem.*, *31*, 483 (1959).

22. W. R. Brode, *J. Amer. Chem. Soc.*, *46*, 581 (1924).

23. M. Kambe, E. Shindo, and M. Marito, *Japan Analyst*, *16*, 1017 (1967).

24. B. N. Mattoo, *Trans. Faraday Soc.*, *52*, 1462 (1956).

25. K. L. Cheng, *Talanta*, *2*, 266 (1959); *5*, 254 (1960).

26. M. Otomo, *Bull. Chem. Soc. Jap.*, *36*, 146 (1962).

27. B. Ricca and G. Fraone, *Gazz. Chim. Ital.*, *79*, 340 (1949); *Chem. Abstr.*, *43*, 8935b (1949).

28. R. T. Foley and R. C. Anderson, *J. Amer. Chem. Soc.*, *72*, 5609 (1950).

29. R. W. Ramette, *J. Chem. Educ.*, *44*, 647 (1967).

30. K. G. Cunningham, W. Dawson, and F. S. Spring, *J. Chem. Soc.*, 2305 (1954).

31. V. C. Barry, J. E. McCormick, and P. W. D. Mitchell, *J. Chem. Soc.*, 222 (1955).

32. E. A. Braude and E. R. H. Jones, *J. Chem. Soc.*, 498 (1945).

33. C. Djerassi and E. Ryan, *J. Amer. Chem. Soc.*, *71*, 1000 (1949).

34. J. P. Riley, *J. Chem. Soc.*, 2108 (1952).

35. A. Griese and C. French, *Appl. Spectrosc.*, *9*, 78 (1955).

36. R. N. Hager, Jr., *Anal. Chem.*, *45*, 1131A (1973).

37. R. E. Santini, M. J. Milano, and H. L. Pardue, *Anal. Chem.*, *45*, 915A (1973).

38. V. Massey and G. H. Gibson, *Fed. Proc.*, *23*, 18 (1964).

39. J. D. Carr, R. A. Libby, and D. W. Margerum, *Inorg. Chem.*, *6*, 1083 (1967).

40. J. I. H. Patterson and S. P. Perone, *Anal. Chem.*, *44*, 1978 (1972).

41. J. W. Strojek, G. A. Gruver, and T. Kuwana, *Anal. Chem.*, *41*, 481 (1969).

42. D. Harrington and H. V. Malmstadt, *Amer. Lab.*, *6*(3), 33 (1974).

43. J. Frank, H. Kuhn, and G. Rollefson, *Z. Physik*, *43*, 155 (1927).

44. R. Hilsch and R. W. Pohl, *Z. Physik*, *64*, 606 (1930).

45. C. N. Reilley and C. M. Crawford, *Anal. Chem.*, *27*, 716 (1955).

46. L. Ramaley and C. G. Enke, *Anal. Chem.*, *37*, 1073 (1965).

47. E. H. Piepmeier, D. E. Braun, and R. R. Rhodes, *Anal. Chem.*, *40*, 1667 (1968); M. L. Franklin, G. Horlick, and H. V. Malmstadt, *Anal. Chem.*, *41*, 2 (1969); K. C. Ash and E. H. Piepmeier, *Anal. Chem.*, *43*, 26 (1971).

PROBLEMS

1. A sodium-vapor lamp emits radiation with a wavelength of 5889.97 Å. Express the wavelength in nm and calculate its frequency. The speed of light in vacuum is 2.99776×10^{10} cm/sec.

2. The energy of the electronic transition for $D\text{-}A \xrightarrow{h\nu} D^+ + A^-$ may be estimated by the equation $h\nu = I_D$ (ionization potential of donor) $- E_A$ (electron affinity of acceptor) $- C$ (mutual electrostatic energy of D^+ and A^-). Gaseous NaCl will absorb in the UV due to a charge-transfer transition. Estimate the energy and wavelength at which absorption may be expected, $I_{Na^+} = 5.14$ eV, $E_{Cl^-} = 3.82$ eV, $C \approx 6.2$ eV. 252 nm

3. The Pd 4,4'-bis(dimethylamino)thiobenzophenone complexation has been reported to be one of the most sensitive color reactions, with a molar absorptivity of 2.12×10^5. Assuming that the minimum measurable absorbance is 0.001 and that a cell with a 10-cm light path is available, what is the lowest possible molar concentration of Pd that can be determined spectrophotometrically? If the volume of the cell is 10 ml, what is the smallest quantity of Pd that can be determined?

4. In 25.0 ml of $0.8\ N$ $HClO_4$, 5.0×10^{-7} mole of Zr forms a 1:1 complex with xylenol orange (XO) giving an absorbance of 0.484 at 535 nm in a 1.00-cm cell. Calculate the molar absorptivity of the Zr-XO complex.

5. A mixture of *ortho* and *para* nitroanilines is analyzed by ultraviolet spectrophotometry, measuring absorbances of the mixture at two different wavelengths. Using the data given below, calculate the molar concentrations of the *ortho* and *para* isomers.

6. A conjugate base of a weak acid, HA, has an absorption maximum at 520 nm. The following data were obtained by measuring the absorbances of solutions of the weak acid having the same concentration but different pH buffers.

pH	Absorbance
2.0	0.00
4.0	0.00
5.0	0.030
6.0	0.180
7.0	0.475
8.0	0.565
9.0	0.590
10.0	0.590
11.0	0.590
12.0	0.590

What is the approximate pK_a of this weak acid?

7. A colored substance X has an absorption maximum at 400 nm. A solution containing 2.00 mg X per liter had an absorbance of 0.840 using a 2.00-cm cell. The formula weight of X is 150. (a) Calculate the absorptivity of X at 400 nm. (b) Calculate the molar absorptivity of X at 400 nm. (c) How many mg of X is contained in 25.0 ml of a solution giving an absorbance of 0.250 at 400 nm when measured with a 1.00-cm cell? (d) How many ppm of X are in the solution in (c)?

8. A 0.200 g sample containing Cu is dissolved, and a diethyldithiocarbamate colored complex is formed in the presence of EDTA. The solution is then diluted to 50.0 ml and the absorbance measured as 0.260. A 0.500 g sample containing 0.240% Cu is treated in the same manner, and the result-

	Absorbance		Molar absorptivity	
	285 nm	347 nm	285 nm	347 nm
o-nitroaniline	——	——	5260	1280
p-nitroaniline	——	——	1400	9200
mixture	0.520	0.458	——	——

ing solution has an absorbance of 0.600. Calculate the percentage of Cu in the sample.

9. A 0.5000 g steel sample is dissolved and the Mn in the sample is oxidized to permanganate by periodate using Ag^+ as a catalyst. After the sample is diluted to 250.0 ml, the absorbance is 0.393 at 540 nm in a 1.00-cm cell. Calculate the percentage of Mn in the steel. The molar absorptivity for permanganate at 540 nm is 2025.

10. ERIO X forms a 1:1 colored complex with Mg^{2+} at pH 10.00. The ERIO X solution was titrated with Mg^{2+} photometrically. This titration showed that, at the equivalence point, [Mg-ERIO X] = [ERIO X] = 5×10^{-7} M. Calculate the formation constant of the Mg complex.

11. A solution containing 0.0150 g of pure weak acid, HA, was titrated with 0.0500 N NaOH. Only the anion, A^-, in the solution absorbed at 350 nm. The following titration data were obtained at 350 nm. What is the molecular weight of this acid?

NaOH, ml	Absorbance
0.0	0.000
0.50	0.185
1.00	0.370
1.50	0.555
2.00	0.680
2.50	0.750
3.00	0.800
3.50	0.842
4.00	0.870
4.50	0.890
5.00	0.900
5.50	0.910
6.00	0.910
7.00	0.910

12. Plot two Job's curves for the Bi-xylenol orange (XO) complex from the following data obtained in 0.1 N H_2SO_4 at 545 nm. (a) What is the molar ratio of Bi to XO? (b) Estimate the formation constant of the Bi-XO complex. I. [Bi] + [XO] = 2.4×10^{-5} M. II: [Bi] + [XO] = 3.2×10^{-5} M.

	Corrected absorbance	
$[Bi^{3+}]/([Bi^{3+}] + [XO])$	I	II
0.0	0.00	0.00
0.1	0.049	0.070
0.2	0.095	0.145
0.3	0.145	0.208
0.4	0.180	0.260
0.5	0.198	0.278
0.6	0.190	0.270
0.7	0.160	0.226
0.8	0.108	0.158
0.9	0.058	0.075
1.0	0.00	0.00

13. The following absorbance values were obtained in preparing a spectrophotometric calibration curve: "blank", 0.03 A; 1.00 mM standard, 0.11 A; 2.00 mM standard, 0.19 A; 4.00 mM standard, 0.35 A. Plot the calibration curve. What is the most probable reason for the noncompliance of the data to Beer's law?

14. Literature values for the molar absorptivities of nucleotides are often used to determine the concentration of nucleotide solutions, since even highly purified nucleotides may contain variable waters of hydration or a variable salt content. A sample of the disodium salt of cytidine 5'-monophosphate (5'-CMP, $C_9H_{12}N_3O_8PNa_2$) was weighed out (0.0814 g), dissolved, and diluted to 25.00 ml in a volumetric flask with distilled water. 5'-CMP has $\varepsilon = 13.0 \times 10^3$ at $\lambda_{max} = 280$ nm in 0.01 M HCl. An aliquot of the CMP stock solution (0.100 ml) was diluted to 10.0 ml with 0.01 M HCl. The absorbance of this solution was 0.831 in a calibrated cuvette of 0.992-cm path length. (a) Calculate the "nominal" or expected concentration of 5'-CMP, assuming it to be a pure anhydrous salt. (b) Calculate the concentration based on spectrophotometric data. (c) Assuming the difference in concentration is due only to absorbed and bound water molecules, what is the average number of water molecules per 5'-CMP molecule?

8

Infrared and Raman Spectroscopy

Eugene B. Bradley

Infrared and Raman spectroscopy are important analytical tools used to investigate a wide variety of molecules in the solid, liquid, and gas states, and yielding complementary information about molecular structure and molecular bonds. Both methods supply information about resonances caused by vibration, vibration-rotation, or rotation of the molecular framework, but because the interaction mechanism between radiation and the molecule differs in the two types, the quantum-mechanical selection rules differ as well. Therefore, not all of the molecular motions recorded by one type of spectroscopy will necessarily be recorded by the other. The geometrical configuration of the molecule and the distribution of electrical charge within that configuration determine which molecular motions may appear in each type of spectrum.

8.1 THEORY AND BACKGROUND

Infrared spectroscopy is used to investigate quantized molecular resonances that absorb electromagnetic energy selectively from a broadband infrared source. Thus, it requires the spectral analysis of infrared energy transmitted through the sample. The spectral analysis is done with a prism or grating monochromator or by autocorrelation (Fourier transform) techniques. The resulting signals are amplified, detected, and recorded in some form.

A molecule will absorb infrared radiation if it vibrates in such a way that its electric dipole moment changes during vibration. The electric dipole moment $\bar{\mu}$ is a vector quantity

$$\bar{\mu} = q\bar{d} \tag{8.1}$$

where q = the electric charge

$\bar{d}$ = the directed distance of that charge from some defined origin of co-ordinates for the molecule

As a molecule vibrates, its charge distribution with respect to that origin may or may not change, depending upon the structure of the molecule. Thus not all vibrations of a particular molecular structure will necessarily absorb infrared radiation, but only those vibrations that cause the electric dipole moment to change.

Raman spectroscopy is used to investigate quantized molecular resonances also, but from a different point of view. The Raman effect is the inelastic scattering of photons by molecules. If a photon is scattered inelastically by a molecule it may gain energy and be scattered at a frequency higher than the original frequency, or it may lose energy and be scattered at a frequency lower than the original frequency. This process is shown in Figure 8.1. The exciting photon $h\nu_L$ may impinge upon a molecule in its ground vibrational state ($n = 0$) or upon a molecule in the first excited vibrational state ($n = 1$) and raise the molecule to a virtual state (sometimes called a pseudo-excited state). If the molecule loses energy and decays back to $n = 1$, a frequency $h(\nu_L - \nu_1)$ is produced if the scattering originated from $n = 0$. If the molecule loses energy and decays back to $n = 0$, a frequency $h(\nu_L + \nu_1)$ is produced if the scattering originated from $n = 1$.

For historical reasons, the shifted frequencies that appear below the exciting frequency are called Stokes frequencies, and those that appear above the exciting frequency are called anti-Stokes frequencies. Notice that the frequency displacement (the Raman shift) of either Stokes or anti-Stokes lines from the exciting line is ν_1, a frequency that is characteristic of a particular molecular mode of vibration. The Stokes lines are more intense because the population of the molecular-energy levels as a function of temperature follows a Boltzmann distribution (most molecules are in the ground vibrational level at room temperature); thus the Stokes lines are recorded with a higher signal-to-noise ratio.

Most collisions of the exciting radiation with molecules are elastic; only about one in 10^6 collisions is inelastic. The incident energy that is scattered with no change in frequency (*elastically* scattered) is called the Rayleigh line and it is much more intense than either Stokes or anti-Stokes lines.

The scattering efficiency of the molecules is proportional to the fourth power of the incident frequency, so visible light, usually from a laser, is used to excite the Raman spectrum. It is important to note that the Raman shift is *independent* of the exciting frequency over a wide range of visible wavelengths, so, for example, one obtains the same lines whether a He-Ne laser (6328 Å) or an Argon-ion laser (4880 Å) is used. Certain molecules photodissociate more easily than others, however, so the laser frequency should be chosen with care. It is a good idea to obtain a spectrum of the sample in the visible region and avoid choosing a laser frequency in a region of strong absorption. (One may use a laser frequency corresponding to a region of strong absorption if resonance Raman scattering is to be studied, but the reader is referred to advanced reading for applications and information on this subject.)

Usually one records the right-angle scattering of intense, monochromatic laser-light incident upon the sample. The vibrating molecules scatter the light at frequencies that are shifted up or down with respect to the exciting frequency, and

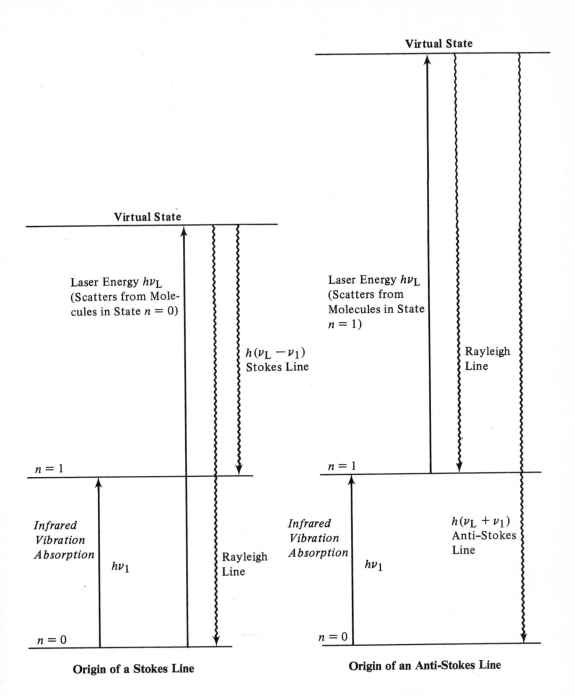

FIGURE 8.1. *Origins of Stokes and anti-Stokes Raman lines.*

these *shifts* (Raman lines) correspond to all, some, or none of the molecular resonances observed in the infrared. The correspondences are called *coincidences*. If a molecule possesses a center of symmetry (for example, C_2H_4, CO_2), then there are *no* coincidences. This case is, of course, particularly easy to spot by a comparison of the infrared and Raman spectra. For example, CO_2 exhibits two fundamental vibrational frequencies in the infrared, at 667 and 2349 cm^{-1}, and one in the Raman at 1340 cm^{-1}.

   A molecule will scatter monochromatic radiation and produce Raman lines if the molecule vibrates in such a way that its polarizability is changed during the vibration. As a molecule vibrates, its electric dipole moment $\bar{\mu}$ or its polarizability α may change, or both $\bar{\mu}$ and α may change:

$$\bar{\mu} = \alpha \bar{E} \tag{8.2}$$

where $\bar{E} =$ the electric field of the incident radiation

The polarizability α is usually a function of the molecular coordinates. The charge distribution of the molecule may be such that $\bar{\mu}$ changes with vibration and α does not change, or vice versa; this is why the quantum-mechanical selection rules differ for infrared and Raman.

   As an example, consider the symmetric stretching mode of vibration of CO_2. The symmetrical stretching motion is

$$\longleftrightarrow \quad O{=}C{=}O \quad \longleftrightarrow$$

the in-phase motion of the two oxygen atoms (in and out). With respect to C, this symmetrical motion involves motions of atoms with the same electronegativity and produces no *net* change in $\bar{\mu}$. For this reason, this mode of vibration does not absorb infrared radiation. The polarizability of a molecule, however, is almost entirely due to the displacements of electrons by the alternating electric field of an incident light beam, and analysis shows that the polarizability of CO_2 does change during this mode of vibration. Therefore this motion in CO_2 will scatter a photon of light inelastically and produce a Raman line.

   The electric-field vector of a Raman line may correspond to partial or total polarization of the electromagnetic radiation in that line, depending upon the degree of symmetry of the molecular motion(s) that spawn the line. Thus, the symmetry of a particular vibrational mode may be inferred from the polarization (or depolarization) of a Raman band.

   The polarization of the light in a Raman line is obtained experimentally by measuring a quantity called the "depolarization ratio," ρ. It is defined by a ratio of the band areas observed when the light is passed through a polarizer turned first perpendicular, then parallel to the scattered light. The expression that results is

$$\rho = \frac{3\bar{\beta}^2}{45\bar{\alpha}^2 + 4\bar{\beta}^2} = \frac{I_\perp}{I_\parallel} \tag{8.3}$$

where $\bar{\alpha} =$ the isotropic part of the polarizability
$\bar{\beta} =$ the anisotropic part of the polarizability

The quantity ρ has no infrared counterpart, and it is usually reported along with the Raman shift. If $\rho = 0$ ($\bar{\beta} = 0$), then polarized radiation is scattered by a totally symmetric mode of vibration. If $\rho = 3/4$ ($\bar{\alpha} = 0$), then depolarized radiation is scattered by the vibration. When the value of the depolarization ratio is less than 0.2, the $\bar{\alpha}$ term is dominating, but if ρ is greater than 0.2, the $\bar{\beta}$ term is becoming more important and there is some degree of asymmetry in the vibrational mode.

The depolarization ratio is measured by first placing a polarization analyzer between the sample and the entrance slit of the monochromator; ρ is obtained by finding the ratio of the band peak-heights when the polarizer is rotated perpendicular ($\perp$) and parallel ($\parallel$) to the scattered radiation coming from the sample. The Raman spectrometer should be standardized first by measuring the polarized 459 cm^{-1} bands of carbon tetrachloride ($\rho = 0.005 \pm 0.002$) and the depolarized band of carbon tetrachloride at 218 cm^{-1} ($\rho = 0.75$).

Depolarization ratios are not obtainable directly on finely ground crystals or powders because refractions and reflections scramble the polarization, but one may measure depolarization ratios of polymer films, liquids, and gases.

The analytical spectroscopist is usually more concerned with "peak intensity" measurement, i.e., I and I_0, whereas the theoretical spectroscopist is often concerned with band areas and band-shape parameters (bandwidth, band contour, etc.). However, before attempting any serious work with areas or shapes, the reader is advised to consult a paper on this subject by Seshadri and Jones [1].

Spectral Region

Chemists work most often in the medium infrared region (2.5–50 μm or 4000–200 cm^{-1}) where most molecular vibrations (in liquids and gases) and vibration-rotations (in gases) occur; purely rotational resonances usually occur in the far infrared between 50 and 1000 μm (or 200–10 cm^{-1}). There are molecules, however, whose motions give rise to (a) vibration or vibration-rotation spectra at wavelengths longer than 50 μm or (b) pure rotation spectra at wavelengths less than 50 μm.

The state of the sample and the environment imposed upon it are clues to the type(s) of spectral frequencies one will observe. Table 8.1 is not complete, but it is representative of what one observes for each of the three states of matter. In

TABLE 8.1. *States of a Sample and Types of Spectra that may Occur for Each*

State of Sample	Types of Spectra
Gas	Fundamental modes of vibration ν_1, ν_2, ν_3, etc.
	Vibration-rotation
	Pure rotation
	Overtones (multiples) of fundamental (for example, 2ν, 3ν, etc.)
	Combinations of fundamentals (for example, $\nu_1 + \nu_2$, etc.)
Liquid	Fundamental modes of vibration
	Overtones
	Combination
Solid	Lattice modes
	Impurity modes
	Absorption edges (semiconductors)

TABLE 8.2. *Information Obtainable from Molecular Infrared Spectra*

1. Far Infrared, 50–1000 μm (200–10 cm^{-1})
   A. rotational constants, internuclear distances, possible geometrical arrangements of atoms
   B. rotational contributions to specific heats
   C. effects of isotopes
   D. molecular symmetry
   E. nuclear spins (from intensities)
   F. fundamental vibrational modes of heavy molecules

2. Medium Infrared, 2.5–50 μm (4000–200 cm^{-1})
   A. fundamental vibrations
   B. vibration-rotation
   C. vibrational contributions to specific heats
   D. force fields inside molecules
   E. characteristic bond frequencies
   F. force constants of potential function
   G. heats of dissociation
   H. structure
   I. effects of isotopes
   J. vibrational amplitudes

3. Near Infrared, 0.7–2.5 μm (14,285–4000 cm^{-1})
   A. fundamental vibrations of X-H (stretching vibrations)
   B. overtone or combination bands of X-H stretching

the infrared, gas spectra usually have well defined lines of absorption; these lines are rather narrow because the number density of molecules is relatively small and the pressure is usually low ($\sim$5–10 cm Hg). When a gas is cooled to its liquid state, the sharp, well defined absorption lines in the spectrum of the gas become reduced in number and broaden somewhat. This reduction and broadening occurs because the number density is much larger in the liquid and free rotation of the molecules is no longer possible (with few exceptions).

Considerable experience is required to interpret the spectra of solids and gases; usually, less is needed for those of a liquid, because most of the spectral bands are relatively strong and broad.

Listed in Table 8.2 is some of the information available from molecular spectra in each region of the infrared.

8.2 INSTRUMENTATION

As in almost all spectroscopic methods, the instrumentation for infrared or Raman spectroscopy consists of a radiation source, a monochromator or wavelength-selection device of some type, a sample holder, and a detector.

Infrared Spectrometers

Infrared spectroscopy produces a spectrum by analyzing the frequency of the radiation that passes through the sample. The frequency analysis is done by a prism or grating monochromator that sorts out the various frequencies contained in the radiation and passes them to a detector, connected to an amplifier system, for recording. Infrared spectrometers are either single-beam or double-beam. The double-beam type is a ratio recording system which, when properly used, cancels background absorption caused by atmospheric gases, particularly CO_2 and H_2O. These are recording instruments in which the ratio is taken automatically and continuously over the entire spectrum. A schematic diagram of a double-beam infrared spectrophotometer is shown in Figure 8.2.

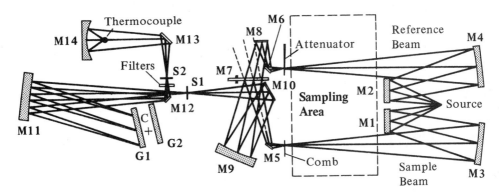

FIGURE 8.2. *A schematic diagram of a typical double-beam infrared spectrometer. The symbols* M1, M2, ... *indicate mirrors;* S1 *and* S2 *indicate slits; and* G1 *and* G2 *indicate gratings. Courtesy of the Perkin-Elmer Corporation.*

The source radiation is split into sample and reference beams that are recombined by the rotating sector mirror M7 after passing through the sampling area. The sample beam and the reference beam travel through the monochromator in alternate pulses. Each pulse is dispersed by grating G1 or G2, depending upon the spectral range desired, and focused on the detector (a thermocouple). No alternating signal is developed by the thermocouple if the intensities of the sample and reference beams are equal at the frequency emerging from the exit slit. If they differ, an alternating voltage is developed by the thermocouple. This alternating signal is amplified and its phase compared with the angular position of the rotating mirror; then it is used to move the attenuator in or out of the reference beam. The attenuator subtracts from the reference beam the same amount of energy as the sample absorbs in the sample beam. What the instrument actually records is the position of the attenuator, which is related to the absorption spectrum of the compound.

One fundamental difference between infrared and ultraviolet-visible spectrophotometers is the position of the sample with respect to the monochromator. In ultraviolet-visible spectrophotometers, the sample is placed after the monochromator to minimize the exposure of the sample to the high-energy radiation. In infrared instruments, the sample is placed before the monochromator to minimize the amount of stray radiation (emanating from the sample and the cell) reaching the detector. Stray light is a particularly serious problem in most of the infrared region, more so than in the ultraviolet-visible region. Chopping the light from the source and measuring the alternating signal from the detector helps to alleviate this problem.

Single-beam systems require a background spectrum and a spectrum of the sample plus background. The ratio of the two spectra is found by dividing the two ordinates (that is, the two intensities) at small frequency increments over the entire range scanned. A plot of these ratios against the frequencies at which each ratio was obtained is the spectrum of the sample. Almost all quantitative and qualitative analysis today is done on double-beam instruments.

Infrared Radiation Sources. In the infrared region, blackbody radiation sources are used. These sources have characteristics not unlike those of a tungsten incandescent lamp. Perhaps the most widely used infrared source is the *Nernst glower*, a sintered rod or hollow tube composed of oxides of such elements as zirconium, thorium, and yttrium. Nernst glowers have operating temperatures as high as 1500°C (attained by electrical heating) and are very intense sources. Another source, the *Globar*, is a rod of silicon carbide operated at somewhat lower temperatures (ca. 1300°C) than the Nernst glower to avoid air oxidation of the silicon carbide (which is not a problem with the metal oxides used in Nernst glowers). A third infrared source is a simple coil of *Nichrome* wire raised to incandescence by electrical heating; this source is simple and rugged, but less intense than the other two. For the near infrared, a tungsten filament lamp is often used.

A major problem in mid-infrared spectroscopy is the generally low intensity of the radiation sources at the wavelengths being used. Most of the radiation emitted by these sources is in the near-infrared and visible regions, and a small, but significant, fraction of this shorter radiation will be present as stray light, a particularly serious problem for long-wavelength measurements.

Infrared Detectors. There are two general classes of infrared detectors: (1) *photon* or *quantum detectors* which detect photons of infrared light via the photoconductive effect that occurs in certain semiconductor materials, and (2) *thermal detectors*, in which absorbed infrared radiation heats the detector and alters one of its physical properties, such as resistance. In general, quantum detectors have a much faster response and a greater sensitivity to infrared radiation than do thermal detectors; but the former can operate only over a very restricted range of wavelengths because there is a limited range of photon energies that will excite electrons in bound states to the conduction band of a semiconductor. Thermal detectors, on the other hand, are usable over a very wide wavelength range: essentially, all that is necessary is that the detector *absorb* a photon; no specific electronic transitions have to occur.

Photon detectors consist of a thin film of semiconductor material, such as lead sulfide, lead telluride, indium antimonide, or germanium doped with copper or mercury, deposited on a nonconducting glass and sealed into an evacuated envelope. Photon flux impinging on the semiconductor increases its conductivity. Lead-sulfide detectors are sensitive to radiation below about 3 μm in wavelength and have a response time of about 10 μsec. Doped germanium detectors cooled to liquid-helium temperatures are sensitive to radiation up to about 120 μm in wavelength, and have a response time of approximately 1 nsec.

There are three types of thermal detectors: the *thermocouple*, the *bolometer*, and the *Golay detector*. The thermocouple, the most widely used infrared detector, is usually composed of a small piece of blackened gold foil, welded to two fine wires made of dissimilar metals, chosen to produce a large thermoelectric emf change on heating and cooling. To minimize conductive heat loss, the entire assembly is sealed in an evacuated housing having an infrared-transmitting window. The cold junction of the thermocouple actually consists of the heavy copper wires attached to the thermocouple wires. Since the incident radiation is chopped and the AC output of the detector is amplified, only the temperature *change* of the thermocouple is important, not the absolute temperature.

A bolometer is a miniature resistance thermometer, usually using a fine platinum wire or a semiconductor thermistor as the sensing element. The resistance of platinum increases by about 0.4% per °C, while that of a typical thermistor decreases by between about 4 and 7% per °C. Two matched sensing elements are used as two arms of a Wheatstone bridge, one of which is shielded from the infrared radiation. A temperature difference between the shielded and nonshielded detectors is thus manifested as a voltage difference which can then be amplified.

The Golay or "pneumatic" detector is based on the increase in pressure of a confined inert gas with temperature. Infrared radiation is absorbed by a rigid blackened metal plate sealed to one end of a small metallic cylinder. The heat is transmitted to the gas, which expands and causes a flexible silvered diaphragm affixed to the other end of the tube to bulge outward. The distortion of the thin diaphragm can be measured either by making it part of an optical system in which a light beam reflects from it to a phototube, or by making it one plate of a dynamic parallel-plate capacitor: the distortion of the flexible diaphragm relative to a fixed plate changes the average plate separation and thus the capacitance.

Raman Spectrometers

Recall that Raman spectroscopy produces a spectrum of a sample by frequency analysis of the light *scattered* from a sample. The sample is "excited" by an intense, monochromatic light-source such as a laser, and the frequency is analyzed with a grating monochromator. Table 8.3 lists some lasers and their characteristics.

TABLE 8.3. *Characteristics of Some Lasers*

Laser	Emission Wavelength (Å)	Typical Power Level (watts)[a]
He-Ne	6328	0.08
Ruby	6943	1–10 MW[c]
Cadmium	4416	0.2
Ar-Kr	4880 (Ar)[b]	0.5
	5145 (Ar)	0.5
	5682 (Kr)	0.5
	6471 (Kr)	0.5

a. Power levels are for *continuous* power output, except for the ruby laser which is pulsed.
b. Most commonly used wavelength.
c. The ruby laser is operated in a pulsed mode, with typical peak-power levels of a few MW and pulse widths of a few nsec.

Some Raman lines are very close to the frequency of the exciting radiation (which is very intense compared to the Raman frequencies). Therefore, it is necessary for the monochromator to have high rejection of scattered light, so those Raman frequencies separated by only a few wavenumbers from the exciting frequency can be observed. A double monochromator is often used for high rejection of scattered light; the detection system often uses a highly sensitive photon-counting technique.

Transform Spectroscopy

Infrared spectra may also be obtained by two other relatively new techniques, Fourier or Hadamard transform spectrometry. The Fourier method utilizes a Michelson

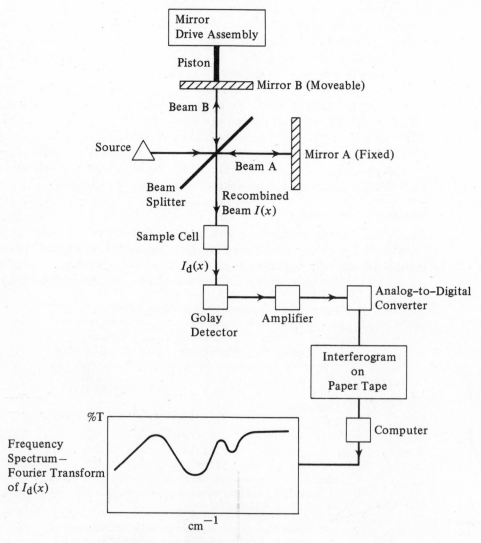

FIGURE 8.3. *An interferometer and associated electronics.*

interferometer constructed to cause interference at infrared frequencies. The interferometer and associated electronics is shown in Figure 8.3. The sample is placed in front of a detector which senses the radiation from the interferometer; that is, radiation exhibiting a variable intensity $I(x)$ as a function of the optical path difference x in the interferometer. The optical path difference is the difference in the distance the light travels in Beam A and in Beam B in Figure 8.3.

The molecules in the sample absorb at their characteristic frequencies, and hence the radiation intensity $I_a(x)$ that reaches the detector is modified by the presence of the sample. The Fourier transform of $I_a(x)$ *is* the absorption spectrum of the sample, and this transform yields percent transmission versus wavenumber (cm^{-1}). This type of spectroscopy is single-beam, so a background spectrum is required in most cases. Also it requires the use of a digital computer to calculate the Fourier transform of $I_a(x)$.

Fourier transform spectroscopy is especially useful for work in the far infrared where photon energy is low, but it may be used throughout the infrared with a typical five-fold improvement in signal-to-noise ratio. The resolution obtainable is inversely proportional to the optical path difference through which the interferometer is scanned.

Hadamard transform spectrometry achieves the performance of the Fourier method but employs the technology of the dispersive prism or grating monochromator. A Hadamard transform instrument utilizes "multiplexing"; that is, it observes all the wavelengths in a spectrum at the same time. This technique also produces a significant gain in the signal-to-noise ratio when compared to more conventional prism or grating monochromators. It is a transform technique because the multiplexing is accomplished by an optical coding so that data points are the transform of the dispersed optical spectrum.

8.3 SAMPLING SYSTEMS

Infrared and Raman techniques may be used to examine solid, liquid, or gas samples, and the samples may or may not be in some imposed environment such as low or high temperatures, applied electric field, and so forth. The state of the sample and its environment is a clue to what type of spectrum to expect.

Infrared Cells

Infrared cells are constructed to transmit infrared energy, so the windows of a cell have to pass the desired range of infrared wavelengths. A bar graph of the spectral transmission of various window materials is shown in Figure 8.4. Most analytical work is done in the range of 4000–400 cm^{-1}, but some work may require spectra extending to 200 cm^{-1}. Commonly used window materials are NaCl, KBr, CsBr, and KRS-5 (a TlBr-TlI mixture). The first three crystals are hygroscopic and must be kept in a desiccator when not in use; they tend to cloud with age and with use and must be polished periodically. The choice of a window material is dictated by cost, the spectral range desired, and the chemical reactivity of the window with the sample. If water solutions are to be analyzed, then AgCl is a good choice for a cell window.

Window thickness is not so critical except in unusual experiments with, for instance, high gas pressures.

Solids are sometimes difficult to sample because some of the incident infrared energy must be transmitted for spectral analysis through a comparatively opaque material. Only a small amount of sample is needed. The sample may be dispersed

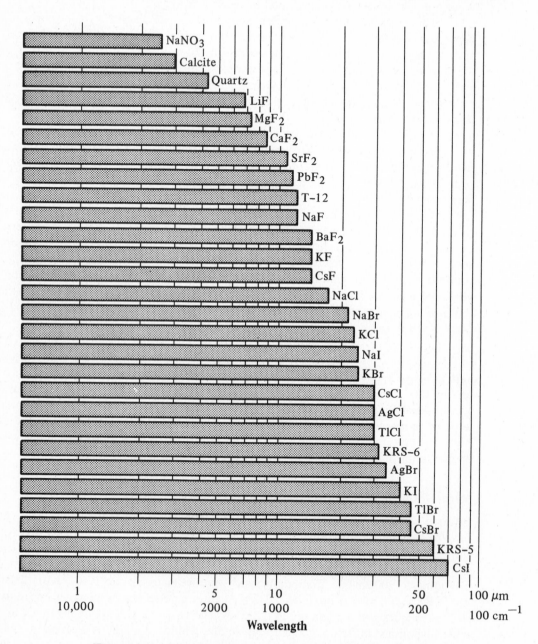

FIGURE 8.4. *Infrared transmission of optical materials. Courtesy of the Harshaw Chemical Company.*

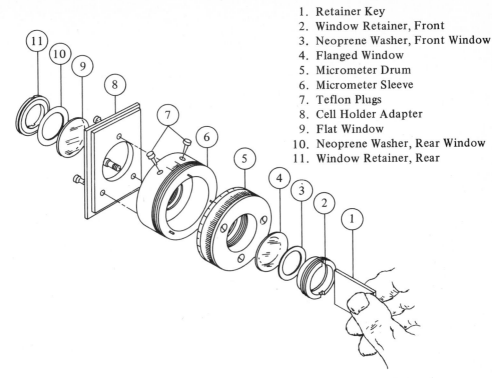

1. Retainer Key
2. Window Retainer, Front
3. Neoprene Washer, Front Window
4. Flanged Window
5. Micrometer Drum
6. Micrometer Sleeve
7. Teflon Plugs
8. Cell Holder Adapter
9. Flat Window
10. Neoprene Washer, Rear Window
11. Window Retainer, Rear

FIGURE 8.5.   *Variable path-length infrared cell.   Courtesy of Beckman Instruments, Inc.*

in a liquid matrix such as Nujol mineral oil (a "mull"), or in a pellet of KBr or CsBr. The pellet is made by first grinding the sample in a "Wiggle-Bug" or with a mortar and pestle; then the powdered sample (typically 10 mg or so) is thoroughly mixed with about 200 mg of the matrix and the combination pressed into a transparent disc in an evacuable die.

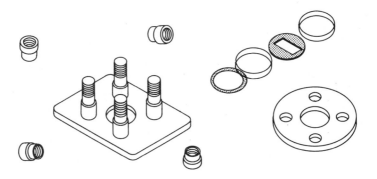

FIGURE 8.6.   *A demountable-type infrared cell for liquids.   Adapted from N. B. Colthup, L. H. Daly, and S. E. Wiberly,* Introduction to Infrared and Raman Spectroscopy, *New York: Academic Press, 1964, by permission of the senior author and the publisher.*

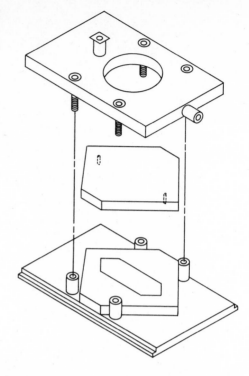

FIGURE 8.7. *A fixed path-length or sealed cell for liquids. Adapted from N. B. Colthup, L. H. Daly, and S. E. Wiberly,* Introduction to Infrared and Raman Spectroscopy, *New York: Academic Press, 1964, by permission of the senior author and the publisher.*

A variety of cells is available for the liquid samples. A liquid cell may be as simple as a drop of liquid sandwiched between two windows to form a capillary film, or as refined as a variable-path cell costing several hundred dollars (see Fig. 8.5). The optical path length required for a liquid is usually less than 1 mm, and spacers of different thicknesses are used to establish a suitable path, often by trial and error. Liquid cells whose path length may be altered are called "demountable" or "sandwich," cells (Fig. 8.6) while others with one fixed path length are termed "fixed-path" cells (Fig. 8.7). If a liquid has to be distilled directly into a cell, then it must be connected to the transfer system by a pipe connection.

Dilution of a liquid sample may be required to weaken the absorption of a strong band in order to observe the band shape, or in order to study solvent effects. Some solvents often used for diluting liquid samples, and the spectral ranges of their usefulness, are illustrated in Figure 8.8.

Gas cells for infrared use range from 2 to 10 cm in length. They are often constructed with a cylindrical glass body, a ground-glass joint, and a vacuum stopcock for filling from a vacuum-transfer system, as shown in Figure 8.9. If a gas absorbs weakly, a longer path length may be needed. Gas cells longer than 10 cm will not fit into most commercial instruments, so multi-pass cells are available for extended path-length. Multi-pass arrangements may also be combined with beam condensors for use with microsamples.

The windows in homemade cells may be held on each end of the cell with hot wax, epoxy cement, or pressure plates tightened against each other over the body of the cell. In the last case, the ends of the glass cell must be carefully polished in order to hold a vacuum of 10^{-5} mm. If epoxy cement is used, it may be loosened for

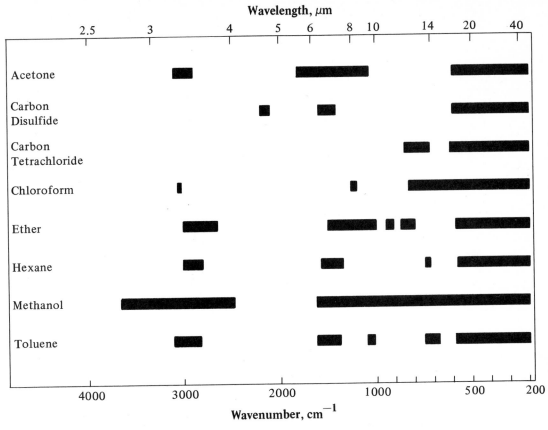

FIGURE 8.8. *Transparent regions of some common solvents used for infrared spectroscopy. The darkened regions are those in which a 0.1 mm thickness of solvent (in an NaCl cell) transmits 30% or less of the incident radiation.*

FIGURE 8.9. *A typical infrared cell for gas samples. Adapted from N. B. Colthup, L. H. Daly, and S. E. Wiberly,* Introduction to Infrared and Raman Spectroscopy, *New York: Academic Press, 1964, by permission of the senior author and the publisher.*

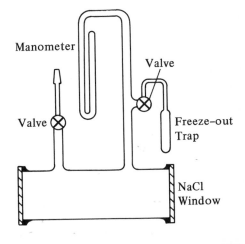

changing windows by soaking the ends of the cell in acetone for several days. The windows of a commercial cell are often mounted permanently, and care must be taken to keep them from fogging since they cannot be dismounted for polishing.

Raman Cells

For routine sampling of liquids that do not need distillation or transferral under vacuum, commercial cells are used for Raman spectroscopy because they are designed to pass the laser beam many times through the sample if necessary, thereby lengthening the optical path through the liquid and increasing the scattered energy available for transfer into the monochromator. Perhaps the most widely used sample cell in Raman work is an ordinary glass capillary tube, sealed at one end. The laser is carefully focused on a small volume of the sample; parabolic collection mirrors and a lens are then used to focus the scattered light on the entrance slit of the monochromator.

Special arrangements must be made if the liquid is to be transferred and kept under vacuum. One of the easiest and cheapest ways to obtain the Raman spectrum of a liquid under vacuum is to distill the liquid into a small glass tube, usually about 3 mm (or less) inner diameter, whose lower end is sealed and flame-polished. The tube is placed vertically and the laser beam directed into the lower end, passing vertically through the tube. A spherical mirror is placed behind the tube to collect the maximum amount of the Raman radiation. A lens system in front focuses the total Raman radiation on the entrance slit of the monochromator.

Solids may be sampled by this technique also, although it takes practice to obtain good spectra. The tube should be tilted slightly in the vertical plane, top end *back* (from the monochromator), so the laser beam grazes the *front* (towards monochromator) of the sample. It is possible, however, to obtain the Raman spectrum of the glass using this technique, so care must be taken to distinguish between sample spectra and the container spectrum.

Water, which is usually a poor infrared solvent because it dissolves most cell windows, is an excellent solvent for Raman work because it has few Raman-active frequencies, and these are relatively weak. Very symmetrical, highly Raman-active molecules such as CCl_4 are generally poor solvents for Raman spectroscopy.

8.4 MOLECULAR BONDS AND MOLECULAR STRUCTURE

Vibrational frequencies, so-called "good group frequencies," are important in applying infrared and Raman spectroscopy to many chemical problems that require the qualitative interpretation of infrared spectra. A *group frequency* is that mode of vibration associated with a particular bond or sets of bonds.

The vibrational frequency of a bond is determined by the bond strength and the masses of the atoms involved, and this frequency is often *unchanged* (or nearly unchanged) by other atoms connected to the original group. For example, the symmetrical stretching vibration of the C–H bond in the —CH, ＼CH$_2$, and –CH$_3$ groups occurs at 2890, 2853, and 2872 cm^{-1}, respectively (with further small shifts, depending on the other substituents on the carbon atom). Using the mathematical model of a harmonic oscillator, the quantized absorption of infrared radiation can be expressed as

$$\bar{\nu} = \frac{1}{2\pi c} \sqrt{\frac{k}{\mu}} \tag{8.4}$$

where $\bar{\nu}$ = the frequency of the bond vibration
c = the velocity of light
k = the force constant of the bond
μ = the reduced mass of the atoms involved

The reduced mass is defined by

$$\mu = \frac{m_1 m_2}{m_1 + m_2} \tag{8.5}$$

where m_1 = the mass of the first atom, in grams
m_2 = the mass of the second atom, in grams

The near-constant absorption frequency of a particular bond or group is used to advantage to check for the presence or absence of certain bonds in a new compound or to follow the progress of a reaction—for example, to determine the presence and type, or absence, of C–H vibrations. Later in this chapter a general procedure for the qualitative interpretation of infrared spectra will be outlined.

Molecular structure may often be inferred for simple molecules (up to 10 atoms) by correlating an assumed geometric structure with the "selection rules" for that structure. This process can be learned by a student without knowing much about the quantum mechanics or group theory that underlies it, but it does take time and practice. The selection rules tell us which modes of vibration are permitted to appear in the infrared and Raman spectrum. Thus, from the actual infrared and Raman spectral patterns and those implied by the selection rules for the *assumed* structure, the structure may be proven or disproven. The process is often like working a crossword puzzle. Bits of information are gathered from several analytical and spectroscopic methods and then fitted properly into place to obtain the structure of the molecule.

In practice, infrared spectroscopy is seldom used alone to infer the total structure of molecules. Usually, much other information is available, and infrared data identify certain molecular features that contribute to a total or final structure determination. Chemists more often need to interpret infrared spectra qualitatively in order to learn what bonds are present or what groups are present, absent, or modified. The general procedure outlined on pages 220 and 221 is useful in many qualitative problems.

FIGURE 8.10. (*Next two pages*). *Correlation chart of group frequencies.*
Courtesy of Dow Chemical Company.

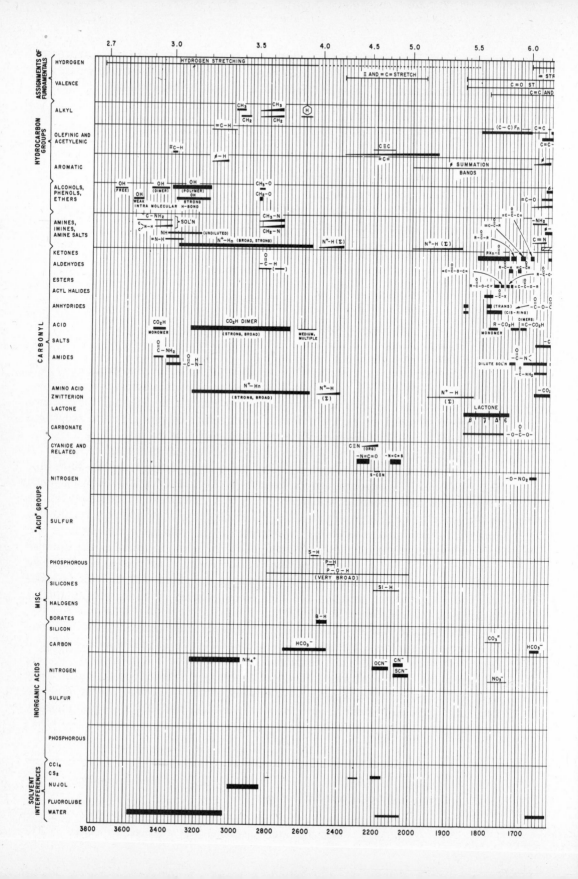

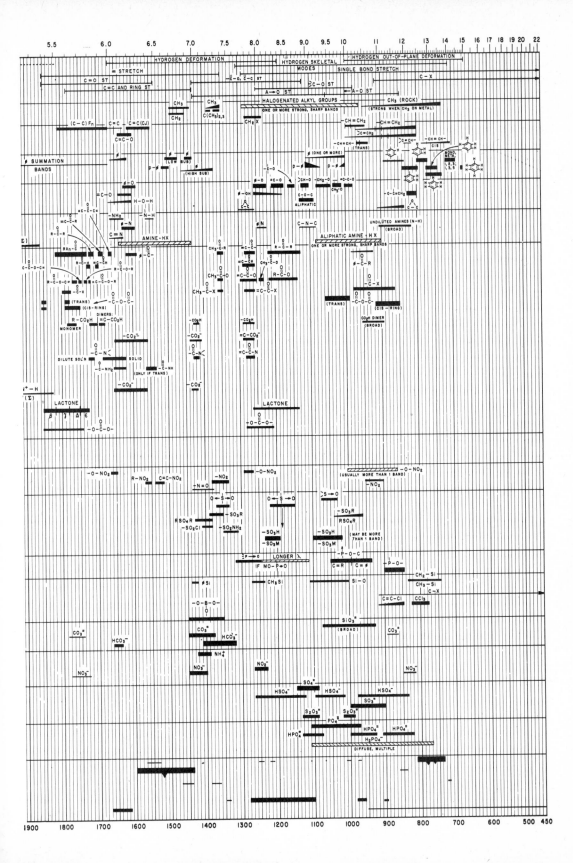

Outline of a General Procedure for Qualitative Interpretation of Infrared Spectra*

1. Bear in mind throughout the interpretation, and apply, all available information about the unknown such as:
   A. Chemical elements known to be present
   B. Chemical elements known to be absent
   C. Physical state and color
   D. Purity of unknown—whether a single compound or mixture
   E. Use which is made of the unknown
   F. Possible component(s)

2. Divide the rocksalt infrared region (2 to 15 μm) into the characteristic functional-group region, 5000–1350 cm^{-1} (2 to 7.5 μm), and the *fingerprint* region, 1350–650 cm^{-1} (7.5 to 15 μm).
   A. Concentrate first on the 5000–1350 cm^{-1} region; consider the strongest absorptions, then medium ones (weak ones only if necessary and helpful).
   B. Determine the presence and type, or absence, of C–H vibrations.
   (1) C–H frequencies occur between 3200 and 2800 cm^{-1}.
   (2) If above 3000 cm^{-1}, then the C atom is unsaturated or a highly halogenated compound is present.
   (3) If below 3000 cm^{-1}, then the C atom is saturated.
   (4) If both above and below 3000 cm^{-1}, then the C's are unsaturated and saturated.
   (5) A band at about 1455 cm^{-1} indicates CH_3 and/or CH_2.
   (6) A band at about 1375 cm^{-1} indicates C–CH_3.
   　a. Use an assignment chart (Colthup) to determine whether this is an ethyl, *n*-propyl, isopropyl, or *t*-butyl group.
   (7) A medium-intensity band at about 725 cm^{-1} indicates a chain of 4 or more methylenes.
   C. Determine, if possible, the type of compound(s) present.
   (1) The presence or absence of medium-strength 1500 and 1600 cm^{-1} bands indicates the presence or absence of aromatics.
   (2) The presence of a medium 1650–1610 cm^{-1} band indicates the presence of olefins (in its absence, olefin may still be present).
   (3) The presence of a weak band at about 2210 cm^{-1}, or a medium one at 3250 cm^{-1} and a medium one at 2115 cm^{-1}, indicates the presence of an acetylenic derivative (in its absence, acetylenics may still be present).
   (4) If CH_2 is present but not CH_3–C, investigate the possibility of alicyclics.
   (5) If CH_2 and CH_3 are present and no aromatics, olefins, or acetylenics are, suspect the presence of aliphatic compound(s).
   (6) After determining the compound type, follow through to learn the type of olefin, number and position of aromatic substituents, etc.
   (7) If only from 3 to 10 bands are present with several broad ones, or if organic assignments of bands lead nowhere, consider the possibility of inorganics.
   D. Proceed to interpret the strong bands, then medium ones. If a band lines up for a functional group(s), follow along to determine whether

---

* Adapted from D. N. Kendall, ed., *Applied Infrared Spectroscopy*, by permission of Van Nostrand Reinhold Company. Copyright © 1966 by Litton Educational Publishing, Inc.

all absorptions of the group are present, and to classify it as closely as possible; e.g., class of ester, type of amide, class of amine, etc.

3. Concentrate next on the 1350–650 cm^{-1} region, proceeding from strong bands to medium ones as in 2D.

4. When the interpretation reaches the stage of suggesting the presence of possible compound(s), comparison should be made with the spectra of knowns for final identification.

   A. If this comparison shows that more than a single component is present, mark off absorptions belonging to the first component identified, then proceed to interpret the remaining bands as above.

5. General considerations to bear in mind:

   A. The absence of an absorption band is more convincing evidence of a functional group's absence, than the presence of a band is evidence of its presence.

   B. All the bands in a spectrum can never be interpreted—some are absorptions characteristic of the molecule as a whole, some are combination bands, and some are overtone bands.

   C. Eight to 10 components is about the most that can be identified in a mixture (sometimes fewer, depending on the similarity and structural complexity of the components).

   D. The presence of bands about 3350 and 1645 cm^{-1} often indicates the presence of water in a sample.

   E. Generally, polymers have fewer, broader, and often less intense bands than the monomers from which they are derived.

   F. Some unknowns we will not be able to identify. Of these, some we may identify later as new correlations are learned and the spectra of new knowns are run—the identification of others may perhaps elude us indefinitely.

The interpretation of infrared spectra requires practice, but the task is eased with the help of correlation charts of group frequencies [2, 3]. Such a chart is shown in Figure 8.10, pp. 218–19. Other charts are available that document group frequencies in the near infrared and the far infrared.

As an example, consider the relatively simple infrared spectrum of ethylene (Fig. 8.11). The sample is contained in a 10-cm cell with NaCl windows (see Fig.

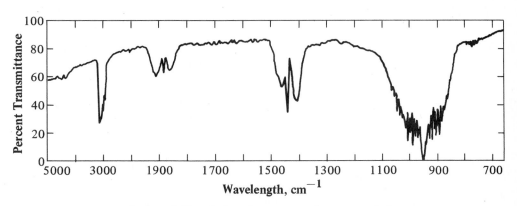

FIGURE 8.11. *Infrared spectrum of gaseous ethylene.*

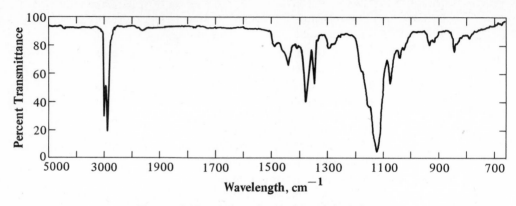

FIGURE 8.12. *Infrared spectrum of diethyl ether.*

8.4 for the spectral transmission of NaCl). The broad spectral bands with fine structure are typical of a low-molecular-weight vapor. Notice the absorption bands from
olefinic CH vibrations (3100, 1440, 950 cm^{-1}). The C=C frequency is absent; this
indicates that ethylene is a symmetrical molecule.

A second example is shown in Figure 8.12. The sample is diethyl ether, a
pure liquid with a low boiling-point. The infrared spectrum is that of a capillary
film of this sample between two salt plates. Notice the aliphatic CH bands (2900,
1460, CH$_3$ at 1380). There is also an aliphatic ether band at 1130 cm^{-1}.

8.5 QUANTITATIVE ANALYSIS

Quantitative analysis of a sample is essentially performed by determining its absorbance and comparing this with the infrared absorptivity a or the molar absorptivity
ε (see Table 7.2 and Sec. 7.3) of pure compounds.

Ideally, the intensity (I_0) of infrared radiation incident upon a sample cell
is reduced (to I) by the absorption of the samples. Actually, some of the incident
energy is scattered by the sample and this scattered energy makes the Beer-Lambert
law inaccurate, especially at high values of absorbance [4]. The baseline method for
quantitative analysis is an empirical method used to establish a calibration curve of
$\log(I_0/I)$ versus concentration. Infrared absorption bands may overlap neighboring
bands or may appear on a sloping background, so transmittance is measured in practice as shown in Figure 8.13. The absorbance, A, is determined from measurements of I and I_0, then a calibration curve of absorbance versus concentration is
plotted.

A corollary of the Beer-Lambert law is the law of additivity of absorbance
($\log I_0/I$), which states that the absorbance of a mixture is equal to the sum of the
absorbances of its components. Stated another way, equal absorbing paths of the
same material will always absorb the same fraction of the incident light. Deviations
from linearity may occur in practice. The Beer-Lambert law is true for monochromatic light passing through the cell; however, all spectrometers (except those
recent ones using tunable, narrowband, infrared lasers) send through the sample a
band of wavelengths centered approximately at the wavelength setting of the spectrom-

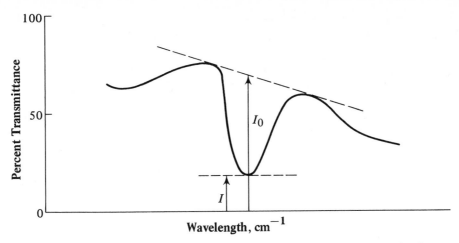

FIGURE 8.13. *Measurement of I_0 and I for an infrared absorption band with a sloping background.*

eter. If the slit width is too wide or the absorption bands too narrow, then rapid changes occur in absorptivity over the wavelength interval established by the slit, and deviations from the Beer-Lambert law will occur. For this reason, the spectral slit-width should be set at about one-tenth the width of the absorption band at one-half the peak height of the band. This is a particularly serious problem in infrared work, because sources are generally not very intense and wide slits are usually employed to compensate for this.

Thus, errors incurred in quantitative analysis by the infrared method include error in measurement of the 100% line, deviations from the Beer-Lambert law, error in the zero line and error in the measurement of %T. The effect of deviations from the Beer-Lambert law is such that one should try to work at values of %T greater than 40% for the most accurate results.

Component Cancellation

If a double-beam spectrometer is used to analyze a multicomponent mixture, then it is possible to eliminate the spectrum of one or more of the components by putting the same amount of the component in the reference beam. In principle, one may cancel the spectrum of each component separately and successively, making it possible to analyze the mixture without overlapping bands. In practice, this is usually limited to three or fewer components. This procedure is useful if small amounts of impurities are to be determined.

A danger in this approach is that strong absorbance in the reference beam can cause loss of servo power in the instrument and the production of erroneous spectra as the instrument tries to take the ratio of two very small signals.

Differential Analysis

The analysis of a mixture by directly comparing a known with an unknown sample in a double-beam spectrophotometer is called differential analysis. When two or more components absorb at or near the same frequency, differential analysis is often the only way to unravel the overlap. The technique has been used in ultraviolet-visible spectroscopy for a long time, so it is not new (see Sec. 7.5).

The Beer-Lambert law is assumed to hold for the components (solvents and solute), and the path length must be known. One of the absorbing components is placed in the reference beam and the mixture is placed in the sample beam. The double-beam spectrophotometer records the ratio of the radiant power of the two beams. The path length should be varied until the solution as a whole transmits about 40% of the incident energy, and the slit width should be *constant*.

Direct Infrared Analysis

Much in the same manner as in ultraviolet-visible absorption spectroscopy, infrared spectroscopy can be used to determine the concentration of a particular compound using the standard quantitative methods discussed in Chapter 7, provided that a sufficiently intense absorption band, relatively free from interferences, can be found. For example, isosorbide dinitrate, a coronary vasodilator, can be determined in pharmaceutical preparations after dissolving it in water, extracting it with CCl_4, and comparing its infrared absorption intensity with a calibration curve [5]. This is a highly specific, rapid, and sensitive analytical method for isosorbide dinitrate because of the strong, sharp band at 1650 cm^{-1} characteristic of nitrate esters. The ultraviolet spectrum of isosorbide dinitrate is of low intensity and noncharacteristic shape; therefore direct ultraviolet techniques cannot be used. Direct infrared analysis is applicable to most organic nitrates, as long as interfering groups such as –COOH, C=N, and ketone and amide functionalities are not present.

Infrared analysis has been used to rapidly determine trace quantities (0.1 to 1 ppm) of various volatile fluoride impurities—such as BF_3, SiF_4, MoF_6, and Freons—in UF_6 used in nuclear applications [6]. The absorption-band wavelengths present indicate the particular impurities present. The precision of the method is about ± 5–10%. Chemical methods of analysis are rather time-consuming and require a good deal of laboratory skill, and gas chromatography or mass spectral analysis cannot be used because of the extremely corrosive nature of fluorides.

One interesting example of infrared analysis is an infrared gas analyzer used to determine breath-alcohol levels of motorists [7].

Total Functional-Group Analysis

One particular advantage of infrared analysis is its ability to determine the total amount of a particular functional group present in even a very complex mixture. For example, the total ketone content of a mixture can be determined because almost all ketone carbonyl bands come at about 1720 cm^{-1}, and the intensity of absorption does not vary a great deal from one compound to another. Therefore, one can determine an "average" absorptivity for a particular functional group from known mixtures, and use this value in the analysis of real samples. The total content of a particular functional group is often an important consideration, particularly in industrial situations.

An example of total functional-group analysis is determining the carboxyl content of carboxyl-terminated polybutadienes (CTPB's), which are polymers (mw ~ 7000) used as elastomeric binders for solid propellants [8]. A solution (approx. 2%) of the CTPB sample in CCl_4 is prepared, and the magnitude of the 1708-cm^{-1} carboxyl-carbonyl band is measured in a 1-mm cell. Quantitation is achieved either by the calibration-curve method, or by the internal-standard method using the 1435-cm^{-1} methylene band or the 1638-cm^{-1} vinyl band as standards. The results for the total carboxyl content by this method agree with those of standard chemical titration procedures to within a relative error of about $\pm 0.03\%$ carboxyl content, for a carboxyl-content range of about 0.5 to 2.5% in commercial CTPB samples.

High-molecular-weight aliphatic amines are used extensively in many industries. The total primary- and secondary-amine content of aliphatic amines can be determined easily and rapidly by functional-group analysis in the near infrared [9], using chloroform solvent and 5-cm fused-silica cells. Primary amines have characteristic absorption maxima at 2.02 μm and 1.55 μm, whereas secondary amines absorb only at 1.55 μm. Quantitation is achieved by the calibration-curve method using a series of standard solutions of primary and of secondary amines. Most other methods for the determination of total primary, secondary, or tertiary amine in a mixture are lengthy or inaccurate, or are unsuitable for small samples.

Raman Analyses

In general, Raman spectroscopy has been used very little, if at all, to perform quantitative analyses; its primary use has been in the study of molecular structure. However, one possible use of laser Raman spectroscopy for quantitative purposes is the identification and determination of trace levels of molecular pollutants in water [10]. The Raman spectrum of distilled water is weak and uncomplicated; thus it is possible to detect and distinguish Raman bands of pollutants in natural waters. For example, it is possible to detect as little as 50 ppm of benzene in distilled water using only 5 mW of laser power from a He-Ne gas laser at 6328 Å. With improved excitation techniques and 50 mW laser power, it should be possible to detect certain Raman-active pollutants at less than 5 ppm levels.

A very unusual application of Raman analysis is the remote detection of atmospheric pollutants [11, 12]. At present, over 40 atmospheric pollutants are monitored at stations across the United States. In general, most of these pollutants are in the gaseous state in concentrations of 0.01 to 10 ppm for molecules and 0.01 to 10 ppb for metal vapors. At present, detecting and quantitatively measuring these pollutants requires fixed monitoring stations using wet chemical techniques. One approach to a remote, instantaneous sensing method involves coupling a very-high-power (50 MW) pulsed laser with a 20″ reflecting telescope to which is attached a monochromator and a photomultiplier tube. The apparatus can be "aimed" at a source of polluted air, such as the emission from a smokestack, up to a mile or so distant. Although quantitation is very difficult and there are many factors involved, the back-scattered laser light of unchanged frequency can be used to measure the amount of particulate matter in the air; and the various Raman lines can be used to measure the molecular species. For example, SO_2 and CO_2 can be accurately measured at the 1 ppm level.

SELECTED BIBLIOGRAPHY

BELLAMY, L. *The Infrared Spectra of Complex Molecules.* London: Methuen; New York: Wiley, 1954.

CONLEY, R. T. *Infrared Spectroscopy.* Boston: Allyn and Bacon, 1966.

FREEMAN, S. K. *Applications of Laser Raman Spectroscopy.* New York: Wiley-Interscience, 1974.

HERZBERG, G. *Infrared and Raman Spectra of Polyatomic Molecules.* New Jersey: Van Nostrand, 1945.

JONES, R. N., and SANDORFY, C. *Chemical Applications of Spectroscopy.* Vol. IX of *Technique of Organic Chemistry,* A. Weissberger, ed. New York: Interscience Publishers, 1956.

SZYMANSKI, H. A. *A Systematic Approach to the Interpretation of Infrared Spectra.* Cambridge Springs, Pa.: Hertillon Press, 1967.

SZYMANSKI, H. A. *Correlation of Infrared and Raman Spectra of Organic Compounds.* Cambridge Springs, Pa.: Hertillon Press, 1969.

SZYMANSKI, H. A., ed. *Raman Spectroscopy, Theory and Practice.* New York: Plenum Press, 1967.

REFERENCES

1. K. S. SESHADRI and R. N. JONES, "The Shapes and Intensities of Infrared Absorption Bands—A Review," *Spectrochim. Acta,* **19**, 1013 (1963).

2. H. A. SZYMANSKI, *A Systematic Approach to the Interpretation of Infrared Spectra,* Cambridge Springs, Pa.: Hertillon Press, 1971.

3. N. B. COLTHUP, L. H. DALY, and S. E. WIBERLY, *Introduction to Infrared and Raman Spectroscopy,* New York: Academic Press, 1964, p 319.

4. D. ROBINSON, *Anal. Chem.,* **23**, 273 (1951).

5. D. WOO, J. K. C. YEN, and P. SOFRONAS, *Anal. Chem.,* **45**, 2144 (1973).

6. R. AUBEAU, G. BLANDENET, and G. BROGNIART, *Anal. Chem.,* **44**, 1628 (1972).

7. Y. FUKUI and Y. YAMAMOTO, *Med. Sci. Law,* **11**, 182 (1971); *Chem. Abstr.,* **77**, 29866n (1972).

8. A. S. TOMPA, *Anal. Chem.,* **44**, 628 (1972).

9. R. B. STAGE, J. B. STANLEY, and P. B. MOSELEY, *J. Amer. Oil Chem. Soc.,* **49**, 87 (1972); *Chem. Abstr.,* **76**, 107688b (1972).

10. E. B. BRADLEY and C. A. FRENZEL, *Water Res.,* **4**, 125 (1970).

11. H. INABA and T. KOBAYASI, *Nature,* **224**, 170 (1969).

12. H. KILDAL and R. L. BYER, *Proc. IEEE,* **59**, 1644 (1971).

PROBLEMS

1. List the upper and lower limits of the near-, mid-, and far-infrared spectral regions in (a) micrometers; (b) wavenumbers (cm^{-1}).

2. Convert 7000 Å to (a) wavenumbers (cm^{-1}); (b) micrometers (μm); (c) eV.

3. Compute the range of energy (in eV) spanned by (a) the near infrared; (b) the mid infrared; (c) the far infrared.

4. The wavelength of the fundamental frequency of vibration of $^{12}C^{16}O$ is 4.663 μm. Express this wavelength in wavenumbers (cm^{-1}); in eV; in cal/mole.

5. In the literature find the infrared and Raman spectra of S_2Cl_2, S_2Br_2, S_2F_2, and H_2O_2. Note similarities in the number of active modes and coincidences. What fundamental frequencies are approximately constant among these molecules? What fundamental frequencies are different? Explain the similarities and differences. By

what reasoning would you assign a structure to each molecule? Do the polarization measurements support the assignments?

6. An infrared spectrophotometer is set at a wavelength of 4 μm and the transmittance of the sample is observed to be 0.50 at this wavelength. Calculate the absorbance at this wavelength if $I_0 = 100$.

7. In what spectral region does one observe (a) the pure rotation spectrum of a gas; (b) the vibration-rotation spectrum of that gas?

8. It is desired to obtain the vibration fundamentals of a gas that contains some "heavy" atoms (say, $z > 30$). In addition, it is suspected that the interatomic forces are weak. In what region(s) of the infrared should one record the spectrum in order to record all of the fundamentals?

9. It is desired to obtain the infrared spectrum of a water solution in the region 2.5–18 μm. What sampling arrangement should be used?

10. Calculate the molar absorptivity of a liquid sample in an infrared cell of thickness 0.1 mm. The absorbance reading of the spectrometer at the frequency of interest is 0.4. The concentration of the sample is 1 M.

11. A band at about 1370 cm^{-1} is indicative of a methyl group. At what frequencies would the first and second overtones be?

12. The symmetrical C–H stretch in alkanes occurs at about 2880 cm^{-1}. At what frequency should this band occur if deuterium were substituted for hydrogen? Tritium?

13. Single, double, and triple bonds have force constants that are approximately 5, 10, and 15×10^5 dynes/cm, respectively. (a) At what frequencies would you expect to find C–C, C=C, and C≡C stretches? (b) What force constant would you expect the carbon-carbon bond in benzene to have? At what frequency should the absorption occur? (c) Compare the calculated frequencies with the actual ones (see Fig. 8.10).

14. The fundamental vibrational frequencies of ethylene are at 3374, 3287, 1974, 729, and 612 cm^{-1}. At what wavelengths will these bands be observed for each of the exciting lines of the Ar-Kr laser—4880, 5145, 5682, and 6471 Å? Discuss the extent of spectral overlap if unfiltered laser light was used.

15. Chloroform exhibits Raman bands at 258, 357, 660, and 760 cm^{-1}. Polarized spectra were taken and peak heights measured. $I_\perp$ was determined to be 30.8, 5.8, 1.3, and 4.7 units; $I_\parallel$ was 40.9, 78.2, 83.2, and 6.0 units, for the four peaks. Calculate the depolarization ratios for these bands, and indicate whether each band is "polarized" or "depolarized."

16. Calculate the relative intensities of a Raman line when excited by each of the four lines from an Ar-Kr laser.

9

Molecular Fluorescence and Phosphorescence

GEORGE H. SCHENK

The mechanism of the absorption of ultraviolet and visible light was discussed in Chapter 7. In this chapter, two processes that involve absorption of radiation as the first step will be discussed; these are fluorescence and phosphorescence.

Both fluorescence and phosphorescence are types of *photoluminescence* (often simply referred to as *luminescence*), the emission of radiant energy (usually visible radiation, but sometimes ultraviolet or infrared radiation) by a molecule, ion, or atom that has reached the excited state by absorbing radiant energy (usually, but not always, ultraviolet radiation):

$$\begin{array}{ccccc} \text{ground} \\ \text{state} \end{array} + \text{UV} \xrightarrow[\text{(excitation)}]{\text{absorption}} \begin{array}{c}\text{excited}\\\text{state}\end{array} \xrightarrow{\text{emission}} \begin{array}{c}\text{ground}\\\text{state}\end{array} + \begin{array}{c}\text{fluorescence}\\\text{(or phosphorescence)}\end{array} \quad \textbf{(9.1)}$$

$$X + h\nu \longrightarrow X^* \longrightarrow X + h\nu'$$

The energy of the fluorescence or phosphorescence ($h\nu'$) is usually much lower than that of the ultraviolet radiation used for excitation. Therefore, since wavelength is inversely proportional to energy, fluorescence or phosphorescence is located at longer wavelengths in the ultraviolet (>300 nm), in the visible region (380–750 nm), or even in the near infrared (>750 nm).

In general, fluorescence emission occurs very soon (10^{-6} to 10^{-9} sec) after a species reaches the excited state. Thus, it is impossible for the eye to perceive a fluorescent substance once the source of ultraviolet radiation has been removed. Phosphorescence emission occurs more slowly ($>10^{-4}$ sec) and with a greater variation in the lifetimes of the phosphorescence emission. Thus, while many phosphorescent substances, including most organic molecules, also cannot be perceived by the eye once the ultraviolet source has been removed, a number of inorganic minerals phosphoresce markedly after ultraviolet excitation has ceased. The longest recorded case is one particular sample of the mineral willemite ($ZnSiO_4$), which phosphoresced for 340 hours!

While the phosphorescence of solids is easily observed at room temperature, it is often impossible to observe the phosphorescence of solutions at room temperature; apparently oxygen molecules, absorbing energy in collisions with the excited species involved, quench its phosphorescence. To avoid this, solutions are cooled in liquid nitrogen (77°K) and allowed to freeze; such solutions are referred to as "rigid solutions" or "glasses." Two organic solvents commonly used to prepare such solutions are ethanol and EPA, a mixture of ethyl ether, isopentane, and ethanol.

Experimental Aspects of Excitation and Emission. Although there are many pathways for a species to reach the excited state, photoluminescence by definition must involve *photoexcitation*, which may occur by absorption of one of the following forms of radiant energy: (1) sunlight, (2) visible radiation, including room light, (3) ultraviolet radiation, or (4) x-rays.

The emission process in photoluminescence is the emission of radiant energy from an excited electronic state. Photoluminescence is called *fluorescence* when the spin of the excited electron does not change as the photoexcited species undergoes a transition from the excited state to the ground state. If there is a change in spin, then the photoluminescence is called *phosphorescence*. For organic molecules, the term fluorescence commonly means emission of radiant energy during a transition from the lowest excited singlet state, S_1, to the singlet ground state, S_0. Phosphorescence of organic molecules commonly means emission during a transition from the lowest excited triplet state, T_1, to the singlet ground state, S_0. For inorganic species, any emission involving a change in the spin of the excited electron is, by definition, phosphorescence.

In contrast to absorption spectrophotometry, fluorescence and phosphorescence spectrometry involve the recording of both an excitation and an emission spectrum; the instruments used are called spectrofluorometers or spectrophosphorimeters.

Excitation and Emission Spectra of UO_2^{2+}. The use of a spectrofluorometer for obtaining emission and excitation spectra will be illustrated with the uranyl (UO_2^{2+}) ion (see Fig. 9.1). To obtain such spectra, one starts by choosing an intense absorption band from the absorption spectrum (250 nm was chosen here). The compound is then excited at this wavelength—that is, energy at this wavelength is pumped in for the compound to absorb—using a grating that limits the incoming radiation to a narrow band about 10–15 nm wide. To obtain the fluorescence emission spectrum, one adjusts the spectrofluorometer to measure and record any radiation emitted from the solution of UO_2^{2+}, starting with a wavelength such as 300 or 400 nm and ending at a wavelength such as 700 nm. The emission spectrum is automatically "scanned" by using a second (motor-driven) grating to vary the wavelengths being measured and recorded by the spectrofluorometer.

The resulting fluorescence *emission* spectrum obtained for the uranyl ion is shown in Figure 9.1. Note that UO_2^{2+} begins to emit fluorescence at 450 nm, and that the most intense bands fall in the green region of the visible spectrum.

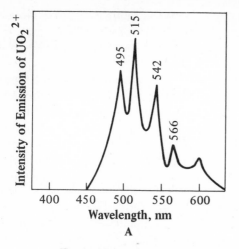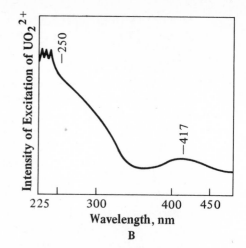

FIGURE 9.1. *Spectra of uranyl nitrate. A: The corrected emission spectrum of 10^{-4} M uranyl nitrate in 0.1 N H_2SO_4–1% H_3PO_4 solution as measured on the Turner absolute spectrofluorometer. B: The corrected excitation spectrum. (The excitation spectrum was measured by setting the emission grating at 515 nm; the emission spectrum was obtained by excitation at 250 nm. Bandwidths were 10 nm.) From G. H. Schenk,* Absorption of Light and Ultraviolet Radiation, *Boston: Allyn and Bacon, 1973, p 102, by permission of the publisher.*

To obtain the fluorescence *excitation* spectrum, the grating through which fluorescence emission passes is generally set at the wavelength of the most intense emission band (for the spectrum in Fig. 9.1, at 515 nm). Then, one adjusts the spectrofluorometer so that it automatically varies the wavelength of exciting radiation striking the solution. (The first grating, which was set at 250 nm when recording the fluorescence emission spectrum, is now driven by a motor, so that the exciting radiation from the source in the spectrofluorometer is continuously varied and measured.) The spectrofluorometer therefore records the emission at 515 nm as a function of the excitation wavelength.

9.1 THEORY OF FLUORESCENCE AND PHOSPHORESCENCE

The theory of luminescence transitions is best described by using a molecular-energy interpretation; for a molecular-orbital interpretation, the reader is referred to specialized monographs [1, 2]. The transitions of an aromatic hydrocarbon, anthracene, will be used to illustrate the molecular-energy interpretation given below.

Excitation and Emission of Anthracene

When interpreting the excitation (absorption) of anthracene, it should be noted that anthracene has two main absorption bands. The higher-energy band is centered at 255 nm; the lower-energy band extends over the 325–375 nm region. Anthracene fluoresces maximally at 380, 402, and 425 nm and phosphoresces at 680 nm. By using a *state* or *molecular-energy diagram*, these energy changes can be portrayed accurately. First the excitation and relaxation processes will be considered, then the fluorescence and phosphorescence processes.

Excitation and Relaxation Processes. For anthracene, there are at least two representative excitation processes:

$$S_0 + UV_{255\,nm} \longrightarrow S_2 \tag{9.2}$$

$$S_0 + UV_{325-375\,nm} \longrightarrow S_1 \tag{9.3}$$

Excitation by either process results in the same fluorescence emission spectrum, implying that only the S_1 state emits, and that anthracene in the S_2 state has to reach the S_1 state before it can emit fluorescence. The molecular-energy diagram in Figure 9.2 symbolizes the steps involved in reaching the S_1 state.

At the extreme left of Figure 9.2 are shown three representative transitions within the $S_0 \rightarrow S_2$ process. Because the S_2 state possesses many vibrational sublevels, there are actually many such transitions. All of the resulting S_2 molecules fall, or relax, to the EV_0 sublevel of the S_2 state by rapid vibrational relaxation. In this process, excess vibrational energy is transferred (within 10^{-13} to 10^{-11} sec) to solvent molecules by thermal relaxation (via collisions). This process also occurs for S_1 molecules in the various sublevels.

Once the S_2 molecule has reached its EV_0 sublevel, it is believed to undergo rapid *internal conversion* to the S_1 state:

$$S_2 \xrightarrow{\text{(10}^{-13}\text{ to 10}^{-11}\text{ sec)}} S_1 \tag{9.4}$$

By definition, this process involves no change in spin of the excited electron, only a conversion of excess electronic energy to excess vibrational energy. At the end of this process, the molecule arrives at the EV_0 sublevel of the S_1 state. The process is as rapid as vibrational relaxation; indeed, if one assumes that electronic energy and vibrational energy are instantly interconvertible, then the slowest part of this process is vibrational relaxation from the EV_n sublevel of the S_1 state to its EV_0 sublevel.

Deactivation of the S_1 State at Room Temperature. There are four important processes that can deactivate the S_1 state at room temperature; that is, allow the S_1 state to lose its excess electronic energy and return to the S_0 state. These are

1. Fluorescence emission: $S_1 \rightarrow S_0 + h\nu_f$ (1st order rate constant $= k_f$)
2. Internal conversion: $S_1 \rightsquigarrow S_0 + heat$
3. Intersystem crossing: $S_1 \rightsquigarrow T_1$ (1st order rate constant $= k_{1sc}$)
4. Collisional quenching: $S_1 + Q \rightsquigarrow S_0 + heat$

Each process will be discussed below in terms of the molecular-energy diagram in Figure 9.2. It should be stressed that each process involves only S_1 molecules in the EV_0 sublevel.

1. *Fluorescence emission.* In this process, S_1 molecules emit photons of various energies, depending on the vibrational sublevel (of the S_0 state) involved in the

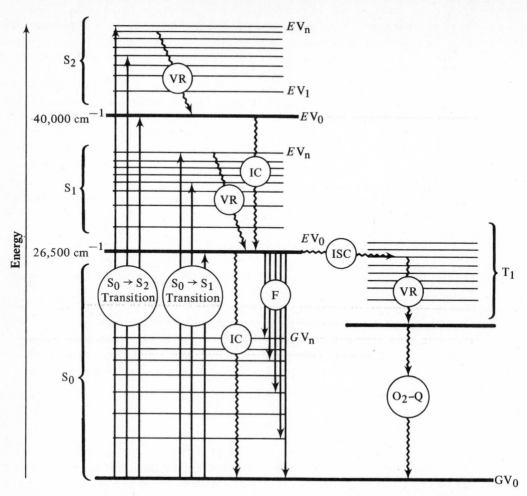

FIGURE 9.2.   A state (molecular-energy) diagram for transitions involving anthracene. S_0 = ground (singlet) state, S_1 = first excited singlet state, S_2 = second excited singlet state, T_1 = first triplet state, VR = vibrational relaxation, IC = internal conversion, F = fluorescence emission, ISC = intersystem crossing, and O_2-Q = quenching of T_1 by oxygen molecules dissolved in the solution. EV and GV refer to the various vibrational sublevels of the excited and ground states. Straight arrows ($\rightarrow$) refer to radiative processes—photon emission or absorption. Wavy arrows ($\rightsquigarrow$) refer to nonradiative processes.

transition.   The smallest amount of energy is involved in the EV_0–GV_n transition, the largest in the EV_0–GV_0 transition.   The molecules do not remain in sublevels higher than the GV_0 sublevel; they undergo further vibrational relaxation, with loss of heat, to the GV_0 sublevel.

Because it is so rapid, fluorescence emission is not generally measured after termination of excitation but during excitation.   The fastest emitters have k_f values near 10^9 sec^{-1}; the slowest emitters, such as benzene, have k_f values in the range of

10^6 or even 10^5 sec^{-1}. The larger the value of k_f, the larger ϕ_f, the quantum efficiency for fluorescence, is likely to be (see Eqn. 9.8).

2. *Internal conversion.* By definition, this process involves no change in spin of the excited electron, only a conversion of excess electronic energy into excess vibrational energy, and loss of this as heat through vibrational relaxation. The kinetics of this process are presumably first order (rate constant, k_c). The S$_1 \rightsquigarrow$ S$_0$ conversion in rigid molecules is thought to be a relatively inefficient (slow) process because of the large amount of electronic energy that must be converted into vibrational energy. According to Lim [3], internal conversion does not occur with aromatic hydrocarbons. Thus, in Figure 9.2, the S$_1 \rightsquigarrow$ S$_0$ conversion involves the equivalent of 26,500 cm^{-1} of energy, whereas the S$_2 \rightsquigarrow$ S$_1$ conversion involves only about half as much.

3. *Intersystem crossing.* In contrast to internal conversion, this process involves a change in the spin of the excited electron and thus a change in spin multiplicity. The details are beyond the scope of this chapter, but one should stress the kinetic competition of this process with fluorescence at room temperature. Where k_{isc} is larger than k_f, S$_1$ molecules will exhibit weak emission or possibly no detectable emission; further, it appears that at room temperature nearly all T$_1$ molecules undergo quenching after colliding and complexing with dissolved oxygen (this process is symbolized in Figure 9.2). Another possible process at room temperature, especially in the absence of oxygen, is the photochemical reaction of T$_1$ molecules.

4. *Collisional quenching.* This process is not shown in Figure 9.2; it can be symbolized as a collision of a quencher Q with an S$_1$ molecule:

$$\text{S}_1 + \text{Q} \xrightarrow{\text{(rate constant = } k_2)} \text{complex} \rightsquigarrow \text{S}_0 + \text{Q} + \text{heat} \qquad (9.5)$$

This type of reaction involves pseudo–first-order kinetics because the concentration of the quencher does not change. The first-order rate-constant is thus equal to $k_2[\text{Q}]$. A typical example of such a quencher is oxygen, which quenches a significant amount of the fluorescence of aromatic hydrocarbons. Oxygen, being paramagnetic, apparently enhances the rate of the S$_1 \rightsquigarrow$ T$_1$ crossing, and the T$_1$ molecule in turn undergoes rapid T$_1 \rightsquigarrow$ S$_0$ crossing with loss of the excess energy as heat [1].

Deactivation of the T_1 State in Solids. In frozen solutions (say, at 77 K) or in a dry solid at room temperature, T$_1$ molecules are not quenched; instead, they return to the S$_0$ state by two slower pathways: (1) phosphorescence emission, and (2) non-radiative intersystem crossing. In the latter pathway, excess electronic energy is converted to vibrational energy as the T$_1$ molecule crosses over to some higher vibrational level (GV$_x$) of the ground state. This is faster than the internal conversion pathway for S$_1$ molecules because much less electronic energy is involved.

Relation Between Concentration and Fluorescence Intensity

The intensity F of fluorescence (or phosphorescence) emission is usually directly proportional to the concentration c of the emitter. At the low concentrations

$(\leq 10^{-5}\,M)$ most often employed in fluorometric measurements, the following equation relating F and c can be derived [2, 4]:

$$F = k\phi_f P_0(1 - e^{-\varepsilon bc}) \approx k\phi_f P_0(2.3\,\varepsilon bc) \tag{9.6}$$

In this equation, ε and b have the same meaning as in Beer's law, Equation 7.9. Thus, $(2.3\,\varepsilon bc)$ represents the fraction of the exciting radiation that is absorbed. Because of the geometry of the fluorometer (see Sec. 9.2), only a fraction (k) of the emitted photons can be measured and recorded as F; thus,

$$k = \frac{\text{photons measured}}{\text{photons emitted}} \tag{9.7}$$

P_0 is the radiant power of the exciting radiation; note that the fluorescence intensity is directly proportional to P_0; ϕ_f is the *quantum efficiency* of fluorescence, i.e., the fraction of excited molecules that fluoresce:

$$\phi_f = \frac{\text{photons emitted/sec}}{\text{photons absorbed/sec}} = \frac{\text{photons emitted}}{\text{photons absorbed}} \tag{9.8}$$

For quantitative analysis, a plot of F versus c is used as a calibration curve. In theory, such a plot should be linear; in practice, it is usually linear over one to four orders of magnitude, but typically curves downward at higher concentrations because of excessive absorption of the exciting radiation (the inner-filter effect [2]).

The relation between the intensity of phosphorescence emission and concentration is similar to that in Equation 9.6, but the full expression is more complicated [5, 6].

9.2 INSTRUMENTATION FOR FLUORESCENCE AND PHOSPHORESCENCE

The two types of fluorescence instruments are the filter fluorometer and the spectrofluorometer; the principal type of phosphorescence instrument is the spectrophosphorimeter.

The four main components of any fluorescence or phosphorescence instrument are the source of excitation, the sample cell, the detector, and the filters or gratings used to select the exciting and emitted radiation. Phosphorescence instruments must also include a Dewar flask for the liquid nitrogen used to freeze samples. Since phosphorescence instruments have the same four main components as fluorescence instruments, the common components of both will be discussed first.

Design of Instruments

Figure 9.3 shows the four essential components of any filter fluorometer or spectrofluorometer. The source is a mercury-arc or xenon-arc lamp (the latter is usually used in spectrofluorometers). The exciting radiation passes through a grating or primary filter, allowing only a certain range of wavelengths to strike the sample. Gratings are used in spectrofluorometers, filters in filter fluorometers. The major advantages of the grating are that it selects any given wavelength from 200 to 600 nm

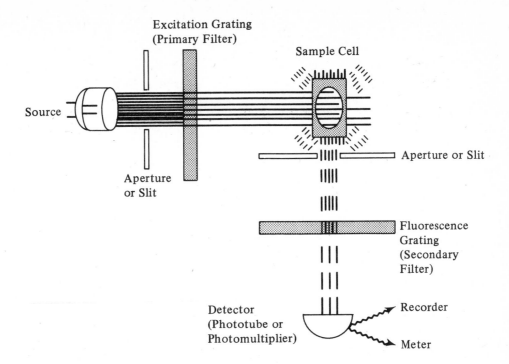

FIGURE 9.3. *Schematic diagram (top view) of the components of a fluorometer (filter fluorometer or spectrofluorometer). The source is a mercury-arc or xenon-arc lamp. The excitation grating or primary filter transmits only a portion of the radiation emitted by the source. Most of the exciting radiation passes through the sample cell without being absorbed. The radiation absorbed causes the sample to fluoresce in all directions, but only the emission that passes through the aperture or slit and through the secondary filter or fluorescence grating is measured by the phototube, or photomultiplier. The output of the detector is either measured on a meter or plotted on a recorder. From G. H. Schenk,* Absorption of Light and Ultraviolet Radiation, *Boston: Allyn and Bacon, 1973, p 260, by permission of the publisher.*

and that it passes a constant bandwidth (such as 10 nm) of radiation, no matter what the wavelength. The major advantage of most filters is that they transmit a greater fraction of the exciting radiation than do gratings, because of the wider bandwidth of the filters. This is a definite advantage for trace analysis, but a disadvantage as far as interferences are concerned—a filter may allow two substances to be excited whereas a spectrofluorometer, with its more selective grating, may be adjusted so that only one substance is excited. The disadvantage of the mercury source (plus filter) is that there are a limited number of mercury lines available with which to excite a sample.

Excitation with a Mercury Arc in a Filter Fluorometer

The usual source employed in filter fluorometers is a 4-watt mercury-arc lamp, either with a clear quartz envelope (emitting primarily 254-nm radiation) or one

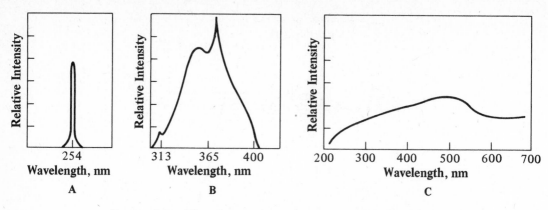

FIGURE 9.4. *The relative intensities of three different sources. A: The emission intensity of the short-wavelength (254 nm) mercury arc. B: The emission intensity of the phosphor-coated mercury arc, showing the intense emission band. C: The intensity of the xenon-arc lamp.*

coated with a white phosphor that emits a continuum from 300 to 405 nm and particularly strongly at 366 nm (see Fig. 9.4).

For excitation at 254 nm, a combination of filters is used that transmits only below 300 nm, namely a 7-54 filter plus a special plastic filter, as shown in Figure 9.5A. Alternatively, because the plastic filter gradually decomposes and must be replaced, a mercury-line interference filter may be used. This is a single, permanent filter for isolating the 254-nm line without transmitting the 313-nm, etc., lines emitted by the low-pressure mercury arc.

A filter that may be used for excitation at longer wavelengths is the 7-60 filter, whose transmittance is shown in Figure 9.5B. This transmits nearly all of the intense band of radiation emitted by the 4-watt low-pressure, phosphor-coated mercury source.

Sample Cells and the Cell Compartment. The sample cell may be made of glass, of optical-grade quartz, or synthetic silica. Glass cells transmit reasonably well down to about 320 nm, depending on the thickness of the cell wall, although there is appreciable absorption below about 360 nm. Ultraviolet grade quartz transmits well down to about 190 nm.

The cell compartment is painted a dull black and constructed so that any

FIGURE 9.5. *A plot of percent transmittance versus wavelength for several types of filters used in fluorescence. A: The 7-54 filter (solid line); a plastic filter that absorbs radiation above 300 nm (dotted line) is used in combination with the 7-54 filter to isolate the 254-nm mercury line. B: The 7-60 narrow-bandpass filter (left) and several sharp-cut filters. The nominal cut-off wavelength for the sharp-cut filters is indicated on each curve. C: Several Bausch-and-Lomb interference filters. The bandwidth at half the peak transmittance is given under each peak. From G. H. Schenk*, Absorption of Light and Ultraviolet Radiation, *Boston: Allyn and Bacon*, 1973, *p 265, by permission of the publisher.*

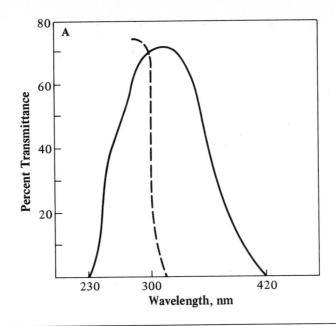

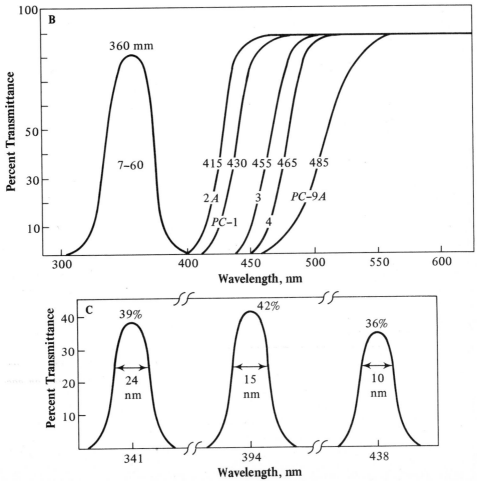

scattered radiation neither leaving the cell nor absorbed by the sample will be absorbed by the paint, not reflected through the fluorescence aperture (or slit). This is important because more than 95% of the exciting radiation is usually not absorbed by the solution, but passes through it.

There are three possible geometrical arrangements of the cell with respect to the source and the detector. The right-angle arrangement shown in Figure 9.3 is the most common, and the most advantageous for dilute solutions. The other two methods [7] are the frontal method and the in-line method.

The advantage of the right-angle arrangement is that stray exciting radiation or other stray light reflected from the cell walls is minimized. Note that in Figure 9.3, the fluorescence aperture blocks the optical path from the cell walls so that the detector cannot "see" reflected radiation from the side walls. Of course, reflection from the wall of the cell facing the detector can still occur.

Selecting a Secondary Filter and Measuring Emission. After penetrating the aperture, the emitted luminescence passes through a secondary filter or fluorescence grating that eliminates any scattered radiation. The bandwidths of the primary and secondary filters should not overlap. For example, if a 7-60 primary filter were used, then the secondary filter chosen should not transmit below about 400 nm; a good choice would be the so-called 2A secondary filter shown in Figure 9.5B.

Three types of secondary filters are available: the narrow-bandpass filter, the sharp-cut filter, and the interference filter. Typical examples of all three are shown in Figure 9.5. The most common type used in filter fluorometers is the sharp-cut filter. Sharp-cut filters are usually made of glass, as are the narrow-pass filters, but they contain chemicals that absorb all ultraviolet and visible radiation up to the wavelength specified. They have a higher transmittance (up to 85%) than do the narrow-pass filters, and have the advantage that they transmit nearly all radiation at wavelengths longer than the specified wavelength. This makes them very satisfactory for trace analysis because they allow a much more intense beam of fluorescence emission to reach the phototube than do narrow-pass or interference filters. For an extensive survey, see the article by Sill [8].

Interference filters consist of (a) two outer layers of glass on whose inner surfaces a thin semitransparent metallic film has been deposited, and (b) an inner layer of some transparent material, such as quartz, calcium fluoride, or magnesium fluoride. Most radiation striking this filter suffers destructive interference, except for the narrow band of radiation that the filter is manufactured to transmit. The bandwidth of the interference filter decreases as the wavelength it is made to transmit increases: thus the 341-nm filter (Fig. 9.5C) has a bandwidth of 24 nm, but the 438-nm filter has a bandwidth of only 10 nm.

The advantages of the fluorescence grating over the secondary filter are the same as those of the excitation grating over the primary filter. However, the secondary filter generally transmits a greater fraction of the emitted radiation than does the fluorescence grating (a possible exception would be some newer grating spectrofluorometers that have wide emission bandwidths). If the secondary filter is a sharp-cut type, then the energy that reaches the detector will be greater than if a narrow-bandpass or interference filter were used. In general, the use of secondary filter and filter fluorometers is recommended for trace analysis.

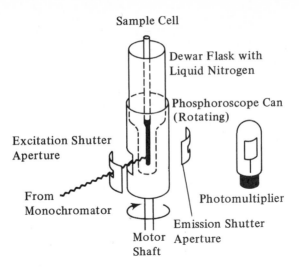

Sample Cell

Dewar Flask with
Liquid Nitrogen

Phosphoroscope Can
(Rotating)

Excitation Shutter
Aperture

From
Monochromator

Photomultiplier

Motor
Shaft

Emission Shutter
Aperture

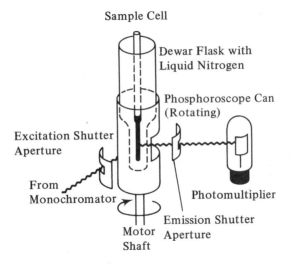

Sample Cell

Dewar Flask with
Liquid Nitrogen

Phosphoroscope Can
(Rotating)

Excitation Shutter
Aperture

From
Monochromator

Photomultiplier

Motor
Shaft

Emission Shutter
Aperture

FIGURE 9.6. *Schematic diagram of rotating-can phosphoroscope used in the phosphoroscope attachment on commercial spectrofluorometers. Top: The slit in the can is in a position to allow exciting radiation to strike the sample, but any fluorescence and phosphorescence emitted from the sample is prevented from reaching the photomultiplier by the wall of the can. Bottom: Further rotation now brings the slit in a position to allow any long-decaying emission (phosphorescence) to pass through and reach the photomultiplier. At the same time, exciting radiation is prevented from striking the sample by the wall of the can, and the sample does not fluoresce. (The phosphoroscope can usually has two slits, but the second is omitted in the diagram for clarity.) From G. H. Schenk,* Absorption of Light and Ultraviolet Radiation, *Boston: Allyn and Bacon, 1973, p 193, by permission of the publisher.*

The detector in some inexpensive filter fluorometers is a phototube, but in most of the better filter fluorometers and in all spectrofluorometers a high-gain photomultiplier tube is used. The photomultiplier is far more sensitive to low radiation levels and is therefore recommended for trace analysis.

In a filter fluorometer the output of the detector is usually displayed on a meter. In a spectrofluorometer, the output is displayed on a recorder to give the excitation and emission spectra. An oscilloscope may also be used, particularly when decay rates are to be measured.

Phosphorimeters. The design of a phosphorimeter is the same as that of the fluorometer, except for the use of a rotating can and Dewar flask. The sample solution is transferred into a small round quartz tube and the tube placed in a special Dewar flask filled with liquid nitrogen to freeze the solution into a glass. The lower part of the flask is smaller than the upper (see Fig. 9.6) and is also made of quartz to permit transmission of the exciting radiation and the phosphorescence emission. The Dewar is placed inside the rotating can, which has two apertures, or slits. As a slit moves into line with the monochromator beam, the sample is excited; but the speed of rotation is such that any fluorescence emission ceases before the slit moves into line with the emission detector, so that only phosphorescence is observed.

Filter Fluorometers

Commercially available filter fluorometers can be grouped into two categories. One category includes those filter fluorometers designed primarily or exclusively for glass cells and hence limited to excitation at wavelengths above 320 nm. In practice, this means wavelengths of 366 nm or higher with a medium-pressure mercury-arc lamp, or 320–400 nm with a phosphor-coated low-pressure mercury-arc lamp. This kind of filter fluorometer is usually modestly priced; the Coleman photofluorometer is a good example. The second category of filter fluorometer includes those instruments designed for mercury-arc excitation at 254 nm, as well as at longer wavelengths. Quartz cells must be used for 254-nm excitation, whereas glass cells can be used at wavelengths above 320 nm. The Turner and the Aminco instruments are examples of this kind of instrument.

Filter fluorometers can be used in automated analytical systems, for example the Technicon AutoAnalyzer®.

Spectrofluorometers

The commercially available spectrofluorometers can be grouped into three categories: (1) Medium-priced uncorrected spectrofluorometers, inexpensive enough to be used for routine analytical work. (2) Uncorrected research spectrofluorometers, more expensive and adaptable for many different types of investigation; one such instrument, for example, can be fitted with a phosphorescence attachment (including a rotating can) that converts it into a spectrophosphorimeter. (3) Corrected, or absolute, spectrofluorometers that *directly* record fluorescence excitation and emission spectra already corrected for instrumental parameters varying with wavelength. Naturally, this type of instrument is very expensive. Examples of each category of instrument will be discussed after the general principles have been introduced.

Components of an Uncorrected Spectrofluorometer. The design of filter fluorometers and spectrofluorometers has already been discussed; here, we shall describe in more detail the components of an uncorrected spectrofluorometer (see Fig. 9.7).

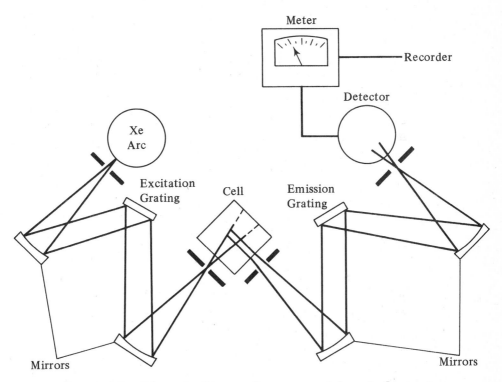

FIGURE 9.7. *Schematic diagram of an uncorrected spectrofluorometer. A high-pressure xenon arc is the usual source. The gratings can be adjusted manually, or driven by a motor for recording. The usual detector is the 1P21 photomultiplier tube. The response of the tube is displayed on a meter and is sometimes recorded. From G. H. Schenk,* Absorption of Light and Ultraviolet Radiation, *Boston: Allyn and Bacon, 1973, p 278, by permission of the publisher.*

A xenon-arc lamp is used as the source in most spectrofluorometers, since it emits continuously over the range 200–700 nm (see Fig. 9.4C) and hence can be used to obtain fluorescence excitation spectra as well as emission spectra. (Emission spectra for many substances could be obtained with a mercury-arc source, but excitation spectra could not, because the emission is discontinuous and the frequency range is so limited.) However, in uncorrected instruments using a xenon-arc lamp, no correction is made for the variation in intensity of the source with changing wavelength.

In many spectrofluorometers, the source is not directly aligned with the sample; instead (Fig. 9.7), mirrors are used to focus the radiation on the cell. The excitation grating has a fixed bandpass (such as 10 nm) on some instruments, so that the spectral bandwidth is fixed. However, on other instruments the spectral bandwidth can be varied by changing the slit-width.

As in filter fluorometers, fluorescence emission is measured at right angles to the path of the incident radiation. The emitted light passes through an exit slit and is focused by a mirror onto the emission grating. The bandwidth of the emission grating should be greater than 10 nm to achieve maximum intensity, unless a fluorescence-emission spectrum is being measured.

All spectrofluorometers are equipped with high-gain photomultipliers as detectors; this partly compensates for the smaller amount of energy that gratings transmit compared to filters. However, uncorrected spectrofluorometers do not compensate for the variable response of the photomultiplier at varying wavelengths, so the measured relative intensities of two fluorescence-emission bands of a given species are not a correct indication of the true intensities.

Medium-Priced Uncorrected Spectrofluorometers.   There are now available a number of so-called "medium-priced" spectrofluorometers. Some are equipped with a mercury source for optimum trace analysis, but a xenon source is also available. The important advantage of these instruments is that the variable-slit-width emission grating allows one to measure fluorescence at the wavelength of maximum emission using as narrow or wide a bandwidth as allowed by the instrumental design.

Uncorrected Spectrofluorometers for Research.   This category of instrument is adaptable to all kinds of research, and is generally much more expensive than the medium-priced spectrofluorometers. The best known example is the Aminco-Bowman SPF instrument. The latter can be used as a spectrofluorometer, but with the attachment of an Aminco-Keirs phosphoroscope, it can also be used as a spectrophosphorimeter. When used as a spectrofluorometer, it consists of essentially the same components as those shown in Figure 9.7.

Corrected Spectrofluorometers.   To obtain "absolute" spectra, the spectra obtained on uncorrected spectrofluorometers must be corrected point by point for instrumental parameters that vary with wavelength. Such corrections are tedious, and it is desirable to obtain spectra on a corrected spectrofluorometer if possible. These instruments correct for variations in the intensity of the xenon source so that the sample is excited at *constant energy* at all wavelengths, and for variations with wavelength in the response of the photomultiplier; emission spectra are presented directly in quanta per unit bandwidth.

Once solvent corrections have been made, *relative* quantum efficiencies (ϕ_f) can be measured directly using fluorescence emission spectra. A standard for the determination of quantum yield, however, must also be run [9]. Typical standards whose quantum yields are known are quinine sulfate ($\phi = 0.55$), fluorescein ($\phi = 0.85$), and 5-dimethylaminonaphthalene-1-sulfonic acid, or DANS acid ($\phi = 0.36$ in 0.1 M NaHCO$_3$ [10]).

9.3 APPLICATIONS

Applications to organic and inorganic substances will be discussed in separate sections. Organic applications will be discussed first since many organic compounds are used to form fluorescent chelates with inorganic cations. The applications will be restricted primarily to fluorescence, which has more analytical uses than phosphorescence at the present time.

Organic Compounds

Planar, conjugated molecules fluoresce, whereas saturated molecules and those with only one double bond do not; usually a molecule must possess at least one aromatic ring if one is to observe fluorescence or phosphorescence. Even conjugated olefins such as 1,3,5-hexatriene do not fluoresce; however, aryl-substituted olefins do. For example, *trans*-stilbene, which is planar, fluoresces; *cis*-stilbene does not, presumably because it is not planar.

The common classes of simple fluorescent organic compounds are listed in Table 9.1 according to functional groups. When a compound possesses two or more such groups, then it can also be expected to fluoresce. For example, 8-hydroxyquinoline is both a phenol (class 10) and a heterocyclic compound (class 7) and is predictably fluorescent.

Fluorescence of Selected Drugs. As an example of the use of fluorescence analysis for the determination of organic compounds, some of the recent work on drugs will be considered. Methods have been developed for the following drugs: "phenylethylamines," barbiturates, and aspirin. The "phenylethylamines" are really substituted 1-amino-2-phenylethanes; the best known phenylethylamine is amphetamine (2-amino-1-phenylpropane). Many of these compounds are excited at 260–270 nm, emit at 282–300 nm, and can be determined fluorometrically at concentrations as low as 0.2 mg/100 ml [11]. Phenylephrine and epinephrine have about the same molar absorptivities as amphetamines, and have quantum efficiencies of about 0.08, so that they can be determined at concentrations as low as 10^{-3} mg/100 ml (0.01 ppm).

Several approaches [12, 13] have been published for the fluorometric determination of barbiturates. A general structure for the "enol" tautomer of most common barbiturates is

Most barbiturates are fluorescent in 0.1 *M* base, but not in acid, because the base removes protons from the 4-hydroxyl group and the 1-nitrogen to form a fluorescent dianion [13]. Where a methyl or ethyl group is substituted on the 1-nitrogen, the barbiturate is not fluorescent. Most barbiturates are excited at 255 nm and emit at 405–420 nm [12].

TABLE 9.1. *Classes of Organic Compounds Exhibiting Usable Fluorescence*

Class	Best Examples (ϕ_f)	Weak or No Fluorescence	Literature Reference
Hydrocarbons			
1. Aryl-substituted olefins	*trans*-Stilbene	*cis*-Stilbene	[1]
2. Unsubstituted aromatic hydrocarbons	Anthracene (0.2), pyrene (0.3)	Benzene (0.04), biphenyl (P)	[1, 2]
3. Alkyl-substituted hydrocarbons	Toluene (0.1), mesitylene (0.2), 9-methylanthracene (0.3)		[7]
Nitrogen Compounds			
4. Aromatic amines	Aniline (0.1), 2-naphthylamine (0.5)	Nitroanilines (P)	[2, 7]
5. Amino acids	Tyrosine (0.2), tryptophan (0.2)	Phenylalanine (0.04)	[2]
6. "Phenylethyl-amines"	Amphetamine (0.02)		[9]
7. Heterocyclics	Quinine (0.55)	Pyridine	[2]
Halogen Compounds			
8. Cl-substituted aromatic hydrocarbons	1-Chloronaphthalene (0.06), *p*-chlorotoluene (0.02)	Chlorobenzene (P)	[2]
9. F-substituted aromatic hydrocarbons	Fluorobenzene (0.1), 1-fluoronaphthalene (0.06)		[1]
Oxygen Compounds			
10. Phenols	Phenol (0.2), 2-naphthol (0.3)	Nitrophenols (P)	[2]
11. Phenyl ethers	Anisole (0.3)		
12. Barbiturates	Phenobarbital (0.001)	5,5′-Dialkyl barbiturates	[9, 10]
13. Aromatic acids	Acetylsalicylic acid (0.02)	Benzoic acid (P)	[11]

Note: The quantum efficiency for fluorescence ϕ_f is indicated in parentheses. A (P) indicates useful phosphorescence properties.

For many years, acetylsalicylic acid (ASA) was thought not to fluoresce and was commonly determined by hydrolysis to salicylic acid, followed by fluorometric determination of the salicylic acid. A tedious separation of the salicylic acid from the acetyl derivative was therefore necessary for the determination of both in aspirin tablets. Recently, it was found that ASA does indeed fluoresce in a solvent of 1% acetic acid in chloroform [14]. ASA is excited at 280 nm and emits at 335 nm, whereas salicylic acid is excited mainly at 308 nm and emits mainly at 450 nm; it is therefore possible to determine each in the presence of the other. It is worth noting that ASA can also be determined in the presence of salicylic acid by measuring its phosphorescence [15].

Inorganic Compounds

Space does not permit a complete survey of all inorganic species; the reader is referred to an extensive account by Lytle [16] of luminescence over the entire periodic table, and to a recent monograph [2]. To be discussed here will be certain simple luminescent ions, chelates of non-transition-metal ions, and chelates of transition-metal ions.

Simple (Unchelated) Luminescent Ions. The most well-known simple ion that luminesces in solution is the uranyl ion, UO_2^{2+} (see spectra in Fig. 9.1); another is the aquated cerium(III) ion. The electron configuration of the latter is $[Xe]4f^15d^0$; the luminescence involves excitation of a $4f$ electron to a $5d$ orbital, after which luminescence occurs during a $5d \rightarrow 4f$ return transition. Cerium(III) is known to be excited at 254 nm [17]; five absorption bands in aqueous solution have been assigned to various $4f \rightarrow 5d$ transitions (those at 200, 211, 221.5, 239.5, and 252.5 nm). Cerium(III) has been determined fluorometrically in $0.4 N$ H_2SO_4 [17] using excitation at 254 nm and measuring the emission at 350 nm. Since cerium(IV) does not fluoresce, cerium(III) can be determined in the presence of cerium(IV).

Of the other lanthanides, europium(III) chloride, an f^6 ion, and terbium(III) chloride, an f^8 ion, have been reported to fluoresce weakly in dimethylformamide solution [16]. The chloride and sulfate salts of samarium(III), an f^5 ion, of gadolinium(III), an f^7 ion, and of dysprosium(III), an f^9 ion, are also reported to luminesce weakly in solution [16]. All five of these lanthanides give rise to weak lines which have been assigned to $f \rightarrow f$ transitions.

The other important ion that is luminescent in solution is the thallium(I) ion. The aquated Tl^+ ion can be excited at 215 nm and emits weakly at 370 nm; the $TlCl_4^{3-}$ ion is excited at 240 to 250 nm and emits strongly at 450 nm. A qualitative test [18] for thallium(I) is based on its violet luminescence following addition of $1 M$ potassium chloride. The fluorometric determination [19] of $10^{-7} M$ thallium(I) in $3.3 M$ HCl plus $0.8 M$ KCl is based on excitation at 250 nm and emission at 430 nm.

Chelates of Non-Transition-Metal Ions. This is the largest class of luminescent inorganic systems, and a full discussion is beyond the scope of this chapter; the reader is referred to the monograph of White and Argauer [20] for the many analytical applications of these systems. In general, the diamagnetic ions of the metals in Groups IA, IIA, IIB, IIIA, and IIIB, as well as Zr^{4+}, can be determined by measuring the fluorescence of their chelates with aromatic organic ligands. The major means of exciting these chelates is by using the π-π^* absorption bands of the chelated ligand [16]. The ions most frequently measured by fluorescence are those in Group IIIA—aluminum(III), gallium(III), indium(III), and thallium(III)—which form metal chelates with a large number of organic ligands: 8-hydroxyquinoline, 2,2'-bipyridine, salicylaldehyde derivatives, and many compounds of the azobenzene type. These ligands are usually weakly fluorescent when uncomplexed, but intensely fluorescent when complexed by these ions.

TABLE 9.2. *Selected Fluorometric Reagents for the Determination of Aluminum*

Organic Chelate	Excitation Wavelength nm	Emission Wavelength nm	Concentration Range (Final Solution)
Morin (2′,3,4′,5,7-Pentahydroxy-flavone)	270 (440)	500	4×10^{-6} to 5×10^{-5} M[a]; 4×10^{-8} to 2×10^{-7} M[b]
Pontachrome Blue Black R (PBBR)	330	635	7×10^{-8} to 6×10^{-7} M[c]
8-Hydroxyquinoline	405 (366)	520	detection limit of 10^{-6} M[d]
Acid-Alizarin Garnet R (AAGR or 2,4,2′-Trihydroxy-azobenzene-5′-sodium sulfonate)	470	575	$\sim 4 \times 10^{-8}$ to 9×10^{-6} M[e]
N-Salicylidene-2-amino-3-hydroxyfluorene (NSAHF)	445	530	$< 3 \times 10^{-8}$ to 3×10^{-7} M[f]

a. C. E. White and C. S. Lowe, *Ind. Eng. Chem. Anal. Ed.*, *12*, 229 (1940).
b. F. Will, III, *Anal. Chem.*, *33*, 1360 (1961).
c. A. Weissler and C. E. White, *Anal. Chem.*, *18*, 530 (1946).
d. W. T. Rees, *Analyst*, *87*, 202 (1962).
e. C. E. White and R. J. Argauer, *Fluorescence Analysis*, New York: Marcel Dekker, 1970, pp 55–57.
f. C. E. White, H. C. E. McFarlane, J. Fogt, and B. Fuchs, *Anal. Chem.*, *39*, 367 (1967).

The metal ion for which the most methods are available is aluminum(III); as an example of the kinds of organic ligands that have been used in fluorescence analysis, some selected organic reagents used for the determination of aluminum(III) are shown in Table 9.2.

Chelates of Transition Metals. Although many transition-metal ions form stable chelates and complexes with aromatic ligands, relatively few such systems are fluorescent. In the case of chelated paramagnetic metal ions, this is because the rate of intersystem crossing from the S_1 state to the T_1 state of the aromatic ligand is greatly increased by the unpaired electrons of metal ions. In solution, most T_1 states lose all their electronic energy by collisional deactivation or by rapid conversion to their S_0 states without emitting a photon. Thus paramagnetic metal ions such as Fe^{3+}, Co^{2+}, Ni^{2+}, and Cu^{2+} are said to quench the fluorescence of their chelates.

Another phenomenon that operates in these chelates to prevent emission is the heavy-atom effect. Heavy diamagnetic atoms such as Hg^{2+}, Au^+, and Tl^{3+} increase spin-orbit coupling, which increases the rate of intersystem crossing [21]. This effect appears to be most effective with Hg^{2+}, for which no well-documented metal-chelate luminescence has been reported. Certain Group VIII d^6 transition-metal ions have been reported to luminesce [2]. When complexed by such strong-field ligands as 1,10-phenanthroline, 2,2-bipyridine, and 2,2,2-terpyridine, iridium(III), ruthenium(II), osmium(II), and rhodium(III) form diamagnetic metal chelates. Such chelates exhibit low-energy charge-transfer absorption $(d \to \pi^*)$ and emission

($\pi^* \rightarrow d$) bands [21, 22]. Iridium(III) has actually been determined [22] by measuring luminescence (which appears to be phosphorescence) at room temperature in ethanol-water solution. It is interesting that no iron(II) chelates have been observed to luminesce, although such chelates exhibit $d \rightarrow \pi^*$ absorption bands. Fink and Ohnesorge [23] have postulated that this is the result of a crossover to a $t_{2g}{}^3 e_g{}^2 \pi^*$ spin state during the lifetime of the initial excited state of the iron(II) chelates. Such a spin state is paramagnetic and undergoes rapid intersystem crossing and rapid internal conversion to the ground state before emission can occur.

Techniques Useful for Analysis of Mixtures

The analysis of simple mixtures of organic or inorganic compounds by fluorometry without any separation is often possible because of the versatility of fluorometers. In contrast to spectrophotometers, these instruments have two instrumental variables instead of one. The analysis of the following hypothetical mixture will illustrate the use of these variables.

Suppose compound A is to be determined in the presence of compound B. Using a fluorometer, three possible techniques may be investigated:

1. If A absorbs ultraviolet radiation in a spectral region where B does not, then the grating or primary filter that selects the excitation wavelength can be adjusted so that only A is excited. Then only A will emit fluorescence and the detector will measure only emission from A.

2. Suppose that B absorbs in the same spectral region as A, but that the term $\epsilon bc\phi_f$ (see Eqn. 9.6) for B is ≤ 0.01 of that of A. It is probable that $\leq 1\%$ of the instrumental readout, F, will be emission from B, and A can still be accurately measured.

3. If A and B both absorb in the same spectral region, but A emits fluorescence in a different spectral region than B, then the fluorometer can be adjusted to measure only fluorescence from A. This is done by manipulating the grating or secondary filter that selects the fluorescence-emission wavelengths falling on the detector. Even though both A and B are emitting light, the detector "sees" only the emission from A.

As an example of the first technique, consider the determination of the aromatic hydrocarbon, anthracene, in the presence of its isomer, phenanthrene. Phenanthrene does not absorb in the ultraviolet at wavelengths longer than 360 nm. Since anthracene has an excitation band above 360 nm, it is possible to excite only anthracene. In an experimental study [24] of this type of mixture, the actual wavelength used was 365 nm. As can be seen from Figure 9.8, the best wavelength at which to measure the fluorescence of anthracene on an uncorrected spectrofluorometer would be about 400 nm. It is also possible to determine phenanthrene by use of the second technique. Phenanthrene and anthracene are excited intensely at 265 nm, but phenanthrene fluoresces at 350 nm where anthracene does not (Fig. 9.8).

It should not be assumed that all simple mixtures can be analyzed by either of the above techniques. Consider the aromatic hydrocarbon pyrene in the presence of an equal amount of anthracene. The ultraviolet absorption (and fluorescence excitation) spectrum of anthracene completely overlaps that of pyrene. It can be

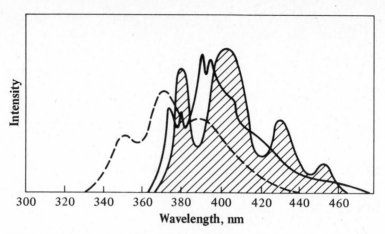

FIGURE 9.8. *The uncorrected fluorescence spectra of phenanthrene (dotted line), anthracene (shaded area), and pyrene (solid line). (Phenanthrene is excited best at 265 nm; anthracene may be excited at 365, 375, or 250 nm; and pyrene is excited at 335 nm.) From G. H. Schenk,* Absorption of Light and Ultraviolet Radiation, *Boston: Allyn and Bacon, 1973, p 175, by permission of the publisher.*

seen from Figure 9.8 that the same is true for the fluorescence emission spectra. Therefore, a separation or chemical reaction is needed before the pyrene can be measured fluorometrically.

In some cases it has been found possible to measure the concentration of each component of a two-component mixture (A and B) by measuring the total fluorescence from both components at two wavelengths. The concentration of each component is calculated by inserting the measured fluorescence intensities into two simultaneous equations, in a manner similar to that used in analyzing ultraviolet-visible absorption measurements (Sec. 7.5).

Quantitative Analysis after Chemical Reaction. A large number of fluorometric analyses have been performed after converting a nonfluorescent or weakly fluorescent compound into an intensely fluorescent species. One example, which involves only hydrolysis, is the measurement of acetylsalicylic acid as salicylic acid or the salicylate anion. Because the *total* concentration of these two acids in blood is very important in the treatment of rheumatic disease, acetylsalicylic acid is converted to salicylic acid by hydrolysis and the total measured as salicylate. First the serum protein is removed, then the acetylsalicylic acid is hydrolyzed under alkaline conditions to salicylic acid and acetic acid (in alkaline solution, an equilibrium mixture of the anions and acids is present). The alkaline solution is then excited at 310 nm and the fluorescence emission is measured at 410 nm.

Instrumental Approaches for Problem Solving

It is of interest to briefly compare the use of a spectrofluorometer and a filter fluorometer in solving analytical problems. The standard procedure is to use the spectrofluorometer to obtain the excitation and emission spectra, and then choose the proper filters so that quantitative measurements can be made on the filter fluorometer. What happens, however, if the excitation band in a routine analysis does not straddle a prominent mercury line? Should one resort to a medium-priced spectrofluorometer with a xenon arc for routine analytical work? Again, what should be done if the emission band of a desired constituent in a mixture overlaps with the band of a second constituent so that it is impossible to use a sharp-cut secondary filter? Possible approaches to these problems can be seen in the filter-fluorometric analysis of aspirin tablets for acetylsalicylic acid (ASA) and salicylic acid [25].

The corrected excitation and emission spectra of ASA and salicylic acid are shown in Figure 9.9. The first problem involved choosing the most efficient method of exciting ASA, since its excitation bands were at 235 and 278 nm. One possible approach was to use the intense 254-nm line emitted by a low-pressure mercury arc (even though this line was not straddled by either excitation band), hoping that its high intensity would compensate for the low ε of ASA at 254 nm. Using this excitation wavelength, however, meant that salicylic acid would also be excited somewhat. This in turn prevented the use of a sharp-cut secondary filter or even the 7-60 narrow-pass filter, since salicylic acid emits between 350 and 400 nm. This problem was solved by using an interference filter with a transmittance range of 329–353 nm, peaking at 341 nm. No interference was encountered from salicylic acid in this region because the emission was so weak, and because the aspirin tablets analyzed contained low levels of salicylic acid.

Obviously, a medium-priced spectrofluorometer could have been equipped with a xenon-arc source and used for the analysis, but the filter fluorometer is usually preferred for routine work. In addition, the latter is more sensitive; for example, the detection limit for ASA on the Turner spectrofluorometer is $10^{-6}\ M$, whereas the detection limit using the Turner filter fluorometer is $10^{-7}\ M$.

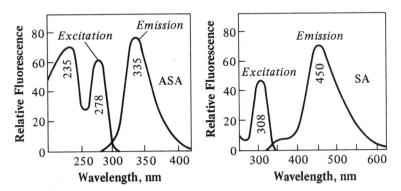

FIGURE 9.9. *Left: The corrected fluorescence excitation and emission spectra of acetylsalicylic acid (ASA). In 1% acetic acid in chloroform, only the 278-nm excitation band can be observed; in ethyl ether-isopentane-ethanol solvent, both the 235- and 278-nm excitation bands are observed. Right: The corrected fluorescence excitation and emission spectra of salicylic acid (SA) as obtained in 1% acetic acid in chloroform. From* G. H. Schenk, Absorption of Light and Ultraviolet Radiation, *Boston: Allyn and Bacon, 1973, p 285, by permission of the publisher.*

Another problem was to choose the most efficient method of exciting salicylic acid, which has only one useful excitation band (at 308 nm). One approach was to use a special phosphor-lamp source emitting between 270 and 340 nm with a peak at 306 nm; this gave good sensitivity for salicylic acid. Another approach was to use the somewhat weak 313 nm line emitted by a low-pressure mercury-arc lamp, selected with a combination primary filter consisting of the 7-54 filter along with a plastic filter used to cut out the 254-nm mercury line. This procedure essentially excited only the salicylic acid, not ASA. In both cases, a sharp-cut filter with 37% T at 465 nm was used to exclude any possible emission by ASA.

In routine analysis for salicylic acid, a medium-priced spectrofluorometer again could have been used. Since the xenon arc has a higher intensity at 308 nm than at 254, a spectrofluorometer with a xenon arc could give a lower detection limit for salicylic acid than would a filter fluorometer. In the analysis for salicylic acid in aspirin tablets, however, it did not prove necessary. The filter fluorometer thus provided a cheaper, more convenient, approach to routine analysis.

Uses of Fluorescence and Phosphorescence in Chromatography

Fluorescence and phosphorescence measurements have long been used to follow the separation of certain luminescent organic compounds in such techniques as liquid chromatography, gas-liquid chromatography, paper chromatography, and thin-layer chromatography (TLC). Such measurements are useful in many cases, but their application to the first three separation techniques is limited, since usually only organic molecules containing an aromatic ring fluoresce or phosphoresce. Thus, luminescence measurements cannot detect acyclic or nonaromatic cyclic organic molecules. In contrast, luminescence measurements find general use in TLC. Before discussing this, some applications of luminescence to the first three separation techniques will be mentioned.

An outstanding example is the separation and characterization of polynuclear aromatic hydrocarbons in polluted air reported by Sawicki and coworkers [26]. Column chromatography employing alumina was used to separate the hydrocarbons; fluorescence, ultraviolet spectrophotometry, and colorimetric tests were used to identify aromatic hydrocarbons in the various fractions.

Fluorescence and phosphorescence have been used by Drushel and Sommers [27] to identify nitrogen compounds in petroleum fractions following gas-chromatographic separations. The nitrogen-rich petroleum fractions investigated were so complex and so small in size that the greater sensitivity of luminescence techniques over other spectroscopic techniques was essential for good analysis.

In the field of paper chromatography, spots of fluorescent organic molecules have been identified on paper chromatograms by inspecting the paper under either short-wavelength (254 nm) or long-wavelength (300–400 nm) ultraviolet radiation. In most cases, the spots appear as blue or violet colors. Sawicki and Pfaff [28] have shown that phosphorescent organic molecules can also be identified on paper chromatograms.

In the more popular TLC separations, on the other hand, adsorbents or precoated TLC sheets containing certain inorganic phosphors are available that emit intense visible radiation over the entire length of the TLC chromatogram *except* where spots of the separated organic compounds are present. Most organic compounds quench the luminescence of the phosphor, and the spots appear as dark shadows against the brilliant luminescent background of unquenched phosphor.

Green (522 nm) is the most common luminescent color used on TLC sheets. Typical green phosphors are (a) pure zinc silicate and (b) calcium silicate with a manganese-lead activator. Most such green phosphors emit only under short wavelength (254 nm) ultraviolet excitation, permitting examination of the TLC sheet for fluorescent organic compounds under long-wavelength excitation. A phosphor of zinc and cadmium sulfides is available that yields an off-white luminescence under both short-wavelength and long-wavelength ultraviolet excitation.

In addition to the qualitative work described above, quantitative measurements on TLC plates are also possible. Lefar and Lewis [29] have measured organic compounds both by the amount of emission on an adsorbent without a phosphor, and by the amount of quenching of a phosphor mixed with an adsorbent. Janchen and Pataki [30] have discussed many examples of direct quantitative measurement on TLC plates of spot luminescence. Another interesting application is the phosphorimetric measurement of nicotine, nornicotine, and anabasine in tobacco after separation by TLC [31].

Applications in Studies of Pollution

Fluorescence and phosphorescence have been used to investigate the pollution of both water and air. Fluorescent compounds, especially, have been used in the study of water flow and water pollution [32]. "Fluorescent tracers" are superior to radioactive tracers because they can be used at concentrations so low (≤ 0.001 ppb) that they constitute neither a real contamination nor a health hazard. A common fluorescent dye, the first such dye to be used, is Rhodamine B; its fluorescence emission is independent of pH from pH 5 to 10 and it can be determined at concentrations above 0.01 ppb.

The use of tracers enables industries and cities to control or reduce pollution before it occurs. Measuring the "time-of-travel" (mean velocity) of rivers and streams and the mixing of those waters into lakes and oceans helps to indicate where to discharge waste, when to discharge it, and at what rate. Tracers have been used, for instance, in San Francisco Bay and in Chesapeake Bay to facilitate correct waste disposal in those waters.

Fluorescence and phosphorescence both find use in the analysis of polluted air for specific chemical pollutants. Fluorescence is especially useful because many aromatic hydrocarbons are intensely fluorescent.

Since aromatic hydrocarbons are one of the chief pollutants in air, the fluorometer has been used by the Public Health Service [33] for determining these compounds. Fluorometry is more useful than ultraviolet spectrophotometry in pollution analysis, not only because it is more versatile, but also because it can measure the very low concentrations of hydrocarbons found in samples collected from the air. Such analyses are all the more important because some aromatic hydrocarbons are carcinogenic. One of the best known carcinogenic aromatic hydrocarbons is benzo[a]pyrene, or 3,4-benzpyrene. A very specific method for determining benzo-

[a]pyrene in the aromatic-hydrocarbon fraction of polluted air samples has been developed, using sulfuric acid as a solvent in which the compound forms a cation with a strong absorption band at 520 nm [33]. A few other aromatic hydrocarbons have weak absorption bands at 520 nm, but none of these emit fluorescent light at 545 nm as does benzo[a]pyrene. To determine benzo[a]pyrene, the sample is excited at 520 nm and the fluorescence emission at 545 nm measured with the fluorometer. It has been shown that benzo[a]pyrene can be estimated in artificial mixtures of over 40 similar compounds without separation. This analysis is also unusual in that visible light, not ultraviolet light, is used to excite a molecule.

Medicine

One of the most useful applications of fluorescence is in the routine determination of certain important molecules in body fluids for diagnostic purposes. Some such molecules are naturally fluorescent, but others must be chemically treated to form fluorescent products. For example, the amino acids tyrosine, tryptophan, and phenylalanine are all measured fluorometrically. Both tyrosine and tryptophan possess aromatic rings that absorb intensely and therefore have an intense natural fluorescence. Tyrosine is excited at both 225 and 280 nm, and emits at 303 nm; tryptophan is excited at 220 and 280 nm and emits at 438 nm [34].

In contrast, phenylalanine possesses a weakly absorbing benzene ring and does not emit fluorescence intensely enough for measurement of trace quantities. The usual analytical methods involve treating it with ninhydrin, copper(II) ion, and L-leucyl-L-alanine [35] to give a highly fluorescent product. Fluorometric measurement of phenylalanine is useful in testing for phenylketonuria, a hereditary metabolic disorder that causes mental retardation. In one series of tests, adult control samples ran 1.5 mg phenylalanine per 100 ml of blood serum; in contrast, parents of phenylketonuriac children ran 1.9 mg per 100 ml, and the phenylketonuriacs themselves ran 30 mg per 100 ml. Since phenylketonuriacs cannot convert phenylalanine efficiently to tyrosine, the levels of tyrosine were about half of those in the blood of control samples.

Advantages and Disadvantages of Fluorescence Analysis

In summary, the two main advantages of fluorescence analysis are that it is capable of measuring much lower concentrations than spectrophotometric analysis (high sensitivity), and that it is potentially more selective because both the excitation and emission wavelengths can be varied. At its best, fluorometric analysis is sensitive to 10^{-8} to 10^{-9} M, depending on the intensity of the source and the quantum efficiency and molar absorptivity of the sample. Where the molar absorptivity or quantum efficiency are small, the source or monochromator can be adjusted to make analysis possible. Such an adjustment is normally not done in absorption spectrophotometry.

Another advantage (also a disadvantage) is that only certain aromatic molecules fluoresce. This excludes from fluorometry all acyclic and alicyclic molecules, as well as those aromatic molecules that do not fluoresce. (This is of course an advantage when analyzing a mixture containing a fluorescent aromatic molecule and several acyclic or alicyclic molecules.)

Other disadvantages to fluorescence analysis have to do with unwanted excited-state interactions. The principal and most serious disadvantage here is quenching; since many nonfluorescent molecules, even in trace quantities, can quench a fluorescent molecule in the S_1 state, the direct analysis of complex mixtures without separation is uncommon. Secondly, since many organic compounds undergo photochemical reactions when irradiated with ultraviolet light, care must be taken to avoid photodecomposition in making quantitative analytical measurements, particularly with intense sources.

Finally, another general disadvantage to fluorescence analysis is that it does not exhibit very high precision or accuracy; a typical level might be $\pm 2\text{--}10\%$. Still, the high sensitivity and selectivity of fluorescence analysis make it the method of choice in many instances.

SELECTED BIBLIOGRAPHY

For further reading in the area of recent developments in fluorescence, the reader is referred to the following monographs:

GUILBAULT, G. G., ed. *Fluorescence: Theory, Instrumentation, and Practice.* New York: Marcel Dekker, 1967.

GUILBAULT, G. G. *Practical Fluorescence: Theory, Methods, and Techniques.* New York: Marcel Dekker, 1973.

SCHENK, G. H. *Absorption of Light and Ultraviolet Radiation: Fluorescence and Phosphorescence Emission.* Boston: Allyn and Bacon, 1973.

UDENFRIEND, S. *Fluorescence Assay in Biology and Medicine.* New York: Academic Press, 1962.

WHITE, C. E., and ARGAUER, R. J. *Fluorescence Analysis.* New York: Marcel Dekker, 1970.

For further reading in the area of recent luminescence work in general, the reader is referred to the following monographs:

PARKER, C. A. *Photoluminescence of Solutions.* New York: Elsevier, 1968.

WINEFORDNER, J. D., SCHULMAN, S. G., and O'HAVER, T. C. *Luminescence Spectrometry in Analytical Chemistry.* New York: Wiley-Interscience, 1972.

ZANDER, M. *Phosphorimetry.* New York: Academic Press, 1968.

REFERENCES

1. D. N. HERCULES, ed., *Fluorescence and Phosphorescence Analysis.* New York: Wiley-Interscience, 1966, chap. 1.

2. G. H. SCHENK, *Absorption of Light and Ultraviolet Radiation: Fluorescence and Phosphorescence Emission.* Boston: Allyn and Bacon, 1973, chap. 4.

3. E. LIM, quoted in *J. Chem. Phys., 41,* 3042 (1964).

4. A. L. CONRAD, *Treatise on Analytical Chemistry,* part I, vol. 5. New York: Wiley-Interscience, 1964, pp 3057–78.

5. J. D. WINEFORDNER, in D. M. Hercules, ed., *Fluorescence and Phosphorescence Anal-*

ysis. New York: Wiley-Interscience, 1966, pp 169–84.

6. W. J. MCCARTHY and J. D. WINEFORDNER, *J. Chem. Educ., 44,* 136 (1967).

7. C. A. PARKER, *Photoluminescence of Solutions.* New York: Elsevier, 1968, pp 220–34.

8. C. W. SILL, *Anal. Chem., 33,* 1584 (1961).

9. G. K. TURNER, *Science, 146,* 183 (1964).

10. C. M. HIMEL and R. T. MAYER, *Anal. Chem., 42,* 130 (1970).

11. C. I. MILES and G. H. SCHENK, *Anal. Chem., 45,* 130 (1973).

12. C. I. Miles and G. H. Schenk, *Anal. Lett.*, *4*, 71 (1971); and *Anal. Chem.*, *45*, 130 (1973).

13. L. A. Gifford, W. P. Hayes, L. A. King, J. N. Miller, D. T. Burns, and J. W. Brides, *Anal. Chim. Acta*, *62*, 214 (1972); *Anal. Chem.*, *46*, 94 (1974).

14. C. I. Miles and G. H. Schenk, *Anal. Chem.*, *42*, 656 (1970).

15. J. D. Winefordner and H. W. Latz, *Anal. Chem.*, *35*, 1517 (1963).

16. F. E. Lytle, *Appl. Spec.*, *24*, 319 (1970).

17. W. A. Armstrong, D. W. Grant, and W. G. Humphreys, *Anal. Chem.*, *35*, 1300 (1963).

18. C. W. Sill and H. E. Peterson, *Anal. Chem.*, *21*, 1266 (1949).

19. G. F. Kirkbright, T. S. West and C. Woodward, *Talanta*, *12*, 517 (1965).

20. C. E. White and R. J. Argauer, *Fluorescence Analysis*. New York: Marcel Dekker, 1970.

21. W. E. Ohnesorge, in D. M. Hercules, ed., *Fluorescence and Phosphorescence Analysis*. New York: Wiley-Interscience, 1966, chap. 4.

22. D. W. Fink and W. E. Ohnesorge, *Anal. Chem.*, *41*, 39 (1969).

23. D. W. Fink and W. E. Ohnesorge, *J. Amer. Chem. Soc.*, *91*, 4995 (1969).

24. G. A. Thommes and E. Leininger, *Talanta*, *7*, 181 (1961).

25. G. H. Schenk, F. Boyer, C. I. Miles, and D. R. Wirz, *Anal. Chem.*, *44*, 1593 (1972).

26. E. Sawicki, W. Elbert, T. W. Stanley, T. R. Hauser, and F. T. Fox, *Anal. Chem.*, *32*, 810 (1960).

27. H. V. Drushel and A. L. Sommers, *Anal. Chem.*, *38*, 10, 19 (1966).

28. E. Sawicki and J. D. Pfaff, *Anal. Chim. Acta*, *32*, 521 (1965).

29. M. S. Lefar and A. D. Lewis, *Anal. Chem.*, *42*(3), 79A (1970).

30. D. Janchen and G. Pataki, *J. Chromatogr.*, *33*, 391 (1968).

31. J. D. Winefordner and H. A. Moye, *Anal. Chim. Acta*, *32*, 278 (1965).

32. G. K. Turner, *Fluorometry Reviews Bulletin on Fluorescent Tracers*, Feb. 1968, Acc. No. 9941.

33. E. Sawicki, W. Elbert, T. W. Stanley, T. R. Hauser, and F. T. Fox, *Int. J. Air Poll.*, *2*, 273 (1960).

34. F. W. J. Teal and G. Weber, *Biochem. J.*, *65*, 476 (1957).

35. P. K. Wong, *Clin. Chem.*, *10*, 1098 (1964).

PROBLEMS

1. (a) Draw a molecular-energy diagram similar to Figure 9.2 for the uranyl (UO_2^{2+}) ion, assuming that the transition in the 225–250 nm region is S_0-S_2 and the transition in the 417 nm region is S_0-S_1. (b) Repeat part (a), assuming instead that the transition in the 225–250 nm region is S_0-S_1 and the transition in the 417-nm region is S_0-T_1. Will the emission be fluorescence or phosphorescence?

2. Draw a molecular-energy diagram showing the transitions involved in the phosphorescence of anthracene, which occurs at 680 nm.

3. Show that each side of Equation 9.8 has the proper units.

4. Compare the slope of a calibration curve for a molecule with a molar absorptivity of 10^5 and a quantum efficiency of 0.01 with that for a molecule having a molar absorptivity of 10^3 and a quantum efficiency of 0.10.

5. Propose two different spectrofluorometric schemes of analysis for the determination of anthracene in phenanthrene, giving all wavelengths. (Only one scheme should use selective excitation of anthracene.)

6. Propose two different filter-fluorometric schemes of analysis for the determination of anthracene in the presence of naphthalene; the schemes must involve two different mercury sources. Assume that $\varepsilon c \phi_f$ for naphthalene is less than 1% that of anthracene at any excitation wavelength employed.

7. Explain what instrumental difficulties might be involved in the filter-fluorometric analysis of acetylsalicylic acid in the presence of a large excess of salicylic acid. Would a spectrofluorometer be superior? Why or why not?

8. A bottle of tonic water is to be analyzed for its quinine content by fluorescence spectrometry, with excitation at 350 nm and emission intensity measured at 450 nm. One milliliter of tonic water is diluted to 100 ml with 0.05 M H_2SO_4; its emission intensity is 8.44 (arbitrary units). A series of quinine standards, in 0.05 M H_2SO_4, is prepared and the emission intensities measured (in parentheses): 100 ppm (293 units), 10.0 ppm (52.3), 1.00 ppm (12.0), 0.100 ppm (1.26), 10 ppb (0.158), and 1.0 ppb (0.015). The emission intensity of 0.05 M H_2SO_4 is negligible. Plot the calibration curve for quinine fluorescence, and determine the quinine content of the original tonic-water sample.

9. Two urine specimens from patients undergoing quinine therapy for malaria are to be analyzed for their quinine level. The following samples are run through the analytical procedure: A. a distilled water blank; B. a standard containing 2.00 μg quinine/ml in distilled water; C. a "blank" urine, which contains no quinine; D. urine specimen #1; and E. urine specimen #2. Two milliliters are taken from each sample, their pH is raised to 9 with concentrated ammonium hydroxide, and they are extracted with 4.00 ml of chloroform. Two milliliters of the chloroform extract is extracted with 2.00 ml of 0.05 M H_2SO_4, which is then placed in a fluorescence cuvette and the fluorescence intensity at 450 nm is determined. The relative emission intensities for the five samples are: A. 1.7; B. 50.2; C. 14.3; D. 82.8; and E. 58.7. Assuming that the emission intensity is directly proportional to the quinine concentration (once allowance has been made for the two "blank" emissions), determine the quinine level in the urine specimens.

10. An organic compound is to be determined by fluorescence spectrometry, with a choice of excitation at 250 nm (with emission at 350 nm) or at 500 nm (600-nm emission). A xenon-arc lamp is to be used as the excitation source of a spectrofluorometer (see Fig. 9.4C, p 236), with an S-5 photomultiplier tube as the detector (see Fig. 10.8, p 267). The compound has a molar absorptivity of 15,000 at 250 nm and of 4,000 at 500 nm. Assume that the quantum efficiencies for fluorescence are the same at the two wavelengths. (a) From this information and that in Figures 9.4C and 10.8, estimate the ratio of the signal obtained with excitation at 250 nm to that with excitation at 500 nm. (b) What other assumptions have to be made?

11. Describe the principles of phosphorescence. Why are phosphorescence measurements frequently made at liquid nitrogen temperatures?

10

Flame Spectroscopy

Gary D. Christian

In this chapter, the spectroscopy of atoms will be discussed. Since free atoms cannot undergo rotational or vibrational transitions as do molecules, only electronic transitions can take place when energy is absorbed or emitted. Because the transitions are discrete (quantized), line spectra are observed.

There are various ways of obtaining free atoms and measuring the radiation they absorb or emit. This chapter will deal with flame spectroscopic and related techniques. The next chapter will describe emission spectroscopic methods using electrical excitation.

In flame spectroscopy, a solution is aspirated into a flame and the inorganic compounds thermally dissociated into atomic vapor. There are three types of flame spectroscopy: atomic absorption, atomic emission, and atomic fluorescence. The first two techniques will be emphasized because commercial instruments are widely available for these, whereas atomic fluorescence is used more for specific applications and as a research tool. Many of the points made with respect to flame chemistry, interferences, and so forth apply also to atomic fluorescence. Various types of atomic fluorescence and the specific instrumentation required are considered at the end of the chapter.

10.1 PRINCIPLES

When a solution is aspirated into a flame, the heat of the flame first causes the solvent to evaporate. The microcrystals remaining are partially or wholly dissociated into elements in the gaseous form (atomization). Some of these atoms can absorb radiant energy of a characteristic wavelength and become excited to a higher electronic state; or, they may absorb energy from the flame and become thermally excited.

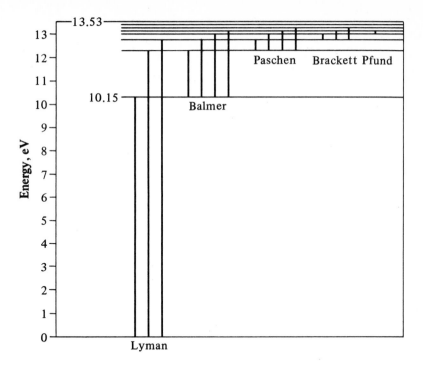

FIGURE 10.1. *Energy-level diagram for hydrogen.*

The atoms lose their excitation energy either as heat by collision with other atoms, or as radiation of a characteristic wavelength as the electron returns to a lower excited state or to the ground state. The absorption of thermal energy from a flame with subsequent emission of some or all of the energy as a spectral line is called *atomic emission*. Measurement of this emitted radiation is known as *atomic emission spectroscopy* or *flame emission spectroscopy* [1]; we will use the first term.

The term *atomic absorption* refers to the absorption of energy from a light source, with a consequent decrease in the radiant power transmitted through the flame. Measurement of this absorption corresponds to *atomic absorption spectroscopy*.

In order to better understand the physical basis of atomic absorption, let us consider the hydrogen atom. In the hydrogen atom, the electron can exist in several well defined and quantized energy states, as shown on the energy-level diagram in Figure 10.1.* The lowest energy state is arbitrarily put at zero on the energy scale. The other energy levels, calibrated relative to this ground state, are represented by the horizontal bars on the diagram.

---

* The names on the series of lines refer to the discoverers of the different series. The series are described accurately by Balmer's law:

$$\frac{1}{\lambda} = R\left(\frac{1}{n^2} - \frac{1}{m^2}\right)$$

where R is a constant (109,677.58 cm^{-1}), and n and m are integers ($m > n$). The Balmer series, for example, corresponds to $n = 2$, and $m = 1, 2, 3, \ldots$. The Lyman series is $n = 1$, the Paschen series is $n = 3$, the Brackett series is $n = 4$, and the Pfund series is $n = 5$.

The diagram indicates that states do not occur beyond a definite energy level (13.53 eV in the case of hydrogen). This limit is called the *ionization potential* and is the "energy level" at which the electron has left the influence of the nucleus.

The vertical lines on the diagram indicate some of the possible transitions the electron can make from one energy level to another. Each transition requires either a gain or a loss of energy equal to the difference between the two energy levels. If this energy is in the form of radiation, it is given by

$h = 4.134 \times 10^{-5} \, eVs.$

$$E_u - E_1 = h\nu = h\frac{c}{\lambda} \qquad (10.1)$$

where E_u = the energy of the upper energy state
E_1 = the energy of the lower energy state

The majority of atoms in a flame are in the ground state (E_0); therefore, many electronic transitions originate from this state. Such transitions are limited in number, since by quantum-mechanical selection rules some energy levels are not directly accessible from the ground state.

Usually, a *resonance wavelength* is defined as the wavelength corresponding to a transition between the ground state and the next accessible level. Here, the term will be used more broadly to include all transitions originating from the ground state. These are the transitions of most interest for the present purpose, because they represent the wavelengths at which absorption or emission is strongest and is usually measured.

The partial energy-level diagrams for lithium, sodium, and potassium are illustrated (in a slightly different form) in Figure 10.2. The dashed lines represent the respective ionization potentials of the elements. Only the major resonance transitions are shown. (Sodium, for example, has over twenty allowed transitions.) The primary resonance lines for these elements are the 671-nm red lithium doublet, the 590-nm sodium doublet, and the 767/769-nm potassium doublet.* Absorption is strongest at these three wavelengths and is followed in intensity by the lines originating in the ground state and ending in a higher excited state. Absorption lines are also observed that arise from transitions involving two excited states. Analytical advantage can be taken of these different absorption intensities for measuring different concentration ranges of a metal, because each absorption line has a different sensitivity.

Figure 10.3 illustrates energy changes in a simple system. The electron has been excited from the ground state to an excited state by the absorption of a quantum of light whose energy is equal to the energy difference between the two states. Within a short time, about 10^{-14} to 10^{-7} sec, the electron is *deactivated* by one of several processes. For instance, it may spontaneously revert to the ground state by emitting a quantum of radiation of the same wavelength as was absorbed (i.e., it fluoresces— cf. Chap. 9). Since this radiation is emitted in all directions, the amount entering

---

* Doublets and higher-order multiplets arise owing to spin (of the valence electrons involved in spectral transitions) which is associated with orbital motion. That is, the spin quantum number, s, may have the value of $+1/2$ or $-1/2$, and so there exist two energy levels for the electron. The occurrence of doublets and multiplets is limited by selection rules (i.e., there are certain forbidden transitions) and by the number of valence electrons.

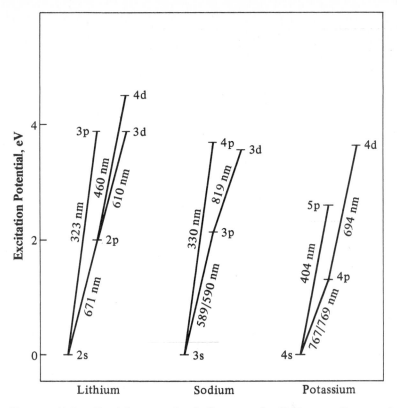

FIGURE 10.2. *Partial energy-level diagrams for lithium, sodium, and potassium. Adapted from G. D. Christian and F. J. Feldman,* Atomic Absorption Spectroscopy: Applications in Agriculture, Biology, and Medicine, *New York: Wiley-Interscience, 1970, p 8, by permission of John Wiley and Sons.*

the monochromator-detector stage of the instrument being used is generally negligible compared to the amount absorbed, and usually does not interfere with the absorption measurement.

Of the other possible methods of deactivation or "energy relaxation," the most common is *quenching*, or radiationless deactivation. This occurs when another atom interacts with the excited atom. The energy of the excited electron is converted into an increase in the kinetic energy of the two atoms; that is, it is usually lost as heat.

A combination of radiation deactivation and radiationless deactivation may occur with a given atomic species if there is another state between the excited state and the ground state. The electron may revert to this intermediate state by emitting radiation of a different wavelength; the wavelength will be longer than that of the radiation absorbed since it corresponds to a smaller amount of energy. The electron may then proceed to the ground state by radiationless deactivation.

The energy required to excite an electron from the ground state may also be acquired thermally, i.e., from collision with other atoms, or with molecules, ions,

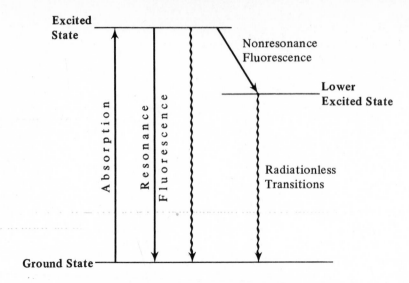

FIGURE 10.3. *Energy changes in a simple system.*

or free electrons present in the flame. Deactivation by emitting a photon following thermal excitation is termed *atomic emission*. For excitation to occur, the flame temperature must be sufficiently high to produce the electronic transition; for this reason, only those elements with long-wavelength (low-energy) emission resonance lines generally exhibit intense flame emission in a relatively cool flame.

10.2 THEORY

It is of interest to know the number of thermally excited atoms relative to the number of ground state atoms at a given flame temperature. In a quantity of atoms, under the same external conditions, the electrons are not all in the same energy level but are statistically distributed among the levels. At a flame temperature T (in K), the ratio of the number of atoms N_u in an excited (upper) state u to the number of atoms N_0 in the ground state is given by the Maxwell-Boltzmann expression

$$\frac{N_u}{N_0} = \frac{g_u}{g_0} e^{-(E_u - E_0)/kT} \tag{10.2}$$

The excited state has energy E_u and the ground state has energy E_0; g_u and g_0 are the *statistical weights* of the excited and ground states, respectively, and k is the Boltzmann constant. The statistical weights can be regarded as the probability that an electron will reside in a given energy level, and can be obtained from quantum-mechanical calculations. Equation 10.2 permits calculation of the ratio (N_u/N_0) at a given flame temperature when the frequency or wavelength for the transition is known. Some typical values are given in Table 10.1.

The statistical weights, g, can be calculated from the equation $g = 2J + 1$, where J is the Russel-Saunders coupling and is equal to $L + S$ or $L - S$. L is the total orbital angular momentum quantum number, represented by the sharp (S),

TABLE 10.1. *Values of N_u/N_0 for Different Resonance Lines*

Resonance lines (nm)	Excitation energy (eV)	g_u/g_0	N_u/N_0		
			2000 K	3000 K	4000 K
Cs 852.1	1.46	2	4.44×10^{-4}	7.24×10^{-3}	2.98×10^{-2}
Na 589.0	2.11	2	9.86×10^{-6}	5.88×10^{-4}	4.44×10^{-3}
Ca 422.7	2.93	3	1.21×10^{-7}	3.69×10^{-5}	6.04×10^{-4}
Zn 213.8	5.80	3	7.29×10^{-15}	5.38×10^{-10}	1.48×10^{-6}

principal (P), diffuse (D), and fundamental (F) series ($L = 0, 1, 2,$ and 3, respectively); S is spin, $\pm 1/2$. The information is generally supplied in the form of *term symbols*, which have the general form $N^M L_J$, where N is the principal quantum number and M is the multiplicity. Hence, the transition for the cesium 852.1-nm line, omitting the principal quantum number N is $^2S_{1/2} - {}^2P_{3/2}$, and $g_u/g_0 = [2(3/2) + 1]/[2(1/2) + 1] = 4/2 = 2$.

Example 10.1. The 228.8-nm cadmium line corresponds to a $^1S_0 - {}^1S_1$ transition. Calculate the ratio of N_u/N_0 in an air-acetylene flame.

Solution: The temperature (Table 10.2, p 271) is 2250°C or 2523 K.

$$g_u/g_0 = [2(1) + 1]/[2(0) + 1] = 3/1.$$

$$\nu = \frac{c}{\lambda} = \frac{2.998 \times 10^{10} \text{ cm/sec}}{2.288 \times 10^{-5} \text{ cm}} = 1.310 \times 10^{15} \text{ sec}^{-1}$$

$$E_u - E_0 = h\nu = (6.626 \times 10^{-27} \text{ erg-sec})(1.310 \times 10^{15} \text{ sec}^{-1})$$
$$= 8.682 \times 10^{-12} \text{ erg}$$

$$\frac{N_u}{N_0} = \frac{g_u}{g_0} e^{-(E_u - E_0)/kT}$$

$$= \frac{3}{1} \exp\left[-\frac{8.682 \times 10^{-12} \text{ erg}}{(1.3805 \times 10^{-16} \text{ erg K}^{-1})(2523 \text{ K})}\right]$$

$$= 3e^{-24.93} = 4.5 \times 10^{-11}$$

The hottest flames generally used in atomic absorption and emission spectroscopy rarely reach temperatures of 4000 K. It is apparent from the data in Table 10.1 that even at the highest temperature, the excited-state population is very small in comparison to the ground-state population. This is true even for the relatively easily excited alkali metals, which are readily determined by atomic emission spectroscopy. Elements such as zinc show poor sensitivity by atomic emission because an extremely small number of the atoms is thermally excited.

Why, then, do the alkali metals exhibit good sensitivity by atomic emission spectroscopy? The answer is that one measures the difference between a theoretically zero signal in the absence of the sample and a finite signal in the presence of the sample. Therefore, the small signal arising from the sample can be readily amplified and measured. The limit of detection is governed by the noise level of the photomultiplier detector, primarily the "shot-noise" (the random fluctuation of the electron current from any electron-emitting surface in a phototube), and by the fact that the atomic emission signal may be superimposed on an intense and noisy flame spectrum.

Some other conclusions can be drawn from the data in Table 10.1. First, note that the relative fraction of atoms in the excited state is very dependent on temperature: a small temperature variation can be expected to have a marked effect on the emission signal. Fortunately, flame temperatures can be adequately controlled so that precise atomic-emission measurements can be made. On the other hand, the total number of ground-state atoms (neglecting ionization and compound-formation effects discussed below) is in principle independent of the temperature. Many elements partially react with flame gases to form molecular oxide and hydroxide species (which do not absorb the resonance lines), the extent of the reaction being temperature-dependent; so atomic absorption in practice is essentially as temperature-dependent as atomic emission. A second conclusion is that since most atoms reside in the ground state, absorption is greatest for lines resulting from transitions originating in the ground state—that is, for the resonance lines.

The strongest absorption line does not necessarily correspond to the most sensitive emission line. The strength of either an absorption or an emission signal is governed by the number of absorbing atoms or emitting atoms plus a quantity known as the *oscillator strength.** In addition, emission intensity is influenced by the spectral region involved—electrons require more thermal energy for shorter-wavelength emission than for longer. In practice, the strongest absorption line is always at a shorter wavelength than the strongest emission line, when the two do not coincide.

A third conclusion to draw from the data in Table 10.1 is that the intensity of emission will vary markedly from one element to another because the relative number of thermally excited atoms varies significantly for the different elements. Atomic absorption, on the other hand, should exhibit more uniform sensitivity for a large number of elements, except for large differences in oscillator strengths. This is true, provided that all the elements can be efficiently converted to atomic vapor.

Relationship Between Atomic Absorption and Concentration

Atomic absorption follows an exponential law for the intensity of transmitted light as a function of the path length b, similar to Lambert's law in molecular spectrophotometry:

$$P = P_0 e^{-k_\nu b} \tag{10.3}$$

The absorption coefficient k_ν characterizes the intensity of an absorption line. It is

---

* The oscillator strength f is an expression of the intensity of a spectral line and represents the probability that an atom will undergo an electronic transition in unit time and absorb or emit a photon.

proportional to the number of absorbing atoms and hence to the solution concentration. It is also proportional to the oscillator strength.

For analytical purposes, the *absorbance A* is the parameter measured.

$$A = \log (P_0/P) = k_\nu b \log e = 0.434 k_\nu b \qquad (10.4)$$

In other words, the absorbance is directly proportional to the absorption coefficient, and therefore to the solution concentration.

One needs to distinguish between the terms *sensitivity* and *detection limit* as used in the atomic absorption literature. Sensitivity is defined as the concentration that gives an *absorption* of 1% (or an *absorbance A* of 0.0044); it is a measure of the absolute signal expected under a given set of conditions, but says nothing about the noise level. Nevertheless, sensitivity is frequently within an order of magnitude of the detection limit, which is typically defined as the concentration that gives a signal twice the root-mean-square (rms) noise level, or twice the standard deviation of the noise.

Broadening of Spectral Lines

Spectral lines are not truly monochromatic or infinitely narrow. Line widths are usually described in terms of half-width, the width of the line profile at half-height (see Fig. 10.6 for a typical line profile). Lines can be broadened by a number of factors. In a flame, an absorption- or emission-line profile is governed almost entirely by the combined effect of *natural broadening, Doppler broadening,* and *collisional broadening.* The first is the result of the finite amount of time that atoms spend in the energy levels between which transitions take place; the second is due to the random thermal motion of the atoms relative to the observer (the detector); and the last is due to interaction or collision of the absorbing or emitting atoms with other molecules or atoms, for example, those of the flame gases.

Natural broadening is generally very small compared to Doppler and collisional broadening, Doppler broadening dominating at the center of the line and collisional broadening dominating at the wings (edges) of the line. Broadening can have a small effect on the sensitivity of atomic-absorption measurements in which the absorption of the center of the line is measured. For most elements at 2000–3000 K, the total half-width of the resonance lines is on the order of 0.002 nm (0.02 Å), although some may be an order of magnitude wider.

10.3 INSTRUMENTATION

Atomic-absorption and atomic-emission spectrophotometers both require an atomizer, a monochromator, and a detector. Atomic absorption requires, in addition, a radiation source.

Radiation Sources

The two principal means of making atomic-absorption measurements are those employing a continuum source and those employing a line radiation-source. A continuum

FIGURE 10.4. *Schematic diagram of a
hollow-cathode lamp.*

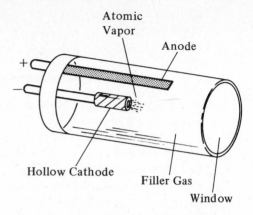

source such as a xenon-arc lamp is rather limited in application because of factors
to be considered below; in practice, line sources are used almost exclusively.

The most commonly used (line) source in atomic absorption is the *hollow-
cathode lamp.* Figure 10.4 is a schematic representation of such a lamp. In the back
of the lamp is a hollow cathode made out of the element to be analyzed or an alloy
containing that element. The open end of the cathode faces the anode (generally a
tungsten wire, ring, or disc) and the window of the lamp, which is constructed of
borosilicate glass or, if ultraviolet radiation is measured, quartz. The lamp is filled
under reduced pressure with an inert gas, usually argon or neon, and a sufficient
potential is applied across the electrodes to cause a current of from 1 to 50 mA to
flow. The potential ionizes the inert gas at the anode and accelerates it at a high
velocity to the cathode, where it hits and causes metal atoms to "sputter" out of the
cathode. Further collisions with the free atoms then produce excited metal atoms
which, upon deactivation, emit the spectrum of the cathode material. (The spectrum
of the filler gas is also emitted by gas atoms struck by the accelerated ions.)

The intensity of the radiation emitted will increase with increased current—

FIGURE 10.5. *Intensity of two copper
spectral lines as a function of hollow-
cathode lamp current. Courtesy of
Westinghouse Electric Corporation.*

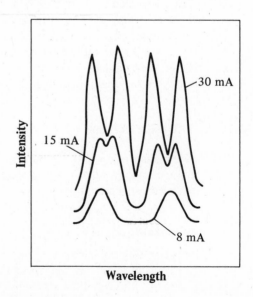

up to a point. At too high a current, Doppler broadening and self-absorption (absorption of part of the emitted radiation by the dense cloud of atoms in the source itself) will occur, with the result that the center of the line (the portion absorbed by the test element) will be decreased in intensity while the wings broaden out (see Fig. 10.5). Although, in principle, line intensity will not affect the absorbance measured, line broadening will. Therefore, an operating current should be chosen that, while avoiding broadening, is high enough to give good lamp stability and signal-to-noise ratio.

A sharp-line source and a continuum source are compared in Figure 10.6. Figure 10.6A illustrates the absorption of light from a line source. The source line and the absorption line are at the same wavelength, but the half-width of the source ($\Delta\lambda_s$) is narrower than that of the absorption line ($\Delta\lambda_a$) because temperatures and pressures are lower in the source than in the flame. Therefore, the entire center of the source line is absorbed in accordance with Beer's law.

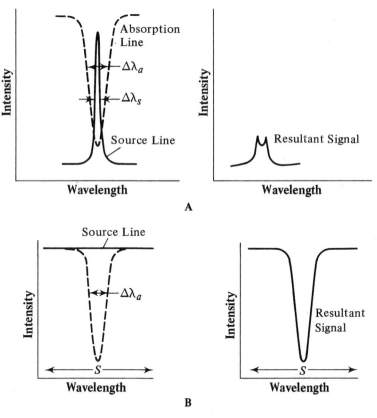

FIGURE 10.6. *Atomic absorption with (A) a sharp-line source and (B) a spectral-continuum source.* $\Delta\lambda_a$ = *absorption line half-width*; $\Delta\lambda_s$ = *source line half-width*; *S* = *spectral bandwidth of monochromator. Adapted from G. D. Christian and F. J. Feldman,* Atomic Absorption Spectroscopy: Applications in Agriculture, Biology, and Medicine, *New York: Wiley-Interscience, 1970, p 58, by permission of John Wiley and Sons.*

Figure 10.6B shows the situation for a continuum source. In this case, only a small fraction of the band of radiation passed by the monochromator is absorbed (even very good monochromators pass a band of radiation on the order of 0.1 Å wide), and a large portion of unabsorbed light falls on the detector. This results in decreased sensitivity (absorbance) and a nonlinear plot of absorbance versus concentration. Figure 10.7 illustrates the difference between calibration curves for line and continuum sources.

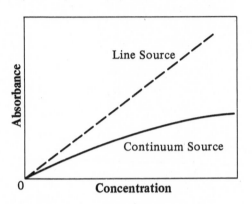

FIGURE 10.7. *Comparison of absorption from continuum and sharp-line sources.*

Linearity and sensitivity using a continuum source will of course be improved as the bandpass of the monochromator (and hence the band of unabsorbed radiation) is narrowed; however, this results in a loss of source intensity and an increased noise level as more gain is required on the detector. In order to approach the sensitivity of a line source, resolution beyond the capabilities of ordinary spectrophotometers would be required.

Monochromators and Detectors

In atomic absorption, the *ratio* of signals is measured with and without absorption. In flame emission, however, the signal intensity is measured directly superimposed on a flame background. For these reasons, the exit-slit adjustment, radiation-detector quality, and so forth are generally less critical in absorption methods than in emission methods.

The major requirement for a monochromator in atomic-absorption measurements is that it has the ability to separate the selected resonance-absorption line from other lines emitted by the source. Although overlap of absorption lines (that is, between two different elements) can occur, this is relatively rare.

Atomic-absorption and emission lines occur in the ultraviolet and visible regions, so a monochromator for either technique should be a general-purpose ultraviolet-visible instrument. Detectors are generally photomultiplier tubes. The most commonly used photomultiplier is the RCA 1P28 tube or the equivalent with an S-5 response curve (Fig. 10.8). This functions well over a broad range of the ultraviolet-visible region (approximately 200–650 nm). For the short-wavelength ultraviolet region below about 200 nm, it may be necessary to use an R106 PM tube which gives about 10-fold better response, whereas in the red region of the visible spectrum, a tube with an S-1 response is preferred.

Atomic-absorption instruments may be either single or double beam. Mono-

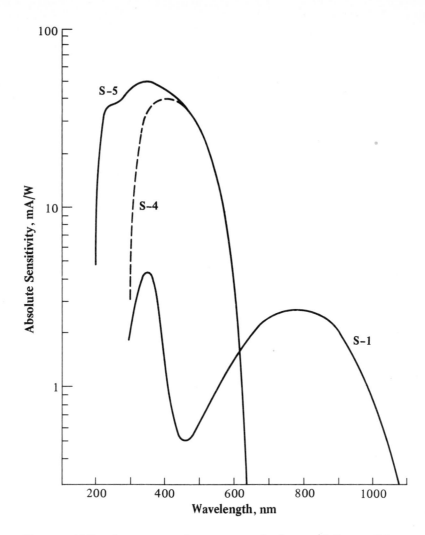

FIGURE 10.8. *Some spectral responses of photomultipliers.* *S-5* = *RCA* 1P28, *S-1* = *RCA* 7102, *S-4* = *RCA* 1P21.

chromator slit-width and photomultiplier-tube voltage will have little effect on most atomic-absorption signals, since a ratio of P/P_0 is recorded; but increasing either one will result in increased emission signals, since either more light enters the mono-chromator, or what light passes it is amplified more in the photomultiplier. However, the noise level will also be increased and an increased signal-to-noise ratio may not result. With some atomic-absorption light sources, such as nickel or cobalt, a non-absorbed line falls close to the resonance absorption line, causing decreased sensi-tivity and nonlinearity of calibration curves. In these cases, decreased slit width will increase the resolution of the absorbed line from the nonabsorbed line, improving sensitivity and linearity.

Instruments designed specifically for the atomic-emission determination of alkali metals (commonly found in clinical chemistry laboratories) may contain simply a single interference filter as the monochromator and a vacuum phototube as the detector. These instruments employ low-temperature flames in which only the most prominent lines of the elements appear. Frequently, a two-filter, two-detector arrangement is employed for making internal-standard measurements; lithium, for example, may be used as an internal standard for sodium measurements. A constant amount of lithium is added to all samples and standards, and the ratio of the intensities of the sodium line and the lithium line is recorded. Such a measurement minimizes the effects of fluctuations in the aspiration rate, flame temperature, and so forth, since the test element and the internal-standard element (if similar enough chemically) should be influenced in the same way, causing the ratio of their spectral intensities to be constant at given concentrations [2].

Burners

The nebulizer and burner system is probably the most important component of the atomic-absorption or emission spectrophotometer, because it is imperative that neutral (un-ionized) atoms of the test element be presented to the optical system. When the sample solution passes into the flame, it must be in the form of small droplets. The process of breaking down a solution into a fine spray is known as *nebulization*. Nebulization is generally carried out with the support or oxidant gas.

There are two major types of nebulizer burners, illustrated in Figures 10.9

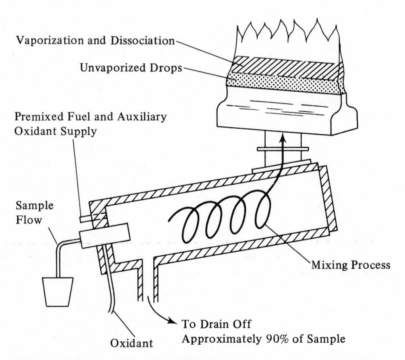

FIGURE 10.9. *Premix nebulizer-burner system. Adapted from G. D. Christian and F. J. Feldman*, Atomic Absorption Spectroscopy: Applications in Agriculture, Biology, and Medicine, *New York: Wiley-Interscience*, 1970, p 80, *by permission of John Wiley and Sons.*

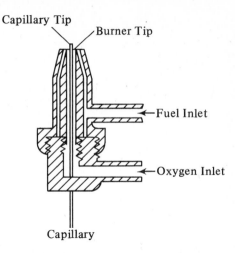

FIGURE 10.10. *Total-consumption burner.* *Courtesy of Beckman Instruments, Inc.*

and 10.10. In the first, liquid is sprayed into a mixing chamber where the droplets are mixed with the combustion gas. This process is called indirect nebulization, and the arrangement is known as the premixed chamber or laminar-flow burner system. In the second type of arrangement, the nebulizer and burner are combined. Nebulization takes place at the burner tip where the combustion gas is mixed with the support gas. The sample aerosol passes directly into the flame. These units are called direct-sprayer burners, total-consumption burners, or turbulent-flow burners.

In the premix burner, the sample is drawn up through the capillary by the decreased pressure created by the expanding oxidant gas at the end of the capillary (the Venturi effect), and is broken into fine droplets. The drops are turbulently mixed with additional oxidant and fuel and then pass into a burner head and out into the flame. Larger droplets condense out and go down the drain.

The total-consumption burner operates essentially as an ordinary pneumatic nebulizer. The oxidizing gas enters the burner through the aspirating gas inlet at a fairly high pressure, about 20–35 psi. It is directed around the capillary aspirator tip where the velocity of the gas produces a Venturi effect, drawing the sample into the stream. The fuel gas, in turn, is directed around the oxidizing stream and mixed with the oxidant and sample, and aids in breaking up the sample. The flame burns at the top of the burner.

In a typical nebulizer, liquid droplets will be produced with particle sizes ranging from a few micrometers in diameter to several hundred micrometers. The majority of droplets have a diameter of 5 to 10 μm, but most of the sample volume is contained in droplets 20 μm or greater in diameter. Whereas in a turbulent burner all droplets will enter the flame, in a premix burner the larger droplets may never reach the flame at all. Particles larger than 10 to 20 μm are either used inefficiently in the flame or are deposited on the premix chamber walls and flow out the drain tube. From 85 to 90% of the sample literally goes down the drain. However, the 10 or 15% that does reach the flame is of fairly small and uniform particle size and is quite efficiently atomized (converted to atomic vapor). The larger particles in a turbulent burner are less efficiently atomized and may never even have time to be desolvated. These particles will scatter the source radiation in atomic-absorption measurements, thus increasing the noise level.

The surface tension and, to a lesser extent, the viscosity of the sample solution are important factors in nebulization efficiency, since work must be performed in the nebulization step to overcome these properties of the liquid. For this reason, the surface tension and viscosity should be maintained as nearly identical as possible in samples and standards. With reasonably concentrated solutions, this can be done quite simply by diluting the test solution. With less concentrated solutions, it may be necessary to match the matrix composition of samples and standards. Concentrated solutions should also be diluted to avoid encrustation of salts on the nebulizer and burner. The same is true when handling heterogeneous systems such as colloids or solutions high in protein content.

One danger in using a premix burner is that certain gas mixtures may detonate (explode) in the chamber, especially when oxygen is used as the support gas. This occurs when the flame front propagates with a speed greater than normal gas-rise speeds. The burning velocity of the O_2-H_2 flame, for example, is 2180 cm/sec and that of the O_2-C_2H_2 flame is 2920 cm/sec. (These compare with speeds of a few tens or hundreds of cm/sec for the commonly used air-supported premix flames!) In the case of detonating flames, the gases obviously cannot be mixed before they are fed into the burner, so a turbulent-flow burner must be used. The turbulent-flow burner is inherently safer than premix burners because flashback is impossible. (The flame will, however, "pop" if it is extinguished by turning off the fuel gas first. This creates a very fuel-lean flame condition when the fuel in the line is used up.)

To summarize the major advantages and disadvantages of the nonpremix and premix burners, the advantages of the turbulent-flow burner are:

1. The entire sample is aspirated into the flame.
2. There is no explosive hazard from a mixture of unburned gases, so high-burning-velocity flames can be used.
3. Solutions containing large amounts of solid solutes can be aspirated, although encrustation of salts can be troublesome.
4. The burner is easy to clean and maintain.

Disadvantages are:

1. Even though the entire sample is aspirated, vaporization and desolvation efficiency is poor, with drop size varying over a broad range, and larger droplets failing to desolvate in the short time spent in the flame.
2. Disturbances such as condensed-phase interferences are more severe because of the desolvation and vaporization problems.
3. The flame temperature is seriously affected by loss of heat used for desolvation.
4. The flame is noisy, both to the ear and to the detector, because of turbulence.
5. The flame geometry is poor (short path-length) for atomic absorption.

The advantages of the premix burner are:

1. Nebulization can be controlled separately, and nearly uniform small droplets are fed to the flame. This leads to less light scattering.
2. Less solvent reaches the flame with less disturbance of the flame.
3. The flame is more homogeneous, and the height dependence for observation is not so critical.

4. Encrustations are reduced because large drops are eliminated.
5. There is low turbulence with less effect on the noise level, and the flame is quiet.
6. There is an elongated absorption path.

Some of the disadvantages of the premix burner are:

1. The relatively large volumes of fuel-oxidant mixture used can be explosive and only low-burning-velocity flames can be used, except under special conditions.
2. There can be a memory effect if large amounts of solids are aspirated.
3. The burner and chamber are harder to clean.
4. Several seconds are required between the initiation of nebulization and the attainment of a steady state within the chamber and in the flame gases.
5. With mixed solvents, the more volatile ones are selectively evaporated.
6. More than 90% of the sample goes down the drain, although that portion reaching the flame is efficiently atomized.

Thus, several factors are involved in the choice of a burner. Generally speaking, a premix burner is preferred for atomic-absorption work, except when a high-burning-velocity flame must be used. Turbulent-flow burners are widely used for atomic-emission measurements, but in recent years premix burners have also found more use, particularly with the high-temperature nitrous oxide–acetylene flame.

Flames

Table 10.2 lists the most commonly used flames in absorption and emission measurements, together with their maximum temperatures. All these flames can be used with a premix burner *except* the two oxygen-supported flames.

Flame Structure. The structure of a typical flame in a premix burner (such as a Bunsen burner) is illustrated in Figure 10.11. The fuel-air mixture emerging from the burner tube is heated in the *preheating zone* by conduction from the *combustion zone*; this heating initiates combustion (oxidation of the fuel). The main combustion reactions take place in the *primary reaction* or *combustion zone* (*inner cone*). This zone, about 0.1 mm thick, is recognized by its bright luminescence (with hydrocarbon fuels, a strong blue-green light due to C_2 and CH radicals). In this zone, thermal

TABLE 10.2. *Flames Used in Atomic Absorption and Emission*

Gas Mixture	Maximum Temperature, °C
Air–Coal Gas	1825
Air-Propane	1725
Air-Hydrogen	2045
Air-Acetylene	2250
Oxygen-Hydrogen	2677
Oxygen-Acetylene	3060
Nitrous oxide–Acetylene	2955
Argon-Hydrogen-Entrained air	1577

FIGURE 10.11.   *Structure of a flame.*

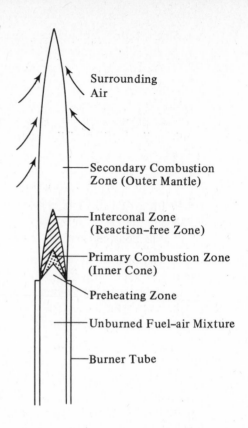

Surrounding Air

Secondary Combustion Zone (Outer Mantle)

Interconal Zone (Reaction–free Zone)

Primary Combustion Zone (Inner Cone)

Preheating Zone

Unburned Fuel–air Mixture

Burner Tube

equilibrium is not achieved, so it is rarely used for atomic emission or absorption measurements.   Gases emerging from the reaction zone of a hydrocarbon flame consist mainly of CO, CO_2, H_2, H_2O and N_2 (if air is the oxidant), with smaller amounts of H, O, and OH radicals.

The *interconal* or *reaction-free zone* is the part usually employed for atomic emission and absorption measurements.   It exhibits nearly complete thermal equilibrium, is not very luminous, and can extend to several millimeters in height.   Under conditions of thermal equilibrium, knowledge of only the temperature suffices to account for atomic emission or absorption phenomena, with no need to consider the manner in which the temperature is generated (for example, the particular fuel and oxidant gases used or their ratio).   The gas mixture expands appreciably after passing from the reaction zone to the interconal zone because of thermal expansion, and sometimes because of an increase after combustion in the total number of moles of gas.

The major part of the flame, the *secondary combustion zone*, consists of the burned gas mixture, which extends around and above the intercone.   By molecular or turbulent diffusion, oxygen and nitrogen from the surrounding air penetrate into the flame, oxidizing carbon monoxide from the interconal gases to carbon dioxide, with weak emission of blue-violet light.   This outer cone is more distinct when the primary combustion is incomplete (that is, in a fuel-rich flame).   Under these conditions, the edge of the outer cone may actually be hotter than the interior of the flame, but because it also emits background radiation, it is not usually sampled for analytical measurements.

The structure of the flame produced by a turbulent burner is more difficult to describe than that of a premix (laminar) burner, because it is obscured by the strong turbulence. The inner cone, while recognizable, is vague, thickened by turbulence. The combustion process in a turbulent burner is somewhat different; the turbulence aids in the ignition of the gases, making the burning velocity higher, but incomplete mixing of the gases above the burner port can cause considerable local variation within the flame. The turbulent flame entrains more air from the surroundings than does a laminar flame, and its temperature, for a given gas composition, is generally higher. Where aspiration of an aqueous solution into a premix flame usually results in a slight decrease in the flame temperature (e.g., 40°C), the drop in a turbulent flame can be much larger (for example, several hundred degrees), depending on the aspiration rate. Hence, substitution of organic solvents can result in striking enhancements in atomic-emission intensities in the turbulent flame.

Selection of Flames. The alkali metals are best determined in the lower-temperature flames (air–coal gas or air-propane) because of their ease of ionization in higher-temperature flames. The neutral atoms are readily excited in these two flames for atomic-emission determination. In many instruments designed specifically for the atomic-emission measurement of these elements, a simple Meker-type burner is suitable.

For the atomic-emission determination of the majority of elements, however, a high-temperature flame is required for excitation. Either an oxyacetylene or a nitrous oxide–acetylene flame can be used. The latter can be used with a premix burner. In order to prevent the burner from overheating, it must be more massive than usual; generally, a thick stainless-steel head is used (sometimes with cooling wings) with a narrower and shorter slot than usual. Under these conditions, the flame is quite safe from flashback unless it is operated in too lean a condition (i.e., with too high an oxidant/fuel flow-rate ratio). Some manufacturers have safety features built into their instruments to prevent igniting a nitrous oxide–acetylene flame using the wrong burner.

When using the nitrous oxide–acetylene flame, an air-acetylene flame is first ignited and adjusted to a fuel-rich condition. Then nitrous oxide is introduced to replace the air. In this manner, one can avoid igniting the flame under lean conditions. The reverse sequence is used to extinguish the flame.

The most commonly used flame for atomic-absorption measurements is the air-acetylene flame combined with a premix burner. Although its advantages are many, certain limitations affect its use for some elements. Metals such as molybdenum, tin, and some alkaline earths are only partially atomized in this flame. Elements that form refractory compounds, including silicon, aluminum, and vanadium, are not appreciably atomized at all. In general, this can be attributed to the tendency of these elements, when heated in the flame, to form refractory oxides that are not decomposed at the temperatures available.

The development of high-temperature, reducing flames has allowed the routine determination of elements that tend to form refractory compounds. Measurements in the nitrous oxide–acetylene flame are generally made in the red secondary zone, which is practically devoid of oxygen. (This red zone has been attributed to long-lived CN and NH species which form a strongly reducing atmosphere.) So, the flame apparently inhibits formation of refractory oxides by its nonoxidizing atmosphere and high temperature.

The high-temperature flames also remove many chemical interferences that occur in the air-acetylene flame for several of the other elements. Chemical interferences may occur, for example, when anions in solution combine with the test element to form thermally stable compounds. These are discussed in more detail below.

A disadvantage of high-temperature flames is that there is a marked increase in the ionization of many elements. Thermal ionization of an element—for example, $Na \rightleftarrows Na^+ + e^-$—is undesirable because it decreases the number of neutral atoms in the flame; thus, sensitivity is lost. This can be circumvented by adding about 200 ppm of an easily ionized element, such as potassium, to suppress the ionization of the other elements. This should be done routinely with all elements with ionization potentials less than about 7.5 eV. This includes the elements Li, Ca, Sr, Ba, Al, Ga, In, Tl, Pb, Sc, Ti, V, Cr, Mn, Y, Zn, Nb, Mo, Ta, and the rare earths.

The air-hydrogen flame is more transparent than hydrocarbon-based flames, and sometimes offers advantages in atomic absorption when working at short wavelengths. This flame has been demonstrated superior to the air-acetylene and nitrous oxide–acetylene flames for the determination of low concentrations of tin, for instance.

An interesting flame useful for atomic-absorption measurements in specific cases is the argon-hydrogen-entrained air flame. The support (oxidant) gas entering the burner is replaced by argon, and combustion is supported by the influx of entrained air from the surrounding atmosphere. This flame can be used with either a turbulent burner or a premix burner. The advantage of this flame is that it is much more transparent at short wavelengths than even the air-hydrogen flame. It exhibits very little emission in the visible region of the spectrum and is nearly colorless to the eye. One can better observe the flame by aspirating tap water and noting the sodium emission. Because of its transparency, this flame offers superior detection limits for elements that absorb below 200 nm. Two specific examples are arsenic at 193.7 and selenium at 196.0 nm. A primary limitation of this flame, however, is its low temperature and the severe chemical interferences allowed by that temperature. For this reason, the nitrous oxide–acetylene flame is preferred for the measurement of arsenic and selenium in most applications. It turns out that this flame also exhibits good transparency below 200 nm, although this is not true at wavelengths around 300 nm. The argon-hydrogen-entrained air flame does find use in newer techniques in which arsenic, antimony, or selenium is converted to a volatile hydride and enters the flame as a gas separated from the sample solution.

Summarizing, then, most atomic-absorption determinations are routinely made with a premix burner using either the air-acetylene flame or the nitrous oxide–acetylene flame. A few specific examples require different conditions, depending on the test element and the sample.

Adjusting Flame Conditions. The optimum ratio of fuel-to-oxidant flows will depend on the types of gases used, the burner, the element determined, and whether absorption or emission is measured. Usually the oxidant is used to aspirate and nebulize the sample solution, so control of the oxidant flow-rate is important in determining the rate at which the sample is introduced. Fuel flow is not usually so critical except under fuel-rich conditions or in emission measurements where flame temperature is important. When optimizing the flows, it is important to keep in mind that the signal-to-noise ratio is as important as, if not more so than, the magnitude of the signal.

One procedure to select the best flow is to set a given oxidant flow-rate and then to vary the fuel flow over a range. The signal and noise levels are measured at each setting while aspirating a solution of the test element. After the initial measurements, the oxidant flow is changed and the process repeated until the conditions for maximum signal-to-noise ratio are found.

Increasing the oxidant flow-rate will increase the rate of uptake of the sample up to a point, while decreasing the efficiency of production of atoms in the flame; usually, a net increase in atom production will result. It should be pointed out that interferences may be reduced under conditions that are not optimum for maximum sensitivity.

To obtain a stoichiometric flame, the flow rate of the gases should be close to the ratio in the chemical reaction. For example, in the oxyacetylene flame, 2.5 moles of O_2 react with each mole of C_2H_2. The flow rate of O_2 should then be about 2.5 times that of C_2H_2; actually, it should be slightly less since atmospheric oxygen is entrained. For a stoichiometric air-acetylene flame, the air flow would be 5×2.5 or 12.5 times the C_2H_2 flow, since air contains only 20% O_2.

A strongly reducing flame is best for elements that form refractory compounds, in order to prevent or minimize the formation of refractory oxides. By making a flame very fuel-rich and perhaps also aspirating an organic solvent, highly reducing species such as free carbon atoms and carbon monoxide are produced in the interior of the flame. (Incandescent unburned carbon particles, in fact, are what make a fuel-rich flame appear yellow.) A stoichiometric flame usually occurs near the point at which yellow incandescence just appears. A fuel-rich oxyhydrogen flame will not usually be as effective as either a fuel-rich oxyacetylene or nitrous oxide–acetylene flame for elements that form refractory compounds; this is because no very strongly reducing species are formed in the oxyhydrogen flame. However, when organic solvents are aspirated, this flame can be quite effective since it is a high-temperature flame.

The position of measurement in the flame is important, particularly in flame emission where the signal is very dependent on the flame temperature. In the typical flame, the maximum-temperature region occurs slightly above the inner cone. Positioning is not as critical in atomic absorption, particularly with the slot burners, although the lateral position is important. Nevertheless, standard practice is to adjust the height of the burner relative to the path of the light beam through the flame to obtain the maximum signal-to-noise ratio for a given element under given conditions of flame stoichiometry and aspiration rate.

The aspiration rate can also affect signals because of the influence of the solvent on flame temperature as well as on droplet size and nebulization losses. An optimum flow will generally be achieved that will represent a compromise between increased introduction of sample atoms and lowering of the temperature by the solvent (usually water). Typical aspiration rates are 1 ml/min for total consumption burners and 3–10 ml/min for premix burners.

We showed previously that, barring formation of molecules, the number of ground-state atoms is essentially independent of the flame temperature. Limits of detection in atomic absorption can, however, be somewhat affected by temperature changes owing to the line-broadening factors and their dependence on temperature. Increased temperatures result in Doppler broadening at the center of the absorption line where absorbance is being measured, which causes a decrease in the peak height of the absorption line. Fortunately, the effect is quite small over small temperature changes, since Doppler broadening is proportional to the square root of the temperature. In practice, temperature control is more necessary for controlling atomization than for controlling Doppler broadening.

A problem encountered in atomic absorption is that of emission from the flame. Emission from the flame gases is normally broadband over a large portion of the spectrum; the instrument can be "zeroed" in the presence of the flame (solvent aspirated) to negate this. In some cases, however, the sample element emits strongly at precisely the same wavelength at which it absorbs; a small fraction of this emission will enter the monochromator, fall on the detector, and be registered as "negative" absorption. Both these emission problems can be overcome by modulating the radiation source, either mechanically with a rotating or vibrating chopper in front of the source, or electronically in the power supply. The detector electronics (amplifier) are tuned to the frequency of modulation of the light source and will record only light modulated at that frequency. High intensity DC emission, however, may "overload" the detector, causing increased noise. When such an AC source and detector are used, flame-emission measurements can be made (with the source turned off) by placing a chopper between the flame and the detector to modulate the emitted radiation at the same frequency.

Furnace Atomizers

Although aspiration into a flame is the most convenient and reproducible means of obtaining atomic vapor, it is one of the least efficient in terms of converting all the sample elements to atomic vapor and presenting this to the optical path. The overall efficiency of atomic conversion and measurement of atoms present in aspirated solutions has been estimated at as little as 0.1%. Also, aspiration methods usually require several milliliters of solution for analysis.

Furnace atomizers have conversion efficiencies much higher than do flame atomizers; absolute detection limits are typically 100 to 1000 times improved over flame-aspiration methods. Our discussion will center on atomizers heated by electrical resistance. Although these are not generally useful for emission measurements, they are well suited for atomic-absorption and atomic-fluorescence measurements [3].

In most of the furnace techniques, a few microliters of sample is placed in a horizontal graphite tube or on a carbon rod or tantalum ribbon; it is dried and (usually) submitted to an ashing step to destroy organic material, using resistive heating of the tube, rod, or ribbon. Finally, it is thermally atomized by resistive heating to produce a transient cloud of atomic vapor above the atomizer. The light path passes through the tube or over the rod or ribbon; a sharp peak of absorbance versus time is recorded. Either the height of the observed peak or its area is directly related to the quantity of metal vaporized. The heating is done in an inert atmo-

TABLE 10.3. *Representative Detection Limits for Furnace Atomic-Absorption Spectroscopy*

Element	Detection Limit, g		
	Perkin-Elmer HGA[a]	Varian CRA-90[b]	IL CTF[c,d]
Ag	2×10^{-13}	2×10^{-13}	5×10^{-13}
Al	3×10^{-12}	5×10^{-12}	4×10^{-13}
Cd	1×10^{-13}	1×10^{-13}	4×10^{-13}
Cr	5×10^{-12}	2×10^{-12}	5×10^{-13}
Cu	1×10^{-12}	3×10^{-13}	8×10^{-13}
Mn	1×10^{-12}	2×10^{-13}	4×10^{-13}
Ni	1×10^{-11}	5×10^{-12}	2.5×10^{-12}
Tl	1×10^{-11}	2×10^{-12}	
Zn	6×10^{-14}	1×10^{-13}	

a. "Perkin-Elmer High Sensitivity Sampling Systems for Atomic Absorption," Brochure L-332A. Courtesy of the Perkin-Elmer Corporation.
b. Varian Carbon Rod Atomizer, Model CRA-90. Courtesy of Varian Associates.
c. "Sensitivities for IL 155 CTF (Controlled-Temperature Furnace) Atomizer." Courtesy of Instrumentation Laboratory, Inc.
d. These numbers represent sensitivities rather than detection limits.

sphere to prevent oxidation of the graphite or tantalum at the high temperatures involved, and also to prevent formation of refractory oxides.

Detection limits quoted by the manufacturers of flameless atomizers are typically in the range of 10^{-10} to 10^{-12} g. Table 10.3 lists representative detection limits for some typical elements. The concentrational detection limit will, of course, depend on the sample volume. The volume will in turn depend on the composition of the sample matrix and on the concentration of the test element. Assuming that a 10-μl sample is analyzed for an element with a detection limit of 10^{-11} g, the concentration detection limit would be 10^{-9} g/ml; this is equal to 1 ng/ml or 1 part per billion. The extreme sensitivity of these techniques is therefore quite apparent, even when dealing with very small samples.

A major difficulty with furnace atomic-absorption methods is that interelement effects or interferences are much more pronounced than in flames, and precision is generally poorer. The interferences can sometimes be minimized by using a standard-addition method for calibration. Often, when the matrix concentration is changed, there is a change in the height as well as in the shape of the analytical peak. In such instances, better accuracy with less influence by the matrix can sometimes be achieved by integrating the signal (measuring its area) rather than by measuring its maximum intensity. Of course, this requires more sophisticated instrumentation.

10.4 INTERFERENCES

Several different types of interferences can occur in atomic-emission and atomic-absorption spectroscopy.

Spectral Interferences

Spectral-line interference, in which two atomic lines overlap or are unresolved, is relatively rare in atomic-absorption analysis. This type of interference is more common in atomic emission, where light is emitted not only by the test element but also by other elements in the sample. If the wavelength of the interfering radiation is close enough to the line of the element being measured, it will not be resolved and will be detected and recorded along with the signal for the element. For example, when small amounts of magnesium are being determined in the presence of large amounts of sodium, the 285.28-nm line of sodium will contribute some emission intensity along with the 285.21-nm line of magnesium. Spectral interference of this type can usually be eliminated by choosing a second resonance line for the test element (probably with a decreased sensitivity), or by removing the interferent by chemical means.

In atomic absorption, the line that is being measured is the resonance line from the source, which has a bandwidth of ~ 0.001 nm and ensures effective resolution. Hence, interference from absorption by another spectral line is quite rare, although some cases have been reported.

A more common type of spectral interference in either emission or absorption measurements arises from the occurrence of band emission-spectra due to molecular species in the flame. (In fact, many elements can be measured by means of the band spectra of the molecules they form in certain flames.) Calcium and strontium, for example, exist partially as molecular hydroxides and oxides in a flame and emit bands in the vicinity of both the sodium and lithium resonance lines. When the alkaline-earth/alkali-metal ratio is high, the interference can become serious, unless a high-resolution monochromator is used.

Molecular-absorption interference, although less common, does occur. For example, a CaOH absorption band occurs in the region of the barium 553.6-nm line. A 1% calcium solution has been reported to give an absorption equivalent to that expected from 75 ppm barium, well within the analytical measurement range for barium (see Table 10.4). High concentrations of alkali-metal and other salts can exhibit appreciable molecular absorption, particularly at wavelengths less than 300 nm.

If a flame contains solid particles or solvent drops that are not vaporized, these particles can scatter the light beam that impinges on them, giving rise to "false" absorption signals; this can be especially troublesome with total-consumption burners.

Molecular-spectral interferences and light-scattering interferences can be fairly easily minimized in either atomic emission or absorption measurements, provided the interferences are not dominant. Molecular-band and light-scatter spectra are approximately constant in intensity within several spectrometer bandpasses (or bandwidths) of a given spectral line. Hence, emission spectra can be corrected for background emission by making measurements at least two bandpasses away on each side of the line wavelength, averaging the two measurements, and subtracting the average from the analytical measurement at the resonance line. Measurements should be made on each side of the line in case the line is sitting on the side of a sharp band. Alternatively, if a scanning monochromator is available, the actual spectrum can be recorded in the vicinity of the resonance line and the background extrapolated to give a baseline for the peak.

Background corrections in atomic absorption are made similarly; that is, by assuming the background absorption to be constant over several bandpasses. A nonresonance line emitted by the test hollow-cathode lamp or by another lamp is selected. This line (often an emission line of the filler gas) must be at least two bandpasses from the resonance line of the test element. After checking to make certain that the test element does not absorb the chosen line, the absorbance of this line by the sample is measured and subtracted from the total absorbance at the resonance wavelength.

A correction can also be made with a hydrogen or deuterium continuum source with the monochromator set at the same wavelength as the resonance line. Sharp line-absorption of the continuum source by the test element is negligible compared to the background over the bandwidth of the monochromator, so the absorbance of the continuum source can simply be subtracted from the absorbance of the resonance line. Several commercial instruments have arrangements that allow automatic background corrections with continuum sources.

A typical setup is shown in Figure 10.12. The two light beams from the lamps are combined by a half-coated mirror (e.g., coated with small reflecting circles so that it will reflect the continuum radiation but will allow space in the mirror for the radiation from the hollow-cathode lamp to pass). Each lamp is pulsed electronically to provide an AC signal, but the two lamps are 180° out of phase. A phase-sensitive detection system then measures the difference of the two signal intensities (which are initially balanced). The sharp-line source measures both atomic absorption and

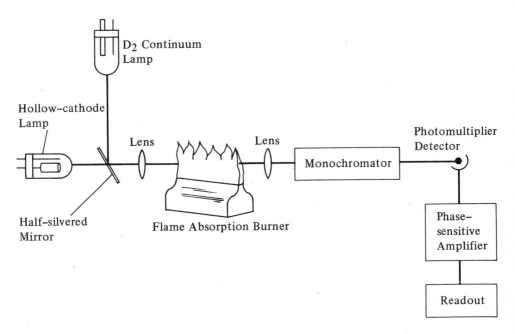

FIGURE 10.12. *Typical setup for atomic-absorption background correction with a continuum source.*

background absorption, but the continuum source measures only the background absorption since any sharp-line absorption removes a negligible portion of its band of radiation. The difference, then, represents the net sharp-line absorption.

Chemical Interferences

Chemical interference, or the chemical combination of the element of interest with other elements in the sample or the flame, is probably the most important interference in flame methods. It directly affects the efficiency of production of neutral atoms in the flame and hence affects both absorption and emission in a similar manner. One of the most common types of chemical interference is the formation of refractory compounds with the test element, usually by an anion in the aspirated solution. The result is a decreased signal. For example, phosphate will react with calcium ions to produce calcium pyrophosphate in the flame. Less frequently, the presence of another cation may result in a decreased signal. For example, aluminum causes low results in the determination of magnesium, owing to the formation of a heat-stable aluminum-magnesium compound. Occasionally, a positive interference will occur in the presence of an interfering substance. The mechanism is not clearly understood, but has to do with the formation of a compound more volatile than the test element.

Chemical interferences, fortunately, can generally be minimized by adding an appropriate *releasing agent*. These agents either compete for the interfering substance or displace it from the test element. For example, phosphate interference with calcium absorption or emission can be eliminated by adding a sufficiently high concentration (about 1%, depending on the actual phosphate levels) of strontium or lanthanum chloride to the solution. The strontium or lanthanum will preferentially combine with the phosphate and prevent its reaction with the calcium. Or, a high concentration of EDTA can be added to form a chelate with the calcium and prevent its reaction with phosphate. The calcium-EDTA chelate is readily dissociated in the flame. Because addition of an external reagent can sometimes change the test signal, the reagent should generally also be added to standards.

The use of high-temperature flames will frequently eliminate chemical interferences. Phosphate interference on calcium, for example, does not occur in the nitrous oxide–acetylene flame. In extremely difficult cases, a chemical separation of the interferent may be required.

Acids will frequently cause a depression of the signal, especially with total-consumption burners. This is particularly so for the alkali metals, probably because of the low-temperature flames used for these elements. Elements that form stable oxides are affected even more. Acids can influence the aspiration rate and nebulization efficiency, a physical interference (see below). Chemical interference by the acid anions may also be involved. For these reasons, matching the acidity in the standards and samples may be required.

Ionization Interferences

Certain elements, particularly the alkali metals and some of the alkaline-earth elements, are appreciably ionized in most flames. This causes a decrease in the number of neutral atoms and a decrease in sensitivity. It is not an interference in itself since standards would be ionized in the same manner; but if a second easily ionized element (e.g., potassium) is added to the test solution, it will contribute free electrons to the flame and cause the equilibrium for the test element (e.g., sodium) to shift toward the formation of a larger fraction of neutral atoms. The result is a positive interference.

Ionization interference can be overcome by adding a large amount (200 to 1000 ppm) of an easily ionized element such as potassium to both sample and standard solutions. This will effectively suppress ionization of the test element to a small and constant value and at the same time increase the sensitivity. Ionization can usually be detected by noting that the calibration curve has a positive deviation (upward curvature) at higher concentrations, because a smaller fraction of the atoms is ionized at higher concentrations.

Physical Interferences

Physical interferences are caused by altering some physical property of the solution, such as its viscosity, surface tension, vapor pressure, or temperature. These alterations will cause a change in aspiration, nebulization, or atomization efficiency. For these reasons, solvent temperature and composition should be maintained reasonably constant.

10.5 APPLICATIONS

More than sixty elements can be determined by atomic-absorption or flame-emission spectroscopy, many at or below about 1 ppm [4]. Only metals and metalloids can be determined by usual flame methods, because the resonance lines for nonmetals occur in the vacuum-ultraviolet region; however, a number of indirect methods for determining nonmetals have been described. For example, chloride can be determined by precipitating it with silver ion and then measuring either the excess or the reacted silver. Phosphorus (525.9 nm) and sulfur (383.7 nm) species (e.g., S_2) exhibit sharp molecular-band emission in the argon-hydrogen flame.

General Considerations

Table 10.4 lists the atomic-absorption and atomic-emission detection limits and wavelengths for the different elements, using the nitrous oxide–acetylene flame for atomic emission and either the air-acetylene or nitrous oxide–acetylene flame for atomic absorption. The detection limits are taken as the concentration required to give a signal equal to twice the standard deviation of the background reading. Generally, at wavelengths shorter than 300 nm, atomic absorption is more sensitive, while at wavelengths in the visible region, certain elements may exhibit improved sensitivity by atomic emission. Some reported detection limits for atomic fluorescence spectroscopy are also given for comparison.

Some elements exhibit maximum emission sensitivity using molecular band emission, but this is more limited in its specificity. Thus, marked improvement in

TABLE 10.4. *Comparison of Detection Limits for Atomic-Emission (AES), Atomic-Absorption (AAS), and Atomic-Fluorescence Spectroscopy (AFS)*

Element	Wavelength (nm)	Detection limit (ppm)		
		AES[a]	AAS[a,b]	AFS[c]
Ag	328.07	0.008	0.001 (A)	0.0001
Al	396.15	0.05		0.005
	309.28		0.1 (N)	
As	193.70	10	0.03[f]	0.1
Au	267.60	2		0.05
	242.80		0.02 (N)	
B	518.0[a]	0.05		
	249.68		2.5 (N)	
Ba	553.55	0.002	0.02 (N)	
Be	234.86	1	0.002 (N)	0.01
Bi	306.77	20		
	223.06		0.05 (A)	0.05
Ca	422.67	0.0002	0.002 (A)	0.000001
Cd	326.11	0.8		
	228.80		0.001 (A)	0.00001
Ce	569.92	10		0.5
Co	345.35	0.03		
	240.72		0.002 (A)	0.005
Cr	425.43	0.004		
	357.87		0.002 (A)	0.004
Cs	455.53	0.6		
	852.11		0.05 (A)	
Cu	324.75	0.01	0.004 (A)	0.001
Dy	404.60	0.05		
	410.39		0.2 (N)	
Er	400.80	0.07	0.1 (N)	0.5
Eu	459.40	0.0005	0.04 (N)	0.02
Fe	371.99	0.03		
	248.33		0.004 (A)	0.008
Ga	417.21	0.06		0.01
	287.42		0.05 (A)	
Gd	440.19	5		
	622.09[d]	0.07		
	368.41		4 (N)	
Ge	265.12	0.4	0.1 (N)	20
Hf	531.16 (II)[e]	20		
	286.64		20 (N)	
Hg	253.65	10	0.5 (A)	0.002
Ho	410.38	0.1	0.1 (N)	
In	451.13	0.003		0.002
	303.94		0.03 (A)	

TABLE 10.4. (*continued*)

Element	Wavelength (nm)	Detection limit (ppm)		
		AES[a]	AAS[a,b]	AFS[c]
Ir	380.01	3		
	550.0[a]	0.4		
	284.97		1 (N)	
K	766.49	0.00005	0.003 (A)	
La	550.13	6	2 (N)	
	441.82[d]	0.01		
Li	670.78	0.00002	0.001 (A)	
Lu	451.86	1		
	331.21		3 (N)	
Mg	285.21	0.07	0.003 (A)	0.001
Mn	403.31	0.008		
	279.48		0.0008 (A)	0.002
Mo	390.30	0.2		
	313.26		0.03 (N)	
Na	589.00	0.0005	0.0008 (A)	
Nb	405.89	1	3 (N)	1
Nd	492.45	0.7		
	463.42		2 (A)	
Ni	352.45	0.02		
	232.00		0.005 (A)	0.003
Os	442.05	2		
	305.87		0.4 (N)	
Pb	405.78	0.1		0.01
	283.31		0.01 (A)	
Pd	363.47	0.05		
	247.64		0.01 (A)	
Pr	495.14	0.07	4 (N)	
Pt	265.94	4	0.05 (A)	
Rb	780.02	0.008	0.005 (A)	
	794.76	3		
Re	346.05	0.2	0.6 (N)	
Rh	343.49	0.03	0.02 (A)	
Ru	372.80	0.3		
	349.89		0.06 (A)	
Sb	252.85	0.6		
	217.58		0.03 (A)	
Sc	402.37	0.8		
	391.18		0.1 (N)	
Se	196.03	100	0.1[f]	0.04
Si	251.61	3	0.1 (N)	
Sm	476.03	0.2		
	429.67		0.6 (N)	
Sn	284.00	0.1		
	235.48		0.05 (A)	

(*continued*)

TABLE 10.4. (*continued*)

Element	Wavelength (nm)	Detection limit (ppm)		
		AES[a]	AAS[a,b]	AFS[c]
Sr	470.73	0.0005	0.005 (A)	0.01
Ta	474.02	4		
	271.47		3 (N)	
Tb	432.65	0.5	2 (N)	
	534.0[d]	0.03		
Te	486.62	2		
	214.28		0.05 (A)	0.05
Th	491.98 (II)[e]	10		
Ti	334.90	0.2		
	364.27		0.1 (N)	
Tl	535.05	0.02		
	276.79		0.02 (A)	
	377.57	0.1		0.008
Tm	371.79	0.08	0.04 (N)	0.1
U	544.8[d]	5		
	351.46		20 (N)	
V	437.92	0.1		
	318.40		0.02 (N)	
W	400.88	0.6	3 (N)	
Y	362.09	1		
	597.2[d]	0.03		
	407.74		0.3 (N)	
Yb	398.80	0.006	0.02 (N)	0.01
Zn	213.86	10	0.001 (A)	0.00002
Zr	360.12	5	4 (N)	

a. Adapted from G. D. Christian and F. J. Feldman, *Appl. Spectrosc.*, *25*, 660 (1971). Nitrous oxide–acetylene flame.
b. Fuel is acetylene. Letter in parentheses indicates the oxidant. A = air, N = nitrous oxide.
c. From V. A. Fassel and R. N. Knisely, *Anal. Chem.*, *46*, 1110A (1974).
d. Band emission.
e. Ion line.
f. Argon-hydrogen-entrained air flame.

sensitivity is found with band emission from gadolinium, iridium, lanthanum, terbium, and yttrium, in addition to boron and uranium which can only be determined by band emission. For analytical measurements, concentrations should be at least ten-fold higher than the detection limits listed in the table, since by definition the precision at the detection limit is no better than $\pm 50\%$.

The analytical application of atomic-absorption or atomic-emission spectroscopy generally involves obtaining the sample in an appropriate solution for measurement and calibrating the instrument properly. Commonly used methods for different materials are described below. Frequently, a releasing agent will have to be added, or a solvent extraction will be required to concentrate the element and increase the sensitivity. Standards should be treated in a similar manner.

Instruments can be calibrated by preparing standard solutions over the concentration range of interest and measuring the absorption or emission of these under the same conditions as sample measurement. At least one standard should be run with each set of samples to determine any correction that should be applied to the calibration curve, because the variables of flame stoichiometry, aspiration rate, and positioning of the burner are difficult to reproduce precisely.

Sometimes, the method of standard additions is used to compensate for chemical and other matrix interference. The principles of this method of calibration, in which the standard is added to an aliquot of the sample, are described in Chapter 2 and elsewhere.

Atomic-absorption and atomic-emission spectroscopy are used for the analysis of a large variety of materials, containing from trace elements (ppm concentrations) to major ($>1\%$) inorganic constituents. Included are agricultural and biological samples, geological samples, petroleum products, glass and its raw materials, cement, ferrous metals and alloys, water, and air. Because of the general ease—or even lack—of sample preparation and because deaeration of the solution is not required, flame methods have largely replaced polarographic methods for many inorganic analyses. Anodic-stripping methods and the more sensitive pulse-polarographic techniques are becoming strong competitors, but furnace atomic-absorption methods rival the detection limits of these. This last technique can often be used for the direct analysis of small solid samples that can be decomposed or "ashed" at temperatures insufficient to vaporize the test elements present, followed by a higher temperature atomization step for the analysis itself. Examples are tissue homogenates and leaves.

The prime instrumental disadvantage of atomic-absorption techniques is that generally only a single element can be measured at a time. A different light source is required for each element. Atomic emission possesses a similar disadvantage, although it is fairly simple to change to a different wavelength for the measurement of another element. Simultaneous multi-element determinations have been made in recent years by atomic-emission spectroscopy using diode array (Vidicon camera) detectors (described in Chap. 7). The array of diodes effectively serves as multiple detectors (as many as several hundred) which can be arranged to detect several different wavelengths over a range.

Organic or biological samples will usually require destruction by dry ashing or wet digestion with oxidizing acids before flame analysis. Biological fluids (blood or urine) frequently can be aspirated after a simple dilution. For blood analysis, serum or plasma is generally preferred since this fraction of the blood generally contains clinically significant concentrations of metals. (An exception is blood-lead analysis for lead poisoning, because lead will concentrate in the red cells.) In other cases, the metal may be more concentrated in the red cells, but concentration changes in the serum or plasma are more clinically indicative; examples are potassium, zinc, iron, and magnesium. In these cases, it is critical that blood samples do not hemolyze (red cells burst) before separation of the serum or plasma is completed.

Serum is the supernatant obtained from clotted blood. Plasma, the liquid portion of circulating blood, is chemically similar to serum except that it contains in addition fibrinogen, the clotting agent in blood. Plasma is obtained by treating the blood with an anticoagulant such as heparin or oxalate, after which the red cells are separated from the plasma by centrifuging. Oxalate should generally be avoided for metal analysis since many metal oxalates are insoluble; an efficient digestion mixture for biological samples is a mixture of HNO_3, H_2SO_4, and $HClO_4$ in the ratio of $3:1:1$ by volume, using about 1 ml per gram of wet material.

Metals and alloys can usually be dissolved in acids, whereas materials such as glass will require alkaline or acid fusion. An important consideration in any analysis is matching the matrix of the standards to that of the sample, or else diluting the sample enough to render the physical effects of the matrix harmless. (Chemical effects may still exist.)

One of the most common applications of atomic-emission spectroscopy is the determination of the alkali metals, particularly in the clinical laboratory. Blood-serum samples need only to be diluted with water (or an internal-standard solution) and aspirated.

Use of Organic Solvents

The overall atomization efficiency in a flame is increased by the use of organic solvents. Such increase is due to a variety of causes, including increased rate of aspiration, finer droplets, more efficient evaporation or combustion of the solvent, and so forth. Thus, increased sensitivity would be obtained by adding a miscible organic solvent such as acetone to the solution. (A three-fold increase is typical.) The problem is that adding the miscible solvent dilutes the sample solution, which more or less defeats the purpose. Therefore, the technique of solvent extraction (Chap. 20) is usually employed to obtain increased sensitivity. The dissolved metal is extracted from the aqueous solution into an immiscible organic solvent in which it is more soluble. The organic phase containing the metal is then aspirated into the flame. A number of advantages accrue. (1) The test element is separated from the bulk matrix of the sample, thereby frequently eliminating possible interferences. (2) It is obtained in a pure organic solvent, which results in maximum atomization efficiency; a ten-fold signal enhancement can be obtained for a given concentration. (3) The test element can be extracted into a smaller volume of organic solvent, with (in many cases) a ten- to hundred-fold gain in concentration. Methyl isobutyl ketone (MIBK) is one of the best materials for solvent extraction and aspiration into a flame. Ammonium 1-pyrrolidinecarbodithioate (APCD) is a commonly used extracting agent because it reacts with a large number of elements in acidic solution [this reagent is often referred to as ammonium pyrrolidine dithiocarbamate (APDC) in the literature].

When using organic solvents, the initial flame adjustment before aspirating the solvent should generally be very lean because the solvent must be burned as well as the fuel. If the flame is too rich in fuel, the solvent will not be completely burned and the flame will be very smoky. The proper flame condition can be adjusted with the solvent aspirating. Solvent should be aspirated between samples because the hot lean flame will tend to heat up the burner.

Determination of Lead in Blood

Lead in unclotted blood can be determined by atomic-absorption spectroscopy. Five ml of heparinized blood is treated with trichloroacetic acid (TCA) to precipitate proteins, which are centrifuged. The pH of the filtrate is adjusted to 3, 1 ml of aqueous ammonium-1-pyrrolidinecarbodithioate (APCD) is added, and the lead is extracted into 5 ml of methyl isobutyl ketone (MIBK) as the Pb(APCD)$_2$ chelate. The organic phase is separated and aspirated into an air-acetylene flame for atomic-absorption measurement. Standards are treated in the same manner, and water-saturated MIBK is used to zero the instrument. The detection limit for this procedure is about 0.1 ppm lead in the blood. The upper level of "normal" blood is 0.6 ppm, with most values being in the range of 0.3–0.4 ppm. Instead of precipitating proteins before solvent extraction, the blood can be hemolyzed with 1 ml of 5% Triton X-100 solution to release the lead from the red cells.

Lead in blood can be determined in microsamples using the Delves microcup sampling procedure. This is a technique similar in operation to furnace atomic-absorption. Ten milliliters of blood is placed in a small nickel crucible, dried on a hot plate at 140°C (ca. 30 sec), and then partially oxidized at 140° with 20 ml of 30% H$_2$O$_2$ until a dry yellow residue is obtained. The crucible is then mounted on a holder and thrust into a flame where the lead is vaporized into a horizontal nickel tube above the flame (through a hole in the bottom of the tube). The light path is through the tube. A transient signal results (as in furnace atomic-absorption), and the peak height of the recorded signal is related to the lead concentration. This technique generally is more precise for blood-lead microanalysis than most other atomic-absorption methods (coefficient of variation = 8% at the 0.4 ppm level). A method of standard additions is used for calibration.

Simultaneous Determination of Sodium and Potassium in Serum

Sodium and potassium in serum are determined in the clinical laboratory by atomic-emission spectroscopy, using an instrument designed specifically for this purpose [5]. Two filter monochromators isolate the sodium and potassium emission lines. A lithium internal standard is used, and the ratios of the Na/Li and K/Li signals are read out on two separate meters. The internal standard compensates for minor fluctuations in flame temperature, aspiration rate, and so forth. A cool flame, such as air-propane, is used to minimize ionization. Typically, the serum sample and standards are diluted 1:200 with a 100 ppm Li solution and aspirated directly. The instrument can be adjusted to read directly in meq/l for sodium and potassium by adjusting the gain while aspirating appropriate standards.

Determination of Zinc in Plants

Zinc is an essential trace element in plants. One gram of dried and ground plant material is dry ashed in a silica crucible overnight at 500°C. The ash is treated with 5 ml of 6 M HCl and slowly dried on a steam bath. This operation is repeated with another 5 ml of acid to hydrolyze pyrophosphate and to dehydrate any silica from the sample or the crucible. The residue is taken up in 20 ml of 0.1 M HCl and filtered. This solution can be aspirated directly into an air-acetylene flame for atomic-absorption measurement. Standards are prepared in 0.1 M HCl. As always, a blank is prepared in the same way as the sample.

Determination of Copper in Sea Water

Major constituents in sea water, such as sodium or magnesium, can be determined by appropriate (at least ten-fold) dilution with distilled water and direct aspiration. Many elements exist in sea water, however, at parts-per-billion or smaller concentrations and must be concentrated prior to analysis. Copper is one of these (1–25 ppb). Common procedures include ion-exchange chromatography, solvent extraction, or a combination of these. Copper can be determined by adjusting the pH of sea water (1 liter) to 3, adding 5 ml of 2% APCD solution and extracting the copper with 25 ml of methyl-*n*-amyl ketone, which has a low solubility in water. The separated ketone layer is aspirated into an air-acetylene flame for atomic-absorption measurement.

Determination of Beryllium in Airborne Particulate Matter

Particulate matter in a measured volume of air can be collected on a cellulose-acetate-membrane filter (e.g., Millipore®). The filter is dry ashed in a low-temperature asher. (This device uses oxygen radicals in a radio-frequency plasma for ashing at below 100°C, thus minimizing losses due to volatility of the test element and retention on crucible walls.) The ash is taken up in dilute HCl and aspirated directly, or the filter can be digested with a mixture of nitric and perchloric acids. For beryllium determination, a nitrous oxide–acetylene flame is used. Results are reported as $\mu g/m^3$ of air.

Determination of Sodium, Potassium, Magnesium, Manganese, and Calcium in Cement

A half-gram sample of cement is decomposed in 4 M HCl and evaporated to dryness, after which the residue is taken up in 4 M HCl. After filtering the solution and diluting it to 100 ml, aliquots are taken to determine each element by atomic-absorption spectroscopy using an air-acetylene flame. Standards for sodium and potassium must contain about the same concentration of calcium as the sample solutions. The presence of the high concentrations of calcium in the sample suppresses interference by aluminum or silicon on magnesium absorption. Phosphate, aluminum, and silicon interference on calcium absorption is eliminated by adding 50 ml of 25,000 ppm strontium solution to 5 ml of the stock sample solution and diluting this to 250 ml with water. Standards all contain the same concentration of acid or other reagents as the samples.

Determination of Molybdenum in Steel

A half-gram sample is dissolved in 10 ml of 1:1 HCl on a hot plate, oxidized with ten drops of concentrated HNO_3, boiled, and diluted to 100 ml when cool. The molybdenum can be determined in either an air-acetylene or nitrous oxide–acetylene flame.

10.6 ATOMIC-FLUORESCENCE SPECTROSCOPY

Although atomic fluorescence is not often used in commercial instrumentation, a good deal of research and special applications are performed with this technique. Hence, some details pertinent to atomic fluorescence are summarized here.

Types of Atomic Fluorescence

As mentioned before, atomic fluorescence involves excitation of atomic vapor by a radiation source, followed by deactivation by the emission of radiation; the emitted radiation is then measured. This process is not unlike molecular fluorescence spectroscopy, described in Chapter 9. Some of the modes of atomic fluorescence were alluded to in Section 10.1 (and in Fig. 10.3); a fluorescent line can be at a wavelength identical to the exciting wavelength, or it can be longer or (very rarely) shorter. There are two main types of fluorescence, resonance and nonresonance. A third type is sensitized fluorescence.

Resonance Fluorescence. Resonance fluorescence occurs when the atoms absorb and reemit radiation at the same wavelength. The most common examples correspond to transitions originating in the ground state (resonance transitions). For example, resonance fluorescence is observed for zinc at 213.86 nm, for nickel at 232.00 nm, and for lead at 283.31 nm. Some atoms may have an appreciable population in a low-lying metastable energy-level and exhibit resonance fluorescence originating from these levels. The intensity of emitted radiation in this case is generally less than for the more abundant ground-state atoms. Resonance fluorescence originating from ground-state atoms is often accompanied by nonresonance fluorescence having the same upper excitation level.

Nonresonance Fluorescence. Nonresonance fluorescence occurs when the exciting wavelength and the wavelength of the emitted fluorescence line are different. There are two basic types: direct-line fluorescence and stepwise-line fluorescence.

In *direct-line fluorescence*, an atom is excited (usually from the ground state) by a radiation source, and then undergoes a direct radiational transition to a metastable level above the ground state. An example is absorption at the 283.31 nm line by ground-state lead atoms, with subsequent emission at 405.78 nm. As with resonance fluorescence, direct-line fluorescence may be excited by absorption of a nonresonance line (e.g., tin fluorescence at 333.06 nm).

In *stepwise fluorescence*, the upper levels of the exciting and the emitted lines are different. In the normal case, the excited atoms lose part of their energy by collisional deactivation (by collision with flame molecules) and then return to the original (usually ground) state by radiational deactivation. Sodium, for example, is excited at the 330.3-nm line and undergoes stepwise fluorescence to emit a line at 589.0 nm. In a second type of stepwise-line fluorescence, the radiationally excited atom is further excited (thermally) to a higher electronic state and then undergoes radiational deactivation to a metastable state (that is, the emitted radiation is still longer in wavelength than the exciting radiation).

A less common type of nonresonance fluorescence is *anti-Stokes fluorescence*, or thermally assisted fluorescence, in which the emitted wavelength is shorter than the absorbed wavelength. This occurs when atoms populating an energy level lying near but above the ground state are excited to a higher energy-level and then undergo a radiational transition to the ground state; or when a ground-state atom is excited to a certain electronic state by absorbing a photon, then raised again to a slightly higher excited state by absorbing thermal energy from the flame, and finally radiationally deactivated to the ground state. The former is a special case of direct-line fluorescence, while the latter is a special case of stepwise fluorescence. Anti-Stokes fluorescence is always accompanied by resonance fluorescence.

All types of nonresonance fluorescence, particularly direct-line fluorescence, can be analytically useful; sometimes it is more intense than resonance fluorescence, and it offers the advantage that scattering of the exciting radiation can be eliminated from the fluorescence spectrum by removing it with a filter or a monochromator. Self-absorption problems (absorption of the emitted radiation by the sample atoms) can also be avoided by measuring fluorescence at a nonresonance line that is not also absorbed.

Sensitized Fluorescence. In this type of fluorescence, an atom emits radiation after collisional activation by a foreign atom that was excited previously by absorbing resonance radiation, but which has not yet been deactivated again. An example is the sensitized fluorescence of thallium atoms in a gas mixture containing a high pressure of mercury vapor and a low pressure of thallium vapor. When irradiated at the 253.65-nm mercury line, the thallium atoms emit at 377.57 and 535.05 nm. This type of fluorescence requires a higher concentration of foreign atoms than can be obtained in flame cells, but presumably it could be observed in nonflame cells.

Instrumentation

The basic instrumentation for atomic-fluorescence spectroscopy is shown in Figure 10.13. The source is placed at right angles to the monochromator so that its radiation (except for scattered radiation) does not enter the monochromator. The source is chopped to produce an AC signal and minimize flame-emission interference. As in molecular fluorescence (Chap. 9), the intensity of atomic fluorescence is directly proportional to the intensity of the light impinging on the sample from the source.

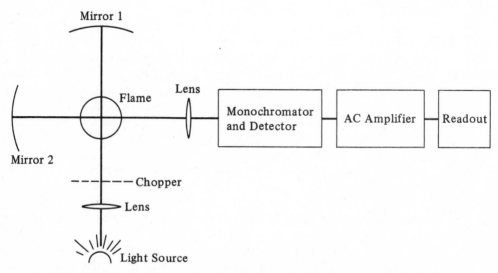

FIGURE 10.13. *Block diagram of atomic-fluorescence setup.*

It is also possible in many cases to increase the signal strength by using mirrors; in Figure 10.13, the light from the source is reflected back into the flame by mirror 1, while the fluorescence radiation that would normally be 180° from the monochromator is reflected back by mirror 2. Other suitable arrangements are possible.

The source can be a continuum source, since it is not necessary to isolate the emitted line from the source wavelengths; a 150-watt xenon lamp is commonly used. A major advantage of a continuum source, of course, is that it can be used for many elements. High-intensity sharp-line sources are also used, however, in an attempt to increase the sensitivity. Since conventional hollow-cathode lamps do not provide the desired intensity, the most widely used sharp-line source for atomic fluorescence is the *electrodeless discharge lamp*. This consists of a small quartz tube into which a small amount of metal or metal iodide is placed. The tube is evacuated, an inert gas (usually argon) at a pressure of 1–5 torr is added, and the tube is sealed. It is then placed in a resonant cavity where it is inductively coupled to a microwave radio-frequency field. The excited electrons produced by the ionization of the inert gas collide with the metal atoms, producing an intense spectrum. Detection limits one or more orders of magnitude lower than those using a continuum source are achieved with these lamps. In recent studies, high-intensity laser sources have been used for further increases in sensitivity.

Both turbulent burners and premix burners have been used for atomic fluorescence. The premix burner is usually round in shape (a modification of the Meker-type burner), since this provides better geometry for fluorescence than does a slot burner. For an optimum detection limit, the premix burner is also "shielded"; that is, an inert gas such as argon or nitrogen is directed in a sheath around the flame. This elongates the interconal zone and lifts the secondary reaction zone above the burner, separating it from the lower part of the interconal zone where the excitation beam passes. The result is less background emission and less noise, particularly in hydrocarbon flames like air-acetylene or nitrous oxide–acetylene. The premix burner, especially when shielded, appears to offer increased sensitivity over the turbulent burner.

For easily atomized elements, hydrogen flames are generally used because of their low flame-emission and flame-flicker noise. For the more refractory elements, however, a fuel-rich nitrous oxide–acetylene flame is required.

A problem with atomic-fluorescence measurements, much as in molecular fluorescence, is quenching of the signal. Quenching in an air-hydrogen flame can be decreased by replacing the nitrogen (in the air) with argon, which has less quenching effect than nitrogen. This would not help appreciably in hydrocarbon flames, however, because the CO and CO_2 present are much better quenchers than even nitrogen.

Non-flame atomizers have also been used in atomic-fluorescence spectroscopy.

Reported detection limits for determination of some elements by atomic-fluorescence spectroscopy are given in Table 10.4. A number of these were obtained using a laser source.

The same detectors are used for atomic-fluorescence measurements as are used for atomic-absorption and atomic-emission spectroscopy. By using a diode-array detector, simultaneous multi-element determinations can be made.

SELECTED BIBLIOGRAPHY

ANGINO, E. E., and BILLINGS, G. K. *Atomic Absorption Spectrometry in Geology*, 2nd ed. Amsterdam: Elsevier, 1972.

BURRIEL-MARTI, F., and RAMIREZ-MUÑOZ, J. *Flame Photometry: A Manual of Methods and Applications.* Amsterdam: Elsevier, 1957.

CHRISTIAN, G. D., and FELDMAN, F. J. *Atomic Absorption Spectroscopy: Applications in Agriculture, Biology, and Medicine.* New York: Wiley-Interscience, 1970.

DEAN, J. A. *Flame Photometry.* New York: McGraw-Hill, 1960.

DEAN, J. A., and RAINS, T. C., eds. *Flame Emission and Atomic Absorption Spectrometry,* vol. 1, *Theory* (1969); vol. 2, *Components*

and Techniques (1971); vol. 3, *Applications* (1975). New York: Marcel Dekker.

MAVRODINEANU, R., ed. *Analytical Flame Spectroscopy: Selected Topics.* New York: Springer-Verlag, 1970.

MAVRODINEANU, R., and BOITEAUX, H. *Flame Spectroscopy.* New York: John Wiley, 1965.

PARSONS, M. L., and MCELFRESH, P. M. *Flame Spectroscopy: Atlas of Spectral Lines.* New York: IFI/Plenum, 1971.

PUNGOR, E. *Flame Photometry Theory.* Princeton: Van Nostrand, 1967.

SYCHRA, V., SVOBODA, V., and RUBESKA, I. *Atomic Fluorescence Spectroscopy.* London: Van Nostrand Reinhold, 1975.

REFERENCES

1. E. E. PICKETT and S. R. KOIRTYOHANN, *Anal. Chem.,* *41*(14), 28A (1969).

2. F. J. FELDMAN, *Anal. Chem.,* *42*, 719 (1970).

3. J. P. MATOUSEK, *Amer. Lab.,* *3*(6), 45 (1971).

4. G. D. CHRISTIAN, *Anal. Chem.,* *41*(1), 24A (1969).

5. P. M. HALD, "Sodium and Potassium by Flame Photometry," in D. Seligson, ed., *Standard Methods of Clinical Chemistry,* vol. 2, New York: Academic Press, 1958, pp 165–85.

PROBLEMS

1. Describe or define the following terms: (a) ground state (b) resonance wavelength (c) line half-width.

2. Describe the various ways by which an electronically excited atom may lose its excess energy.

3. For the elements listed in Table 10.1, calculate the ratios of N_u/N_0 given for the different temperatures.

4. Describe the factors that cause broadening of a spectral line.

5. Why will a nonlinear calibration curve and a loss in sensitivity generally occur in atomic-absorption spectroscopy when using a continuum light-source as compared to a sharp-line source?

6. Why is the half-width of a line emitted from a hollow-cathode lamp narrower than the absorption line half-width for an element in a flame?

7. Compare the resolution requirements of a monochromator for atomic-absorption measurement and atomic-emission measurement.

8. Compare the advantages and disadvantages of the total-consumption burner and the pre-mix burner in atomic-absorption spectroscopy.

9. Although chemical interferences are generally more prevalent in "cool" flames, a relatively cool flame like air-propane is preferred for the alkali metals. Why?

10. Why is a high-temperature flame, for example, the nitrous oxide–acetylene flame, sometimes required in atomic-absorption spectroscopy?

11. Why is a high concentration of a potassium salt sometimes added to samples and standards in flame-spectroscopic measurements?

12. Why is it important to have a steady flame temperature in atomic-absorption as well as in atomic-emission measurements?

13. Why is the light source in atomic-absorption instruments generally modulated?

14. Why do furnace atomizers provide greatly increased sensitivity over flame atomizers in atomic-absorption measurements?

15. Identify and describe the major types of interferences encountered in flame atomic-emission and atomic-absorption measurements. Discuss how each can be minimized.

16. Why are organic solvents sometimes used in flame-spectroscopic measurements?

17. A 12-ppm solution of lead gives an atomic-absorption signal of 30% absorption. What is the atomic-absorption sensitivity?

18. A serum sample is analyzed for lithium by atomic-emission spectroscopy using the method of standard additions. Three 0.500-ml aliquots of sample are added to 5.00-ml portions of water. To these are added (a) 0 μl, (b) 10.0 μl, and (c) 20.0 μl of standard 0.0500 M LiCl solution. The emission signals (in arbitrary units) are 23.0, 45.3, and 68.0 for solutions (a), (b) and (c), respectively. What is the concentration of lithium in the serum sample in parts per million (wt/vol)?

19. You are asked to analyze for calcium and aluminum in a glass sample. Outline a procedure, including sample preparation, method of measurement, type of flame used, and method of calibration.

20. A sample of an unusual amino-acid analog —L-canavaninosuccinic acid, $C_9H_{16}N_4O_7$— was synthesized and converted to its barium salt to prevent a slow internal cyclization reaction during storage. A barium assay was performed by atomic-absorption spectroscopy to obtain an indication of the purity of the compound: 21.0 mg of the compound was dissolved in dilute HNO_3 and diluted to 100.0 ml; 20.0 ml of the resultant solution was further diluted to 100.0 ml. Five replicate atomic-absorption readings were taken on a blank, 6 standards, and the test sample. The data are:

Sample	Average Meter Reading ± Standard Deviation (arbitrary absorbance units)
Blank	0 ± 7
1 ppm Ba	44 ± 3
4 ppm	178 ± 4
10 ppm	483 ± 12
14 ppm	684 ± 21
20 ppm	993 ± 36
30 ppm	1512 ± 88
Test Sample	762 ± 18

(a) Plot the calibration curve and determine the percentage of barium by weight in the original compound. (b) Compare this result with the expected Ba content for the "pure" compound, and comment on the purity of the synthesized sample.

21. The following atomic absorption data were obtained with solutions made up with varying amounts of methanol and a 1.00 mM aqueous stock solution of a metal ion:

Sample	Added Methanol (ml)	1 mM Stock Solution (ml)	Percent Absorption
#1	0	12.0	31.6
#2	1.0	11.0	31.8
#3	3.0	9.0	34.5
#4	4.0	8.0	28.5
#5	6.0	6.0	22.6
#6	8.0	4.0	16.3

(a) Explain the results. (b) What are the most favorable conditions for the analysis of aqueous solutions of the metal ion (that is, highest sensitivity)? (c) Calculate the concentration of the metal ion required to give 1% absorbance in the absence of added methanol, and with the optimum amount of added methanol.

22. A sodium solution is analyzed by flame emission using the 589-nm sodium-doublet line. In developing a procedure for the analysis, the analyst notes that a 1 ppm solution of sodium gives an emission reading of 112, while the same solution containing 10 ppm potassium gives a reading of 123. In view of the fact that a 10 ppm solution of potassium gives no appreciable reading at 589 nm, give a probable explanation for the enhancing effect of the potassium.

11

Emission Spectroscopy

RAMON M. BARNES

This chapter describes methods of observing the emission spectra of atoms, ions, and molecules using excitation sources powered by electrical energy. The common names *emission spectroscopy* or *optical-emission spectroscopy* are applied to these methods.

In emission spectroscopy, the excitation source transforms the sample from its initial state as solid, liquid, or gas into a plasma of atoms, ions, and molecular radicals that can be electronically excited. The radiative deactivation of these excited states produces light quanta which are sorted by wavelength in a spectrometer or spectrograph; the resulting emission spectrum is detected by either photographic or photoelectric means. Many aspects of these measurements resemble those described in Chapter 10 for flame-emission spectroscopy; but electrical arcs or sparks, glow or plasma discharges, or lasers replace the flame as the means of atomization and excitation of the sample. Most of the electrical-discharge excitation sources provide greater energies than do flame sources, and they produce more complex spectra that require spectrometers and spectrographs with better resolution.

Since every element possesses characteristic spectra, emission spectroscopy is applicable in both theory and practice to the entire periodic table. However, the emission spectra for some elements, notably halogens and the noble gases, require more energy to produce than do those for a metallic element, and special excitation conditions must be applied. Normally, the emission spectra of all metals and metalloids in a sample occur simultaneously when the sample is electrically excited.

Emission spectroscopy forms the basis for numerous practical qualitative and quantitative analyses in industrial quality-control and research applications. Quantitative analyses are very rapid once the procedure is defined and the instrument standardized, and analyses are generally simultaneous, multi-element ones; the determination of 25 to 35 metals and metalloids in steel or aluminum in a fraction of a minute is common. Furthermore, emission spectroscopy is customarily used to obtain a rapid qualitative or semiquantitative survey of elements contained in unknown materials, because of the ability of electrical excitation-sources to atomize and excite samples submitted in many forms—powders, solids, liquids, or gases. A spectrographic qualitative analysis may take no more than 20 minutes.

This chapter will describe the instrumentation required, the types of samples generally studied, and typical examples of techniques and applications of emission spectroscopy.

11.1 PRINCIPLES AND THEORY

The principles and theory described in Chapter 10 for atomic emission apply also to emission spectra produced by electrical excitation-sources. In those sources for which the Maxwell-Boltzmann expression (Eqn. 10.2) describes the distribution of energy levels for an atom or ion, the absolute temperature T represents the equilibrium temperature of the discharge. Since the temperatures of electrical sources are generally higher than those of flames, sufficient energy is available to produce ions. The concentrations of electrons and ions are uniquely related to the temperature and to the composition of the gas (all charged particles originate from thermal ionization of the gaseous form of the elements). The basic concept of thermal ionization introduced by Saha is the application of the law of mass action to ionization. The equilibrium constant can be expressed as a function of the absolute temperature in an expression known as the *Saha relationship* [1].

$$K_{nj} = \frac{n_{ij}n_e}{n_{aj}} = \frac{(2\pi mkT)^{3/2}}{h^3} \frac{2Z_{ij}}{Z_{aj}} e^{-E_{ij}/kT} \tag{11.1}$$

where n_{ij} = the density or concentration (in number per cm³) of the singly-charged ions of the component j

n_{aj} = the density of the neutral atoms

m = the mass of the electron

k = the Boltzmann constant

h = Planck's constant

Z = the partition function

E = the ionization energy

The subscripts *a, i, e* refer to the neutral *a*tom, the *i*on, and the *e*lectron, respectively.

The practical version of the Saha formula (for a total pressure of one atmosphere) is given as follows:

$$\frac{n_{ij}n_e}{n_{aj}} = 4.83 \times 10^{15} T^{3/2} \frac{Z_{ij}}{Z_{aj}} 10^{(-5040V_{ij}/T)} \tag{11.2}$$

V_{ij}, the ionization potential, is expressed in electron volts. For calcium ($V_{ij} = 6.1$ eV) at T = 6000 K, the exponential factor is $10^{-5.12}$, whereas Z_{ij}/Z_{aj} for the Ca ($^1S_0$) and Ca$^+$ ($^2S_{1/2}$) ground states is ~ 2; so the equation gives a value of 3.4×10^{16}. For $n_e = 10^{17}$/cm³, as might be found in a high-current arc, $n_{ij} = 0.34 n_{aj}$, or 25% ionization.

In an arc discharge ($T = 4000$ to 7000 K), at least 0.01 to 0.1 percent of all particles exist as ions. Electrical discharges require this minimum level of ionization to be conductive and remain self-supporting. The discharges, however, are essentially neutral because the negative charge carried by the free electrons is balanced by the total positive charge of the ions. Spectral lines from neutral atoms are designated with a Roman numeral I and those from singly charged ions with a Roman numeral II. The intensities of the lines depend upon the degree of ionization, the concentration of the element in the source, and the partition function, as well as the absolute temperature, the Boltzmann constant, the statistical weight, the frequency, the transition probability, and the excitation or ionization energies.

Thus, for electrical sources in thermal equilibrium, the processes of dissociation, excitation, and ionization can be treated as if the gas mixture were contained in a furnace at the same temperature. Excitation is described by the Maxwell-Boltzmann distribution law (Eqn. 10.2), ionization by the Saha relationship (Eqn. 11.1), and dissociation by the general relationships for chemical equilibrium.

Some electrical discharges, such as spark discharges, are transient in nature; others, such as glow discharges, operate at subatmospheric pressures. In both, the equilibria that characterize thermal atmospheric discharges are absent, so that the Boltzmann distribution and Saha relationship are no longer applicable. In practice, this means that one method will produce spectra with absolute intensities different from those produced by another. For instance, the emission spectrum of a spark discharge differs significantly with time from that of an arc; also, the excitation of halogens in a hollow-cathode discharge is more efficient than in an arc.

11.2 INSTRUMENTATION

The measurement of emission spectra requires a number of instrumental components, some common in principle to other spectrometric methods (Chap. 6). An excitation source powered by a suitable generator converts the sample into an emitting discharge plasma. The sample is held or contained in an excitation chamber or stand, and the radiation emitted from the electrical discharge is transferred by suitable optics to a spectrometer or spectrograph, which sorts the radiation according to wavelength. The readout translates the photoelectric (spectrometric) or photographic (spectrographic) record of the spectrum into an analog or digital display of the wavelengths and intensities. The wavelength region generally encompasses 180 to 900 nm; vacuum instrumentation permits investigation of shorter wavelengths, and many commercial systems do not operate at wavelengths longer than 500–600 nm.

Spectrometers

The components of a spectrometer include an entrance slit and at least one exit slit, a dispersive element such as a prism or grating, and optical components such as mirrors or lenses to collimate the entering light and to focus the spectrally resolved wavelengths on the exit slits. The term spectro*meter* implies that the detectors are photoelectric *measuring* devices such as photomultipliers, whereas the name spectro*graph* implies that the detector is an emulsion supported on either a glass or film backing that makes a direct photographic *representation* of a complete spectrum.

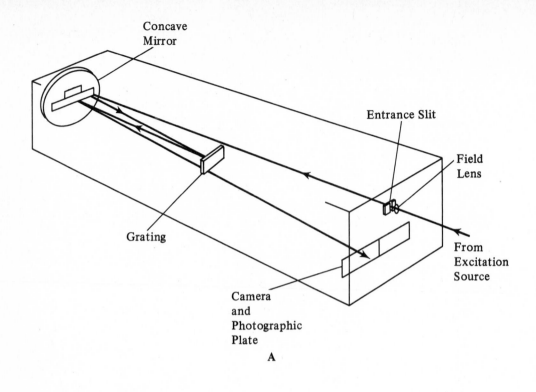

Concave
Mirror

Entrance Slit

Field
Lens

Grating

From
Excitation
Source

Camera
and
Photographic
Plate

A

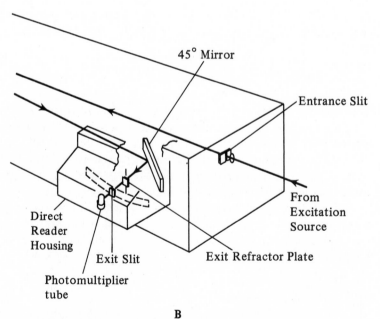

45° Mirror

Entrance Slit

Direct
Reader
Housing

Exit Slit

Photomultiplier
tube

Exit Refractor Plate

From
Excitation
Source

B

FIGURE 11.1.   *Fastie-Ebert plane-grating convertible spectrograph-spec-trometer.   Courtesy of Jarrell Ash Division, Fisher Scientific Co.*

Figure 11.1 illustrates a Fastie-Ebert arrangement which can be used either as a spectrograph or a spectrometer by simply deflecting the spectrum with a large 45° plane mirror. One large, concave mirror is used both to collimate the entering light illuminating the grating and to focus the dispersed light onto the exit focal plane. Since its rediscovery in 1952, the Fastie-Ebert arrangement and the closely related Czerny-Turner arrangement have become the most popular monochromator-spectrometer-spectrograph instruments in atomic spectroscopy.

The use of photomultipliers in spectrometers requires the accurate positioning of exit slits along the spectrometer's focal curve, allowing the selection of individual spectral lines and groups of lines to detect many elements simultaneously. Emission spectrometers often have room for as many as 90 different exit slits, although only 20–35 separate detectors and readouts, called channels, might be used for a particular analysis. For some types of analysis, more than one spectral line from an element can be monitored to provide appropriate concentration ranges for the elements in various samples. Other channels may be used for background detectors or internal reference lines. Such instruments are sometimes called *direct-reading spectrometers* or *direct readers*.

Associated with each phototube is an electronic system in which the phototube current is converted to a voltage that is generally collected or integrated on a storage capacitor. The capacitor voltage is read during or at the end of the exposure, and analog devices or digital processors record and compute the concentration of the element detected. Many modern spectrometer readout systems operate with digital mini- or microcomputers. The computers control sample handling, excitation conditions, exposure times, and other spectrometer parameters, as well as data acquisition, computation, and presentation. Very rapid, precise readings can be obtained in this manner.

Spectrographs

Spectrographs employ a photographic emulsion to record the entire emission spectrum at one time, so exit slits or multiple detectors are not required. The record is permanent and can be inspected later for more detailed information, which cannot be done with readings obtained from spectrometers. Scanning the entire spectrum with a single-channel spectrometer (monochromator) requires approximately the same time as exposing and processing a spectrogram.

After the photographic emulsion is exposed in the spectrograph, the latent image (the spectrogram) is developed. A dark image appears for each emission line detected (Fig. 11.2). These dark images are generally in the shape of the entrance slit of the spectrograph, and the amount of darkening or blackening is directly related to the intensity of the emission signal for each emitting species in the discharge source —that is, to the number of photons striking the emulsion in unit time at each frequency.

In order to determine the positions of these darkened images or spectral lines, the plate or film is positioned in a comparator or microphotometer which projects a portion of the spectrum onto a viewing screen for direct comparison with a known or standard spectrum. The optical arrangement and photograph of a commercial microphotometer is shown in Figure 11.3. Typically, an iron spectrum will also be

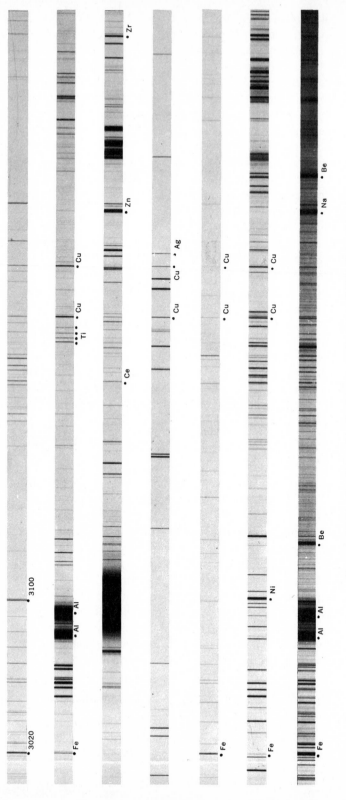

FIGURE 11.2. Portions of typical spectra taken on a JACO 3.4-m Fastie-Ebert spectrograph employing a 15,000 line/inch grating giving a dispersion of 5 Å/mm at the focal plane. From top down, materials are: iron, aluminum, magnesium, lead, steel, nickel, and beryllium ore. Courtesy of Jarrell Ash Division, Fisher Scientific Co.

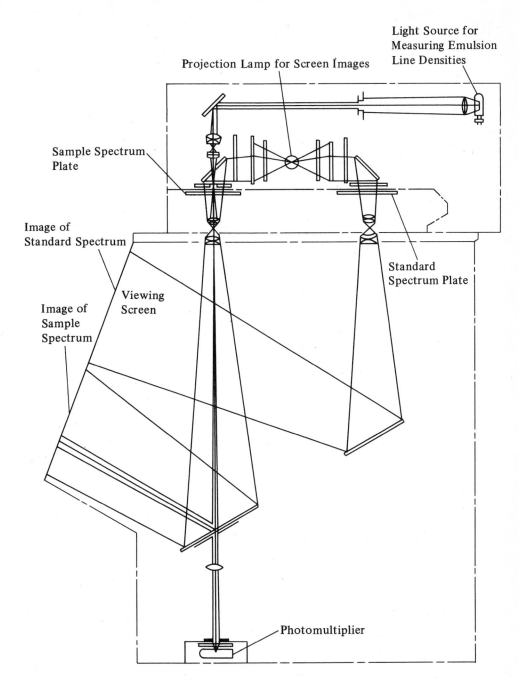

FIGURE 11.3. *Optical system for a microdensitometer. Courtesy of Spectrochemical Division, Baird-Atomic, Inc.*

recorded on the sample film; this allows one to align the sample spectrum with the standard spectrum. To determine the darkening of the spectral lines, the transmittance of the line is measured photometrically with the microphotometer [2]; the radiation from the light source is focused on a line, and the light passing through the line is detected by the photomultiplier tube. A galvanometer or digital readout is obtained. Since the blackening of the photoemulsion is not a linear function of the exposure, the emulsion has to be calibrated; this can be done easily using a laboratory computer [3].

Excitation Sources

A number of electrical excitation-sources are available for emission spectroscopy. In most commercial spectrochemical instruments, more than one excitation source is contained in a single power-supply cabinet; a typical combination may include a spark, a direct-current arc, and an alternating-current arc. A list of the various electrical excitation-sources, some of their characteristics, their approximate cost and the types of samples generally required is given in Table 11.1. Because of the actual or potential widespread use in emission spectroscopy, only the arc, spark, and inductively coupled plasma discharges will be described here in detail.

DC Arc. The DC arc is the least complex of the electrical excitation-sources discussed here; it consists of a low-voltage (10–50 V), high-current (1–35 A) discharge between a sample electrode and a counter electrode. The DC power supply may consist of no more than a full-wave rectifier and a filter.

The sample, most often prepared as a finely ground powder, is placed in a graphite cup electrode (see Fig. 11.4); the counter electrode is also fabricated from a graphite rod. The sample is usually (but not always) made the anode, and the

TABLE 11.1. *Some Emission Spectroscopy Sources*

Type	Characteristics	Samples Used	Price
DC Arc	Continuous, self-maintaining, direct-current discharge with low voltage and high current between sample and counter electrodes.	powders, solids, residues	$1000–6500
AC Arc	A series of separate discharges individually initiated once during each half-period of supply voltage and extinguished when voltage across the gap falls and becomes too low to sustain the discharge. Current continuous during conduction periods, similar to DC arc.	powders, solids, residues	$3000–4000

TABLE 11.1. (*continued*)

Type	Characteristics	Samples Used	Price
Spark	Transient discharge reaching high instantaneous current, produced by the discharge of a capacitor between the sample and counter electrodes with a duration of a few hundreds of microseconds and reoccurring 1–5000 times each second.	solid flats or rods, pressed pellets, liquids, residues	$3000–7000
DC Arc Plasma Jet; Gas Stabilized Arc	DC arc discharge formed between nonsample electrodes in flowing gas streams of argon or helium. Sample introduced separately.	liquids, powders	$1500–3500
Inductively Coupled Plasma Discharge	An electrodeless radio-frequency discharge produced by magnetically induced eddy currents in flowing argon confined in a quartz tube at atmospheric pressure.	liquids, powders, gases	$6000–10,000
Microwave Plasma Discharge	A discharge produced with or without electrodes by microwave fields in stationary or flowing gas streams in a microwave cavity.	liquids, gases	$1500
Glow Discharge Lamp	A low-pressure discharge in an inert gas, characterized by abnormal glow and sputtering of solid sample cathodes.	solids, residues	$10,000
Hollow Cathode Lamp	A low-pressure discharge in inert gas characterized by normal glow and sputtering of solid cathode.	solids, residues, gases	$2000–3500
Laser Microprobe	A plasma produced by the absorption of laser radiation, forming an emitting vapor cloud. Sometimes supplemented by auxiliary excitation by spark.	conducting and nonconducting solids	$19,000

counter electrode the cathode. The arc is initiated either by momentarily touching the two electrodes together or, more commonly, by applying an initial high-voltage spark. Once the discharge is formed, a bright, self-sustaining, electrically conducting path is established between the two electrodes. The electrodes heat rapidly and the sample is vaporized into the arc discharge. Graphite electrodes are generally used for routine samples, because graphite does not melt under these conditions and is a

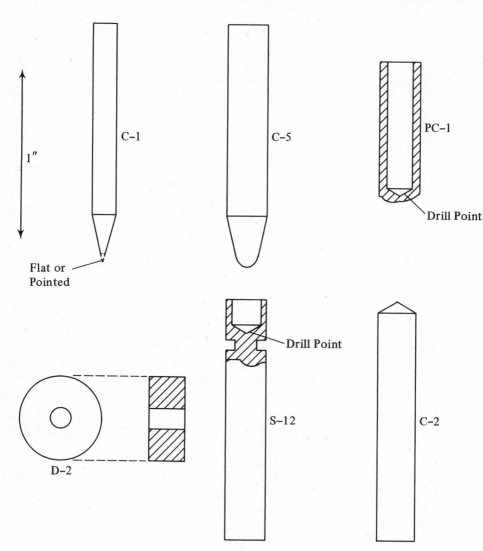

FIGURE 11.4. *Some standard forms of graphite sample and counter electrodes. Counter electrodes represented by "C", sample electrodes by "S", rotating disk by "D", and porous cup by "PC."* Adapted from Methods for Emission Spectrochemical Analysis, *6th ed., Philadelphia: American Society for Testing and Materials, 1971, pp 105–10, by permission of the publisher. Copyright © 1971 by the American Society for Testing and Materials.*

good electrical conductor. The anode reaches a temperature of about 4200 K, whereas the cathode is at ≤ 3500 K; the conducting channel between the two electrodes ranges at equilibrium between 4000 and 7000 K, depending upon the atmosphere and the composition of the channel plasma. This conducting channel or arc is surrounded by a region of heated gas known as the mantle or envelope. The mantle reaches a temperature of approximately 3000–4000 K, but does not serve as a conducting pathway.

The sample does not simply "boil out of" the hot electrode, introducing the sample vapor into the arc region. Elements do not all vaporize at the same rate unless some additional steps are taken; the vaporization rate depends upon the chemical composition of the sample and upon the chemical and physical reactions that occur in the hot electrode. From a very simple point of view, the graphite electrode acts like a high-temperature oven in which each element is vaporized according to its thermal properties. However, factors such as the reduction of oxides, the formation of volatile compounds such as chlorides, alloying, and carbide formation alter these vaporization processes and, hence, the sequential appearance of emissions from the various elements. Refractory materials such as silicates may remain behind in the electrode cup long after other, more volatile, elements have escaped. In some applications, this separation of volatile from nonvolatile elements is deliberately enhanced by the addition of other compounds (the *carrier distillation* method). The determination of trace elements in uranium by addition of a carrier such as AgCl is an example: the trace elements rapidly volatilize along with the AgCl during the first 10–20 sec of arcing, but the uranium matrix remains mostly nonvolatilized and, thus, its complex spectrum is greatly diminished in intensity. In other situations, additional compounds are mixed with the sample to promote uniform and simultaneous vaporization. This admixture might include powdered graphite or salts with an easily ionized cation, such as Li_2CO_3, as diluents. The presence of lithium in the mixture will also provide a uniform arc temperature during vaporization of the sample. If lithium were not present, the ionization current flow and hence the arc temperature would change as each element or group of elements evaporated from the sample electrode. The arc temperature remains relatively constant in the presence of a sufficient quantity of lithium because the lithium is readily ionized and provides the arc with a constant supply of ions and electrons. In this application, Li_2CO_3 is called a *spectrochemical buffer*.

The high temperatures of electrodes and arcs result in consumption of the graphite electrodes. When the carbon from the electrode reacts with nitrogen in the ambient air, cyanogen (CN) forms, which emits an intense and complex molecular spectrum that obscures some useful atomic-emission spectra. One way to avoid cyanogen bands, and to stabilize the arc discharge at the same time, is to exclude air from the arc by operating it in a closed chamber filled with argon [4] or in a flowing stream (3–4 l/min) of mixed argon (70–80%) and oxygen (20–30%). The latter arrangement is called a *Stallwood jet*.

The evaporation of sample from the electrode and the consumption of the electrode during arcing also cause the arc column to shift its position on the electrode surface. This movement or wander of the arc relative to the optical axis of the spectrograph drastically reduces the precision of arc analysis. The Stallwood jet also aids in reducing arc wander.

The spectra of DC-arc discharges are considerably different from those observed for flames and sparks. Because of the high temperature of the arc column, sufficient energy is available to populate higher atomic states. A complex spectrum, generally composed of neutral-atom and ion emission, results.

The high efficiency of atomization and excitation shown by the DC arc, together with the line-rich spectra it produces, make the arc technique valuable for qualitative analysis and multi-element quantitative analysis. Large emission signals for relatively small amounts of sample characterize the sensitivity of the DC-arc source.

Spark. The chief characteristic of the spark discharge is its dependence upon short times and short-time processes. In routine use, the spark signal is time-integrated by a photographic emulsion or by the electronics associated with photoelectric detectors. The spark is typically produced by the discharge of a capacitor between the sample and counter electrodes; Figure 11.5 is a simplified circuit diagram of a

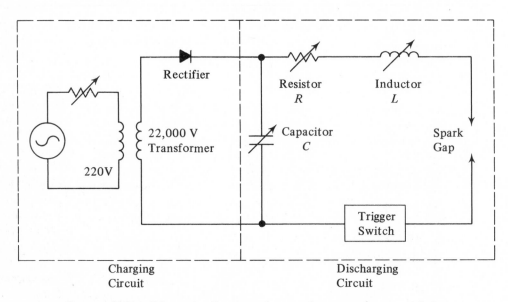

FIGURE 11.5. *Schematic diagram of a spark source for an emission spectrograph.*

typical spark source. A capacitor of 5–100 nf is charged to 1–30 kV and is then discharged (by the trigger switch) to form a conducting discharge channel or *spark* between the electrodes. There are typically 2 to 30 sparks per cycle of the line signal, or 120 to 1800 sparks per second. The amplitude of the oscillating discharge current flowing through the spark gap decays exponentially with time. The amplitude, frequency, and duration of the oscillation depend upon the discharge circuit parameters—resistance (R), capacitance (C), and inductance (L)—and on the voltage across the capacitor. For a particular analysis, these various parameters are specified after considerable trial-and-error experimentation to achieve the best quantitative results. Recently, a new design has markedly improved the operation of spark sources [5], and research into the mechanisms of the spark discharge [6] has led to ways of electronically shaping the waveform of the spark discharge for improved analytical results.

Although numerous spark-source arrangements have been developed, two types are most common: the high-voltage source (with or without a diode rectifier) shown in Figure 11.5, and a medium-voltage (1000 V) source.

Events happen very rapidly in the spark discharge, and what happens is substantially different from what happens in an arc. For example, during the first oscillation of the current, which may last only about 10 μsec, the spark-discharge channel is formed and the sample material is vaporized, atomized, ionized, excited, and propelled into the spark gap at velocities of up to 10 km/sec. As the excited atoms and ions travel away from the sample electrode, they emit their characteristic spectra. As the spark current falls, the spark-discharge channel contracts, ions recombine into excited atoms, and the sample is vapor-deposited on the counter electrode. The process is repeated in subsequent half-cycles until the capacitor voltage is insufficient to maintain the spark discharge. Clearly, the emission spectra from a spark discharge depend not only upon the part of the spark gap viewed by the spectrograph (near the anode, near the cathode, or in the middle) but on the selected time during the spark discharge. Without special equipment, spark-emission spectra are integrated over the total time of all these events.

Although the spark discharge appears complex, the quantitative application of the spark provides a very efficient means for transforming solid samples into emitting atomic vapors. The spark discharge provides fast, precise analysis; in quality-control steel analysis, for example, the time is less than 10 sec. Although the sensitivity is commonly not as high as that obtained with a DC arc, high precision can be obtained without special techniques.

The spark discharge is often applied to solid samples in the form of rods approximately a quarter-inch in diameter or cast disks or flats a half-inch thick by 1 to 3 inches in diameter. Powders are most often pressed into pellets and treated as solid samples for spark analysis. Liquid samples are also analyzed by spark discharges in many cases. Several different ways of analyzing liquid samples have been developed:

1. The porous-cup electrode (Fig. 11.4) is a quarter-inch graphite rod hollowed out by drilling, leaving a few millimeters at the end of the rod to form a bottom through which solutions can seep. The hollow electrode is filled with a few milliliters of sample solution, and the bottom is sparked against a graphite rod below it.

2. The rotating-disk electrode is a graphite disk about a half-inch in diameter held vertically; it dips into a solution and carries a thin film of the solution to the top of the electrode, where it is sparked. The disk is rotated at about 5 to 30 rpm.

3. Liquids can also be dried onto the top of quarter-inch graphite or metal rods, or on half-inch graphite disks, and the dried residue sparked. The *copper-spark* method uses a dried residue on a quarter-inch copper rod, and the *rotating-platform* method employs a half-inch graphite disk onto which the residue is dried and which is rotated horizontally during sparking. Both methods give good precision, and the copper-spark method is characterized by excellent sensitivity (cf. Table 11.2).

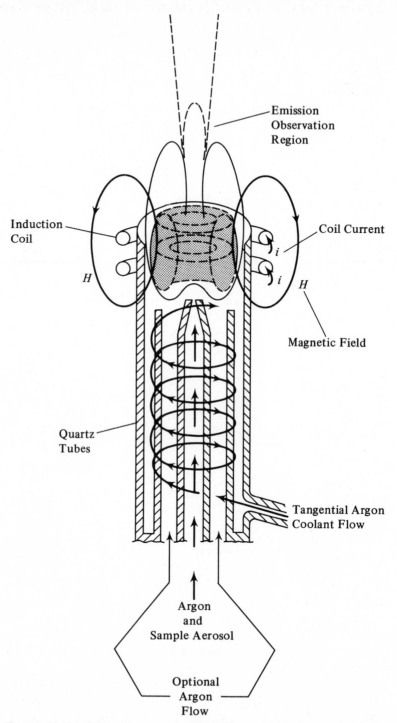

FIGURE 11.6. *Schematic representation of an inductively coupled plasma discharge. Adapted from V. A. Fassel and R. N. Kniseley,* Anal. Chem., *46, 1110A (1974), by permission of the publisher. Copyright © 1974 by the American Chemical Society.*

Inductively Coupled Plasma (ICP) Discharge. The arc and spark sources date to the early development of emission spectroscopy in the mid-1800s; the inductively coupled plasma (ICP) discharge is a relatively recent development, and is perhaps the most promising emission spectroscopic source today. Commercial ICP systems became available only in 1974, but research on this source has been going on since the early 1960s [7].

The ICP discharge is caused by the effect of a radio-frequency field on a flowing gas. In Figure 11.6, it is induced without electrode contact in argon flowing upward through a quartz tube inside a copper coil or solenoid. The coil is energized by a radio-frequency generator operating between about 5 to 75 MHz; a typical frequency is 27 MHz. The radio-frequency signal creates a changing magnetic field H inside the coil in the flowing argon gas.

A changing magnetic field induces a circulating (eddy) current in a conductor, which in turn heats the conductor. At room temperature, argon is not a conductor, but it can be made electrically conductive by heating it. To start the ICP discharge, a pilot spark, arc, or Tesla discharge is applied to the argon. This pilot discharge absorbs energy from the changing magnetic field and turns rapidly into a stable discharge plasma that is thermally very hot and spectrally very intense. The equilibrium temperature in the core of an ICP discharge operating at 1–2 kw input power is about 9,000–10,000 K.

More than one stream of argon is often used for spectrochemical analysis with the ICP discharge. One argon stream is confined to a volume near the tube walls to protect the quartz from the high-temperature discharge. A second argon stream carries the sample into the center of the discharge to produce an effective pathway through the discharge. If this pathway were not formed, the sample might flow around the hot discharge and be less effectively heated.

Although samples may be injected either as powders or as liquids, an arrangement similar to the spray-chamber nebulizer assembly used in flame spectroscopy (Chap. 10) is presently utilized. A complete nebulizer, spray chamber, and ICP discharge assembly is illustrated in Figure 11.7 [8]. The solvent is evaporated from the solution droplets formed in the spray chamber, so that only dried particles flow with the argon into the high-temperature discharge.

Because of the high temperatures available and the inert atmosphere of the ICP discharge, some of the difficulties found in flame, arc, and spark techniques are not present in the ICP discharge. Chemical interferences caused by the formation of stable compounds in flames (see Chap. 10) are negligible with the ICP discharge, so that releasing agents or special conditions are not needed. All compounds are likely to be atomized completely during their passage through the hot pathway in the center of the discharge. Ionization interferences occur in excitation sources with high temperatures such as the DC arc and the ICP plasma; however, adding a spectroscopic buffer such as 1000 ppm LiCl remedies any difficulty in the ICP discharge.

Spectral interferences with the ICP source are also possible, especially when the hot region of the discharge is viewed. However, the continuum background from the hot discharge does not extend appreciably beyond the end of the induction coil, and very high signal-to-background ratios are obtained just a short distance (1–3 cm) above the induction coil. Background from the argon continuum and interference from Ar(I) emission is minimal.

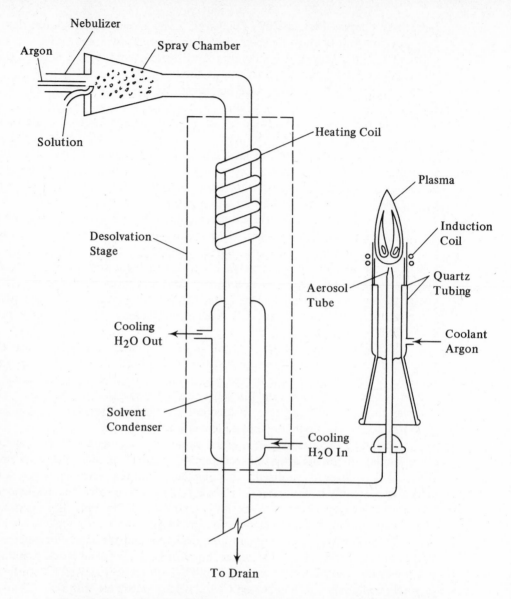

FIGURE 11.7. *Sample nebulizer, spray chamber, and desolvation apparatus for ICP discharge spectrometry. (Not to scale.) Adapted from R. N. Kniseley, V. A. Fassel, and C. C. Butler,* Clin. Chem., *19, 807 (1973), by permission of the publisher.*

The spectrum of an element in the ICP discharge resembles most closely one obtained in the DC arc rather than in a spark or a flame, so that the ICP discharge provides a rich spectrum for qualitative and simultaneous multi-element quantitative analysis. Even molecular spectra such as that due to CN are minimized in the ICP discharge or are located in a separate region of the discharge. In addition, the stabilities of the signal intensities observed in the ICP discharge are comparable to those of the flame rather than the arc or spark discharges.

The temperature distribution of the ICP discharge differs from other electronic excitation-sources owing to the induction coupling effect. Instead of finding the highest temperature along the axis of the discharge, as in the DC arc, the highest temperatures of the ICP discharge are found off-axis in the induction-coil region.

All of these properties of the ICP discharge provide excellent capabilities for quantitative analysis. Flow and operating conditions can be readily selected, so that nearly optimum signal-intensities for most elements can be obtained in a single spectroscopic viewing region above the hot discharge. This allows the simultaneous determination of 35 elements, for example, in a single sample without modifying the conditions for each element.

Table 11.2 presents detection limits for emission spectroscopy with several excitation sources. (These may be compared with those given in Table 10.4 for flame methods.) Generally less than 5 ml of sample solution is required for both emission analysis and the flame methods. The ICP discharge has been found to have both the precision of flame methods and the sensitivity of arc methods [9]. (For precise determinations, concentrations should generally be 100 times the detection limits listed.)

Although quantitative analysis with the ICP discharge may be performed with a spectrograph, the ICP discharge is more efficiently used with a spectrometer. One of the major reasons is that the high signal-to-background ratio and high stability provide linear analytical curves (readout signal as a function of concentration) over ranges of 10^4 to 10^5 [10]. This linearity exceeds by orders of magnitude that ob-

TABLE 11.2. *Comparison of Some Experimentally Determined Emission Spectroscopic Detection Limits ($\mu g/ml$)*

Element	DC Arc[a]	Spark[b]	ICP[c,d]
Ag	0.0006	0.2	0.004
Al	0.05	0.05	0.00008
As	0.1	5	0.002
Au	0.05	0.1	0.04
B	0.07	0.5	0.0001
Ba	0.005	0.02	0.00001
Be	0.0006	0.0002	0.000003
Bi	0.03	0.1	0.05
Ca	0.01	0.05	0.0000001
Cd	0.02	1	0.0002
Ce	0.02	0.3	0.0004
Co	0.01	0.05	0.003
Cr	0.01	0.05	0.0008
Cu	0.0003	——	0.0006
Fe	0.01	0.5	0.00009

(continued)

TABLE 11.2. (*continued*)

Element	DC Arc[a]	Spark[b]	ICP[c,d]
Ga	0.02	0.02	0.0002
Ge	0.02	——	0.0005
Hf	1	0.25	0.01
Hg	0.07	1	0.01
In	0.03	0.3	0.03
La	0.03	0.02	0.0001
Mg	0.007	0.05	0.000003
Mn	0.003	0.01	0.00002
Mo	0.006	0.03	0.0001
Na	0.005	0.1	0.00002
Nb	5	0.10	0.0002
Ni	0.02	0.05	0.0001
P	0.15	4	0.015
Pb	0.005	0.1	0.001
Pd	0.02	0.02	0.0008
Pt	0.04	0.4	0.08
Rh	0.02	0.05	0.003
Sb	0.07	2	0.2
Sc	0.2	0.01	0.003
Se	——	——	0.03
Si	0.1	0.20	0.01
Sn	0.05	0.30	0.003
Sr	0.00003	0.002	0.00003
Ta	30	0.3	0.03
Te	60	4	0.08
Th	0.02	0.5	0.003
Ti	0.0001	0.01	0.00003
Tl	0.07	0.8	0.2
U	——	2	0.03
V	0.02	0.02	0.00006
W	0.3	0.4	0.0007
Yb	0.0009	0.005	0.00002
Zn	0.01	0.5	0.00001
Zr	0.004	0.01	0.00006

a. V. Svoboda and I. Kleinmann, *Anal. Chem.*, *40*, 1534 (1968).
b. J. P. Faris, *Proc. 6th Conf. Anal. Chem. Nucl. Reactor Tech.*, TID-76655, Gatlingburg, Tenn., 1962.
c. V. A. Fassel and R. N. Kniseley, *Anal. Chem.*, *46*, 1110A, 1155A (1974).
d. P. W. J. M. Boumans and F. J. de Boer, *Proc. Anal. Div. Chem. Soc.*, *12*, 140 (1975).

tained in routine spark and arc analyses, as well as in flame methods. The linearity of the photographic emulsion is insufficient to cover this range, and only photo-multipliers have the capability needed.

11.3 QUALITATIVE AND QUANTITATIVE ANALYSES

Emission spectroscopy is widely used for both qualitative and quantitative analysis. The high sensitivity and the possible simultaneous excitation of as many as 72 elements, notably metals and metalloids, makes emission spectroscopy especially suited for rapid survey analysis of the elemental content in small samples at the level of $10\ \mu g/g$ or less. With control over excitation conditions to maintain constant and reliable atomization and excitation, the spectral line intensities can be used for quantitatively determining concentrations. An analytical curve must be constructed with known standards, and often the ratio of analyte intensity to the intensity of a second element contained in, or added to, the sample (the internal-standard method) is used to improve the precision of quantitative analyses. Preparation of standards for arc and spark techniques requires considerable care to match chemical and physical forms to the sample; this is not commonly required for ICP discharge.

Qualitative Analysis

Emission spectroscopy is especially well suited to the identification of elements contained in a sample, because meaningful results are obtained in less than an hour in a single exposure requiring only a few mg of sample in almost any form. Conventionally, DC-arc excitation is used for qualitative analysis because of its high sensitivity for metals and metalloids. To perform a DC-arc qualitative analysis, the sample (as a powder, small chunks, chips, filings, residue, or other form) is placed in a graphite-cup electrode (Fig. 11.4), and the electrode arced until the entire sample is vaporized. The spectrum is integrated photographically, providing a permanent record over a comprehensive wavelength range. Generally, several spectra are recorded on one photographic film or plate by moving (racking) this film in the camera between each run (see, e.g., Fig. 11.2). One of the spectra is usually that of iron to allow alignment with master plates. Processing the photoplate takes about ten minutes, and the spectrum is compared on a comparator-densitometer (Fig. 11.3) with either a master plate or a series of spectra of known elements (Fig. 11.3). The master plate, available commercially, contains a standard iron-arc spectrum, a wavelength scale, and wavelength markers for the persistent or most sensitive characteristic lines for each element. A portion of a master plate is shown in Figure 11.8. After aligning the unknown spectrum with the master plate, major line coincidences are identified for characteristic lines on the master. Three lines are generally required for positive identification of an element. An additional aid is that certain elements have characteristic patterns or groupings of spectral lines, which, with a little practice, are rapidly found and used for positive identification. Reference to standard wavelength tables provides additional lines that may be found in the unknown spectrum but not on the master plate.

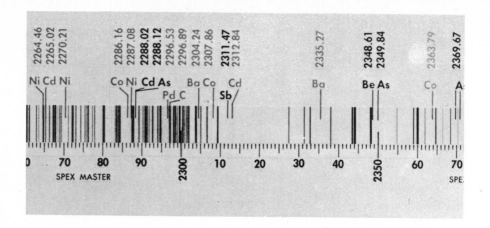

FIGURE 11.8. *Segment of Spex Master plate. In the complete plate, persistent lines of about* 70 *elements are given with color-coded labeling for ease of identification. Lines are superimposed on an iron spectrum. Units are angstroms. Courtesy of Spex Industries, Metuchen, N.J.*

Qualitative analysis by laser microprobe is popular for identifying small inclusions or areas in conducting and nonconducting samples. The laser can be focused to sample areas of 10 to 50 μm in diameter.

Often, qualitative analyses are performed with slightly more control over the various experimental conditions to obtain a rough estimate of the concentration range of the elements identified as major, minor, or trace. For better concentration estimates, semiquantitative or quantitative techniques, demanding greater control over parameters, are applied.

Quantitative Analysis

Emission spectroscopy is an important quantitative technique widely used in many industrial and research laboratories. In order to achieve an absolute concentration error of less than $\pm 10\%$, sample preparation and handling, experimental variables, and operating parameters must be strictly controlled. With conventional arc and spark procedures, absolute errors of ± 1–5% can be achieved. The development of a routine spectrometric analysis may take months, but once the method is optimized, high-quality quantitative results are obtained rapidly and routinely for large numbers of similar samples.

Fluctuations in electronic excitation-sources (described in Sec. 11.2), together with sample irregularities, constitute the major sources of error in emission spectroscopy. Modern spectrometers provide excellent stability and precision, and new sources like the ICP discharge and the controlled-waveform spark discharge have reduced many of the previous limitations. Photoelectric detection generally provides precision superior to that of photographic methods.

Some other critical considerations in quantitative emission spectroscopy include obtaining a representative sample, treating the sample to provide a suitable form without contamination, and matching standards with samples.

Electrodes. For arc and spark analyses, graphite electrodes are commonly used as sample and counter electrodes; some standardized electrode shapes are presented in Figure 11.4 [11]. The purity of these electrodes must be high, and most suppliers provide a quantitative DC-arc analysis for at least 15 elements with each box of electrodes. Electrodes are generally guaranteed to have a total ash content of less than 1 ppm, a maximum allowable impurity per element of 2 ppm, and total maximum impurities of 6 ppm.

High-purity graphite powder for DC-arc mixtures, or for pressed pellets for spark analysis, is also analyzed and guaranteed by manufacturers. In spark methods, the sample (if conductive) is often one of the two electrodes, and only a counter electrode is needed. Graphite electrodes are common, but metal counter electrodes, especially silver (to permit determination of carbon), are routinely employed in vacuum spark analysis.

Samples. Careful control of sampling and sample preparation is essential in quantitative emission spectroscopy. Even in the routine spark analysis of steel or aluminum, which requires only the grinding or machining of the surface of cast samples, the detailed characteristics of the sample-casting procedures had to be studied extensively during the method-development phase.

In arc analyses, the sample may require treatment before analysis; this can contribute contaminants or cause loss of some elements. For example, samples with high carbon content, like coal, require the removal of the organic portion by ashing in a muffle furnace at elevated temperatures or in a low-temperature oxygen plasma. Coal is ashed in platinum or silica crucibles at 500°C to eliminate the organic portion, but these high temperatures may cause volatilization and loss of some trace elements. Other inorganic materials such as rock, cement, slag, or chemicals need only to be dried, ground, and sieved. However, each step can also contaminate the sample. Typically, samples are ground so that known sources of contamination are eliminated. For example, in the analysis of beryllia (BeO) for other elements, samples are ground with a high-purity BeO mortar and pestle. (The use of a mortar and pestle made of tungsten carbide or of alumina will contaminate the specimen with iron and cobalt traces from the tungsten carbide or with aluminum from the alumina.) Sieving with metal screens can also contaminate the sample with traces of the screen material.

Sample contamination must also be taken into account when adding internal-reference and spectrochemical-buffer compounds. High-purity materials used for these special purposes are commercially available, since most laboratory chemicals are not pure enough.

Standards. The preparation of solid and powder standards for quantitative emission analysis is an important phase of the development and testing of new emission methods. Sometimes the lack of suitable standards hinders the analysis or limits the obtainable accuracy. Standard reference materials are being continually tested and authorized by the National Bureau of Standards, and a number of major steel and aluminum companies have developed standard disk samples for emission and x-ray spectrometry. Standards for trace metals in oil are also produced commercially.

In arc- and spark-emission spectroscopy, one of the critical aspects of quantitative analysis is the need to match the standard as closely as possible to the sample. Dilution of sample and standards by a common matrix in DC-arc methods somewhat reduces the dependence upon exact matches. Gordon and Chapman devised a common matrix-dilution technique for DC-arc analysis which is almost totally independent of the forms of the sample and the standard [4].

Internal-Standard Method. In emission spectroscopy, some of the variables in the excitation and processing of spectra can be minimized or eliminated by adopting the internal-standard technique. The technique is based upon measuring the ratio of the analyte signal-intensity and the reference-line signal-intensity. The internal standard is added to both the sample and the standards at the same concentration. The method assumes that as the excitation-source and spectrometer-readout conditions vary, the signal from the internal standard will change in the same way as those for the analyte elements. Thus, a ratio of the line intensities should minimize variations. Barnett et al. [12] has detailed the factors considered in selecting an internal standard. The technique is applied in both photographic and photoelectric detection systems; for photographic emulsions, the internal standard tends to correct for differences in processing and in emulsion properties from one plate to the next.

In routine industrial analysis, multi-channel spectrometers under computer control generally acquire, store, and update analytical curves for numerous elements simultaneously as part of a periodic check on standards. Excellent precision and accuracy can be obtained with these procedures.

In developing an emission spectroscopic method, especially arc and spark techniques, considerable effort must be devoted to the selection of internal-standard materials and spectral lines. Some arc and all ICP methods exhibit good precision without use of an internal standard.

Analytical Curves. Emission spectroscopy is not an absolute technique, and the intensity response for each analyte element must be calibrated for various known amounts of the element introduced into the excitation source. The analytical curve from the microphotometer (Fig. 11.3) represents this calibration. The transmittance of the analyte line is measured along with a nearby background, and these values are transformed into relative intensities using the emulsion calibrations. The selection of photographic emulsion depends upon the wavelength range to be covered and on the strengths of the spectral signals. Operating parameters, including exposure conditions and film-developing time and temperature, are selected in preliminary experiments to provide calibration linearity and good signal-to-noise ratio. Once determined, these conditions must then be maintained rigorously throughout the calibration and analysis stages.

Concentration is the independent variable, and the relative intensity or intensity ratio is the dependent variable. Some analytical curves are plotted on logarithmic coordinates, but computer curve-fitting procedures readily allow wide-range rectilinear calibrations, as well as calculation of the concentration values for unknown samples. For very accurate work, emulsion calibrations are repeated for each spectrum by adopting the sample spectrum as the source of the emulsion calibration.

Accuracy and Precision. The accuracy and precision required of an atomic-emission spectroscopic method affect the approach used in the analysis as well as the time involved. A qualitative analysis requires a minimum of effort, but as better accuracy and precision are demanded, increasing care is needed. Even if a representative sample has been obtained, errors inherent in the method, human errors, and random errors contribute to inaccuracies. Spectrochemical equipment is largely responsible for the random errors that influence precision, and both method and individual laboratory errors influence the accuracy. In addition, relative precision and accuracy depend upon concentration levels. The standard deviation increases with increasing concentration, but the relative standard deviation decreases; the latter may vary from a few percent to less than one percent using photographic detection, depending on the element and the concentration.

Precision is usually improved with a photoelectric detector. Electronic stabilities determined with a stable excitation source have a relative standard deviation ranging over ± 0.03–0.2% (with modern instruments, using 10-sec integrations and 10 runs). Precision may range over ± 0.3–3.0% for homogeneous samples with concentration levels above about 0.5% in spark analysis, or for solution samples with concentration levels about 100 times greater than the limit of detection for the ICP discharge. The precision of DC-arc techniques for determining trace elements in powdered samples at concentrations greater than 20 ppm is typically in the range ± 2–12% relative standard deviation.

Evaluation of accuracy requires comparing results against standard materials or the results obtained using other independent techniques. Figure 11.9 illustrates the correlation for iron in orchard leaves determined by atomic-absorption, DC-arc, and x-ray-fluorescence spectroscopy, and ICP-emission spectrometry. The standard deviations are also indicated.

FIGURE 11.9. *Comparison of results for iron in six samples of orchard leaves. The "average value" for each sample is the average of the values obtained by a number of independent laboratories using one or more of the techniques given in parentheses. The standard deviation of these values is given for each sample by the error bars, as well as the standard deviation of the results obtained by ICP emission spectroscopy for 7 dissolutions. A recent atomic-absorption value is also given, indicated by ■. Adapted from R. H. Scott and A. Strasheim, Anal. Chim. Acta, 76, 71 (1975), by permission of the author and publisher.*

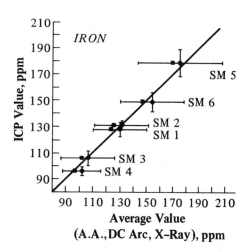

Typically, the accuracy and precision change with the composition of the sample, since the different matrices introduce errors; however, the ICP discharge is particularly free of errors caused by the sample type. For example, determination of some 16 elements in samples as varied as distilled water, steel, blood serum, whole blood, food, and soil showed the detection limits to be within a factor of 2 to 3; the detection limit is proportional to the slope of the analytical curve and the precision (or noise).

11.4 APPLICATIONS

The applications of emission spectroscopy with electrical excitation-sources are diverse and extensive. A few examples are selected in this section to illustrate typical analyses. A number of annual and biennial reviews collect and describe new applications as they are published.

Analysis of Metals by Spark Discharge

The determination of 23 elements in aluminum and its alloys by the *point-to-plane* spark technique with an emission spectrometer [13] represents an example of the type of routine quality-control analysis performed on metals and alloys in mills and foundries. Preheated sample molds designed to produce homogeneous castings free of voids or porosity in the regions to be sparked are filled from a sampling ladle containing molten metal taken from the aluminum furnace. After cooling, the disks are transported to the spectroscopy laboratory where an operator machines a smooth surface on the sample. The sample is placed on a Petrey stand that aligns the sample with the entrance slit of the spectrometer. Only predetermined locations on the disk are sparked. A freshly cut graphite counter-electrode (C-5 in Fig. 11.4) is positioned 3.0 mm from the machined surface.

A spark discharge is produced between the flat surface of a chill-cast aluminum sample and the tip of a pointed graphite counter electrode. The emission intensities for 31 different spectral lines and an aluminum internal-reference line are measured simultaneously by 32 photomultiplier tubes positioned behind exit slits. At the end of the 10–15 sec exposure period, the accumulated capacitor potentials for each analytical line relative to the potential for the aluminum internal reference line are automatically measured and recorded. The unknown values are calculated automatically in terms of percent concentration.

Secondary standards and blank standards of similar metallurgical composition as the unknown samples are used for the principal analytical curve. The averages of 20 results on standards and 20 readings from the blank standards establish the analytical curve. The 20 readings are produced by five separate spark spectra obtained on each of four different occasions.

This overall approach remains basically the same for analysis of steel, brass, zinc, or other metals, although there are specific differences in spectrometers, analyte spectral lines, sample-preparation techniques, and excitation conditions.

Metals in Lubricating Oils

The determination of wear metals in the lubricating oils used in aircraft, truck, locomotive, and other engines can provide an excellent indication of the mechanical condition of the engine. In fact, as the presence of certain metals is noticed or their concentrations begin to increase, the parts or components of the engine that are wearing out can be identified and replaced or repaired. This routine program of wear-metal analysis saves tens of millions of dollars annually, and the analysis is one of the largest analytical operations in the world. Tens of thousands of samples are run monthly. The most important wear metals are iron, aluminum, magnesium, copper, and silver. Iron appears as an indicator of more than 80 percent of all failures detected by wear-metal analysis. Aluminum usually relates to wear of oil pumps, cases, housings, pistons, and cylinder heads, and copper to wear of bronze parts such as bushings and retainers. Silicon is useful as an indicator of lubricant contamination from dust and dirt.

The spark analysis is performed with a rotating graphite disk electrode. The spectra of ten or more elements in the 0.1 to 500 ppm range are determined with a spectrometer during a 45-sec exposure after a 30-sec prespark [14]. For calibration, eight analyses of each of five standards containing the wear metals are used to establish the analytical curves. The samples are agitated in the original container until all sediment is dispersed homogeneously in the oil. The graphite electrode disk is mounted as the cathode on a graphite spindle and positioned in the spark stand. A graphite counter electrode spaced 3 mm above the top of the rotating disk is centered on the optical axis. An aluminum or porcelain boat holding the oil sample is positioned on the spark stand and raised until the disk dips into the oil. The spark is started after the turning disk is evenly coated with the oil sample. Duplicate determinations are made with new electrodes on each sample.

Trace Elements in Airborne Particulate Matter

Emission spectrography has been used extensively for the determination of trace elements in atmospheric particulates, especially in large-scale survey studies in which simultaneous multi-element analysis is important [15, 16]. Airborne particulate matter is routinely collected by drawing a measured volume of air through filter materials such as fiberglass, asbestos, cellulosic paper, porous plastic, or graphite in the form of disks or electrodes. However, for the determination of trace elements, the chemical composition of the filter is important. For example, glass filters show high concentrations of Ba, Sr, Rb, Zn, Ni, Fe, Ca, As, and other elements. The composition of the filter materials is particularly significant in sampling relatively clean atmospheres because of the low particulate levels collected in reasonable sampling times.

A membrane filter which can be dissolved in acetone, or a spectrochemically pure graphite filter which can be examined directly with a powder DC-arc technique, can provide passable results. After air has been drawn through a previously weighed filter, the membrane filter is dissolved in acetone, then centrifuged. The particulates are collected, dried, and weighed; then a spectroscopic buffer is added composed of 1 part NaF and 1 part graphite powder, with 100 ppm indium oxide and 20,000 ppm tantalum oxide as internal standards. About 35 mg of the final mixture is placed in a graphite electrode and arced at 15 A for 60 sec in a controlled (90% Ar–10% O_2) atmosphere.

Alternatively, the graphite filter can be a standard porous-cup spectrographic electrode (Fig. 11.4) through which air is drawn. An indium internal-reference solution is dried in the electrode before sampling. When excited in a 28 A DC arc for 20 sec in an argon atmosphere saturated with HCl, this technique gives absolute detection limits between 0.1 and 5 ng for 14 elements.

Trace Elements in Plant Material, Soil, and Blood

The routine determination of trace elements in agricultural, geological, and biological samples is of considerable interest. Ideally, many trace elements in each sample should be determined simultaneously using a single group of standards. Atomic-emission spectroscopy using the ICP source provides that capability.

Inorganic analysis of plant materials for certain trace elements is frequently used in agricultural studies. For example, orchard leaves can be examined for their Fe, Mn, Cu, Al, B, and Zn content [17]. The leaves are first dried and finely ground, then ashed in silica crucibles in a muffle furnace at 500°C. The ash is dissolved in HNO_3 and diluted to a known volume. Once the linearity of response for each element is established by use of standards, calibration is carried out with only one composite standard solution containing all the elements. The ICP discharge results compare well with those obtained by other methods. An example for iron is given in Figure 11.9. Agreement among alternative methods provides a good test for the accuracy of determination. The standard deviations are indicated by the horizontal and vertical lines in the figure. Better precision was obtained for the ICP discharge method.

The sampling and analysis of soils is extensively used in exploring for minerals. The application of the ICP-discharge technique for Cu, Zn, Ni, Co, and Pb is rapid and free from certain interference effects common to atomic-absorption analysis [18]. After drying and screening, weighed samples are dissolved in a 9:1 mixture of concentrated perchloric and nitric acids.

In health-care programs, knowledge of the concentrations of biologically essential or toxic elements in body fluids is important. Moreover, one must be able to measure accurately small changes in concentration that can be significant with respect to diseases. The ability to determine rapidly and simply several trace elements, some at the ppb level, in body fluids such as blood and urine is achieved by the ICP discharge [8]. This analytical system is able to determine many elements simultaneously, which conserves both sample and time. For biological fluids, only very small volumes (less than 1 ml) are usually available, and sample volumes of 10–25 μl can be used with the ICP discharge.

SELECTED BIBLIOGRAPHY

AHRENS, L. H., and TAYLOR, S. R. *Spectrochemical Analysis*, 2nd ed., Reading, Mass: Addison-Wesley, 1961.

BARNES, R. M. "Emission Spectroscopy," *Anal. Chem.*, *44*, 122R (1972); *46*, 150R (1974).

BARNES, R. M. *Emission Spectroscopy*. Stroudsburg, Pa.: Dowden, Hutchinson, & Ross, 1975.

GROVE, E. L., ed. *Analytical Emission Spectroscopy*, vol. 1, parts I and II. New York: Marcel Dekker, 1971 and 1972.

HARRISON, G. R. *M.I.T. Wavelength Tables*, 2nd ed., Cambridge, Mass.: MIT Press, 1969.

MIKA, J., and TOROK, T. *Analytical Emission Spectroscopy*, New York: Crane, Russak, & Co., 1974.

SLAVIN, M. *Emission Spectrochemical Analysis*, New York: Wiley, 1971.

ZEIDEL, A. N.; PROKOFEV, V. K.; RAISKII, S. M.; SLAVNYI, V. A.; and SCHREIDER, E. Y. *Table of Spectral Lines*, New York: IFI/Plenum, 1970.

REFERENCES

1. P. W. J. M. BOUMANS, *Theory of Spectrochemical Excitation*, New York: Plenum Press, 1966.

2. "Description and Performance of the Microphotometer," in *Methods for Emission Spectrochemical Analysis*, 6th ed., Philadelphia: American Society for Testing and Materials, 1971, pp 296–98, ASTM E 409-71.

3. "Photographic Photometry in Spectrochemical Analysis," in *Methods for Emission Spectrochemical Analysis*, 6th ed., Philadelphia: American Society for Testing and Materials, 1971, pp 74–96, ASTM E 116-70a.

4. W. A. GORDON and G. B. CHAPMAN, *Spectrochim. Acta, 25B,* 123 (1970).

5. J. P. WALTERS, *Appl. Spectrosc., 26,* 323 (1972).

6. J. P. WALTERS, *Appl. Spectrosc., 26,* 17 (1972).

7. V. A. FASSEL and R. N. KNISELEY, *Anal. Chem., 46,* 1110A, 1155A (1974).

8. R. N. KNISELEY, V. A. FASSEL, and C. C. BUTLER, *Clin. Chem., 19,* 807 (1973).

9. P. W. J. M. BOUMANS and F. J. DE BOER, *Spectrochim. Acta, 27B,* 391 (1972).

10. C. C. BUTLER, R. N. KNISELEY, and V. A. FASSEL, *Anal. Chem., 47,* 825 (1975).

11. "Designation of Shapes and Sizes of Graphite Electrodes," in *Methods for Emission Spectrochemical Analysis*, 6th ed., Philadelphia: American Society for Testing and Materials, 1971, pp 106–11, ASTM E 130-66.

12. W. B. BARNETT, V. A. FASSEL, and R. N. KNISELEY, *Spectrochim. Acta, 23B,* 643 (1968).

13. "Spectrochemical Analysis of Aluminum and Its Alloys by the Point-to-Plane Technique Using an Optical Emission Spectrometer," in *Methods for Emission Spectrochemical Analysis*, 6th ed., Philadelphia: American Society for Testing and Materials, 1971, pp 196–207, ASTM E 227-67.

14. "Proposed Spectrochemical Method of Test for Wear Metals in Used Diesel Lubricating Oils by a Rotating-Disk Electrode Technique Using a Direct-Reading Spectrometer," in *Methods for Emission Spectrochemical Analysis*, 6th ed., Philadelphia: American Society for Testing and Materials, 1971, pp 375–82, ASTM D-2-1968.

15. A. SUGIMAE, *Anal. Chem., 46,* 1123 (1974).

16. J. L. SEELEY and R. K. SKOGERBOE, *Anal. Chem., 46,* 415 (1974).

17. R. H. SCOTT and A. STRASHEIM, *Anal. Chim. Acta., 76,* 71 (1975).

18. R. H. SCOTT and M. L. KOKOT, *Anal. Chim. Acta., 75,* 257 (1975).

PROBLEMS

1. Explain why the simultaneous determination of several elements would be more difficult by means of atomic-absorption spectrophotometry than by atomic-emission spectrometry using either flame, arc, or ICP excitation sources.

2. Alkali and alkaline-earth metals in solution are in the ionic form and appear colorless, but in an excitation source, emission from neutral atoms and ions is observed, perceived as bright colors in the visible region. (a) To go from ions to atoms, these

species must acquire one or more electrons. From where do these electrons come? (b) How do you account for the colorful emission from these metals? (c) What color would you predict each of these metals to show in an arc or ICP discharge?

3. In Table 11.2, the halogens and gases are conspicuously absent from the lists of elements. What reasons can you give for the difficulty in determining these elements by arc or spark sources in air? Suggest one or two methods that you would try if you were required to determine halogens, permanent gases, or rare gases by emission spectrometry.

4. Would a DC arc make a very good source for production of neutral atoms for atomic absorption? Explain your answer.

5. If you were given a brass block for analysis and told that the tin and zinc distributions in the block were very heterogeneous, would you or would you not choose a spark point-to-plane technique for analysis? On what grounds do you make your selection? If you chose not to use a spark point-to-plane technique, what alternative spark techniques might you employ for the analysis of zinc and tin?

6. A sample of an unknown light-metal alloy was analyzed using the point-to-plane spark technique. By means of a projection comparator the following wavelengths were identified. What elements are present? (Hint: the CRC *Handbook of Chemistry and Physics* contains lists of wavelengths.) What is the alloy matrix?

236.706 nm	283.307	327.926
251.612	288.158	328.233
252.852	288.958	330.259
255.796	294.920	330.294
256.799	296.116	330.628
259.373	307.399←(internal	332.513
261.020	reference)	334.502
266.039	317.933	334.557
270.170	318.020	343.823
270.574	322.129	396.153
277.983	324.754	403.076
278.142	327.396	481.053

7. The accompanying figure illustrates the emission signals from Mn in 25-μl aliquots

of human whole blood, and of blood to which spikes of a Mn standard solution were added. The whole blood had first been diluted tenfold with 0.1 M HCl, and an ICP source was used. What is the concentration of Mn in the blood sample?

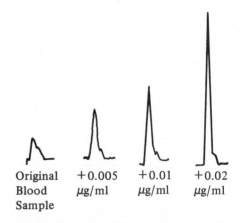

| Original Blood Sample | +0.005 μg/ml | +0.01 μg/ml | +0.02 μg/ml |

Signals obtained for Mn in human whole blood (10-fold dilution) and from addition standards. Adapted from R. N. Kniseley, V. A. Fassel, and C. C. Butler, Clin. Chem., 19, 807 (1973), by permission of the publisher.

8. The reproducibility of the signals for the Mn 403.0-nm line in problem 7 is indicated by the recordings in the following figure. What is the precision of these signals expressed as standard deviation and relative standard deviation?

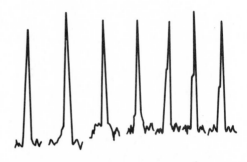

Reproducibility of signals for Mn from 25 μl samples of whole blood (undiluted). Adapted from R. N. Kniseley, V. A. Fassel, and C. C. Butler, Clin. Chem., 19, 807 (1973), by permission of the publisher.

9. Describe the considerations involved in selecting (a) an internal-standard element and spectral line (b) a spectrochemical buffer (c) a matrix diluent.

10. Predict the change in atomic-absorption sensitivity when a flame of temperature $T = 2500$ K is replaced by an arc of temperature $T = 5000$ K for the resonance transition of calcium corresponding to a wavelength of 422.673 nm. (The transition is $3p^6 4s^2\, {}^1S_0 \leftarrow 3p^6 4s^1\, {}^1P_1{}^0$, corresponding to $E = 2.93$ eV.) Will ionization make an appreciable contribution?

Arc Number	Sample	Si line ($\%\ T$)	Na line ($\%\ T$)
1	0.0001% standard	> 99	> 99
2	0.001% standard	96	92
3	0.01% standard	66	71
4	0.1% standard	< 1	23
5	Pure dolomite	< 1	< 1
6	1 part dolomite + 9 parts graphite	58	16
7	1 part dolomite + 99 parts graphite	95	65

Plot a calibration curve (log absorbance versus log concentration), and determine

11. A sample of dolomite was analyzed semi-quantitatively for its Si and Na content using a DC arc with a matrix-dilution technique. Standards are available (Spex Industries, Inc.) which contain about 50 elements, each at a specified concentration level, mixed with a high-purity spectroscopic graphite powder; for example, 0.1% by weight of each of 50 elements in one standard, 0.01% of each in a second standard, and so forth. The following data were obtained from a densitometer measurement of an exposed film on the silicon 288.16-nm line and the sodium 330.23-nm line:

the concentration of Si and Na in the dolomite sample.

12

Nuclear Magnetic Resonance Spectroscopy

S. STERNHELL

Like other forms of spectroscopy (for instance, infrared and ultraviolet), nuclear magnetic resonance spectroscopy (NMR) deals with the measurement of energy gaps between states of different energy. However, unlike most other forms of spectroscopy, the phenomenon requires the presence of an external magnetic field and concerns nuclei rather than electrons. This is the origin of the terms "nuclear" and "magnetic" in *nuclear magnetic resonance spectroscopy*.

NMR spectroscopy is of relatively recent origin and has had a spectacular rise, owing principally to its applications in organic chemistry—it is at present the most powerful technique for structural analysis available to the organic chemist, because it utilizes commonly found elements (in particular, hydrogen) as "chromophores." With the aid of NMR it is possible to define the environment of practically all commonly occurring functional groups, as well as of fragments (such as hydrogen atoms attached to carbon) which are not otherwise accessible to spectroscopic or analytical techniques. NMR may also be utilized for quantitative determination of compounds in mixtures and hence for following the progress of chemical reactions. More sophisticated applications often yield kinetic and thermodynamic parameters for certain types of chemical processes; and others, in particular spin-spin coupling, often give accurate information about the relative positions of groups of magnetic nuclei within molecules. The principal limitations of the method are its inherently low sensitivity and its virtual nonapplicability to samples in the solid state.

The phenomenon of nuclear resonance was first observed in 1946 by two teams of physicists: Purcell, Torrey, and Pound at Harvard and Bloch, Hansen, and Packard at Stanford, who shared a Nobel Prize for this discovery. The first observation of the *chemical shift*, the phenomenon on which all chemical applications are based, was made by Knight in 1949 and the first systematic applications to organic chemistry were reported in 1953 by Meyer, Saika, and Gutowsky. The first commercial instruments appeared in about 1956 and, in spite of their high cost, several thousand are now in use. Relatively inexpensive models are now available that, although not as sophisticated as the more expensive models, are easier to operate and are capable of handling many routine measurements.

12.1 THEORY AND INSTRUMENTATION

Two elementary principles of classical electromagnetism, summarized in Figures 12.1 and 12.2, should be recalled. Atomic nuclei have charge (they contain protons) and some also behave as if they spin. A spinning charge is equivalent to a current in a conductor loop; therefore, nuclei with nonzero spin will generate a magnetic field, i.e., will have a *magnetic moment* or a magnetic dipole.

FIGURE 12.1. *Right-hand rule. A current i flowing in a conductor loop generates a magnetic field H in the direction shown.*

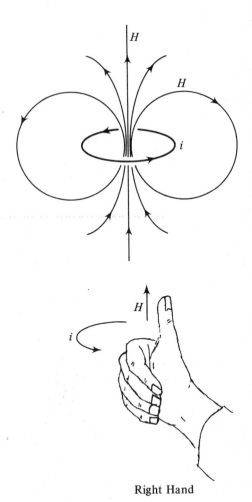

Right Hand

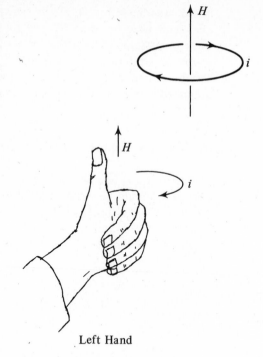

FIGURE 12.2. *Left-hand rule. A magnetic field H causes current i to flow in the conductor loop in the direction shown. As given, this rule is incomplete, since relative motion of the field and conductor is necessary in the macroscopic case, but the rule gives the correct direction of the effect in the nuclear case.*

Left Hand

Depending on the shape of the nuclear charge and the number and type of nucleons, the *spin quantum number*, I, can have values 0, 1/2, 1, 3/2, and so on. There are three principal groups of nuclei:

1. $I = 0$ (nonspinning nuclei). These have no magnetic moment and are composed of even numbers of protons and neutrons, e.g., $^{12}_{6}C$, $^{16}_{8}O$.
2. $I = 1/2$ (spherical spinning charges). These nuclei have a magnetic moment but no *electric quadrupole*. This group is by far the most important from the chemical point of view. Chemically useful nuclei in this group, in decreasing order of importance, are: $^{1}_{1}H$, $^{13}_{6}C$, $^{19}_{9}F$, $^{31}_{15}P$, $^{15}_{7}N$. Of these, the proton (^{1}H) alone accounts for well over 90% of all NMR observations made.
3. $I > 1/2$ (nonspherical spinning charges). These nuclei have both magnetic dipoles and electric quadrupoles; examples are $I = 1$: $^{2}_{1}H$, $^{14}_{7}N$; $I = 3/2$: $^{11}_{5}B$, $^{35}_{17}Cl$, $^{37}_{17}Cl$, $^{79}_{35}Br$, $^{81}_{35}Br$, $^{7}_{3}Li$; $I = 2$: $^{36}_{17}Cl$, $^{58}_{27}Co$; $I = 5/2$: $^{25}_{12}Mg$, $^{27}_{13}Al$, $^{17}_{8}O$.

A fundamental quantum law is that: *In a uniform magnetic field, a nucleus of spin I may assume 2I + 1 orientations.* Thus, for a nucleus of $I = 1/2$ (for instance, the proton), there are $2(1/2) + 1 = 2$ permissible orientations. This makes a nucleus of $I = 1/2$ analogous to a bar magnet in a magnetic field (Fig. 12.3). Since we shall deal exclusively with nuclei of spin $I = 1/2$ in this chapter, and almost exclusively with protons, the "bar-magnet analogy" will be useful.

As with the bar magnet, the two orientations of the nuclear magnet in the magnetic field (of strength* H_0) have different energies, and it is possible to induce a

---

* The units are *gauss*: 1 gauss is defined as the strength of a magnetic field that induces a voltage of 1 V in a conductor 1 cm long moving at 1 cm/sec.

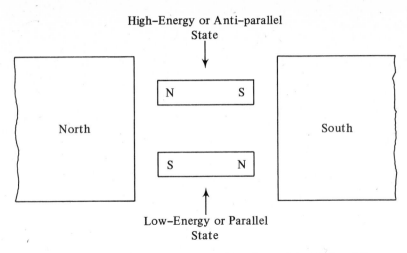

High–Energy or Anti–parallel
State

North

N   S

S   N

South

Low–Energy or Parallel
State

FIGURE 12.3.   *The bar-magnet analogy for nuclei with I = 1/2.*

nuclear transition, analogous to the flipping of the bar magnet, by applying electromagnetic radiation of an appropriate frequency ν given by

$$\nu = \frac{\gamma H_0}{2\pi} \tag{12.1}$$

where γ = a fundamental constant known as the *gyromagnetic ratio* or *magnetogyric ratio*, and is characteristic of the particular nucleus concerned

It can be seen that Equation 12.1 can be reduced to

$$\nu = \text{constant} \times H_0 \tag{12.2}$$

Equation 12.1 is known as the *Larmor equation*; it shows that one could observe a nuclear transition (*spin flip*) by keeping the magnetic field constant and varying the applied frequency (or vice versa) until the combination of field strength and irradiating frequency characteristic of the nucleus concerned is reached. This condition is often described as *resonance* and is, of course, the origin of the term "resonance" in *nuclear magnetic resonance*. The term *resonance frequency* is also sometimes used, but it must be remembered that the term would be meaningless without specifying the field strength H_0. Thus, the resonance frequency of the proton is 60 MHz *at 14,092 gauss*. In practice, NMR spectrometers may be capable of varying (or "sweeping") either the frequency or the magnetic field, and one often uses the terms *frequency-sweep spectrometer, frequency-sweep spectrum, field-sweep spectrometer,* and *field-sweep spectrum.*

The magnitudes of the various constants involved are such that the energy gap corresponding to the spin flip, given by $\Delta E = h\nu$, is very small; 60 MHz corresponds to only 6×10^{-6} kcal/mole. Thus, all NMR frequencies at usable field strengths fall in the radio-frequency (RF) region of the electromagnetic spectrum; the source of the radiation is a radio-frequency transmitter, generally a crystal oscillator.

Now consider the details of the energy transfer to a nuclear magnet placed in an external field H_0. The magnet, in either the parallel or the antiparallel

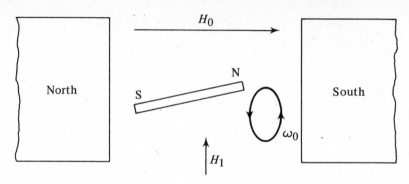

FIGURE 12.4. *The relation between precession and the exciting field H_1.*

orientation (Fig. 12.3), will not remain stationary, but will precess (Fig. 12.4) in a magnetic field H_0 with an angular velocity ω_0 given by

$$\omega_0 = \gamma H_0 \tag{12.3}$$

Combining Equations 12.1 and 12.3, we get

$$\omega_0 = 2\pi\nu \tag{12.4}$$

Thus, if one can get ω_0, one can also determine ν, the resonance frequency. This is done as follows: a second magnetic field (H_1) is generated at right angles to H_0 by passing a very-high-frequency alternating current supplied by an RF oscillator through a coil (the transmitter coil). When the angular component of H_1 matches ω_0, the frequency of this alternating current is equal to ν and a transition, or spin flip, can occur. The geometry of the arrangement in Figure 12.4 follows from the simple rules of electromagnetism stated at the beginning of the chapter, and the NMR experiment can be seen to amount to "nuclear induction."

We can now construct an *NMR spectrometer*. A typical arrangement is shown in Figure 12.5. This diagram represents a *field-sweep, crossed-coil spectrometer*, but the essential features are the same for other types of spectrometers. The essential parts of any high-resolution (the significance of this term will become apparent later) NMR spectrometer are:

1. The *magnet*, which may either be a permanent magnet or an electromagnet, but which must be capable of generating a very strong, very stable, and very homogeneous magnetic field. (These magnetic-field requirements are the principal reasons for the cost and complexity of NMR spectrometers.) To average out small magnetic-field inhomogeneities throughout the sample, the sample tube is rotated at several hundred rpm.

2. The *sweep generator*, which is used to vary the magnetic field over a small range by passing a variable direct current through coils that are coaxial with the direction of the main magnetic field H_0.

3. The *transmitter coil*, which is placed at right angles to the sweep coils and is used to generate the exciting field H_1.

4. The *receiver coil*, which is placed around the sample holder in the remaining orthogonal plane. A small current is generated in it when the resonance condition is achieved (see nuclear induction, above).

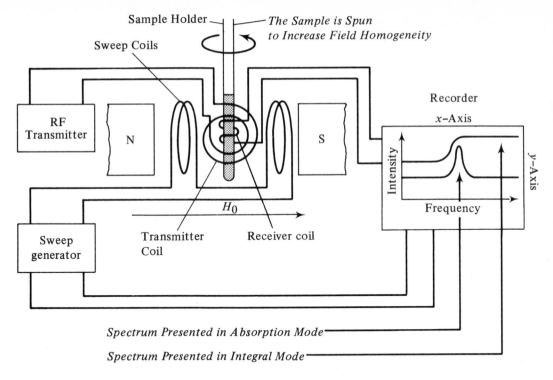

Sample Holder

Sweep Coils

The Sample is Spun to Increase Field Homogeneity

RF Transmitter

N

S

Recorder

x–Axis

Intensity

Frequency

y–Axis

H_0

Sweep generator

Transmitter Coil

Receiver coil

Spectrum Presented in Absorption Mode

Spectrum Presented in Integral Mode

FIGURE 12.5. *Schematic diagram of an NMR spectrometer.*

The signal from the receiver coil is suitably amplified and is made to deflect the recorder pen along the *y*-axis while the *x*-axis is synchronized with the sweep generator. Thus one plots the signal from the receiver coil as a function of the field strength; the intensity of the signal is proportional to the number of nuclei undergoing the transition. This is the *field-sweep experiment*. The *frequency-sweep experiment* is analogous, except that the field is kept constant while the frequency is swept and synchronized with the *x*-axis of the recorder. In either case one can express the *x*-axis scale in terms of "signal frequency" because, by Equation 12.1, the field strength and frequency for the resonance condition are always directly connected.

The intensity of the signal is proportional to the area under the absorption curve (Fig. 12.5) and is usually obtained by electronic integration, yielding a step function whose height is a direct measure of the relative intensity of the absorption signal.

There are certain consequences of the small size of the energy gap involved in a nuclear-spin transition. The Boltzmann relation gives the populations of nuclear spins in the upper energy state (N_2) and in the lower energy state (N_1) in terms of the energy gap ΔE between them:

$$\frac{N_1}{N_2} = e^{\Delta E/RT} \tag{12.5}$$

When the energy gap is very small, as is the case here, the right-hand side approaches e^0 (unity), and the excess population in the lower energy state, given by $N_1 - N_2$ and called the "Boltzmann excess," becomes very small. Since an absorption signal can only originate from the Boltzmann excess (typically only 1 nucleus in 100,000 in an NMR experiment), it follows that the method is inherently not very sensitive and that sophisticated signal amplification must be used in an NMR spectrometer. One of the reasons for the use of very high magnetic fields becomes apparent: the Larmor equation shows that high magnetic fields require high resonance frequencies. This in turn widens the energy gap between the spin states ($\Delta E = h\nu$), thereby increasing the Boltzmann excess and the sensitivity of the experiment.

A consequence of the small Boltzmann excess in NMR experiments arises from the general spectroscopic principle that absorption cannot occur unless some mechanism exists for a radiationless transition that can restore the excess population in the lower energy state. This is related to the fact that upward and downward transitions are equally probable on collision with an appropriate energy quantum. Therefore excess absorption, that is, observable absorption signals, can only originate from unequal populations, as stated above.

The mechanisms of radiationless transitions from the upper to the lower energy states are particularly critical in NMR spectroscopy because of the small Boltzmann excess. These mechanisms are termed *relaxation* and are characterized by their *relaxation times T*, which are equal to half the time necessary to restore equilibrium by the mechanism considered. Clearly, large values of T indicate inefficient relaxation. Two relaxation mechanisms are important:

1. *Spin-spin* or *transverse relaxation* (characterized by T_2) occurs when the energy is lost by spin exchange, that is, by transmission to neighboring spins. This operates extremely efficiently in solids, where magnetic nuclei are close together. However, the positive effects of this efficiency are offset by another general spectroscopic principle, the uncertainty principle, which states that the width of a spectral line is inversely proportional to the time spent in the upper energy state,

$$\text{line width} = \frac{\text{constant}}{\text{time in upper state}} \tag{12.6}$$

Since the spin-spin relaxation mechanism in solids is so efficient, very small values of T_2 result, producing very broad lines. Further, such spin exchanges between identical nuclei average the resonance frequencies of nuclei whose environments are not quite identical, and broaden the spectral lines further (dipolar broadening). For these reasons, solids give spectra with lines about 1000 times too broad to give information of much chemical interest (see below). Spectra of solids, or *wide-line spectra*, will therefore not be further discussed here, although they are of interest in solid-state physics.

2. *Spin-lattice* or *longitudinal relaxation* (characterized by T_1) occurs when the energy is lost to the "lattice," i.e., to any component of the sample, inter- or intramolecular. The lattice contains magnetic nuclei in rapid thermal motion in a magnetic field, generating a variety of electric currents and magnetic dipoles; energy may be lost to them by the nuclear magnets observed, thus restoring the equilibrium. This mechanism operates with gases, liquids, and solutions and is of just the right efficiency to produce narrow lines, or so called *high-resolution spectra*.

Interactions between nuclear magnetic dipoles and nuclear electric quadrupoles in nuclei where $I > 1/2$ offer another relaxation mechanism that prevents the observation of the NMR signals from some elements.

Interactions of the nuclear magnet with unpaired electrons (for example, in free radicals and in atoms of the transition metals) can also result in efficient relaxation. Since an unpaired electron has about 1000 times the strength of a nuclear magnet, line broadening often occurs in solutions containing even small amounts of paramagnetic impurities, which must therefore be rigorously excluded from NMR samples; even dissolved oxygen causes some broadening.

If for some reason the spin-lattice relaxation mechanism is not operating efficiently, as when high viscosity interferes with the thermal movement of the lattice, the signal strength will diminish with time even during the relatively short interval needed to scan the signal, thus causing the phenomenon of *saturation*. The same phenomenon will occur if the current in the transmitter coil, and therefore the strength of the RF field, is increased to too high a value, flipping the nuclei into their upper states faster than the relaxation processes can restore the equilibrium. The onset of saturation is also accompanied by some line broadening, because it is the nuclei exactly at resonance, and hence in the middle of the signal line, that are saturated first.

With most spectrometers operating under routine conditions, the line widths are controlled by the inhomogeneity of the magnetic field (line widths are generally measured as the width at half height of a single line and denoted by W_H or $W_{1/2}$). In a slightly inhomogeneous field, different parts of the sample will experience slightly different magnetic fields and hence resonate over a range of frequencies, broadening the spectral lines. Line widths of as little as 0.1 Hz are sometimes desirable; line widths in excess of about 1 Hz result in the loss of considerable information. Clearly, this imposes very stringent demands upon the magnet as regards homogeneity. A line of 1 Hz width obtained with a spectrometer operating at the equivalent of 100,000,000 Hz requires a homogeneity of better than 1 in 10^8; however, this is routinely available with modern spectrometers.

To summarize: some nuclei, notably protons, have magnetic moments. "Spin-flip" nuclear-magnetic transitions of these nuclei can be observed at frequencies predicted by the Larmor equation, using complicated and expensive apparatus. The strength of the signal is directly proportional to the number of nuclei involved.

If this were all NMR had to offer, it would not be considered particularly useful in chemical investigations, since all one achieves is a costly and inconvenient estimate of the total hydrogen, fluorine, etc., content in a sample. In practice, all applications of NMR to chemistry are from three secondary phenomena: the *chemical shift*; the *time-dependence* of NMR phenomena; and *spin-spin coupling*. These effects will now be discussed.

12.2 THE CHEMICAL SHIFT

From now on, unless otherwise indicated, we shall refer to protons and deal with PMR (*proton magnetic resonance*) rather than with NMR. However, the principles are strictly analogous for all magnetic nuclei with $I = 1/2$.

The statement that protons resonate at 60 MHz at 14,092 gauss is only an approximation. Actually, protons in organic molecules are found to resonate, at 14,092 gauss, over a frequency range of about 1000 Hz at approximately 60 MHz. The exact frequency at which a proton resonates within this range is related to its chemical environment (hence the term *chemical shift*). The resonance of ^{19}F at 56.54 MHz in the same magnetic field is the closest resonance to that of ^{1}H; this is some 3,500,000 Hz away. It is apparent that the proton chemical shift range of about 1000 Hz is actually the fine structure of a single line.* To put it pictorially, at a chart width where the chemical-shift range of protons corresponds to about 2 feet, the fluorine resonances will turn up $2\frac{1}{2}$ miles away; the ^{13}C range will be found 48 miles away.

Since the chemical shift reflects molecular structure, it can be used to determine the structures of unknown compounds; and since hydrogen is an almost universal constituent of organic compounds, the method is very widely applicable. Furthermore, as mentioned before (Fig. 12.5), the intensity of the signal caused by any group of protons (the area under the curve, generally determined by electronic integration) is directly proportional to the number of protons in it. We can therefore determine the environments of hydrogen atoms in an organic molecule and obtain the relative distribution of hydrogens between the various environments.

Measurement of the Chemical Shift

Modern NMR spectrometers can determine resonance frequencies of sharp lines to a precision of better than 0.05 Hz. It would be almost impossible to measure a frequency of (say) 60,000,000 Hz to an absolute accuracy of 0.05 Hz, as this implies an absolute accuracy of 1 part in 10^{10}. Instead, all chemical shifts are measured relative to some standard substance which is added to the sample being investigated; one can then express the chemical shift in terms of displacement in Hz from the signal caused by the standard. As the range of proton chemical shifts at 14,092 gauss is approximately 1000 Hz, measurement to a precision of 0.05 Hz implies an accuracy of 1 part in 10^4—which is realistic, but still requires high stability of the magnetic field over the time necessary to scan the spectrum, and hence an advanced magnet technology.

The standard substance almost universally used is tetramethylsilane (Me$_4$Si), commonly abbreviated as TMS. This standard was chosen because it gives rise to a single sharp line as a result of the identical environment of all the protons in the symmetrical molecule and because the chemical environment of protons in TMS is such that they resonate at a higher field than practically any other proton. Further, TMS is an inert, low-boiling liquid and can be easily removed from the sample after the spectrum has been run. Therefore, in practice, the procedure is nondestructive. The sample size required for examination by NMR, however, is relatively large, generally at least 10 mg, because of the inherently low sensitivity of the method.

The chemical shift of any proton can be expressed in terms of "Hz from TMS." By convention, the absence of a sign implies "Hz to lower field, or downfield, from TMS," remembering at all times that "field" and "frequency" can be

---

* The ability to resolve this line defines *high-resolution NMR*.

used interchangeably. The chemical shift thus expressed depends upon the operating field of the spectrometer (Eqn. 12.1) so that one would have to state: "Proton X resonates at Y Hz from TMS at Z MHz spectrometer frequency." However, if one divides this value by the spectrometer frequency, one obtains the chemical shift in terms of dimensionless units. In practice, a factor of 10^6 is also introduced to avoid handling very small numbers, so the dimensionless unit turns out to be parts per million (ppm). Chemical shifts expressed in ppm versus TMS are usually designated as δ. Thus:

$$\text{Chemical shift in ppm } (\delta) = \frac{\text{Chemical shift in Hz vs. TMS}}{\text{Spectrometer frequency in Hz}} \times 10^6 \quad \textbf{(12.7)}$$

The δ scale ranges from 0 to about 12 ppm. Another system sets TMS arbitrarily at 10 and expresses the chemical shifts in terms of τ values, so that:

$$\tau = 10 - \delta \quad \textbf{(12.8)}$$

The unit is still ppm, only the scale is different. In other words, with the numbers reading in ppm, we have:

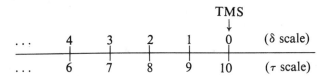

Chart paper for NMR spectrometers is marked in either, or both, scales and also (nearly always) with a grid scaled in Hz, thus ensuring maximum confusion for the beginner. (The τ-system is no longer recommended usage.)

Physical Causes of the Chemical Shift

The chemical shift occurs because the resonance frequency depends not upon the gross field (H_0) between the poles of the magnet of an NMR spectrometer, but on the actual field at the resonating nucleus. Only for the hypothetical case of an isolated proton will the field at the nucleus be equal to the gross field. For all other cases

$$H_{\text{nucl.}} = H_0(1 - \sigma) \quad \textbf{(12.9)}$$

where σ = the *shielding constant* for the particular situation

The shielding constant cannot in general be predicted, but the factors governing it, and hence determining the chemical shift, are qualitatively understood.

Consider an isolated hydrogen atom—a proton with its electron. Under the influence of H_0, the $1s$ electron will circulate in the direction given by the left-hand rule, thus becoming equivalent to a current in a circular loop. This current will generate (by the right-hand rule) a small magnetic field H_e which, in the region of the nucleus, will be in such a direction as to oppose H_0 (Fig. 12.6). The electron is then said to *shield* the proton in a hydrogen atom. Therefore, for a hydrogen atom, the gross field H_0 required for resonance at a fixed frequency will be slightly larger than that required for an isolated (unshielded) proton.

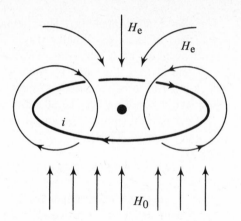

FIGURE 12.6. *Shielding of the proton by the electron in an isolated hydrogen atom.*

Now consider a hydrogen atom bonded to a carbon atom—that is, one existing as a part of a molecule. From simple bonding theory, we know that the electron density about the hydrogen will be reduced because the carbon atom is more electronegative; hence, the shielding effect of the circulating $1s$ electron (now part of a σ bond) is smaller than that in an isolated hydrogen atom. In other words, a hydrogen atom bonded to carbon is *deshielded*, compared to an isolated hydrogen atom. Clearly, the exact amount of deshielding is related to the electron distribution in the bond joining the hydrogen atom to the rest of the molecule. Thus, through the operation of the inductive mechanism in chemical bonding, one would expect the protons of methane to be more shielded than those of methyl chloride, and therefore to resonate at a higher field (closer to TMS). This is, in fact, borne out by experiment:

Compound	δ (ppm vs. TMS)
CH_4	0.23
CH_3Cl	3.05 (2.82 ppm downfield of CH_4)
CH_2Cl_2	5.33 (2.28 ppm downfield of CH_3Cl)
$CHCl_3$	7.24 (1.91 ppm downfield of CH_2Cl_2)

This series also shows that the effect of increasing electron withdrawal on the chemical shift of the remaining proton(s) is cumulative, but not strictly additive.

As is typical of all inductive effects, this type of deshielding decreases rapidly with increasing distance from the electronegative atom. Thus, the methyl group of ethyl chloride resonates at $\delta = 1.33$ ppm. In general, factors influencing electron density in the proximity of the proton are reflected in the chemical shift. Electron deficiency is associated with deshielding and therefore results in downfield shifts from TMS.

The second major effect, besides deshielding by bonding, that governs the chemical shifts of protons is the influence of *magnetically anisotropic* neighboring groups. A group (which can be a bond or the environment of an atom, but which is here considered a collection of electrons) is said to be magnetically anisotropic if the circulation of electrons within it under the influence of a magnetic field depends upon its orientation with respect to this field.

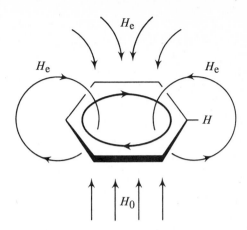

FIGURE 12.7. *Induced circulation of π-electrons in the benzene ring.*

For instance, when a molecule of benzene is oriented with respect to the magnetic field H_0 as shown in Figure 12.7, a movement of the delocalized π-electrons occurs (left-hand rule) which is known as the *ring current*. This current generates (according to right-hand rule) a subsidiary magnetic field H_e whose direction is such that it reinforces H_0 at the periphery of the benzene ring while opposing H_0 above and below the plane of the benzene ring. Thus, the aromatic protons, which are at the periphery of the benzene ring, are deshielded, and are found to resonate at a field considerably lower than that expected solely on the basis of the electron-density distribution.

When the benzene ring assumes, with respect to the field H_0, an orientation orthogonal to that shown in Figure 12.7, little circulation of electrons takes place, so the net effect results only from the phenomenon shown above. It can be demonstrated, by an extension of such arguments, that magnetically *isotropic* groups will not exert any net shielding effects on neighboring magnetic nuclei, because thermal motion will average all shielding influences.

Magnetically anisotropic groups can be considered to be surrounded by volumes of space in which protons will be shielded $(+)$ or deshielded $(-)$, that is, moved upfield or downfield, respectively. The best-established effects are associated with the groups shown in Figure 12.8.

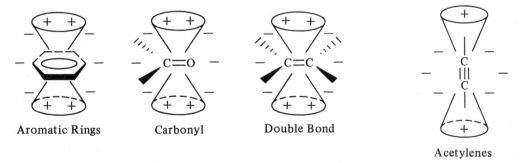

Aromatic Rings   Carbonyl   Double Bond

Acetylenes

FIGURE 12.8. *Shielding zones associated with some magnetically anisotropic groups.*

It can be seen that both of the effects discussed above depend upon the circulation of electrons in the magnetic field of the spectrometer. Their magnitude will therefore be directly proportional to the spectrometer field, H_0, or the "spectrometer frequency." This is the physical rationalization of the statement made in Section 12.2, that chemical shift expressed in Hz depends upon the spectrometer frequency.

The chemical shift of any given proton depends upon the combination of effects, which are (roughly) additive; the effects reinforce or cancel one another. Thus, acetylenic protons are deshielded by the inductive effect (acetylene is acidic) but shielded by the anisotropy of the triple bond; a value of $\delta = 1.80$ ppm results.

Because it is almost impossible to disentangle the various contributory effects, the theory of chemical shifts can be used only as a general guide. For the solution of problems, empirical correlations are almost invariably used. Some of the more fundamental of these are given in Table 12.1.

The choice of solvent is important. Since the standard (TMS) and the sample are in the same environment, one would expect negligible solvent effects. However, different solvents, which may have different degrees of magnetic anisotropy, will generally interact with various molecules in different ways, and the molecules will on the average be oriented in some preferred manner. Therefore solutions used for accurate measurements of chemical shifts should be as dilute as possible (preferably less than 10%) to avoid solute-solute interactions, and the solvent should not interact strongly with the sample (as do, for instance, hydrogen-bonding solvents). Carbon tetrachloride is a preferred solvent because it is magnetically isotropic and has no sites for strong interactions. Further, CCl_4 has no protons, so there will be no

TABLE 12.1. *Chemical Shift Data for Protons (δ scale)*

Aliphatic protons (cyclic or acyclic excluding cyclopropane derivatives):
  Methyl (with only H or alkyl substituents on both α and β carbon): 0.9
  Methylene (with only H or alkyl substituents on both α and β carbon): 1.25
  Methine (with only H or alkyl substituents on both α and β carbon): ca. 1.6

Presence of electron-withdrawing substituents on the α-carbon (e.g., halogens, $-OH$, $-OR$, $-O-CO-R$, $-NH_2$, $-NO_2$) shifts the proton by 2–4 ppm downfield. Carbonyl groups, $C=C$, and aromatic rings have a similar but less pronounced effect, the downfield shift being generally about 0.5–1.5 ppm.

Benzylic protons: 2–3 (toluene methyl: 2.34)

Acetylenic protons: 2–3

Olefinic protons: 5–7, varying regularly with substitution. Ethylene: 5.30

Aromatic and heterocyclic protons: 6–9. Benzene: 7.27

Aldehydic protons: 9–10

Hydroxylic and amino protons: Anywhere between 1 and 16 ppm, depending on the state of hydrogen bonding (strong H-bonding is deshielding). Signals due to such protons may be easily recognized by shifts with temperature, which alters the degree of hydrogen bonding, and by their facile exchange with D_2O. The latter procedure can be carried out in an NMR sample tube and the signals due to $-OH$, $-NH_2$, etc., simply vanish.

blanked-out areas in the spectrum. The most commonly used solvent is deutero-chloroform ($CDCl_3$), whose dissolving power for most compounds is greater than that of CCl_4 and which is also proton-free. Chemical shifts in CCl_4 and $CDCl_3$ are generally very similar.

In summary, the phenomenon of chemical shift enables the chemist to obtain some fundamental information about electronegativities, bond anisotropies, and so on. Above all, the ability to observe the chemical shift causes hydrogen atoms (and to some extent other nuclei) to become *functional groups* that can be qualitatively and quantitatively estimated.

12.3 TIME-DEPENDENCE OF NMR PHENOMENA

The time scale of the NMR phenomenon is best realized when it is recalled that NMR transitions occur at the low-frequency end of the electromagnetic spectrum.

Consider two protons situated in different environments. They will give rise to two separate resonances in the NMR spectrum, say $\Delta\nu$ Hz apart (Fig. 12.9C). However, if, by one of the mechanisms discussed below, the two protons exchange their environments at a rate *faster* than $\Delta\nu$ times per second, one obtains only one signal, at an intermediate frequency (Fig. 12.9A); the two nuclei are *equivalent* on the NMR time scale.

The definition of equivalence is important in NMR spectroscopy. A group of nuclei is defined as *chemically equivalent* if they possess the same chemical shift. Thus, by symmetry, the six protons of the benzene molecule are inherently chemically equivalent. However, the three protons of a methyl group are chemically equivalent only by virtue of the normally fast rotation about the bond joining the methyl group to the rest of the molecule. A group of nuclei is *magnetically equivalent* when they not only have the same chemical shift but also the same spin-spin coupling (see below) to all nuclei outside the group.

NMR spectra are characteristic of exchange rates. Thus, at slow (on the NMR time-scale) exchange-rates, one can simply observe separate signals for each of the environments and estimate the relative populations at each site. At intermediate exchange-rates, characteristically broadened spectra are observed (Fig. 12.9B) from which information about the rate of the process taking place can be extracted. At high exchange-rates, the single averaged signal occurs at a frequency determined by the relative populations at each site. Given the characteristic frequency of the individual resonances from the slow-exchange case (typically from low-temperature spectra), it is possible to determine the relative populations at two sites from the averaged (typically high-temperature) spectra.

The most common observable mechanisms for averaging the environments of protons, or of groups of equivalent protons, that can be observed on the NMR time-scale are proton exchange, conformational changes, and rotation about partial double-bonds. An example of each follows:

1. *Proton exchange.* In dilute solutions in aprotic solvents, the hydroxylic protons of mixtures of ethanol and water give rise to separate signals. However, an increase in temperature or concentration, or a change in pH, speeds up the proto-tropic exchange so that only one signal for the –OH protons is observed.

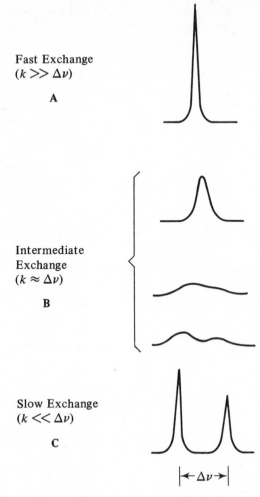

Fast Exchange
$(k \gg \Delta\nu)$

A

Intermediate
Exchange
$(k \approx \Delta\nu)$

B

Slow Exchange
$(k \ll \Delta\nu)$

C

$|\leftarrow\Delta\nu\rightarrow|$

The chemical shift of the –OH protons of just ethanol in an aprotic solvent will also vary with concentration and temperature, because of different degrees of hydrogen bonding. Further, at low exchange-rates, the –OH signal of ethanol shows splitting due to spin-spin coupling with the methylene protons (see below); but at high exchange-rates it gives rise to a singlet because the methylene protons "see" only the average spin-state of the –OH protons.

2. *Conformational changes.* At room temperature, the NMR spectrum of cyclohexane consists of a single sharp line, because the rate of conformational inversion between the two equivalent chair forms, which is associated with the interchange between axial and equatorial positions, is fast compared with the difference (in Hz) between the chemical shifts of axial and equatorial protons. At about –160°C, this inversion slows down enough to make separate signals for the axial and the equatorial protons observable.

3. *Rotation about partial double-bonds.* At low temperatures, the signals caused by the *N*-methyl groups of *N,N*-dimethylformamide appear as two bands of

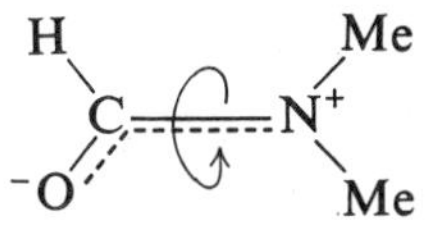

equal intensity. At higher temperatures, they coalesce to a single band midway between the original signals.

12.4 SPIN-SPIN COUPLING

Many signals in PMR spectra exhibit fine structure because of the splitting of spin-state energy levels of the protons by other magnetic nuclei in the neighborhood.

As an analogy, consider pairs of small bar magnets constrained into a specific spatial relation to each other (as nuclei are in real molecules) and which can assume just two North-South directions (as nuclei of spin $I = 1/2$ do). It is immediately obvious that, for the relative arrangements depicted in Figure 12.10, the antiparallel arrangement A has a lower energy than the parallel arrangement B.

FIGURE 12.10. *The bar-magnet analogy for spin-spin coupling.*

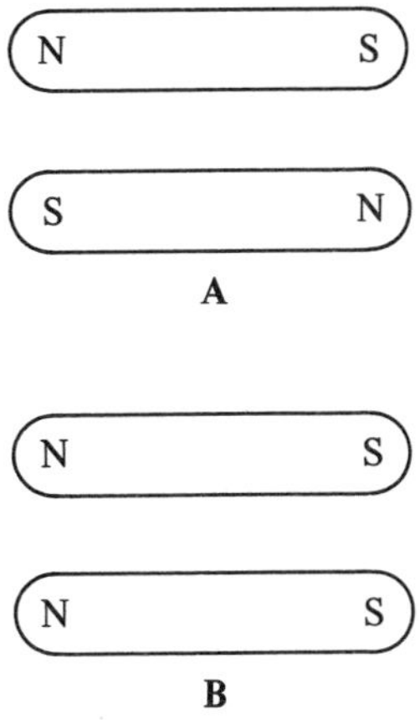

In the case of the nuclear magnets, the interaction does not take place through space, but through the agency of the binding electrons. The strength of this interaction is expressed by the parameter J, the *coupling constant*, which is related to the degree of splitting of resonances and which is expressed in Hz. The value of J depends only upon the electronic and steric relationship between the interacting protons, and hence does not depend on the spectrometer frequency. Thus, obtaining the NMR spectra of the same compound at two frequencies allows one to distinguish between multiple lines caused by protons of different chemical shift and those caused by the splitting of energy levels as a result of spin-spin coupling.

A detectable interaction between protons takes place only across a limited number of bonds. In general, no significant spin-spin coupling is observed between protons separated by more than four σ-bonds (or by more than four σ-bonds and one π-bond).

Two separate problems are involved in obtaining chemically useful information from spin-spin coupling; first the multiplets in question must be analyzed so as to yield the values of J and the chemical shifts of the interacting protons; and second, these values must be interpreted in terms of molecular structure.

Analysis of Spin-Spin Multiplets

In principle, any set of multiplets due to a number of interacting protons (or groups of equivalent protons) can be analyzed by computerized quantum-mechanical calculations. Such calculations are always tedious and often very difficult; fortunately, the multiplets can be analyzed by direct measurement in a large number of cases. Such spectra are known as *first-order spectra*; we shall deal with the analysis of first-order spectra and with some general features of the more complex *second-order spectra*.

The parameter that determines whether a group of protons (a *spin system*) will give rise to a first- or second-order spectrum is the ratio, $\Delta v/J$, of the chemical-shift difference between the relevant protons and the coupling constant J between them, both expressed in Hz. Large $\Delta v/J$ ratios, indicating *weakly coupled* systems, are associated with simple first-order spectra. For a true first-order spectrum, *all* $\Delta v/J$ ratios within the spin system must be large. Quite often a spin system has sets of both strongly and weakly coupled nuclei in it, and straightforward application of first-order rules to such cases will lead to errors in analysis. For most purposes, $\Delta v/J \geq 3$ can be considered "large."

Because chemical shifts, and therefore Δv, increase with increasing strength of the magnetic field while coupling constants do not, it follows that spectra taken at higher frequencies are easier to interpret. This is the principal reason why, despite the considerably greater expense, spectrometers operating at ever higher frequencies are being built. (The limits of field strengths obtainable with reasonably sized permanent magnets or iron-core electromagnets have apparently been reached. The latest high-field NMR instruments use superconducting (liquid-helium cooled) solenoids, and reach fields corresponding to an operating frequency of 360 MHz for protons.)

There are certain conventions used in naming spin systems. The letters A, B, C, D, ... are used to describe groups of protons whose chemical-shift differences are small compared with the values of their coupling constants; that is, strongly coupled sets. Subscripts are used to give the number of protons in an equivalent group. A break in the alphabetical sequence shows which groups are weakly coupled. For example, writing A_2BMXY describes a six-spin system. The two A nuclei and the B nucleus are strongly coupled to each other, but only weakly coupled to the nuclei M, X, and Y. The nucleus M is weakly coupled to all other nuclei. The nucleus X is strongly coupled to the nucleus Y, but weakly coupled to the other nuclei.

Primes are used to denote protons that are chemically equivalent but are not coupled identically to other protons and therefore are not magnetically equivalent.

The A_nX_m system will give rise to a first-order spectrum (A yielding $m + 1$ lines and X yielding $n + 1$ lines, with all spacings equal to J_{AX}), while the A_nB_m system will give a complex spectrum. Fortunately, the number of spins in a spin system, and hence its complexity, is limited by the rapid attenuation of J with the number of bonds separating the coupled nuclei.

The rules for interpreting first-order spectra are as follows:

1. When a proton (or a group of magnetically equivalent protons) is spin-spin coupled to n equivalent protons with a coupling constant of J Hz, its NMR signal is split into $n + 1$ lines* separated by J Hz. The relative intensities of the lines are in the ratio of the binomial coefficients of $(x + y)^n$. The true chemical shift of the protons concerned lies at the center of the multiplet.

Splitting by one proton therefore results in a doublet of equal intensity; splitting by two protons results in a triplet of relative component intensities of $1:2:1$; splitting by three protons results in a quartet of relative component intensities $1:3:3:1$; splitting by four protons results in a quintet of relative intensities $1:4:6:4:1$; and splitting by six protons results in a septet of relative component intensities $1:6:15:20:15:6:1$. (Compare Table 13.2, p 376.)

2. If there are more than two interacting groups of protons ($A_nM_mX_p \cdots$), the multiplicity of the signal due to the A protons is given by $(m + 1)(p + 1) \cdots$; i.e., the part of the spectrum due to nuclei A takes the form of a multiplet of submultiplets. Note that the number "n" does not enter into the expression. Clearly, the appropriate J values control splittings.

3. In first-order spectra, equivalent protons appear not to split one another; in other words, the transitions corresponding to such interactions are forbidden, or of zero probability. However, interactions between equivalent protons do take place and the corresponding coupling constants can be obtained from some second-order spectra.

The physical basis of the first-order rules is quite clear. Consider a system of two protons, H_A and H_X, and let the two allowed spin-states be α (high energy) and β (low energy). Then for upward transitions of the nucleus H_A we can have:

$$H_A\beta \text{ to } H_A\alpha \text{ with } H_X \text{ in state } \alpha \quad \text{and} \quad H_A\beta \text{ to } H_A\alpha \text{ with } H_X \text{ in state } \beta$$

Since the populations of H_X in the α and β states are almost completely equal (recall the vanishingly small Boltzmann excess discussed previously), the two transitions are of equal probability and hence H_A will give rise to a symmetrical doublet.

Similarly, for a system of three spins, one H_A and two H_X, we can have the following upward transitions for H_A:

$H_A\beta$ to $H_A\alpha$ with the first H_X in state α and the second in state β
$H_A\beta$ to $H_A\alpha$ with the first H_X in state β and the second in state α
$H_A\beta$ to $H_A\alpha$ with both H_X nuclei in state α
$H_A\beta$ to $H_A\alpha$ with both H_X nuclei in state β

The first two transitions are equivalent (*degenerate*) and hence H_A will give rise to a triplet with the intensity ratios $1:2:1$.

---

* More generally, splitting by a nucleus of spin = I gives $2nI + 1$ lines.

However, this sort of reasoning is not the full theoretical treatment for the system; the full treatment merely reduces to this description for cases where $\Delta\nu/J$ assumes large values; in other words, for first-order spectra.

We shall now deal with the spectral characteristics of some commonly encountered spin systems.

Two-Spin Systems. This can, by definition, be either an AX spectrum (i.e., a doublet of equal-intensity lines for H_A centered on the chemical shift δ_A of H_A with a separation of J_{AX}, and an identical doublet centered on δ_X) or a second-order AB spectrum.

The AB spectrum also consists of two doublets whose separations are exactly equal to J_{AB}, but the "inner" lines are more intense than the "outer" lines. The chemical shifts of H_A and H_B are given by the following expression

$$\nu_A - \nu_B = \sqrt{(1 - 4)(2 - 3)} \qquad (12.10)$$

where $\nu_A - \nu_B$ is the separation of the chemical shifts of H_A and H_B, and the numbers refer to the frequencies of the lines as marked in Figure 12.11. Once $\nu_A - \nu_B$ (in Hz) has been determined, δ_A and δ_B can be located by measuring from the center of the always perfectly symmetrical AB systems (often referred to as an "AB quartet").

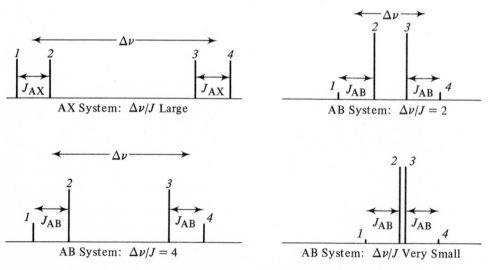

FIGURE 12.11. *Calculated spectra of two-spin systems.*

As δ_A and δ_B become more nearly identical, the intensities of the inner lines increase at the expense of the outer lines until, at the limit of $\nu_A - \nu_B = 0$, the transitions corresponding to the outer lines become forbidden and the system reduces to a singlet of two-proton intensity, i.e., the trivial A_2 case.

The characteristic of a part of the spectrum "sloping" away from the position of the other part is common to all spectra that are not strictly first order; practically speaking, this means nearly all observable spectra.

Three-Spin Systems. A system of three protons can always be described by no more than six parameters. Thus, the first-order AMX case is described by: δ_A, δ_M, δ_X, J_{AM}, J_{AX}, and J_{MX} (obviously J_{AX} and J_{XA} are the same). In this first-order case, one observes four lines for each proton (a doublet of doublets) with separations corresponding to the coupling constants with the other nuclei for a total of 12 lines. Many experimental spectra, such as the one shown in Figure 12.12, approach the ideal AMX case, i.e., the directly measured line spacings are very close to the true coupling constants, as computed by the appropriate quantum mechanics ("ABC analysis"). Note that even here the intensities depart from the first-order ideal, where all lines within each doublet-of-doublets should be equal. Thus, the lines in the H_A and H_M multiplets slope toward each other (cf. the AB case above). The lines of the H_X multiplet appear broader because of small additional unresolved coupling to the protons on the phenyl ring.

If all the protons have similar chemical shifts and are coupled—that is, in the ABC case—a spectrum of up to 15 lines results, which is so distorted that it is often not possible to recognize it as such. A very common system is the partially strongly coupled ABX case, which must not be analyzed as an AMX case. Where two of the protons are equivalent, one can get an A_2X or an A_2B system.

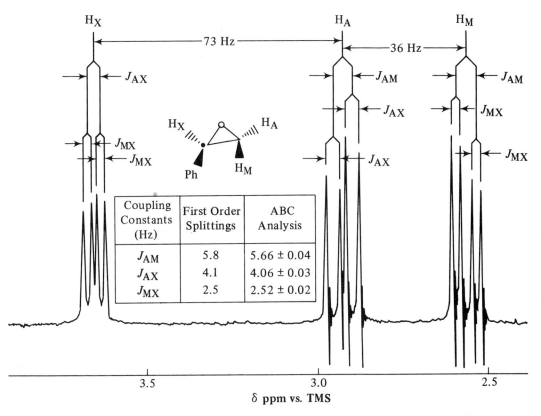

Coupling Constants (Hz)	First Order Splittings	ABC Analysis
J_{AM}	5.8	5.66 ± 0.04
J_{AX}	4.1	4.06 ± 0.03
J_{MX}	2.5	2.52 ± 0.02

FIGURE 12.12. *100-MHz spectrum of styrene oxide (25% in CCl₄). The part of the spectrum due to aromatic protons is not shown.*

By first-order rules, the A_2X system gives rise to a doublet of two-proton intensity and a triplet of one-proton intensity. The A_2B spectrum may have up to 9 lines and can be highly asymmetrical.

Four-Spin Systems. The system AX_3 is quite common and occurs, for example, in the spectrum of the fragment CH_3–$\overset{\diagup}{\underset{\diagdown}{C}}H$. The X resonance is a doublet of three-proton intensity, with spacings equal to J_{AX}, while the A resonance is a 1:3:3:1 quartet with the same spacings.

The intensity distribution in the three commonly encountered "four-line" patterns—namely, the AB quartet, the AMX doublet-of-doublets, and the AX_3 quartet—are very characteristic and can be distinguished on sight (see Fig. 12.13).

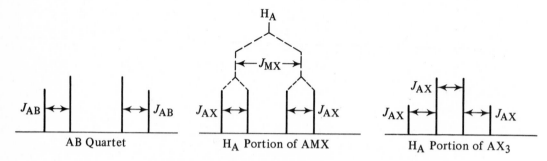

FIGURE 12.13. *The intensity distribution in four-line patterns.*

The system AB_3 is only of theoretical interest. The systems A_2X_2 and A_2B_2 are very common and are found in the spectra of compounds with freely rotating pairs of nonequivalent methylene groups:

$$R\text{–}CH_2\text{–}CH_2\text{–}R'$$

In the extreme first-order A_2X_2 case, each methylene group gives rise to a triplet with spacings J_{AX}, but the A_2B_2 system may give up to 24 lines. However, it can be easily recognized because it always consists of two identical mirror-image halves.

By definition, an A_2B_2 system can be described by the three parameters J_{AB}, δ_A, and δ_B, although J_{AA} and J_{BB} will enter into the second-order case. However, there are systems where the two sets of chemically equivalent (by symmetry) nuclei have unequal coupling constants to each other because they lack magnetic equivalence. Such systems, denoted by AA'BB' or AA'XX', are associated with *para*-disubstituted benzenes and it is easily seen that an additional parameter must be used to describe them:

$$
\begin{array}{ll}
\text{R} & \delta_A \\
H_A \quad\quad H_{A'} & \delta_B \\
& J_{AA'} \\
& J_{BB'} \\
H_B \quad\quad H_{B'} & J_{AB}\ (= J_{A'B'}) \\
\text{R}' & J_{AB'}\ (= J_{A'B})
\end{array}
$$

Other types of four-spin systems, including the general (and quite formidable) ABCD case, have no obvious qualitatively distinguishing characteristics.

Five-Spin and Higher Systems. The asymmetrical first-order A_2X_3 case is very common since it is associated with the ethyl group attached to an electronegative center (e.g., ethyl chloride). The completely distorted A_2B_3 case is not very common, but gradual transitions can be observed in many spectra. The partially symmetrical AA′BB′C system and its first-order analogue AA′MM′X are both common, since they are observed in the spectra of pyridine and also of all monosubstituted benzenes. Complete analysis involves the placing of up to 124 lines.

The symmetrical AX_4 system, as in $R–CH_2–\overset{|}{CH}–CH_2–R'$, gives rise to a doublet and a quintet. Similarly, the AX_6 (seven-spin) system exhibited in the spectra of isopropyl derivatives gives rise to a doublet and a septet. Second-order examples of these spectra are rare.

Common Errors in Analysis of NMR Spectra

The obvious effects associated with second-order spectra (for instance, extra lines, distorted intensity patterns, and unequal spacings) generally preclude any injudicious attempts to analyze such systems by first-order rules. However, in some cases second-order spectra have features that are qualitatively indistinguishable from some features of first-order spectra, and so are often misinterpreted. It must be understood that the three cases discussed below are not physical phenomena—they are simply the result of certain combinations of the chemical-shift and spin-coupling parameters.

Partially Strongly Coupled Spectra. The X portion of an ABX spectrum gives rise to four lines, which are often regularly spaced and appear identical to the X portion of an AMX spectrum. However, the spacings *cannot* be used to obtain the values of J_{AX} and J_{BX}, although the distance between the outer lines does correspond to $J_{AX} + J_{BX}$. When the AB portion of the spectrum can be clearly resolved, no misinterpretation should result, because it is more complex than the AM portion of an AMX spectrum. However, when only the X portion is visible (for example, when the remainder is hidden by overlapping resonances) the problem is not simple and the possibility of a partially strongly coupled system must be considered.

Virtual Coupling. A resonance due to a proton may be complicated (split) because of a proton which is *not* directly coupled to it, but which is strongly coupled to a proton which *is* coupled to it. This "phenomenon" is really a special case of the trap described above. Consider, for example, a linear system of 3 protons:

$$-\overset{|}{\underset{H_A}{C}}-\overset{|}{\underset{H_B}{C}}-\overset{|}{\underset{H_C}{C}}-$$

Although protons H_A and H_C are usually not significantly coupled (they are separated by four σ-bonds), the resonance due to H_A may not be a simple doublet with spacing

J_{AB} if H_B and H_C are strongly coupled; that is, if at the spectrometer frequency employed, $(\nu_B - \nu_C)/J_{BC}$ is a small number. Clearly, mistakes are most likely to occur if the B and C portions of the spectrum cannot be discerned, as in the case discussed above.

Deceptive Simplicity. Sometimes the combination of parameters is such that a deceptively simple spectrum results. Consider the spectrum of furan,

$$H_{B'} \quad H_B$$

$$H_{A'} \quad O \quad H_A \qquad J_{AB} \neq J_{AB'}$$

The 60-MHz spectrum of this compound gives rise to two triplets suggesting an A_2X_2 case, whereas symmetry considerations show that it should give rise to an AA'XX' or AA'BB' spectrum. Deceptive spectra should always be suspected when a first-order analysis appears to yield a number of apparently equal coupling constants while structural considerations suggest coupling constants of widely different magnitudes. Thus, the incorrect analysis of the spectrum of furan leads to a postulation of equal *ortho* and *meta* coupling constants. More sophisticated analysis shows that this is not the case, as should be expected on structural grounds.

Signs of Coupling Constants

Coupling constants have sign (+ or −) as well as magnitude. By convention, the sign of the coupling constant between two nuclei is taken to be positive if the state with the two spins in an antiparallel orientation is of lower energy. The relative signs of coupling constants cannot be obtained from first-order spectra but may be determined from more strongly complexed spectra and from some multiple-resonance experiments (see below). The absolute signs of coupling constants cannot be obtained from spectral analysis because the reversal of all signs leaves the spectrum unchanged. Many absolute signs have been determined from the NMR spectra of compounds in a nematic (partially oriented) phase.

Aids to Spectral Analysis

Besides first-order approximations and quantum-mechanical calculations, several other (essentially experimental) aids are available.

Examination of NMR Spectra at More than One Frequency. As mentioned before, coupling constants do not depend on the operating frequency of the NMR spectrometer, whereas the chemical shifts on the Hz scale do. It follows that what is a second-order spectrum at 60 MHz may become a first-order spectrum at 100 MHz.

Solvent Shifts. Chemical shifts are often strongly influenced by the nature of the solvent used, whereas coupling constants are essentially solvent-independent. Thus, a change of solvent may simplify a spectral pattern. Although experiments of this nature are essentially shots in the dark, the procedure is widely used; the common solvent pairs are deuterochloroform and benzene or pyridine.

Deuterium Substitution. Substitution of deuterium (D or $^2_1$H) for protium ($^1_1$H) tends to simplify NMR spectra in two ways. First, it removes that part of the spectrum due to the replaced proton(s), and second, it simplifies the remainder because, while deuterium is magnetic and will split the resonances of the remaining protons, the coupling constants between ^{1}H and ^{2}H are only about one-seventh of the corresponding coupling constants between ^{1}H and ^{1}H. For example, while the methyl resonance of ethanol is a triplet (X part of A_2X_3), the methyl resonance of CH_3CH_2OH is a slightly broadened singlet.

Spin Decoupling. It is possible to introduce one (or more) irradiating radio-frequencies into the transmitter coil of an NMR spectrometer, thus generating one or more perturbing magnetic fields in addition to H_1. Such experiments are known as *double-* (or *multiple-*) *irradiation* experiments and give rise to *double-* (or *multiple-*) *resonance spectra. Spin decoupling,* in which the second (and further) fields are relatively strong and are directed at the resonances of protons coupled to the protons being observed, is a special case and is the most common experiment of this type.

If the resonance from proton A (which is coupled to proton B) is observed while simultaneously proton B is strongly irradiated at its resonant frequency, the normal doublet expected of H_A (half of an AB quartet) will collapse to a singlet. This results from the fact that the second irradiating field causes rapid transitions of H_B between its two spin states, so that H_A experiences only the averaged spin state of H_B and hence no splitting in its energy levels results. Clearly, this phenomenon is related to the time dependence of NMR.

The capacity of spin decoupling in simplifying spectra is obvious. However, strongly coupled protons cannot be decoupled because the introduction of the second radio-frequency field perturbs the region near the field and hence makes the resonances impossible to observe.

There are two basically different methods of spin decoupling: *field-sweep decoupling,* in which the frequency difference between the decoupling field (H_2) and the observing field (H_1) is kept constant as the spectrum is swept, and *frequency-sweep decoupling,* in which the value of H_2 is kept constant as the value of H_1 changes. The latter is more commonly used for routine studies and the results are easier to interpret.

Shift Reagents. In 1970, Williams, elaborating on the preliminary work of Hinckley, discovered that adding *tris-β-diketonate* lanthanide complexes to solutions of substances with lone pairs of electrons available for coordination (such as oxygen- and nitrogen-containing organic compounds) resulted in vastly more dispersed NMR spectra. This phenomenon, named *lanthanide-induced shift* (LIS), arises from the

unusual combination of paramagnetic properties in most lanthanides, whereby large local changes in the magnetic fields are produced in the immediate vicinity of the lanthanide. This type of induced shift is known as *pseudo-contact shift* and is propagated through space in a normal manner, in contrast to the *contact shifts* found with other paramagnetic species where the effect is transmitted through bonds.

As lanthanide-induced shifts often have values of up to 20 ppm, the increased dispersion, and hence interpretability, of NMR spectra afforded by this method is enormous. Moreover, pseudo-contact shifts diminish regularly with the distance from the paramagnetic center, r in Figure 12.14, and since this can be approximately located (the lanthanide complex is attached to the lone pair), their magnitudes give valuable structural information.

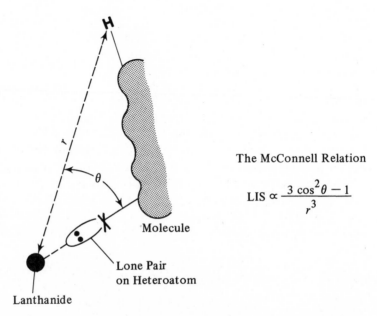

The McConnell Relation

$$LIS \propto \frac{3 \cos^2 \theta - 1}{r^3}$$

FIGURE 12.14. *The magnitude of the lanthanide-induced shift (LIS) as a function of molecular geometry. H is a proton on the molecule whose resonance is being shifted by the presence of the lanthanide.*

The most commonly used shift reagents are based on europium (downfield shifts) and praseodymium (upfield shifts) and contain either dipivaloyl methane ($R_1 = R_2 = t$-butyl, $R_3 = H$) or fluoroalkyl derivatives of β-diketones as ligands.

Interpretation of Spin-Spin Coupling in Terms of Structure

The magnitudes of coupling constants (J) are very characteristic of molecular environment and are especially sensitive to stereochemistry. Further, multiplicities of resonances can give information about the number of neighboring protons. The theory of spin-spin coupling is far too complex to be routinely used and empirical correlation tables are invariably resorted to. The common correlations given below are well established. All coupling constants are quoted as their absolute magnitudes only.

Geminal Coupling Across an sp³ Carbon.

Typical range: 12–18 Hz

The full range is 0–22.4 Hz. Double bonds adjacent to the central carbon give larger values (e.g., an aromatic ring or a carbonyl group for R_1). Smaller values are associated with $R_1 =$ a heteroatom.

Vicinal Coupling Across Three Single Bonds.

$$H_A\text{–}C\text{–}C\text{–}H_B$$

The magnitude of J_{AB} is dominated by the size of the dihedral angle (ϕ) and is given by the Karplus equation:

$$J_{AB} = J^0(\cos^2 \phi) - 0.3 \quad \text{for angles } 0\text{–}90°$$
$$J_{AB} = J^{180}(\cos^2 \phi) - 0.3 \quad \text{for angles } 90\text{–}180° \tag{12.11}$$

The values of the constants J^0 and J^{180} are substituent-dependent, with the ranges $J^0 = 9\text{–}12$ and $J^{180} = 14\text{–}16$ covering most situations. Within the variations caused by substituents those due to the cases

$$H\text{–}\overset{|}{\underset{|}{C}}\text{–}\overset{|}{\underset{|}{C}}\text{–}H, \qquad H\text{–}\overset{\|}{C}\text{–}\overset{|}{\underset{|}{C}}\text{–}H, \quad \text{and} \quad H\text{–}\overset{\|}{C}\text{–}\overset{\|}{C}\text{–}H$$

can usually be ignored. Typical values for freely rotating methyl and methylene groups are 6–8 Hz. The Karplus relation has obvious importance in determining the stereochemistry of organic compounds and is summarized graphically in Figure 12.15.

Olefinic Systems. Typical values are:

$$J_{cis} (J_{AB}) = 6\text{–}14 \text{ Hz}$$

10 Hz

$$J_{trans} (J_{AC}) = 11\text{–}18 \text{ Hz}$$

6 Hz

$$J_{gem} (J_{BC}) = 0\text{–}3 \text{ Hz}$$

4 Hz

Electronegative substituents (i.e., R = heteroatom) lead to smaller values of olefinic coupling constants.

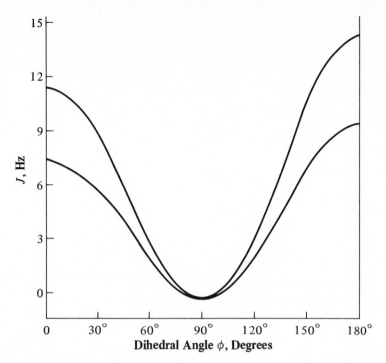

FIGURE 12.15. *The dependence of vicinal coupling constants on dihedral angles.*

Long-Range Coupling. This is defined as coupling across more than 3 bonds. Long-range coupling constants are rarely larger than 3 Hz, but may be highly characteristic of structure. The most common type of long-range interactions is *allylic coupling*, which is due to the protons in H–C–C=C–H, *cisoid* (J_{AX}) or *transoid* (J_{BX}), and which is highly dependent on stereochemistry (see Fig. 12.16).

Homoallylic coupling, i.e., the coupling across 5 bonds in the fragment H–C–C=C–C–H, takes up a slightly larger range of values and also has a characteristic stereochemical dependence. In general, coupling between two protons separated by 4 single bonds becomes significant ($J = 1$–3 Hz) only if the 5 atoms of the system H–C–C–C–H take on a planar "W" (or "M") arrangement.

Aromatic Systems. Typical values in benzenoid compounds are:

$$J_{ortho} = 7\text{–}10 \text{ Hz}$$
$$J_{meta} = 1\text{–}3 \text{ Hz}$$
$$J_{para} = 0\text{–}1 \text{ Hz}$$

Similar ranges apply for heterocyclic systems, except that the J_{ortho} involving protons on carbons α to a heteroatom takes on lower values (cf. olefinic systems) and that a

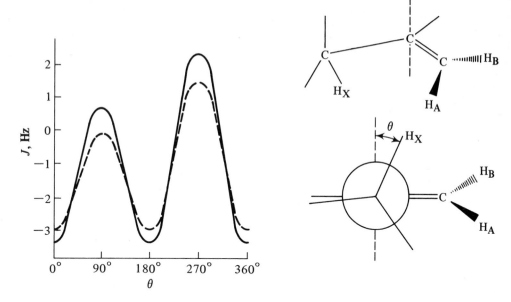

FIGURE 12.16. *Dependence of allylic coupling constants on stereochemistry. Solid lines: Transoid (J_{BX}); dashed lines: Cisoid (J_{AX}). θ is the dihedral angle formed by the C–H_X bond and the (dashed) line perpendicular to the plane formed by the C=CH_AH_B moiety.*

ring-size dependence of J_{ortho} (analogous to that in cycloölefins) is also observed. Such influences are cumulative, so that $J_{\alpha,\beta}$ in furans is only 1–3 Hz.

12.5 NMR SPECTROSCOPY OF NUCLEI OTHER THAN PROTONS

By accident, almost all the nuclei of interest to the vast majority of chemists have spins $I = 1/2$ and hence do not differ at all from protons in their basic theoretical aspects. However, their usefulness does not warrant the effort of learning any empirical parameters relating to them, so the remarks below do not reflect the amount of data available.

It must be realized that the effect of spin-spin coupling of protons to other magnetic nuclei may be observed in the *proton* spectra, and hence some idea of the magnitudes of coupling between protons and some commonly occurring magnetic nuclei may be useful in interpreting proton spectra.

^{19}F Spectra

Fluorine resonates over a range of some 300 ppm, i.e., its chemical shift is more sensitive than ^{1}H to the changes of environment. In saturated systems, J_{H-F} for H–C–F (geminal) ranges from 40–80 Hz and for H–C–C–F (vicinal) from 0–30 Hz. The latter has a Karplus-like dependence on stereochemistry (Eqn. 12.11).

^{31}P Spectra

Phosphorus resonates over about 400 ppm. J_{P-H} (direct), as in phosphine derivatives, is in the range of 200–700 Hz, i.e., of an entirely different order of magnitude from interproton coupling constants. The J_{H-P} coupling constants for H–C–P, H–C–C–P, and H–C–O–P (as in phosphate esters) vary between 0 and 30 Hz. In phosphate esters it is generally in the range of 5 to 20 Hz and shows a Karplus-like stereochemical dependence.

^{13}C Spectra

The natural abundance of ^{13}C is only 1%, and thus ^{13}C spectra are difficult to observe in unenriched samples. A further disadvantage is that ^{13}C is a "less good magnet" than a proton. The overall loss of sensitivity compared to ^{1}H is approximately 6000-fold. However, because of the central importance of carbon in organic chemistry, constant efforts to obtain ^{13}C NMR data have been made over the last 15 years. Recently (1970–1971) Fourier Transform NMR spectroscopy (see Sec. 12.6) has been routinely applied to this problem, and this method in conjunction with blanket decoupling of protons (to collapse the large, direct, ^{13}C–H coupling constants and obtain further enhancement due to the Nuclear Overhauser Effect) affords spectra whose signal-to-noise ratio is comparable with that of proton NMR spectra.

There is little doubt that ^{13}C–NMR ("CMR") will become of great importance in the near future as instrumentation becomes more widely available. The structural implications are considerable; the chemical shifts of ^{13}C cover over 200 ppm and fall into very characteristic ranges. Further, by using the "off-resonance de-

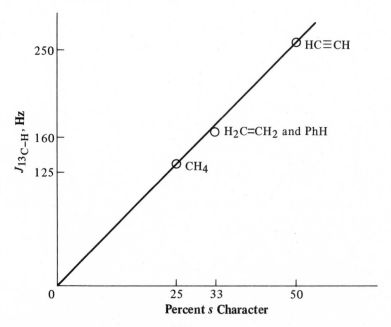

FIGURE 12.17. *The relation between direct* ^{13}C–H *coupling constants and the hybridization of the carbon atom.*

coupling technique," the direct coupling between carbon and protons may be diminished in magnitude, but not completely eliminated, thus permitting us to distinguish methyl carbons (quartet), methylene carbons (triplet), methine carbons (doublet), and tertiary carbons (singlet), by inspection.

The effect of direct (i.e., across one bond) coupling between ^{13}C and protons can often be observed in proton spectra in the form of so-called ^{13}C satellites, from which the ^{13}C–H coupling constants can be obtained by direct measurement. To a first degree of approximation, this coupling is directly proportional to the percent s character in the carbon (Fig. 12.17).

Unfortunately, quantitative applications of CMR spectroscopy are less straightforward than those of PMR because, under the usual experimental conditions, the relative intensities of ^{13}C signals do not reflect accurately their relative abundances. This is due principally to relaxation phenomena and makes proton rather than carbon NMR the method of choice for the analysis of mixtures.

12.6 SPECIAL TOPICS

Pulse Spectroscopy

The normal method of scanning NMR spectra (or, for that matter, other spectra) consists of altering the wavelength of the electromagnetic energy supplied and observing absorption whenever the Larmor relation for a particular nucleus is met. This is known as continuous-wave (CW) spectroscopy.

By contrast, it is possible to apply electromagnetic energy effectively over the whole range of the spectrum in a short, intense burst (pulse) and to observe the spectral effect produced by the nuclei promoted to their upper energy state as they fall back to their lower energy state. The record thus obtained (*free induction decay, FID*) is not identical to the normal absorption spectrum but is related to it, and may be converted to it by performing a Fourier transformation. Consequently, spectra of this type are often called *Fourier Transform Spectra* and the apparatus is often described as a *Fourier Transform (FT)* spectrometer. The advantage of this method is that the information obtained in each pulse is equivalent to scanning the whole spectrum and thus, for equivalent acquisition time, FT spectroscopy leads to a great improvement in sensitivity.

In practice, the data from hundreds, or thousands, of such pulses are stored in a minicomputer and are then processed (Fourier transformed) into an absorption spectrum.

Spectra of Compounds Dissolved in Nematic Phases

As already stated, rapid reorientation of molecules is a necessary prerequisite for the observation of high-resolution NMR spectra; solids give rise to "wide-line" spectra of little chemical interest. However, at intermediate rates of molecular reorientation, it is possible to obtain high-resolution NMR spectra without averaging out through-space interactions between magnetic nuclei.

These rates are attainable for molecules dissolved in the nematic phases of liquid crystals; such spectra give information about molecular geometry, in particular about interproton distances, which is not easily available from other physical measurements.

Nematic-phase spectra are considerably more complicated than those obtained in liquids or gases. Thus, the spectrum of benzene in nematic phase consists of at least 50 observable lines, whereas benzene in the liquid or gas phase gives rise only to a single sharp line in its high-resolution NMR spectrum.

The Nuclear Overhauser Effect (NOE)

One of the important ways in which magnetic nuclei may relax from their upper to their lower energy levels is through a dipolar spin-spin interaction with another magnetic nucleus. This process takes place through space, and its efficiency is inversely proportional to the sixth power of the internuclear distance involved. It follows that the most efficient relaxation by that route can take place when two magnetic nuclei are in close spatial proximity in the same molecule.

This phenomenon must not be confused with spin-spin coupling, which is transmitted through bonds and which leads to the splitting of energy levels. Only relaxation times are involved.

Consider now two magnetic nuclei, A and B, which are in sufficiently close spatial proximity to influence each other's relaxation times. If the nucleus A is observed while the nucleus B is simultaneously irradiated (see Sec. 12.4 for multiple irradiation), the relaxation process in nucleus A becomes more efficient because nucleus B, which is undergoing rapid up-and-down transitions, becomes effectively a rotating magnetic field. This results in a perturbation of the usual Boltzmann distribution of nuclei A towards the lower state and increases up to 50% the intensity of the signal due to the nucleus A. This enhancement of intensity is known as the Nuclear Overhauser Effect and is diagnostic for the presence of magnetic nuclei in close spatial proximity. Structural information can thus be obtained, for example, in connection with *cis-trans* isomerism.

Commercially Available Instruments

High-resolution NMR spectrometers are complex and expensive instruments produced by a very limited number of manufacturers—Varian (USA), Perkin-Elmer (UK), Bruker (Germany), and Jeol (Japan) account for virtually all instruments. They range from proton-only routine instruments (e.g., Varian EM360 and Perkin-Elmer R24) operating at 60 MHz* and costing approximately $10,000 to flexible research spectrometers, operating usually at 90 or 100 MHz, which may cost up to $150,000 with accessories (e.g., Varian XL100-15 and Bruker HX-90). At the extreme ends of the scale Varian offers its model EM300 which can be used only to observe protons (at 30 MHz) and costs about $5,000, while several manufacturers offer high-field systems (220–360 MHz) based on helium-cooled superconducting magnets, which may cost up to $300,000.

---

* NMR spectrometers are usually described in terms of their operating frequency for protons even if they are not used to obtain proton NMR spectra, rather than in terms of the more logical parameter, the strength of the magnetic field.

The vast majority of analytical applications of NMR spectroscopy can be classified under two headings: determination of structures of pure compounds and quantitative determination of mixtures. The monitoring of the progress of reactions is, of course, only a subcategory of the latter class.

In practice, structural determination is not carried out solely by means of NMR spectroscopy, although proton NMR is probably the most important single method available in this area. For this reason, a detailed discussion of structure determination by NMR alone is generally not included even in extensive general texts on NMR spectroscopy and is best considered in conjunction with other major techniques.

Quantitative applications of NMR have, however, certain inherent strengths and limitations that are summarized below:

1. NMR spectroscopy is nondestructive—a sample may be recovered completely unchanged after being subjected to an NMR experiment because the energy changes involved are negligible compared with the strengths of chemical bonds. The solvents used are usually easily evaporated, and the cell (a glass test-tube) is easily washed out.

2. It is often possible to identify the components of a mixture and to carry out a quantitative analysis in one step—that is, it is not always necessary to carry out precalibration procedures.

3. The results of quantitative analysis by NMR, while not inherently of great accuracy, tend to be quite positive. Thus, even a small number of resonances can lead to a positive identification because chemical shifts can be determined very accurately, and the substances identified can then be quite positively estimated in a mixture. In addition, the integration of several resonance signals often leads to internal verification.

4. When applicable, quantitative analysis by NMR can be very fast (a typical spectrum takes less than 5 min to run) and convenient (simple sample preparation).

5. The principal limitation of NMR spectroscopy as an analytical tool is its inherently poor sensitivity. This is particularly important in examining mixtures, because with pure compounds one may assume that protons resonating at different frequencies are present in ratios of whole numbers whereas the corresponding ratios in mixtures can only be determined to within the accuracy of integration. It is difficult to determine a small amount of impurity, except when it gives rise to well separated signals; therefore, NMR is very rarely used for this purpose. This insensitivity is not wholly a disadvantage because, by converse reasoning, samples used for structural determination need not be highly purified. As a rule of thumb, a purity of 90% is adequate and even larger quantities of impurity can be tolerated provided they can be identified.

6. The integrated intensities of resonances in an NMR spectrum give only relative abundances of magnetic nuclei in the various environments. This limitation is not serious, since precalibrating the integrator with samples of known composition or introducing internal standards can be used to convert the relative values

into absolute numbers. Using an internal standard avoids errors arising from changes of spectrometer response with time, so it is the preferred procedure. Substances suitable for this use should give rise to easily observed resonances (preferably singlets) not overlapping with those being determined, should be chemically inert toward the other components, and should be easy to weigh accurately. The most useful internal standards for nonaqueous systems are 1,3,5-trinitrobenzene and methylene bromide, and for aqueous systems the salts of terephthalic acid.

7. It is obvious that with the aid of an internal standard it is possible to determine the total weight of hydrogen in a known weight of a pure compound and thus obtain a rapid and nondestructive analysis for this element. Furthermore, by making certain assumptions (e.g., that the resonance of lowest intensity corresponds to a single proton in a molecule or that a sharp singlet near $\delta = 4$ ppm is due to a methoxy group), it is possible to obtain the molecular weight of an unknown substance. If the assumption was wrong, it would typically result in the apparent molecular weight becoming equal to the "equivalent" weight with respect to the fragment whose resonance is considered. This must be less than the true molecular weight and therefore represents a very useful check on molecular weights determined by mass spectrometry (Chap. 16): when the molecular weight obtained by NMR is higher than the m/e ratio of the peak of highest mass in the mass spectrum, the molecular ion is not detectable in the latter. This condition is not uncommon with many compounds (for instance, with many iodo-derivatives where the molecular ion cannot be observed even at the lowest practicable electron energy).

Experimental Considerations

The operation of NMR instruments is far too complex to be discussed within the present framework, but the user should know some of the experimental variables, even if he or she does not normally operate the instrument.

Sample Preparation. As mentioned above, very high purity is not normally essential, but certain types of impurities such as paramagnetic substances must be excluded. The presence of solid impurities of any sort in the solution of a substance will degrade the homogeneity of the magnetic field and hence cause line broadening. For this reason solutions should be filtered before being placed in the NMR sample tube.

Solvent. For all practical purposes, NMR spectra are recorded in solution, although pure ("neat") liquids and even gases can, in principle, also be examined. The solvents must meet certain requirements (Sec. 12.1) and a compromise must often be employed between using concentrated solutions (for high sensitivity) and dilute solutions (for measuring chemical shifts uninfluenced by solute-solute interactions). Besides the commonly used carbon tetrachloride, deuterochloroform, and D_2O, a range of deuterated solvents (dimethyl sulfoxide, benzene, pyridine, acetone, dioxane) is commercially available. It must be emphasized that direct comparison of chemical shifts obtained in different solvents is invalid, as solvent-induced changes of up to 0.5 ppm are by no means uncommon.

Instrumental Variables. Most of these serve self-evident purposes (e.g., amplification, noise filtering, phasing of signals, width of sweep, and adjustments of field homogeneity) but two variables are of particular importance in analytical applications. As mentioned above, the strength of the irradiating field H_1 (the amplitude of the RF radiation) may cause saturation when set at too high a value, but high RF field also causes increased sensitivity. For this reason, the RF field is often set at a value that saturates *some* of the resonances over the finite range of relaxation times in a real sample. Deviations from the ideal behavior (the exact correspondence between the number of protons and the height of the integral step) caused by such settings will not lead to error when examining pure substances where the ratios between the various steps can be legitimately rounded off to whole numbers, but may become a source of serious error in quantitative work on mixtures. For this reason, such measurements should be repeated with at least two settings of the RF field strength. Also, since saturation is a function of the duration of exposure of magnetic nuclei to the RF field H_1, as well as its strength, the parameters governing the scanning velocity (*sweep time*) and RF-field strength cannot be considered independently. Furthermore, a pure absorption signal corresponds only to an infinitely slow sweep-time, while very rapid sweep-times will be associated with various distortions.

SELECTED BIBLIOGRAPHY

General Texts

BECKER, E. D. *High Resolution NMR.* New York: Academic Press, 1969.

BOVEY, F. A. *NMR Spectroscopy.* New York: Academic Press, 1969.

EMSLEY, J. W.; FEENEY, J.; and SUTCLIFFE, L. H. *High Resolution NMR Spectroscopy,* vols. I and II. Oxford: Pergamon Press, 1965.

JACKMAN, L. M., and STERNHELL, S. *Applications of NMR Spectroscopy in Organic Chemistry,* 2nd ed. Oxford: Pergamon Press, 1969.

MATHIESON, D. W., ed. *Nuclear Magnetic Resonance for Organic Chemists.* London: Academic Press, 1967.

Analysis of NMR Spectra

ABRAHAM, R. J. *Analysis of High Resolution NMR Spectra.* Amsterdam: Elsevier, 1971.

CORIO, P. L. *Structure of High-Resolution NMR Spectra.* New York: Academic Press, 1966.

DETAR, D. F., ed. *Computer Programs for Chemistry,* vol. 1. New York: W. A. Benjamin, 1968.

ROBERTS, J. D. *An Introduction to Spin-Spin Splitting in High Resolution NMR Spectra.* New York: W. A. Benjamin, 1962.

Carbon-13 NMR Spectroscopy

CLERC, J. T.; PRETSCH, E.; and STERNHELL, S. ^{13}C *Kernresonanzspectroscopie.* Frankfurt: Akademische Verlagagesellschaft, 1973.

LEVY, G. C., and NELSON, G. L. *Carbon-13 NMR for Organic Chemists.* New York: Wiley-Interscience, 1972.

STOTHERS, J. B. *Carbon-13 NMR Spectroscopy.* New York: Academic Press, 1972.

Collections of NMR Data

BHACCA, N. S. et al. *High Resolution NMR Spectra Catalog,* vols. 1 and 2. Palo Alto: Varian Associates, 1963.

BOVEY, F. A. *NMR Data Tables for Organic Compounds,* vol. 1. New York: Interscience, 1967.

BRÜGEL, W. *NMR Spectra and Chemical Structure.* New York: Academic Press, 1967.

HOWELL, M. G.; KENDE, A. S.; and WEBB, J. S., eds. *Formula Index to NMR Literature Data,* vols. 1 and 2. New York: Plenum Press, 1966.

JOHNSON, L. F., and JANKOWSKI, W. C. *Carbon-13 NMR Spectra*. New York: Wiley-Interscience, 1972.

Special Topics

BOVEY, F. A. *High Resolution NMR of Macromolecules*. New York: Academic Press, 1972.

CASEY, A. F. *PMR Spectroscopy in Medicinal and Biological Chemistry*. London: Academic Press, 1971.

DWEK, R. A. *NMR in Biochemistry*. Oxford: Clarendon Press, 1973.

FARRAR, T. C., and BECKER, E. D. *Pulse and Fourier Transform NMR*. New York: Academic Press, 1971.

KASLER, F. *Quantitative Analysis by NMR Spectroscopy*. London: Academic Press, 1973.

NOGGLE, J. H., and SCHIRMER, R. E. *The Nuclear Overhauser Effect*. New York: Academic Press, 1971.

Determination of Molecular Structure by Combined Spectroscopic Methods (including NMR)

SILVERSTEIN, R. M.; BASSLER, C. G.; and MORRILL, T. C. *Spectrometric Identification of Organic Compounds*, 3rd ed. New York: Wiley-Interscience, 1974.

SIMON, W., and CLERC, T. *Structural Analysis of Organic Compounds by Spectroscopic Methods*. London: Macdonald, 1971.

WILLIAMS, D. H., and FLEMING, I. *Spectroscopic Methods in Organic Chemistry*, 2nd ed. London: McGraw-Hill, 1973.

PROBLEMS

1. The methyl protons of *n*-propyl alcohol show an absorption peak 352.3 Hz upfield from a benzene external-reference peak, using a radio-frequency field of 60 MHz. (a) If the benzene peak occurs at $\delta = 6.73$ ppm (downfield) from the TMS peak, what is the chemical shift of the sample peak relative to TMS? (b) If the applied frequency had been 50 MHz, at what equivalent frequency from the benzene peak would the absorption peak have occurred?

2. Match the following NMR spectra (pp 360–61) with the following compounds: (a) ethyl bromide; (b) 1,1-dibromoethane; (c) 1,2-dibromo-2-methylpropane; (d) 1,1,2-tribromoethane; (e) ethyl alcohol; and (f) *p*-(*t*-butyl)toluene. The number in a circle near a set of peaks refers to the relative area for those peaks.

3. Predict the relative shape of the NMR spectrum for methyl ethyl ketone, 2-butanone. Compare with that for acetone. Include the number of peaks and their relative areas.

4. Predict the relative shapes of the NMR spectra for propane and 1-nitropropane.

5. Using the Larmor equation and the fact that hydrogen resonates at 60 MHz in a field of 14,092 gauss, (a) calculate the gyromagnetic ratio for hydrogen; (b) calculate the resonance frequency for hydrogen in a spectrometer with a magnetic field strength of 23,487 gauss. (c) If the spectrometer described in (b) above is used to obtain ^{13}C spectra, resonance occurs at 25.1 MHz. What is the resonance frequency for ^{13}C in a spectrometer that obtains ^{1}H signals at 80 MHz?

6. Define, illustrate, or explain each of the following terms or phrases: (a) frequency-sweep spectrometer; (b) spin-lattice relaxation; (c) chemical shift; (d) TMS; (e) ring current; (f) LIS; (g) pulse FT NMR; and (h) NOE.

7. (a) What is the chemical shift of a proton whose NMR signal is observed at 320 Hz downfield from TMS in a spectrometer whose basic resonance frequency for hydro-

gen is 90 MHz? (b) What is the chemical-shift difference between two different hydrogens whose NMR signals are observed at 180 and 400 Hz from TMS in a spectrometer operating at 60 MHz? (c) An NMR signal is observed at 7.3 ppm downfield from TMS in a spectrometer operating at 100 MHz. Calculate the position in Hz of that same signal in a spectrometer operating at 60 MHz.

8. Explain why the ^{1}H-NMR spectrum of N-methylacetamide shows signals for two different N-methyl groups.

9. Sketch the first-order splitting patterns you would expect to observe for the following spin systems (your sketches should be similar to those in Figs. 12.11 and 12.13): (a) AX (b) A_3X_2 (c) A_3X (d) AMX with $J_{AM} > J_{MX} > J_{AX}$.

10. Sketch the ^{1}H-NMR spectrum you would expect to observe for each of the following compounds: (a) ethyl chloride; (b) t-butyl amine; (c) toluene; (d) methyl methacrylate; (e) 1,1,1-trifluoroethane.

11. The ^{1}H-NMR spectrum of a mixture of toluene and benzene showed two signals; one at 7.3 ppm (integral = 85) and one at 2.2 ppm (integral = 15). From the relative intensities of these signals, calculate the ratio of benzene to toluene in the mixture.

12. Propose structures for the unknown compounds whose ^{1}H-NMR spectra (60 MHz) and molecular formulas are given on pp 362–64. In each instance explain your analysis of the spectrum and how it leads to the structure you propose. The number in a circle by a set of peaks refers to the relative area under the peaks for that set.

13. A particular chlorination reaction could have yielded one of the following isomers: $CH_3(CO)CCl_2CH_2COOH$, $CH_2Cl(CO)CHClCH_2COOH$, or $CHCl_2(CO)CH_2CH_2COOH$. From the 60-MHz proton-NMR spectrum of the isolated product (p 364), determine which compound was actually formed, and explain your selection.

14. Gas chromatographic separation of a mixture of halocarbons gave two isomeric compounds whose molecular formula was found to be $C_2HCl_3F_2$. What are the structures of the two isomers whose 60-MHz NMR spectra are given on p 365? [Hint: Remember that ^{19}F has a spin of 1/2 and splits hydrogen signals as if it were another hydrogen.]

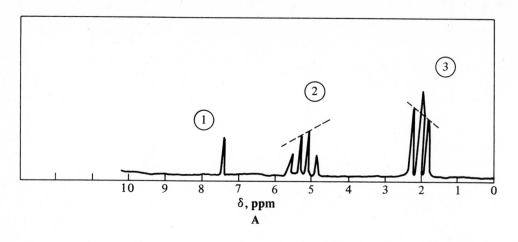

A

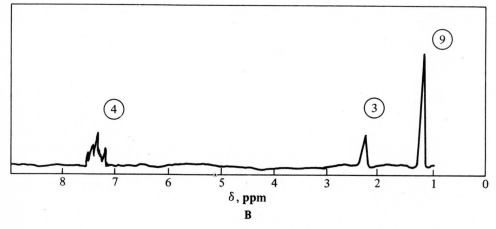

B

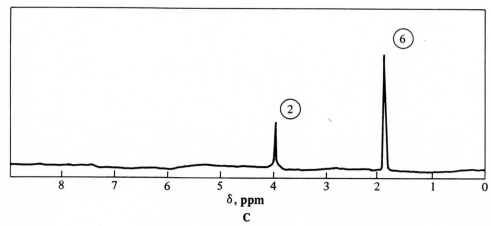

C

Spectra for Problem 2

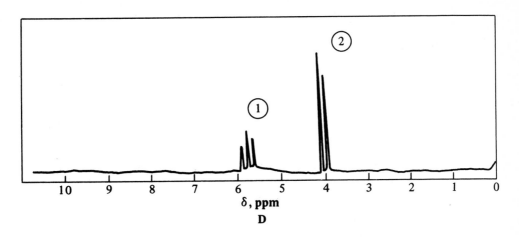

D

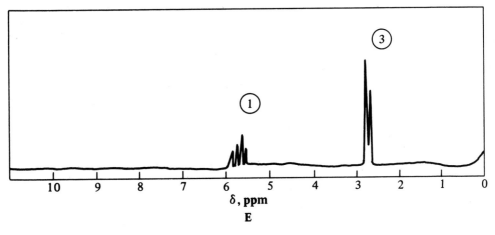

E

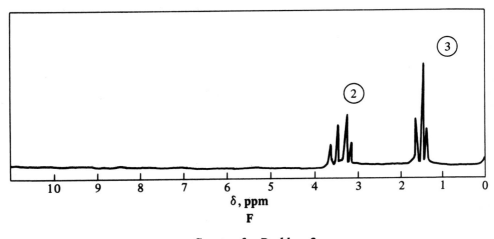

F

Spectra for Problem 2

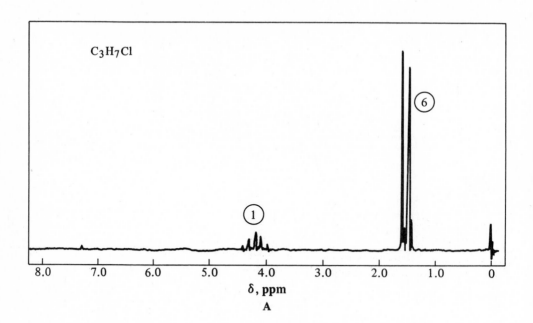

C_3H_7Cl

①

⑥

δ, ppm

A

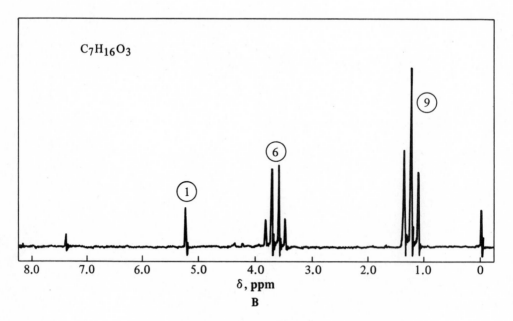

$C_7H_{16}O_3$

⑨

⑥

①

δ, ppm

B

Spectra for Problem 12

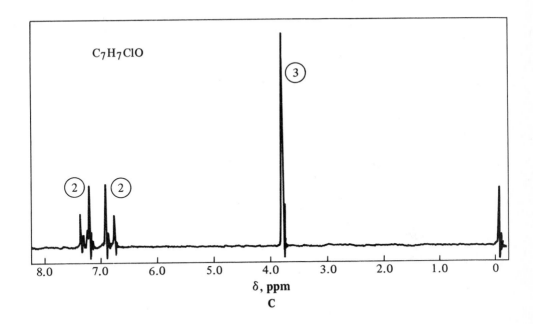

C

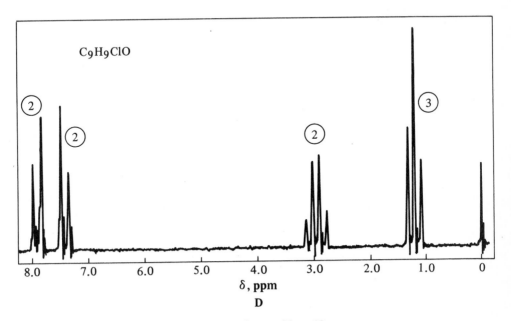

D

Spectra for Problem 12

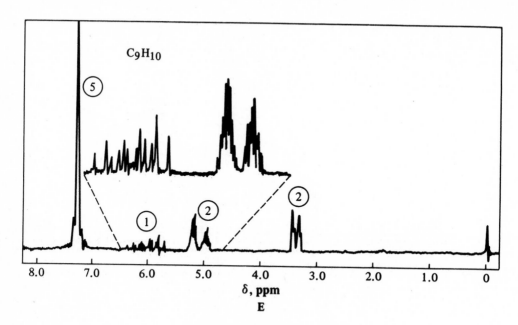

Spectrum for Problem 12

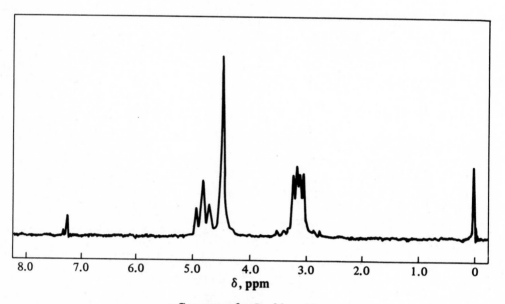

Spectrum for Problem 13

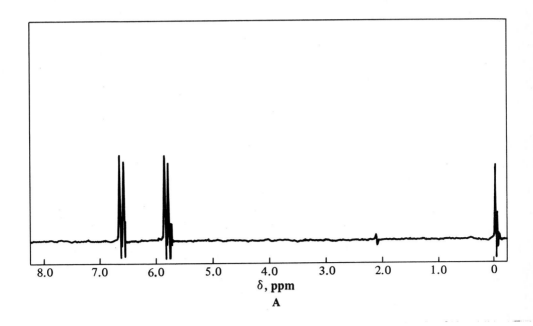

A

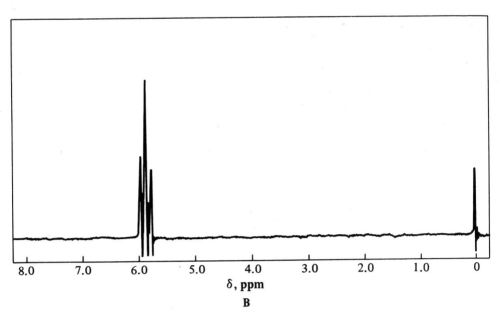

B

Spectra for Problem 14

13

Electron Spin Resonance Spectroscopy

JOHN R. WASSON

Since its discovery by Zavoisky in 1944, *electron spin resonance* spectroscopy (ESR) (also called *electron paramagnetic resonance* spectroscopy [EPR]) has become an essential tool for the study of the structure and dynamics of molecular systems containing one or more unpaired electrons. Such paramagnetic systems can frequently be examined using magnetic susceptibility techniques as well, but these do not provide the detailed information that ESR spectroscopy does. ESR spectroscopy and magnetic susceptibility methods each have their strengths and limitations and often provide complementary information.

The theory of ESR spectroscopy shares much in common with that of nuclear magnetic resonance spectroscopy; however, the magnetic moment of the electron is about 1000 times as large as the nuclear moment and the constants employed in NMR theory frequently are different in magnitude and sign. Here, the concern is only with the fundamentals and applications of ESR spectroscopy to chemistry. The texts and specialized monographs cited at the end of the chapter should be consulted for more detailed treatments of the technique.

It is appropriate at this juncture to mention that practical aspects of the use of ESR spectroscopy are discussed most often in the thesis literature (see *Dissertation Abstracts*), where the space limitations of the research literature do not apply. The book by Alger is particularly valuable for descriptions of experimental techniques.

Types of Materials Studied by ESR

ESR spectroscopy is used to study a wide variety of materials, of which the following is a sample:

1. Inorganic and organic free radicals which possess an odd number of electrons, such as Fremy's radical, $ON(SO_3)_2^{2-}$, and diphenylpycrylhydrazyl (DPPH):

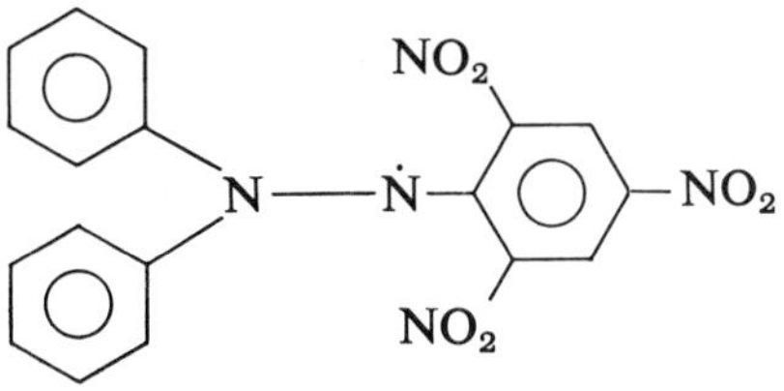

These radicals can be generated by a variety of methods, including pyrolysis and the irradiation of a sample with γ-rays. Free radicals are frequently encountered as intermediates in such chemical reactions as enzyme-substrate reactions. Most free radicals, being unstable, cannot be readily purchased and stored. However, Fremy's radical (obtained from Fremy's salt, $K_4[ON(SO_3)_2]_2$), DPPH, and various nitroxide radicals can be obtained from commercial sources.

2. Odd-electron molecules such as NO, NO_2, and ClO_2. Many molecules of this type have been examined by gas-phase ESR techniques.

3. Triplet-state molecules, such as O_2 and S_2. These systems have two unpaired electrons. Optical irradiation of solids and solutions can often permit investigation of photoexcited triplet states, which are important in photochemistry.

4. Transition-metal complexes, organometallic compounds, and catalysts containing metal ions with incomplete $3d$, $4d$, or $5d$ electron subshells. The detection of V(IV) (which has the $1s^2 2s^2 2p^6 3s^2 3p^6 3d^1$ configuration) in crude petroleum is one notable application of ESR spectroscopy.

5. Rare earth and actinide compounds containing incomplete $4f$, $6d$, or $5f$ subshells.

6. Impurities in solids, such as semiconductor materials. Odd electrons gained by an acceptor or lost by a donor impurity may be associated with energy bands in crystals.

7. Metals. The electrons in conduction bands of metals can be examined by ESR spectroscopy.

Although ESR spectroscopy can be utilized to probe the structure of many materials, it has certain limitations. Many materials, particularly those containing more than one unpaired electron (Ni(II) compounds, for instance) do not exhibit room-temperature ESR spectra because of large zero-field splitting (discussed later) or unusually large line-broadening. These materials are best examined using conventional magnetic susceptibility methods, although on occasion NMR studies are possible. It is also important to be aware that ESR spectroscopy is concerned with a particular electronic state, the ground state (which may be a photoexcited state), and that other electronic states of a system are important only insofar as they become "mixed in" the electronic state being studied via perturbations or structural dynamics.

13.1 THE RESONANCE CONDITION

The electron is a charged particle with angular momentum (orbital and spin) and, as such, it possesses a magnetic moment, μ_e, given by

$$\mu_e = -g\beta J \tag{13.1}$$

Here J (in units of $h/2\pi$, where h = Planck's constant) is the *total angular momentum vector*, g is a dimensionless constant (the *g-value*, *g-factor*, or *spectroscopic splitting factor*), and β is a constant, the *Bohr magneton*. The negative sign in Equation 13.1 is a consequence of negative electronic charge. Neglecting orbital angular momentum and considering only the total spin angular momentum S, Equation 13.1 can be written as

$$\mu_e = -g\beta S \tag{13.2}$$

The g-value for the free electron, g_e, is 2.0023. The approximation made in Equation 13.2 is valid for most discussions of the ESR spectra of the organic free radicals and transition-metal complexes whose orbital angular momentum can be considered to be "quenched." Treating the g-value as an experimental quantity does not harm the present discussion, since deviations of g-values from g_e can be accounted for by introduction of spin-orbit coupling.

Magnetic moments can be detected by their interactions with magnetic fields. In zero field, the magnetic moments of unpaired electrons in a sample are randomly oriented. In the presence of a magnetic field H, electron moments assume orientations with respect to the applied field, giving rise to $2S + 1$ energy states (Zeeman splitting). The measurable components of μ_e are $g\beta m_s$ where m_s is the magnetic spin quantum number, which can take the values $+S$, $+(S - 1), \ldots, -(S - 1), -S$. The application of a magnetic field to an $S = 1/2$ (or larger) system is said to remove the *spin degeneracy* (i.e., the equal energy values of m_s in the absence of an applied magnetic field).

The energy of an electron moment in a magnetic field is given by

$$E = -\mu_e \cdot H \tag{13.3}$$

Upon combining Equation 13.2 and 13.3, the expression

$$E = g\beta H m_s \tag{13.4}$$

results (assuming that the direction of the applied field defines the z-axis). When $S = 1/2$, there are two energy levels

$$E_{m_s = +1/2} = +\tfrac{1}{2}g\beta H \tag{13.5}$$

FIGURE 13.1. *Energy levels and spectra in ESR spectroscopy. A: Energy levels for an unpaired electron in a magnetic field. B: ESR absorption peak: RF power (P) absorbed vs. magnetic field. C: ESR first-derivative presentation—change of power absorbed per unit change in magnetic field vs. magnetic field. ΔH is the peak-to-peak line width. The first-derivative spectrum is the usual form obtained using ESR spectrometers, since phase-sensitive crystal detection of the microwave power absorbed by the sample is usually employed.*

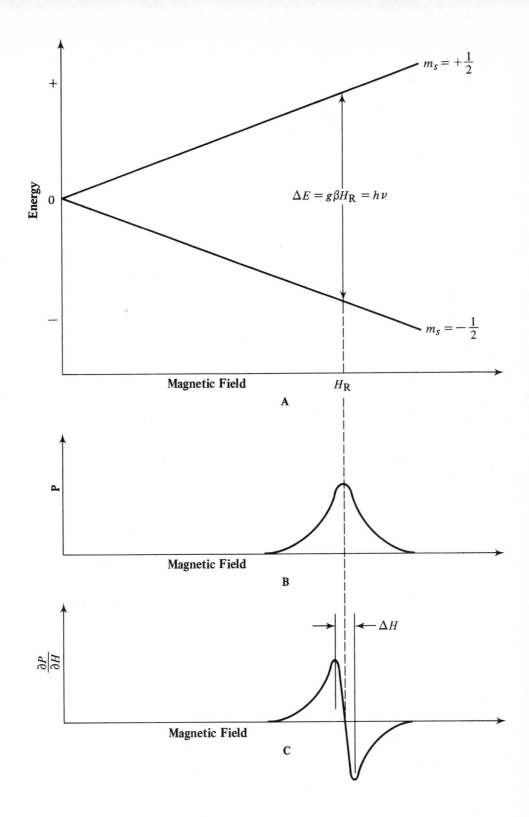

$$\Delta E = g\beta H_R = h\nu$$

$m_s = +\frac{1}{2}$

$m_s = -\frac{1}{2}$

Energy

Magnetic Field

H_R

A

P

Magnetic Field

B

$\frac{\partial P}{\partial H}$

ΔH

Magnetic Field

C

TABLE 13.1. *Spectrometer Frequencies and g_e, Resonance Field Strength*

Designation	Spectrometer Frequency			g_e (oe)[a]
	ν(Hz)	λ(cm)	ν(cm^{-1})	
X-band	$\sim 9.5 \times 10^9$	3.156	0.317	3390
K-band	$\sim 23 \times 10^9$	1.303	0.767	8207
Q-band	$\sim 35 \times 10^9$	0.856	1.168	12,489

a. For the purposes of magnetic resonance spectroscopy, Oersteds (oe) and Gauss (G) are effectively the same and are employed interchangeably.

and

$$E_{m_s = -1/2} = -\tfrac{1}{2}g\beta H \tag{13.6}$$

whose energy is linearly dependent on H. The separation between these energy levels (Fig. 13.1) at a particular value of the magnetic field, H_R, is

$$\Delta E = +\tfrac{1}{2}g\beta H_R - (-\tfrac{1}{2}g\beta H_R) = g\beta H_R \tag{13.7}$$

In an ESR experiment, an oscillating magnetic field perpendicular to H_R induces transitions between the $m_s = -1/2$ and $m_s = +1/2$ levels, provided the frequency, ν, is such that the resonance condition

$$\Delta E = h\nu = g\beta H_R \tag{13.8}$$

is satisfied. The frequency is held constant and the magnetic field is varied. At a particular value of the magnetic field, H_R, resonance absorption of energy occurs, resulting in a peak in the spectrum (Fig. 13.1B). The frequencies commonly employed in ESR experiments are in the microwave region; these frequencies and magnetic field strengths for g_e resonance absorption signals are given in Table 13.1.

13.2 ESR INSTRUMENTATION

As in most other types of spectroscopy, the instrumentation employed in ESR spectroscopy consists of a source of electromagnetic radiation, a sample holder, and appropriate detection equipment for monitoring the amount of radiation absorbed by the sample. In ESR spectroscopy a magnetic field provided by an electromagnet is also required. Monochromatic radiation of the various frequencies employed in ESR work (Table 13.1) is obtained from klystrons, which are electronic oscillators producing microwave energy. Spectrometers operating at X-band (3-cm wavelength) are the ones most commonly employed. The microwave radiation is transmitted along hollow rectangular metal pipes called waveguides.

Figure 13.2 gives a block diagram of a simple ESR spectrometer. The sample is placed at the center of the sample cavity where the magnetic vector is at a maximum. Quartz tubes (~ 3 mm o.d.) are generally employed to contain solid and solution samples. Unlike the NMR technique, the sample tubes are not rotated. The magnetic field is slowly and linearly increased until the resonance condition (Eqn. 13.8) is satisfied, at which point power is absorbed by the sample and a change in current in the detector crystal is monitored. A pair of Helmholtz coils are mounted around the cavity to increase sensitivity. Feeding the coils from an oscillator superimposes a variable amplitude sinusoidal modulation on the slowly varying magnetic field. The signal detected by the phase-sensitive detection system is proportional to the slope of the ESR absorption as the magnetic field passes through resonance. The recorder then presents the first-derivative spectrum. Many spectrometers are also equipped to present second-derivative spectra.

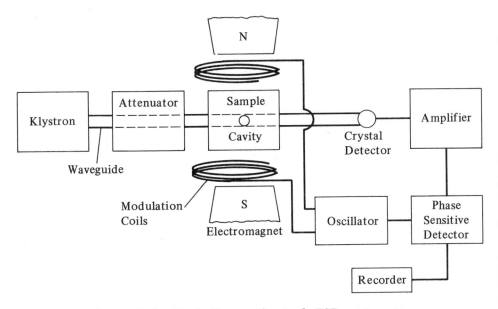

FIGURE 13.2. *Block diagram of a simple ESR spectrometer.*

The sample tube must be chosen with careful attention to the physical, chemical, and magnetic properties of each sample. For instance, when the sample is dissolved in a polar solvent with an appreciable dielectric constant, quartz sample tubes are usually not suitable and capillaries or thin rectangular cells of glass are used. Again, when studying free radicals with $g \approx g_e$, Pyrex tubing can be used, whereas only quartz can be used for triplet ($S = 1$) compounds because of paramagnetic impurities such as Fe^{3+} in most laboratory-grade glassware. Finger sized Dewar flasks (of the appropriate materials) and other cryogenic equipment permit ESR spectra to be obtained as a function of temperature.

The spectral sensitivity of ESR depends on a variety of factors, but with a response time of 1 sec, as few as 10^{11} spins ($\sim 10^{-12}$ moles) can be detected with currently available spectrometers. This sort of sensitivity suggests that ESR spectroscopy would be useful for trace analysis. A minimum detectable concentration is perhaps 10^{-9} M in samples with very small dielectric loss. For qualitative measurement in aqueous solutions, 10^{-7} M is more reasonable, while for quantitative measurements the sample concentration should be greater than about 10^{-6} M. Unfortunately, ESR spectra are more applicable to qualitative and semiquantitative than to quantitative analysis—to answering "What?" rather than "How much?"—because of the variety of instrumental variables in the method and the absence of suitable standards. Additional work in this area should markedly extend the utility of ESR techniques for quantitative analytical purposes.

In any ESR experiment it is important to monitor the microwave frequency at which the spectrometer operates and the magnetic field range swept during the experiment. Although the frequency is constant during an experiment, the frequency available from a given klystron will vary a little with tuning of the instrument. The frequency can be determined using a built-in frequency meter or appropriate transfer oscillators and frequency counters. The magnetic field can be monitored using an NMR gaussmeter or by using samples of known g-value; for instance, the DPPH free radical for which $g = 2.0036$. The magnetic field sweep can also be checked using Fremy's radical or oxobis(2,4-pentanedionato)vanadium(IV).

13.3 THERMAL EQUILIBRIUM AND SPIN RELAXATION

For a sample in thermodynamic equilibrium containing N spin systems ($S = 1/2$) in a magnetic field, there is a population difference between the two m_s levels arising from each $S = 1/2$ system; the difference follows the Boltzmann distribution.

$$\frac{N_{m_s = +1/2}}{N_{m_s = -1/2}} = e^{-h\nu/kT} \approx 1 - \frac{h\nu}{kT} \quad \text{where } kT \gg g\beta H \qquad (13.9)$$

In this expression $N_{m_s = \pm 1/2}$ is the number of spins having $m_s = +1/2$ and $m_s = -1/2$. Under normal conditions there is a slight excess population in the lower ($m_s = -1/2$) level. Absorption of microwave energy by the sample induces transitions from the $m_s = -1/2$ to the $m_s = +1/2$ level. To maintain steady-state conditions, electrons promoted to the excited state must lose energy and return to the lower level; otherwise, saturation would occur and no resonance absorption would be observed. This is similar to the situation in NMR spectroscopy.

Saturation is normally avoided by working at low RF power levels. The electrons lose energy and return to the ground state by two relaxation mechanisms, spin-lattice and spin-spin relaxation, similar to mechanisms encountered in NMR spectroscopy. In spin-lattice relaxation, nonradiative transitions from the $m_s = +1/2$ to the $m_s = -1/2$ state occur because of interactions between the electrons and their surroundings that cause the spin orientation to change. Strong spin-lattice coupling of this type enables the spin system to lose energy to the lattice (surroundings) as rapidly as the oscillating field can supply it; thermal equilibrium values of the spin-state populations are maintained and energy is continuously absorbed as long as the resonance condition is satisfied. Weak spin-lattice coupling leads to saturation at comparatively low microwave power levels, whereas strong coupling can only be overcome by increasing the microwave power. Strong interactions are characterized by short relaxation times giving rise to wide lines (recall the Heisenberg Uncertainty Principle, which can also be written $\Delta E \Delta t \geq h/2\pi$). If spin-lattice relaxation leads to an m_s-level lifetime of about the period of the microwave radiation, or less, it is impossible to observe ESR spectra, since the microwave-induced transitions are lost among those due to relaxation.

The ESR spectra of samples with short relaxation times can be sharpened just by reducing the temperature, since this stabilizes the excited state, thereby lengthening the relaxation time. Spin-lattice relaxation is enhanced (relaxation times shortened) by the presence of energy levels separated from the ground state by the order of kT. This situation is often encountered in paramagnetic ions and radicals where spin-orbit coupling (interaction of electron spin and orbital moments) is relatively large.

Unpaired electrons can interact with other magnetic dipoles in the system. Such interactions do not dissipate energy and hence do not directly contribute to returning the spin systems to equilibrium. However, the spin-lattice transition may be enhanced if the interaction with the magnetic dipoles brings the excess energy to a position for transfer to the lattice. A variety of dipoles are frequently part of an unpaired electron's environment; for example, other unpaired electrons, magnetic nuclei of the lattice, and various electronic and impurity dipoles. Since dipolar interactions decrease with the cube of the separation, i.e., $E_{\mathrm{di}} = \mu_1 \cdot \mu_2 / r_{12}^3$, many of the spin-spin (spin dipolar) interactions can be eliminated by diluting the paramagnetic material of interest into a diamagnetic ($S = 0$, i.e., no unpaired electrons) and (hopefully) isomorphous lattice. The reduction of spin-spin relaxation results in the sharpening of ESR spectra and improved resolution of g-values, hyperfine structure, and so forth. This will be referred to again later in this chapter.

Energy Levels and Spectral Parameters

The energy of an ion can be considered to consist of a number of parts,

$$E_{\mathrm{tot}} = E_{\mathrm{C}} + E_{\mathrm{CF}} + E_{\mathrm{SO}} + E_{\mathrm{SS}} + E_{\mathrm{Z}} + E_{\mathrm{HF}} + E_{\mathrm{Q}} + E_{\mathrm{N}} \qquad \textbf{(13.10)}$$

where E_{C} = the free ion or Coulomb energy ($\sim 10^5$ cm^{-1})

E_{CF} = the Stark crystalline-field or electrostatic energy associated with the environment of the ion ($\sim 10^4$ cm^{-1})

E_{SO} = the spin-orbit interaction energy ($\sim 10^2$ cm^{-1})

E_{SS} = the electronic spin-spin interaction energy (~ 1 cm^{-1})

E_{Z} = the Zeeman-interaction energy of the electron with the external magnetic field (~ 1 cm^{-1})

E_{HF} = the hyperfine interaction energy—the energy of coupling between electron and nuclear magnetic moments ($\sim 10^{-2}$ cm^{-1})

E_{Q} = the nuclear quadrupole energy ($\sim 10^{-3}$ cm^{-1})

E_{N} = the Zeeman-interaction energy of the nucleus with the external field ($\sim 10^{-4}$ cm^{-1})

An additional energy term describing the effects of electron exchange between ions is sometimes added to Equation 13.10. In Table 13.1 it is noted that the energies associated with ESR are on the order of 1 cm^{-1}. This means that electronic transitions requiring energies greater than ~ 1 cm^{-1} are not of immediate concern, so the energy levels accessible to ESR spectroscopy will primarily involve the last five terms of Equation 13.10. The calculation of these energies requires some knowledge of quantum mechanics, particularly angular-momentum theory, and cannot be effectively dealt with here.

The simplest free radical is the hydrogen atom. In freshman chemistry, the electronic configuration of the ground state is given as $1s^1$ and, at that time, the student is more or less lucidly informed that the spin quantum number m_s can take the values $+\frac{1}{2}$ or $-\frac{1}{2}$. From the preceding discussion (Eqns. 13.1 to 13.8), ESR spectroscopy requires these values and configurations. The energy levels and observed ESR spectrum of the hydrogen atom are sketched in Figure 13.3. If only electron spin is considered, the situation depicted in Figure 13.1 would result; however, the nuclear spin of hydrogen ($I = 1/2$) interacts with the electron spin and with the external magnetic field as well. The result of these two interactions (analogous to the interactions producing spin-spin splitting in a NMR spectrum) is that the ESR spectrum consists of two peaks separated by 506.8 gauss with the resonant field H_R centered between them at a strength such that $g_0 = 2.00232$. If A_0, a measure of the hyperfine coupling energy, were equal to zero, only a single derivative peak, centered at H_R, would be observed corresponding to a transition between the dashed levels in Figure 13.3. The components of m_I are shown in Figure 13.3, where it is seen that each spin level

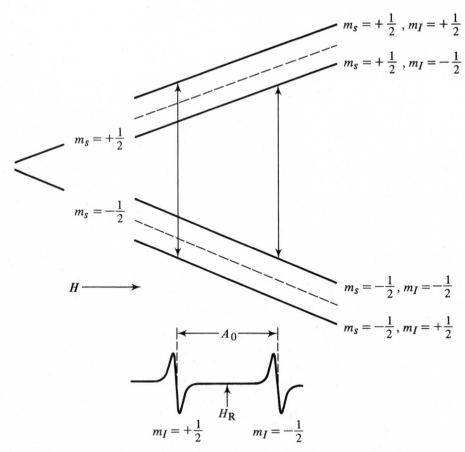

FIGURE 13.3.   *The ESR spectrum and energy levels for the hydrogen atom.*

is split into two levels by the hyperfine interaction between electron and nuclear spins. The derivation of this energy level diagram is lucidly presented in the text by Wertz and Bolton.

It is to be noted that A_0, the isotropic electron-spin–nuclear-spin hyperfine coupling constant, can be qualitatively related to the amount of time the unpaired electron spins in an s-orbital on the nucleus in question; the larger A_0, the greater the probability of finding the electron at the nucleus.

For an ion with a nonzero nuclear moment I, $2I + 1$ lines can be expected centered around g_0 with a hyperfine spacing A_0 between them. For example, for ^{63}Cu(II) (a $3d^9$ ion), $I = 3/2$; four lines are expected and generally observed in the first-derivative spectrum (see Fig. 13.4). The A_0 value is taken as the separation between the two central ESR lines, and the g_0 value is calculated from the magnetic field halfway between those lines. For V(IV) compounds (^{51}V, $I = 7/2$), eight lines are expected for the solution ESR spectra. The selection rules for ESR spectroscopy, as implied in Figure 13.3, are $\Delta m_s = \pm 1$ and $\Delta m_I = 0$.

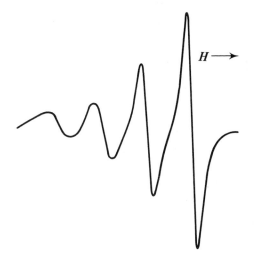

FIGURE 13.4. *The general shape of the ESR spectra for* $^{63}Cu^{2+}$ *(a $3d^9$ ion), where* $I = 3/2$.

$H \longrightarrow$

Organic free radicals in solution generally exhibit hyperfine coupling with several nuclei. When the nuclei are chemically equivalent, the number of lines is given by

$$2n_i I + 1 \qquad\qquad (13.11)$$

where n_i is the number of equivalent nuclei having nuclear spin I. Thus, the methyl radical, $H_3C\cdot$, exhibits a four-line spectrum from splitting by three equivalent hydrogens. The p-benzosemiquinone radical anion (A)

(A)   (B)

exhibits a five-line spectrum while the benzene radical anion (B) gives a seven-line

TABLE 13.2.   *Relative Intensities of ESR Lines*

Number of Equivalent Atoms with $I = 1/2$ (n)	Relative Intensities of ESR Lines	Number of Lines ($n + 1$)
1	1:1	2
2	1:2:1	3
3	1:3:3:1	4
4	1:4:6:4:1	5
5	1:5:10 : 10:5:1	6

spectrum.   Note that in hydrocarbon radicals the abundance of ^{13}C (1.108%, $I = \frac{1}{2}$) is so low that satellite peaks due to interaction of the unpaired electron with the ^{13}C atoms are not readily resolved.   For hydrocarbon radicals in which the unpaired electron interacts only with hydrogen atoms, Equation 13.11 reduces to $n + 1$.

When an organic radical possesses two or more sets of equivalent atoms, the total number of lines in the ESR spectrum is given by

$$\prod_{i=1}^{j} (2n_i I_i + 1) = (2n_1 I_1 + 1)(2n_2 I_2 + 1) \cdots (2n_j I_j + 1) \qquad \textbf{(13.12)}$$

For example, for the hypothetical $(H_2N)\dot{B}(PF_2)$ radical where $I = 3$ for ^{10}B, $I = 1$ for ^{14}N, $I = 1/2$ for ^{31}P, and $I = 1/2$ for ^{19}F, a total of 378 lines could be expected if the unpaired electron interacted appreciably with each of the nuclei.

The number of lines in the ESR spectrum of a radical is a clue to its identity. Of further assistance is the intensity pattern in the spectrum.   For n equivalent nuclei with $I = 1/2$, the $n + 1$ lines have intensities proportional to the binomial expansion of order n.   Table 13.2 lists the relative intensities up to $n = 5$.   The intensity patterns for sets of equivalent nuclei with $I > 1/2$ are handled in a similar fashion.   Figure 13.5 shows the ESR spectrum of diphenylpicrylhydrazyl (DPPH) free radical in benzene.   Under low-resolution conditions, the proton hyperfine coupling is not observed and the five-line spectrum with the intensity distribution 1:2:3:2:1 results from the interaction of the unpaired electron with two (effectively equivalent) ^{14}N ($I = 1$) nuclei; for nuclei with $I > 1/2$, the intensity distribution is more complex than a simple binomial expansion, and is beyond the scope of this text.

FIGURE 13.5.   *Low-resolution ESR spectrum of the diphenylpicrylhydrazyl (DPPH) radical in benzene.*

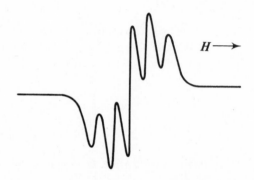

$H \longrightarrow$

Magnetically nonequivalent protons will normally have different splitting constants, and the observed ESR spectra can be analyzed by reconstructing the spectrum from the splitting patterns and intensity distributions expected for each equivalent set of protons. Some examples should serve to illustrate this procedure. The photolysis of hydrogen peroxide in methanol produces the $\cdot CH_2OH$ free radical. The protons bound to carbon and the proton bound to the oxygen atom comprise two nonequivalent sets. For $\cdot CH_2OH$, either a doublet of triplets (Fig. 13.6A) or a triplet of doublets (Fig. 13.6B) could be expected, depending on whether the A value for the OH proton is larger or smaller than the A value for the CH_2 protons. Experiments show that a triplet of doublets appears, with a 1:2:1 intensity distribution, $A_{CH_2} = 17.4$ gauss, and $A_{OH} = 1.15$ gauss in accordance with the stick diagram given in Figure 13.6B [1]. More complicated spectra are analyzed similarly but, as can be imagined, the difficulty of interpretation increases with the increasing number of sets of equivalent protons.

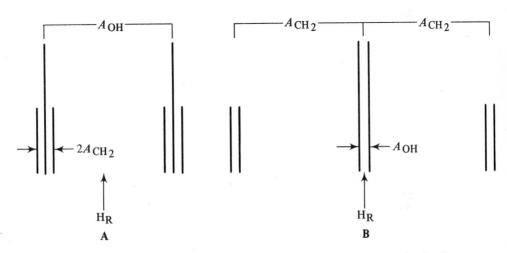

FIGURE 13.6. *Possible ESR splitting patterns for the $\cdot CH_2OH$ radical. A: The hyperfine splitting constant for the OH proton (A_{OH}) is larger than that for the CH_2 protons (A_{CH_2}). B: The hyperfine splitting constant for the OH proton is smaller.*

The origin of the proton hyperfine splitting in the ESR spectra of hydrocarbon radicals can be explained by quantum-mechanical calculations. These results give rise to the well-known McConnell relation [2]

$$A = \rho Q \tag{13.13}$$

where A = the hyperfine coupling constant for a proton in a C–H fragment having an unpaired π-electron density of ρ

Q = a constant having a value of 22.4 gauss

This relation permits unpaired electron distributions in π-electron radicals, such as the benzene radical anion and the *p*-benzosemiquinone radical anion, to be mapped experimentally; while at the same time, the ESR spectra of π-electron radicals can be calculated using simple Hückel-molecular-orbital theory of the type taught in sophomore-level organic-chemistry courses.

Transition-Metal Complexes

Generally, the spectra of transition-metal complexes are associated with the central metal ion. Frequently, *superhyperfine* splitting is also encountered which demonstrates that the unpaired electron of the ligand is delocalized over the metal complex. Figure 13.7 shows the ESR spectrum of $VO[S_2PC_2H_5(OCH_3)]_2$ in chloroform solution. Each of the eight vanadium hyperfine lines is split into three by interaction of the unpaired electron with two equivalent phosphorus nuclei ($I = 1/2$), each line having roughly the 1:2:1 intensity distribution expected. Line overlapping contributes to deviation from the anticipated intensity distribution.

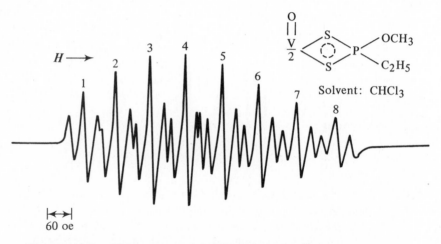

FIGURE 13.7. *ESR spectrum of $VO[S_2PC_2H_5(OCH_3)]_2$ in chloroform. The eight vanadium hyperfine lines are numbered; each of these is split into a triplet from interaction with the two equivalent phosphorus nuclei.*

In oxovanadium(IV) complexes ($3d^1$ systems) of this type, it can be shown [3] that the ^{31}P superhyperfine splitting arises from interaction of the ground-state vanadium(IV) $3d_{x^2-y^2}$ orbital with the phosphorus 3s orbitals. This *trans*-annular interaction can be pictorially represented as in Figure 13.8. The $d_{x^2-y^2}$ orbital is not σ-bonding with respect to the sulfur atoms, but does possess the correct symmetry to interact directly with phosphorus 3s and 3p orbitals. The essentially isotropic nature of the phosphorus superhyperfine splitting constants indicates that phosphorus 3p orbitals are not appreciably involved in the *trans*-annular interaction. Ligand superhyperfine splitting in the ESR spectra of metal complexes provides detailed

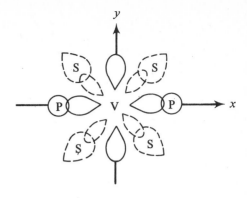

FIGURE 13.8. *Pictorial representation of the orbital interaction in certain oxovanadium(IV) complexes.*

information regarding the covalency of metal-ligand bonding. The above example is only one of the many that can be cited.

13.5 ANALYTICAL APPLICATIONS

The chief application of ESR spectroscopy to chemical problems is the identification of the presence and nature of species containing unpaired electrons. Determination of concentrations of electron spins in a given sample is not very precise; in general, only order-of-magnitude estimates of spin concentrations can be obtained. Accurate quantitative analyses can seldom be performed using ESR spectroscopy.

ESR lines usually exhibit shapes very close to those of Gaussian or Lorentzian functions. The intensities of ESR lines may be obtained by integration of the full absorption curve, by two consecutive integrations of the first-derivative curve, or by the approximation

$$\text{intensity} = \text{derivative height} \times (\Delta H)^2 \tag{13.14}$$

where ΔH is defined as in Figure 13.1, which yields the relative intensities of lines in a spectrum.

Applying first principles to measurements of the ESR signal and to all pertinent instrumental parameters, absolute numbers of spins can be determined. However, this is rarely done since the number of variables to be controlled is considerable and the labor involved is disproportionate. Relative concentrations of species with the same spectral shape and line widths can be determined simply by comparing peak heights of the normal first-derivative curve under identical conditions, i.e.,

$$\frac{N_1}{N_2} = \frac{h_1}{h_2} \tag{13.15}$$

If the linewidths differ, Equation 13.15 can be modified to yield (cf. Eqn. 13.14)

$$\frac{N_1}{N_2} = \frac{h_1}{h_2} \frac{(\Delta H_1)^2}{(\Delta H_2)^2} \tag{13.16}$$

Again, employing a standard sample as a reference, intensities of ESR lines obtained by one or more integrations can be compared to yield spin concentrations.

Quantitative Analysis of Metal Ions

In analytical work, the biggest problems are associated with maintaining identical instrumental conditions for both reference compounds and samples, and finding a suitable reference material. The reference sample should be a stable, easily handled material with line-shape, line-width, and power-saturation properties similar to those of the test sample. Reasonably good semiquantitative information can be obtained by preparing calibration curves using standard samples, and comparing them with data for test samples. A good example of this technique is the detection of Cu(II) in sea water at the parts-per-billion level [4]. In this example, copper is extracted from sea water with 8-hydroxyquinoline in ethyl acetate. The ESR-line intensities of the extracted solutions are then compared to those obtained for standard samples of known copper concentration similarly prepared. The curve of standard-line intensity versus copper-concentration can lead to a deviation of ± 0.2 ppb in the copper analyses; this means that the relative deviation is about $\pm 8\%$. While a deviation of this magnitude is intolerable for macroscopic methods, such as gravi-metric analysis, it is more palatable with trace analyses. Since this approach to monitoring copper concentration is rather rapid and fairly reliable, its semiquantitative nature can often be tolerated.

Another representative type of analysis by ESR is that of Fe(III) [5]. Fe(III) can be extracted from 1.8 M hydrochloric acid with tributyl phosphate. The ESR intensity of the extracted iron, presumably $FeCl_4^-$, can then be determined relative to the signal from the DPPH radical employed as an external standard. The relative intensity is proportional to concentration in the range 10–200 ppm of Fe(III) in the extract.

Other metal ions that can be determined quantitatively by ESR include V(IV), Cr(III), Mn(II), and Ti(III).

Spin-Labeling of Biological Systems

Spin labels are stable, paramagnetic molecules that, by their structure, easily attach themselves to various biological macromolecular systems such as proteins or cell membranes. Examples of spin labels that can be covalently bonded to specific sites of biological systems include nitroxide derivatives of N-ethylmaleimide, which bind specifically to –SH groups, and nitroxide derivatives of iodoacetamide, which bind specifically to methionine, lysine, and arginine residues of amino acids. Nonco-valently bonded spin-labels that can be incorporated into biological systems include nitroxide derivatives of stearic acid, of phospholipids, and of cholesterol.

Spin labels provide information about the static and dynamic nature of the system, including structure, relative polarity, fluidity, viscosity, conformational changes, phase transitions, and chemical reactions.

In recent years the systems most often studied by the spin-label method have been biological membranes and various models thereof. For example, using nitroxide derivatives of stearic acid, the organization of the phospholipid phase of biological membranes has been studied [6]. One interesting practical application of this type of spin-labeling is in the study of disease-state membranes. Intact erythrocyte membranes were shown to be in a more fluid state near the membrane surface in patients suffering from myotonic muscular dystrophy as compared to those from normal controls [7], thus providing an early diagnostic test for this disease.

Determination of Surface Area

Because of its specificity for molecules with unpaired electrons, ESR has been used to determine the active surface area of catalysts. The total area of the ESR signal is proportional to the number of unpaired electrons in the sample. A comparison is made of the catalyst, which has had a paramagnetic molecule adsorbed on its surface, with a standard containing a known number of unpaired electrons, usually DPPH which has 1.53×10^{21} unpaired electrons per gram.

In a study of the surface area of an MnO_2 catalyst [8], ESR measurement of the surface area based on adsorption of DPPH indicated a surface area of 46 m^2/g, whereas ESR measurement of active adsorbed oxygen indicated a surface area of 42 m^2/g. These two values compared favorably with the results from the usual BET method, which gave a surface area of 61 m^2/g. The BET method consists of volumetric or gravimetric measurements of the quantity of gas that will completely cover the surface of the solid with an adsorbed layer.

SELECTED BIBLIOGRAPHY

ABRAGAM, A., and BLEANEY, B. *Electron Paramagnetic Resonance of Transition Ions.* Oxford: Clarendon Press, 1970.

ALGER, R. S. *Electron Paramagnetic Resonance: Techniques and Applications.* New York: Interscience Publishers, 1968.

ATHERTON, N. M. *Electron Spin Resonance.* New York: John Wiley, 1973.

GERSON, F. *High Resolution E.S.R. Spectroscopy.* New York: John Wiley, 1970.

SWARTZ, H. M.; BOLTON, J. R.; and BORG, D. C., eds. *Biological Applications of Electron Spin Resonance.* New York: Wiley-Interscience, 1972.

WERTZ, J. E., and BOLTON, J. R. *Electron Spin Resonance: Elementary Theory and Practical Applications.* New York: McGraw-Hill, 1972. *This is probably the best basic text on ESR now available.*

REFERENCES

1. R. LIVINGSTON and H. ZELDES, *J. Chem. Phys.*, 44, 1245 (1966).

2. H. M. McCONNELL, *J. Chem. Phys.*, 24, 632, 764 (1956).

3. D. R. LORENZ, D. K. JOHNSON, H. J. STOKLOSA, and J. R. WASSON, *J. Inorg. Nucl. Chem.*, 36, 1184 (1974).

4. Y. P. VIRMANI and E. J. ZELLER, *Anal. Chem.*, 46, 324 (1974).

5. T. TAKEUCHI and N. YOSHIKUNI, *Bunseki Kagaku*, 22, 679 (1973).

6. H. M. McCONNELL and B. G. McFARLAND, *Quart. Rev. Biophys.*, 3, 91 (1970).

7. D. A. BUTTERFIELD, A. D. ROSES, M. L. COOPER, S. H. APPEL, and D. B. CHESNUT, *Biochemistry*, 13, 5078 (1974).

8. A. T. T. OEI and J. L. GARNETT, *J. Catal.*, 19, 176 (1970).

PROBLEMS

1. Calculate the resonant field strengths for substances which have g-values of 2.100 and 1.989 when $\nu = 9.4$, 23, and 35 gigahertz (1 GHz $= 10^9$ Hz $= 10^9$ sec^{-1}), respectively. (Note: Planck's constant, $h = 6.6256 \times 10^{-27}$ erg-sec, and the Bohr magneton, $\beta = 0.9273 \times 10^{-20}$ erg/gauss.)

2. What are the separations between resonant field strengths for substances having g-values of 1.964 and 1.989; 2.080 and 2.073, when $\nu = 9.4$, 23, and 35 GHz, respectively?

3. What are the values of $h\nu$ (cm^{-1}/molecule) when $\nu = 9.4$, 23, and 35 GHz? (Planck's constant, $h = 33.3586 \times 10^{-12}$ cm^{-1}-sec).

4. Evaluate the ratios of populations in $m_s = +1/2$ and $m_s = -1/2$ spin states when $\nu = 9.4$, 23, and 35 GHz and $T = 298$, 77, 20, and 4 K. Boltzmann's constant, $k = 1.3804 \times 10^{-16}$ erg/K.

5. How many ESR lines can be expected for the 1,2-; 1,3-; and 1,4-difluorobenzene radical anions? ($I = 1/2$ for ^{19}F.)

6. How many ESR lines could be expected for the tetrahedral P_4^- radical? ($I = 1/2$ for ^{31}P.)

7. How many ESR lines can be expected for $Cu[S_2P(OCH_3)_2]_2$ and $VO[S_2P(OCH_3)_2]_2$ ($I = 3/2$ for Cu; $I = 7/2$ for V) if only the metal hyperfine and phosphorus hyperfine splittings are observable?

14

X-Ray Spectroscopy

William J. Campbell

Since the discovery of x-rays by Roentgen in 1896, this region of the electromagnetic spectrum has been a source of significant contributions to our fundamental knowledge of atomic structure and to our techniques for chemical analysis. By 1927, six Nobel prizes in physics had been awarded for studies on the physics of x-rays and the interaction of x-rays with matter.

The analytical importance of the x-ray technique can be judged by the growth from fewer than 50 x-ray spectrometers in use in 1953 to over 10,000 now. Following the successful development and utilization of laboratory-type instrumentation, the field has expanded to include a wide range of process-control instrumentation: probes for analyzing millimeter- and micrometer-size areas, portable analyzers using radioisotopes to excite x-rays, and ion accelerators for measuring surface concentrations and trace elements.

14.1 INTRODUCTION

X-rays are generated by bombarding matter with either high-energy particles such as electrons or alpha particles or with x-ray photons. When an atom is so bombarded, an electron is ejected from one of the inner shells of the atom. This vacancy is immediately filled by an electron from a higher energy shell, creating a vacancy in that shell that is, in turn, filled by an electron from a yet higher shell. Thus, by a series of transitions, $L \rightarrow K$, $M \rightarrow L$, $N \rightarrow M$, each new vacancy is filled until the excited atom returns to its ground state.

Each electronic transition (apart from radiationless transitions) results in the emission of a characteristic x-ray spectral line whose energy $h\nu$ is equal to the difference between the binding energies of the two electrons involved in the transition (see

Fig. 14.1). Only certain electronic transitions are permitted by quantum-mechanical selection rules, which are described in various text books on atomic physics. The x-ray spectral lines are designated by symbols such as Ni $K\alpha_1$, Fe $K\beta_2$, Sn $L\alpha_2$, and U $M\alpha_1$. The symbol of an x-ray line represents the chemical element (Ni, Fe, Sn, and U); the notations K, L, or M indicate that the lines originate by the initial removal of an electron from the K, L, or M shell, respectively; a particular line in the series is designated by the Greek letter α, β, etc. (representing the subshell of the outer electron involved in the transition), plus a numerical subscript. This numerical subscript indicates the relative strength of each line in a particular series—for example, $K\alpha_1$ is more intense than $K\alpha_2$. Because there are a limited number of possible inner-shell transitions, the x-ray spectrum is much simpler than the complex optical spectrum that results from the removal or transition of valence electrons; in addition,

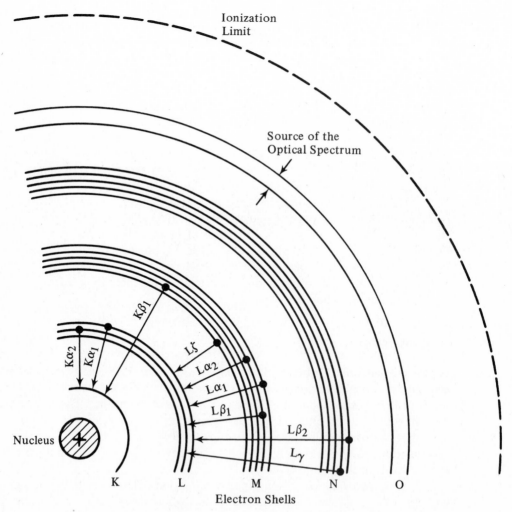

FIGURE 14.1. *Origin of characteristic x-ray lines.*

both the intensity and wavelength of x-rays are essentially independent of the chemical and physical state of the element emitting them.

There are a number of approaches to x-ray analysis. In *x-ray absorption*, the absorption of energetic x-rays that occurs when an electron is removed from its orbital is related to the concentration of the absorbing species. In *x-ray emission*, the sample is bombarded with an electron beam in an x-ray tube and the emitted x-ray photons are measured. Measurements are generally restricted to qualitative or, at best, semiquantitative determinations because of the heating and selective volatilization of different elements by the impinging electron beam. In *x-ray fluorescence*, or *secondary x-ray emission*, the sample is bombarded with an x-ray beam and the reemitted x-radiation (at a longer wavelength) is measured. The difficulties found in using x-ray emission for quantitative analysis are not experienced in x-ray fluorescence, so this technique is widely used for that purpose.

Crystalline materials, in which the atomic spacing is about the same magnitude as x-ray wavelengths, are capable of diffracting x-rays. This serves as the basis of *x-ray diffraction* analysis; qualitative identification of crystalline materials is readily made from a measurement of the angles of diffraction. X-ray diffraction also serves as a means for isolating x-rays of a particular wavelength in an x-ray spectrometer.

X-ray fluorescence spectroscopy is the most widely used x-ray technique for quantitative analysis; this chapter will be primarily concerned with this method of analysis. X-ray absorption and x-ray diffraction analysis are treated briefly at the end of the chapter.

14.2 INSTRUMENTATION

An x-ray fluorescence spectrometer needs an x-ray source, a means of dispersing the x-rays, and a detector. This is illustrated in Figure 14.2. The conventional x-ray spectrometer consists of a high-intensity x-ray tube with a stabilized, high-voltage power supply; a multi-sample chamber that can be evacuated; a goniometer (for measuring the diffraction angle) with either a parallel-plate collimator or a slit system, depending on the x-ray optics; and a proportional or scintillation-counter detector, together with its associated electronics which include a DC power supply, scaler-ratemeter, linear amplifier, single-channel analyzer, and recorder (see Chap. 19 for a detailed description of ionizing-radiation detectors). Many of the newer units have the output of the single-channel analyzer coupled to magnetic or paper-tape storage and a dedicated or time-sharing computer. Research-type, single-channel x-ray spectrometers cost on the order of $25,000 to $50,000; control instrumentation can range in cost from a few thousand dollars for a portable analyzer to $200,000 for a 15- to 20-element simultaneous analyzer with computer and automatic sample transports.

Generation of X-Rays

For most analytical applications, primary x-rays are produced by bombarding a suitable target with 10- to 100-keV electrons. This is a Coolidge-type x-ray tube and is illustrated in Figure 14.3. The spectrum resulting from electron excitation consists of a broad band of energies (the *continuum* or *Bremsstrahlung*) plus photons of dis-

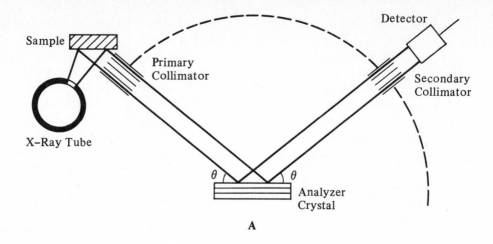

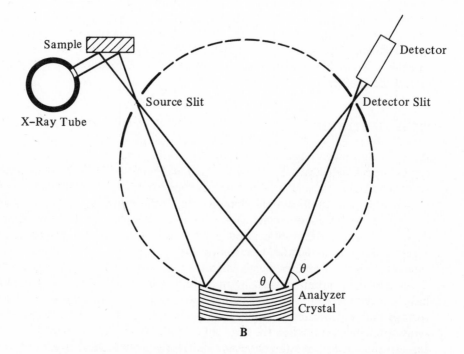

FIGURE 14.2. *Wavelength dispersion using nonfocusing (A) and focusing (B) optics.*

crete energies that are characteristic of the target element (see Fig. 14.4). The frequency of the characteristic photons is described by Moseley's law:

$$\nu = k(Z - 1)^2 \qquad (14.1)$$

where Z = the atomic number of the target element
k = a constant

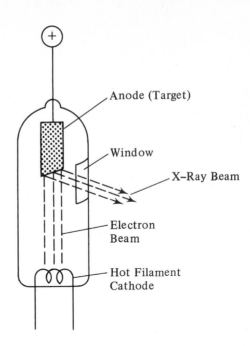

FIGURE 14.3. *Schematic diagram of a Coolidge high-vacuum x-ray tube.*

Anode (Target)

Window

X–Ray Beam

Electron Beam

Hot Filament Cathode

The integrated intensity (I) of the continuum is related to the current, voltage, and atomic number of the target by

$$I = kiZV^2 \qquad (14.2)$$

where $\quad i =$ the x-ray tube current in mA
$\quad\quad\quad\ V =$ the voltage in kV

Inspection of Equation 14.2 shows that the integrated intensity of the continuum is proportional to the atomic number; therefore, higher-atomic-number elements such as tungsten or platinum are often used as targets. Other essential properties of a target besides high atomic number are a high melting point and good thermal conductivity. The efficiency of primary x-ray production is less than one percent; the other 99+ percent of the electron energy is released into the target as heat.

As indicated in Equation 14.2, the continuum intensity is proportional to the square of the applied voltage. The distribution of the continuum from an yttrium target as a function of applied voltage is shown in Figure 14.4. Note that, as the voltage is increased, the peak of the continuum moves to a higher energy (shorter wavelength). As a first approximation, the wavelength of maximum intensity in the continuum is $3\lambda_0/2$, where λ_0 is the short-wavelength limit in Å set by the relationship

$$\frac{hc}{\lambda_0} = Ve \qquad (14.3)$$

where $\quad V =$ the potential in volts
$\quad\quad\quad\ h =$ Planck's constant
$\quad\quad\quad\ c =$ the speed of light in vacuum
$\quad\quad\quad\ e =$ the charge on the electron

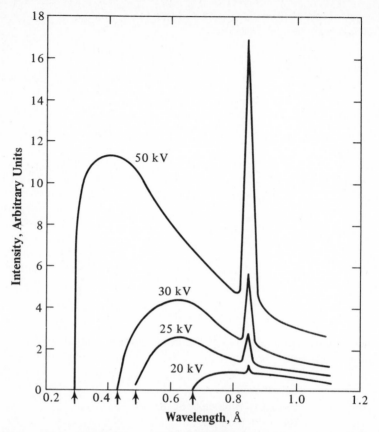

FIGURE 14.4. *Variation in x-ray distribution with voltage (yttrium target). The characteristic Y Kα line is at 0.83 Å. The short wavelength cutoff is indicated by an arrow for each voltage. From F. J. Welcher, ed.,* Standard Methods of Chemical Analysis, *6th ed., vol. IIIA, p 169, by permission of Van Nostrand Reinhold Company. Copyright © 1966 Litton Educational Publishing, Inc.*

At the short-wavelength limit, all the energy of the electron hitting the target is converted to a single photon, with none left over for heat loss or multiple emission.

The voltage required to produce the characteristic lines of each spectral series also increases with increasing atomic number. Minimum voltages, in keV, for the K, L, and M series are in the following ranges:

K series: 1.1 for ^{11}Na to 115 for ^{92}U
L series: 1.2 for ^{30}Zn to 21.7 for ^{92}U
M series: 0.41 for ^{40}Zr to 5.5 for ^{92}U

Each of these minimum (critical) voltages, corresponding to the minimum photon or electron energy that can expel an electron from a given level in the atom, is known as the *absorption edge* of that level for the particular element. Each element has as many absorption edges as it has excitation potentials—one K, three L, five M. For example, the K edge for calcium is 4.038 keV; the three L edges for lead (L_I, L_{II}, and L_{III} corresponding to the different L electrons—see Fig. 14.1) are 15.870, 15.207, and 13.044 keV, respectively.

The intensity of a characteristic line excited by electrons is related to the applied voltage by the expression

$$I = ki(V - V_0)^n \tag{14.4}$$

The value of n (which ranges over the interval between 1 and 2) depends on the ratio between the applied voltage V and the critical voltage V_0; for voltages less than $4\,V_0$, the value of n is close to 2.

In x-ray fluorescence spectroscopy, the characteristic x-rays of the sample are generated (excited) by both the characteristic and continuum x-rays of the source. An important consideration is the relative excitation of secondary x-rays by the

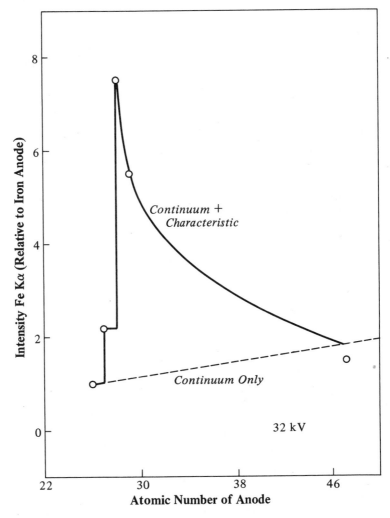

FIGURE 14.5. *Secondary excitation of iron using various x-ray tube targets.*

continuum as compared to those generated by primary characteristic x-rays. Although the total intensity of the characteristic primary peak or peaks is low compared to the continuum, the efficiency of excitation by the characteristic lines is significantly greater in many instances because of the higher absorption of these x-rays close to the surface. This higher excitation efficiency is a result of the limiting depth beyond which all secondary (fluorescence) x-rays are absorbed within the sample (the depth being related to the linear absorption coefficient of the sample for the spectral or "analytical" line). The depth of sample analyzed will range from less than 1 mm to 1 cm, depending on the energy of the spectral line and the composition of the sample. Because of this internal absorption, only those incident photons absorbed close to the surface are efficient producers of fluorescence x-rays.

Figure 14.5 shows the relative intensity of the secondary Fe Kα line emitted from an iron sample, using as primary targets in the x-ray tube some of the elements whose atomic numbers are in the range of 26 to 47. With an iron target (atomic number 26), the only source of excitation is the continuum and, therefore, that intensity is considered as unity. With targets of nickel and copper ($Z = 28$ and 29, respectively), the characteristic primary x-rays just exceed the critical energy of the Fe K-absorption edge, so excitation of Fe K radiation is a maximum. When using a high-Z target such as silver ($Z = 47$), the characteristic Ag K radiation is not absorbed near the surface of the iron sample, so the resultant Fe Kα radiation, generated relatively deep in the sample, is absorbed before escaping to the surface.

Radioisotopes (for instance, alpha emitters) can be used as sources for exciting x-ray fluorescence and are used in portable x-ray spectrometers. These are discussed later.

Dispersion of X-Rays

Chapter 6 described the use of diffraction gratings to disperse electromagnetic radiation in the ultraviolet-to-infrared regions. The radiation is diffracted if the spacings between lines on the grating are of the same magnitude as the wavelength of the radiation. This condition would be very difficult to meet for x-rays, since their wavelengths are only a few angstroms at most. The spacings of atoms in crystals, however, are small enough to diffract x-rays; this has led to the widespread use of x-rays for determining crystal structures and, conversely, to the use of crystals to disperse x-rays in spectrometers.

There are two general approaches to sorting x-rays of different wavelengths (different energies) in a spectrometer: by *wavelength dispersion*, in which the x-rays are identified after the original beam has been spread out by an analyzing crystal, and by *energy dispersion*, in which the undispersed x-rays are sorted into 100 to 1000 energy groups by means of a high-resolution frequency-sensitive semiconductor detector coupled to a multi-channel analyzer. Until approximately 1970, essentially all x-ray spectrometer analyses were made by the wavelength-dispersion technique. At present, energy-dispersion analysis using a dedicated computer for processing the data is becoming competitive with the wavelength method. The energy-dispersion technique is described below in the sections on detectors and radioisotope-source portable instruments.

The condition for diffraction of x-rays can be described by considering the

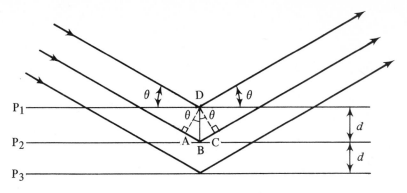

FIGURE 14.6. *Diffraction of x-rays from the planes of a crystal.*

diffraction of a monochromatic beam impinging on a row (plane) of atoms (or ions) as shown in Figure 14.6. Lines AD and CD are perpendicular to the incident and diffracted beams, respectively. The beam diffracted from plane P_2 must travel a distance $\overline{ABC}$ further than that diffracted from plane P_1. Since angles ADB and BDC are equal to the angle of incidence and diffraction θ,

$$\overline{AB} = d \sin \theta \qquad (14.5)$$

or

$$\overline{ABC} = 2d \sin \theta \qquad (14.6)$$

where $d =$ the distance between planes in the crystal

Those waves out of phase after diffraction will interfere destructively and not be observed. Only those in phase will reinforce and be observed. This occurs when $\overline{ABC}$ is an exact multiple of the wavelength of the incident beam λ. Hence,

$$n\lambda = 2d \sin \theta \qquad (14.7)$$

where $n =$ the *order* of the diffraction pattern

When n is unity, the diffracted radiation is called first order. Higher orders of diffracted radiation fall off in intensity. Equation 14.7 is known as *Bragg's law*, and may be compared to Equation 6.6 for the diffraction of radiation from a grating. For x-rays of a given wavelength, then, diffraction will be observed at only certain values of θ (determined by d). These θ values can be determined by rotating the crystal and measuring the angle of diffracted x-rays with respect to the angle of the incident beam. The d-spacings of a given plane can therefore be calculated. Or, if the d-spacing of a crystal is known, the angle at which a given x-ray will be diffracted (in a spectrometer, for instance) can be calculated.

> *Example 14.1.* The first-order diffraction of the Mo Kα 0.712 Å line from a plane of calcium fluoride is observed as strong radiation at 6.48°. What is the distance between planes?
>
> *Solution:*
> $$n\lambda = 2d \sin \theta$$
> $$1(0.712) = 2d \sin (6.48)$$
> $$d = 3.16 \text{ Å}$$

Bragg originally used this relationship to determine the wavelengths of x-rays. He diffracted x-rays from a sodium-chloride crystal and used as the *d*-value that calculated from the density of the crystal and Avogadro's number. Once λ was determined, then x-ray diffraction could be used to determine *d* spacings in other crystals, and x-ray crystallography (the study of crystals) was born.

The two types of x-ray optical systems used in spectrometers are *nonfocusing* (flat-crystal) and *focusing* (curved-crystal) systems (see Fig. 14.2). In flat-crystal optics, the x-ray beam is collimated by a closely spaced series of parallel metal foils (see Fig. 14.2A), where the beam divergence is limited by the spacing between the foils and the lengths of the foils. In curved-crystal optics, either a small region of the sample is excited using a pinhole collimator to limit the size of the primary x-ray beam, or a large area is irradiated and a divergence slit serves as the "optical source" of secondary x-rays (see Fig. 14.2b). With focusing optics, a cylindrical concave crystal focuses the diffracted x-rays onto a circle having a radius equal to one-half the radius of curvature of the crystal. The crystal has been mechanically bent to a radius 2*r*, then ground to the radius *r* of the focusing circle. The x-ray source, crystal surface, and detector slit all lie on the focusing circle. Focusing and nonfocusing optics give essentially the same intensity and line-to-background ratio for large samples, whereas for small samples, focusing optics are at least an order of magnitude more efficient.

Analyzer crystals must satisfy the Bragg relationship for the analytical line without exceeding the maximum 2θ angle available with commercial instrumentation, approximately 150°. In general, the analyzing crystal should be composed of elements of low atomic number to avoid high background from fluorescence x-rays generated in the analyzing crystal itself. The dispersion of x-rays is inversely related to the *d*-spacing and to the Bragg angle, so

$$\frac{d\theta}{d\lambda} = \frac{n}{2d \cos \theta} \qquad (14.8)$$

TABLE 14.1. *Properties of Analyzing Crystals*

Crystal	Reflecting Plane (hkl)	2*d*, Å	Comments
Lithium fluoride	200	4.03	Optimum crystal for all wavelengths less than 3 Å
Silicon	111	6.27	Suppresses even-ordered reflections, $n = 2, 4, 6, \ldots$
Pentaerythritol	002	8.74	Optimum for atomic numbers 13 to 17
Mica	002	19.93	Used primarily in curved-crystal optics for long-wavelength x-rays
Potassium hydrogen phthalate	002	26.63	Used for atomic numbers 6 to 12
Barium stearate	——	100	Used with curved- or flat-crystal optics for wavelengths greater than 20 Å

Therefore, crystals of low *d*-spacing (high dispersion) are used to disperse partially overlapping x-ray spectral lines. The characteristics of some of the more widely used crystals are given in Table 14.1.

Detectors

Four types of detectors are used in x-ray analysis: Geiger, proportional, scintillation, and semiconductor detectors. These are described in detail in Chapter 19. (They detect ionizing radiation, of which x-rays are an example.) Geiger tubes are simple to operate and do not require highly stabilized electronic circuitry. However, they have two principal disadvantages: first, the counting loss (nonlinear response) is significant even at moderate x-ray intensities because of the relatively long dead-time between counts; second, discrimination of x-ray energies is not possible.

The spectral sensitivity of proportional detectors is similar to that of Geiger counters, but proportional detectors can be used at relatively high counting rates (high x-ray intensities), since the dead-time is small. Also, the output voltage of this detector is proportional to the energy of the incident x-ray photon, so that direct energy-discrimination is possible without the need for a dispersing medium. For x-rays longer than 2 Å, the windows of these detectors are very thin organic films of mylar, formvar, or nitrocellulose, all of which have a high transmittance for long-wavelength x-rays. Since these windows are porous, the counting gas is passed in a continuous stream through the detector (*flow-proportional detectors*).

The most generally useful detector in conventional x-ray spectrometry is the scintillation counter, which incorporates a very low dead-time and excellent sensitivity for x-rays of wavelength less than 2 Å. Since the output voltage is proportional to the energy of the incident x-ray photon, electronic pulse-amplitude discrimination can be used to reject x-rays whose energies are sufficiently different from those of the spectral lines being measured. The resolving power of the scintillation counter is approximately one-half to one-third that of the proportional detector. However, a high degree of energy resolution is not generally required in wavelength-dispersion applications, since the discrimination is against higher-order x-rays whose energies are multiple integer values of the desired radiation.

Table 14.2 presents some guidelines for selecting the optimum detector for a specific application using wavelength discrimination or dispersion.

The excellent resolution provided by the more recently developed lithium-drifted silicon [Si(Li)] and germanium [Ge(Li)] semiconductor detectors (see Chap.

TABLE 14.2. *X-Ray Detectors and Guidelines for Use*

Detector	Application
Geiger	Routine control analysis where low counting rates and physical discrimination are adequate.
Flow-proportional	Determination of all elements of atomic number 24 or below.
Proportional	Unique applications where the maximum resolution of a detector is required.
Scintillation	Determination of all elements of atomic number 25 and above.

19) has been a significant breakthrough in x-ray analysis. To obtain optimum pulse-resolution and performance with these solid-state detectors, low-noise preamplifiers and amplifiers are required, in addition to liquid-nitrogen cooling of the detector and the first stage of the preamplifier. Because of their smaller size, greater complexity, and higher cost, the use of semiconductor detectors is generally limited to energy-dispersion applications where the increased resolution is required.

In Figure 14.7, the energy resolution of proportional, scintillation, and semiconductor detectors is compared to wavelength-diffraction resolution. The energy resolution of the three types of detectors has approximately the same slope, that is, it is proportional to the square root of the photon energy. The resolving power of

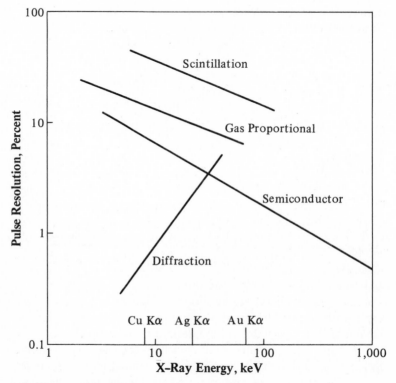

FIGURE 14.7. *Resolution of energy-proportional detectors and of crystal diffraction as a function of photon energy.*

the semiconductor detector is approximately a factor of ten better than that of the scintillation counter and a factor of three better than the gas-proportional detector. For lower energies, the resolution provided by a LiF-crystal (diffraction) spectrometer is a factor of 5 to 10 superior to the best semiconductor detector. With increasing photon energy, the semiconductor detector becomes more favorable and, at high energy, provides superior resolution since high-reflectivity crystals of very low d-spacing are not available.

The initial applications of semiconductors utilized radioisotopic sources (see below); currently the trend is toward direct excitation with low-powered x-ray tubes.

Some advantages of the energy-dispersion semiconductor approach are: simultaneous multi-element analysis, high collection efficiency, no higher-order diffraction lines, and low sensitivity to surface preparation of the sample. In comparison, wavelength dispersion offers superior resolution for most elements, higher count-rate per element, better peak-to-background ratio, and is applicable to the low-energy x-ray region where chemical effects (valence, coordination) can be measured using high-resolution x-ray spectroscopy. There is a wide variety of energy-dispersion systems commercially available, ranging from very simple and compact portable analyzers to completely computerized semiconductor systems.

Energy Dispersion With Radioisotope Sources— Portable Instruments

Until the early 1960s, the application of radioisotopes in x-ray spectroscopy was limited to the calibration of proportional or scintillation detectors. At that time, simple and compact energy-dispersion instruments using radioactive sources were developed for specific applications where resolution and sensitivity requirements are not severe. Radioisotopic sources have a flux 6 to 8 orders of magnitude lower than high-powered sealed x-ray tubes; therefore, any application based on radioisotopic sources must be limited to those energy-dispersion techniques in which there is a close coupling of the radioisotopic sources, the sample, and the detector. These portable analyzers employ the technique of balanced filters to isolate the line of analytical interest. These filters consist of two thin metallic foils with K-absorption edges on the low- and high-energy sides of the x-ray line of interest. For example, as shown in Figure 14.8, the Sn Kα line just exceeds the K edge of the palladium filter, and therefore is absorbed, whereas the Sn Kα x-rays are readily transmitted by the silver foil. The thicknesses of the two filters are carefully controlled so that their

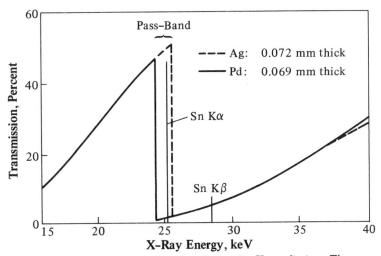

FIGURE 14.8.   *Balanced filters for isolating Sn Kα radiation. The transmission and absorption filters are made of silver and palladium, respectively. From S. H. V. Bowie, A. G. Darnby, and J. R. Rhodes, Trans. Inst. Min., Met. 74, 36 (1964–65), by kind permission of J. R. Rhodes, Columbia Scientific Industries, P.O. Box 9908, Austin, Texas.*

absorption characteristics are virtually the same for all radiation, except in the narrow pass-band. The difference in measured intensity, using first the silver and then the palladium filter, is related to the tin content of the sample. The portable analyzers complement the conventional x-ray spectrometer for process control and field applications, but are not competitive in the laboratory.

Radioactive Sources

Radioisotopes commonly used for energy-dispersion analysis are listed in Table 14.3. Sealed sources of all types are now commercially available. The price of a source depends on the cost of the radioisotope and the complexity of the instrument design.

Alpha emitters such as polonium-210 and curium-242 are used to excite emission of low-energy x-rays. They offer the advantage of large signal-to-background ratio, but the thickness of sample analyzed is extremely small. The alpha emitters are health hazards and generally have very limited application in energy-dispersion analysis.

Beta emitters are used to generate continuum plus characteristic x-rays that collectively excite the sample. These beta sources may be a thin layer of the isotope on a suitable target, or a mechanical or chemical mixture of isotope and target.

Isotopes that decay by K-electron capture emit essentially monoenergetic x-radiation; for example, ^{109}Cd and ^{55}Fe emit Ag K and Mn K x-rays, respectively. Large signal-to-background ratios can be achieved with these "monoenergetic" sources. Many analysts recommend the use of a K-capture isotope whose characteristic radiation just exceeds the absorption edge of the element being determined. This criterion is applicable to wavelength dispersion. However, for energy dispersion one must allow for the poorer resolution of the analytical system, so the criterion must be modified so as to resolve the characteristic x-ray emitted by the sample from the incoherent "Compton radiation" (see Chap. 19) and the coherent scattered incident radiation. To achieve this resolution, the primary x-rays must either be significantly higher in energy than the K or L absorption edge of the element being

TABLE 14.3. *Radioisotopes Commonly Used in Energy-Dispersive X-Ray Analysis*

Radio-isotope	Half-life (years)	Principal Mode of Decay	Principal Radiation
^{55}Fe	2.7	electron capture	Mn K x-rays
^{109}Cd	1.3	electron capture	Ag K x-rays, 88 keV gamma
^{125}I	0.16	electron capture	Te K x-rays, 35 keV gamma
^{3}H/Zr	12.3	β emission	Bremsstrahlung 3–12 keV
^{147}Pm/Al	2.6	β emission	Bremsstrahlung 10–50 keV
^{241}Am	458.0	α emission	Np L x-rays, 26 and 60 keV gamma
^{153}Gd	0.65	electron capture	Eu K x-rays, 97 and 103 keV gamma
^{57}Co	0.74	electron capture	Fe K x-rays, 14, 122, and 136 keV gamma
^{242}Cm	17.6	electron capture	Pu L x-rays
^{238}Pu	86.4	electron capture	U L x-rays

determined, or so close to the edge that the incoherent scatter falls below the energy of the analytical line.

Two examples of source-sample-detector geometries used with beta, gamma, and x-ray emitting isotopes are shown in Figure 14.9. The central source (Fig. 14.9A) is more widely used for portable radioisotopic analyzers than the annular source. The important parameters of the central and annular geometries are the sample-source-detector distances and the relative sizes of the three components. The x-ray filters are usually placed between the source and the detector window. Using the central source, counting rates of 10^3 to 10^5 counts/sec are obtained from pure samples of the element being analyzed. Shielding is provided by a shutter and by the sample.

Gamma emitters are often used in a source-target configuration in which the principal radiation for exciting the sample is the secondary emission from the target.

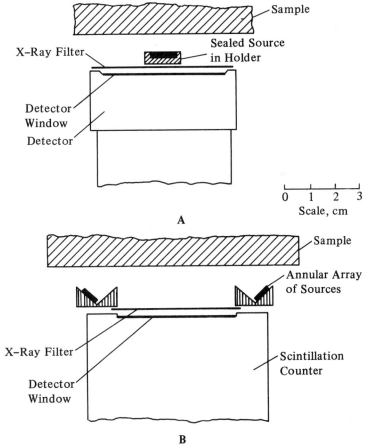

FIGURE 14.9. *Central (A) and annular (B) source geometries used with portable radioisotopic x-ray analyzers. From S. H. V. Bowie, A. G. Darnby, and J. R. Rhodes, Trans. Inst. Min., Met. 74, 36 (1964–65), by kind permission of J. R. Rhodes, Columbia Scientific Industries, P.O. Box 9908, Austin, Texas.*

By appropriate choice of gamma emitter and target, the analyst has available a "monoenergetic" excitation source. There are a number of commercially available source-target assemblies that allow the analyst to easily change the target material. The source, a high-intensity gamma emitter, is positioned in a cup formed by the target element. The high-energy gamma radiation from the source excites characteristic x-rays that are superimposed on a scattered gamma background. Annular source-targets are used extensively with semiconductor detectors. By removing the target and aiming the source directly at the sample, direct excitation of the sample may be utilized. These high-energy gamma photons increase the depth of sample analyzed by a factor of ten or more compared to their lower-energy L lines. Increased penetration into the sample is very important for applications such as analysis of inhomogeneous samples and in situ analyses of ore samples. Thus, particle-size effects, a common problem in the analysis of powdered samples, are reduced by the use of high-atomic-number K radiation.

14.3 PREPARATION OF SAMPLES FOR X-RAY FLUORESCENCE ANALYSIS

X-ray fluorescence spectroscopy is applied to virtually every type of elemental determination encountered by control and research laboratories. The types of samples analyzed include ashes, ores, minerals, ceramics, metals and alloys and films and coatings. The samples may be in the form of powders, solutions, rods, sheets, films, or particulates. The method is, in general, nondestructive; the sample can be retained for other analyses.

Solid samples used in x-ray fluorescence analysis include metallurgical specimens, briquetted powders, and borax discs. For quantitative analysis, both standards and unknowns must be in the same matrix and subjected to the same preparation. Because of the limited escape depth of secondary x-rays, particularly in the long-wavelength region, the surface layers must be representative of the entire sample.

Surface preparation is an essential step in achieving good quantitative results. For metallurgical samples the surface is generally prepared by grinding, followed by polishing. (Etching techniques are not used, since some elements may be preferentially removed from the surface layer.) Particle size and particle-size distribution are very important variables in the analysis of powdered samples. Powdered samples are either processed by adding a small amount of binder and forming into a briquet using high pressure, or by fusing with a suitable flux such as sodium tetraborate and casting the molten sample into a glass disk. Fusion methods are generally preferable to briquetting, as the fused sample is homogeneous on a scale of micrometers, thus eliminating particle-size effects. Also, the fluxing reagent serves as a diluent for the sample, thereby reducing interelement effects.

Solution samples are held in plastic or metallic containers with thin mylar windows transparent to x-rays. The most convenient procedure is to use cup-like containers with 0.006- or 0.02-mm mylar windows, with the sample held in an inverted position over the x-ray tube.

Samples in the gaseous or vapor state require cells with x-ray–transparent windows that can withstand high pressure-differentials. Some type of pressure regulation must be used to maintain the number of atoms in the x-ray beam at a specified level.

Preparation of Samples for Trace Analysis

Trace analyses are conveniently classified into two types: Minor or trace constituents in large samples (e.g., gold in low-grade ores) and major constituents of very small samples (e.g., titanium in a flake of paint). Samples of the first type can be converted to the second by physical or chemical concentration of the desired elements. Limits of detectability for the first type range from 0.1 to 100 ppm, depending on the elements being determined, the overall sample composition, and the complexity of the x-ray spectra. This is a concentration detection limit. Limits of detectability with the second type of sample are expressed in micrograms (generally about 0.01 to 1 μg) and may represent ppm, ppb, or lower concentrations in the original sample, depending on the sensitivity for the element and the size of the starting sample. The minimum amount. detected is an absolute detection limit. Good examples of these sample types that are of environmental concern are aqueous discharges from industrial plants (type 1) and particulates collected on filter disks from air samples (type 2).

For the determination of trace elements in aqueous samples, the best approach is to use ion-exchange techniques to isolate and collect the elements of interest and to provide a sample that can be directly inserted in the x-ray instrument. Using papers impregnated with cation and anion resins (see Chap. 21 regarding strong exchangers), groups of elements can be quantitatively collected from dilute aqueous solutions, as shown in Table 14.4 for anions. These strong-acid and strong-base papers are not selective; therefore, the analyst has to be aware that all the ions present are competing for the available exchange sites. A very high concentration of

TABLE 14.4. *Collection Efficiency of Anions by Paper Impregnated With a Strong Anion-Exchanger*

Anion	Collection efficiency, percent	
	Resin in Cl$^-$ form	Resin in OH$^-$ form
IO$_3^-$	71	90
HPO$_4^{2-}$	76	99
BrO$_3^-$	88	98
Br$^-$	97	>99
VO$_3^-$	98	>99
PtCl$_6^{2-}$	99	>99
SO$_4^{2-}$, Cr$_2$O$_7^{2-}$	>99	>99
CrO$_4^{2-}$, MnO$_4^-$	>99	>99
MoO$_4^{2-}$, Fe(CN)$_6^{4-}$	>99	>99

Note: This data is for SB-2 anion exchange paper, available from H. Reeve-Angel and Company.

one particular ion may "swamp" the ion exchanger, and the particular ion of interest may not be effectively retained.

Other types of exchange media include chelate-resin–loaded paper, reagent-impregnated paper, cellulose-phosphate paper, and cellulose–sulfuric-acid paper. The chelate-resin–loaded and reagent-impregnated papers can selectively collect one or more elements; for example, there is a chelating resin that is highly selective for Hg^{2+}, CH_3Hg^+, Au^{3+}, and some of the platinum-group metals. Other approaches for collecting either groups of elements or individual elements are coprecipitation, wherein the elements of interest are collected on filter paper after treatment with a precipitation reagent, or electrochemical preconcentration by plating onto the surface of a pyrolytic-graphite electrode. Standards are prepared by treating aliquots of known solutions in the same manner as the unknowns. Standards prepared with resin-loaded papers have a very long shelf-life and are easily stored.

When the separation-collection procedure is not quantitative, a radiotracer of the element being determined can be added to the initial sample to serve as a collection monitor. For example, in the determination of gold in low-grade ores, radioactive ^{195}Au is added to the ore prior to dissolution and subsequent collection on chelate-resin–loaded paper. The intensity of the Pt K x-rays from the K-capture decay of the ^{195}Au is a linear function of the fraction of gold collected on the resin-loaded paper. Radiotracers of $^{203}Hg^{2+}$ and $CH_3{}^{203}Hg^+$ are used to determine the collection efficiency for inorganic and organic mercury in aqueous effluents. The actual chemical form in which the mercury is present, as well as the total mercury content, is an important parameter in environmental studies.

In the analysis of particulates in air, the samples are collected by passing measured volumes of air through filter paper (or some other suitable filter media). One method of standardization is to pipette small volumes of solution containing known amounts of the elements to be determined onto the same filter medium. Depending on the energy of the x-ray line and the size of the particulates, there may be systematic errors in the analysis using standards prepared from solutions. Another approach to standardization is to disperse known quantities of elements in the form of finely divided powders onto paper or glass-fiber filters. Problems with this approach include variation in particle size between standards and unknowns, and quantitative collection of the standard powders by the filter.

14.4 QUANTITATIVE X-RAY FLUORESCENCE ANALYSIS

Quantitative analysis is achieved by comparing intensities from unknowns to those from primary or secondary standards. Depending on the degree of similarity between unknown and standard, small or large correction factors may be necessary.

Because of the limited penetration of characteristic x-ray lines from the source, most samples can be assumed to be infinitely thick; that is, the intensity of the measured x-ray fluorescence line will not increase if the sample thickness is increased. For "infinitely" thick samples, the intensity of fluorescence from element x is related to concentration by the relationship

$$I_x = \frac{kW_x}{\mu_{\lambda_1} + \mu_{\lambda_2}} \tag{14.9}$$

where I_x = the measured line intensity

W_x = the weight fraction of the element being determined

μ_{λ_1} = the averaged linear-absorption coefficient of the sample as a whole for the incident radiation λ_1

μ_{λ_2} = the averaged linear-absorption coefficient of the sample as a whole for the fluorescent radiation λ_2

k = a proportionality constant

The value of the averaged linear-absorption coefficient for the sample, μ_s, for any wavelength is equal to the summation of the linear-absorption coefficient of each element x times its weight fraction

$$\mu_s = \sum \mu_i W_i \qquad (14.10)$$

Although Equation 14.9 is oversimplified, the main points are correctly indicated; the measured intensity depends on both the concentration of the element being determined and on the overall composition of the sample. For example, the intensity of the Ag Kα line from various silver ores depends on both the total silver content and the matrix composition (Fig. 14.10). These samples represent matrices containing various amounts of lead, barium, and transition elements, plus minerals

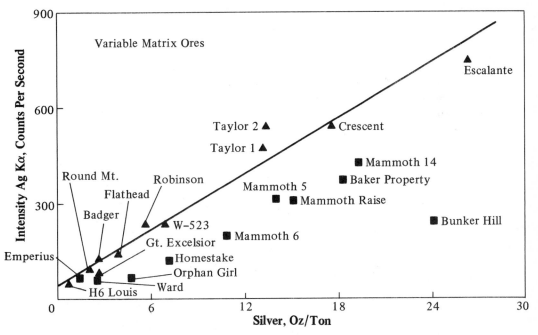

FIGURE 14.10. *Variation in Ag Kα intensity with mineralogical composition.* ▲ = *low-Z matrix;* ■ = *high-Z matrix. The line is a calibration curve derived from silver standards prepared in a silica matrix. From P. G. Burkhalter,* Anal. Chem., *43, 10 (1971), by permission of the publisher. Copyright © 1971 by the American Chemical Society.*

such as quartz and feldspar. Therefore, the analyst must have adequate knowledge regarding the composition of the unknowns, or employ some technique that will minimize the compositional dependence. This dependence, commonly called the matrix effect, is the principal source of systematic error in quantitative x-ray analyses.

Six general procedures are available to reduce or correct for the matrix dependence: comparison standards, internal standards, standard addition, dilution, thin films, and scatter correction. Each of these is discussed below. One essential requirement for both samples and standards in all methods (other than those using thin films) is homogeneity on a micrometer scale because of the low penetration of incident x-ray photons. Other practical factors to be considered for quantitative results include surface preparation and particle-size distribution.

Comparison Standards

The most widely used method of calibration is the comparison of intensities from unknowns with those from standards of similar composition. Obviously, this direct comparison requires knowledge regarding the probable composition of the sample (in industrial-control analyses, for example, the approximate composition of the sample is frequently known). When unknowns and standards are very close in composition, a simple ratio of intensities and composition is adequate, for example

$$\frac{I_u}{I_s} = \frac{c_u}{c_s} \tag{14.11}$$

where the subscripts u and s refer to unknowns and standards, respectively. Applications in which the unknowns vary over a wide range of compositions require the use of graphical or mathematical correction techniques. The present trend in process control is to use simultaneous equations to derive correction factors (for absorption and for enhancement by higher-energy x-rays emitted within the sample). Then, using these correction factors, the composition of the unknown is obtained by a multiple-regression technique. Originally, the mathematical approach was limited to a few laboratories having access to large computers. Nowadays, dedicated computers are an integral part of many modern industrial-control x-ray spectrometers.

Internal Standards

In the internal standardization method, a known concentration of a reference element is added to the sample being analyzed. For x-ray spectroscopy, the reference should have a characteristic radiation that will be excited and absorbed to a similar extent as the characteristic radiation of the element being determined. Therefore, the internal standard is generally an element one atomic number higher or lower than the element being determined. In some instances, it may be necessary to use an element of much higher atomic number and to make use of its L or M radiation, for example Br Kα (11.9 keV) and Au Lβ_1 (11.4 keV).

Regardless of the reference line used, the matrix may affect the relative intensities of the reference and analytical lines in one of the following ways:

1. the matrix will have a slightly higher absorption coefficient for the longer-wavelength line;
2. another element in the matrix will have an absorption edge between the reference line and the analytical line of interest;
3. an emission line from the matrix will preferentially excite the element of lower atomic number.

Classes of samples representing each of these situations are shown graphically in Figure 14.11. The matrix M is considered to be the third element and the symbols X and R represent the element being determined (the unknown) and the reference element, respectively. If the matrix element emits lines L_1 or L_3 or has absorption edges E_1 or E_3, there is no significant preferential absorption or enhancement of either the unknown or reference emission line. In contrast, if the matrix element has an absorption edge at E_2, then X $K\alpha$ is preferentially absorbed by the matrix element so that the internal standard is not applicable. Another source of systematic error is when the matrix element emits a strong line of wavelength L_2, whereby the reference element R is preferentially excited (by absorption at RE). The original sample, of course, must not contain appreciable amounts of the reference element.

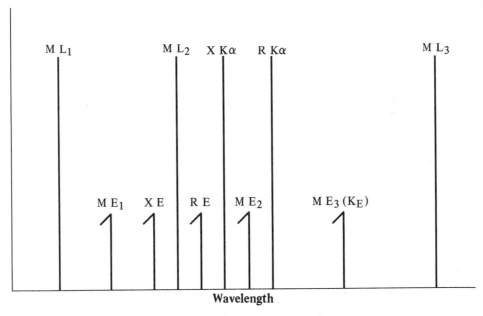

FIGURE 14.11. *Possible interfering lines and absorption edges when using internal standards. M is the matrix element, X is the element being determined, R is the reference element, E_1 represents an absorption edge, K_E is the K absorption edge, and vertical lines represent emission wavelengths.*

Within these limitations, the internal-standard method has enjoyed wide application in mineral and ore processing. It is essential that the reference element be intimately mixed with the sample on a micrometer scale. Various procedures have been used to achieve this blending, such as grinding the sample and reference with an abrasive such as silicon carbide, or by fusion using borax, carbonate, or pyrosulfate as a flux.

Standard Addition

The standard-addition method is similar to the internal-standard method, except that the element being determined serves as the reference standard itself. Analysis is accomplished by measuring the intensity of the characteristic spectral line before and after the addition of a known amount of the element being determined. It is assumed that a linear relationship exists between line intensity and concentration (over a limited concentration range), and that the matrix is not significantly altered by the addition. In general, the addition method is limited to the determination of trace and minor elements. All of the comments regarding sample preparation for internal standards apply directly to the standard-addition approach.

Dilution

One general method of reducing the matrix effect is to dilute standards and unknowns in a common "solvent." With sufficient dilution, the small weight-fraction of the solute makes its contribution to the matrix negligible:

$$\lim_{W_A \to 0} \mu_{\text{sample}} = \mu_{\text{solvent}} \tag{14.12}$$

where W_A = the weight fraction of the sample

As a result of dilution, the element or elements being determined are now present as minor constituents, so the intensity-to-concentration relationship is linear and thus minimizes the matrix effects.

Dilution may be achieved by dissolving the sample in an inorganic or organic solvent (for example, water or chloroform), or by fusing it with a flux (such as borax, carbonate, or pyrosulfate). Another approach is to add a strong absorber of x-rays, such as lanthanum oxide, to the flux to minimize the degree of dilution required to reduce matrix effects; that is, to swamp out the effects of a variable sample matrix. A typical application of the La_2O_3-flux approach is determining copper in a series of ore samples having a variable iron concentration. The dilution plus the strong absorber minimizes the absorption of Cu $K\alpha$ by the iron.

Thin Films

Interelement effects are small or negligible in thin-film samples, because neither the primary nor the secondary x-rays are strongly absorbed. Thus, the intensities of the secondary x-rays are directly proportional to the amount of the element present; matrix effects are minimized by this technique. Because standards and unknowns are prepared in a similar manner, linear comparison of intensities is valid.

In order to prepare thin-film samples, the desired elements must usually be chemically or physically separated from the host compound. The elements being determined are collected in a physical form suitable for x-ray analysis using such methods as ion exchange, solvent extraction, or precipitation. Metallic ions, for example, may be collected on resin-loaded paper, which also serves as the mechanical support in the x-ray spectrometer. The absolute sensitivity for elements isolated from the host compound is 0.01 to 1 μg; analysis of elements present in trace concentrations is possible with this preconcentration approach, if the total sample size is sufficiently large.

Scatter Correction

The basic assumption in the scatter-correction approach is that both scattered source and emitted fluorescence x-rays are subject to similar losses owing to absorption. Therefore, for samples with widely varying matrices, the ratio of emitted to scattered x-ray intensities I_e/I_s is relatively constant. In general, scatter-correction methods significantly improve the reliability of the analytical results, although the ultimate accuracy is poorer than that of other, more reliable, methods such as dilution. Scatter correction is one area where considerably more research is needed.

Accuracy and Precision

The accuracy and precision of the x-ray fluorescence method is related to the care taken in sample preparation, to the stability of the instrument, and ultimately to counting statistics.* With modern instrumentation, minor or major constituents may give counting rates of 10,000 counts/sec or higher above background, so that a relative precision of 0.1% can be achieved in 100-sec counting times. The accuracy of the analyses is related to the similarity of composition between the unknowns and the standards or to the analyst's ability to apply appropriate correction factors. In routine industrial-control applications, a relative analytical accuracy of 1% is not unusual, whereas for many unknown samples the relative accuracy may be 5–10% or poorer. X-ray fluorescence methods can be applied for concentrations ranging from several ppm in favorable cases to essentially 100% by weight. Times are on the order of several minutes or less for control applications (total analytical time may be considerably longer, depending on the amount of sample preparation required).

14.5 SPECIAL TOPICS AND OTHER X-RAY METHODS

Coating and Film-Thickness Determinations

An important application of x-ray spectroscopy in the metallurgical industry is measuring the thickness of coatings or films. The thickness can be calculated by determining either the intensity I_s of the characteristic radiation emitted from the substrate (after being attenuated by the coating) or by measuring the intensity I_f of

---

* The counting error is inversely proportional to the square root of the number of photons counted for each analytical line being measured.

a characteristic line emitted from the coating (see Fig. 14.12). These measurements are correlated to data obtained with coatings of known thickness. Virtually all coating-thickness monitors used in the metallurgical industries are based on such x-ray intensity measurements. The methods are rapid, nondestructive, and can be applied to a variety of coatings and thicknesses; measurements are not affected by physical properties such as hardness or magnetism, and only to a minor or negligible extent by oils used to protect metal surfaces. Compared to wavelength dispersion, the energy-dispersion analyzers using radioisotopic sources of x-rays or gamma rays have the advantages of compactness, reduced maintenance, stability, lower price, and can be used with much lower radiation fluxes.

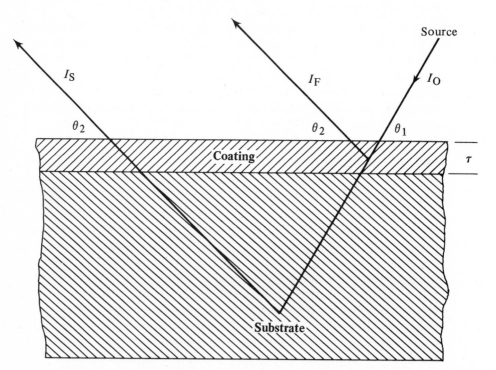

FIGURE 14.12. *Film-thickness measurements using characteristic x-rays emitted by the coating or the substrate.*

A typical "thickness gauge" of this type will measure an area of 40 cm² with a repeatability of 1%. The measurement ranges for tin and zinc gauges using different sources are given in Table 14.5. Errors due to changes in hardness, chemical composition, and thickness are less than 0.3%.

One of the first important applications of x-rays to the measurement of the thickness of coatings was in the control of tin plate on steel, using attenuation of the Fe Kα line. The incident radiation may be either polychromatic or monochromatic (the latter makes isolation of the signal from background easier). However, it is essential that the primary radiation be of sufficient energy to excite the substrate. In the example of tin on steel, x-rays or γ-rays in the 10 to 25 keV range will excite

TABLE 14.5. *Typical Instrument Specifications for Determining Tin and Zinc Plating Thickness*

	Electrolytic Tin	Hot-Dipped Zinc	Electrolytic Zinc
Measurement Range (One Side of Sample)	1–15 g/m²	60–450 g/m²	5–30 g/m²
Approximate Plating Thickness	0.1–2 μm	8–60 μm	0.7–4 μm
Preferred Source and Energy	^{241}Am 17 keV Secondary γ-rays	^{241}Am 60 keV γ-rays	^{241}Am 17 keV Secondary γ-rays

Source: Adapted from J. F. Cameron and C. G. Clayton, *Radioisotope Instruments*, New York: Pergamon Press, 1971, by permission of the publisher.

Fe K lines without exciting the characteristic Sn K lines. Referring to Figure 14.12, the coating thickness τ is related to the intensity I_s from the substrate by

$$\frac{I_s}{I_{s(\tau = 0)}} = e^{-(\mu_1 \csc \theta_1 + \mu_2 \csc \theta_2)\tau} \qquad (14.13)$$

where $\quad I_{s(\tau = 0)}$ = the intensity when coating thickness equals 0
$\quad \mu_1$ = the linear-absorption coefficient (in cm^{-1}) of the coating for the primary radiation
$\quad \mu_2$ = the linear-absorption coefficient of the coating for the secondary radiation
$\quad \tau$ = the coating thickness in cm

Example 14.2. Calculate the thickness (τ) in μm of a tin coating ($\rho = 7.3$ g/cm³) deposited uniformly on an iron substrate, using Equation 14.13. Use the following parameters: Cu Kα (1.54 Å) as the monochromatic source; Fe Kα (1.93 Å) as the secondary radiation; $\theta_1 = \theta_2 = 45°$; and the measured value $I_s/I_{s(\tau = 0)} = 0.50$.

Solution: The magnitude of τ will depend on the values of μ_m, the *mass absorption coefficient*, $\mu_m = \mu/\rho$ where ρ is the density of the material. The following values were taken from the *Handbook of Chemistry and Physics*: (1) μ_m for tin = 247 at 1.54 Å; (2) μ_m for tin = 470 at 1.93 Å.

$$\mu_1 = \mu_{(m, 1.54 Å)}\rho = 247 \, (7.3) = 1800 \text{ cm}^{-1}$$
$$\mu_2 = \mu_{(m, 1.93 Å)}\rho = 470 \, (7.3) = 3400 \text{ cm}^{-1}$$

Substituting these values, and noting that csc 45° = 1.41:

$$0.50 = e^{-[1800\,(1.41) + 3400\,(1.41)]\tau} = e^{-7300\tau}$$
$$-0.69 = -7300\tau$$
$$\tau = 9.4 \times 10^{-5} \text{ cm} = 0.94 \, \mu\text{m}$$

An important point from the problem is that input parameters will vary 2–10 percent or more; therefore, the reliability of the calculated value is related proportionally. The range of thicknesses over which this method can be used is determined primarily by the average value of μ_1 and μ_2. The higher the value of μ, the smaller the range of thicknesses that can be measured. In the case of electroplated tin on steel, the usual range is 0.1–2.5 μm.

Most determinations of coating thickness are based on measurements of characteristic radiation from the coating. The thickness can be considered to fall into one of three regions: linear, exponential, and infinite thickness. In the linear region, absorption of the incident and fluorescent radiation by the very thin coating is negligible; therefore, the intensity is linearly related to the coating thickness. For films of intermediate thickness, the intensity is an exponential function of thickness. As the thickness approaches infinity, the intensity becomes constant.

A typical example of the use of characteristic radiation is measuring the thickness of nickel coatings on steel. The function of the nickel is to provide a thin, but strong, bond between an enamel or porcelain coating and the steel substrate. Current practice in the enamel-coating industry is to cut samples from the sheet and submit them to the x-ray laboratory. With a portable analyzer, however, satisfactory results can be obtained by semiskilled personnel directly on the sheets.

Energy-dispersion x-ray spectroscopy has received considerable attention for the determination of lead on interior walls of houses in the inner cities of the United States (ingestion of lead-bearing paints is a significant health hazard to young children). The highly penetrating Pb K radiation is used for these measurements, since the lower-energy Pb L lines may be absorbed in overlayers of nonlead paints, giving a false negative reading.

Positive-Ion Excitation

The use of highly energetic positive ions for the generation of low- and medium-energy characteristic x-rays from samples is receiving considerable attention for applications in surface-structure analysis and in the environmental sciences. The important features of positive-ion excitation are the high sensitivity for low-atomic-number elements, the small depth of sample analyzed, and the relatively low level of continuous radiation scattered from the sample. Generally, protons in the 100-keV to 5-MeV range are used; however, alpha particles and higher-atomic-number positive ions have some unique advantages.

In surface studies, particularly in the fields of corrosion and thin-film technology, low-energy x-ray spectra generated by 100- to 300-keV protons are used in conjunction with Auger and photoelectron spectroscopy (Chap. 15) to analyze changes in the surface caused by implantation, oxidation, diffusion, etc. Fractions of a monolayer of various elements on the surface can be determined by this new analytical technique. The sampling depth is of the order of 1–5 monolayers using protons for excitation of low-energy x-rays. Depth profiles can be obtained by sputtering successive monolayers and analyzing the new surface. The beam diameter can be reduced to approximately 1 mm if spatial resolution is required.

For trace applications, microgram amounts of sample are supported on a very thin substrate. The detection limits for most elements using a 1.5-MeV proton beam at 5 μA current are of the order of 10^{-9} to 10^{-12} g, the detection limit being a function of the thickness of the support material. Trace applications include examination of water residues, biological specimens, tissue sections, and air particulates.

Electron-Probe Microanalysis

In the early 1940s, Hillier of the Radio Corporation of America conceived the idea of using a focused electron beam for localized x-ray spectroscopic analysis. Several years later, the first practical electron-probe x-ray spectrometer was designed by Castaing at the University of Paris. This microanalyzer proved to be a major breakthrough, since the instrument made possible the nondestructive analysis of micrometer-sized volumes.

In *electron-probe x-ray spectroscopy* (EPXS), an electron beam of moderate energy, 10 to 50 keV, is focused on the sample at the location where elemental composition is to be determined. The atoms in a minute volume, one-half to several μm in diameter and one or more μm in depth, are excited by the incident electrons and, upon returning to the ground state, emit x-rays characteristic of the excited elements. The actual volume of sample analyzed depends on such variables as the diameter and energy of the electron beam, the diffusion of electrons in the sample, and the path length of the scattered primary and secondary x-rays.

Until the late 1960s, commercial EPXS instruments consisted of four major components: an electron-optical system for producing a stable electron beam of 1-μm (or smaller) diameter, light optics for viewing the microscopic area under investigation, a precision stage for accurately locating and translating the sample under the electron beam, and one or more focusing x-ray spectrometers for measuring the characteristic x-rays (see Fig. 14.13). More recently, EPXS has been superseded by *scanning electron microscopy* (SEM). In the scanning electron microscope, the sample image is obtained by either backscattered or transmitted electrons, and the elemental composition is determined by energy-dispersion x-ray methods.

Quantitative analysis is accomplished by the use of standards similar in composition to the sample being analyzed, or by using pure elements as standards and applying theoretical and semiempirical corrections for differences in absorption, secondary fluorescence, and atomic number. The mathematical methods using pure-element standards have received the greatest attention because of the difficulty in obtaining multi-element standards that are homogeneous on a submicrometer scale. Computer programs are available for performing the complex corrections. Since the development of SEM, it has been realized that qualitative or semiquantitative analysis is adequate for many practical applications. Therefore, pictorial displays of concentration across the sample surface, obtained by sweeping the electron beam across the sample, are generally adequate, as contrasted to the older technique of point-by-point analysis.

For most elements, the sensitivity of the EPXS method is approximately 0.01–0.1 weight-percent with a relative accuracy of 1–5 percent, depending on the correction procedure, the availability of suitable standards, and the reliability of the parameters used in the calculations. Elements from boron, atomic number 5, to all higher-atomic-number elements can be determined. Although the EPXS method is not applicable to trace elements in a homogeneous sample, its absolute detection limit—10^{-12} to 10^{-14} g—is very impressive.

The EPXS or modified SEM methods have been applied extensively to virtually all fields of science. Applications include the qualitative identification of the composition of small inclusions, determination of diffusion rates of elements in solids,

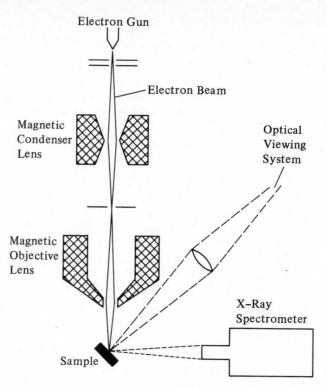

FIGURE 14.13. *Electron optics for the excitation of x-rays in a micro-meter-sized volume.*

phase-equilibria studies, the determination of the thickness and uniformity of films, and the qualitative and quantitative analysis of minute samples such as airborne particulates. Specific applications include the study of the metallic phases in meteorites, the depletion of uranium in the grain boundaries of iron alloys, the diffusion of chromium during oxidation of steels, and inorganic inclusions in oil shale.

Essentially all types of samples can be analyzed by this technique. Ideally, samples should be good electrical conductors to avoid charge buildup; however, a very thin conducting film, for example gold or carbon, can be deposited on nonconductors such as ceramics, glasses, and biological samples.

X-Ray Absorption Spectroscopy

The intensity of an x-ray beam is attenuated (decreased) during passage through matter by a dual process—*photoelectric absorption* and *x-ray scattering*. The amount of attenuation can serve as the basis of quantitative analysis in specific cases. In photoelectric absorption, virtually all of the energy of the incident x-ray quantum is converted into the kinetic energy of the photoelectron ejected; this is the process that results in the emission of characteristic (fluorescence) x-rays. The extent of attenuation is governed by the linear-absorption coefficient μ, which is similar to *absorptivity* in molecular absorption (Beer's law). For a given element, this is equal to the sum of the photoelectric-absorption coefficient τ and the scattering coefficient σ.

Photoelectric absorption predominates, except for low values of Z and high values of λ. By application of Beer's law, x-ray transmittance (P/P_0) can be used to determine either composition or thickness:

$$\frac{P}{P_0} = e^{-\mu_m \rho b} \tag{14.14}$$

where μ_m = the mass absorption coefficient
  ρ = the density of the sample in g/cm³
  b = the thickness in cm

Values for the mass-absorption coefficient, which is equal to μ/ρ, are listed in standard reference tables. As a first approximation, μ_m is proportional to $Z^4\lambda^3$ up to the K or L absorption edge; thus, the absorption coefficient is dependent on both the element composition and the wavelength of the x-ray (see Fig. 14.14). As mentioned before, there can be one K-absorption edge, three L edges, and five M edges.

FIGURE 14.14. *Relationship of the mass-absorption coefficient to wavelength.*

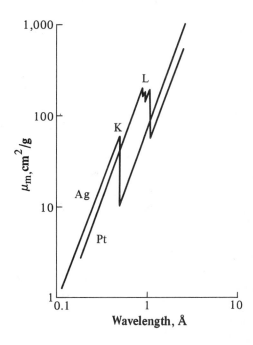

X-ray absorption measurements have been utilized for two types of analytical applications. The principal application has been for process monitoring in which the sample composition is essentially constant except for a variable amount of the element of interest. Examples are tetraethyl lead in gasoline or sulfur in fuel oil, where intense continuous radiation provides adequate signal for instantaneous process control. This approach, using a polychromatic source, has essentially no specificity, so that the sample parameters are very limited. Unknown samples can be analyzed by measurement of two monochromatic x-ray line intensities, one on each side of a characteristic absorption edge of the element being determined. This absorption-edge technique is then specific for the element being determined.

Quantitative calculations when there is more than one absorber are based on the additive absorption of different elements. The mass-absorption coefficient of a sample containing different elements is given by an equation similar to Equation 14.10.

$$\mu_{m(s)} = \sum_{i=1}^{j} \mu_{m(i)} W_i \qquad (14.15)$$

where $\mu_{m(i)}$ = the mass-absorption coefficients (in cm^2/g) of the individual elements m(i) at the given wavelength

W_i = the weight fractions of the elements

Strictly speaking, this equation holds only for monochromatic light. The sensitivity for a given element depends markedly on the sample composition. Very small concentrations of elements with large mass-absorption coefficients can be determined in samples where the bulk matrix has a low mass-absorption coefficient. Thus, for example, 10^{-10} g of phosphorus can be determined in biological tissues. Classical examples of quantitative x-ray absorption analysis are the determination of lead tetraethyl in gasoline and sulfur in petroleum.

Example 14.3. A 3.00-ml gasoline sample is placed in a cell of 0.250-cm thickness. The sample, which contains a small amount of lead tetraethyl in n-octane and has a density of 0.720 g/cm^3, absorbs 75.0% of the Cu Kα line from an x-ray source. If the mass-absorption coefficients ($\mu_m = \mu/\rho$) for the Cu Kα line for lead, carbon, and hydrogen are 230 cm^2/g, 4.52 cm^2/g, and 0.48 cm^2/g, respectively, what is the percent of lead tetraethyl in the sample?

Solution: We must first calculate the mass-absorption coefficients for the two compounds present and then for the sample. Then we can calculate the weight fraction of lead tetraethyl. The formula weight of lead tetraethyl, $Pb(CH_2CH_3)_4$, is 323.4, so

$$W_{Pb} = \frac{207.2}{323.4} = 0.6407$$

$$W_C = \frac{8(12.011)}{323.4} = 0.2971$$

$$W_H = \frac{20(1.0080)}{323.4} = 0.06234$$

Therefore, for lead tetraethyl

$$\mu_{m(LTE)} = 230(0.641) + 4.52(0.297) + 0.48(0.062)$$
$$= 149 \text{ cm}^2/\text{g}.$$

The formula weight of n-octane, $CH_3(CH_2)_6CH_3$, is 114.23, so

$$W_C = \frac{8(12.011)}{114.23} = 0.8412$$

$$W_H = \frac{18(1.0080)}{114.23} = 0.1588$$

Therefore, for octane,

$$\mu_{m(o)} = 4.52(0.841) + 0.48(0.159) = 3.88 \text{ cm}^2/\text{g}.$$

We can calculate the mass-absorption coefficient for the sample, $\mu_{m(s)}$, from Equation 14.14,

$$\log \frac{100}{25.0} = \frac{\mu_{m(s)}(0.720)(0.250)}{2.303}$$

$$\mu_{m(s)} = 7.70 \text{ cm}^2/\text{g}.$$

Let W be the weight fraction of lead tetraethyl in the sample. Therefore,

$$\mu_{m(s)} = \mu_{m(LTE)}W + \mu_{m(o)}(1 - W)$$
$$7.70 = 149W + 3.88(1 - W)$$
$$W = 0.0264 \text{ wt. fraction of tetraethyl.}$$

Therefore, the sample contains 2.64% lead tetraethyl.

Mass-absorption coefficients at different wavelengths for the various elements are available in various handbooks such as those in the bibliography at the end of this chapter. As in conventional spectrophotometry (Chap. 7), the optimum absorbance range for x-ray absorption analysis is about 0.1 to 1.

Although specific examples like those mentioned above are well suited for x-ray absorption analysis, with good selectivity using the absorption-edge technique, in general the method does not offer significant advantages over x-ray fluorescence analysis. Since the latter technique is easier to apply, it is more widely used.

X-Ray Emission Spectroscopy

In this technique, the sample to be studied is the target of an electron beam in an x-ray tube; x-rays are emitted by the sample and are measured. Metals and alloys can be studied in this way. Measurements are generally restricted to qualitative or, at best, semiquantitative determinations. Selective volatilization of different elements by the impinging electron beam make quantitative analysis difficult.

X-Ray Powder Diffraction Analysis

Although x-ray diffraction by single crystals is a useful technique for determining crystal structure, a more useful analytical technique is *powder* diffraction; the sample crystals are ground to a powder, after which the diffraction pattern can readily be used to identify unknown substances, based on tables of known diffraction patterns.

The powdered sample (200–300 mesh) in the form of a cylinder is placed in the path of a narrow beam of essentially monochromatic x-rays. The diffraction pattern is recorded on a photographic film at right angles to the incident beam. The powder contains fine, randomly oriented crystals. Hence, the requirements of Equation 14.7 (the proper θ) are fulfilled by many of these crystal orientations. The random orientation results in a circular cone of diffracted beam for a given reflecting plane with the incident beam as the axis. Since there are planes at different angles in the crystal, several different cones are observed. The film strip is too narrow to

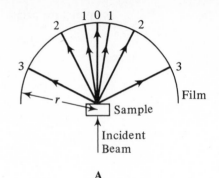

FIGURE 14.15. *Typical x-ray powder diffraction pattern. The numbers represent opposite arcs of the same cone. A: The instrumental arrangement. B: The developed film strip. The radius of the film is r; the S's are the distances between the arcs of a given cone.*

A

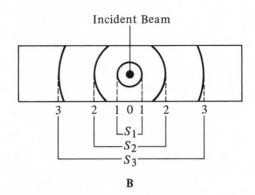

B

record the entire circle of the cone impinging upon it, so the developed film contains curved lines marking the intersection of the various cones with the film (see Fig. 14.15).

The film strip is placed circularly (either half or full circle) around the sample, which is at the origin. For this geometry,

$$4\theta = \frac{S}{r} \tag{14.16}$$

where r = the radius of the film
         S = the distance between the two recorded arcs of a given cone of diffracted x-rays
         θ = the angle of diffraction in radians

Converting from radians to degrees (1 radian = 57.296 degrees),

$$4\theta = \frac{S}{r}(57.296) \tag{14.17}$$

If r is set as a multiple or fraction of 57.296, measurement of θ becomes simple. For example, camera diameters are often set at 57.296 mm, so

$$S = 2\theta \tag{14.18}$$

where S is in millimeters.

Diffraction patterns are usually identified from the three most intense lines by comparing the distances between lines and their relative intensities with standard catalogued spectra.

Example 14.4. Using a camera with a diameter of 57.296 mm and a Cu Kα 1.54-Å (first-order) source, diffraction lines are observed with the following distances between their arcs: 28.66 mm, 52.20 mm, and 82.08 mm. Comparing with the x-ray data in tables listed in the bibliography, what is the probable compound?

Solution: From Equation 14.18, we calculate

$$\theta_1 = \frac{28.66}{2} = 14.33°$$

$$\theta_2 = \frac{52.20}{2} = 26.10°$$

$$\theta_3 = \frac{82.08}{2} = 42.04°$$

Therefore, from Equation 14.7,

$$d_1 = \frac{1.54}{2\sin(14.33)} = 3.04 \text{ Å}$$

$$d_2 = \frac{1.54}{2\sin(26.10)} = 1.75 \text{ Å}$$

$$d_3 = \frac{1.54}{2\sin(42.04)} = 1.15 \text{ Å}$$

From comparison of measured and tabulated d-values, the substance is probably cesium bromide.

Cameras are calibrated by running the spectrum of a substance (such as sodium chloride) with accurately known d-values. A commonly used x-ray source is the Cu Kα doublet at 1.54 Å with the Kβ line filtered out by a nickel foil. Some elements exhibit x-ray fluorescence upon irradiation by the Cu Kα line, which causes fogging of the film, so another target of longer wavelength is chosen for the x-ray source. Although resolution increases with wavelength, lines of x-rays longer than 2–3 Å tend to be scattered by air and lose their sharpness. It should be remembered that the angles 2θ are dependent upon the wavelength of the diffracted radiation. The absorption paths, and consequently the relative intensities, also vary with the wavelength of the source. The tabulated d-values are within 0.001 Å for d of 1 Å or less, but may vary by 0.01–0.05 Å for d up to 8 Å.

The cylindrical sample is kept as small as possible to minimize the absorption of diffracted radiation. The optimum thickness is $1/\mu_m\rho$, where ρ is the sample density. Cylinders are generally kept at 0.5-mm or less diameter. When dilution is necessary, an amorphous substance such as flour is used as the diluent. It is best that the cylindrical sample not be in a container, but in many cases this is not possible. Satisfactory container materials include lithium borate ("Lindemann" glass) or various plastics because of their low mass-absorption coefficients; the container is a tube with a wall-thickness of about 0.01-mm.

Although quantitative measurements can be made, x-ray powder diffraction is used primarily as a qualitative tool to obtain information about the actual compounds appearing in a sample. Selectivity and sensitivity will depend on the composition of the sample; identification of minor components will be rather limited because of the overlap of their diffraction patterns with weak lines of the various major constituents.

It is more convenient nowadays to use a direct-recording x-ray diffraction spectrometer for powder-diffraction measurements than to use film detection. The detector (for instance, a scintillation counter) is placed on a goniometer and slowly rotated about the sample. The intensity of diffracted radiation is recorded on chart paper as a function of the angle of rotation; the resultant spectrum is a series of peaks at different angles. These and their relative intensities are correlated with the tabulated *d*-values.

SELECTED BIBLIOGRAPHY

Books

Advances in X-Ray Analysis, Proceedings of the Annual Conference on Applications of X-Ray Analysis, University of Denver, vols. 1–16. New York: Plenum Press, 1958–1973.

BERTIN, E. P. *Principles and Practices of X-Ray Spectrometric Analysis*. New York: Plenum Press, 1970.

BIRKS, L. S. *Electron Probe Microanalysis*. New York: Interscience, 1963.

JENKINS, R., and DEVRIES, J. L. *Practical X-Ray Spectrometry*. Phillips Technical Library, New York: Springer-Verlag, 1967.

JENKINS, R. *An Introduction to X-Ray Spectrometry*. New York: Heyden, 1974.

JENKINS, R. H., and DEVRIES, B. *Worked Examples in X-Ray Spectrometry*. New York: Springer-Verlag, 1970. *An excellent set of problems for students.*

LIEBHAFSKY, H. A.; PFEIFFER, H. G.; WINSLOW, E. H.; and ZEMANY, P. D. *X-Rays, Electrons, and Analytical Chemistry*. New York: Wiley-Interscience, 1972.

Tables of Wavelengths, 2θ Angles, Photon Energies, and Mass-Absorption Coefficients

BEARDEN, J. A. *X-Ray Wavelengths*. U.S. Atomic Energy Commission Report, N.Y.O. 10586, 1964.

FINE, S., and HENDEE, C. F. "A Table of X-Ray K and L Emission and Critical-Absorption Energies for All the Elements." *Nucleonics*, *13*(3), 36 (1955).

STAINER, H. M. *X-Ray Absorption Coefficients: A Literature Survey*. Bureau of Mines Information Circular 8166, 1963.

WHITE, E. W.; GIBBS, G. V.; JOHNSON, G. G., Jr., and ZECHMAN, G. A., Jr. *X-Ray Emission Line Wavelength and Two-Theta Tables*. ASTM Series 37. Philadelphia: American Society for Testing and Materials, 1965.

SWITZER, G.; AXELROD, J. M.; LINDBERG, M. L.; and LARSEN, E. S. *Tables of Spacing for Angle 2θ, Cu Kα, Cu Kα₁, Cu Kα₂, Fe Kα, Fe Kα₁, Fe Kα₂*. Circular 29, Geological Survey, Washington, D.C.: U.S. Department of the Interior, 1948.

Sources of Standards

Catalog of Standard Reference Materials. Special Publication 260. Washington, D.C.: National Bureau of Standards, 1975.

Standard Reference Materials and Meaningful Measurements. 6th Materials Research Symposium, National Bureau of Standards, Washington, D.C.

Report on Available Standard Samples and Related Materials for Spectrochemical Analysis. Special Technical Publication 58-D. Philadelphia: American Society for Testing and Materials, 1960.

PROBLEMS

1. You have been asked to determine low concentrations of tantalum and niobium in an ore concentrate in which the tantalum-to-niobium ratio is 1:50. Discuss methods to achieve maximum fluorescence signal from tantalum with minimum interference from niobium.

2. Using wavelength dispersion, which detector would you use for the x-ray fluorescence measure of Si $K\alpha$, U $M\alpha$, Cu $K\alpha$, and I $K\alpha$?

3. For the determination of 1–10 weight-percent lead in an ore concentrate, what elements and characteristic lines can be used as internal standards for x-ray fluorescence?

4. An analytical laboratory was requested to determine potassium (present as KCl) in a silica matrix. Suggest some possible approaches to the problem.

5. Discuss methods for determining the thickness of a zinc coating on a iron substrate; include discussion on the preparation of standards and on calibration.

6. Outline a method for calculating the energies of the $K\alpha$ and $L\alpha$ lines of plutonium ($Z = 94$).

7. Discuss methods for extending the limits of detectability of x-ray fluorescence spectroscopy down to the ppm–ppb range. Also include comments regarding possible sources of systematic errors.

8. Describe the operation of a Coolidge tube.

9. What is an absorption edge?

10. Describe the principles of x-ray emission, x-ray absorption, and x-ray fluorescence analysis. Distinguish between each technique with respect to instrumentation requirements.

11. A powder-diffraction x-ray spectrometer uses a Cu $K\alpha$ x-ray source (1.54 Å, first-order). The spectrum of an unknown pure substance gives three intense peaks at the following 2θ values: 25.70°, 40.50°, and 31.38°. The relative intensities of the three peaks are 100:40:35, respectively. What is the probable substance?

12. An analyst, using an x-ray fluorescence spectrometer with a molybdenum target source and a sodium-chloride analyzer crystal, wishes to determine nickel in a meteorite sample. At what 2θ value would he look for the nickel peak?

13. A powdered ammonium thiosulfate sample was given to a student as an unknown. The diffraction pattern was obtained using a camera with a radius of 57.3 mm and using a cobalt x-ray source with an iron filter. What would be the distances between corresponding arcs of the three strongest lines?

14. Using a tungsten x-ray tube and a LiF analyzing crystal ($d = 2.01$ Å), a very strong x-ray fluorescence peak for a pure but unknown metal was observed at $2\theta = 69.36°$. Calculate the wavelength of the fluorescence radiation and identify the metal.

15. An x-ray tube with a copper target is operated at 50 kV. What will be the cutoff wavelength for the continuous radiation?

16. Calculate the transmittance of a monochromatic x-ray beam from a copper target ($K\alpha$ line) passing through a 1 cm³ sample of carbon tetrachloride in benzene (1% by weight) contained in a cell with a cross-sectional area of 9.80 cm². The density of the solution is 0.880 g/cm³.

15

Electron Spectroscopy

Lo I Yin
Isidore Adler

In recent years there has been a rapid development of instrumental techniques; one of the fastest growing areas is that of electron spectroscopy. This is a technique for studying the energy distribution of electrons ejected from a material that has been irradiated with a source of ionizing radiation such as x-rays, ultraviolet light, or electrons.

It is convenient to distinguish among the various electron spectroscopies on the basis of the excitation sources used. When x-ray radiation is employed, the technique is commonly called ESCA [1] (for *electron spectroscopy* for *chemical analysis*); it is also sometimes called *x-ray photoelectron spectroscopy* (XPS). When ultraviolet excitation is used, the method is generally called *photoelectron spectroscopy* (PES) or *ultraviolet photoelectron spectroscopy* (UPS). A third variation, in which electrons are generally used as the ionizing radiation, is commonly referred to as *Auger spectroscopy*.

Of the three types of electron spectroscopy, ESCA has perhaps been the most widely used for chemical studies. For this reason, this chapter will concentrate most heavily on ESCA. Although simple quantitative chemical analysis can be performed by ESCA, this probably represents the least effective use of this powerful tool, which provides quantitative information about such basic parameters as binding energies, charges, valence states, etc., which involve the atom as a function of its chemical environment.

We thank S. O. Grim, Professor of Chemistry at the University of Maryland, for many helpful discussions.

15.1 PRINCIPLES OF ELECTRON SPECTROSCOPY

A unique quality of ESCA is that it permits direct probing of the valence and core electrons, where much chemical information is contained. This is achieved mainly through the photoelectric process: when any material is bombarded by photons with energy greater than the binding energy of an electron in a given atomic shell or subshell, there is a finite probability that the incident photon will be absorbed by the atom and an atomic electron either promoted to an unoccupied level or ejected as a photoelectron. Figure 15.1 illustrates schematically the process of photoelectron production by absorption of a photon. The probability of photoelectric absorption

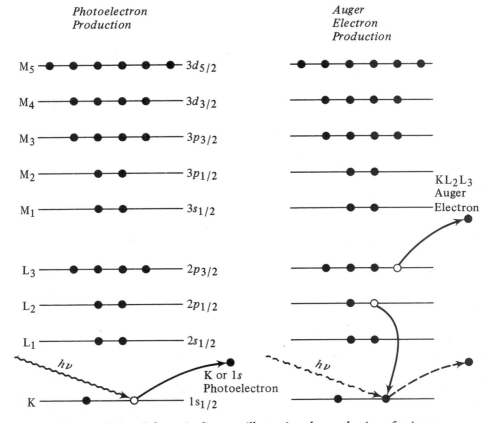

FIGURE 15.1. *Schematic diagram illustrating the production of primary photoelectrons and Auger (secondary) electrons in an atom. In primary-photoelectron production, an atom absorbs an x-ray photon that causes the ejection of a core electron (in this case, a K-shell electron). An Auger electron is produced when,* after *the primary photoelectron has been ejected from the inner shell (indicated by the dotted lines), an electron from a higher shell (in this case, from the L shell) fills the orbital vacancy. The excess energy, instead of being emitted as a secondary x-ray, is simultaneously transferred to another electron (the Auger electron) which is ejected from the atom; in this case the Auger electron is also from the L shell.*

depends on the energy of the incident photon and the atomic number of the element being irradiated.

The kinetic energy of the photoelectron is, to a first approximation (ignoring solid-state and relaxation effects), given by

$$E_p = h\nu - E_b \tag{15.1}$$

where E_p = the kinetic energy of the photoelectron
           $h\nu$ = the energy of the incident photon
           E_b = the binding energy of the electron in its particular shell

It is clear from Equation 15.1 that, if the incident photons are "monoenergetic," the photoelectrons ejected from a given shell will also be monoenergetic. Thus, at a given energy of the incident photons, the photoelectron spectrum of a material reflects the various occupied electronic levels and bands in the material.

Because the energies of the various electronic levels are usually different among different materials, photoelectron spectra are characteristic of the material. It is important to emphasize that the photoelectrons possess characteristic energies as they leave the atom, but that only a relatively small fraction of the electrons emerge from the target material with their energies undisturbed, since energy is lost by a variety of mechanisms.

Figure 15.2 illustrates the excitation of a solid sample by x-ray photons. Although the x-rays may penetrate deeply into the sample to produce photoelectrons, most of these electrons lose energy in numerous inelastic collisions; only those atoms residing in the top few monolayers give rise to undistorted photoelectron spectra. Thus, a typical spectrum resulting from a group of initially monoenergetic photo-electrons will consist of a single peak due to the "undisturbed" electrons (i.e., those that are directly ejected), plus a large continuum on the low-kinetic-energy side of the peak. Since the typical escape depth in ESCA and Auger spectroscopy is only about 3–50 Å, these are truly techniques for surface analysis.

The electron continuum, however, does not begin at the photoelectron peak but rather at a discrete distance away from the peak. This is because an electron emerging from a solid loses its kinetic energy in quantized amounts by exciting plasma oscillations (plasmons). For example, Figure 15.3A shows a wide-range scan (170–1480 eV) of a germanium sample. The x-axis is the kinetic energy of the electrons (E_p). For the purpose of display, the electron counts (intensity) are compressed into a logarithmic scale on the y-axis. We see the photoelectrons from the various L and M shells as well as the LMM Auger-electron lines.* We also note a small, broad shoulder at the same distance (~ 17 eV) from the low-energy side of each peak. This is the plasma-loss peak, which is common to all electrons (whether photo-electrons or Auger electrons) emerging from the solid sample. In Figure 15.3B, two of the more prominent electron lines are shown in detail, with electron intensity displayed linearly on the y-axis. In this case, the plasma-loss peaks are situated far enough from the main peak to allow the precise positions of the various electron

---

*An LMM Auger electron is one emitted by the following mechanism: A vacancy, initially created in the *L shell* by the photoejection of an electron, is filled by the fall of an M-shell electron, accompanied by the ejection of another *M-shell* electron from the atom. The second M-shell electron is the LMM Auger electron.

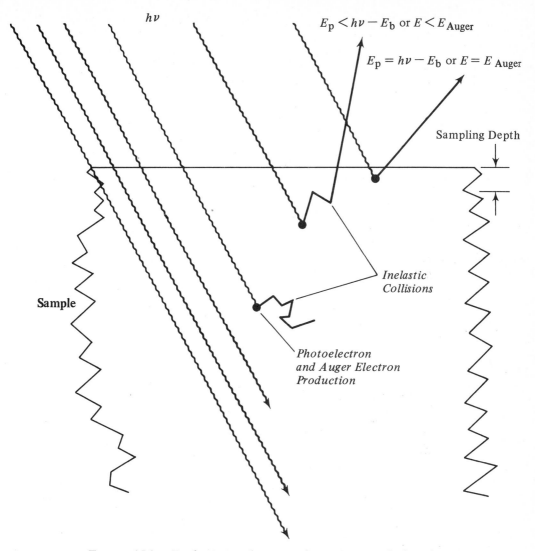

$h\nu$

$E_p < h\nu - E_b$ or $E < E_{Auger}$

$E_p = h\nu - E_b$ or $E = E_{Auger}$

Sampling Depth

Sample

Inelastic
Collisions

Photoelectron
and Auger Electron
Production

FIGURE 15.2. *Production and escape characteristics of photoelectrons and Auger electrons in a solid sample. Because most electrons lose energy by inelastic collisions, the effective sampling depth is about 3–50 Å. E_p is the kinetic energy of the ejected photoelectron and E_b is its binding energy; $h\nu$ is the (monoenergetic) energy of the incident x-ray photon. In the case of Auger electrons, E_{Auger} is its original kinetic energy and E is that seen by the spectrometer.*

lines to be identified unambiguously. However, plasma-loss peaks can occasionally cause confusion in the identification of fine structure associated with some electron lines.

Because the positions of photoelectron lines can be precisely determined from these spectra, and the photoelectron energies are characteristic of the atomic levels of a given element, these energies can be used as the basis for elemental identification.

On closer examination, one finds that the kinetic energy of the "undisturbed" emerging photoelectrons is not entirely constant for a given shell in a given element, even for a monoenergetic photon source: there are variations as the chemical environment of the atom changes. As the outer electrons participate in forming chemical bonds, the net charge on the atom changes, which in turn affects the binding energy of the core electrons. For example, in electropositive elements (such as metals), the outer-shell electrons move away from the nucleus as bonds are formed, after which the core electrons become more strongly bound because the atom now has a net positive charge. As a consequence, the kinetic energies of the photoelectrons shift toward lower values relative to the uncombined element (see Eqn. 15.1). On the other hand, the electronegative elements show a net increase in negative charge as they form chemical bonds, so the ejected photoelectrons emerge with higher kinetic energies, reflecting the decreased binding energies the core electrons have to overcome to escape.

This is a highly simplified picture of the effects of chemical bonding on photoelectron spectra. There are a variety of other factors that affect the binding energy of the electron and the kinetic energy of the ejected photoelectron: for example, relaxation effects, stereochemistry, crystal structure, and lattice energy, to name a few. The electron senses the total of all these effects; their proportionate contributions are very difficult to assign.

An excellent discussion of the various factors involved in binding energies is given in a recent paper [2] dealing with a series of metal-dithiene compounds of the type $[M(S_2C_2R_2)_n]^z$ where M is one of a large variety of transition metals; n is generally 2 or 3; R is one of a variety of substituents such as CN, C_6H_5, CH_3; and z is 0, -1 or -2. The problem presented by these compounds is the possible oxidation states of the metal necessary to satisfy stoichiometrically the possible charges of the complex. For instance, the nickel species in both $[(C_2H_5)_4N]_2\{Ni[S_2C_2(CN)_2]_2\}$ and $[(C_2H_5)_4N]\{Ni[S_2C_2(CN)_2]_2\}$ have identical ligands, have square-planar geometry, and are diamagnetic. Tests using ESCA showed that the binding energies of the Ni electrons were identical in both. By contrast, the binding energies of the sulfur ($2p$) electrons decreased as the negative charge on the complex increased. This evidence shows clearly that the "oxidation state" of the Ni remains relatively constant and that the increased negative charge of the complex mainly resides on the anionic ligands, specifically on the sulfur atoms. Some investigators use such observations to deduce the chemical environment around an atom, whereas others use theoretical calculations to predict the binding energies.

Resolution

The resolving power needed for ESCA is defined more by binding-energy shifts caused by chemical changes than by overlaps between the binding-energy values of

---

FIGURE 15.3. *A: Al-K*$\alpha_{1,2}$ *x-ray excited electron spectrum of germanium. Photoelectron peaks from various atomic shells are labelled "photo." Note the presence of a plasma-loss shoulder, indicated by an arrow, about 17 eV on the low-energy side of each prominent electron line. B: Expanded display of the Auger portion of the germanium spectrum showing plasma-loss ("plasmon") peaks adjacent to the main peaks.*

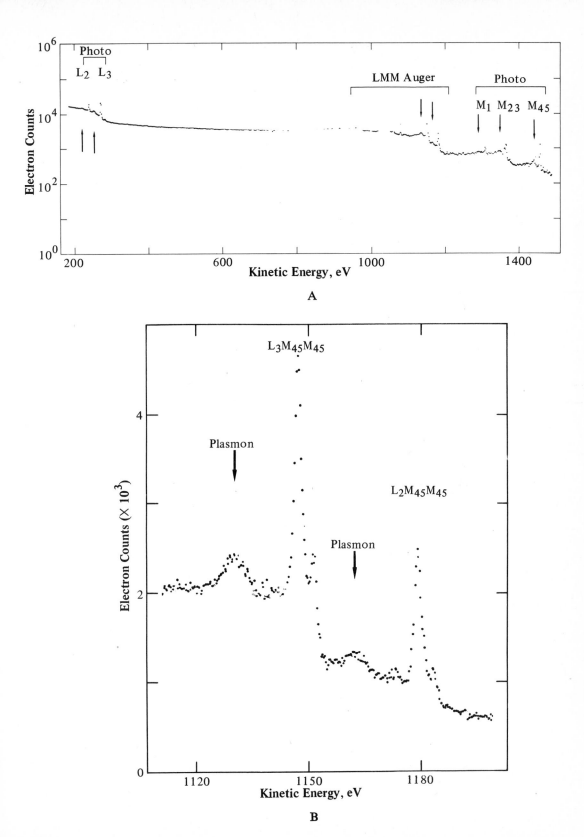

A

B

elements. For a normal range of chemical phenomena, the binding energy for a particular photoelectron can change by about 0.1–10 eV, whereas the energy separation between corresponding electrons of different elements is considerably greater, 50–100 eV. (The binding energies of $1s$ electrons in boron and carbon atoms, for instance, differ by 96 eV [see Table 15.1].) There is some energy overlap between electrons in *different* orbitals of different elements—the scandium $2p$ electrons at 407 and

TABLE 15.1. *Selected ESCA Binding Energies*

Atomic No.	Element	Binding Energy, E_b (eV)	Type of Electron
3	Li	55	$1s$
4	Be	111	
5	B	188	
6	C	284	
7	N	399	
8	O	532	
9	F	686	
10	Ne	867	$1s$
11	Na	1072; 63	$1s, 2s$
12	Mg	89	$2s$
13	Al	74; 73	$2p_{1/2}, 2p_{3/2}$
14	Si	100; 99	
15	P	136; 135	
16	S	165; 164	
17	Cl	202; 200	
19	K	297; 294	
20	Ca	350; 347	
21	Sc	407; 402	
22	Ti	461; 455	
23	V	520; 513	
24	Cr	584; 575	
25	Mn	652; 641	
26	Fe	723; 710	
27	Co	794; 779	
28	Ni	872; 855	
29	Cu	951; 931	
30	Zn	1044; 1021	$2p_{1/2}, 2p_{3/2}$
32	Ge	129; 122	$3p_{1/2}, 3p_{3/2}$
47	Ag	373; 367	$3d_{3/2}, 3d_{5/2}$
78	Pt	74; 70	$4f_{5/2}, 4f_{7/2}$
79	Au	87; 83	$4f_{5/2}, 4f_{7/2}$

Source: These values are taken from Appendix 1 of K. Siegbahn, C. Nordling, A. Fahlman, R. Nordberg, K. Hamrin, J. Hedman, G. Johansson, T. Bergmark, S. Karlsson, I. Lindgren, and B. Lindberg, *ESCA: Atomic, Molecular, and Solid-State Structure Studied by Means of Electron Spectroscopy*, Uppsala: Almquist and Wiksells, 1967, by permission of the senior authors.

402 eV are very close in energy to the nitrogen $1s$ electron at 399 eV—but these overlaps are not usually significant. The chemical changes, being relatively small (< 10 eV) compared to the usual kinetic energies of photoelectrons (500–1500 eV), require resolutions of up to about $\pm 0.01\%$ for adequate measurements. These requirements will be discussed in more detail in the section on instrumentation.

Auger Spectra

The nature of atomic-deactivation processes is such that photoelectrons are accompanied by x-ray emission or by Auger electron emission. For the lighter elements and for the outer atomic shells of the medium and heavy elements, Auger-electron emission is the predominant mode by which an atom deactivates. Moreover, when using high-energy electrons rather than x-rays to bombard a sample, Auger-electron emission predominates.

When a vacancy is produced in an inner shell by photoelectron ejection, the filling of this vacancy by an electron from a higher-energy shell is either followed by the emission of a fluorescence x-ray photon or by the simultaneous ejection of another outer-shell electron—the Auger or secondary electron (Fig. 15.1). Like the fluorescence x-rays, these electrons have characteristic energies for each atomic shell and each element. However, the Auger spectrum is generally more complex than the x-ray spectrum. For instance, two prominent x-ray peaks, $L\alpha$ and $L\beta$, are observed with initial vacancies in the $L_3(2p_{3/2})$ and $L_2(2p_{1/2})$ shells of copper ($L\iota$ and $L\eta$ are extremely weak). In contrast, Figure 15.4 shows the corresponding Auger spectrum of Cu with vacancies in the L_2 and L_3 shells. There are many more groups of prominent peaks, as well as fine structures in the peaks themselves. Most of these Auger

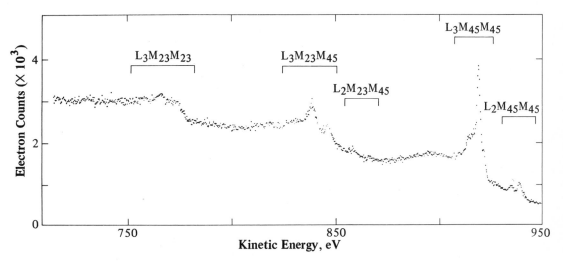

FIGURE 15.4.   *Detailed $L_{2,3}MM$ Auger spectrum of copper. These lines are due only to vacancies in the L_2 and L_3 shells of copper. Note the abundant fine structure in the spectrum. The separation between a particular $L_3M_iM_j$ group and the corresponding $L_2M_iM_j$ group is equal to the binding-energy difference between L_3 and L_2 shells.*

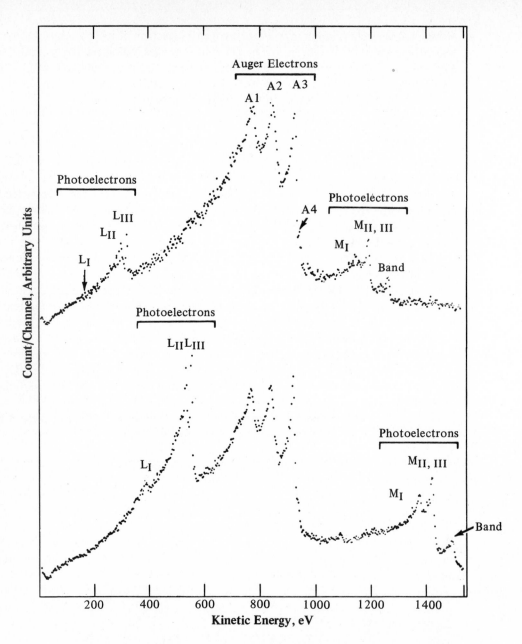

FIGURE 15.5. *Electron spectra of copper. Top: Mg* $K\alpha_{1,2}$ *x-ray (1254 eV) excitation. Bottom: Al* $K\alpha_{1,2}$ *x-ray (1487 eV) excitation. Note that, whereas the kinetic energies of the photoelectrons are proportional to the energies of the incident x-rays, those of the Auger electrons are independent. "Band" means the conduction band. The details of the Auger portion of the spectra are shown in Figure* 15.4. *From L. Yin, E. Yellin, and I. Adler, J. Appl. Phys.,* **43**, *3595 (1971); by permission of the authors and the American Institute of Physics.*

spectral lines have been catalogued for various elements and can be identified by reference to these tables. Like photoelectrons, the Auger electrons are sensitive to chemical environment, which may produce some ambiguities in identification; so the tables must be used with care.

Some characteristics of Auger lines can be used to distinguish them from photoelectron lines. This is important since photoelectron lines are so frequently accompanied by Auger lines. One useful fact is that the position (energy) of the Auger lines is always independent of the energy of the exciting photon because the Auger process occurs after the atom is ionized. A wide-range scan of the electron spectrum of copper is shown in Figure 15.5. The top spectrum was obtained by using Mg $K\alpha_{1,2}$ x-rays (1254 eV) as an excitation source, the bottom by using Al $K\alpha_{1,2}$ x-rays (1487 eV). Whereas the kinetic energies of the groups of peaks labeled "photoelectrons" increase with the incident x-ray energies (Eqn. 15.1), the energies of the group labeled "Auger electrons" remain unchanged. In practice, however, changing the energy of the incident radiation is not a trivial matter, because it generally involves changing the x-ray anode.

Fortunately, in some instances there are other methods of distinguishing Auger electrons from photoelectrons. In the case of KLL Auger electrons, there is a single group of lines which one identifies from appropriate tables, keeping in mind a possible discrepancy of a few eV caused by chemical shifts. For outer-shell Auger electrons, there are groups of lines corresponding to vacancies produced in subshells. Although these groups may contain complex features, the component lines of these groups are separated by energies corresponding to the difference in binding energies. For example, the L_3MM group of Auger lines is separated from a comparable group of L_2MM Auger lines by the difference in binding energy between the L_3 and L_2 shells (Fig. 15.4). Further, this difference is usually independent of the chemical environment.

Another practical generalization is that, for any given group of Auger lines from a major shell, the most intense group results from vacancies in the outermost subshell. This follows quite naturally, because in a given major shell the electron population is greatest in the outermost subshells. Therefore, roughly speaking, the probability of producing a vacancy by x-ray absorption is also highest for the outermost subshell. Furthermore, after photoionization, physical processes occur that reorganize the vacancy distribution among the subshells. Such reshuffling always results in increased vacancies in the outermost subshell. Thus, for example, one would predict (and actually find) that for the L-shell Auger groups, the intensities are as follows: $L_3MM > L_2MM > L_1MM$; similarly, for the M-shell groups, $M_5NN > M_4NN > M_3NN > M_2NN > M_1NN$; and so forth for higher shells.

15.2 INSTRUMENTATION

As in many fields, ESCA instrumentation was initially designed and built by pioneering investigators and thus was found in very few laboratories. Today ESCA instrumentation may be purchased commercially. There are excellent instruments available which offer relative ease of operation, high sensitivity, and good resolution.

In this section we shall review the principles underlying the instrumentation,

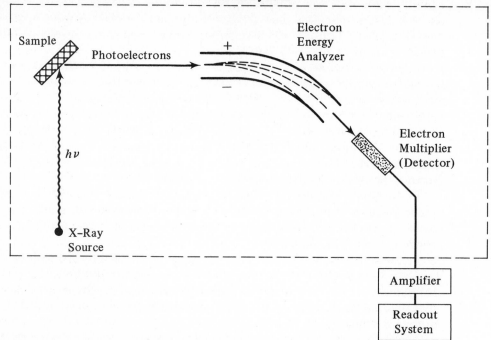

FIGURE 15.6. *Schematic diagram of an electron spectrometer. The electrostatic analyzer "sorts" or spreads out the photoelectrons, Auger electrons, and other secondary electrons of various energies so that only monoenergetic electrons reach the detector. In this, the energy analyzer serves much the same function as does a monochromator in optical spectroscopy.*

which consists of the following components: an excitation source, an electron-energy analyzer, a detector and associated electronics, and a sample-handling device. Figure 15.6 is a block diagram of an ESCA spectrometer.

Excitation Source

There are alternate methods of excitation in ESCA. We shall concentrate on photon excitation—in particular, x-ray excitation. As Equation 15.1 implies, the exciting source must be "monoenergetic." The important question in ESCA is "how monoenergetic," since this is a relative term. Because the demands of ESCA require the measurement of line shifts on the order of 0.1–1 eV, the energy spread of the exciting source must be of the same magnitude or less. ESCA systems are generally quite inefficient, which demands a high-intensity source as well.

The best way of obtaining such a source is to make use of the characteristic x-rays from an x-ray anode. However, it is a well known fact that characteristic x-ray lines have a finite width or energy spread. Such widths decrease with decreasing atomic number. It should be noted also that K x-ray lines are preferable as excitation sources because the L spectra are inherently more complex. Using these criteria (as well as the following practical considerations) the characteristic Al or Mg K lines (1487 eV or 1254 eV, respectively) were chosen for use in ESCA. The elements heavier than Al or Mg produce x-rays with higher efficiency, but the lines are inherently too broad and the $K\alpha_1$ and $K\alpha_2$ components begin to become distinct, so the radiation is no longer monoenergetic. The elements lighter than Mg or Al are either gases, or (if solid) the width of the K line begins to increase because the x-rays are now coming from transitions of electrons in the valence bands. In the case of Mg or Al, the $K\alpha_1$ and $K\alpha_2$ lines are so close in energy that for practical purposes they can be considered as a single line; the total energy spread is about 0.7 and 0.9 eV for Mg and Al, respectively. Power dissipation on the order of 1 kW or more is required to produce adequate electron intensities.

A recent development for producing monoenergetic x-rays involves a crystal monochromator in conjunction with an Al x-ray source to further reduce the energy spread of the characteristic x-rays and the background continuum. Because of the greatly reduced x-ray intensities following the use of the monochromator, it has been necessary to develop an ingenious method for processing the electron output from the spectrometer. The solution is analogous to a parallel-processing procedure that permits a band of electron energies to be measured simultaneously. The total energy spread of the exciting x-rays and the spectrometer is of the order of 0.5 eV for such instruments.

Another readily available monochromatic source uses the resonance lines of He I at 21.2 eV or He II at 40.8 eV, which have linewidths of about 0.005 eV. These are the major sources used in vacuum-ultraviolet photoelectron spectroscopy (UPS). Unfortunately, good photon sources with energies between 1000 and 40 eV are still not easily available.

Electron Spectrometer

Because of the commercial availability of very adequate electron spectrometers (the heart of the ESCA instrument), it will not be necessary to furnish here the detailed theory of operation. The discussion will concern itself only with the principles of operation.

Three types of electron spectrometers are presently in use: magnetic, electrostatic, and retarding-grid types. Of these, the first two are focusing instruments whereas the last is not. Historically, the magnetic spectrometer was the first type, used notably in the work of Siegbahn and coworkers [1]. Today the most common type of spectrometer in photoelectron spectroscopy, whether x-ray or ultraviolet, is the electrostatic type. The third variety (retarding grid) is employed mainly with electron excitation and is usually used in conjunction with the LEED (*low energy electron diffraction*) apparatus for studying Auger spectra.

The magnetic spectrometer is a momentum analyzer—the momentum of the electron is proportional to the applied magnetic field. In such instruments the percentage momentum resolution ($\Delta mv/mv$) is an instrumental constant. The momentum resolution achieved by Siegbahn et al. is about 0.01%. Instruments of this type are usually very large and very sensitive to stray magnetic fields. It is usually necessary to cancel any extraneous magnetic fields by the use of large Helmholtz coils and to place the spectrometer in iron-free rooms. These are essentially custom-built research instruments with low efficiency and are found in very few laboratories.

Electrostatic instruments come in a variety of forms: complete concentric hemispheres, hemispheric and spherical sectors, coaxial cylinders, etc. In such analyzers, the kinetic energy of the electron is proportional to the applied potential between the two conducting surfaces. Owing to the spherical or axial symmetry of such spectrometers, most have double-focusing properties. In general, the percentage energy resolution ($\Delta E/E$) is a constant of the instrument; resolutions of the order of 0.05% have been achieved. Because the percentage resolution is a constant, the absolute resolution ΔE is directly proportional to the energy E of the electron. In other words, at low electron energies the absolute resolution is better (ΔE is smaller). Consequently, there are two approaches to achieving good resolution in electrostatic analyzers: (1), building an instrument with a high enough resolution that the absolute resolution ΔE is small enough even at high kinetic energies to contribute little to the measured linewidth; and (2), reducing the energy of the electron entering the spectrometer by a constant value so that ΔE becomes small and constant. This is done by the simple expedient of applying a retarding potential, or by using a retarding lens which reduces the initial kinetic energy of the electron to the desired value prior to entering the spectrometer. At present, most commercial ESCA instruments employ the latter technique and offer resolutions of the order of 0.1 eV. Like the magnetic analyzer, the electrostatic analyzer is sensitive to stray magnetic fields, but less critically so; some form of magnetic shielding is usually required, but not the use of Helmholtz coils as in magnetic spectrometers.

The third type of spectrometer, which uses retarding grids and electronic differentiation for energy analysis, is rather uncommon in conventional photoelectron spectroscopy. The reader is referred for further details to texts on LEED and Auger spectroscopy.

Detection Systems

As a general rule, the electron energies and intensities measured in ESCA are both relatively low because of the various factors discussed above. The low electron-energies dictate the use of windowless detectors and the low intensities dictate the use of pulse-counting techniques; most of the available ESCA instruments employ both. The low counting-rates also make automated data-acquisition and analysis attractive; thus, many commercial instruments offer on-line computers as part of the entire ESCA system.

Sample Systems

Because ESCA can be applied to a great variety of problems, sample-handling capabilities should have enough flexibility that investigations can be performed on solids, liquids, or gases. These requirements are not easy to meet in practice and generally require specially engineered sample devices.

Vacuum System. It is essential to have strict control over the sample surface because the response in ESCA is entirely determined by the surface. A minimum requirement is a "very clean vacuum"; that is, a vacuum relatively free of vapors that can be adsorbed on the surface of the sample and thus distort and contaminate the observed spectra. As a rule of thumb, a vacuum of 10^{-8} torr or better is necessary for general purposes, because surface contamination is very rapid and the surface in poorer vacuums may be contaminated to an unknown extent; a vacuum in the range of 10^{-10} torr is often required. In fact, since most surfaces are already contaminated by the time the sample is introduced into the sample chamber, it is also very desirable to have auxiliary surface-cleaning capabilities in the sample chamber itself, such as sample-heating and ion-sputtering devices (an argon-ion gun, for example), to clean the samples in place so they can be quickly studied before the surface becomes contaminated again.

Surface Charging. The ESCA investigator working on nonconducting samples must be constantly aware of the problem of surface charging. Surface-charge buildup will affect the values of the observed kinetic energies of photoelectrons from which chemical information is subsequently obtained. Surface charge occurs as a consequence of the ejection of electrons from the sample by the incident x-rays. The surface of a nonconductor becomes electron-deficient (positively charged) because there are not enough charge carriers to neutralize the deficiency, as would happen in a conductor. The electrons now must leave a surface that attracts them and thus experience a retardation and consequent loss of kinetic energy. Sample charging is not a simple effect but is sensitive to the geometry and environment of the sample and its container. The amount of charging will thus vary from instrument to instrument, even for the same sample.

There are various techniques for dealing with sample charging—some instrumental, some involving special sample-preparation, and some involving both. Instrumental techniques include using an electron gun to flood the sample with low-energy electrons and designing special geometries to surround the sample with a cage that discharges it. Among sample-preparation methods are such techniques as depositing on the nonconducting sample a very thin conducting film of a noble metal (such as gold or platinum) that has strong photoelectron lines with well established energies. The deposited film must be thin enough not to obscure the sample of interest underneath, should not have electron lines with energies similar to those of the sample, and must not react with the sample. Other methods to minimize sample charging include depositing a thin film of nonconducting sample onto a conducting substrate and incorporating the nonconducting sample into a conductive wire mesh.

The phenomenon of charging is important only when absolute energy values are required; provided the degree of charging is constant or quickly reaches an equilibrium value, the relative energies are unaffected.

Another parameter that affects the measured electron energies and which must be taken into account in determining the electron binding energies is the *work function*. The kinetic energy the spectrometer sees is not necessarily the energy the electron has as it leaves the atom; every electron that escapes the surface of the sample must overcome a surface potential known as the work function, usually on the order of a few eV. Although work functions differ from sample to sample, it has been shown that only the work function of the entrance material to the spectrometer needs to be accounted for in the determination of absolute kinetic energies.

Because the work function of a particular spectrometer is an instrumental constant, it can readily be determined either by direct measurement or by reference to some standard electron energy. For example, the well known 83.8-eV binding energy of the $4f_{7/2}$ level of gold is often used to calibrate the spectrometer work-function. The work function can then be subtracted from the right side of Equation 15.1 to give

$$E_p = h\nu - E_b - E_{wf} \tag{15.2}$$

15.3 APPLICATIONS

In current applications, the somewhat limited usefulness of ESCA in the area of simple quantitative elemental analysis does not detract from its potential in a myriad of other chemical studies. In order to demonstrate the principles of the technique, we will show how to go about interpreting ESCA data in the following examples. Some of these are from our own work and were selected merely for convenience. These examples, although typical, are by no means exhaustive; they only serve to highlight some of the current applications of ESCA.

Elemental Analysis

Examination of the literature discloses very few examples of classical quantitative elemental analysis. ESCA is an extraordinarily sensitive surface technique involving the top twenty or so angstroms; in this sense, almost vanishingly small amounts of an element, about 0.001 monolayer, can be detected. To attempt an elemental analysis of a sample, however, immediately presents the analyst with the question of how representative the surface is of the rest of the sample, particularly in view of the possibility of surface contamination. Sample preparation is critical and must contend with a wide variety of surface phenomena such as adsorption and chemisorption, oxidation, and mechanical contamination, as well as more subtle phenomena that will be brought out in greater detail below. One important point is that both ESCA and Auger spectroscopy are essentially nondestructive techniques.

In summary, the use of ESCA for elemental analysis is primarily limited to the qualitative identification of surface elements, and monitoring the presence or absence of these elements. Nevertheless, progress is being made in the application of both ESCA and Auger spectroscopy to quantitative analysis.

Valence States

Studies of chemical bonding, charge distribution, and valence state are perhaps the best established applications of ESCA at present and account for the bulk of the published papers in this area. In contrast to the heretofore more classical techniques which are essentially inferential in character, ESCA is able to directly probe both the valence electrons, which actually participate in bonding, and the core electrons, which are directly influenced by the behavior of the valence electrons. It is this capability of ESCA that has led to its rapid growth; it is perhaps the most powerful and direct tool for these types of studies.

The transition metals are excellent examples of elements capable of various valence states, some of which are stable. In a systematic study of Fe_2O_3 and FeF_2 under argon-ion bombardment [3], the Fe $2p_{3/2}$ photoelectron peak was examined after various periods of ion bombardment (Fig. 15.7). With extended periods of bombardment, the peak shifts toward higher kinetic (lower binding) energy until its position coincides with that for metallic iron. In other words, Fe^{2+} and Fe^{3+}

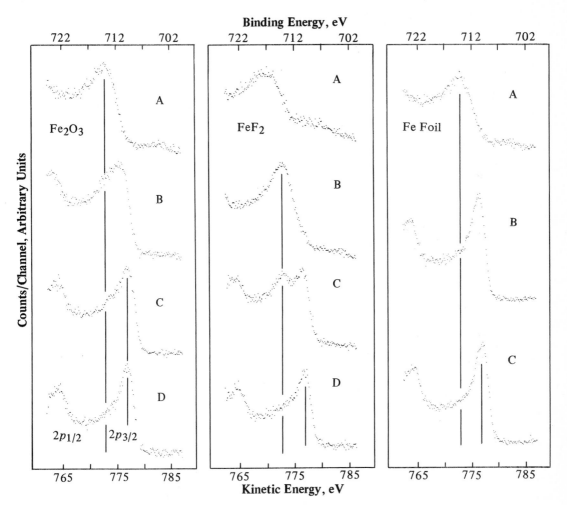

FIGURE 15.7. *Al Kα$_{1,2}$ x-ray excited photoelectron spectra of the Fe $2p_{3/2}$ (L$_3$) level in Fe$_2$O$_3$, FeF$_2$ and Fe foil, showing chemical reduction induced with argon-ion sputtering. Sputtering was performed at a pressure of 25 microns, a voltage of 1.5 kV, and a current density of 0.2 mA/cm^2. Fe$_2$O$_3$ sequence: A, prior to ion-sputtering; B, after 12 min; C, after 72 min; D, after 120 min of sputtering. FeF$_2$ sequence: A, prior to sputtering; B, after 15 min; C, after 120 min; D, after 210 min of sputtering. Fe foil sequence: A, prior to sputtering; B, after 60 min; C, after 160 min of sputtering. From L. Yin, S. Ghose, and I. Adler,* Appl. Spectr., **26**, 355 (1972); *by permission of the publisher.*

are being reduced to their metallic state under argon-ion bombardment. This is a clear example of how one can study surface reactions in a dynamic or time-dependent way. The spectra also show what we assume to be FeO as an intermediate product in the case of Fe_2O_3 samples. It is well known that FeO is unstable in air and would normally be prepared only with extreme difficulty. We have no way of knowing whether the observed FeO is stoichiometric. This kind of chemical reduction under ion bombardment is fairly common among the $3d$ transition-metal compounds.

The effect of surface contamination is shown by the fact that initially the position of the photoelectron line from the "metallic iron" actually is indistinguishable from that for Fe_2O_3. This is caused by a surface layer of oxidized iron that is subsequently sputtered away by the ion bombardment.

The examples cited above demonstrate a need for caution in the use of ion-sputtering as a cleaning technique in the preparation of sample surfaces for ESCA analysis; the ion-sputtering process itself can produce chemical changes on the sample surface.

Stereochemistry

Because ESCA can directly probe the electronic structures of substances ranging from free atoms to solids, it is useful in a host of related fields such as stereochemistry, geochemistry, crystallography, and atomic and solid-state physics. Among the phenomena lending themselves to study are stereostructures, band structures, paramagnetism, atomic lifetimes, and Auger transitions.

An example of the use of ESCA to study the effect of steric arrangements concerns the binding energies of the core electrons of Ni in nickel compounds [4]. Some 70 compounds containing Ni in all of its known oxidation states were examined. Among other things, the results indicate that when Ni is bonded to the same ligand under different geometries, the binding energy of the Ni-ion electrons increases in the order: planar < tetrahedral < octahedral. This is not surprising because, for a given type of ligand, the nickel-to-donor distances increase in the same order; thus, since the valence electrons in the octahedral case are farthest removed from the Ni core, the binding energy of the remaining electrons is greatest. This relationship will not necessarily hold if the ligand is varied.

There is also a direct correlation between Ni $2p$ binding energy and the estimated charge on Ni for some simple Ni(II) compounds, as shown in Figure 15.8. Similar correlations have been observed recently for a large number of copper compounds [5].

Surface Studies

One of the more important practical applications of ESCA is in the study of surface phenomena. Such areas as the direct study of surface reactions, diffusion processes under preselected conditions, the study of dopants in solids, surface-catalysis phenomena, sputtering processes, and gas-surface interactions are open to investigation.

Some contributions in this area have been made by the LEED method, with the instruments modified to measure the energies of the emerging Auger electrons.

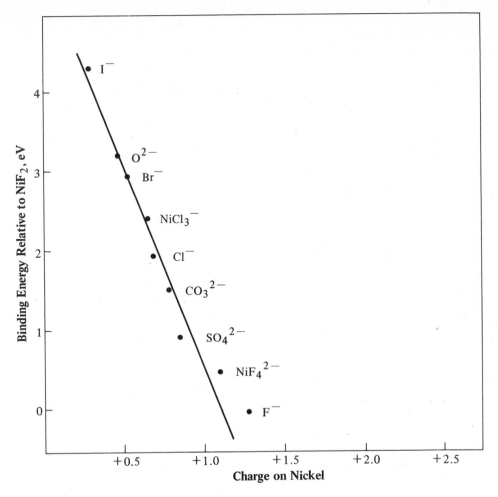

FIGURE 15.8. *Correlation between the Ni $2p_{3/2}$ (L_3) binding energy (relative to NiF_2) and the estimated charge on nickel for some simple Ni(II) compounds.*

Because LEED is based on excitation of the sample by electrons (typically, samples are bombarded with a focused beam of electrons in the energy range up to 5 keV), these studies are limited to the use of Auger spectra. Further, electron excitation requires electronic differentiation of the energy spectra to minimize the high background of scattered electrons. Therefore, Auger spectra have the shapes shown in Figure 15.9 rather than the hump-shaped peaks of ESCA spectra. The degraded resolution, the complexity of Auger spectra, and the uncertainty of Auger chemical shifts limit such surface studies to the identification of elements and the monitoring of the presence or absence of surface constituents, rather than their chemical states or activities. Nevertheless, a great deal of surface information can be extracted even from the simple elemental identification of the presence, absence, or change of surface constituents.

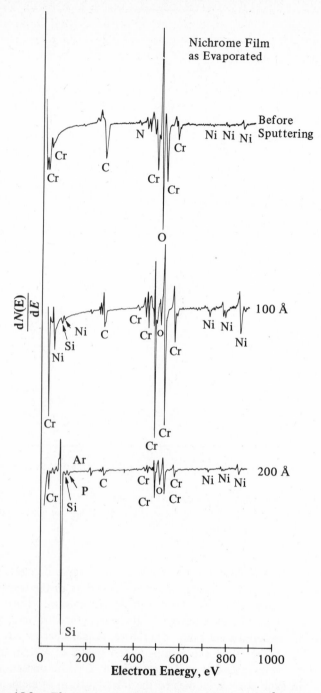

FIGURE 15.9. *Electron-excited Auger spectra from a 150-Å nichrome film deposited on a silicon substrate. The spectra represent a profile of the film from the surface down to a depth of 200 Å as various amounts of the material have been sputtered off. Note that the unit on the ordinate is the derivative of the electron intensity, dN(E)/dE, rather than the intensity N(E). From R. E. Weber,* J. Crystal Growth, *17, 342 (1972),* by permission of the author and the North Holland Publishing Company.

An excellent example of surface studies is given by Weber [6] using ion-sputtering to determine the in-depth composition of thin films on selected substrates. Figure 15.9 shows the effect of sputtering and surface thickness on sequentially observed Auger spectra. Note that the unit on the y-axis is $dN(E)/dE$, the first derivative of the number of electron counts, rather than $N(E)$. The top spectrum is that of a 150-Å nichrome film deposited on a silicon substrate. The Ni and Cr from the nichrome as well as the surface oxygen are visible, but not the substrate. In the middle spectrum, after 100 Å has been sputtered away, an Auger line from the silicon substrate appears while the oxygen-line intensity drops greatly. In the bottom spectrum, after 200 Å of material has been removed, the Si from the substrate shows very strongly, whereas the Ni and Cr peaks have almost disappeared. Auger peaks for argon from the sputtering source have also begun to appear. The amplitudes of the various Auger peaks are shown as a function of material sputtered in Figure 15.10. By contrast, these same amplitude profiles are shown for a heat-treated film in Figure 15.11. It is clear that in the latter case the first 75 Å of the surface consists

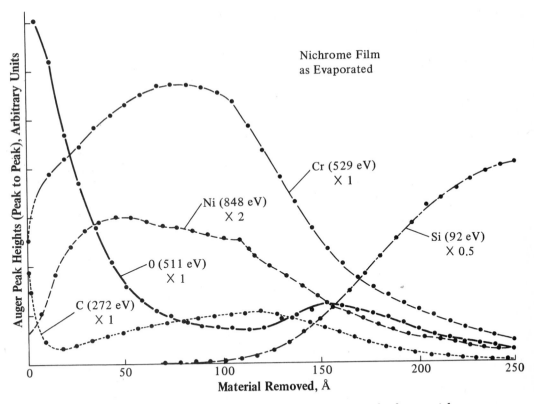

FIGURE 15.10. *Amplitudes of the various Auger peaks from a nichrome film on a silicon substrate as a function of the amount of material sputter-etched from the film. From R. E. Weber, J. Crystal Growth, 17, 342 (1972), by permission of the author and the North Holland Publishing Company.*

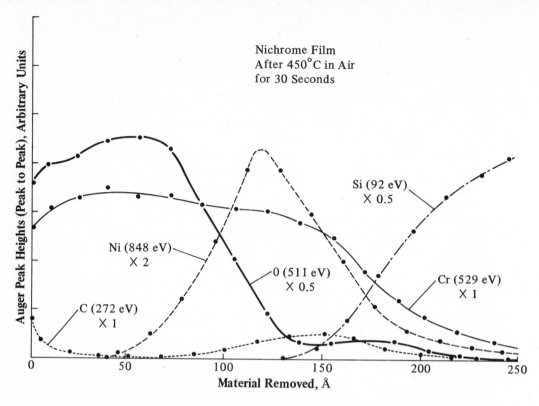

FIGURE 15.11. *Amplitudes of the Auger peaks from a heat-treated nichrome film as a function of the amount of material sputter-etched from the film. From R. E. Weber, J. Crystal Growth, 17, 342 (1972). Reproduced with the permission of the author and the North Holland Publishing Company.*

of Cr and O, whereas the Ni has now diffused to the interface between the film and the silicon substrate.

Other examples of surface phenomena that have been studied involve grain boundaries, surface diffusion, corrosion, etc.

One significant advantage of Auger spectroscopy with electron bombardment is that the electron beam can be focused on a very small area of the sample surface. Typical beam diameters have been as little as 25 μm, although the use of Auger spectroscopy in conjunction with the scanning electron microscope allows the use of beam diameters below 5 μm. At present, ESCA photon-beam diameters are limited to about a mm or so. With scanning capability and small beam-diameters, one can now perform lateral or even two-dimensional characterization of a surface. For a two-dimensional semiquantitative analysis of a surface, the spectrometer is locked onto the energy of an Auger peak characteristic of a particular element. The electron beam is scanned systematically across the surface of the sample, and the position of the probe beam is correlated with the *x-y* position of the light beam on an oscilloscope screen. Finally, the light intensity of the oscilloscope signal is made proportional to the intensity of the Auger signal. The net result is an oscilloscope picture of the sample surface magnified perhaps $400\times$, with the bright areas on the screen corresponding to the "image" of the element analyzed on the surface. One can then "lock" on to the Auger peak of a second element, get its "picture," and so on. By this sequential multi-element capability, the presence of several elements at specific sites can be correlated.

Examples of this type of application abound in the literature. Segregation of impurities in metals and alloys often occurs at grain boundaries. A study of the embrittlement and stress-failure of a tungsten sample showed a nearly uniform distribution of phosphorus across the sample, except for certain grains that appeared to be completely free of it; this complete absence of phosphorus can be interpreted as related to cleavage failure at these points.

Surface Catalysis

For the most part, the behavior of surface catalysts have not been well understood; as a result, their development is still something of an art. ESCA offers perhaps the best potential for studying such phenomena because, since the suspected mechanisms probably involve some form of charge transfer, there should be an associated change in binding energy.

One such example is the study of the binding energy of platinum in a series of complexes [7]. The ESCA binding-energy data show that the coordination of "neutral ligands" can lead to a considerable transfer of charge from the metal to the ligands, thus confirming that the catalytic behavior of these platinum complexes is indeed related to charge transfer. Other typical examples of this sort have been given by Kelly and Tyler [8] and Larsson et al. [9].

Quantum Structure of Free Molecules

Studies of molecular structure and molecular energy-levels by ultraviolet photoelectron spectroscopy are being conducted by a large number of investigators. Such studies are fundamental in nature and to a large extent theoretical. In order to provide meaningful data free of solid-state effects, the samples are usually gaseous. Further, in order to see the closely spaced molecular orbitals and final-state vibrational structures, very high instrumental resolution (a few meV) and (usually) ultraviolet excitation are required. This subject is well covered in review articles and texts [10–13].

Valence-Band Structure

Photoelectron spectroscopy provides a useful (because direct) tool for studying the valence-band structure of solids. It is unlike soft x-ray emission spectroscopy where one must contend with transitions (to inner shells) that are constrained by selection rules and where one must take into account the character of the shell to which the transitions occur. In photoelectron spectroscopy, any of the occupied states in the band can be examined by ejecting the band photoelectrons. Thus, the photoelectron spectral shape essentially reflects the structure of the occupied band itself.

Consequently, ESCA has been widely used to study the band structures of metals, alloys, and compounds. These data in turn are compared with density-of-state or molecular-orbital calculations.

Because band structures are of interest to investigators in a wide variety of disciplines besides chemistry (such as solid-state physics, geochemistry, and crystallography), this area of application of ESCA is growing rapidly. This is especially so with the improved vacuum and resolution of second-generation instruments.

In principle, ultraviolet-excited photoelectron spectroscopy would be ideally suited for valence-band-structure studies because of its extremely high resolution. However, ultraviolet-photoelectron spectra may not truly represent the band structure being probed; because the energy of the ultraviolet source is so low, it tends to induce valence-electron transitions and thereby distort the intensity distribution of the resulting photoelectron spectrum. X-ray excitation, on the other hand, while providing poorer resolution, is essentially free of such distortions. Thus, the two types of photoelectron spectra serve to complement each other and provide a more complete picture of the valence-band structure.

REFERENCES

1. K. SIEGBAHN, C. NORDLING, A. FAHLMAN, R. NORDBERG, K. HAMRIN, J. HEDMAN, G. JOHANSSON, T. BERGMARK, S. KARLSSON, I. LINDGREN, and B. LINDBERG, *ESCA: Atomic, Molecular, and Solid-State Structure Studied by Means of Electron Spectroscopy*, Uppsala: Almquist and Wiksells, 1967.

2. S. O. GRIM, L. J. MATIENZO, and W. E. SWARTZ, Jr., *Inorg. Chem.*, *13*, 447 (1974).

3. L. YIN, S. GHOSE, and I. ADLER, *Appl. Spectrosc.*, *26*, 355 (1972).

4. L. J. MATIENZO, L. YIN, S. O. GRIM, and W. E. SWARTZ, Jr., *Inorg. Chem.*, *12*, 2762 (1973).

5. D. C. FROST, A. ISHITANI, and C. A. McDOWELL, *Mol. Phys.*, *24*, 861 (1972).

6. R. E. WEBER, *J. Crystal Growth*, *17*, 342 (1972).

7. C. D. COOK, K. Y. WAN, U. GELIUS, K. HAMRIN, G. JOHANSSON, E. OLSON, H. SIEGBAHN, C. NORDLING, and K. SIEGBAHN, *J. Amer. Chem. Soc.*, *93*, 1904 (1971).

8. M. A. KELLY and C. E. TYLER, *Hewlett-Packard Journal*, July, 1973, pp 1–14.

9. R. LARSSON, B. FOLKESSON, and G. SCHÖN, *Chemica Scripta*, *3*, 88 (1973).

10. K. SIEGBAHN, C. NORDLING, G. JOHANSSON, J. HEDMAN, P. F. HEDÉN, K. HAMRIN, U. GELIUS, T. BERGMARK, L. O. WERME, R. MANNE, and Y. BAER, *ESCA Applied to Free Molecules*, Amsterdam: North-Holland, 1969.

11. D. W. TURNER, C. BAKER, A. D. BAKER, and C. R. BRUNDLE, *Molecular Photoelectron Spectroscopy*, London: Wiley-Interscience, 1970.

12. C. R. BRUNDLE, *Appl. Spectrosc.*, *25*, 8 (1971).

13. D. W. TURNER, *Phil. Trans. Roy. Soc. Lond.*, *A268*, 7 (1970).

PROBLEMS

1. Identify the elements present in the sample which gives the ESCA spectrum pictured at top of facing page.

2. Identify the elements present in an organic compound which has the ESCA spectrum shown at foot of facing page.

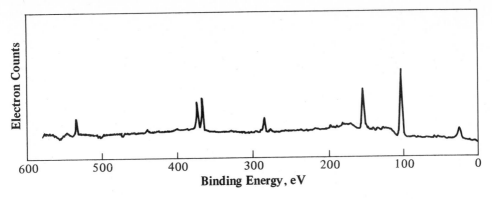

Problem 1

3. Determine the binding energies ($2p_{3/2}$ electrons) for iron in the compounds whose spectra are shown in Figure 15.7. Compare the shifts in binding energy caused by the differing chemical environments with the binding energy differences between elements near iron in the periodic table.

4. What are the advantages and disadvantages of ESCA as a method for analysis of surfaces? Compare ESCA with Auger spectroscopy.

5. In an attempt to solve an analytical problem in the design and production of a semiconductor device, you are trying to determine the approximate detection limit for silver vacuum-deposited on a silicon substrate. Given that the beam-probe diameter in ESCA is about one millimeter, that the analysis depth is about 20 Å, and that ESCA can detect about 0.001 of a monolayer of an element, answer the following questions: (a) What is the absolute "detection limit"

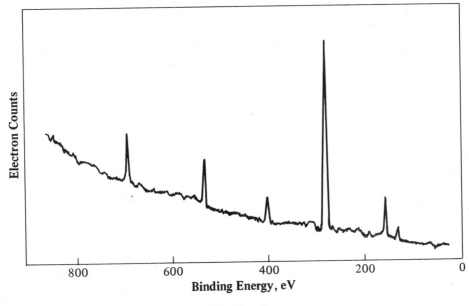

Problem 2

for Ag in grams? (b) How many atoms does this correspond to? (c) If the Ag were homogeneously distributed in the Si substrate, what would be the concentration detection limit in g/cm^3 and in ppm? The densities of elemental Ag and Si are 10.5 and 2.33 g/cm^3; the atomic radii are 1.44 and 1.32 Å; and the atomic weights are 107.87 and 28.086 g/mole, respectively.

6. The ESCA spectrum of an inorganic compound is taken using Al $K\alpha$ radiation. The photoelectron energy (E_p) of the $4f_{7/2}$ level for gold, a thin layer of which has been deposited on the sample, is measured at 1353 eV. (a) At what photoelectron energy should you look for the carbon $1s$ photoelectron peak to determine whether the surface of the sample has been contaminated with vacuum-pump oil? (b) With the same spectrometer, at what photoelectron energy should the carbon $1s$ peak be if Mg $K\alpha$ radiation were used?

7. An ESCA spectrum of a gaseous mixture of CO, CO_2, and CH_4 is taken. Prominent peaks are noted at binding energies of 290.1, 295.8, 297.9, 540.1, and 541.3 eV. Assign the observed peaks to the element and compound responsible.

8. The surface of an aluminum sample was thoroughly cleaned by abrasion and immediately put into the sample chamber of an ESCA spectrometer. Two prominent peaks in the spectrum occurred at binding energies of 72.3 and 75.0 eV, whose relative intensities were 15.2 and 5.1 (arbitrary) units. After a week's exposure to laboratory air, the same sample was rerun under the same conditions; the two peaks were again observed (at 72.2 and 74.5 eV), although the intensities were now 6.2 and 12.3 units. Explain.

9. ESCA can be used for the quantitative analysis of MoO_3/MoO_2 mixtures, compounds for which an instrumental method was not previously available [W. E. Swartz, Jr., and D. M. Hercules, *Anal. Chem.*, 43, 1774 (1971)]. This is done by analyzing the Mo $3d_{3/2}$–$3d_{5/2}$ region of the electron spectrum. Mo(VI) in MoO_3 has a peak at 235.6 eV for $3d_{3/2}$ and 232.5 eV for $3d_{5/2}$; Mo(IV) in MoO_2 has corresponding peaks at 233.9 and 230.9 eV. Thus, the electron counts at 235.6 eV are due primarily to MoO_3 and those at 230.9 to MoO_2. The following data were obtained on standard MoO_3/MoO_2 samples.

% MoO_2	$N_{235.6}:N_{230.9}$
100	1.30 ± 0.10
95	1.41 ± 0.20
90	1.70 ± 0.10
80	2.10 ± 0.20
75	2.30 ± 0.20
60	2.95 ± 0.05
55	2.99 ± 0.20
50	3.31 ± 0.10
45	3.46 ± 0.06
40	3.60 ± 0.17
25	4.17 ± 0.05
20	4.53 ± 0.20
10	5.00 ± 0.30
5	5.05 ± 0.20
0	5.07 ± 0.05

Three unknowns gave the following count ratios: 1.94 ± 0.15, 2.55 ± 0.15, and 4.08 ± 0.10. Determine the % MoO_2 in the three unknowns.

16

Mass Spectrometry

MICHAEL L. GROSS

The practice of mass spectrometry is carried out with rather sophisticated instruments (mass spectrometers) which produce, separate, and detect both positive and negative gas-phase ions. Since samples are typically neutral in charge, they must be first ionized in the spectrometer. Ionization of molecular substances is often followed by a series of spontaneous competitive decomposition or fragmentation reactions which produce additional ions. The ion masses (more correctly, their mass-to-charge ratios) and their relative abundances are displayed in a *mass spectrum*. Most compounds produce unique or distinctive patterns, so most substances can be identified by their mass spectra.

Mass spectrometry is noteworthy among modern structural tools because the information produced is of a chemical nature. The signals produced by a spectrometer are the direct result of chemical reactions (ionization and fragmentation) rather than energy-state changes that typify most other spectroscopic tools. To intelligently apply mass spectrometry, it is important to understand how this chemical information is produced. This chapter is intended to introduce the reader to the instrumentation necessary to carry out and identify these chemical reactions and to the procedure used in interpreting the information obtained.

Mass spectrometry is one of the oldest instrumental methods used in chemical analysis. The most important contribution of early mass spectrometry was the discovery of nonradioactive isotopes. The first study was reported by J. J. Thomson in 1913 [1] on the gaseous element neon. He showed that neon consists of two isotopes: ^{20}Ne and ^{22}Ne.

Major instrumental improvements followed closely just after World War I. F. W. Aston [2] in England constructed a more elaborate mass spectrograph which was used to verify the neon work and to identify other isotopes. The first mass spectrometer that utilized electrical rather than photographic detection was built in the United States by A. J. Dempster [3]. Whereas the mass spectrograph was better suited to measuring the exact masses of the isotopes, the spectrometer excelled in determinations of isotopic abundances. By the mid-thirties, most of the stable isotopes had been identified, and exact mass measurements established the idea that atomic masses are not whole numbers, a fact crucial to the understanding of nuclear chemistry. It was not until 1942, however, that the first commercial mass spectrometer was put into use, for petroleum analysis at the Atlantic Refining Corporation.

More general application of mass spectrometry as an analytical tool in the organic and biochemical areas was not developed until the 1960s. Within a period of a few years a number of chemists in the United States (McLafferty, Bieman, and Djerassi) and in England (Beynon) demonstrated that molecular structure could be elucidated for a wide variety of substances using mass spectrometry. Since then, the technique has become a standard addition to most research and analytical laboratories.

16.1 INSTRUMENTATION IN MASS SPECTROMETRY

To obtain a mass spectrum, the sample must be vaporized, ionized, and then (provided the substance is molecular) allowed to fragment or decompose. The various ions must then be separated according to their mass-to-charge ratios (m/e values) and finally detected. The instrumentation necessary to accomplish these requirements has four major components: (1) inlet systems for vaporization; (2) a source which serves to ionize and then detain the ions for a short period of time (usually about 1 μsec) so that fragmentation may occur; (3) a method of mass analysis; and (4) a detection scheme.

Inlet Systems

A generally useful inlet system must be able to vaporize molecules of quite low vapor pressure such as high-molecular-weight organic and organometallic compounds. Since many substances of interest to chemists do not have large equilibrium vapor pressures at room temperature, the inlet must operate at low pressure (10^{-4}–10^{-7} torr) and high temperature (up to 300°C). Actually, the full development of mass spectrometry in the organic and inorganic areas had to await the development of these inlet systems. The problems involved with leak-tight high-temperature vacuum systems with many remotely operated valves are not trivial, and these problems have only been overcome in the last 15 to 20 years.

Most analytical mass spectrometers have two inlet systems: a batch inlet for gases and liquids and for solids of moderately high vapor pressure, and a direct inlet for high-molecular-weight nonvolatile solids and for thermally unstable compounds. A typical design for a batch inlet is shown in Figure 16.1.

A small quantity of solid or liquid sample (approximately 10–100 μg) is introduced via the detachable sample tube into the reservoir. The sample is maintained in the gaseous state by the low background pressure of the inlet (10^{-5}–10^{-6} torr) and the high temperature of the surrounding oven. It should be obvious that a sample whose vapor pressure at the oven temperature is less than the background pressure

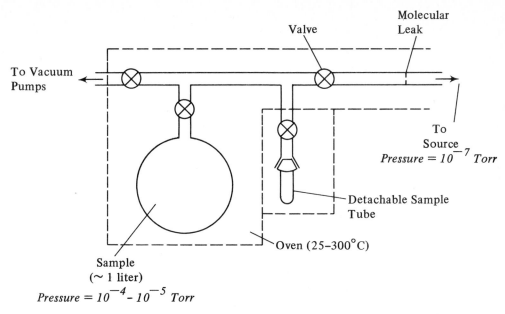

FIGURE 16.1. *Schematic diagram of a typical batch-inlet system. This inlet is used for gases, volatile liquids, and volatile solids.*

of the inlet cannot be admitted to the spectrometer using this inlet. In fact, it is preferable that the sample have a vapor pressure of 10^{-2}–10^{-3} torr at the operating temperature so that a steady stream of the vapor can be admitted to the source through the leak—a glass or metal diaphragm containing a pinhole—for ionization. The flow is often molecular, which means the rate of effusion is inversely proportional to the square root of the molecular weight. This is the case when the opening is very small (ten times smaller than the mean free path of the gas particles). Since the lower-weight molecules pass more quickly through the leak, the inlet reservoir slowly becomes enriched in the higher-weight molecules. [This is not a serious problem unless very precise data are needed (e.g., in isotope-ratio work), because leak rates are usually quite slow.]

Solid samples that do not have a high enough vapor pressure to evaporate under conditions of the batch inlet, or that are thermally sensitive, are admitted directly to the source. Usually the sample is placed in a small cup and introduced into the source through a vacuum lock. The sample cup can be cooled (e.g., with liquid nitrogen) or heated by infrared radiation or by thermal contact with a hot metal block surrounding the container. Using this technique, it is no longer necessary to fill the sample reservoir with vapor and, thus, smaller sample sizes (as low as 1 ng) and lower-vapor-pressure substances can be readily admitted. The direct inlet provides a dramatic increase in the versatility of mass spectrometry. No other analytical tool can produce as much information on such small quantities of complex organic or organometallic compounds. Mass spectra can be obtained for such diverse and nonvolatile samples as steroids, carbohydrates, dinucleotides, and low-molecular-weight polymers.

In many cases, nonvolatile substances are converted into more volatile derivatives prior to mass-spectral analysis. Examples include trimethylsilyl derivatives of alcohols or molecules containing sugar groups, ester derivatives of acids, and volatile chelates of trace-metal ions. Usually, a suitable volatile derivative can be synthesized by well established and relatively simple procedures.

Another method for sample introduction is the gas chromatograph (GC), discussed in Chapter 22. Components separated by a GC can be admitted to the source of a mass spectrometer after enriching the eluent vapor (that is, separating the helium carrier-gas from the sample vapor with a molecular separator.) A common design (Fig. 16.2) uses either a porous glass or Teflon membrane through which the small, mobile helium atoms preferentially diffuse and are then pumped away. The larger sample molecules continue through the separator into the source for ionization and finally mass analysis.

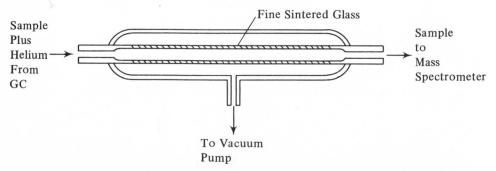

FIGURE 16.2. *A molecular separator used as an interface in GCMS. The GC and interface serve as inlet for the mass spectrometer. The carrier gas (H_2 or He) preferentially effuses through the porous glass and is pumped away.*

Since the width of GC peaks is on the order of a few seconds, a fast-scanning mass analyzer is necessary. The combination of gas chromatography and mass spectrometry (usually given the acronym GCMS) is perhaps the most versatile and sensitive tool in mixture analysis and is often used in petroleum, environmental, and biochemical research.

Electron-Impact Source

The ion source is the heart of the mass spectrometer—the region where the sample ionizes and fragments. One may look at the source as a rather sophisticated chemical reactor initiating a series of characteristic degradation reactions (fragmentation) of an ionized sample. The decompositions take place in a very short time (usually 1 μsec), so a mass spectrum can be obtained very rapidly—as will be seen, some instruments can produce up to 1000 spectra per second.

The most common method of ionization is by electron impact (EI); that is, a high-energy electron beam dislodges an electron from a sample molecule to produce a positive ion.

$$M + e^- \longrightarrow M^+ + 2e^- \qquad \textbf{(16.1)}$$

where M = the molecule under study
M^+ = the *molecular* or *parent ion*

The beam produces M^+ in a variety of energy states. Some are produced with rather large amounts of internal energy (rotational, vibrational, and electronic) that is dissipated by fragmentation reactions; for instance,

$$M^+ \underset{\searrow}{\overset{\nearrow}{}} \begin{matrix} M_1^+ \longrightarrow M_3^+ \\[6pt] M_2^+ \longrightarrow M_4^+, \text{ etc.} \end{matrix} \qquad \textbf{(16.2)}$$

where $M_1^+, M_2^+, \ldots$ are lower-mass ions. Other molecular ions resist decomposition because they are formed with insufficient energy for fragmentation. It should be noted that most fragmentation processes are endothermic, and thus low-energy molecular ions will not fragment in the source and will be detected at the molecular mass.

A schematic of a typical electron-impact source is given in Figure 16.3. The device consists of an *electron gun* that accelerates and focuses electrons emitted by a thin, red-hot filament usually made of rhenium or tungsten. The electrons are accelerated by placing a negative bias of 70 V on the filament, producing a beam with a Gaussian distribution of kinetic energies around a maximum at 70 eV (1 eV = 23.06 kcal/mole). Since most covalent molecules have ionization potentials of around

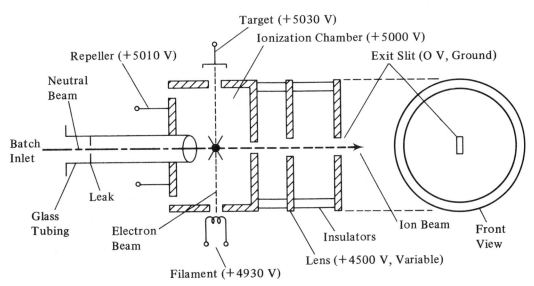

FIGURE 16.3. *Typical electron-impact source. The source is mounted on a frame and inserted into the flight tube of the mass spectrometer. The voltages in parentheses are typical values for the component parts of a spectrometer operating at 5000 V accelerating potential. Note that the target is at $+100$ V with respect to the filament, and the filament is at -70 V with respect to the ionization chamber.*

TABLE 16.1. *Ionization Potentials of Some Common Organic Molecules*

Compound	Ionization Potential (eV)
Methane	12.98
n-Hexane	10.17
Benzene	9.25
Naphthalene	8.12
Ethanol	10.48
Ethylamine	8.86
Acetone	9.69
Acetic Acid	10.35

Source: J. L. Franklin, J. G. Dillard, H. M. Rosenstock, J. T. Herron, K. Draxl, and F. H. Field, *Nat. Stand. Ref. Data Ser. Nat. Bur. Stand.*, *26* (1969).

10 eV (see Table 16.1), 70-eV electrons are sufficient to dislodge an electron from one of the higher-energy molecular orbitals and produce a molecular ion with a distribution of internal energies. Molecular ions in higher energy states can then decompose, producing various fragment ions. Since fragmentation patterns do not change significantly above 25–30 eV of ionizing energy, 70 eV is simply an arbitrary choice, and 50 eV or 80 eV would be equally acceptable. It is possible to vary this ionization energy by simply changing the voltage applied to the filament. A useful technique is to obtain a spectrum at a low voltage, such as 15 eV; this spectrum will be considerably simplified because of decreased fragmentation. In addition, ionization potentials of complex molecules can be measured by studying the decrease in the molecular-ion signal as a function of ionizing voltage.

The electron beam is collected on a target usually operated at a positive voltage (100 V) with respect to the filament. The target and filament are incorporated into the proper electronic circuitry to insure a constant current or flow of electrons through the ionization region. The regularity of the electron beam is important to achieve a constant number of ionizing events per unit time. (Under normal conditions, only about one neutral molecule out of every 1000 introduced into the source is ionized; the remainder are pumped away by the large-capacity diffusion pumps located outside the source.)

The second important feature of the source is the *ion gun* which accelerates all the molecular and fragment ions out of the source into a mass-analysis sector (the region in which sorting of ions occurs according to m/e value). Accelerating voltages are unique for each spectrometer and are in the 1000–10,000 V range. If a spectrometer operates with 5000 V accelerating potential, the voltages applied to the various components are shown in Figure 16.3.

The repellers are charged to a slightly higher voltage than the chamber to draw the positive ions into the ion gun. The lens plates are two semicircular discs to which is applied a variable voltage to focus the ion beam. Thus, the ions are formed in a positive field whose strength decreases in the direction of the exit slit and therefore accelerates positive sample ions in that direction. As was mentioned previously, the residence time of the ions is about 1 μsec in the ionization chamber. Since the time is short and the pressure low (10^{-6}–10^{-7} torr), each ion acts as an independent entity and will remain as a molecular ion or as a fragment, depending on the amount of internal energy imparted to it by the electron beam.

To review: A steady stream of neutral molecules is drawn into the source from an inlet system and ionized where the stream of molecules intercepts the electron beam. The positive ions created are constantly drawn out with the ion gun, while the remaining neutral molecules are steadily pumped away. Thus, the source operates on a steady-state principle: constant input of neutral molecules and output of ions (and leftover neutral molecules).

The electron-impact source is the work horse of analytical mass spectrometry. It is efficient, durable, and capable of producing a steady, intense beam of positive ions. Like all instruments, it must be periodically disassembled and cleaned, in addition to being equipped with a new filament. However, a well cared-for source may operate for 6 months or more.

Spark Source

Of course, the electron-impact source cannot be used if nonvolatile inorganic samples such as metal alloys or ionic residues are to be analyzed. These substances can be investigated using a different kind of ionization chamber called a spark source, similar to the excitation sources used in emission spectroscopy (Chap. 11). The other parts of the spectrometer can be the same as a general-purpose instrument; however, a Mattauch-Herzog double-focusing instrument is preferred (Fig. 16.7 below), because the spark source produces ions with a wide spread of kinetic energies. The entire device is known as a *spark-source mass spectrometer* (SSMS).

Ions are produced by applying a pulsed radio-frequency voltage of approximately 30 kV to a pair of electrodes mounted directly behind the ion gun; i.e., about where the electron beam is located in an electron-impact source (see Fig. 16.3). The electrodes may be made of the sample itself if it is an electrical conductor or (for a nonconducting specimen) from a mixture of graphite and sample mixed and pressed into an electrode. The high-voltage spark causes localized heating of the electrode with simple vaporization as atoms or simple ions. As in electron impact, the ions are accelerated through the ion gun and then mass analyzed.

There are a number of advantages of SSMS that recommend it as a general-purpose tool for trace elemental analysis in a variety of different samples. First, the method has uniformly high sensitivity for almost all the elements; as little as 1 ppb can be detected. Second, extremely complex samples can be submitted to elemental analysis; as many as sixty different elements have been determined simultaneously in a given sample. Third, the information is relatively simple—only the mass-to-charge ratios of the elements are observed. Complications can arise if the element has a large number of isotopes or if the probability of forming multi-charged ions is large, but nonetheless, the mass spectrum is much simpler than the spectrum obtained in emission spectroscopy. Fourth, the response of the instrument is linear over a wide range of concentrations of a given element in the sample; therefore, it is not necessary to use a wide range of standards to calibrate the measurements.

The detection systems used in SSMS are either photographic plates or electron multipliers (discussed below). The former has the advantage of being an integrating detector and is used for rapid monitoring of the elemental composition of a complex sample. If accurate data are required, electrical recording is preferred.

Thus, SSMS is an extremely powerful technique for routine elemental analysis of complex nonvolatile samples. The chief disadvantages are the high cost of the equipment and the fact that a skilled technician is needed to operate the instrument. Some specific applications will be discussed in Sec. 16.4.

Mass Analysis by Magnetic Sectors

A number of methods of mass analysis can be employed in mass spectrometry. The most common type uses a magnetic sector. Once outside the source, the ion beam moves down a straight, evacuated tube toward a curved region placed between the poles of a magnet (see Fig. 16.4). This region is called the magnetic sector and its purpose is to disperse the ions in curved trajectories that depend on the m/e of the ion. Low-mass ions (beam 1 in the figure) are deflected most, and the heavier mass ions (beam 3) the least.

The kinetic energy of the ions leaving the source is given by the product of the ion charge e and the accelerating voltage V

$$\frac{mv^2}{2} = Ve \tag{16.3}$$

where m = the mass of the ion
           v = its velocity

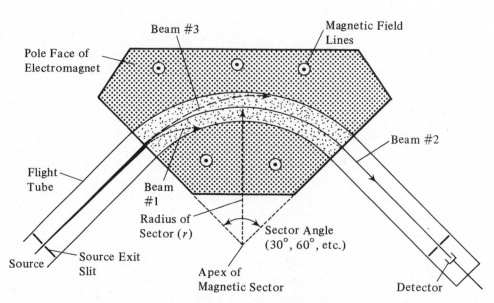

FIGURE 16.4. *Mass analysis in a sector magnetic field. Poles of the electromagnet are located above and below the plane of the page. The magnetic field H points perpendicularly out of the plane of the page. Note that the two slits and the apex of the sector are colinear.*

In the magnetic field, the ions experience a centripetal force of Hev, where H is the field strength that causes deflection. This force must be balanced by the centrifugal force of the ions, mv^2/r, where r is the radius of curvature. Therefore,

$$\frac{mv^2}{r} = Hev \tag{16.4}$$

or

$$v = \frac{Her}{m} \tag{16.5}$$

If the ion velocity is substituted into Equation 16.3, one obtains

$$\frac{m}{2}\left(\frac{Her}{m}\right)^2 = Ve \tag{16.6}$$

or

$$m/e = \frac{H^2r^2}{2V} \tag{16.7}$$

This equation may be rewritten in a form where mass is in atomic mass units, e is the number of charges ($+1$, $+2$, and so on), H is in gauss, r is in centimeters, and V is in volts:

$$m/e = \frac{H^2r^2}{20,740V} \tag{16.8}$$

The radius of deflection necessary for an ion to impinge on the detector is determined by the curvature built into the flight tube, and is therefore a constant. A scan of mass spectrum is accomplished either by keeping H constant and decreasing the accelerating voltage so that ever-increasing ion masses are brought to focus (that is, are given a deflection equal to the radius-of-curvature of the flight tube) or by increasing H at constant V to accomplish the same result. Older instruments that used permanent magnets were scanned by the first method; however, most modern instruments are equipped with electromagnets and are scanned by increasing the electric current in the magnet coils.

Mass spectrometers with only a sector magnetic field for mass analysis are known as single-focusing instruments. A well designed single-focusing spectrometer may have resolution as high as 5000. In mass spectrometry, resolution R is defined as

$$R = \frac{m}{\Delta m} \tag{16.9}$$

where Δm = the mass difference between two resolved or separated peaks
m = the nominal mass at which the peaks occur

A resolution of 5000 would indicate that $m/e = 5000$ would be resolved from $m/e = 5001$ (or $m/e = 50.00$ from 50.01). A resolution of 500 is sufficient for many applications in organic chemistry, and low-cost instruments offering such resolution may be adequate to solve many problems.

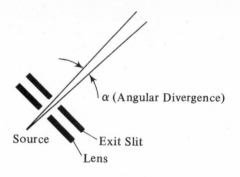

FIGURE 16.5. *An angular divergent beam at the exit of an electron-impact source.*

α (Angular Divergence)

Source   Exit Slit
       Lens

Double-Focusing Mass Spectrometers. If resolution greater than about 5000 is required, a double-focusing mass spectrometer is necessary. Two factors that limit resolution in the single-focusing instruments are the angular divergence and spread in kinetic energy of the ion beam as it leaves the ion gun (see Fig. 16.5). The various ions in the beam always have a small spread of kinetic energies (on the order of a few eV) because they are formed in different regions of the ionization chamber and, therefore, experience different total accelerations. In addition, the neutral molecules enter the source with a Boltzmann distribution of thermal energies, which must be added to the ionization and acceleration energies to obtain the total kinetic energy.

To correct for these aberrations, an *electrostatic analyzer* (ESA) or sector is introduced, usually before the magnetic sector. This device consists of two cylindrical electrodes; a positive voltage is applied to the outer one and a negative voltage of equal magnitude to the inner (see Fig. 16.6). The radius of curvature of an ion beam through this sector is determined by the kinetic energy of the beam for a constant voltage—the higher the kinetic energy, the greater the radius. Ultimately, high-energy ions will be deflected so little that they will impinge on the positive electrode. Ions of low kinetic energy are discharged on the negative electrode. Thus, the ESA serves as a kinetic-energy analyzer.

More specifically, the ESA serves to sort out ions of equal kinetic energy and bring them to a common focus. Thus a beam emanating from a single point (the source) is brought to focus at many points, each representing a common kinetic energy (only two are shown in Fig. 16.6). In turn, the magnetic-field shape can be designed, by proper machining of the pole faces, to refocus the separate beams at one point for each mass-to-charge ratio.

Resolution as high as 150,000 with mass-measuring accuracy of 0.3 ppm can be achieved with one commercial double-focusing spectrometer, and a resolution of 20,000–50,000 is not uncommon. Thus, the exact weight of a compound of nominal molecular weight 600 could be measured to ca. ±0.0002 mass units using the 150,000 resolution instrument. This accuracy allows unambiguous assignment of the elemental composition (chemical formula) of the sample ion and consequently of the neutral sample. Detailed applications will be considered in a later section.

Two designs are prevalent for double-focusing or high-resolution mass spectrometers: (1) Nier-Johnson and (2) Mattauch-Herzog (both shown in Fig. 16.7). The Nier-Johnson design operates only with an electrical detector. The Mattauch-Herzog design uses either a photographic film detector at the focal plane or an electrical detector placed at one point of the plane. The advantage of a photoplate is that it

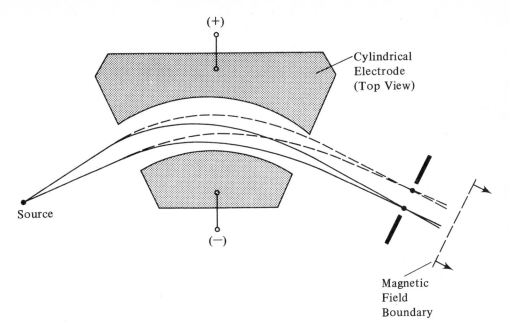

(+)

Cylindrical
Electrode
(Top View)

Source

(−)

Magnetic
Field
Boundary

FIGURE 16.6. *Focusing of a divergent beam of two slightly different kinetic energies (solid and dashed lines) by an electrostatic analyzer (ESA). The ESA is followed by a sector magnet, see Figures 16.4 and 16.7.*

is an integrating detector and can give a reliable spectrum even when evaporation of the sample is discontinuous or sporadic. It is also useful for very small samples because the operator does not have to wait for the magnetic field to be scanned; instead, the entire spectrum is exposed at once.

The disadvantage of film detection is that the plate must be developed and the lines identified to obtain the mass spectrum. Also, intensity data suffer in accuracy (at best, ion abundances can be measured to 10% relative error). Identification of line position and intensity is done with a microdensitometer (as in x-ray crystallography or emission spectroscopy); high-resolution measurements can be made in this manner. The densitometer is usually interfaced to a computer.

Using a Nier-Johnson design, the exact (high resolution) mass measurement is obtained by peak matching. The exact mass of an unknown peak is determined by a high-precision measurement of the changes in accelerating voltage and ESA voltage that are necessary to superimpose the unknown peak on a peak of known mass produced by a mass standard introduced with the unknown sample. Typical mass standards are perfluorinated hydrocarbons or amines. Since $m/e = H^2 r^2 / 2V$,

$$\frac{m_{\mathrm{s}}}{m_{\mathrm{st}}} = \frac{V_{\mathrm{st}}}{V_{\mathrm{s}}} \tag{16.10}$$

where V_{st} = the accelerating voltage needed to focus the standard ions at constant H and r

V_{s} = the voltage needed to focus the sample ions at constant H and r

These measurements are very time-consuming and are usually used to obtain exact mass measurements for only a few important peaks in an unknown spectrum.

A more convenient and expeditious means of mass measurement with either design is to interface an electronic detector with an on-line computer that acquires and stores all the data, both m/e values and intensity data, while the spectrum is being scanned. After identifying the m/e ratios of the mass standard, the computer calculates the exact masses of all the unknown peaks from the scanning time between standard and unknown and, within a few minutes, prints on a teletype the exact masses and intensities of all the peaks in the mass spectrum. This is possibly the most elegant technique in mass spectrometry, for it provides the analyst with exact masses which can be used to determine the elemental compositions of all peaks in a mass spectrum.

For example, a molecular mass of 150.0681 ± 0.003 (2 ppm accuracy) is unique for the composition $C_9H_{10}O_2$ and rules out other samples of nominal mass 150 such as $C_5H_{10}O_5$ ($m/e = 150.0528$), $C_7H_6N_2O_2$ ($m/e = 150.0429$), or $C_9H_{14}N_2$ ($m/e = 150.1157$). Similar arguments can be made for fragment ions as well. Certainly, sample identification using this technique is greatly facilitated compared to that using a low-resolution spectrum, which yields nominal masses only. As might be expected, the high-resolution mass spectrometer equipped with computer is quite expensive ($150,000–$200,000) and complicated to operate and maintain.

Time-of-Flight Mass Analysis

Time-of-flight (TOF) mass spectrometers are equipped with a modified electron-impact source and a long, straight flight-tube. Different masses are distinguished by their different arrival times at the detector located at the end of the tube. Since the kinetic energy of the ions after acceleration is given by Equation 16.3, we can write

$$v = \left(\frac{2Ve}{m}\right)^{1/2} \tag{16.11}$$

Every ion has its own unique velocity, inversely proportional to the square root of the mass. Now if the ions should be accelerated into a long flight-tube of length L, the time necessary for an ion to reach the end of the tube is

$$t = L/v \tag{16.12}$$

The difference in time, Δt, which separates ion 1 from another ion 2, is

$$\Delta t = L(1/v_1 - 1/v_2) \tag{16.13}$$

$$\Delta t = L \frac{\sqrt{m_1} - \sqrt{m_2}}{\sqrt{2Ve}} \tag{16.14}$$

and depends on the difference in the square roots of the masses.

FIGURE 16.7. *Schematic diagrams of the two most commonly used double-focusing mass spectrometers. The Nier-Johnson is really a modified design capable of resolution of 150,000 because of the added hexapole lenses.* From S. Evans and R. Graham, Advan. Mass Spectrom., *6*, 429 (1974), *by permission of Applied Science Publishers, Ripple Road, Barking, Essex, England.*

Mattauch–Herzog

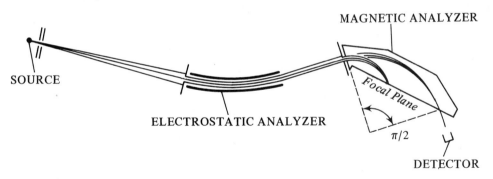

SOURCE

MAGNETIC ANALYZER

ELECTROSTATIC ANALYZER

Focal Plane

$\pi/2$

DETECTOR

Nier–Johnson

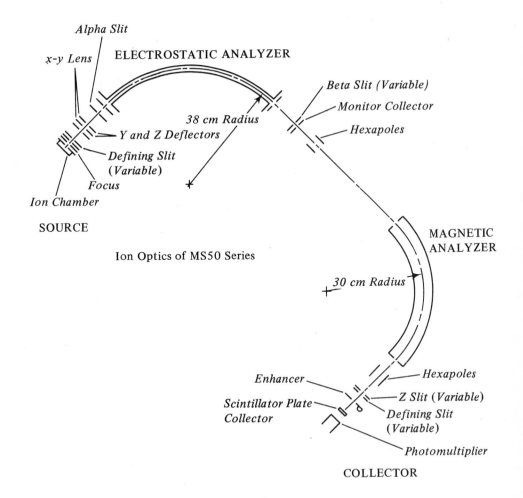

Alpha Slit

x-y Lens

ELECTROSTATIC ANALYZER

Beta Slit (Variable)

Monitor Collector

Hexapoles

38 cm Radius

Y and Z Deflectors

Defining Slit (Variable)

Focus

Ion Chamber

SOURCE

Ion Optics of MS50 Series

MAGNETIC ANALYZER

30 cm Radius

Enhancer

Hexapoles

Z Slit (Variable)

Scintillator Plate Collector

Defining Slit (Variable)

Photomultiplier

COLLECTOR

The instrument is operated in a pulsed mode because continuous ionization and acceleration would lead to a continuous output at the detector with intractable overlapping of various masses. A typical sequence of events for pulsed operation is as follows: (1) The electron gun is turned on for about 10^{-9} sec to form a packet of ions. (2) The accelerating voltage is turned on for about 10^{-4} sec to draw the ions out into the flight tube. (3) All power shuts off for the rest of the millisecond pulse interval, allowing the ion packet to "coast" unhindered down the flight tube. (4) The electron gun turns on again, forming a fresh packet of ions. The spectrum is recorded by bringing the amplified signals from the detector to the vertical deflection plates of a storage oscilloscope. The horizontal axis of the scope is a time base and starts when the accelerating voltage is activated (see Fig. 16.8). With this instrument, as many as 1,000 spectra per second can be obtained.

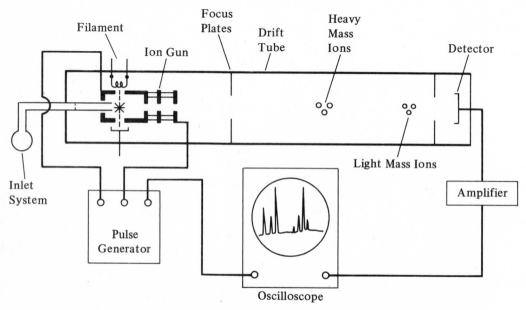

FIGURE 16.8. *Schematic diagram of a time-of-flight mass spectrometer.*

The advantage of a TOF mass spectrometer is its rapidity in scanning a spectrum. The device is extremely useful in monitoring fast gas-phase kinetics, flash photolysis, and shock-tube experiments, and can be used in GCMS applications. It can be used in routine analytical applications, and the best designs have a resolution of around 500 with an upper mass limit of 1000.

Quadrupole Mass Analyzers

Another means of accomplishing mass analysis without the use of magnetic fields is a *path-stability mass spectrometer* (often called a *mass filter*). In these devices, an ion beam from a conventional source is injected into a dynamic arrangement of electromagnetic fields. Certain ions will take a "stable" path through the analyzer and be collected; others will describe "unstable" paths and be filtered out. The quadrupole is one example of this type of mass spectrometer and has become quite popular in recent years, especially in the area of GCMS.

The quadrupole mass analyzer consists of four poles arranged as shown in Figure 16.9. Ions are injected along the z-axis into a radio-frequency field formed by application of a DC voltage U and an RF voltage $V \cos \omega t$ to the four electrodes. The voltage of the positive electrode is $+(U + V \cos \omega t)$ and that of the negative electrode is $-(U + V \cos \omega t)$. Because V is larger than U, the opposite poles change polarity at twice the RF frequency. The polarity changes are 180° out of phase

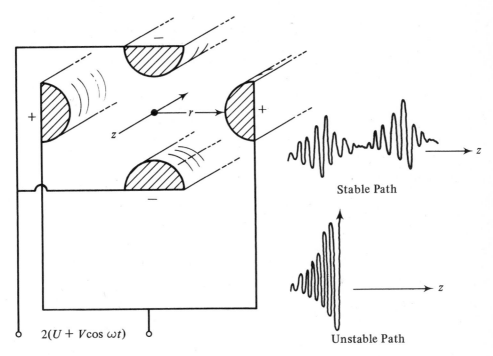

FIGURE 16.9. *Quadrupole mass-analyzer. Ions are injected from the electron-impact source along the z-axis. Ideally, the poles are hyperbolic in cross-section; in practice, circular poles are used. Pole length is approximately 20 cm and r about 2 cm.*

(that is, when the vertical poles are positive, the horizontal poles are negative). Solution of the differential equations of motion for the ions is rather complicated; it is sufficient here to point out that two types of solution are obtained, representing either a stable path or an unstable path. Both paths involve oscillation about the z-axis because of the alternating field, but as can be seen from Figure 16.9, those ions (ideally of one mass only) in a "stable" path will pass through whereas all others will take the unstable course and be discharged on collision with the poles (they are filtered out). As U and V are varied while keeping the U/V ratio constant, ions of one mass after another will take the stable path and be collected on a detector located at the end of the mass analyzer.

Quadrupoles have a number of distinctive advantages. First, the path does not depend on the kinetic energy or the angular divergence of the incoming ions, so these instruments have high transmission. Second, they are relatively inexpensive and compact. Third, a complete scan can be achieved very rapidly since only a change in voltage is required. As a result of these advantages, such instruments are often used in the GCMS combination (where rapid scanning is a requirement) and in space or satellite work. They perform fairly well as routine analytical instruments; for some designs, an upper mass limit of ~ 1000 amu with resolution of 700–800 can be achieved.

Ion Cyclotron Resonance

A recent and exciting development in mass spectrometry is *ion cyclotron resonance* (ICR), a technique used for the study of ion-molecule reactions [4–6]. Here ions are formed by electron impact in crossed electric and magnetic fields. The ions then drift along the length of the cell with a velocity given by cE/H, where E is the static electric field, H is the magnetic field strength, and c the speed of light (see Fig. 16.10). Since the electric field (drift field) is quite small (~ 0.1–1.0 V/cm), the residence time is greater than 1 msec—approximately 10^3 times longer than in a conventional mass spectrometer. As a result, reactions between the ions and any neutral molecules present can take place.

Mass analysis occurs in the analyzer section using the cyclotron principle.

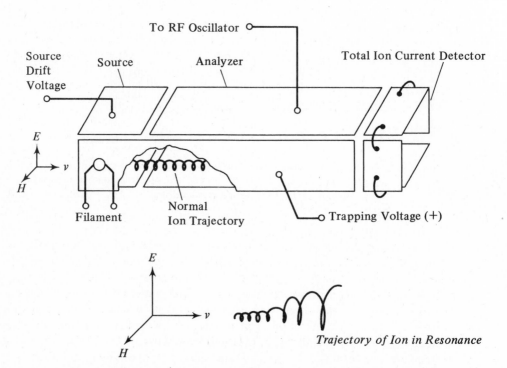

FIGURE 16.10. *The cell used in ion-cyclotron resonance spectroscopy. The cell is located in a vacuum chamber, placed between the poles of an electromagnet with the E and H fields as shown by the axes.*

Drifting ions formed in a uniform magnetic field will travel in a cycloid with a frequency given by

$$\omega = \frac{eH}{mc} \qquad (16.15)$$

where ω = the frequency in radians/sec

If an alternating electric field is applied to the plates of the analyzer, an ion with a cyclotron frequency equal to the electric-field frequency will absorb energy and begin to spiral (a resonance condition). This energy absorption is detected using a "marginal" oscillator as the source of the alternating voltage (usually in the radio-frequency region), much as in NMR. Using a constant RF input, a mass spectrum of both the primary ions and the secondaries produced in the ion-molecule reactions can be obtained by varying the magnetic field H. The final section of the cell simply collects all the ions and is used to register the total ion current in the cell.

Ion-molecule reactions add a new dimension to mass spectrometry. In addition to the unimolecular decomposition reactions (which are also observed in conventional instruments), bimolecular reactions can be observed. Investigations of these reactions are useful in increasing our understanding of the fundamentals of chemical kinetics and for studying structures and properties of ions without solvation effects (acidity, basicity, stability, etc.). The structure of neutral molecules can also be investigated by allowing them to react with reagent ions. Conventional instruments can be used for ion-molecule reaction studies, but a high pressure (0.01–1 torr) of the neutral molecules must be employed because of the short residence time, thus restricting the reaction studies to molecules with a high vapor pressure. ICR has the advantage of a long residence time and a low kinetic energy of the ions, which means that lower pressures (10^{-5} torr) are adequate.

Methods of Ion Detection

The most useful and sensitive method of detection is to focus the mass-analyzed beam of ions on an *electron multiplier*. (The design of electron multipliers is much the same as that of a photomultiplier tube in ultraviolet-visible spectroscopy [see Chap. 7].) The tube current is amplified and sent to a strip-chart recorder, which often contains, instead of a pen, a mirrored galvanometer that reflects high-intensity light onto photographic paper. The mirror method allows faster scanning than a pen trace; it also allows simultaneous recording of the spectrum at a number of different sensitivities using several galvanometers.

Another, less common, method of detection is a photographic film placed along the focal plane of a Mattauch-Herzog instrument.

16.2 INTERPRETATION OF A MASS SPECTRUM

Certainly the most important applications of mass spectrometry are the identification of complex molecules and the elucidation of their structures. It might be expected that a given molecule would give a unique fragmentation pattern that would distinguish it from all other substances. This expectation is realized often, but not always. As in other forms of spectroscopy, the analyst must be able to interpret the pattern he observes; this requires considerable skill and experience. In the following pages, we will discuss the types of ions found in a mass spectrum in order to present some rather basic procedures in interpretation. More thorough approaches can be found in specialized monographs.

Mass spectrometry is an extremely information-rich technique, producing many signals or peaks for a single substance. Its chief advantage over other information-rich tools (such as NMR, IR, and x-ray spectroscopy) is its sensitivity—useful spectra can be obtained for samples as small as one nanogram. However, a complete understanding of all the fragmentation mechanisms has not yet been achieved.

Assignment of the Molecular Ion

As previously discussed, the *molecular ion* has a mass that corresponds to the molecular mass of the neutral sample. Because one electron has been removed, it is a radical cation, symbolized by $M^{\ddot{+}}$ or often just M^+. Most substances produce a recognizable molecular ion, although there are important exceptions. High-molecular-weight hydrocarbons, aliphatic alcohols, ethers, and amines produce only a small number of molecular ions that may be difficult to find if the signal-to-noise ratio is small. Polyfunctional compounds such as carbohydrates and polyamines often do not yield a molecular ion upon electron impact. On the other hand, molecules possessing an aromatic ring often give abundant molecular ions, presumably because of their ability to delocalize positive charge.

The first problem in dealing with an unknown spectrum is the identification of the molecular ion. Some simple rules are helpful. First, M^+ should have the highest mass, ignoring isotopic contributions. Second, the molecular mass will be an even mass-number if it contains an even number $(0, 2, 4, \ldots)$ of nitrogen atoms, and will be an odd mass number otherwise; this is known as the "nitrogen rule." Some examples are: benzene, C_6H_6, $M^+ = 78$; ethanol, C_2H_5OH, $M^+ = 46$; cholesterol, $C_{27}H_{46}O$, $M^+ = 386$; dimethyl hydrazine, $CH_3NHNHCH_3$, $M^+ = 60$; methylamine, CH_3NH_2, $M^+ = 31$; pyridine, C_5H_5N, $M^+ = 79$. A final test of a correct M^+ assignment is that no illogical losses should be found. Seldom do organic molecules lose more than 4 hydrogen atoms, to give $(M - 4)$ fragments. The next reasonable fragmentations of molecular ions are losses of a methyl group $(M - 15)$, NH_2 or O $(M - 16)$, OH or NH_3 $(M - 17)$, H_2O $(M - 18)$, F $(M - 19)$, HF $(M - 20)$, and C_2H_2 $(M - 26)$. Thus, if a tentative molecular ion has lost 4 to 14 or 21 to 25 mass units, either the assignment of M^+ is incorrect or the spectrum is of a mixture.

Elemental Composition of the Molecular Ion

In the spectrum of methane (CH_4), a small peak located at $m/e = 17$ has an intensity 1.1% that of the M^+ peak at $m/e = 16$. The signal at $m/e = 17$ arises because carbon consists of two naturally occurring stable isotopes: ^{12}C and ^{13}C. Assigning the value 100% to the quantity of ^{12}C (an incorrect, but useful, procedure), we find that ^{13}C is 1.1%. Thus $m/e = 17$ in methane is $^{13}CH_4^+$. A molecule that contains six carbon atoms, such as benzene (C_6H_6), will have M^+ at $m/e = 78$ and $^{13}CC_5H_6$

TABLE 16.2. *Relative Isotopic Abundances of Some Common Elements*

Element	M		M + 1		M + 2	
	Mass	Percent	Mass	Percent	Mass	Percent
H	1	100	2	0.015	———	
C	12	100	13	1.08	———	
N	14	100	15	0.36	———	
O	16	100	17	0.04	18	0.20
S	32	100	33	0.80	34	4.4
Cl	35	100	———		37	32.5
Br	79	100	———		81	98.0

at $m/e = 79$, but now the intensity at 79 is 6.6% ($1.1\% \times 6$), since the probability of finding one ^{13}C is six times greater.

The analyst can make use of the natural abundance of ^{13}C to assign the number of carbon atoms in M^+. For example, if M^+ is 100% and $(M + 1)^+$ is 7.7%, M^+ contains 7 carbons. Often M^+ is not the largest peak in a mass spectrum and therefore is not assigned an intensity of 100% (the largest peak in a spectrum is usually arbitrarily assigned an intensity of 100% and all other peaks are measured relative to this). In that case, a useful formula is

$$\text{No. of carbon atoms} = \left(\frac{M + 1}{M}\right)\Big/ 0.011 \qquad (16.16)$$

where $M + 1$ and M are the intensities of the respective peaks. This procedure works fairly well if M^+ contains 10 or fewer carbon atoms. A relative error of 10% in the measurement of $M + 1$ or impurities in the spectrum make the number of carbon atoms a maximum rather than exact number at best. If $M^+ = 100\%$ and $M + 1 = 17.8\%$, the maximum number of C's is 16 ($1.1\% \times 16 = 17.6\%$); although the molecule may contain 15 carbons, it cannot contain 17 carbon atoms.

Other elements have isotopic contributions helpful in determining how many atoms of that element are contained in M^+. Table 16.2 gives some examples. The halogens are noteworthy: an M^+ that contains one Cl must have an $M + 2$ peak with at least 1/3 the abundance of M^+, and a bromine-containing molecule will have nearly a 1:1 ratio of $M:(M + 2)$.

Using the data in the table, the chemist can predict the pattern at M, M + 1, and M + 2 for a suspected compound and compare it with experiment. For example, with 4-chloropyridine one would expect the following:

Ion		Composition	m/e	Abundance (calculated)
M^+	=	$C_5H_4N^{35}Cl$	113	100%
$M + 1$	=	$\left.\begin{array}{l}{}^{13}CC_4H_4N^{35}Cl \\ C_5H_4{}^{15}N^{35}Cl\end{array}\right\}$	114	$5(1.1) + 1(0.4) = 5.9\%$
$M + 2$	=	$C_5H_4N^{37}Cl$	115	$1(32.5) = 32.5\%$
$M + 3$	=	$\left.\begin{array}{l}{}^{13}CC_4H_4N^{37}Cl \\ C_5H_4{}^{15}N^{37}Cl\end{array}\right\}$	116	$0.325[5(1.1) + 1(0.4)] = 1.9\%$

If the observed pattern at $m/e = 113$–116 agrees with the calculation, the evidence is strong that M^+ is C_5H_4NCl.

Most other elements have distinctive isotopic compositions which can be obtained by referring to a handbook. These patterns are useful for confirming the presence of that element in M^+.

The procedures outlined above for estimating the elemental composition of molecular ions can be applied to fragment ions as well. For example, a common ion in hydrocarbons or molecules with large alkyl substituents is $C_3H_7^+$ ($m/e = 43$). Molecules containing acetyl groups will give a CH_3CO^+ ion, also at $m/e = 43$. The $m/e = 44$ in the former case will be 3.3% of the intensity at 43, whereas in the latter $m/e = 44$ will be 2.2%. A cautionary note must be interjected: to apply the rules, one must be certain that the $F + 1$ and $F + 2$ masses (where F is a fragment mass) consist only of isotopic contribution to F and not of other fragment ions.

Fragment Ions from Simple Cleavage Reactions

After ionization, most molecules fragment by the simple loss of a portion of the molecule in the form of a free radical. For example, isobutane can readily lose a methyl radical to form the propyl ion ($m/e = 43$).

$$
\begin{array}{c}
\overline{CH_3} \quad \rceil^{\pm} \\
| \\
CH_3\overset{}{C}HCH_3
\end{array}
\longrightarrow CH_3\overset{+}{C}HCH_3 + \dot{C}H_3
\qquad (16.17)
$$

The fragment ions formed in these reactions are often gas-phase carbonium ions, the same ions observed as intermediates in certain solution reactions of organic compounds. Many mass-spectral fragmentations produce the thermodynamically most stable carbonium ions. Notice that the propyl ion has an odd mass-number ($m/e = 43$), which is typical for all simple cleavage ions possessing an even number of nitrogen atoms. (Molecular ions with an even number of nitrogen atoms have even masses, by the nitrogen rule described above.) Although a complete treatment of simple cleavage reactions is not possible here, a brief introduction in terms of structural types will be presented [7–9].

Aliphatic Hydrocarbons. The mass spectra of two isomeric hydrocarbons are given in Figure 16.11. Straight-chain hydrocarbons and molecules containing large *n*-alkyl groups typically give a pattern similar to that shown in Figure 16.11A. The data are reported in bar-graph form with the largest peak (called the *base peak*) assigned an abundance of 100%. The right-hand axis is expressed as a percentage of all ion intensities summed together. Another common method of presenting mass-spectral data is in tabular form, a list of all m/e ratios and their relative abundances (again normalized to the most intense peak).

Various alkyl ions such as $C_3H_5^+$, $C_3H_7^+$, $C_4H_7^+$, $C_4H_9^+$ ($m/e = 41$, 43, 55, and 57) dominate hydrocarbon spectra, but these do not come from initial simple

FIGURE 16.11. *A: Electron-impact spectrum of n-decane, $C_{10}H_{22}$, at 70 eV ionizing energy. B: Electron-impact spectrum of 3,3,5-trimethyl-heptane, an isomer of n-decane. Notice the change from the "normal" alkyl pattern.*

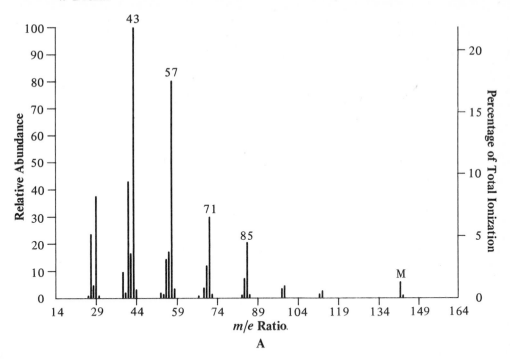

n-Decane

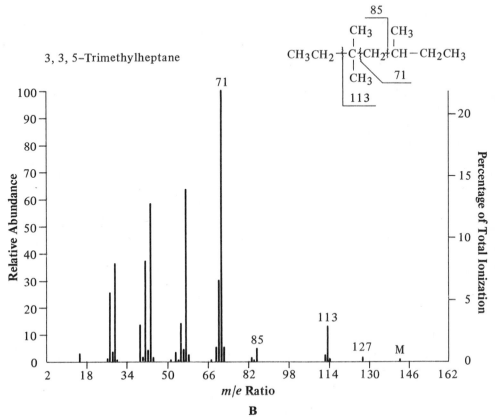

3, 3, 5–Trimethylheptane

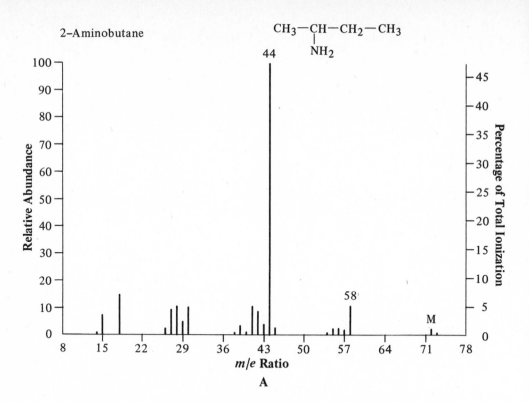

FIGURE 16.12. *Mass spectra of a series of sec-butyl compounds. Major features of the spectra can be interpreted in terms of simple initial cleavage reactions. All are at 70 eV ionizing energy.*

cleavages of M^+, but rather from subsequent decomposition of the initially formed ions. Branching in an alkyl chain can be detected by slight perturbations of the straight-chain spectrum caused by preferential cleavages at the branch points (see Fig. 16.11B). Thus, the most significant fragments are not the high-abundance ions at low mass, but rather the low-abundance high-mass ions formed by simple cleavage at branch points.

Saturated Aliphatic Compounds Containing Heteroatoms. A great variety of organic matter falls in this classification—for example, alcohols, ethers, mercaptans, amines, and halides. Two types of simple cleavage reactions may occur that are initiated or directed by the presence of the heteroatom (O, S, N, X, etc.), as exemplified by Equations 16.18 and 16.19 for ethyl ether. Heteroatoms that can stabilize the positive

$$CH_3CH_2OCH_2CH_3^+ \longrightarrow \cdot CH_3 + [CH_3CH_2O\overset{+}{C}H_2 \longleftrightarrow CH_3CH_2\overset{+}{O}=CH_2]$$

$$m/e = 59 \ (51\% \ \text{Rel. Abund.}) \qquad \textbf{(16.18)}$$

$$CH_3CH_2OCH_2CH_3^+ \longrightarrow CH_3CH_2O\cdot + \overset{+}{C}H_2CH_3 \qquad \textbf{(16.19)}$$

$$m/e = 29 \ (40\% \ \text{Rel. Abund.})$$

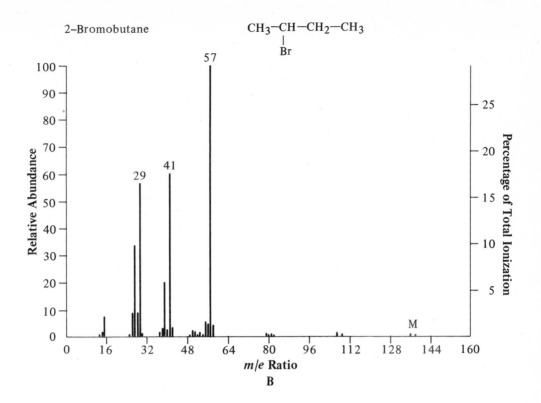

2-Bromobutane

CH₃—CH—CH₂—CH₃
         |
         Br

B

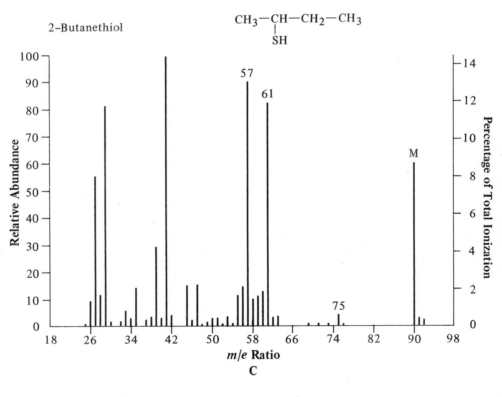

2-Butanethiol

CH₃—CH—CH₂—CH₃
         |
         SH

C

charge by resonance prefer path 16.18. Other, more electronegative, heteroatoms prefer path 16.19. Aliphatic amines fragment almost exclusively by path 16.18; alcohols, ethers, and thio compounds fragment by both pathways; and halogen compounds preferentially lose the X· (path 16.19). Thus, 2-aminopropane undergoes loss of both hydrogen and a methyl group to give $m/e = 58$ and 44, respectively; whereas 2-bromopropane loses Br almost exclusively.

$$
\left[\overline{\underset{\underset{CH_3-CH-NH_2}{|}}{CH_3}} \right]^{+} \cdot
\longrightarrow
\begin{cases}
CH_3-CH=\overset{+}{N}H_2 + \cdot CH_3 \\
\quad m/e = 44\ (100\%\ \text{Rel. Abund.}) \\[1.2em]
\underset{\underset{CH_3-\overset{+}{C}=NH_2 + \cdot H}{|}}{CH_3} \\
\quad m/e = 58\ (10\%\ \text{Rel. Abund.})
\end{cases}
\tag{16.20}
$$

$$
\left[\overline{\underset{\underset{CH_3-CH-Br}{|}}{CH_3}} \right]^{+}
\longrightarrow
\underset{\underset{CH_3\overset{+}{C}H + Br\cdot}{|+}}{CH_3}
\tag{16.21}
$$
$$
m/e = 43\ (100\%\ \text{Rel. Abund.})
$$

Try to rationalize the three spectra in Figure 16.12 using the rules just discussed!

Notice that when there is a choice between the loss of various radicals (hydrogen, methyl, ethyl, etc.), the larger group is preferred, as in reaction 16.20. This is generally true of all simple cleavage reactions at 70 eV of ionizing energy.

Alkenes and Doubly Bonded Heteroatoms. One might expect that a double bond in a long hydrocarbon chain, such as a fatty acid, could be located by mass spectrometry since formation of allyl ions would be preferred:

$$
R-CH_2-CH=\overline{CH}\big|^{+} \xrightarrow{-H} R=CH=CH-\overline{CH_2}\big|^{+} \longrightarrow \text{etc.}
$$
$$
\big\lfloor \xrightarrow{-R} \overset{+}{C}H_2-CH=CH + \text{other fragments}
\tag{16.22}
$$

This possibility is not realized because the double bond rearranges or migrates after ionization but prior to fragmentation. As a result, isomeric olefins tend to give nearly identical spectra. Examples of this kind constitute a serious drawback of electron-impact ionization if complete sample identification is required.

If the molecule contains a double bond to a heteroatom, such as in a carbonyl group, the simple cleavage reaction occurs adjacent to this group and locating the functional group is often straightforward. Here, double-bond migration is not a problem. An example is 2-butanone, which gives a base peak corresponding to loss of an ethyl group, but also experiences some loss of methyl.

$$
\underset{\underset{CH_3\overset{O}{\overset{\|}{C}}CH_2CH_3}{}}{}^{+} \cdot
\longrightarrow
\begin{cases}
CH_3\overset{O}{\overset{\|}{C}}{}^{+} + CH_3\dot{C}H_2 \\
\quad m/e = 43\ (100\%\ \text{Rel. Abund.}) \\[1.5em]
CH_3CH_2\overset{O}{\overset{\|}{C}}{}^{+} + \cdot CH_3 \\
\quad m/e = 57\ (7\%\ \text{Rel. Abund.})
\end{cases}
\tag{16.23}
$$

Note again that loss of the larger alkyl is preferred. This type of fragmentation is found in most carbonyl compounds (acids, aldehydes, esters, etc.).

Aromatic Compounds. The spectrum of benzene (Fig. 16.13) is archetypal of unsubstituted aromatic compounds. Usually one of the most intense peaks is M^+, and the fragmentation pattern is quite simple (compare with Fig. 16.11). The reason is that aromatic compounds are readily able to stabilize a positive charge by delocalization. The only possible single cleavage in benzene is loss of H to give $C_6H_5^+$ ($m/e = 77$). Ring opening and cleavage give rise to $C_4H_4^+$ ($m/e = 52$) and $C_3H_3^+$ ($m/e = 39$).

Substituted aromatics such as shown in Equation 16.24 fragment preferentially by loss of R to give the stable benzyl ion, which is known to rearrange to the symmetrical tropylium ion (*A*)

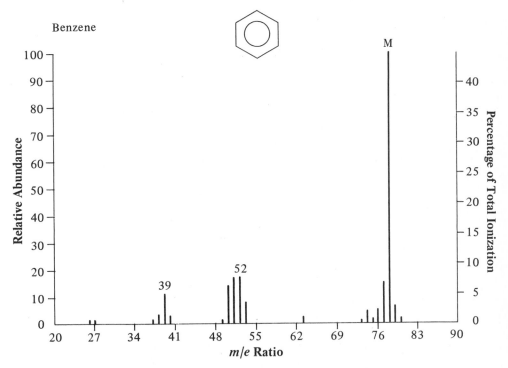

The spectra of *ortho-*, *meta-*, and *para*-substituted compounds are often identical because the substituent location is lost in the 7-membered ring ion. Except for

FIGURE 16.13. *Electron-impact mass-spectrum of benzene at 70 eV of ionizing energy.*

specific *ortho*-disubstituted compounds, the chemist cannot use mass spectrometry for assigning ring-substituted isomers in various aromatics.

Fragment Ions from Rearrangements of M⁺

Since rearrangements may alter the original skeleton of a molecule, one might think that they are troublesome in mass-spectral interpretation. Actually, a number of fragmentations of M^+ involving rearrangement are analytically very useful. Most of these processes occur by loss of a neutral molecule, rather than a radical, and are found at even masses in a mass spectrum (if the number of nitrogen atoms is even). Thus, a rather abundant even-mass ion at the higher-mass end of the spectrum should be singled out for special attention. We will discuss only a few examples to illustrate the interpretive procedure.

The McLafferty Rearrangement. In many compounds containing a doubly bonded heteroatom (C=X), a hydrogen will transfer to X from the third carbon down the chain from C=X, with the loss of an olefin. The process is illustrated for 2-hexanone:

$$m/e = 58 \tag{16.25}$$

The transfer is highly specific, involving only the hydrogen shown. This fragmentation is known as the *McLafferty rearrangement.* Notice the fragment ion has an even mass-number ($m/e = 58$), which is typical for rearrangements of this kind. Because most initial fragmentations are cleavage reactions that yield odd mass-numbers (unless the number of nitrogen atoms is odd), highly abundant rearrangements are easy to pick out of the spectrum. The fragmentation occurs in many other carbonyl compounds (acids, esters, amides, aldehydes, and so on), provided a hydrogen is situated 3 atoms from the carbonyl.

The analytical utility of the McLafferty rearrangement is illustrated for 3-methyl-2-pentanone, an isomer of 2-hexanone:

$$m/e = 72 \tag{16.26}$$

The molecular ion is again of the correct structure to give a McLafferty rearrangement, but this time to yield $m/e = 72$, indicating that the methyl substituent is in position 3. Rather subtle differences in molecular structure, such as the position of the branch point, can be often uncovered using information from this rearrangement.

Rearrangements in Aromatic Compounds. An important fragmentation in various substituted aromatic compounds involves the transfer of a side-chain hydrogen atom to X (where X = CH_2, O, S) or to the aromatic ring:

$$\text{C}_6\text{H}_5\!-\!X(CH_2)_n\overline{CH_3}\Big]^{+\cdot} \longrightarrow \quad \text{C}_6\text{H}_5\!-\!\overline{XH}\Big]^{+\cdot} \quad \text{or} \quad \Big]^{+\cdot} \qquad (16.27)$$

$$[n = 1, 2, \ldots]$$

Thus, the base peak in the spectrum of phenyl ethyl ether is $m/e = 94$ (C_6H_5OH); and an important peak (55% relative abundance) in the spectrum of butyl benzene is $m/e = 92$ (C_7H_8). Isotopic labeling studies with deuterium show that H-transfer occurs from any one of the four carbon atoms in phenyl butyl ether, suggesting a nonspecific rearrangement. Nevertheless, the fragmentation is analytically useful—only phenyl ethyl ether, of the other $C_8H_{10}O$ isomers shown, gives loss of C_2H_4.

We have only discussed two types of rearrangement involving M^+ processes. Many others are highly specific and quite useful in elucidating molecular structure; others, less specific, can still yield information (for instance, the side-chain rearrangement above). Rearrangements invariably involve the loss of small neutral molecules such as olefins, H_2O (in alcohols), small alcohols (in some esters), acids, carbon monoxide, formaldehyde, etc. They are readily identified in the high-mass region of the spectrum as even-mass-number ions (for an even number of nitrogen atoms) and are usually useful in mass-spectral interpretation.

Further Fragmentation Reactions

Enough energy is often deposited in the molecular ion by the ionization process to again decompose the initially formed fragments, producing secondary, tertiary, etc., ions at lower masses. The mass spectra for complicated molecules often contain very abundant fragment ions of low mass, which are products of these consecutive decompositions. In the hydrocarbon spectra (Fig. 16.11), notice the abundant peaks around $m/e = 29$, 43, and 57. These are not initially formed fragments, but rather arise by successive rearrangement reactions. For example, $m/e = 43$ ($C_3H_7{}^+$) probably originates by the loss of C_2H_4 from $C_5H_{11}{}^+$, C_3H_6 from $C_6H_{13}{}^+$, or of other neutral olefins from higher-mass primary ions. These rearrangements are less useful for interpretation than the initial fragmentations and may even be misleading to the inexperienced analyst. There is a strong tendency, for instance, to incorrectly interpret abundant $C_3H_7^+$ as indicating a branched propyl group, although in some instances this may be the case. [An abundant $m/e = 43$ ($C_3H_7^+$) would be significant if the abundances at $m/e = 57$ ($C_4H_9^+$) and $m/e = 29$ ($C_2H_5^+$) were very small.]

The extensive fragmentation that often occurs in complex molecules can be attenuated so as to emphasize the initial cleavages. This is done by lowering the ionizing energy to 15–20 eV or by using other methods of ionization (e.g., chemical or field), which are discussed later.

Multiply Charged Ions

Besides the singly charged ions that dominate a mass spectrum, some doubly charged fragments can be found. For example, a weak peak at $m/e = 38.5$ (77/2) in the spectrum of benzene is $C_6H_5^{2+}$. Gas-phase metal ions from organometallic compounds or from volatile metals such as mercury are often found in $+2$ or even $+3$ states. Usually, multiply charged ions are of low abundance and not very useful in interpretation.

Metastable Ions

In all mass spectrometers, fragmentation continues to occur outside the source (that is, after full acceleration). If, in a sector instrument, an ion (M_1^+) decomposes to M_2^+ prior to entering the magnetic field [$M_1^+ \rightarrow M_2^+ + (M_1 - M_2)$], the M_2^+ will no longer have the same kinetic energy as the "normal" ions and, therefore, will not be mass analyzed at M_2. Instead, its kinetic energy is $M_2(M_2/M_1)$ because of energy conservation, and the ion will be analyzed at a lower apparent mass $m^* = M_2^2/M_1$.

Metastables are usually identified by broad low-abundance peaks occurring at fractional masses. For example, in acetophenone, one might postulate that a methyl group is lost to form the $m/e = 105$ ion, which then loses CO to form $m/e = 77$. An alternate route is the direct, one-step loss of CH_3CO. Both processes are

$$m/e = 120 \qquad m/e = 105 \qquad \xrightarrow[-CO]{*} C_6H_5^+ \qquad m/e = 77 \tag{16.28}$$

verified by the observation of two metastable peaks (designated by * in 16.28) at $77^2/105 = m/e = 56.5$ and at $77^2/120 = m/e = 49.4$. Metastable peaks, then, are invaluable aids in determining which decompositions took place to give the observed mass-spectral patterns.

Negative Ions

Negative ions can be investigated by reversing the polarity of the accelerating voltage and the magnetic field. Usually they are formed by one of two processes: (a) the neutral molecule captures an electron from the ionizing beam to form M^-, or (b) ion-pair production ($AB + e^- \rightarrow A^+ + B^- + e^-$), which yields fragmentary negative ions. The abundances of negative ions are 10–1000 times less than those of positive ions, and it is not yet clear how useful the technique of negative-ion mass spectrometry will be in identifying compounds.

16.3 ANALYTICAL APPLICATIONS OF ELECTRON-IMPACT MASS SPECTROMETRY

Identification and Structural Elucidation of Compounds

It should be clear from the last section that a mass spectrum yields a wealth of information from very small samples (10^{-6}–10^{-9} g). If the mass spectrum has been previously reported, identification of the unknown is accomplished by checking for a match. However, caution must be employed because spectra obtained with different instruments using different temperatures and source conditions will not match identically; small quantitative differences in relative abundances arise because of different residence times in the source and because certain instrument designs may discriminate against low- or high-mass ions. Checking for a match can be done rapidly using a computer with a data file of previously determined spectra. Compilations are available on magnetic tape or in book form (see bibliography). Ideally, the file spectra should be determined using the same instrument under the same conditions; proof of identity is then a peak-to-peak match of the unknown spectrum with a reference.

The use of mass spectra to identify dangerous drugs, both for diagnosis in a hospital setting and in forensics, is an important application. Applications in other fields include identifying such substances as pollutants (environmental work), natural products (biochemistry), flavor components (the food industry), or hydrocarbons (the petroleum industry). Often, the analyst begins with a complex mixture which can be separated by gas chromatography on-line with a mass spectrometer.

Proof of structure for new compounds is more difficult since the mechanisms of mass-spectral fragmentations are not well enough understood to be used to predict the entire spectrum of a postulated structure from basic principles. Using mass-spectral information together with infrared, ultraviolet-visible, and nuclear-magnetic resonance data is a powerful approach. High-resolution mass spectrometry expedites structural studies by providing the formulas (elemental compositions) of M^+ and the fragment ions.

Analysis of Mixtures

Mass spectrometry made important contributions in the analysis of petroleum mixtures during the Second World War. However, GC (gas chromatography) is now preferred because of the convenience and simplicity inherent in a chromatographic procedure. Mass spectra of different hydrocarbons contain many identical peaks, and it is difficult to find one peak characteristic of each component; the reverse is often the case in GC. Nevertheless, the percent composition of a mixture can be obtained by quantitative mass spectrometry using a series of simultaneous equations, much as is done in analyzing mixtures by ultraviolet or visible spectrophotometry (see Chap. 7).

Mass-spectral analysis of simple mixtures may be used in one-time experiments for which the set-up and calibration of a gas or liquid chromatograph are too time-consuming, even though the mass spectrometer must also be calibrated. The convenience of mass-spectral methods for gaseous mixtures recommends this approach, especially if the appropriate gas-handling apparatus is not readily available for GC. However, GC is often preferred for routine work.

With complex mixtures, it may only be necessary to know the types of compounds present. For example, it is important in the petroleum area to determine the approximate concentrations of saturated hydrocarbons, alkenes and cycloalkanes, and aromatics or substituted aromatics in some mixture. The lower-mass series of ions are useful in this pursuit. Alkanes yield abundant fragments at $C_2H_5^+$, $C_3H_7^+$, $C_4H_9^+$, . . . ; alkenes and saturated cyclic alkanes at $C_2H_3^+$, $C_3H_5^+$, $C_4H_7^+$, . . . ; and aromatics at $C_6H_5^+$, $C_7H_7^+$, $C_8H_9^+$. The sum of the intensities of the fragment peaks for any of these series is proportional to the concentration of each type of hydrocarbon.

For complex mixtures, which often occur in biochemical and environmental problems, the mass spectrometer can serve as a highly specific detector for a gas chromatograph. For example, the organic extract of polluted waters may contain hundreds of organic compounds which cannot be perfectly separated by one pass through a GC. Thus, what appears to be a single peak by GC may actually be a

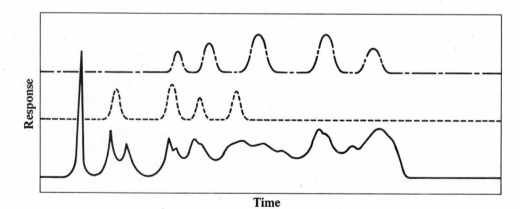

FIGURE 16.14. *Comparison of a total gas-liquid chromatogram obtained from the output of the GC detector or the total ion-current monitor of the mass spectrometer, along with two hypothetical chromatograms obtained by monitoring specific peaks in the mass spectra. Solid line is the total chromatogram; dashed line is the chromatogram made by monitoring one specific ion; broken solid line is the chromatogram made by monitoring another specific ion.*

mixture of a number of components. Each component may have unique M^+ or fragment peaks. To make use of this fact, mass spectra are rapidly obtained at many points across the GC peak and the data stored in an on-line computer. The abundance of certain ions can then be plotted versus time; each ion is specific for one compound in the unresolved GC peak (see Fig. 16.14).

The procedure can be simplified by rapid switching from one peak to another over the GC profile. This is accomplished most efficiently on a sector magnetic instrument by varying the accelerating voltage at a constant magnetic-field strength, and is even more easily carried out with a quadrupole or time-of-flight instrument. The technique is known as *mass fragmentography*.

In inorganic chemistry, mixtures of metal ions in solution can be analyzed by electron-impact mass spectrometry. First the metal ions are complexed with an organic ligand (usually various substituted acetylacetonates) to form volatile metal chelates. If many metal ions are anticipated, the mixture is separated by GC and the separated fractions identified by mass spectrometry. Simple mixtures can be analyzed directly using the mass spectrometer. Because of the high sensitivity of mass spectrometry, trace analysis is possible.

Biochemical Applications

The need for sophisticated analytical tools in the biochemical and health-science areas continues to grow each year. Mass spectrometry is ideally suited for many problems because of its high sensitivity. For instance, the action of drugs in living systems can be better understood if the drug metabolites are isolated and identified. A urine or blood specimen will contain metabolites in trace quantities, and a mass spectrum can be obtained after extraction, concentration, and separation.

Many compounds of biochemical interest have been thoroughly investigated by mass spectrometry. The mechanisms of fragmentation of alkaloids, steroids, and terpenes are fairly well understood [10]. Mass-spectral studies have been reported for amino acids, carbohydrates, and various lipids [11]. However, some molecules of biochemical importance (for example, proteins and nucleic acids) are highly polar, thermally sensitive and of high molecular weight. Thus, it is impossible to vaporize these substances in the source of a mass spectrometer. Prior chemical conversion to various volatile derivatives is helpful, provided the molecular weight is not too high. In this way, small polypeptides (containing 10–12 amino acids) have been analyzed, and the amino-acid sequence determined by mass spectrometry. Spectra can also be obtained of mono- and di-nucleotides after converting the OH groups to $OSi(CH_3)_3$ to break the hydrogen bonding.

Isotope Abundance Studies

Mass spectrometry was originally developed to identify and analyze quantitatively the natural abundances of stable isotopes. The determination of isotopic abundances is still important today, but for different reasons. Isotopic labeling of molecules is quite important in studies of chemical mechanisms and kinetics, both in the organic and biochemical areas. Prior to studies of this kind, the extent of labeling must be determined, and mass spectrometry is usually the method of choice. For example, the amounts of benzene-d_5, -d_4, etc. in benzene-d_6 can be determined by measuring the abundances of $C_6D_6^+$ ($m/e = 84$), $C_6D_5H^+$ ($m/e = 83$), $C_6D_4H_2^+$ ($m/e = 82$), etc. The best procedure is to lower the ionizing energy so that no peaks corresponding to loss of H or D interfere [12].

Sometimes the position of an isotopic label (^2H, ^{13}C, ^{15}N, etc.) can also be determined. The analyst must know whether the compounds undergo prior scrambling reactions before attempting studies of this nature. It would be folly to search for the position of a deuterium in an olefin by mass spectrometry because of the tendency for double-bond migrations to occur while the compound is in the mass spectrometer. However, for compounds giving no scrambling, or only well-understood rearrangements, mass spectrometry can be utilized to locate the label.

Precise isotope ratios are also necessary in studies of kinetic isotope-effects, isotope-dilution studies, and dating work.

The isotope-dilution technique involves "spiking" the sample with the element of interest; the added element, however, has an appreciable difference in isotope-abundance ratios from the natural abundance. As an example, consider a trace analysis of organic bromide, say bromobenzene. If the sample were spiked with 1 μg of C_6H_5Br which contains only bromine-81, and the observed ratio of $^{79}Br : {}^{81}Br$ changes from 1:1 (natural abundance) to 1:2, then the original sample must contain 2 μg of bromobenzene. The method is sensitive to trace amounts of particular elements and has been used for determination of carbon, nitrogen, oxygen, and sulfur in organic and biochemical samples and for analysis of metals in geological specimens.

As one example of dating work, the age of rocks can be determined by measuring the ratio of argon-40 to argon-36 using the mass spectrometer. Argon-40 is a product of potassium-40 decay with a half-life of 1.3×10^9 years. The exact amount of argon-40 is obtained by measuring the ratio of argon-36 to argon-40 with argon-38 added as a tracer. In this way, ages of meteorite and geological samples have been determined in the one-million to one-billion year range.

If high precision is required (1 part in ten thousand), an isotope-ratio mass spectrometer is used. These instruments are normal magnetic-sector instruments with dual inlets and dual collectors. The ion containing one isotope is focused on one collector (^{40}Ar) and an adjoining detector collects the other peak (^{36}Ar). The signals are accurately compared using precision resistors and null detection.

Another timely example is tracing the origin of nitrate in ground and surface waters. At high concentration this substance is toxic, and can only be dealt with if its source can be identified. Different sources (animal waste, fertilizers, natural rocks) have different $^{15}N/{}^{14}N$ ratios; however, the differences are so small that precise ratios requiring an isotope-ratio instrument are needed.

Thermodynamic Studies

An ionization-efficiency curve is a plot of the decrease in intensity of a certain peak (molecular ion or fragment) as the ionizing energy is lowered. There is usually a particular "threshold" energy below which a negligible number of ions appear; this is the ionization potential.

In one method, the energy of the electron beam is varied by changes in the voltage applied to the filament; a more elegant way is to use an intense light source and a monochromator (photoionization). Because most molecules have ionization potentials around 10 eV (124 nm), a rather costly and complicated vacuum monochromator is required to select the ionizing wavelength. Of course, a mass spectrometer is used to monitor ion intensities.

From ion-efficiency curves, the ionization potential of M and the "splitting" potentials of the fragments can be obtained and in turn, bond-dissociation energies and heats of formation of gas-phase ions can be obtained from the ionization potentials [13].

16.4 NEW DEVELOPMENTS AND SPECIALIZED APPLICATIONS

Chemical- and Field-Ionization Mass Spectrometry

Certainly, the molecular weight of the unknown is one of the most important pieces of information to gain from a mass spectrum, but the M^+ peak for certain types of compounds is often absent or of low intensity. Another related drawback to mass spectrometry is consecutive ion-fragmentation in complex molecules, which results in low-mass ions carrying a large share of the total intensity (see Fig. 16.11). Thus, the more analytically important molecular ion and primary fragments (those formed in the initial fragmentation of M^+) are of low abundance or even missing in the spectrum. A major advance is the development of chemical- (CIMS) [14, 15] and field-ionization (FIMS) [16] techniques, which are gentler ionization procedures. The result is enhancement of the abundance of ions containing molecular-weight and initial-fragmentation information.

Instead of ionizing with an energetic electron beam, *chemical ionization* occurs via ion-molecule reactions. The ion, often referred to as a reagent ion, reacts with a sample molecule by transferring a proton or by abstracting an H^- or an electron, which imparts a $+1$ charge to the sample molecule.

Typically, the source of a conventional mass spectrometer is redesigned to operate at a higher pressure (1–10 torr). Methane is admitted and ionized to produce CH_4^+ and CH_3^+. These react to form CH_5^+ and $C_2H_5^+$ as follows:

$$CH_4^+ + CH_4 \longrightarrow CH_5^+ + CH_3 \cdot \tag{16.29}$$

$$CH_3^+ + CH_4 \longrightarrow C_2H_5^+ + H_2 \tag{16.30}$$

The CH_5^+ and $C_2H_5^+$ do not react further with the neutral methane, but once a small amount of sample (XH) is admitted to the source (1 part in 1000 parts methane), the sample molecules are ionized by proton and hydride-ion transfers:

$$CH_5^+ + XH \longrightarrow XH_2^+ + CH_4 \tag{16.31}$$

$$C_2H_5^+ + XH \longrightarrow X^+ + C_2H_6 \tag{16.32}$$

XH_2^+ and X^+ may then fragment, giving a mass spectrum. No molecular ion per se is observed, but the molecular weight is readily obtained from the $M + H$ or $M - H$ peaks.

Other reagent ions, which are weaker gas-phase acids than CH_5^+, may be employed to further simplify the spectrum. Examples include $C_4H_9^+$ (from isobutane), NH_4^+ (ammonia), or H_3O^+ (water). These acids also ionize by proton transfer, but the energies are somewhat less, and the fragmentation of XH_2^+ is minimized. Figure 16.15 shows the electron-impact and chemical-ionization spectra of ephedrine, a biologically important amine. Notice the striking absence of M^+ by electron impact and the abundant M + 1 in the CI spectra. The fragmentation is also simplified by CI.

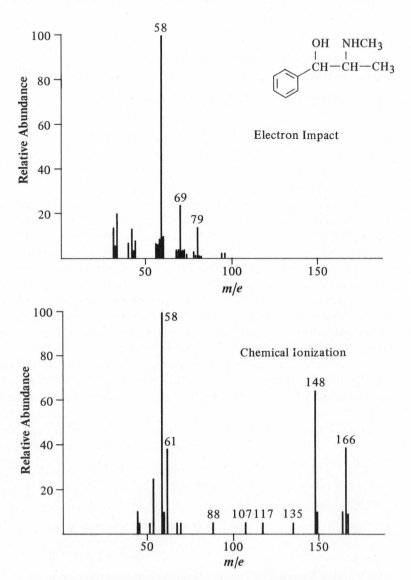

FIGURE 16.15. *Comparison of the electron-impact (EI) and chemical-ionization (CI) mass spectra of ephedrine. From H. M. Fales, H. A. Lloyd, and G. A. W. Milne, J. Amer. Chem. Soc., 92, 1590 (1970), by permission of the publisher. Copyright © 1970 by the American Chemical Society.*

Field ionization employs a conventional mass analysis with a modified source. A small wire or sharp-edged anode is mounted at the input end of the ion gun as shown in Figure 16.16, and a very large electric field (10^5 V/cm) is applied between the anode and cathode. (The anode is first activated so that its surface contains many sharp points (whiskers) by filling the chamber with acetone at 0.04–0.1 torr and applying 10,000 V for several hours.) The electric field is then sufficient to remove an electron from gaseous molecules in the field. It is thought that the high field so distorts

FIGURE 16.16. *Schematic diagram of a typical field-ionization source. This source is simply substituted for the conventional electron-impact source. The remainder of the mass spectrometer is the same. Combined EI/FI sources have been used.*

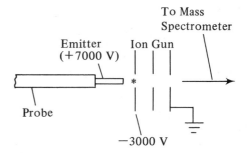

the potential-energy surfaces of the sample molecule that an electron is quantum-mechanically tunneled through the energy barrier to the anode. The practical consequence of this is that the molecular ion so formed is not excited, and very little fragmentation results. Almost every compound gives an abundant M^+ or $(M + 1)^+$ by field ionization, and considerably simplified fragmentation patterns. The electron-impact and field-ionization spectra of ribose are compared in Figure 16.17.

Chemical- and field-ionization are important complements to electron-impact mass spectrometry because they emphasize the molecular-ion region producing small numbers of primary fragmentations and almost no secondary and further fragmentations. By contrast, electron impact gives a wealth of fragmentations at the expense of the molecular ion and of primary fragments. In most cases, the analyst can combine this information to identify the sample. As a result, CI and FI are especially useful for analysis of complex molecules, and in direct analysis of mixtures because of the simple spectra that are produced. Chemical ionization is often a hundred times more sensitive than electron impact, for two reasons: First, the ionization of the sample is concentrated in only a few peaks rather than dispersed over hundreds of peaks as in the electron-impact ionization of complex molecules. Second, the efficiency of ionization by electron impact is approximately 0.1%; that is, only one out of every thousand sample molecules is ionized. The un-ionized sample molecules are lost to the vacuum pumps. Because chemical ionization takes place by ion-molecule reactions, ionization efficiency could be raised significantly by increasing the reagent gas pressure and thus the concentration of reagent ions, and by extending ion-residence times.

Spark-Source Mass Spectrometry

As mentioned previously, mass spectrometry can be applied to nonvolatile inorganic substances by using a spark source. One important analytical application is the

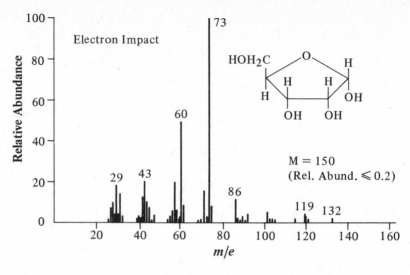

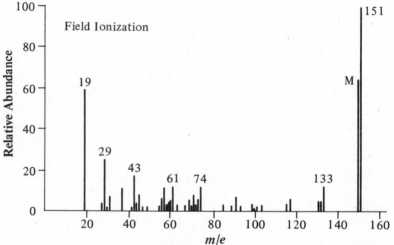

FIGURE 16.17. *Comparison of the electron-impact and field-ionization mass-spectra of d-ribose. The molecular ion is found at m/e = 150. The abundant peak at m/e = 151 is formed by a protonation ion-molecule reaction occurring in the vicinity of the emitter. From H. D. Beckey,* Field Ionization Mass Spectrometry, *Braunschweig-Vieweg, 1971; New York: Pergamon Press, 1971, p 284, by permission of the publisher.*

analysis of fossil fuels, fly ash, and coal dust for trace metals. Because many metals such as mercury, cadmium, arsenic, beryllium, and lead are environmental hazards, it is important to determine their concentration in coal for evaluation of suitable fuels. Another useful application is the analysis of semiconductors for trace elements that affect the electrical properties of the material.

In the biological area, *spark source mass spectrometry* (SSMS) is an ideal tool for trace elemental analysis. First, the sample is ashed by strong heating or by a microwave discharge in oxygen to remove the organic material. The residue is then mixed with pure graphite and sparked in the spectrometer. The presence of elements at ppb levels has been verified in samples such as plant leaves, human and animal tissue, bones, and plasma. A major advantage is that multi-element analysis is possible, although the precision may be less than in other trace element techniques such as anodic stripping voltammetry or atomic absorption spectroscopy.

Surface Analysis

Analysis of solid surfaces in terms of elemental composition is an important problem in modern research. Mass spectrometry, as *secondary-ion mass spectrometry* (SIMS) or *ion-probe analysis* [17], can play a useful role.

The procedure involves bombarding the sample surface with a fast-moving (5–20 keV) ion beam. This beam is produced in a highly efficient discharge source called a duoplasmatron (see Fig. 16.18). The primary ions are focused by a series

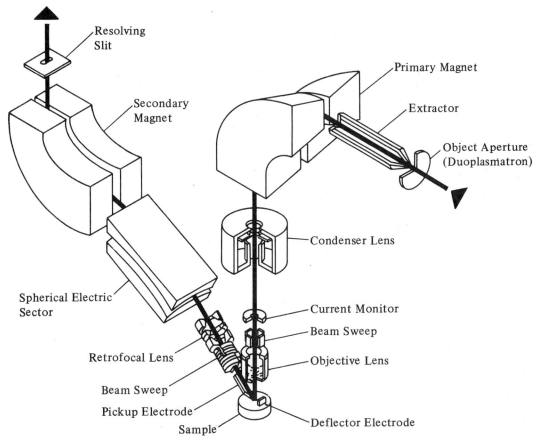

FIGURE 16.18. *Schematic diagram of a secondary-ion mass spectrometer. This particular design is called the Ion Microprobe because very small areas can be investigated with it. From* Chemical and Engineering News, *August* 19, 1968, *p* 30, *by permission of the American Chemical Society, copyright owner.*

of lenses to obtain a narrow, well defined beam. The impacting ions dislodge ("sputter") atoms and ions from the sample as gas-phase species. The secondary ions are drawn into the mass spectrometer for mass analysis. Figure 16.18 shows the use of a double-focusing spectrometer to perform an energy analysis on the secondary beam before a mass analysis. Suitable primary ions can be either inert (Ar^+ or N_2^+) or reactive (O_2^+, O^+).

When the primary ion beam impacts the surface, energy transfer occurs to break lattice bonds and vaporize ions or atoms. Some of the atoms may possess sufficient internal excitation to eject an electron, forming additional gas-phase ions. The majority of the secondary ions are singly charged and monoatomic. One mechanism for ion loss is neutralization at the surface before entering the gas phase. This can be minimized if the surface is a nonconducting matrix, such as a metal oxide, or if the primary ion beam is O_2^+, which reacts at the surface to form a less conducting oxide region. Thus, an oxide-coated metal surface bombarded with Ar^+ will release more ions than a pure metal surface.

This phenomenon brings up a disadvantage of the technique. The ion yield or ionization efficiency of a surface depends on the nature of the element and on the chemical composition at the bombardment location. The yield of an ion from one element relative to another will change as the composition and conditions vary. The results may be complicated because a change in ion output as the surface is sputtered does not necessarily mean a change in the relative elemental composition. Another problem occurs because the sputtering may be nonuniform, i.e., certain elements are removed more efficiently than others. This effect can be minimized by scanning the ion beam across the surface.

Nevertheless, there are many important advantages of secondary ion mass analysis.

1. The technique is highly sensitive, permitting detection of ppb concentrations.
2. Surface areas between 1 mm² to 1 μm² can be investigated, depending on the width of the primary-ion beam. The narrower limits are approached with instrumentation called an *ion microprobe.*
3. Like SSMS, the technique is applicable to all elements and is especially useful for light elements (H through Na), which are not amenable to techniques such as the electron microprobe (Chap. 14).
4. Changes in isotopic composition can be examined because the procedure is mass spectral in nature. Again this is not true for electron microprobes.
5. Three-dimensional analysis is possible with depth resolution of approximately 50–100 Å.

Although secondary-ion mass analysis is still relatively new in terms of applications, it is clear that it will be extremely useful for studies of metallurgical, geological, and semiconductor surfaces and for samples from corrosion and metal-catalyst studies. There may be biochemical and organic applications as well. A number of units are commercially available, including instruments with double-focusing and quadrupole mass-analyzers for the secondary beam. However, the expense is high, ranging from $100,000 to $250,000.

Another technique that permits in-depth profiling of solid surfaces is *ion-*

scattering spectrometry (ISS). A commercial instrument is available from the 3M Company at lower cost than SIMS.

In this method, a sample is mounted in a vacuum chamber and bombarded with noble-gas ions at 0.5 to 3 keV. The primary ions scattered at 90° pass into an electrostatic analyzer identical in principle with those used in double-focusing mass spectrometers. By scanning the voltage to the ESA, velocity analysis is accomplished.

It can be shown that the energy loss of the primary beam at the first monolayer of surface is determined by the mass of the surface atom responsible for the scattering. The relevant equation is

$$E_1/E_0 = (m_s - m_0)/(m_s + m_0) \qquad (16.33)$$

where m_0 = the mass of the primary beam
E_0 = the kinetic energy of the primary beam
E_1 = the energy of the ions scattered at 90°
m_s = the mass of the surface atom

It is clear that if E_1 is measured and m_0 and E_0 are known, the mass of the surface atom, m_s, can be determined and the element identified. The method involves an indirect mass measurement. The number of ions scattered at a certain intensity is proportional to the amount of the element present.

This technique possesses many of the advantages of secondary-ion mass analysis, including studies of isotopic abundances. The method is not as extensively evaluated as SIMS; however, it appears to be capable of major-component analysis extending down to the 0.1 part per thousand range.

Mass-spectrometry principles and techniques have been employed in other kinds of surface studies in which sample atoms are sputtered by interaction with a laser beam or by RF glow discharges. These approaches are more highly specialized, but it should be clear that mass spectrometry is an important tool in surface chemistry. The student should compare SIMS and ISS with other surface analytical techniques such as ESCA, Auger spectroscopy, electron microprobe, and low-energy electron diffraction (see Chaps. 14 and 15).

SELECTED BIBLIOGRAPHY

Instrumentation in Mass Spectrometry

BEYNON, J. H. *Mass Spectrometry and Its Applications to Organic Chemistry.* Amsterdam: Elsevier, 1960.

BLAUTH, E. W. *Dynamic Mass Spectrometers.* Amsterdam: Elsevier, 1966.

KISER, R. W. *Introduction to Mass Spectrometry and Its Applications.* Englewood Cliffs, N.J.: Prentice-Hall, 1965.

MELTON, C. E. *Principles of Mass Spectrometry and Negative Ions.* New York: Marcel Dekker, 1970.

ROBOZ, J. *Introduction to Mass Spectrometry: Instrumentation and Techniques.* New York: Interscience, 1968.

Compilations of Standard Spectra

Catalog of Mass Spectral Data, API Research Project 44. Pittsburgh, Pa.: Carnegie Institute of Technology.

CORNU, A., and MASSOT, R. *Compilation of Mass Spectral Data.* London: Heyden, 1966.

Index of Mass Spectral Data. Philadelphia, Pa.: American Society for Testing and Materials, 1969.

STENHAGEN, E.; ABRAHAMSSON, S.; and MC-LAFFERTY, F. W., eds. *Atlas of Mass Spectral Data.* New York: John Wiley, 1969.

STENHAGEN, E.; ABRAHAMSSON, S.; and MC-LAFFERTY, F. W., eds. *Registry of Mass Spectral Data.* New York: John Wiley, 1974.

Interpretation of Mass Spectra

BIEMAN, K. *Mass Spectrometry: Organic Chemical Applications.* New York: McGraw-Hill, 1962.

HILL, H. C. *Introduction to Mass Spectrometry.* London: Heyden, 1966.

MCLAFFERTY, F. W. *Interpretation of Mass Spectra.* Reading, Mass.: W. A. Benjamin, 1973.

REED, R. I. *Application of Mass Spectrometry to Organic Chemistry.* London: Academic Press, 1966.

REFERENCES

1. J. J. THOMSON, *Rays of Positive Electricity and Their Application to Chemical Analyses*, London: Longmans, Green, and Co., 1913.

2. F. W. ASTON, *Phil. Mag.*, *38*, 707, 709 (1919).

3. A. J. DEMPSTER, *Phys. Rev.*, *11*, 316 (1918).

4. J. D. BALDESCHWIELER and S. S. WOODGATE, *Acc. Chem. Res.*, *4*, 114 (1971).

5. M. L. GROSS and C. L. WILKINS, *Anal. Chem.*, *43*(14), 65A (1971).

6. J. L. BEAUCHAMP, *Ann. Rev. Phys. Chem.*, *22*, 527 (1971).

7. H. BUDZIKIEWICZ, C. DJERASSI, and D. H. WILLIAMS, *Mass Spectrometry of Organic Compounds*, San Francisco: Holden-Day, 1967.

8. J. H. BEYNON, R. A. SAUNDERS, and A. E. WILLIAMS, *The Mass Spectra of Organic Molecules*, Amsterdam: Elsevier, 1968.

9. Q. N. PORTER and J. BALDAS, *Mass Spectrometry of Heterocyclic Compounds*, New York: Wiley-Interscience, 1971.

10. H. BUDZIKIEWICZ, C. DJERASSI, and D. H. WILLIAMS, *Structure Elucidation of Natural Products by Mass Spectrometry*, vol. I, *Alkaloids;* vol. II, *Steroids, Terpenoids, Sugars, and Miscellaneous Natural Products*, San Francisco: Holden-Day, 1964.

11. G. R. WALLER, ed., *Biochemical Applications of Mass Spectrometry*, New York: Wiley-Interscience, 1972.

12. K. BIEMAN, *Mass Spectrometry: Organic Chemical Applications*, New York: McGraw-Hill, 1962, pp 204–50.

13. R. W. KISER, *Introduction to Mass Spectrometry and Its Applications*, Englewood Cliffs, N.J.: Prentice-Hall, 1965, pp 162–206.

14. F. H. FIELD, *Acc. Chem. Res.*, *1*, 42 (1968).

15. B. MUNSON, *Anal. Chem.* *43*(13), 28A (1971).

16. H. D. BECKEY, *Field Ionization Mass Spectrometry*, Oxford: Pergamon Press, 1971.

17. C. A. EVANS, Jr., *Anal. Chem.*, *44*(13), 67A (1972).

PROBLEMS

1. A sector instrument is designed to operate with a radius of 30.00 cm and an accelerating voltage of 3000 V. Calculate the magnetic field (in gauss) necessary to focus the M^+ of methane. What would be the radius of trajectory for CH_3^+ under these conditions?

2. Repeat the calculation for the necessary field to focus the M^+ of naphthalene ($C_{10}H_8^+$). What would be the radius of curvature for the $M - 1$ ion in naphthalene? Comment on the resolution necessary to separate M and $M - 1$ in methane and naphthalene.

3. A sector mass-spectrometer is built to scan to $m/e = 500$ with the maximum field of the electromagnet at 6000 gauss and an accelerating voltage of 3000 V. To examine the molecular ion of a compound of molecular mass 850, what modification in the accelerating-voltage power-supply is required?

4. Draw a schematic diagram of an electron-impact source showing what voltages should be applied to the various components using an accelerating voltage of 1765 V, an ionizing energy of 50 eV, a repeller voltage of 10 V, and a target voltage of 80 V.

5. An unknown compound gives a nominal molecular mass of 220. A mixture of the unknown and perfluorotributylamine $[(C_4F_9)_3N]$ is admitted to a double-focusing mass spectrometer with an accelerating voltage of 5000 V. With $C_4F_9{}^+$ in focus ($m/e = 218.9856$), the accelerating and ESA voltages are reduced to exactly 99.463% of the originals to bring the unknown peak to an identical focus. What is the exact mass of $m/e = 220$? From the data below, what is the elemental composition of $m/e = 220$?

Compound	m/e
$C_{17}H_{16}$	220.1251
$C_{10}H_{20}O_5$	220.1311
$C_{13}H_{20}N_2O$	220.1576
$C_{11}H_{24}O_4$	220.1674
$C_{15}H_{24}O$	220.1827

6. The exact mass of CO is 27.9949 and that of C_2H_4 is 28.0313. What resolution is necessary to just separate CO^+ and $C_2H_4{}^+$ found in a mixture of carbon monoxide and ethylene? Compare this requirement with that necessary to separate $C_{20}H_{40}{}^+$ and $C_{19}H_{36}O^+$, both nominally at $m/e = 280$.

7. The mass spectrum of benzene is obtained on a time-of-flight mass spectrometer of length 100 cm with an accelerating voltage of 3000 V. Calculate the time required for $C_2H_2{}^+$ (one of the low-mass ions), $C_6H_5{}^+$, and $C_6H_6{}^+$ to reach the detector. (Note: the voltage must be expressed in erg/esu,

where 300 volts = 1 erg/esu. The magnitude of the electronic charge is 4.803×10^{-10} esu.)

8. What is the residence time for M^+ of benzene in an ion-cyclotron-resonance cell of length 10 cm with a drift field in both the source and analyzer of 0.25 V/cm? The magnetic field is set at 7,800 gauss. Compare with the residence time of around 10^{-6} sec for a conventional mass-spectrometer source.

9. An electric field of what frequency (in kHz) is necessary to observe the $m/e = 78$ ion from benzene under the conditions in problem 8?

10. Calculate the M + 1, M + 2, etc., abundances for the following molecular ions. To approximate the probability of finding two ^{13}C atoms in a molecule, the following relation can be employed:

$$\frac{M + 2}{M} = \frac{(1.1n)^2}{200}$$

where (M + 2)/M is expressed in percent and n is the number of carbon atoms. Consider the abundance of M^+ to be 100%. (a) C_6H_6; (b) $C_2H_4O_2$; (c) $C_2H_8N_2$; (d) C_3H_7Cl; (e) C_4H_4S; (f) $C_{16}H_{34}$.

11. Mercury as an environmental pollutant is sometimes found as dimethyl mercury. Look up the natural abundance of the mercury isotopes and calculate the pattern to be expected in the molecular-ion region.

12. The methyl group in acetophenone can be deuterated by refluxing a mixture of acetophenone and D_2O with a little base catalyst.

At 15 eV of ionizing energy, no M − 1 is detected for unlabeled acetophenone, and

M + 1 is 8.8%. Calculate the percentage of $-d_3$, $-d_2$, and $-d_1$ after one exchange, if the following abundances are found in the mass spectrum. Remember to correct for ^{13}C.

m/e	Rel. Abund.
124	8.75
123	100.00
122	7.01
121	4.42
120	——

13. Postulate a structure for the compound with the following mass spectrum. After you have settled on a structure, account for the ions found in the spectrum.

m/e	Rel. Abund.	m/e	Rel. Abund.
25	0.10	61	0.74
26	0.36	62	0.64
27	0.77	63	0.51
28	0.14	64	0.07
35	0.12	72	0.35
36	0.30	73	2.1
37	2.0	74	4.3
37.5	0.84	75	4.6
38	5.71	76	3.4
38.5	0.33	77	45.2
39	1.10	78	3.0
40	0.05	79	0.06
47	0.18	84	0.70
48	0.19	85	0.89
49	1.5	86	0.89
50	9.6	87	0.32
51	12.0	88	0.22
52	1.0	97	0.26
53	0.03	99	0.07
54	0.05	108	0.11
54.5	0.08	109	0.04
55	0.34	110	0.10
55.5	0.07	111	0.78
56	3.91	112	100.00
56.5	0.28	113	6.9
57	1.25	114	32.9
57.5	0.09	115	2.1
60	0.47	116	0.06

14. The following mass spectrum was obtained for an amine containing four carbon atoms. What is the compound?

m/e	Rel. Abund.	m/e	Rel. Abund.
15	1.9	43	3.1
27	0.75	44	100.0
28	4.2	45	2.8
29	9.1	56	2.3
30	2.9	57	1.6
31	4.1	58	10.0
32	0.39	59	0.41
33	1.1	71	0.39
39	2.0	72	2.3
40	0.75	73	1.2
41	9.4	74	0.07
42	6.0		

15. The first evidence to prove the existence of a certain inorganic compound was the mass spectrum taken on a time-of-flight mass spectrometer. The data below were measured from a photograph of the oscilloscope display, and as such the M + 1 peaks were too weak to measure. Identify the compound.

m/e	Rel. Abund.	m/e	Rel. Abund.
111	100	128	6
112	10	129	15
113	100	130	7
114	12	144	33
127	15	146	33

16. The following compounds are isomeric C-6 *ketones*. Complete identification should be possible by considering carbonyl-directed cleavages and the McLafferty rearrangement (or lack of it). Identify the compound using these processes.

	Ketone #1		Ketone #2
m/e	Rel. Abund.	m/e	Rel. Abund.
27	14.8	27	49.4
28	4.4	28	10.9
29	33.7	29	68.3
30	0.8	30	1.7
39	7.7	39	12.8
40	1.0	40	1.6
41	26.2	41	23.0
42	3.8	42	8.0
43	100	43	100
44	2.2	44	3.3
55	2.7	55	3.1

Ketone #1		Ketone #2	
m/e	Rel. Abund.	m/e	Rel. Abund.
56	9.0	56	1.9
57	27.4	57	76.1
58	1.3	58	2.5
71	0.9	71	45.6
72	17.1	72	2.5
73	0.8	73	——
85	2.4	85	2.0
100	3.5	100	19.9
101	0.2	101	1.3

17. The following spectrum is that of a compound containing C, H, and O. Also present in the molecule is an aromatic ring. Identify the material.

m/e	Rel. Intensity	m/e	Rel. Intensity
26	0.10	67	0.35
27	4.0	74	0.40
28	0.2	75	0.35
39	6.0	76	0.39
40	1.4	77	7.2
41	4.8	78	0.80
42	0.3	79	0.81
43	4.1	93	0.70
44	0.10	94	100.00
49	0.05	95	6.6
50	1.3	96	0.42
51	4.6	107	2.0
52	0.43	108	0.40
55	1.1	121	0.20
56	0.06	122	0.03
62	0.34	135	0.20
63	1.2	136	25.0
64	0.50	137	2.5
65	4.3	138	0.18
66	5.9		

18. What resolution is necessary to distinguish between molecular oxygen and sulfur in a mass spectrometer?

19. The mass spectrum of methyl alcohol has peaks at $m/e = 15, 28, 29, 30, 31,$ and 32. A broad, low intensity, metastable peak was found at $m/e = 27.13$. Determine the mother and daughter ions.

20. The decomposition of ions with the elemental composition $C_2H_5O^+$ has been studied by Shannon and McLafferty [*J. Amer. Chem. Soc.*, **88**, 5021 (1966)]. A. Metastable peaks caused by the following decompositions were observed:

(a) $C_2H_5O^+ \longrightarrow H_3O^+ + C_2H_2$; and
(b) $C_2H_5O^+ \longrightarrow CHO^+ + CH_4$.

At what m/e values would the metastable peaks caused by these decompositions be found? B. Of the following structural formulas, $HOCH_2CH_2Y$, $CH_3CH(OH)Y$, CH_3OCH_2Y, CH_3CH_2OY, one was found to decompose by route (a) one hundred times less often than any of the other three structures did. Predict which structure it was.

21. The mass spectra of two different trimethylpentanes showed the following relative abundances. [H. W. Washburn et al., *Ind. Eng. Chem., Anal. Ed.* **17**, 75 (1945).]

m/e	Relative Abundance	
	(a)	(b)
43	20	50
57	80	9
71	1	40
99	5	0.1
114	0.02	0.3

Of the two isomers, 2,2,4- and 2,3,4-trimethylpentane, which is more likely to produce the abundances given in column (a)? Write the structures of the ions most likely responsible for the m/e values found.

22. From the following table of mass spectral data deduce the probable structure of the unknown $C_xH_yN_z$.

m/e	Rel. Abund.	m/e	Rel. Abund.
15	3.7	43	2.7
27	3.3	44	0.29
28	4.1	55	2.0
29	3.6	56	2.7
30	6.2	57	5.6
31	0.10	58	100
39	4.8	59	3.6
40	1.4	60	0.05
41	18	73	0.41
42	11	74	0.02

23. The mass spectrum of an unknown compound had the following relative intensities for the M, ($m/e = 86$), M + 1, and M + 2 peaks respectively: 18.5, 1.15, and 0.074 (percentage of base peak). From the following partial list of isotopic abundance ratios, determine the molecular formula of the unknown.

Isotope Abundance
Ratios (M = 100%)

Formula	M + 1	M + 2
$C_4H_6O_2$	4.50	0.48
C_4H_8NO	4.87	0.30
$C_4H_{10}N_2$	5.25	0.11

Isotope Abundance
Ratios (M = 100%)

Formula	M + 1	M + 2
$C_5H_{10}O$	5.60	0.33
$C_5H_{12}N$	5.98	0.15
C_6H_{14}	6.71	0.19

24. Determine the m/e order in which the following gases will appear in the mass spectrum of a mixture containing them: C_2H_4, CO, N_2.

25. Compare and contrast ESCA, Auger spectroscopy, ISS, and SIMS as methods for surface analysis.

17

Thermal Methods of Analysis

NEIL JESPERSEN

In thermal methods of analysis, either temperature change is measured or the temperature is manipulated to produce the measured parameter. Thermogravimetry (TG), differential thermal analysis (DTA), and differential scanning calorimetry (DSC) are the three major methods that use temperature change as the independent variable. Thermometric titration (TT) and direct-injection enthalpimetry (DIE) use temperature as the dependent variable. These five methods will be discussed primarily from an analytical point of view. Each method has its unique characteristics and capabilities; for that reason, the major aspects of each method are considered individually.

17.1 GENERAL CHARACTERISTICS OF THERMAL METHODS

Thermogravimetry involves measuring the mass of a sample as its temperature is increased. A plot of mass versus temperature permits evaluation of thermal stabilities, rates of reaction, reaction processes, and sample composition.

Differential thermal analysis is the monitoring of the difference in temperature between a sample and a reference compound as a function of temperature. These data can be used to study heats of reaction, kinetics, phase transitions, thermal stabilities, sample composition and purity, critical points, and phase diagrams.

Measurement of the differential power (heat input) necessary to keep a sample and a reference substance isothermal as temperature is changed (scanned) linearly is the basis of *differential scanning calorimetry*. In addition to the capabilities mentioned for DTA, DSC can provide more precise values for heats of reaction; it allows quantitative measurement of effects that involve little or no heat of reaction (but do involve finite changes in heat capacity) and may be used to determine heat capacities as a function of temperature. DSC is very sensitive to heat-capacity changes, and allows for more precise measurement of these effects than does DTA.

Thermometric titrations involve monitoring of temperature change as a function of the volume of titrant added. From this, concentrations may be evaluated as in normal titrimetry; ΔH^0, ΔG^0, and ΔS^0 for the reaction may also be calculated under appropriate conditions.

Direct-injection enthalpimetry data are similar to those from TT. However, titration is replaced by a virtually instantaneous injection of reagent, and temperature is monitored as a function of time. As a result, more rapid analysis is possible. Heats of reaction can be readily deduced, and kinetics may be studied in favorable situations.

General Thermodynamic Relationships

Since thermal analyses are usually run under conditions of constant pressure, the underlying thermodynamic equation is the Gibbs-Helmholtz expression:

$$\Delta G^0 = \Delta H^0 - T \Delta S^0 \tag{17.1}$$

where G = the free energy of the system
H = the enthalpy of the system
S = the entropy of the system
T = the temperature in K

The general chemical reaction

$$aA + bB \longrightarrow cC + dD \tag{17.2}$$

is spontaneous as written if ΔG is negative, is at equilibrium if $\Delta G = 0$, and does not proceed if ΔG is positive.* Thermal analysis involves the monitoring of spontaneous reactions.

Methods involving temperature change as the independent variable (TG, DTA, and DSC) take advantage of the $T \Delta S$ term in Equation 17.1. Differentiating the Gibbs-Helmholtz equation with respect to temperature, one obtains†

$$\frac{d(\Delta G)}{dT} = -\Delta S \tag{17.3}$$

This shows how to move from a stable situation (ΔG positive) to one where reaction will occur. If ΔS is positive, an increase in temperature will eventually cause ΔG to become negative, whereas if ΔS is negative, decreasing the temperature will achieve the desired spontaneous reaction.‡ Once the reaction is made to occur, each of the

---

* It is important to note that in some cases the reaction may not proceed under certain conditions even though ΔG is negative. A mixture of oxygen and hydrogen is a case in point. Such metastable states, while of considerable interest, are outside the scope of this discussion.

† Equation 17.3 is a gross oversimplification: it assumes that neither ΔS nor ΔH varies with temperature. This is not so. However, the possible variations of ΔH and ΔS will usually only affect the temperature at which ΔG becomes negative, not the fact that it will eventually do so.

‡ Once the spontaneous reaction starts, it proceeds at a rate dependent upon the kinetic characteristics of the sample.

three methods may be used to detect the process, often yielding different and complementary information.

The second group of methods (TT and DIE) involves the creation of a spontaneously reacting mixture by combining two or more chemical species. Then,

$$\Delta T = \frac{-\Delta H n_{\mathrm{p}}}{C'_{\mathrm{p}}} \tag{17.4}$$

where n_{p} = the number of moles of product formed
          C'_{p} = the heat capacity (cal/deg) for the entire system

Since the amount of product (n_{p}) may be equilibrium controlled (as in TT) or kinetically controlled (as in DIE), Equation 17.4 may be expanded in various ways in order to calculate the parameters listed previously.

These relationships have been presented in their simplest forms; later discussions will illustrate the complexities involved. For instance, the thermodynamic terms calculated are not usually standard-state terms (e.g., ΔH calculated is not ΔH°). The additional effort necessary to extrapolate to standard states (e.g., infinite dilution) is usually excessive for analytical situations, and in some cases the quality of the data does not warrant such treatment. References will be given to treatments of data or theory beyond the scope of this text that may interest those who wish to become more deeply involved with methods of thermal analysis.

17.2 THERMOGRAVIMETRY

Thermogravimetry (TG) involves continuously measuring the mass of a sample as a function of its temperature. Plots of mass versus temperature are called *thermogravimetric curves* or *TG curves*. The use of other names is discouraged.

General Considerations

Suitable samples for thermogravimetry are solids that undergo one of the two general types of reaction:

$$\text{Reactant(s)} \longrightarrow \text{Product(s)} + \text{Gas}$$

$$\text{Gas} + \text{Reactant(s)} \longrightarrow \text{Product(s)}$$

The first process involves a mass loss, whereas the second involves a mass gain. Processes occurring without change in mass obviously cannot be studied by TG (e.g., the melting of a sample).

A simple thermogram, for the dehydration of copper sulfate pentahydrate, is shown in Figure 17.1. There are two points of major interest to the analytical chemist. First is the general shape of the thermogram and the particular temperatures at which changes in mass occur. From this information, individual compounds may be identified under given conditions. Unfortunately, the reproducibility of the temperatures at which mass changes occur is severely affected by many experimental conditions, as noted later. For this reason, the obvious qualitative analytical capabilities of TG have yet to be fully realized.

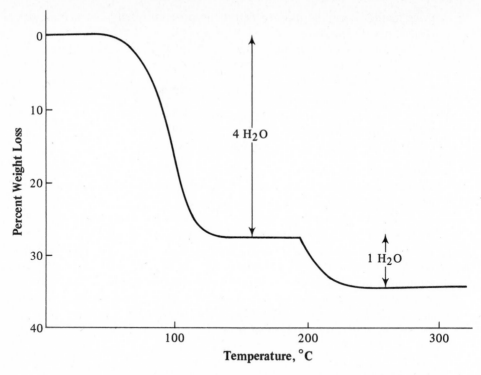

FIGURE 17.1. *A thermogravimetric curve for the dehydration of copper sulfate hydrate.*

The second major feature of the curve (the magnitudes of the mass changes observed) has found much more use, because it is independent of the many factors that affect the shape of the thermogram. Mass changes are directly related to the specific stoichiometries of the reactions occurring, independent of the temperature. As a consequence, precise quantitative analysis of samples whose qualitative composition is known can be made, or else the composition of novel compounds can be deduced.

Instrumentation

Thermogravimetric instrumentation should include several basic components in order to provide the flexibility necessary for the production of useful analytical data. These components are (a) a balance; (b) a heating device; (c) a unit for temperature measurement and control; (d) a means for automatically recording the mass and temperature changes; and (e) a system to control the atmosphere around the sample.

Balances. Balances must remain precise and accurate continuously under extreme temperature and atmospheric conditions, and should deliver a signal suitable for continuous recording. These requirements may be met in many ways: the two books by Duval and Wendlandt (see bibliography) show at least ten different commercial thermobalances that perform satisfactorily. The basic characteristics of such balances will be illustrated by describing one, the Cahn Electrobalance (Ventron Instruments

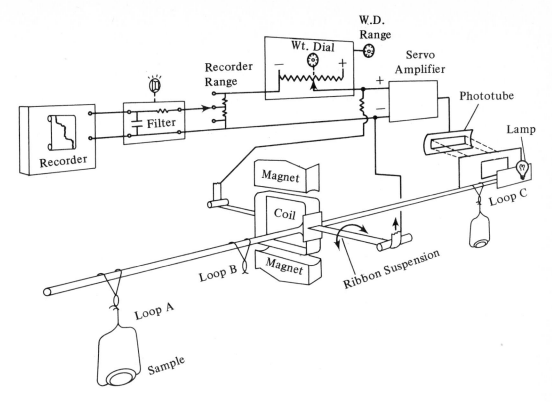

FIGURE 17.2. *Schematic diagram of the Cahn Electrobalance. Courtesy of Cahn Instruments Div., Ventron Instruments Corp.*

Corp., Cahn Div., Paramount, California. See Fig. 17.2). It operates as a null-type device by providing an electrical force to restore the beam to a predetermined position as the mass of the sample changes. As the beam is moved off balance, a shutter affixed to the beam changes the amount of light reaching a phototube, which causes a restoring force to be generated by passing a current through an electromagnet that serves as the pivot for the balance beam. A permanent magnet above and below the pivot point supplies magnetic attraction to the electromagnet. The force necessary to restore the beam is proportional to the current passed through the electromagnet, which is recorded. Additional features of the balance are two loops for hanging sample pans (loop A affording 2.5 times the sensitivity of loop B) and controls that adjust the range of the recorder and set the initial balance of the instrument (mass dials).

Null and other types of balances are available that have the capability of measuring the mass of a sample between 100 and 0.02 g to a precision of 0.01–1%. As will be shown later, the smaller the sample, the better the results often will be.

Heating Devices. The sample can be heated by resistance heaters, infrared or microwave radiation, or by heat transfer from hot liquids or gases. Resistance heaters are the most common.

Furnaces should be designed so that the sample is heated uniformly and symmetrically. The furnace must also be designed so that the heat generated is localized on the sample. Heat flow into the environment is an inconvenience to the operator, and heat flow to the balance results in serious errors. These are minimized by cooling the exterior of the oven, and by locating the oven as far as possible from the balance itself. Convection currents can be minimized by designing the sample holder so that it provides the least possible resistance to air flow, and by installing appropriate baffles. Apparent mass changes are always observed at the start of an experiment because of convection currents. Best results are obtained when these currents are held constant after start-up.

Temperature Measurement and Control. Temperature-sensing devices are usually thermocouples placed as close to the sample as possible. Thermocouples are inexpensive, rugged, and fairly linear in their response to temperature changes. Platinum resistance thermometers are also used in this application. The emf generated by the thermocouple may be used to drive one axis of an x–y recorder, or a feedback circuit to the heater may be used to obtain a programmed linear heating rate. In the latter case, the time axis of a strip-chart recorder is proportional to temperature. Instruments that depend upon a linear increase in power to the heater often have severely nonlinear temperature increases because of heat losses to the environment.

Recording the Signal. Electrical signals from the balance (see Fig. 17.2) and from the measuring thermocouple (after amplification) are fed into a recording potentiometer. If a strip-chart recorder is used, then the time-base axis is also the sample-temperature axis; an event marker may be used to indicate the temperature in increments of 10, 25, 50, or 100 degrees in order to monitor the linearity of heating. The x–y recorder is also used, but this method of recording suffers from the disadvantage that any nonlinearity in the heating rate will not be observed.

Control of the Atmosphere. The composition of the atmosphere surrounding the sample can have large and (if properly used) advantageous effects. For that reason, most thermogravimetric instruments provide some means of altering this atmosphere; in most cases, a static or flowing atmosphere of any desired composition can be provided. In addition, thermogravimetric determinations can be done in a vacuum (many systems can achieve pressures of 10^{-3} torr or less), or at elevated pressures.

TG Theory and Experimental Considerations

Figure 17.1 is a typical thermogravimetric curve. In virtually all TG analyses, the mass is monitored as the temperature is increased; accurate measurements under decreasing temperature are difficult and tend to yield little additional information. As discussed earlier, a reaction occurs when ΔG for the process becomes zero or negative, and its start is indicated when the mass deviates from the initial plateau. When the reaction stops, a new plateau is reached. The temperatures at which the reaction appears to start (T_i) and end (T_f), as well as the shape of the curve, depend upon many factors. Some of these are heating rate, heat of reaction, furnace atmosphere, amount of sample, nature of sample container, particle size, and packing of the sample.

The major use of TG is in the precise determination of mass changes for several sequential reactions. Necessarily, each reaction involving a change in mass must begin with and be followed by a plateau in order to distinguish sequential events. Two processes may occur more or less simultaneously, resulting in shoulders or complete merging of the decomposition reactions. Proper use of the variables listed above can often be used to avoid this. A rather simplified discussion of these variables is presented to illustrate the possibilities.

Heating Rate. In any heating process, there is always a difference in temperature between the sample and the oven. The magnitude of this thermal lag is roughly proportional to the rate at which the sample is heated. As a result, if a change in mass of a sample occurs always at a temperature T_i^0, then the observed T_i (measured outside the sample) will always be greater than T_i^0. Because of the thermal lag, the difference between T_i and T_i^0 will increase as the heating rate is increased. T_f is the temperature at which the end of mass change occurs. This value will depend upon the heating rate in a similar fashion. It is also found that the temperature range of mass loss $(T_f - T_i)$ tends to increase with heating rate. Figure 17.3 shows the effect of a much slower heating rate for the sample as in Figure 17.1.

Heat of Reaction. Since this is an intrinsic property of the material studied, it cannot be altered; however, its effects can be modified. An endothermic process will show a

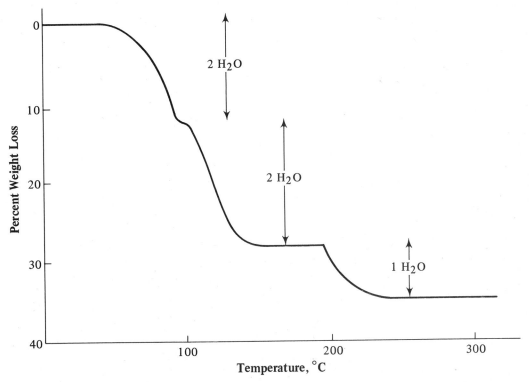

FIGURE 17.3. *Increased resolution of thermogravimetric curves by lower heating-rate* (*compare to Fig.* 17.1).

larger thermal lag than an exothermic one; the latter will sometimes cause the sample to be hotter than the observed temperature. Obviously, T_f is greatly affected whereas T_i is not. If T_f increases greatly, other processes may be obscured. This increase only occurs in endothermic reactions and may be minimized by heating the sample at a low rate so that the heat absorbed by the reaction can be replaced by heat flow from the oven. Decreasing the temperature range of mass loss $(T_f - T_i)$ increases the probability of obtaining usable plateaus.

Furnace Atmosphere. This is perhaps the most useful variable in altering TG curves. The basic feature is that, by providing an atmosphere rich in the reaction product, decomposition is delayed to higher temperatures. Conversely, in an inert atmosphere or vacuum the reaction will proceed at lower temperature. Simultaneous reactions can be separated by the choice of atmosphere, provided that different gases are liberated.

In addition to moving the temperatures of the decompositions, it is possible to alter the reaction that occurs. A notable example of this is found in the heating of organic samples: oxidation will occur in the presence of oxygen, whereas pyrolysis will occur if oxygen is excluded.

Nature of Sample Container. The container is important in that (a) the material used to hold the sample may catalyze an entirely unexpected reaction and (b) the container may trap some of the gases generated. The former may be evaluated by analyzing the reaction products. In the latter case, irreproducible mass changes can occur because of adsorption of the gas, or the curve can be displaced by a self-generated atmosphere around the sample. Metallic sample holders reduce the chances of adsorption, and self-generated atmospheres can be removed by flowing an inert gas past the sample during analysis.

Physical Characteristics of Sample. The amount, particle size, and packing of the sample generally affect its thermal homogeneity. Large systems have large temperature-gradients whereby the outer portions may be reacting while the inner portions are still cool and stable. The result is a greater thermal lag for larger samples, with the effects noted above. Smaller particle size tends to decrease thermal lag, but tighter packing increases it. Nonuniformity of particle size and packing leads to irreproducible curves.

Depending upon the processes studied, it may be necessary to have very good control over some or all of these variables. Generally, to distinguish between reactions that occur within 50–100°C of one another, very stringent control is needed. If long plateaus separate the decompositions, control is less critical.

In addition to gravimetric analysis, TG has also been used to elucidate the kinetics of decomposition reactions. This involves analyzing the shape of the TG curve. In general, the rate of reaction at any measured temperature is proportional to the slope of the curve, but a number of uncertainties sometimes make these analyses of questionable value. Freeman and Carroll [*J. Phys. Chem.*, *62*, 389 (1958)] describe the most popular of the kinetics-analysis methods, while Clarke et al. [*Chem. Comm.*, 266 (1969)] present the major objections to kinetics analysis by TG.

Analytical Calculations

Under controlled and reproducible conditions, quantitative data can be extracted from the relevant TG curves. Most commonly, the mass change observed is related to sample purity or composition.

> **Example 17.1.** A mixture of CaO and $CaCO_3$ is analyzed. The thermogram shows one reaction between 500 and 900°C, where the mass of the sample decreases from 125.3 mg to 95.4 mg. What is the percentage of $CaCO_3$ in the sample?

Solution: mmoles CO_2 = (mg lost)/(MW CO_2) = 29.9/44.0 = 0.682

mmoles CO_2 = mmoles $CaCO_3$

mg $CaCO_3$ = mmoles $CaCO_3$ (MW $CaCO_3$) = 0.682 × 100.1 = 68.2 mg

% $CaCO_3$ = (68.2/125.3)(100%) = 54.6%

> **Example 17.2.** A pure compound may be either MgO, $MgCO_3$, or MgC_2O_4. A thermogram of the substance shows a loss of 91.0 mg from a total of 175.0 mg used for analysis. What is the formula of the compound? The relevant possible reactions are

$$MgO \longrightarrow \text{no reaction}$$
$$MgCO_3 \longrightarrow MgO + CO_2$$
$$MgC_2O_4 \longrightarrow MgO + CO_2 + CO$$

Solution: % mass loss sample = (91.0/175.0)(100%) = 52.0

% mass loss if $MgCO_3$ = (44.01/84.33)(100%) = 52.3

% mass loss if MgC_2O_4 = $\left(\dfrac{44.01 + 28.00}{112.3}\right)$(100%) = 64.3

If the preparation was pure, the compound present is $MgCO_3$.

Applications of TG

Books by Duval, Vallet, and Wendlandt (referenced at the end of this chapter) contain a good summary of TG work. A few interesting analytical applications are given below.

Mixtures of divalent-cation oxalates can be analyzed successfully with a high degree of precision. A mixture of calcium, strontium, and barium oxalate monohydrates will lose all its water of hydration between 100° and 250°C; the three anhydrous oxalates will decompose simultaneously to the carbonates between 360° and 500°; and the carbonates will in turn decompose to the oxides in the following order: calcium (620–860°C), strontium (860–1100°C), and barium (1100° and up). In addition to the rather common oxalates, the precipitates formed with other organic precipitating agents have been studied, including those of the very similar lanthanide metals. Examples of precipitating agents are cupferron and neocupferron, and significant differences in the decomposition curves of their chelates may be needed for analysis of mixtures.

Direct analysis of solid materials eliminates the precipitation steps referred to above. Clays and soils can be evaluated by TG to determine water content, carbonate content, and organic matter content.

Thermograms can be used to compare the stabilities of similar compounds (e.g., of metal carbonates by studying the thermal decomposition to their respective oxides). Qualitatively, the higher the decomposition temperature, the more positive is the ΔG value at room temperature and the greater the stability.* The example given earlier of the dehydration of copper sulfate pentahydrate is interesting in that one of the five water molecules is not equivalent to the other four. This is confirmed by x-ray crystallography, which shows that four water molecules surround the copper(II), whereas the more tightly bound water molecule is hydrogen-bonded to two neighboring sulfate ions.

17.3 DIFFERENTIAL THERMAL ANALYSIS

In *thermal analysis* (TA), the temperature of a sample is monitored while heat is supplied at a uniform rate. In the more sophisticated method of differential thermal analysis, the difference in temperature between a sample and a reference is measured as they are heated.

General Considerations

Differences in temperature between the sample and an inert reference substance will be observed when changes that involve a finite heat of reaction, such as chemical reactions, phase changes, or structural changes, occur in the sample. If ΔH is positive (endothermic reaction), the temperature of the sample will lag behind that of the reference. If ΔH is negative (exothermic reaction), then the temperature of the sample will exceed that of the reference. Figure 17.4 shows TA and DTA curves for these two cases. DTA is more widely applicable than TG because it is not limited to reactions in which a change in mass occurs. On the other hand, a reaction with a ΔH of zero will not be observed. However, if a measurable change in heat capacity accompanies the process, a change in the position of the baseline will be noted. Table 17.1 lists the various reaction types observable and the expected nature of ΔH.

DTA heating curves are useful both qualitatively and quantitatively. The positions and shapes of the peaks can be used to determine the composition of the sample. (Sadler publishes an index of DTA curves similar to the tabulations of optical spectra.) The area under the peak is proportional to the heat of reaction and the amount of material present, and thus permits quantitative analysis. In addition, the shape of the heating curve can be used in evaluating the kinetics of the reaction under carefully controlled conditions.

Instrumentation

Implementing differential thermal analysis requires the following components: (a) a circuit for measuring differences in temperature, (b) a heating device and temperature-control unit, (c) an amplifying and recording apparatus, and (d) an atmospheric-control device.

---

* This assumes a constant ΔS for the reactions compared, and is most valid when a homologous series of compounds is studied.

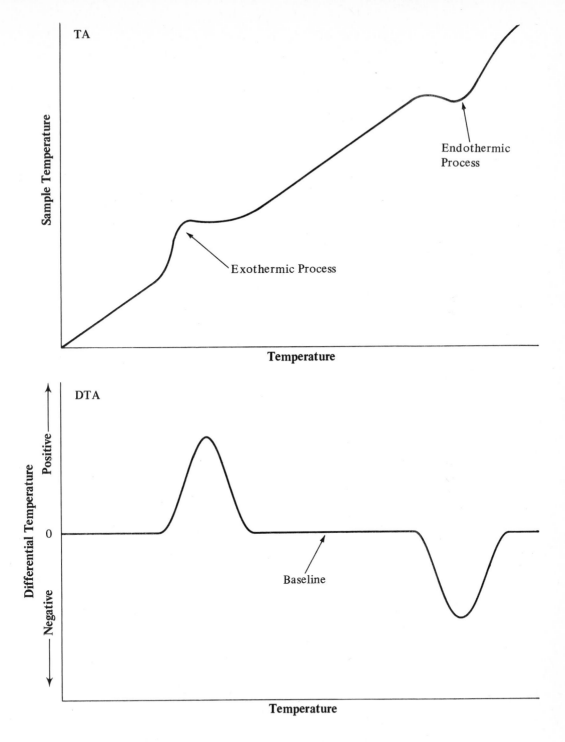

FIGURE 17.4. *A comparison of thermal analysis (TA) and differential thermal analysis (DTA) curves, illustrating exothermic and endothermic peaks.*

TABLE 17.1. *Processes Observable Using DTA, and the Heats of Reaction Typically Observed*

Phenomena	Heat of Reaction	
	Exothermic	Endothermic
Physical		
Crystalline transition	×	×
Fusion	——	×
Vaporization	——	×
Sublimation	——	×
Adsorption	×	——
Desorption	——	×
Absorption	——	×
Chemical		
Chemisorption	×	——
Desolvation	——	×
Dehydration	——	×
Decomposition	×	×
Oxidative degradation	×	——
Oxidation in gaseous atm.	×	——
Reduction in gaseous atm.	——	×
Redox reactions	×	×
Solid-State reactions	×	×

Source: Adapted from S. J. Gordon, *J. Chem. Educ.*, *40*, A87 (1963), by permission of the publisher.

Temperature Measurement. Thermocouples are by far the most reliable devices for monitoring temperature in DTA. A typical arrangement is shown in Figure 17.5.

One of the major considerations in DTA is obtaining valid readings of the actual temperature of the sample and reference materials conveniently and reproducibly. As in TG, thermal equilibrium is of utmost importance. There is always a definite temperature difference between the outer and inner portions of the sample; indeed, reactions often occur at the surface of the sample while the interior is still unreacted. This effect is minimized by using as small a sample as possible with uniform particle-size and packing. Depending upon the instrument used, the thermocouple may be imbedded in the sample, or at the other extreme, may simply be in direct contact with the sample holder. In any case, the thermocouple must be precisely positioned for every experiment. To obtain the best results, the reference and sample thermocouples should be matched in temperature response and the geometric arrangement of the sample and reference thermocouple should be perfectly symmetrical within the oven.

Heating and Temperature Control. The heating and temperature-control units are very similar to those used in TG. Ovens should be constructed to avoid electrical interference with the thermocouples. To reduce this possibility even further, most instruments have an inner metallic chamber for the sample and reference, to act as

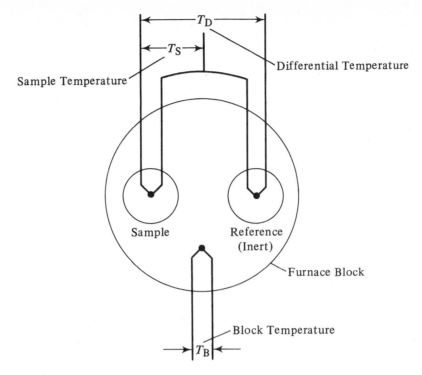

FIGURE 17.5.   *Schematic of the thermocouple arrangement in the DTA cell.   Adapted from S. J. Gordon*, J. Chem. Educ., *40, A87 (1967), by permission of the journal editor.*

an electrical shield and to minimize thermal fluctuations.   Needless to say, convection currents are no longer important, and atmospheric control is much more easily achieved—particularly a flowing atmosphere.

Recording the Signal.   Amplifying the signal and recording the results is done in much the same as in TG, replacing the signal for mass changes with the potential difference between the thermocouples.   Figure 17.6 shows a schematic of a typical DTA apparatus.

The similarities of TG and DTA are obviously great, at least instrumentally. As a consequence, many commercial instruments are designed to perform both types of analysis; the heating device, temperature-control unit, atmospheric control, and recording device are essentially used in common and are contained in a single control unit, only the thermobalance and DTA sample compartments being separate.

Theoretical and Experimental Considerations

The equation for heat flow from the environment to the sample or vice versa is given by the Newtonian cooling equation:

$$\frac{dQ}{dt} = c(T_s - T_e) \qquad (17.5)$$

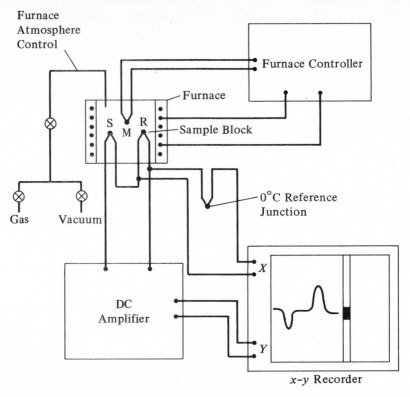

FIGURE 17.6. *Schematic of the entire differential thermal analysis setup.*
S, R, and M represent the sample, reference, and furnace-monitoring
thermocouples, respectively. Adapted from W. W. Wendlandt, Thermal
Methods of Analysis, *New York: John Wiley, 1964, by permission of the*
publisher.

where c = a constant related to the thermal conductivity of the system
T_s = temperature of the sample
T_e = the temperature of the environment

The flow of heat (Q) is from the environment to the sample if dQ/dt is negative; this is always the case in a heating curve, in the baseline regions. The equation for the rate of heat production for chemical processes is

$$\frac{dQ}{dt} = (-\Delta H)\frac{dn_p}{dt} \tag{17.6}$$

where n_p = the number of moles of product formed

The net heat-change in the sample is given by the sum of Equations 17.5 and 17.6. For an exothermic process, the start of the reaction causes an increase in the rate of gain of heat (Eqn. 17.6) but the rate of transfer of heat from the environment is decreased [in Eqn. 17.5, $(T_s - T_e)$ tends to decrease]. When Equation 17.5 is equal to Equation 17.6, the maximum (or minimum) of the DTA peak is observed.

If the constant c in Equation 17.5 is known, the exact point at which the reaction ends can be calculated. Usually, however, the magnitude of c is not known and all that can be said is that the reaction ends at some point after the maximum. This behavior may be compared to that in TG, where the reaction unambiguously ceases when a new plateau is reached.

DTA peak areas depend mainly upon the amount of material, the heat of reaction, and the thermal flow to or from the sample. These are related by the equation

$$A = \frac{-m\,\Delta H}{gc} \tag{17.7}$$

where g = a constant related to the geometry of the sample
c = a constant related to the thermal conductivity
m = the amount of reactive component in the sample (in moles)

Although the constants g and c can be evaluated experimentally, they are usually combined into a simple empirical conversion factor, c', to give:

$$A = c'm(-\Delta H) \tag{17.8}$$

The parameters discussed below also have some effect upon the observed areas, but the proportionality given by Equation 17.8 holds well under controlled experimental conditions.

As in TG, the maintenance of thermal equilibrium throughout the system becomes the overriding consideration in obtaining reproducible results. As noted previously, the placement of the thermocouple becomes critical; slight displacements in the position of the thermocouple from the center of the sample can contribute to irreproducible results. Placing the thermocouple outside the sample cell in good thermal contact with it assures consistent positioning, while simplifying the experimental procedure.

The magnitude of the difference in temperature between the exterior and the interior of the sample depends upon two factors: the rate of heating (as in TG), and the thermal conductivity of the sample and sample holder. Thus, a metal sample (which has a high thermal conductivity) is close to isothermal, even at high rates of heating. An apparent solution to the problem of thermal equilibrium is to increase the thermal conductivity of the sample appreciably (for instance, by mixing it with a diluent of high conductivity). This approach has limitations, however: Equation 17.5 shows that the heat produced or absorbed by the reaction will then be partially or completely compensated for by heat flow to or from the environment.

The best solution is to use a cell whose thermal conductivity is low relative to that of the sample. This minimizes the effect described by Equation 17.5 so that a large proportion of the effects described by Equation 17.6 can be measured. Therefore, ceramic sample-holders are used in reactions where ΔH is relatively small, and more convenient metallic sample-holders are used in reactions involving great amounts of heat. Best results are obtained with well powdered samples, and uniformity of results is enhanced by consistently using samples of the same particle-size and density of packing.

Table 17.2 summarizes the major factors that affect the shape and size of the DTA heating curve. The effects of the atmosphere around the sample are precisely

TABLE 17.2. *Some Common Factors That Influence DTA Heating Curves*

Factor	Effect	Correction or Control
Heating rate	Changes in peak size and position	Use low heating-rate
Sample size	Changes in peak size and position	Decrease size or lower the heating rate
Thermocouple placement	Irreproducible curves	Use the same location for each run
Sample particle size	Irreproducible and erratic curves	Use small, uniform particle size
Thermal conductivity of sample	Changes in peak position	Mix with thermally conductive diluent or lower the heating rate
Thermal conductivity of cell	Affects peak area	Decrease thermal conductivity to increase peak area
Reaction with atmosphere	Changes in peak size and position	Control carefully (can be used advantageously)
Sample packing	Irreproducible curves	Control carefully (affects thermal conductivity)
Diluent	Changes heat capacity and thermal conductivity	Choose carefully (can be used advantageously)

the same as those in TG and may either be a serious problem or a tool to use to analytical advantage.

Reference Materials. The subject of reference materials is important and often neglected. The major requirements are that the reference material should be inert over the temperature range of the analysis, that it should not react with the sample holder or thermocouples and that its thermal conductivity should match that of the sample. The last item is important since changes in thermal conductivity or heat capacity

TABLE 17.3. *Common Diluents and Reference Materials for DTA*

Compound	Approximate Temperature Limit, °C	Reactivity
Silicon carbide	2000	May be a catalyst
Glass beads	1500	Inert
Alumina	2000	Reacts with halogenated compounds
Iron	1500	Crystal change at ~700°C
Iron(III) oxide	1000	Crystal change at 680°C
Silicone oils	1000	Inert
Graphite	3500	Inert

with temperature result in sloping baselines. Table 17.3 lists some of the more common reference materials.

Diluents. The materials listed in Table 17.3 can also be used as diluents. Naturally, the diluent must also be inert in the presence of the sample.

One purpose of using a diluent has already been discussed: it permits the thermal conductivities of sample and reference to be matched. In addition, it may be used to maintain a constant sample-size while the amount of the reacting component is varied; this will decrease the influence of many of the factors listed in Table 17.2. A diluent can also be used where the sample is so small that weighing it out directly is inconvenient.

Analytical Calculations

Equation 17.8 predicts a direct proportionality between peak area and mass. Hence, for quantitative analysis, the peak area (A) of a sample of known mass (m_k) is compared to that for an unknown sample run under identical conditions:

$$m_{unk} = m_k \left(\frac{A_{unk}}{A_k} \right) \tag{17.9}$$

Similarly, the heat of reaction may be determined by comparison with a sample of known ΔH, although particular caution has to be exercised in determining heats of reaction: the constant in Equation 17.8 which relates peak area and ΔH varies with temperature. As a result, the known sample should react at the same temperature as the unknown, and the peak areas of the known and unknown should be roughly equal.

> ***Example 17.3.*** Compound A has a molecular weight of 98.4 and a heat of fusion of 1.63 kcal/mole. Compound B has a molecular weight of 64.3 and melts at approximately the same temperature as compound A. 500-mg samples of each yield DTA peak areas of 60.0 cm² and 45.0 cm² for A and B, respectively. What is the heat of fusion of B?
>
> *Solution:* From Equation 17.8,
>
> $$\Delta H_B = \Delta H_A \left(\frac{A_B}{A_A} \right) \left(\frac{m_B}{m_A} \right)$$
>
> m_A and m_B must be expressed in molar quantities to compare different compounds.
>
> $$\Delta H_B = 1.63 \text{ kcal/mole} \left(\frac{45.0 \text{ cm}^2}{60.0 \text{ cm}^2} \right) \left(\frac{500/64.3}{500/98.4} \right) = 1.87 \text{ kcal/mole}$$

Calculation of the area under the peak of the heating curve (see Fig. 17.7) can be subject to ambiguity, since, more often than not, the initial and final baselines do not coincide—the thermal conductivity or heat capacity has changed as a result of the reaction. A method for rapidly estimating the area of interest is illustrated in the figure. Both baselines are extended to a perpendicular line drawn from the maximum of the curve, and the areas under the two halves of the curve are determined and summed to give the total area.

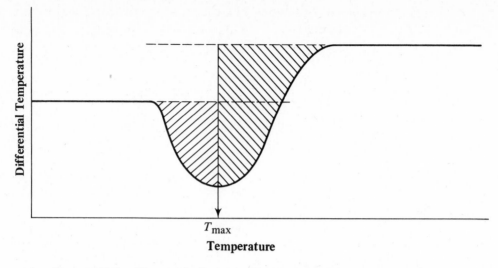

T_{max}

Temperature

FIGURE 17.7. *Illustration depicting the calculation of DTA peak areas. The displacement of the baseline indicates a change in heat capacity.*

The rates and activation energies of the reactions observed in DTA can be calculated from observed changes in DTA curves as the heating rate is changed; the essential data are the rate of heating b and the temperature at the curve maximum T_{max} (in K). The applicable equation is

$$d[\ln (b/T_{max}^2)]/d(1/T_{max}) = -E^*/R \qquad (17.10)$$

where $E^* =$ the activation energy of the reaction
             $R =$ the gas constant

A plot of $\ln (b/T_{max}^2)$ versus $1/T_{max}$ yields a line of slope $-E^*/R$ [1].

The order of the reaction process (first-order, second-order, etc.) can be determined from the asymmetry of the DTA curve [1] (see Fig. 17.8). The asymmetry of the peak is simply x/y, and the reaction order is estimated from:

$$\text{Reaction Order} = 1.26(x/y)^{1/2} \qquad (17.11)$$

There are many more complete treatments, and interested readers are referred to the bibliography at the end of this chapter for more detail. The problems associated with kinetic analysis by TG are also present with DTA.

FIGURE 17.8. *Parameters used to calculate the DTA peak asymmetry. Adapted from H. E. Kissinger, Anal. Chem., 29, 1702 (1957), by permission of the publisher. Copyright © 1957 by the American Chemical Society.*

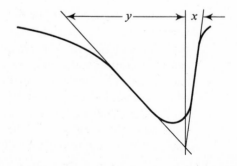

Applications of DTA

The general reference books of MacKenzie and Wendlandt summarize a large number of DTA studies and analytical applications. A few of these are outlined below.

Heat capacity estimates may be made using DTA. In the ideal system, with identical reference and sample materials, the "true" baseline of the instrument is obtained. Using a reference and sample of different heat capacities, the baseline will not be the same; and an estimate of the heat capacity of an unknown may be obtained by comparing the baseline shift with that for a sample of known heat capacity. A shift in the baseline is almost always observed after a DTA peak because of change in heat capacity of the sample. In addition, some reactions such as the glass transition of polymers yield virtually no DTA peak, but there is a rather sharp shift in the baseline after the transition temperature.

Polymer analysis is perhaps the most common application of DTA. Under carefully controlled conditions, the shape of the heating curve indicates both the type of polymer and the method used to prepare it; consequently, not only can the polymer be identified, but often (when production processes differ) the particular manufacturer as well. The "crystallinity" of a polymer determines its physical properties to a great extent. In DTA, there are commonly two peaks, one for the reaction of the crystalline part of the sample and another for that of the noncrystalline part (these two peaks often overlap). The magnitudes of these peaks can be used to evaluate the percent crystallinity. A significant advantage of DTA in this application is that the untreated polymer can be studied, thus avoiding possible changes caused by pretreatment (such as dissolution or grinding) of the sample.

Fuels (such as coal) can be evaluated rapidly to determine the source and BTU rating. As with TG, clays and soils can be analyzed using DTA.

Some of the most interesting analyses are of biological materials. Heating curves of such materials (e.g., plant leaves, cell cultures) give characteristic plots; indeed, cell cultures of the same strain of bacteria yield different heating curves, depending on the growth medium. In addition, the calorific value of organic material and foods can be evaluated using DTA.

17.4 DIFFERENTIAL SCANNING CALORIMETRY

In DTA, reactions are observed by measuring the deviation of the sample temperature from that of the reference material. This deviation causes thermal fluxes (Eqn. 17.5) which complicate the theoretical description of the curves and decrease the sensitivity. It would be advantageous to keep the sample and reference at the same temperature and to measure the rate of heat flow into each that was necessary to maintain the constant temperature. This is achieved by placing separate heating elements in the sample and reference chambers; the rate of heating by these elements can be controlled and measured as desired. This is the basis of differential scanning calorimetry (DSC).

DSC plots are graphs of the differential rate of heating (in cal/sec) versus temperature (see Fig. 17.9). The area under the peak is directly proportional to the heat evolved or absorbed by the reaction, and the height of the curve is directly

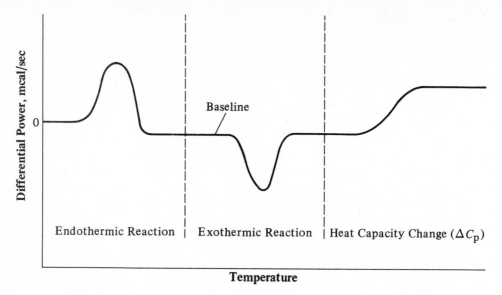

FIGURE 17.9. *Ideal representation of the three processes observable via differential scanning calorimetry.*

proportional to the rate of reaction. Although a proportionality constant similar to c' in Equation 17.8 exists, it is an electrical conversion factor rather than one based on sample characteristics; that c' is now independent of temperature is a major advantage of DSC over DTA.

Instrumentation

Figure 17.10 illustrates the circuitry of a differential scanning calorimeter. There are two separate heating circuits, the average-heating controller and the differential-heating circuit. In the average-temperature controller, the temperatures of the sample and reference are measured and averaged and the heat output of the average heater is automatically adjusted so that the average temperature of the sample and reference increases at a linear rate. The differential-temperature controller monitors the difference in temperature between the sample and reference and automatically adjusts the power to either the reference or sample chambers to keep the temperatures equal. The temperature of the sample is put on the x-axis (time) of a strip-chart recorder and the difference in power supplied to the two differential heaters is displayed on the y-axis. The power difference is calibrated in terms of calories per unit time.

A simple differential scanning calorimeter can be constructed to monitor endothermic reactions, since heat can be added to the sample compartment without affecting the heating rate. If the process is exothermic, however, the mere addition of heat to the reference will, while keeping the sample and reference isothermal, make the rate of heating nonlinear. The circuit in Figure 17.10 avoids this problem: when an exothermic process occurs, the average-temperature circuit decreases the

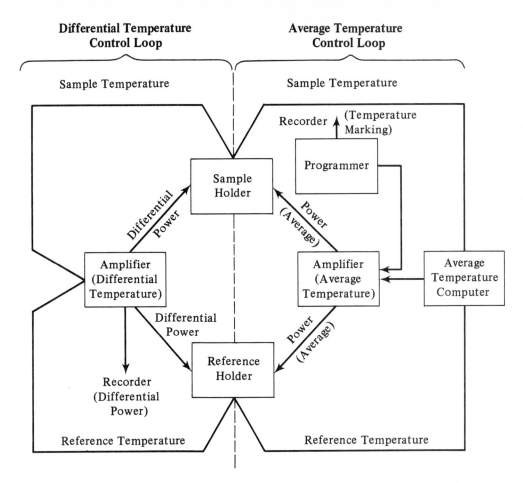

Differential Temperature Control Loop

Average Temperature Control Loop

Sample Temperature

Sample Temperature

Recorder

(Temperature Marking)

Programmer

Sample Holder

Differential Power

Power (Average)

Amplifier (Differential Temperature)

Amplifier (Average Temperature)

Average Temperature Computer

Differential Power

Power (Average)

Reference Holder

Recorder (Differential Power)

Reference Temperature

Reference Temperature

FIGURE 17.10. *Schematic diagram of the DSC apparatus. Adapted from E. S. Watson, M. J. O'Neill, J. Justin, and N. Brenner,* Anal. Chem., *36, 1233 (1964), by permission of the publisher. Copyright © 1964 by the American Chemical Society.*

rate of heating of both the reference and sample equally. In the sample compartment, this decrease in the rate of heating is compensated for by the heat of the reaction, while the differential heater in the reference compartment compensates for the decreased heating by the average heater.

Samples for analysis range in size from 1 to 100 mg and are sealed in a foil or metallic container for direct contact with the heaters and temperature sensors. The sample and reference compartments are well isolated to avoid flow of heat from one to the other, and heat flow to the environment is equalized by careful choice of material and geometry in the compartments. A wide range of heating rates (0.5 to 80°C/min) can be used, and instruments are generally sensitive enough to detect heat evolution or absorption at a rate of less than one millicalorie per second. Electrical signals are amplified and recorded as in TG and DTA. The use of sealed sample-containers eliminates atmospheric considerations in most cases. Temperatures are monitored using platinum resistance devices.

Experimental Considerations

The amount of heat generated by the differential heaters per unit time is

$$P = \frac{dQ}{dt} = i^2 R \tag{17.12}$$

where P = the power in watts
Q = the quantity of heat in joules
i = the current in amperes
R = the resistance in ohms

Chemical reactions liberate or absorb heat according to Equation 17.6. Thus, when ΔH is positive (endothermic reaction), the sample heater is energized and a positive signal is obtained; when ΔH is negative, the reference heater is energized and a negative signal is obtained (see Figure 17.9). The integral of the peak is equal to the heat evolved or absorbed by the reacting sample.

Not only is DSC sensitive to processes where there is a finite ΔH, but it is also very sensitive to differences in the heat capacities of the sample and reference. If the sample has a greater heat capacity than the reference, the sample differential heater will be operating even in the baseline region, giving a positive signal; similarly, a higher heat capacity for the reference will yield a negative baseline. A change in the heat capacity of either the sample or reference will be seen as a displacement of the baseline. The difference between the actual baseline and the zero of the instrument (in cal/sec), divided by the heating rate (°C/sec), is equal to the difference in heat capacities (cal/°C) between the sample and reference systems.

If the heat capacity of the reference is known, then the heat capacity of the sample can be determined over a wide range of temperatures. There is a great interest in this type of application; for example, changes in structure of many large polymers have a very small ΔH (virtually undetectable by DTA), but a ΔC_p quantitatively measurable by DSC.

The factors in Table 17.2, which have detrimental effects on DTA curves, have minimal effects on DSC curves. In particular, measurements obtained from the total area under the curve (calculation of ΔH and sample mass) are not affected. However, these factors still have an effect on the rate of reaction, particularly if large thermal gradients are allowed to develop in the sample or reference, that have a severe effect upon the apparent rate of reaction and any values calculated from these rates.

The rate at which heat is evolved in exothermic reactions must be taken into account in DSC; rapid exothermic reactions may cause the rate of temperature increase of the sample to be greater than the programmed rate of heating, even when both the average and differential heaters are off. A similar problem sometimes occurs with endothermic processes, where a rapid endothermic reaction may cool the sample so severely that the combined maximum heating of the two heaters cannot maintain a linear heating rate and isothermal conditions. Both these situations can be easily rectified by adjusting the heating rate or the sample size.

Analytical Calculations

Virtually every chemical process involves a change in the heat capacity of the sample. When measured by differential scanning calorimetry, such changes produce a curve similar to Figure 17.7 (except with a y-axis in cal/sec). The area under the DSC curve is determined in the same manner as in DTA. This area is proportional to the amount of heat evolved or absorbed by the reaction, and the heat of reaction is obtained by dividing this by the moles of sample used. If the heat of reaction is known, the moles of sample present can be calculated from essentially the same equation (i.e., the integral of Equation 17.6). All determinations should be preceded by an analysis of a standard sample of known mass and ΔH in order to calibrate the particular instrument used.

Processes where ΔH is zero yield no area for the curve (see Fig. 17.9C). In this case, the change in the specific heat is determined from

$$\Delta C_p(\text{cal}/°\text{C-g}) = \frac{\Delta \text{ Baseline}}{mb} \qquad (17.13)$$

where m = the mass of the sample
         b = the heating rate

Analytical Applications of DSC

Because of the great similarity between DSC and DTA, the analyses previously described and referred to for DTA are amenable to DSC studies.

The unique feature of DSC is the determination of heat capacities (specific heats). As noted, the differential power (cal/sec) divided by the heating rate (°C/sec) yields the difference in heat capacities between the sample and the reference (in the baseline regions only). A change in heat capacity is seen by a shift in the baseline. A sharp increase in the baseline of the plot is typical of glass transitions in polymers. By comparing the heat capacity of the sample with the known heat capacity of the standard, the absolute heat capacity of the sample can be calculated.

17.5 THERMOMETRIC TITRATION AND DIRECT-INJECTION ENTHALPIMETRY

Early thermometric measurements were laborious and time consuming and not very sensitive, although many excellent thermometric studies were reported up to the early 1950s, when thermometric titration became suitably automated for routine analytical use. Around that time, the thermistor temperature-sensor, the constant-delivery pump and sophisticated thermostatic control were introduced in rapid succession.

Thermometric titrations (TT) and direct-injection enthalpimetry (DIE) are both calorimetric techniques; the heat evolved or absorbed serves as an indicator of the progress of the reaction. Nowadays, TT and DIE are used for routine analysis and in fundamental research involving the chemical equilibrium, reaction kinetics, and thermochemistry of processes not readily studied by other methods.

Thermometric titration plots are characteristically graphs of temperature change versus titrant added. Direct-injection enthalpimetry yields plots of temperature versus the time following injection of a titrant. Both are illustrated in Figure 17.11. The methods are discussed together in this section because of the many similarities between them.

In TT, temperature changes occur only when titration is in progress and when there is sample reactant present. As a consequence, the start and endpoint of a titration are readily observed, and the number of moles titrated is calculated as in regular titrimetry. By determining the heat capacity of the system under study, heats of reaction can be readily determined. In addition, equilibrium constants can be evaluated under the appropriate conditions.

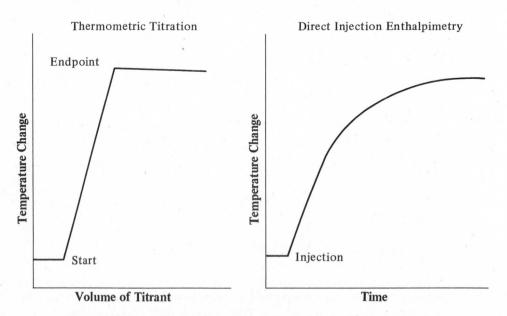

FIGURE 17.11. *Characteristic curves obtained from thermometric titration and direct-injection enthalpimetry.*

In direct-injection enthalpimetry, the titrant at the same temperature as the sample is injected rapidly into the sample and the data obtained as a temperature-versus-time curve. No endpoint is obtained, but the magnitude of the temperature change is proportional to the concentration. Also, one can generate kinetic curves to evaluate slow reactions. The speed of analysis is enhanced, and processes with equilibria unfavorable for titration are readily studied by using a large excess of one reactant.

Both DIE and TT are subject to the same restrictions as in classical calorimetry. If TT is used simply as an endpoint detection method, the restrictions also apply, but to a much lesser degree.

Instrumentation

Thermometric titrations can be implemented with a buret, a Dewar flask, and a Beckman thermometer, as in early studies. In modern instrumentation, however, automated electronic methods are used to obtain and often to evaluate the data. A typical TT setup consists of (a) a constant-delivery pump, (b) a temperature-control system, (c) an adiabatic cell, (d) a calibration unit, (e) an electronic temperature-sensing system, and (f) an amplifying and data-processing system.

Delivery Pump. A constant-delivery pump permits the time axis of a strip-chart recorder to be used as the volume-of-titrant axis (with a simple conversion factor). Typically, a syringe driven by a synchronous motor (that drives a carriage or screw) is used, and solutions can be delivered at constant rates ranging down to a few microliters per minute. Because of their variable flow rates, the more common peristaltic pumps are not often used for thermometric titrations.

In DIE, the syringe is rapidly emptied at the start of the experiment to deliver the titrant virtually instantaneously into the sample cell.

Temperature-Control Requirements. The temperature control needed in the TT apparatus depends upon the results desired. It is often possible to obtain useful endpoints in titrations simply by bringing both the sample and titrant to room temperature. However, for precise calorimetric results, the titrant and sample must be as close to the same temperature as possible. This is the main purpose of the thermostat.

Currently, using modern temperature-controllers, it is possible to maintain the temperature of the system at a wide range of set temperatures to a precision of $\pm 0.001°C$ or less. As a rule of thumb, the temperature change caused by the reaction observed must be at least as great as the temperature difference between the titrant and sample (i.e., the precision of the thermostat). Consequently, letting the random heat flows of the environment control the temperature of the apparatus is only sufficient for highly exothermic or endothermic processes.

Adiabatic Cell. The "adiabatic" cells used for TT and DIE have widely varying designs. They range from an insulated beaker to a Dewar flask to the highly elegant and efficient Dewar-type cell of Christiansen et al. [2] (Fig. 17.12). All are designed to minimize the heat transfer from the cell to the environment, thus maximizing the temperature change observed. When only titration endpoints are of interest, the simplest cell suffices; but if quantities such as heats of reaction, equilibrium constants, or kinetic parameters are sought, better cells are necessary.

These cells may be evaluated in terms of their heat-leak modulus, which is defined by the Newtonian cooling equation

$$\frac{dT}{dt} = -C(T_c - T_e) \tag{17.14}$$

where C = the heat-leak modulus
           T_c = the temperature of the cell
           T_e = the temperature of the environment

The Christiansen cell has the very low heat-leak modulus of 1.1×10^{-3} min^{-1}. Another factor is the mass of the cell and its contribution to the overall heat capacity and response; the better cells have thin walls to minimize the heat capacity and maximize the speed of response to temperature changes.

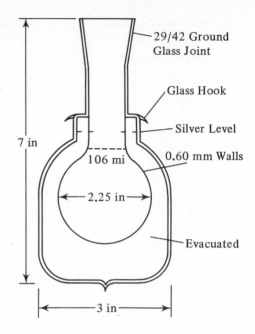

FIGURE 17.12. *An efficient adiabatic cell used for TT and DIE. Adapted from J. J. Christensen, R. M. Izatt, and L. D. Hansen, Rev. Sci. Instr., 36, 779 (1965), by permission of the senior author.*

Whereas it is relatively easy to maintain the titrant at any particular temperature by having it in good thermal contact with the thermostat bath, the cell temperature is not controlled easily in this manner, and an external means is usually employed to bring the cell quickly to thermal equilibrium. This is done using the calibration heater.

Calibration Unit. The calibration circuitry has two purposes: to determine the heat capacity of the system, and to control the temperature in the cell itself.

The heat evolved or absorbed is calculated from the temperature change using the relation

$$\Delta Q = \Delta T C_{\mathrm{p}}' \tag{17.15}$$

C_{p}' is the heat capacity of the system, readily measured as the amount of heat necessary to raise the cell temperature a known amount by electrical-resistance heating.

$$C_{\mathrm{p}}'(\text{joules/}^\circ\text{C}) = i^2 R t / \Delta T \ (\text{watts-sec/}^\circ\text{C}) \tag{17.16}$$

where t = the time of heating
i = the current (measured)
R = the resistance (known)

Division by 4.184 joules/cal permits conversion to cal/°C. The voltages V_{s} and V_{h} across a standard resistor (R_{s}) and the heater (R_{h}) connected in series are the measurements of interest, since $i^2 R_{\mathrm{h}} = V_{\mathrm{s}} V_{\mathrm{h}} / R_{\mathrm{s}}$. The heater can be used to advantage in hastening the cell to a thermal equilibrium with the thermostat bath and titrant by heating the cell and its contents to a temperature very close to that at which the thermostat is set.

Temperature-Sensing System. Temperature sensing is the heart of the thermometric titration technique. The principal temperature-sensors used are thermistors. A thermistor is a temperature-sensitive semiconductor whose resistance obeys the equation

$$R_T = Ae^{B/T} \tag{17.17}$$

where A and B are constants whose values depend upon the nature of the thermistor. In general, thermistors decrease in resistance as the temperature increases, by 3–6%/ °C. If the thermistor is incorporated into a Wheatstone bridge, the off-balance potential caused by the change in R_T can be recorded on a strip-chart recorder; when the input potential of the Wheatstone bridge is about 1 V, the output voltage changes by approximately 10 mV/°C (thermocouples produce a voltage of approximately 10 μV for a similar temperature change).

Both the thermistor response and the Wheatstone bridge readout are not linear with temperature. However, it has been found that the nonlinearity is un-important over a small enough temperature range (less than 0.1°C). Other factors that make thermistors ideal for TT and DIE are their small size, fast response to temperature change, and (when encapsulated with glass) inertness to most chemicals.

Amplification and Recording. Although the thermistor is already as sensitive as a thousand-junction thermocouple would be, it is often advantageous to amplify the signals obtained. Using a DC amplifier, it is possible to obtain good signals for temperature changes of the order of 10^{-4} °C or less. An AC Wheatstone bridge with a lock-in amplifier can detect temperature changes of the order of 10^{-6} °C [3].

The two most popular data-acquisition systems are the strip-chart recorder and the digital data-storage system. The latter is used when a great deal of data processing is anticipated.

Experimental Considerations

Figure 17.13 represents an idealized thermometric titration curve. Region 1 is the baseline. Ideally horizontal, in practice is has a finite slope as a result of frictional heat added by stirring, resistive heat added by the thermistor (Eqn. 17.12), and the transfer of heat from the cell to the thermostat (Eqn. 17.14). If frictional and resistance heating are constant and equal to W, then the slope in Region 1 is

$$\frac{dT}{dt} = -C(T_c - T_e) + W \tag{17.18}$$

The slope in Region 2 is due to the same effects, plus the following: the temperature change generated by the reaction, the heat of dilution of the reactants (ΔH_D), and the difference in temperature between titrant and sample after the start of titration (ΔT_R). This may be expressed as

$$\frac{dT}{dt} = -C(T_c - T_e) + W + (-\Delta H/C'_p)\left(\frac{dn_p}{dt}\right) + \Delta H_D/C'_p + \Delta T_R k \tag{17.19}$$

where k = a constant

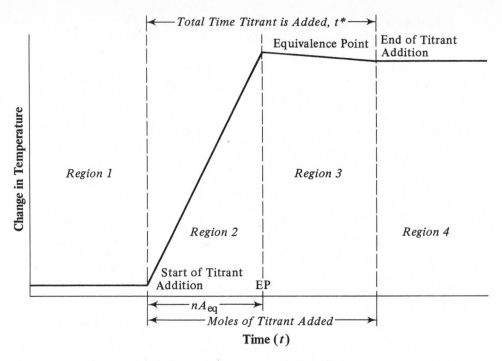

FIGURE 17.13. *Idealized representation of the four major regions of the TT curve. With a constant-delivery pump, the x-axis can be in units of time or moles of titrant.*

In Region 3, where the equivalence point has been passed, the slope of the curve is described by

$$\frac{dT}{dt} = -C(T_c - T_e) + W + \Delta H_D / C_p' + \Delta T_R \qquad (17.20)$$

When no further titrant is added (Region 4), the slope again obeys Equation 17.18. (There is usually some rounding at the equivalence point in real titrations.)

These expressions can be combined to obtain the heat of reaction ΔH and, if the production of product (n_p) is equilibrium controlled, the equilibrium constant of the reaction can also be calculated [4].

In DIE, temperature-versus-time curves indicate the progress of the reaction. Kinetic processes can be evaluated (usually for reactions having half-reaction times greater than 5 sec), and from the total temperature change, heats of reaction can be evaluated. The general equation for a DIE curve is

$$\frac{dT}{dt} = \frac{-\Delta H}{C_p'} \left(\frac{dn_p}{dt} \right) + W \qquad (17.21)$$

where dn_p/dt is governed by the appropriate rate expression. An obvious advantage of this type of kinetic analysis is that the system is not disturbed (and is continuously monitored) in obtaining the data.

Equations 17.18 to 17.21 are straightforward, but often it is not necessary to solve them rigorously to obtain useful and reliable results—see the following section.

In applying the equations, however, there are a few points to consider. First, the heat capacity of the system in TT is continuously changing in Regions 2 and 3; thus, C'_p in Equation 17.19 is not truly a constant. As the volume of the system increases during the titration, the change in temperature per unit time decreases, even though the amount of heat released remains constant; this can cause a large error if not corrected [5]. The correction is made by replotting the entire curve in terms of Q (calories of heat evolved)—instead of T—versus volume of titrant added. To obtain Q, the change in temperature at each point on the curve is multiplied by the heat capacity (C_p) at that point. The heat capacity at every point in Regions 2 and 3 can be determined by measuring C_p in Regions 1 and 4 of the curve, obtaining C_{p1} and C_{p4}. At any point t in Regions 2 and 3, the heat capacity is given by

$$C_{pt} = C_{p1} + (t/t^*)(C_{p4} - C_{p1}) \qquad (17.22)$$

where t^* is the total time interval over which titrant is added (this assumes a linear increase in heat capacity during the course of titration). The curve of heat evolved (Q) versus volume of titrant is called an *enthalpogram*. This procedure is tedious, and can be avoided by using a titrant that is 100 or more times as concentrated as the sample [6]; the term ($C_{p4} - C_{p1}$) in Equation 17.22 then approaches zero.

... equivalent to enthalpograms, since the heat capacity does not ... e the reactants are mixed.

... ns

... tion of either the titrant or the sample, the volume added to ... ds the concentration of the unknown. Heats of reaction are ... ous solution of Equations 17.18 to 17.20 [4].

... hermometric titration of acid A with base B was performed, ... ilar to that in Figure 17.13 was obtained. The slopes of the ... the curve were 1.0×10^{-5}, 8.0×10^{-4}, -1.0×10^{-5}, and ... C/sec, respectively. The overall temperature change was ... to the experiment, the heat capacity of the cell was deter- ... 0 cal/°C. The titration rate was 6.0×10^{-8} moles B/sec. In ... found that the titration of B into pure water gave a slope ... C/sec under identical experimental conditions. Use these ... e the heat of reaction.

... uation 17.18, the slope in Region 1 corresponds to the value W, since $T_c = T_e$. The same equation applies to Region 4, but now the constant C can be evaluated since W and ($T_c - T_e$) are known. The value of C is 1.5×10^{-4} sec^{-1}. The heat of dilution factor in Equation 17.20 is the difference between the slope of the titration of B into pure water and the slope in Region 1

$$\Delta H_D/C'_p = 2.0 \times 10^{-5} - 1.0 \times 10^{-5} = 1.0 \times 10^{-5} \text{ °C/sec}$$

Now it is possible to solve Equation 17.20 for T_R, obtaining a value of -1.5×10^{-4} sec^{-1}. Lastly, all of the above information is used in Equation 17.19 to obtain

$$8.1 \times 10^{-4} = \frac{-\Delta H}{C'_p} \left(\frac{dn_p}{dt}\right)$$

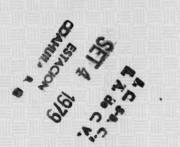

The term dn_p/dt is equal to the titration rate and C_p' was given as 1.000 cal/°C. The heat of reaction is then: $\Delta H = -8.1 \times 10^{-4}/6.0 \times 10^{-8} = -13.5 \times 10^3$ cal/mole $= -13.5$ kcal/mole.

In the above data, the terms in units of °C can be replaced by any other value proportional to the temperature (e.g., recorder deflection); similarly, the terms in units of sec can be replaced by any measure which is directly proportional to time. Equation 17.19 can also be integrated and then evaluated. This requires a knowledge of the variation of T_c and C_p' with time in Region 2.

Instead of using the equations, heats of reactions can be estimated graphically to a few percent knowing the change in temperature, the heat capacity at the midpoint of the titration curve, and the moles of product formed (not the molarity). The heat capacity at the midpoint of the curve is obtained by extrapolating the part of the curve in Region 3 back to Region 2 and measuring Q from the baseline to the extrapolated line at the midpoint of the titration.

Estimates of equilibrium constants can be made from TT curves when there is distinct curvature near the equivalence point. Taking the general reaction

$$A + B \rightleftharpoons AB$$

at the equivalence point, the analytical concentrations (A) and (B) can be calculated. The equilibrium concentrations [A] and [B] are then calculated as

$$[AB] = \frac{h}{h_t}(A) \tag{17.23}$$

$$[A] = (A) - [AB] \tag{17.24}$$

$$[B] = (B) - [AB] \tag{17.25}$$

These concentrations can then be combined to obtain the equilibrium constant. Figure 17.14 illustrates the meaning of h and h_t. As the equilibrium constant increases, the degree of curvature decreases and h approaches h_t.

Example 17.5. Figure 17.14 is a titration curve where chemical equilibrium causes curvature near the endpoint. An estimate of the equilibrium constant is made by measuring h and h_t as diagrammed. The concentration of the sample must be known. Assume that the reaction of a metal (M) with a ligand (L) takes place to form the complex ML. The sample concentration is given to be 0.0100 molar initially. Calculate the stability constant of the complex.

Solution: At the endpoint, the following relationships hold:

$$C_L = 0.0100 = [ML] + [L]$$
$$C_M = 0.0100 = [ML] + [M]$$

Then

$$[ML] = C_M\left(\frac{h}{h_t}\right) = C_L\left(\frac{h}{h_t}\right)$$

$$[L] = [M] = C_M - [ML] = C_L - [ML]$$

ING. RUFFO IBARRA H.

No 107584

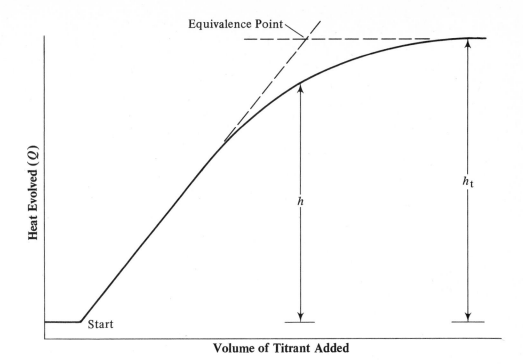

FIGURE 17.14. *Equilibrium curvature of enthalpograms, illustrating parameters h and h_t used to estimate equilibrium constants.*

The stability constant is

$$K_s = \frac{[ML]}{[M][L]} = \frac{C_M(h/h_t)}{(C_M - [ML])^2}$$

If h and h_t are measured to be 77.8 and 87.3, respectively, then

$$K_s = \frac{(0.0100)(77.8/87.3)}{[0.0100 - 0.0100(77.8/87.3)]^2} = 7.50 \times 10^3$$

The units of h and h_t cancel in the above expressions, and any appropriate and convenient measure of their relative magnitudes may be used (e.g., °C, cm, mV, etc.).

Once the heat of reaction and equilibrium constant have been determined, the entropy change, ΔS, of the reaction can be calculated from

$$-RT \ln K_{eq} = \Delta H - T\,\Delta S \tag{17.26}$$

Often, titrations can be done with samples of 10^{-2} M or less. When dilute solutions are used, it may be safely assumed that the measured thermodynamic parameters are essentially the same as in the standard state of infinite dilution (i.e., $\Delta H_{mean} \approx \Delta H^0$, etc.).

Analytical Applications of TT and DIE

The monograph by Tyrell and Beezer lists many of the analyses possible using these two methods; some of these analyses are listed in Table 17.4.

TABLE 17.4. *Reaction Types Amenable to Thermometric Enthalpy Titration*

Reaction Type	ΔH_r (kcal/mole) [a]	Precision
Neutralization		
Strong acid + strong base	−13.5	±0.1%
Weak acid + strong base	−13.5 to −4	±0.1–5%
Weak base + strong acid	−13.5 to −4	±0.1–5%
Polyprotic or basic systems	−14 to −4	±0.1–10%
Oxidation-Reduction		
Inorganic [b]	−40 to −10	±0.1%
Organic [b]	−40 to 0	±0.1–10%
Complexation		
EDTA [b]	−15 to +10	±0.1–5%
Other [b]	−20 to +20	±0.1–10%
Precipitation		
Inorganic [b]	−20 to −5	±0.1–10%
Organic [b]	−20 to −5	±0.1–10%
Heats of Mixing		
Dilution of inorganic ions	−15 to +10	——
Organic solvents	−15 to +15	——

a. ΔH_r is the approximate overall heat of the process; 1 cal = 4.184 joules.
b. These processes may have slow kinetics which severely affect the results.

An almost classical example of the advantages of TT is in the titration of boric acid ($K_a = 6.4 \times 10^{-10}$) with a strong base. This titration is impossible by classical methods without pretreating the sample. However, as shown in Figure 17.15, TT yields results differing little from those obtained with a strong acid such as HCl, the reason being that the ΔH for the two processes is essentially the same, whereas ΔG and ΔS are significantly different.

Analysis of mixtures is possible when the two species have different equilibrium constants and heats of reaction with the titrant. This occurs, for example, in the titration of a mixture of calcium and magnesium with EDTA. Calcium ($K_f = 10^{11}$) reacts first and exothermically ($\Delta H = -5.7$ kcal/mole); magnesium ($K_f = 10^{9.1}$) reacts second and endothermically ($\Delta H = +5.5$ kcal/mole). This titration is illustrated in Figure 17.16.

It is also possible to titrate biochemical species. Antibodies have been titrated with antigen, and enzyme-substrate mixtures have been titrated with appropriate coenzymes. Proteins are readily titrated with acid or base, or precipitated with phosphotungstic acid, yielding very informative thermometric titration curves [7, 8].

DIE permits rapid analysis. For instance, SO_2 and CO_2 in air [8] can be determined by injecting air samples into concentrated KOH. Sharp temperature changes or pulses indicate the presence of reactants, and the magnitude of the temperature change gives the concentration. Analysis time is very short (ca. 3 min)

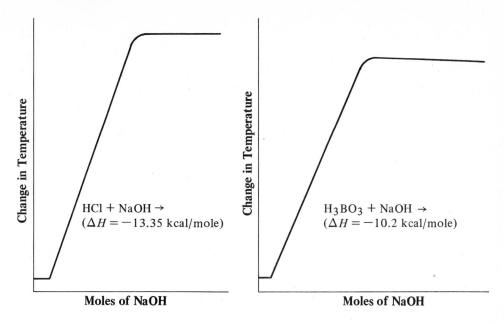

FIGURE 17.15. *Comparison of the titration of H_3BO_3 and HCl with NaOH, observed thermometrically.*

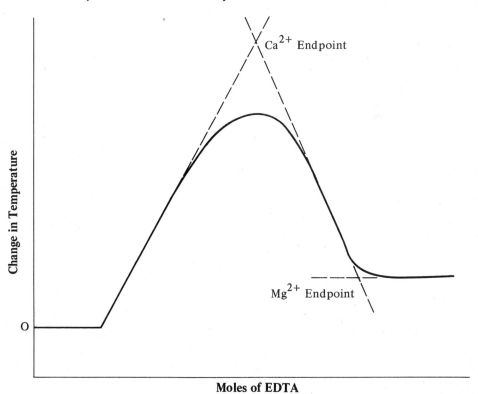

FIGURE 17.16. *Thermometric titration of a mixture of Ca^{2+} and Mg^{2+} with EDTA.*

for this type of determination, and the precision and accuracy, although not as good as with TT, are acceptable.

Kinetic studies have been made by DIE of the hydrolysis of organic nitrates and of esters. Enzyme reactions have also been studied. In all cases, a continuous recording of the process is obtained, and the system is not disturbed by sampling. This can be quite important in sensitive biochemical reactions.

SELECTED BIBLIOGRAPHY

DUVAL, C. *Inorganic Thermogravimetric Analysis*, 2nd ed. Amsterdam: Elsevier, 1963.

MACKENZIE, R. C. *Differential Thermal Analysis*, vol. 1. New York: Academic Press, 1970.

TYRRELL, H. V., and BEEZER, A. E. *Thermo-metric Titrimetry*. London: Chapman and Hall, 1968.

VALLET, P. *Thermogravimetrie*. Paris: Gauthier-Villars, 1972.

WENDLANDT, W. W. *Thermal Methods of Analysis*. New York: Interscience, 1964.

REFERENCES

1. H. E. KISSINGER, *Anal. Chem.*, *29*, 1702 (1957).

2. J. J. CHRISTENSEN, R. M. IZATT, and L. D. HANSEN, *Rev. Sci. Instr.*, *36*, 779 (1965).

3. E. B. SMITH, C. S. BARNES, and P. W. CARR, *Anal. Chem.*, *44*, 1663 (1972).

4. J. J. CHRISTENSEN, J. RUCKMAN, D. J. EATOUGH, and R. M. IZATT, *Thermochim. Acta*, *3*, 203, 219, 233 (1972).

5. N. D. JESPERSEN and J. JORDAN, *Anal. Lett.*, *3*, 323 (1970).

6. P. W. CARR, *Thermochim. Acta*, *3*, 427 (1972).

7. E. B. SMITH and P. W. CARR, *Anal. Chem.*, *45*, 169 (1973).

8. P. G. ZAMBONIN and J. JORDAN, *Anal. Chem.*, *41*, 437 (1969).

PROBLEMS

1. List some of the factors that influence (a) thermogravimetry curves, (b) differential thermal analysis curves, and (c) differential scanning calorimetry curves, indicating which are most important for the various techniques.

2. What is a self-generated atmosphere? What effect may it have on DTA and TG?

3. A thermogravimetric curve shows that a compound will not start to decompose until the temperature reaches 150°C. However, upon storage overnight at 140°C this same compound decomposes totally. Suggest why.

4. Figure 17.1 is a typical TG curve. What would an ideal curve look like? (Hint: See footnotes.)

5. A hydrate of Na_2HPO_4 weighing 150 mg decreases to a weight of 119 mg after heating to 150°C. Calculate the number of waters of hydration.

6. From the information in the text, draw a fully labeled diagram of the TG curve obtained by heating a mixture of 50 mg of $CaC_2O_4 \cdot H_2O$ and 50 mg of $BaC_2O_4 \cdot H_2O$ to 1200°C. Calculate the magnitude of all weight losses.

7. Sketch a DTA curve for the process in Problem 6. Assume no additional reactions.

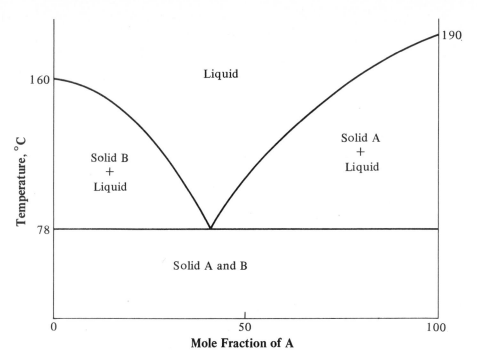

Problem 10

8. Calculate, from data in handbooks, the TG curve for the thermal decomposition of 100 mg of urea (see *Merck Index*). Assume all processes are quantitative.

9. A. Show mathematically the direction in which the reaction temperatures will move when (a) the atmosphere contains the gaseous product and (b) when the atmosphere contains the gaseous reactant. B. Show how the stoichiometric coefficient of the gaseous reactant can be deduced by varying the atmosphere.

10. Phase diagrams can be deduced from DTA curves. A simple phase diagram is given. Sketch the heating curves obtained when the mole percent of A is 0, 25, 50, 75, 100%. Assume that the heat of fusion of A is twice that of B and that both are endothermic.

11. Comment on the advisability of using DTA for routine melting- and boiling-point determinations.

12. On heating, a sample of bismuth gives an endothermic peak at 270°C, whereas on cooling, an exothermic peak appears at 257°C. What is occurring?

13. The heat of fusion of naphthalene is 4.63 kcal/mole at 80°C and the DTA peak observed using 100 mg of sample is 36.3 cm². Water has a heat of fusion of 1.43 kcal/mole at 0°C. What should the peak area for 100 mg of ice be under the same conditions? From experimental considerations, would it be expected to be slightly larger or smaller? Why?

14. Calculate the heat capacity of a thermometric titration system (cal/°C system) given the following data: $\Delta T = 0.0235°C$, $V_s = 1.234$; $V_h = 1.876$; $t = 64.3$ sec, and $R_s = 10.003$. What is the resistance of the heater R_h? Is the answer too high or too low if the heater leads have an appreciable resistance? Why?

15. Why is the TT curve for boric acid so sharp (Fig. 17.15), although the ionization constant indicates that it should be otherwise? (Hint: There is another chemical process occurring.)

16. Using the data in Figure 17.15, what is the heat of ionization of boric acid?

17. Calculate K, ΔG, ΔH, and ΔS at 25°C for the reaction $M + L \rightleftharpoons ML$, given the following data: Sample concentration (L) = $1.00 \times 10^{-2}\ M$; sample volume = 100.0 ml; titrant (M) = $1.00\ M$; titration rate = 0.0400 ml/sec.

Time, sec	Cal Evolved
5.0	1.95
10.0	3.87
15.0	5.73
20.0	7.42
25.0	8.68
30.0	9.30
35.0	9.56
40.0	9.69
50.0	9.89
60.0	9.97
70.0	10.0
80.0	10.0

Assume all appropriate corrections have been made. Sketch the titration curve.

18. Ignoring the heat capacity of the adiabatic cell, show that ΔT is independent of the sample volume for a given titration. What effect does the cell have?

19. If a reaction is slow, what sort of error (positive or negative) can be expected in calculating unknown concentrations?

20. The heat of ionization of *tris*-(hydroxymethyl)aminomethane (TRIS) is $+11.45$ kcal/mole. Sketch the thermometric titration curve of 50.0 ml of 0.01 M TRIS with 1 M HCl. Sketch the titration curve of the resulting cation with 1 M NaOH. Estimate the temperature change for each titration.

21. The DSC curve for an inorganic complex exhibits an endotherm at 375°C. A TG trace shows no weight loss at this temperature. What transition may be occurring?

22. Silver nitrate is thermally stable up to 473°C, at which point NO_2 and O_2 are gradually lost, leaving a residue of metallic silver at about 608°C. $Cu(NO_3)_2$, on the other hand, decomposes below 470°C in two steps to CuO, which is stable up to at least 950°C. Suggest a method for determining the percent composition of the alloy formed by heating an unknown mixture of silver and copper nitrates above 950°C.

18

Kinetic Methods

HARRY B. MARK, JR.

In chemical analysis, the species to be determined is usually accompanied by one or more substances that interfere with its analysis. Separation techniques are commonly employed to isolate the desired species prior to the actual measurement; but frequently, especially in complex biological and natural-environment systems, quantitative separations are virtually impossible or at best laborious. Obviously, performing analyses without prior separation is always more convenient.

Methods for the in situ chemical analysis of a mixture of species having closely related chemical and physical properties can be placed in two general classes, according to the technique employed to eliminate (or reduce) the interference by the other components of the system. A *thermodynamic* approach involves changing the equilibrium conditions of the system to render all reactions thermodynamically unfavorable except the one of analytical interest. A *kinetic* approach involves adjusting, or simply taking advantage of, the differences in reaction rates of the components of the mixture in order to measure the reactions of the desired species.

The concept of employing reaction-rate parameters to determine the initial analytical concentration of reactants dates back over 50 to 60 years to the early literature in biochemistry, radiochemistry, and gas-phase diffusion; furthermore, among all the analyses performed in all the laboratories around this country, the number carried out by kinetic-based methods probably exceeds that carried out by thermodynamic methods and direct instrumental measurement combined. This comes as a surprise at first, until one considers the large numbers of enzymatic and other determinations done on multi-channel autoanalyzers used in clinical laboratories. Most of these rapid automated instruments use kinetic methods.

Thus, it is somewhat surprising that it was not until the 1950s that several research groups started to point out to *chemists* the broad inherent possibilities and advantages of kinetic-based analyses. In spite of considerable activity in development of methods, there has still not been any large surge in the application of kinetic-based techniques to routine analytical problems in chemistry; and most undergraduate textbooks on analytical chemistry and instrumental analysis do not mention the subject, or at best devote a few pages to outmoded methods.

There are two main reasons for this lack of use. First, almost all commercial instruments for chemical measurement are expressly designed for steady-state or equilibrium measurement, and do not perform satisfactorily when used for quantitative time-dependent measurement. Second, the practice of analytical chemistry is conservative, and new methods are accepted slowly, particularly methods that introduce another parameter that is difficult to control—in this case, time. However, recent developments in instrumentation are likely to change the present situation, and kinetic-based analytical techniques are likely to become commonplace in the next decade. Consequently, a chapter on this subject is included in this text.

18.1 COMPARISON OF KINETIC AND THERMODYNAMIC METHODS

Kinetic techniques often have advantages over equilibrium or thermodynamic techniques despite the greater difficulty of making measurements on a dynamic system. Equilibrium differentiations (free-energy differences) for the reactions of very closely related compounds (such as homologues or isomers) are often too small to permit direct resolution of the components of a mixture. However, the kinetic differentiations obtained when these compounds are reacted with a common reagent are often quite large. The reason is that the free energy of activation for the formation of the activated complex in such reactions is much more sensitive to the small structural differences between similar compounds than is the overall free-energy change for the reaction. These differences may involve polar effects, inductive effects, steric effects, or resonance effects, among others. Table 18.1 gives values for the relative rate-constants for the reactions of several alkyl halides with a variety of reagents.

Another advantage of kinetic methods is that they permit a larger number of chemical reactions to be used analytically. Many chemical reactions cannot be employed analytically in equilibrium or thermodynamic-based techniques: the reactions attain equilibrium too slowly, side reactions or subsequent reactions of the products occur as the reaction proceeds to completion, or the reactions are not sufficiently quantitative (equilibrium constants are too small) to be applicable. However, kinetic-based techniques can be employed in many of these cases. For example, complications arising from an unfavorable equilibrium constant, slow reaction, side reactions, reverse reactions, and so forth are circumvented by measuring the reaction rate during the initial 1–2% of the overall reaction (where the mechanism is usually straightforward). Thus, virtually any chemical reaction whose initial rate can be measured can be employed in a kinetic-based method.

Kinetic-based methods employing catalytic (especially enzymatic) reactions are inherently more selective than many comparable chemical equilibrium methods. For example, of the approximately sixty oxidizable sugars and their derivatives, only two (β-D-glucose and 2-deoxy-D-glucose) are enzymatically oxidized by glucose oxidase at a significant rate. The oxidation of all others, including the isomeric

TABLE 18.1. *Relative Reaction Rates of Alkyl Halides with Various Reagents*

Reaction[a]	Relative Rate-Constants								
	R = CH$_3$	C$_2$H$_5$	i-C$_3$H$_7$	i-C$_4$H$_9$	n-C$_3$H$_7$	i-C$_4$H$_9$	n-C$_4$H$_9$	Allyl	Benzyl
1. RCl + I$^-$ → RI + Cl$^-$	——	1	0.0077	0.0092	0.53	——	0.52	41	95
2. RI + C$_6$H$_5$O$^-$ → C$_6$H$_5$OR + I$^-$	1	0.22	0.077	——	0.086	0.032	0.080	4.7	——
3. RI + C$_6$H$_5$CH$_2$O$^-$ → C$_6$H$_5$CH$_2$OR + I$^-$	1	0.091	0.021	——	0.035	0.033	0.025	——	——
4. RI + N(C$_2$H$_5$)$_3$ → (C$_2$H$_5$)$_3$NR$^+$ + I$^-$	1	0.0087	0.0017	v.sl.[b]	0.0017	0.00027	0.0012	——	——
5. RI + C$_6$H$_5$N(CH$_3$)$_2$ → C$_6$H$_5$N(CH$_3$)$_2$R$^+$ + I$^-$	1	0.0657	——	——	0.0208	——	——	7.55	~20
6. RI + Ag$^+$ → R$^+$ + AgI	1	2.35	~90	——	1.05	0.148	0.734	——	——
7. RBr + H$_2$O → ROH + HBr	1	0.413	0.641	2700	——	——	——	——	——

Source: H. B. Mark, Jr., G. A. Rechnitz, and R. A. Grienke, *Kinetics in Analytical Chemistry*, New York: Wiley-Interscience, 1968, pp 178–79, by permission of John Wiley and Sons. Copyright © 1968 by John Wiley and Sons.
a. Notes on reactions: 1. Allyl chloride and potassium iodide in acetone at 60°C, in some cases extrapolated from data at lower temperatures. 2. Alkyl iodide and sodium phenolate in ethanol at 42.5°C. 3. Alkyl iodide and sodium benzyloxide in ethanol at 30°C. 4. Alkyl iodide and triethylamine in acetone at 100°C. 5. Alkyl iodide and dimethylaniline in ethanol at 40°C. 6. Alkyl iodide and silver nitrate in ethanol at 25.4°C. 7. Solvolytic hydrolysis of alkyl bromide in 80% ethanol at 25°C.
b. v.sl. = too slow for measurement.

aldo-D-hexoses and the anomer α-D-glucose, is catalyzed at less than a few percent of the rate at which β-D-glucose and 2-deoxy-D-glucose are oxidized. The catalytic activity of urease, which hydrolyzes urea, is even more specific. With respect to sensitivity, the enzyme-catalyzed luminescent reaction of luciferin

$$\text{Luciferin} + O_2 + \text{ATP} \xrightarrow[\text{Mg}^{2+}]{\text{Luciferase}} \text{Oxyluciferin} + \text{ADP} + h\nu \qquad (18.1)$$

the "firefly reaction," can be used to measure as little as 4×10^{-13} mole of ATP. In cases where the catalyst or enzyme itself is the species being measured, or where chemical amplification techniques have been used, it has been shown that these methods are capable of measuring such species as NAD$^+$ at the 10^{-16} mole level, and can determine the activity of single molecules of the enzyme. These are, of course, special reactions.

Closely similar functional groups on the same molecule can be determined by kinetic differentiation—for example, analysis of both the primary and secondary alcohol groups on the polymeric molecule, poly(propyleneglycol). This is an important problem, since the ratio of primary to secondary alcohols on the chain affects the physical properties of the material and, hence, its price. Obviously, separation is impossible and any reagent for alcohol functional groups will give only total –OH content. However, by taking advantage of the difference in the reaction rates of primary and secondary –OH groups with acetic anhydride, a kinetic technique has been developed to determine the concentrations of each. Similar techniques have been employed to measure the ratio of internal to external (terminal) double bonds in polyalkenes.

For reactions that do not attain equilibrium virtually instantaneously, kinetic methods are also more rapid than those relying on measurements made after equilibrium has been reached. The kinetic approach does imply poorer sensitivity limits for a given reaction, however, since the rate is measured when only a fraction of the reaction has been completed.

One last point in comparing kinetic and equilibrium measurements is the wide variety of techniques that can be used to control the rates (and rate constants) of reactions and thus optimize measurements. The free energy of activation of a reaction is very sensitive to temperature, to the nature of the solvent and to ionic strength, among other factors.

18.2 MEASUREMENT OF REACTION RATES

Chemical reaction rates cover a very wide range. Some reactions, such as the neutralization of a strong acid with a strong base, are so rapid that they appear to reach equilibrium instantaneously, whereas others, such as the (noncatalyzed) reaction between oxygen and hydrogen at room temperature, are so slow that no reaction can be detected at all.

In order to determine the initial concentration of a desired species by kinetic-based methods, the rate of the chemical reaction must be measured by monitoring the concentration of at least one of the reactants or products as a function of time. Chemical methods (titration) or physical methods (spectrophotometry or conductivity) can be employed. If chemical methods are used, the rates of reaction must be quite slow or, if the reaction has suitable properties, quenching methods can be utilized when some reaction occurs at a significantly fast rate. Continuous measurement of the reaction rate is possible by physical, but not by chemical, methods: the reaction rates observable are limited only by the response times of the instruments.

In Figure 18.1 is a schematic presentation of the change with time of a measured experimental parameter P. P is proportional to the concentration of product formed on reaction of a five-component mixture (A, B, C, D, and E, which have widely varying rate-constants). Thus, if A reacts faster than B, etc., the product that is formed during the early stage of the reaction results mostly from A. Likewise, if E is the slowest reacting of the five components, the product formed in the latter stages results almost entirely from the reaction of E. Reactions with half-times larger than about 10 sec are considered "slow," whereas those with half-times smaller than 10 sec are considered "fast." The methods for measuring each type and the experimental limitations for each are briefly discussed below.

Slow Reactions

The rates of slow chemical reactions in solution can generally be studied by quite simple and conventional methods. The reactants are mixed in some vessel and the progress of the reaction is followed by titrating aliquots of the mixture or by measuring, at known times, a physical property of the solution such as optical absorption or polarographic diffusion current.

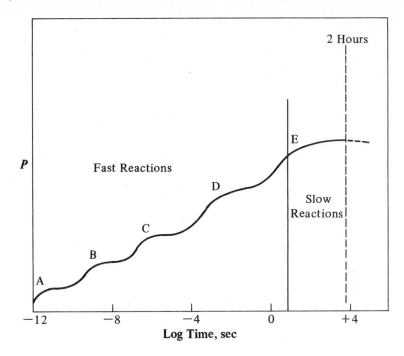

FIGURE 18.1. *Experimental parameter P (proportional to concentration) vs. time t for a five-component mixture (A, B, C, D, and E). From H. B. Mark, Jr., G. A. Rechnitz, and R. A. Grienke,* Kinetics in Analytical Chemistry, *New York: Wiley-Interscience, 1968, by permission of John Wiley and Sons. Copyright © 1968 by John Wiley and Sons.*

The speed of initial mixing of the components in the vessel places a definite limit on the minimum half-time that can be measured in this way. If the mixing is accomplished by simple stirring devices such as magnetic stirring bars, the mixing time is a few seconds, and reactions with half-times smaller than 10 sec are difficult to measure with acceptable accuracy.

On the other hand, the kinetics of reactions with long half-times can be determined, but such determinations consume considerable time and are, therefore, undesirable for analytical purposes. A 2-hr time limit (Fig. 18.1) is arbitrarily considered the longest acceptable time for routine analysis.

If the reaction rate is greater than 2 hr or less than 10 sec, several simple techniques can be employed to adjust the rate so that the half-time will lie within the desired range. These are: (1) changing the temperature of the reaction system, (2) changing the concentration of the reactants, and (3) changing the solvent medium or ionic strength of the solution.

Change in Temperature. The relationship between temperature and the rate constant k of a chemical reaction is given by the Arrhenius equation

$$\frac{d(\ln k)}{dT} = \frac{E^*}{RT^2} \tag{18.2}$$

or (in its integrated form)

$$k = Ae^{-E^*/RT} \tag{18.3}$$

where E^* = the activation energy
         R = the universal gas constant
         A = the frequency factor

For a large number of homogeneous reactions, the rate constant increases 2 or 3 times for each 10°C rise in temperature.

Reactions that are fast at room temperature can be slowed by cooling to allow measurement by "convenient" or "conventional" physical or chemical methods. For example, the conductometric analysis of a mixture of certain aliphatic aldehydes by differential reaction rates can be carried out at 0–5°C, whereas, at room temperature, the reactions are too fast. On the other hand, slow reactions can be made to proceed at considerably faster rates by raising the temperature. For example, fructose reacts with anthrone at room temperature in the presence of glucose and within 10 min develops a highly colored product. Glucose does not react appreciably even over a long period of time, but by elevating the temperature of the reaction mixture to 100°C after the fructose has reacted, the glucose can be made to react to completion in a few minutes and can be determined.

Change in Concentration. Reactions with very large rate-constants can be measured simply by using low concentrations of reactants, provided that sensitive enough methods are available to measure the small changes in concentration. For example, the bromination of N,N-diethyl-m-toluidine is extremely fast in aqueous solution, but since 10^{-8} M bromine can be estimated from the redox potential of a platinum electrode, the concentration of the free amine can be reduced to 10^{-8} M and the reaction can then be readily followed. Spectrophotometric methods can be used to measure extremely small concentrations of highly colored compounds. A reaction involving color change and a large rate-constant is that between ferrous ion and cobaltioxalate ion in aqueous solution.

$$Fe^{2+} + [Co(C_2O_4)_3]^{3-} = Fe^{3+} + [Co(C_2O_4)_3]^{4-} \tag{18.4}$$

High concentrations of the reacting species can be employed to speed up reactions with small rate-constants, although changes in activity coefficients may hamper the calculation of initial concentration when high concentrations of reactants are used.

Change in Solvent or Ionic Strength. The rate constant of a chemical reaction can be considerably altered by changing the solvent or by adding a salt to the reaction medium, partly as a consequence of changes in the dielectric constant of the solvent or the ionic strength of the solution. More specifically, as the dielectric constant increases, (1) the rate of a reaction between two ions of the same sign increases, (2) the rate of a reaction between two ions of the opposite sign decreases, (3) the rate of a reaction between two neutral species that form a polar product increases, and (4) the rate of reaction between an ion and a neutral molecule is not significantly changed. As the ionic strength of the medium increases, (1) the rate of reaction between two ions of the same sign increases, (2) the rate of reaction between two ions of opposite sign decreases, (3) the rate of reaction between two neutral species that form a polar product changes only slightly, and (4) the rate of reaction between an ion and a neutral molecule changes only slightly.

Fast Reactions

The kinetic methods of analysis discussed in this chapter have mostly been applied to slow reactions, but many of these methods are also applicable to fast reactions, provided that sufficient accuracy in the measurement of the reaction rate can be achieved. Special techniques to measure fast reactions have become more accurate in recent years, and practical analytical applications of them are now being devised.

For the most part, experimental methods for studying fast reactions can be classified into four groups: mixing, relaxation, periodic, and continuous methods. The approximate upper limit of reaction rates that can be measured by each of these techniques depends upon the mixing time or, in the case of relaxation and periodic methods, the displacement time, which is the time required to bring the system to a suitable nonequilibrium condition.

Mixing Methods. Mixing methods, the most common experimental method employed in kinetic studies of fast reactions, involve the actual rapid mixing of reacting species that were initially separated. They are of special interest because they are the only methods that do not rely on displacing an established equilibrium. Hence, reactions that are virtually irreversible under conditions of interest can be studied; it is for this reason that mixing methods are also the most applicable to pseudo-first-order reactions.

The most widely used fast mixing method is the *continuous-flow method.* The reactants flow in separate continuous streams that meet in a mixing chamber and then pass along an observation tube or chamber with detection devices at appropriate points along its length (see Fig. 18.2). The detection devices, which measure the composition of the flowing sample, may be optical, thermal, chemical, electrical, or any other method applicable to a rapidly moving sample. Reactions with half-times of the order of 10^{-3} sec can be observed by this method.

The *stopped-flow* method is perhaps the next most commonly used mixing method. This technique employs a pair of driven syringes to force the reactants into a mixing chamber and then into the observation cell. As soon as the mixed solution reaches the observation cell, the flow is stopped in order to observe changes in the measured parameter without interference from artifacts arising from flow and turbulence.

Other mixing methods have been employed with considerable success for monitoring reaction rates of intermediate magnitude.

Relaxation and Periodic Methods. Relaxation methods involve a single sudden alteration of one or more conditions of a system initially at equilibrium, whereas periodic methods involve a periodic alteration or disturbance of the system. These two methods can be subdivided into two classifications, based on the parameter altered: either the *equilibrium constant* is changed (ΔK methods), or the *concentration* of one or more of the species of the system is changed (Δc mthods). These methods

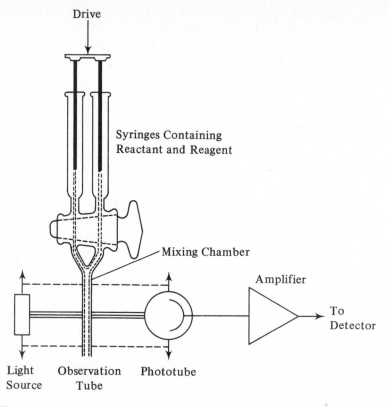

Drive

Syringes Containing
Reactant and Reagent

Mixing Chamber

Amplifier

To
Detector

Light   Observation   Phototube
Source   Tube

FIGURE 18.2. *Schematic diagram of a continuous-flow apparatus. From H. B. Mark, Jr., G. A. Rechnitz, and R. A. Grienke,* Kinetics in Analytical Chemistry, *New York: Wiley-Interscience, 1968, by permission of John Wiley and Sons. Copyright © 1968 by John Wiley and Sons.*

can be used to measure rate constants of the order of 10^{12}/mole-min; hence, they are applicable to fast ionic reactions such as neutralization and hydrolysis, which typically have half-times of 10^{-9} sec or less.

ΔK Methods. After a rapid alteration of K by changing an external condition, the solution composition readjusts at a finite rate in an attempt to reattain equilibrium; this process of adjustment is called *relaxation*. Several experimental techniques for achieving the necessarily rapid alterations of K have been developed. These include a pressure-jump (sound-absorption) method, an electric-field (dissociation) method, and a temperature-jump method. A temperature jump is brought about by passing an electrical current through the solution in a special cuvette, producing an abrupt, nearly instantaneous, rise in the temperature of the solution. A reaction then takes place as the concentrations adjust to the new temperature. Regardless of the type of perturbation used, the treatment of the data is essentially the same.

Δc Methods. A rapid change is made of the concentration of one or more species in a system initially at equilibrium; changes in the concentrations of all the species then occur as the system moves back toward equilibrium. Commonly employed methods are flash photolysis (minimum $t_{1/2} \sim 10^{-5}$ sec), which can measure first-order rate constants as large as 5×10^6 min^{-1}, and electrochemical potential-step, coulostatic, and galvanostatic methods, used for studying fast electrode reactions or the homogeneous reactions following the electron-transfer step.

18.3 MATHEMATICAL BASIS OF KINETIC METHODS OF ANALYSIS

The past few years have seen the development of many methods for calculating the initial concentration of the species of interest from reaction-rate data. These methods involve, in general, manipulating and rearranging the differential or integral forms of the classical reaction-rate equations to put them in a convenient form for calculating the initial concentrations of the unknown reactants. Such methods can be classified into two main categories: methods for a single species and methods for the simultaneous (in situ) analysis of mixtures. Within each of these two categories, the methods can be subdivided according to the kinetic order of the reactions employed: pseudo-zero-order or initial-rate methods, first-order and pseudo-first-order methods, and second-order methods.

Although most investigators classify reactions by their rate order, the actual mechanisms of the chemical reactions employed in virtually all of these methods (except those involving catalytic reactions or radiochemical decay) are bimolecular reactions of the type

$$A + R \underset{k_b}{\overset{k_f}{\rightleftharpoons}} P \qquad (18.5)$$

where $A =$ the species of analytical interest
$R =$ the added reagent
$P =$ the product (or products)
$k_f =$ the forward rate constant
$k_b =$ the backward rate constant

The general differential rate expressions then have the form

$$-\frac{d[A]_t}{dt} = -\frac{d[R]_t}{dt} = \frac{d[P]_t}{dt} = k_f[A]_t[R]_t - k_b[P]_t \qquad (18.6)$$

($[A]_t$, $[R]_t$, and $[P]_t$ represent the concentrations of these species at any time t.) Thus, the nomenclature zero, first, and second order actually refers to the experimental conditions under which the rate measurements are made or to the relative concentrations of the reactants A and R.

If the rate data are taken only during the initial 1–2% completion of the total reaction, then the concentrations of A and R remain virtually unchanged and equal to the initial concentrations ($[A]_0$ and $[R]_0$, respectively); and the reverse reaction can be ignored, since only a negligible amount of product is formed. Thus, Equation 18.6 simplifies to a pseudo-zero-order form

$$\left(\frac{d[P]_t}{dt}\right) \approx k_f[A]_0[R]_0 \approx \text{Constant} \qquad (18.7)$$

Experimentally, only the rate of initial change of concentration of product is followed, since the change in concentration of either A or R is very small under these conditions and cannot be measured accurately.

If Reaction 18.5 is run under such conditions that the initial concentration of one of the reactants (either A or R) is very large compared to that of the other, then the concentration of that reactant will remain virtually unchanged as the reaction proceeds to equilibrium and can be considered equal to the initial concentration. Also, the reverse reaction can usually be neglected since the large excess of one of the reactants drives the reaction to virtual completion. Under these conditions, the reaction is pseudo-first-order and the rate expression takes the form (for R in excess)

$$-\frac{d[A]_t}{dt} \approx k_f[R]_0[A]_t = k_f'[A]_t \tag{18.8}$$

A completely analogous expression can be written for $-d[R]_t/dt$ for the case where A is in large excess.

If the rate of Reaction 18.5 is measured while the reaction goes to a significant degree of completion under conditions where $[A]_0$ is of the same order of magnitude as $[R]_0$, then the method is called a second-order method and the exact differential-rate expression (Eqn. 18.6) must be employed in analyzing the data. Note also that only when the reaction mechanism is virtually irreversible can the reverse reaction be ignored in Equation 18.6. Furthermore, for the special case $[R]_0 = [A]_0$, a modified form of the calculation of initial concentrations must be used.

It is obvious from the discussion above that any kinetic-based analytical procedure must take into account the degree of approximation made in the various rate equations with respect to the period of measurement, the relative initial concentrations of reactants, and, in some cases, the reversibility of the reactions. Care must be taken, for example, in using a pseudo-first-order method when the initial concentration of the unknown varies over several orders of magnitude; the error introduced in assuming the validity of the pseudo-first-order approximation of Equation 18.8 is a function of $[A]_0$. Although the reaction mechanisms and rate equations for enzymatic and other catalyzed reactions in general are somewhat more complex, similar assumptions and simplifications (and, therefore, restrictions in validity) apply to the rate-measurement techniques employed in the analytical use of these systems.

Within each of the classifications of reaction-rate methods, there are many different methods of display or mathematical manipulation of the data or equations used to calculate the initial concentration of the species being determined. The calculating technique used can have very significant effects on the accuracy of the analysis. For example, the kinetic role of the species being determined in methods employing first-order or enzymatic or other catalyzed reactions has a strong effect on the choice of measurement of the reaction rate. For the simultaneous, in situ, analysis of several components of a mixture, the choice of method is even more critical with respect to accuracy. Both the relative and absolute values of the rate constants, as well as the initial concentrations of the species to be determined, dictate the choice of method. Furthermore, within the mathematical framework of each of these calculation procedures, there are generally optimum or limited times at which rate data should be taken in order to minimize the effects of random and absolute error in measurement. The choice of procedure and optimization of the measurement is very complex and no simple rules can be given, but some of the general principles are discussed below.

18.4 RATE EQUATIONS FOR THE DETERMINATION OF A SINGLE SPECIES

Three types of reactions have been employed in kinetic techniques for determining a single species: first- (or pseudo-first-) order, enzyme-catalyzed, and other catalyzed reactions.

First- (or Pseudo-First-) Order Reactions

A first-order or pseudo-first-order irreversible reaction of a reactant A to form the product P can be written as

$$A \xrightarrow{k_A} xP \tag{18.9}$$

where $\quad k_A$ = the rate constant
$\qquad x$ = a number describing the stoichiometry of the reaction

The rate of disappearance of A as a function of time is

$$-\frac{d[A]_t}{dt} = k_A[A]_t \tag{18.10}$$

where $\quad [A]_t$ = the concentration of A at any time t

Integrating Equation 18.10 yields a relationship between $[A]_t$ and the initial concentration $[A]_0$, which is the quantity to be measured in a kinetic-based analysis:

$$[A]_t = [A]_0 e^{-k_A t} \tag{18.11}$$

Substituting Equation 18.11 into 18.10 defines the rate of the reaction in terms of $[A]_0$,

$$-\frac{d[A]_t}{dt} = k_A[A]_0 e^{-k_A t} \tag{18.12}$$

Equation 18.12 is the basis for the *derivative* approach to rate-based analysis, which involves directly measuring the reaction rate at a specific time or times and relating this to $[A]_0$. Equation 18.11 is the basis for the two different *integral* approaches to kinetic analysis. In one case, the amount of A reacted during a fixed time is measured and is directly proportional to $[A]_0$ (*fixed-time* method); in the other case, the time required for a fixed amount of A to react is measured and is also proportional to $[A]_0$ (*variable-time* method). Details of these methods will be discussed in Section 18.5. Primarily because of difficulties in reproducing mixing times, Equation 18.11 is not often applied directly. Some time t_1 ($t_1 \neq 0$), when the solution is homogeneously mixed, is used as the initial point from which Equation 18.10 is integrated. Thus, the difference in concentration ΔA over a time interval Δt ($\Delta t = t_2 - t_1$) is related to $[A]_0$ by

$$\Delta A = [A]_0(e^{-k_A t_2} - e^{-k_A t_1}) \tag{18.13}$$

In many situations, the concentration of the product P is the experimentally measured variable, rather than the concentration of A. In such cases, since $\Delta[P] = -x\,\Delta[A]$, Equations 18.12 and 18.13 can be rewritten as

$$\frac{d[P]_t}{dt} = xk_A[A]_0 e^{-k_A t} \tag{18.14}$$

and

$$\Delta[P] = x[A]_0(e^{-k_A t_1} - e^{-k_A t_2}) \tag{18.15}$$

When the concentration is measured instrumentally, it is related to the magnitude of some electrical signal $\mathscr{S}$ produced in the detector or sensor portion of the instrument. When $\mathscr{S}$ is linearly related to the concentration of the product—for example, in conductance or amperometric measurements—$\Delta\mathscr{S} = \nu\,\Delta[P]$ and $d\mathscr{S} = \nu\,d[P]$, where ν is the proportionality constant or *transfer function* in electrical units per concentration unit. Substituting for $\Delta[P]$ and $d[P]$ in Equations 18.14 and 18.15, and replacing t_2 by the term $(t_1 + \Delta t)$, yields

$$\frac{d\mathscr{S}_t}{dt} = \nu x k_A[A]_0 e^{-k_A t} \tag{18.16}$$

and

$$\Delta\mathscr{S} = \nu x[A]_0 e^{-k_A t_1}(1 - e^{k_A\,\Delta t}) \tag{18.17}$$

Thus, $[A]_0$ in both cases is directly related to the signal output of the instrument.

Often an instrumental method is employed in which $\mathscr{S}$ is not a linear function of $[P]$. For example, in optical absorption or potentiometric measurements, the output of a photomultiplier or an electrode is a logarithmic function of concentration. In such cases, the direct instrumental response can be written in a general form as

$$\mathscr{S} = f([P]) \tag{18.18}$$

where $f[P]$ = an arbitrary function

The mathematics becomes more complicated and, in general, nonlinear calibration curves result.

Enzyme-Catalyzed Reactions

Enzyme-catalyzed reactions are used analytically to determine both enzyme activities $[E]$ and substrate concentrations $[S]$, and are very important in clinical diagnoses. The usual Michaelis-Menten mechanism for enzymatic reactions is

$$E + S \underset{k_{-1}}{\overset{k_1}{\rightleftarrows}} E \cdot S \xrightarrow{k_2} P + E \tag{18.19}$$

In this equation, $E \cdot S$ is the intermediate enzyme-substrate complex. A steady-state treatment of this reaction mechanism gives the rate law

$$\frac{-d[S]_t}{dt} = \frac{d[P]_t}{dt} = \frac{k_2[E]_0[S]_t}{K_M + [S]_t} \tag{18.20}$$

The enzyme concentration appears only as the initial concentration in Equation

18.20, since the enzyme is cyclically regenerated during the reaction. K_M, the so-called Michaelis constant, is equal to $(k_{-1} + k_2)/k_1$. Equation 18.20 is the basis for the derivative techniques for determining both $[E]_0$ and $[S]_0$. If the concentration of product is monitored by a linear-response sensor, the resulting electrical signal at a given time is

$$\frac{d\mathscr{S}_t}{dt} = \frac{vk_2[E]_0[S]_t}{K_M + [S]_t} \qquad (18.21)$$

If the substrate concentration is large compared to K_M, then the reaction is pseudo-zero-order and the rate of change of the signal with time is directly proportional to $[E]_0$. Under conditions where $[S]_t \ll K_M$, the rate of change of the signal is also directly proportional to $[S]_t$ and, when initial reaction rates are measured, $[S]_t \approx [S]_0$.

Integrating Equation 18.20 between two substrate concentrations $[S]_1$ and $[S]_2$ (the concentrations at times t_1 and t_2 respectively) yields

$$-K_M \ln\left(\frac{[S]_2}{[S]_1}\right) - \Delta[S] = k_2[E]_0(t_2 - t_1) \qquad (18.22)$$

which is the basis of the integral methods.

Other Catalyzed Reactions

Homogeneous catalyzed reactions (other than enzyme-catalyzed reactions) have been used extensively in trace analysis. The general approach is to employ a reaction in which the species of analytical interest acts as a catalyst. Since the mechanisms of such reactions are varied and complex and often are not completely known, it is impractical or impossible to give exact rate equations for such mechanisms here. However, the rate expressions in terms of the rate of formation of product can usually be written in the general form

$$\frac{d[P]_t}{dt} = K[C]_0 f([X_1], [X_2], \ldots, [X_i]) \qquad (18.23)$$

where $[X_i]$ = the reactant and product concentrations
f = an arbitrary function
K = the proportionality constant
$[C]_0$ = the initial catalyst concentration

It can be seen from the form of Equation 18.23 that the derivative approach can be used to determine $[C]_0$. The mathematical relationships for the integral methods can be obtained by rearranging and integrating.

18.5 METHODS FOR DETERMINING A SINGLE SPECIES

Two types of techniques are employed for analyzing a single-component system. The most straightforward is the *derivative* or *slope* method in which one obtains the derivative of the electrical signal by electronically differentiating the signal from the transducer. The second approach uses the integral forms of the rate equations, and one of two possible types of measurement: the *fixed-time* or *constant-time* method in which the reaction is allowed to proceed for a fixed time, and the *variable-time* method in which the signal output varies between two fixed limits and the time Δt required for the complete sweep is measured.

The Derivative Technique

For first- and pseudo-first-order reactions monitored by an instrument with a linear response, Equation 18.16 is solved for $[A]_0$ to yield the relationship between the rate of change of the signal and the initial concentration of A:

$$[A]_0 = \left(\frac{e^{k_A t}}{\nu x k_A}\right)\left(\frac{d\mathcal{S}_t}{dt}\right) \tag{18.24}$$

There are two modes in which Equation 18.24 is employed. If the derivative measurement is made at a specified time after the reaction is initiated, the first term is a constant and $[A]_0$ can be obtained directly from the measured value of $d\mathcal{S}_t/dt$. A more common approach is to make the derivative measurement during the initial 1% of the overall reaction, before $e^{k_A t}$ differs significantly from unity. Then the initial rate is virtually independent of time, and Equation 18.24 simplifies to

$$[A]_0 \approx \left(\frac{1}{\nu x k_A}\right)\left(\frac{d\mathcal{S}_t}{dt}\right)_{\text{initial}} \tag{18.25}$$

During the initial portion of the reaction, the slope is approximately constant (to within 1%) and pseudo-zero-order kinetics apply.

For enzyme-catalyzed reactions used to measure enzyme activities with a linear-response instrument, solving Equation 18.21 for $[E]_0$ gives

$$[E]_0 = \left(\frac{K_M + [S]_t}{\nu k_2 [S]_t}\right)\left(\frac{d\mathcal{S}_t}{dt}\right) \tag{18.26}$$

If the measurement is at a fixed value of $[S]_t$, $d\mathcal{S}_t/dt$ is directly proportional to $[E]_0$ since the first term is a constant. However, measurement at constant $[S]_t$ is obviously difficult, and the analysis itself can be greatly simplified by arranging experimental conditions so that $[S]_t \gg K_M$. In this case, the initial rate is obtained and

$$[E]_0 \approx \left(\frac{1}{\nu k_2}\right)\left(\frac{d\mathcal{S}_t}{dt}\right)_{\text{initial}} \tag{18.27}$$

The determination of the substrate concentrations using enzyme-catalyzed reactions by the derivative method follows from Equation 18.20, under the following conditions: (1) a linear instrumental response, (2) reaction conditions where $[S]_t \ll K_M$, (3) a fixed value for $[E_0]$, (4) a measured initial rate ($[S]_t \approx [S]_0$).

$$[S]_0 = \left(\frac{K_M}{\nu k_2 [E]_0}\right)\left(\frac{d\mathcal{S}_t}{dt}\right)_{\text{initial}} \tag{18.28}$$

Because of the complexity of other catalyzed reactions, initial reaction-rates are usually measured for analytical purposes. Equation 18.23 shows that, if all reactant concentrations are approximately equal to their initial concentrations, a direct proportionality is obtained between the catalyst concentration and the initial measured rate, provided the instrument has a linear response. With a nonlinear response, it is necessary to make the measurement at a fixed signal level in order to have a direct proportionality between $[C]_0$ and the derivative.

Fixed-Time Method

The fixed-time approach is an integral technique, although conditions are usually so arranged that measurement times and concentration changes are small enough to produce a good approximation to the instantaneous reaction-rate.

If the product concentration in a first- or pseudo-first-order reaction is measured by a linear-response instrument, Equation 18.17 can be solved for $[A]_0$ to give

$$[A]_0 = \left(\frac{e^{k_A t_1}}{\nu x (1 - e^{k_A \, \Delta t})} \right) \Delta \mathscr{S} \tag{18.29}$$

If all measurements are begun at the same value of t_1 after the start of the reaction and Δt is constant, the quantity in brackets will be constant for all experiments, and $[A]_0$ is directly proportional to $\Delta \mathscr{S}$. This is true for any fixed time-interval during the reaction and, thus, the fixed-time method is not restricted to measurements of initial rates. However, the analysis can be considerably simplified if the measurement is made before 1–2% of A has reacted.

$$[A]_0 \approx \left(\frac{1}{\nu x k_A \, \Delta t} \right) \Delta \mathscr{S} \tag{18.30}$$

The use of this equation in the fixed-time method is shown in Figure 18.3. It is clear from the format of the fixed-time method and Equations 18.29 and 18.30 that, if $\Delta \mathscr{S}$ is not directly proportional to $\Delta[P]$ (as is the case with nonlinear-response instruments), the fixed-time method will lead to a nonlinear relation between $\Delta \mathscr{S}$ and $[A]_0$; this virtually rules out the use of this method with such instruments.

When enzyme-catalyzed reactions are employed to measure enzyme activities, Equation 18.22 can be solved for $[E]_0$ to give

$$[E]_0 = \frac{-K_M \ln \left(\frac{[S]_2}{[S]_1} \right) - \Delta[S]}{k_2 \, \Delta t} \tag{18.31}$$

where $\Delta t = t_2 - t_1$. If the relation $[S]_2 = \Delta[S] + [S]_1$ is substituted into Equation 18.31 and the logarithmic term expanded in a Maclaurin series, one obtains

$$[E]_0 = \frac{-K_M \left[\frac{\Delta[S]}{[S]_1} - \frac{1}{2} \left(\frac{\Delta[S]}{[S]_1} \right)^2 + \frac{1}{3} \left(\frac{\Delta[S]}{[S]_1} \right)^3 - \cdots \right] - \Delta[S]}{k_2 \, \Delta t} \tag{18.32}$$

In order to use the fixed-time approach, several approximations to simplify this equation are necessary. First of all, the relative change of concentration ($\Delta[S]/[S]_1$) must be made very small (less than 2%) during the interval Δt so that the higher-order terms of the series can be ignored, which gives

$$[E]_0 = \frac{-1}{k_2 \, \Delta t} \left(\frac{K_M}{[S]_1} + 1 \right) \Delta[S] \tag{18.33}$$

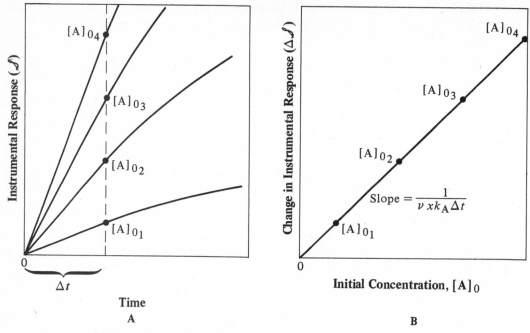

FIGURE 18.3. *The fixed-time method for uncatalyzed reactions, in the case where $t_1 = 0$ and $\mathscr{S}_{t=0} = 0$. (a) Variation of $\mathscr{S}$ as a function of time for various different initial concentrations of A. (b) Variation of $\Delta\mathscr{S}$ at a fixed time-interval Δt with change in $[A]_0$.*

This equation is further simplified if the condition $[S]_1 \gg K_M$ is employed, which yields

$$[E]_0 \approx \left(\frac{-1}{k_2\,\Delta t} \right) \Delta[S] \tag{18.34}$$

and which, for a linear-response instrument ($\Delta S \approx \Delta\mathscr{S}$), gives a direct proportionality between $\Delta\mathscr{S}$ and $[E]_0$. Again, a nonlinear-response instrument will lead to nonlinear relations between ΔS and $[E]_0$, and the fixed-time method is not readily applicable.

The fixed-time technique for determining substrate concentrations using enzyme-catalyzed reactions follows much the same mathematical development as given above.

With respect to the use of catalyzed reactions, the catalyst concentrations can be determined using the fixed-time method, but strict adherence to pseudo-zero-order conditions (initial reaction-rate measurement) is generally necessary to obtain linear calibration curves.

The Variable-Time Method

The variable-time method, like the fixed-time method, is an integral method which, for short measurement times and small changes in concentration, also gives results approaching the instantaneous reaction-rate.

The variable-time method, as employed for first- or pseudo-first-order reactions, also uses the integral form of the first-order rate equation (Eqn. 18.15). Solving for $[A]_0$ yields

$$[A]_0 = \frac{\Delta[P] e^{k_A t_1}}{x(1 - e^{-k_A \Delta t})} \tag{18.35}$$

In the variable-time method, $\Delta[P]$ is held constant and Δt is the measured parameter that is related to $[A]_0$. If measurements are carried out during the first 1–2% of the overall reaction (initial-rate conditions), the exponential term, $e^{k_A t_1}$, is approximately equal to unity; and if the measurements are begun very near zero reaction-time, Equation 18.35 becomes

$$[A]_0 = \left(\frac{\Delta[P]}{x k_A}\right) \frac{1}{\Delta t} \tag{18.36}$$

Thus, in contrast to the fixed-time procedure, it is absolutely necessary to employ pseudo-zero-order conditions (initial-reaction conditions) in order to obtain a linear calibration curve. For a linear-response instrument, $\Delta[P]$ can be replaced by $\Delta \mathscr{S}/v$ to give

$$[A]_0 = \left(\frac{\Delta \mathscr{S}}{v x k_A}\right) \frac{1}{\Delta t} \tag{18.37}$$

The application of this equation to rate data is shown in Figure 18.4. The variable-time procedure has several advantages over the fixed-time procedure when used with instruments having a nonlinear relationship between signal output and concentration.

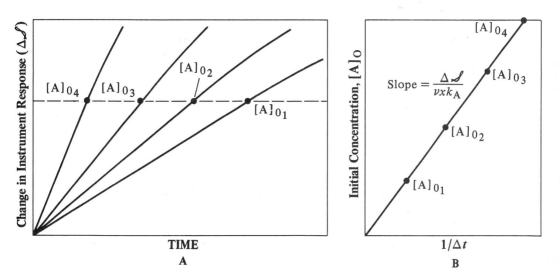

FIGURE 18.4. *Variable-time method for uncatalyzed reactions.* (a) *Variation of $\mathscr{S}$ as a function of time for various different initial concentrations of A.* (b) *Variation of $1/\Delta t$ required to reach a fixed value of $\Delta \mathscr{S}$ as a function of $[A]_0$.*

The variable-time approach is ideally suited to the determination of enzyme activities; rearrangement of the integral form of the rate law (Eqn. 18.22) yields

$$[E]_0 = \left[-K_M \ln \left(\frac{[S]_2}{[S]_1} \right) - \Delta[S] \right] \left(\frac{1}{k_2 \, \Delta t} \right) \tag{18.38}$$

Since $[S]_2$, $[S]_1$, and (thus) $\Delta[S]$, are held constant in the variable-time method, a linear relation between $[E]_0$ and $1/\Delta t$ always exists because the bracketed term is a constant. Again, if $[S] \gg K_M$ and $\Delta[S]/[S]_1$ is kept small (initial-rate conditions), Equation 18.38 can be simplified to

$$[E]_0 = - \left(\frac{\Delta[S]}{k_2} \right) \frac{1}{\Delta t} \tag{18.39}$$

If a linear-response instrument is used, the $\Delta[S]$ term in this equation simply becomes $\Delta \mathscr{S}/v$; with a nonlinear-response instrument $\Delta[S]$ becomes $[f(\mathscr{S}_2) - f(\mathscr{S}_1)]$. Thus, a linear relationship between $[E]_0$ and $1/\Delta t$ is independent of the linearity of the instrumental response and measurements need not be made during the initial stages of the reaction.

The variable-time method, however, is not as well suited for determining substrate concentrations as the fixed-time method; there will be a nonlinear relationship between $[S]_0$ and $1/\Delta t$ unless pseudo-zero-order conditions are used during the interval Δt and the measurements are begun very close to $t = 0$.

For other types of catalyzed reactions, the variable-time method is well suited for determining catalyst concentrations. Initial-rate procedures and linearity of instrumental response are not necessary.

Summary and Comparison of Single-Component Techniques

In choosing between the three single-component approaches, the most important factors are the type of reaction, the species sought for, and the characteristics of the instrumental response. The derivative technique is the most straightforward approach and gives the desired read-out of instantaneous reaction-rate. For noisy signals, however, the two integral approaches are more reliable. If the instrumental response is linearly related to concentration, the fixed-time approach is superior for pseudo-first-order reactions and for the determination of substrate concentrations using enzyme reactions. Reaction-rate analyses of enzyme activities and the determination of other catalysts are best carried out by the variable-time method. If the instrumental response is a nonlinear function of concentration, the variable-time approach is of great advantage. The two integral approaches are complementary, and both should be available for the maximum usefulness of reaction-rate methods.

18.6 RATE EQUATIONS AND METHODS FOR MIXTURES

Often, the reaction rates of closely related components of a mixture with a common reagent are similar, and the rates cannot be sufficiently separated by either a thermodynamic or a kinetic masking technique to permit the faster or slower reacting component to be neglected. When this specific situation occurs, *differential reaction-rate methods* can be employed for analyzing the mixtures without resorting to separation techniques.

Consider the irreversible bimolecular reactions of a binary mixture of A and B with a common reagent R.

$$A + R \xrightarrow{k_A} P \tag{18.40}$$

$$B + R \xrightarrow{k_B} P' \tag{18.41}$$

The range of concentrations of reactant and reagent for which general differential reaction-rate methods have been developed is illustrated in Figure 18.5. When the concentration of common reagent is very large with respect to the total concentration of A and B, the reaction proceeds by pseudo-first-order kinetics (Region I) and several general methods are available. The rates of change of the concentrations of either the product or the total reactants (total A and B) are monitored as a function of time.

As [R] becomes less than 50 times the total concentration of reactants ([A] + [B]), pseudo-first-order kinetics are no longer valid (Region II); however, as [R] approaches ([A] + [B]) in magnitude, simple second-order kinetic treatments of the rates of reaction can be used. Regions III, IV [special cases where [R] = ([A] + [B])], and V of Figure 18.5 represent the concentration ranges where the

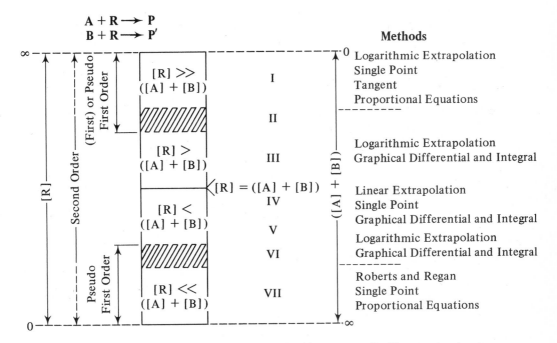

FIGURE 18.5. *General analytical techniques applicable to second-order reactions. From H. B. Mark, Jr., G. A. Rechnitz, and R. A. Grienke,* Kinetics in Analytical Chemistry, *New York: Wiley-Interscience, 1968, by permission of John Wiley and Sons. Copyright © 1968 by John Wiley and Sons.*

second-order treatment is employed. General methods based on second-order kinetics have been developed in which either [R], ([A] + [B]), or [P] can be followed.

As [R] decreases further, the kinetics again approach pseudo-first-order rates (Region VI), but now with respect to R. As [R] ≪ ([A] + [B]) (Region VII), a pseudo-first-order rate again applies, and general differential reaction-rate methods have been developed for this situation. There are also differential methods based on measurements of *initial* reaction-rates, where the kinetics become pseudo-zero-order.

Theoretical treatments for analysis based on second-order kinetics are considerably more involved than those for first-order or pseudo-first-order processes. Therefore, whenever possible, the conditions of a bimolecular reaction are adjusted so that the reaction follows pseudo-first-order kinetics; a 50-fold or greater excess of reagent (Region I) or reactants (Region VII) is necessary. There are systems, however, for which pseudo-first-order conditions cannot be employed—for example, with a large excess of either reagent or reactants, the reactions of interest may be too fast for practical measurements.

Three of the more commonly used first-order differential kinetic methods are discussed in detail in this section. These are the *logarithmic-extrapolation method*, the *method of proportional equations*, and the *method of Roberts and Regan*.

Logarithmic-Extrapolation Method

The logarithmic-extrapolation method is suitable for reactions that are first-order or pseudo-first-order with respect to the reactants; that is, in Region I of Figure 18.5, where $[R]_0 \gg ([A]_0 + [B]_0)$. Consider two competing irreversible reactions of the type

$$A \xrightarrow{k_A} P \tag{18.42}$$

$$B \xrightarrow{k_B} P \tag{18.43}$$

in which A and B react to form a common product P, whose concentration at any time t is given by the expression

$$[P]_\infty - [P]_t = [A]_t + [B]_t = [A]_0 e^{-k_A t} + [B]_0 e^{-k_B t} \tag{18.44}$$

After A has reacted essentially to completion ($[A]_t \approx 0$) in the case where $k_A \gg k_B$, one can take the logarithm of both sides of Equation 18.44 and obtain:

$$\ln ([P]_\infty - [P]_t) = \ln ([A]_t + [B]_t) = -k_B t + \ln [B]_0 \tag{18.45}$$

Thus, a plot of $\ln ([A]_t + [B]_t)$ or $\ln ([P]_\infty - [P]_t)$ versus time yields a straight line with a slope of $-k_B$ and an intercept (at $t = 0$) of $\ln [B]_0$. The value of $[A]_0$ may then be obtained by subtracting $[B]_0$ from the total initial concentration of the mixture; the latter can be determined either by independent methods or calculated from $[P]_\infty$, provided the reaction mechanism does not change during the final stages. A typical reaction-rate curve of this type is illustrated in Figure 18.6. Because of its simplicity, this method is one of the most widely used differential kinetic methods; it gives somewhat greater accuracy than do the other methods for mixtures where the ratio of rate constants is relatively large.

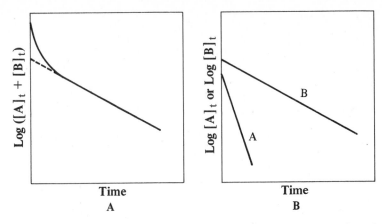

FIGURE 18.6. *Logarithmic-extrapolation method for a mixture of species A and B reacting by first-order kinetics.* (a) *Rate data obtained for the mixture.* (b) *Rate data for each component separately.* From H. B. Mark, Jr., G. A. Rechnitz, and R. A. Grienke, Kinetics in Analytical Chemistry, *New York: Wiley-Interscience, 1968, by permission of John Wiley and Sons. Copyright © 1968 by John Wiley and Sons.*

Method of Proportional Equations

This method is based on the principle of constant fractional life (usually called "half-life"), which applies to a species undergoing reaction in such a way that, after any time interval, a constant fraction of the amount left unreacted at the end of the previous interval has reacted (or a constant fraction remains unreacted), irrespective of the initial concentration. This property is associated with first-order or pseudo-first-order reactions—such as radioactive decay—for which "half-lives" are often quoted as a measure of reaction rate. This property of constant fractional life also applies to more complex reactions—such as successive and parallel reaction-sequences—involving first-order reactions. The initial concentration of a species reacting with constant fractional life is directly proportional to the amount of product formed at any given time.

For Reaction 18.9,

$$[P]_t = x([A]_0 - [A]_t) = x[A]_0[1 - e^{-k_A t}] = G_A[A]_0 \qquad (18.46)$$

Therefore, the concentration of P at any given time is directly proportional to the initial concentration of A. The proportionality constant is a function only of the stoichiometry, the reaction time, and the rate constant.

Instead of the actual concentration, any parameter directly proportional to $[P]_t$, such as absorbance of light, electrical conductivity of the solution, polarographic diffusion-current, or volume of reagent required for a titration, can be measured. Then, since $\mathscr{S} = v[P]$,

$$\mathscr{S}_t = K_A[A]_0 \qquad (18.47)$$

where $K_A = vG_A$
v = the proportionality constant

Consider the analysis of a mixture of two similar species, A and B. If B also reacts by first-order kinetics to produce P (not necessarily with the same stoichiometry as A), the same treatment given above for A can be applied. For the reaction of B alone,

$$[P]_t = G_B[B]_0 \tag{18.48}$$

where $\quad G_B = x_B[1 - e^{-k_B t}]$ and is a constant at any specified time t

If the reactions of A and B are independent of one another,

$$[P]_{t_1} = G_{A_1}[A]_0 + G_{B_1}[B]_0 \tag{18.49}$$

$$[P]_{t_2} = G_{A_2}[A]_0 + G_{B_2}[B]_0 \tag{18.50}$$

The numerical values of constants G_A and G_B at times t_1 and t_2 are determined by measuring the amount of P produced by known amounts of pure A and pure B after times t_1 and t_2. Alternatively, the constants can be calculated by substituting known reaction-rate constants (k_A and k_B), stoichiometries, and times into the equations for G_A and G_B. Usually, the former procedure is preferred because it minimizes the influence of the numerous experimental variables.

Thus, the analysis of a two-component mixture is accomplished by measuring the concentration of P at times t_1 and t_2. These data are then substituted into Equations 18.49 and 18.50, which are then solved simultaneously to yield the concentrations $[A]_0$ and $[B]_0$. This method can also be applied to situations in which two species react to form different products,

$$A \longrightarrow nC \tag{18.51}$$

$$B \longrightarrow mD \tag{18.52}$$

provided [C] and [D] are both directly proportional to the same parameter, the instrumental signal $\mathscr{S}$. This may be the case, for instance, in analyzing a mixture of two organic compounds containing the same functional group. If the two reactions proceed independently, one can write

$$\mathscr{S}_t = K_A[A]_0 + K_B[B]_0 \tag{18.53}$$

The initial concentrations of the two species can be found by determining $\mathscr{S}_t$ at two reaction-times and solving the resulting simultaneous equations.

This method can also be used for mixtures containing more than two reacting species. For a series of compounds (A, B, ..., N) that react with constant fractional lives to yield products directly proportional to $\mathscr{S}$, a series of n equations analogous to Equation 18.53 can be written for n different reaction-times, and, in theory, can be solved for the initial concentration of each species.

Method of Roberts and Regan

The method developed by Roberts and Regan is used for reactions in which it is possible to detect and follow concentration changes of R with high sensitivity. It is applicable to reactions that are pseudo-first-order with respect to the reagent (Region VII of Fig. 18.5). For example, an excellent reagent for carboxylic acids is diphenyldiazomethane, because it is very highly colored. The reaction between these two species can be made to proceed by a pseudo-first-order reaction with respect to the reagent, and thus the reaction can be followed spectrophotometrically even though the concentration of the reagent is small compared to that of the acid.

The rate of disappearance of R, reacting with a two-component mixture of A and B, is given by

$$\frac{-d[R]}{dt} = k_A[A]_0[R] + k_B[B]_0[R] = K^*[R] \tag{18.54}$$

where $K^* = k_A[A]_0 + k_B[B]_0$

The amounts of A and B consumed during the course of the reaction are negligible because the concentrations of these species are in great excess.

An analysis is accomplished by measuring K^* in the usual manner for first-order reactions, for example from

$$K^* = \frac{\ln \dfrac{[R]_0}{[R]_1}}{t_1 - t_0} \tag{18.55}$$

and by determining k_A and k_B, by reacting the pure components, A and B, with the reagent. The total initial concentration of the reactants, $[M]_0$, is found by an independent method

$$[M]_0 = [A]_0 + [B]_0 \tag{18.56}$$

Equations 18.54 and 18.56 are solved simultaneously for $[A]_0$ and $[B]_0$.

Comparison of General First-Order Methods for Mixtures

In the preceding sections, the general kinetic methods have been discussed in terms of their mathematical framework. Relatively little comparative work has been reported utilizing the various kinetic methods, so that it is difficult to compare these methods critically with respect to actual experiments. In other words, experimental verification of the theory is lacking. The following comparisons are based primarily on the mathematical framework of the methods and on the limitations of commonly employed analytical techniques.

Below is a list of practical aspects that must be considered before selecting a kinetic method for a given circumstance and system. The relative advantages and disadvantages of each method are discussed with respect to each aspect.

Ratios of $[A]_0/[B]_0$ and k_A/k_B. The limitations of the logarithmic-extrapolation method lie in the fact that A must react essentially to completion [i.e., $[A]_0 e^{-k_A t} \ll [B]_0 e^{-k_B t}$] before any significant data can be obtained. Hence, the main limitations of the method are really in the ratios k_A/k_B and $[A]_0/[B]_0$. Figure 18.7 illustrates calculated curves for cases in which $[A]_0/[B]_0 = 1$ and for several values of k_A/k_B; the curves are normalized for all values of k_B by plotting with respect to $k_B t$ as the time axis.

The accuracy of the method increases as the ratio $[A]_0/[B]_0$ grows smaller. Figure 18.8 illustrates calculated curves for the cases in which $k_A/k_B = 7.5$ for several values of $[A]_0/[B]_0$. The solid circles indicate the time at which the ratio

$k_A[A]_t/k_B[B]_t = 1/30$; this is the time at which the extrapolation becomes valid. The error will increase as the ratio $[A]_0/[B]_0$ increases, because t becomes larger. Thus, accurate experimental methods are required for determining concentration in cases where $[B]_t$ is small when the reaction of A is complete. In addition, the kinetics must be sufficiently well behaved for a lengthy extrapolation to be meaningful. The method of proportional equations is less limited with respect to $[A]_0/[B]_0$ and k_A/k_B, because it does not demand that $k_A[A]_t$ be negligible compared to $k_B[B]_t$ in order to collect analytically useful data.

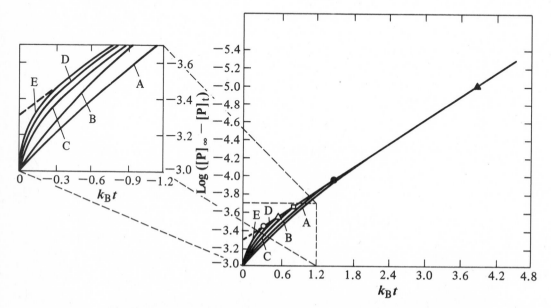

FIGURE 18.7. *Effect of rate-constant ratio in the logarithmic-extrapolation method.* $[A]_0/[B]_0 = 1$; $k_A/k_B = (A)$ 2; (B) 4; (C) 7.5; (D) 10; (E) 25. *The symbols* $\bigcirc$, $\triangle$, $\square$, $\bullet$, *and* $\blacktriangle$, *respectively, indicate the points beyond which the curves can be considered linear.* $[P]$ *is the concentration of product. Adapted from H. B. Mark, Jr., G. A. Rechnitz, and R. A. Grienke,* Kinetics in Analytical Chemistry, *New York: Wiley-Interscience, 1968, by permission of John Wiley and Sons. Copyright © 1968 by John Wiley and Sons.*

The method of Roberts and Regan has a wider range of applicability with respect to $[A]_0/[B]_0$ and k_A/k_B than either of the other two. In fact, a useful advantage of this method is that small k_A/k_B ratios can be tolerated rather easily because this method does not depend on the manner in which the fractions of A and B remaining vary with respect to each other. This method depends on measuring a composite pseudo-first-order rate constant K^* for the mixture (Eqn. 18.55), and $[A]_0$ can be determined over a wide range of $[A]_0/[B]_0$ as long as $k_A[A]_0$ contributes significantly to the measured value of K^*. Under these conditions, as $[A]_0/[B]_0$ changes, K^* likewise changes. It is possible to determine smaller values of $[A_0]$ with this method than is possible with the others, provided that k_A/k_B is large. This is,

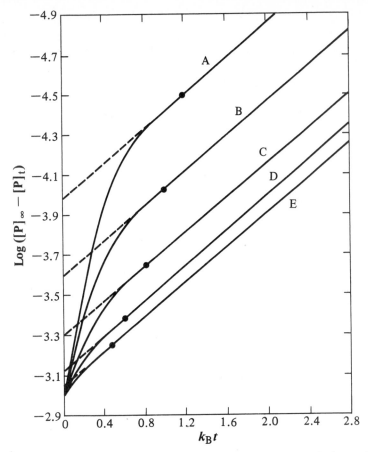

FIGURE 18.8. *Effect of the ratio of sample concentrations in the logarith-mic-extrapolation method for* $k_A/k_B = 7.5$. $[A]_0/[B]_0 = (A)$ 9; (B) 3; (C) 1; (D) 0.25; (E) 0.1. $[A]_0 + [B]_0$ *is constant throughout;* $[P]$ *is the concentration of the product. From H. B. Mark, Jr., G. A. Rechnitz, and R. A. Grienke,* Kinetics in Analytical Chemistry, *New York: Wiley-Interscience, 1968, by permission of John Wiley and Sons. Copyright © 1968 by John Wiley and Sons.*

perhaps, its chief advantage.   In general, as the ratio of $[R]_0$ to $([A]_0 + [B]_0)$ decreases, the minimum amount of $[A]_0$ that can be determined decreases also, reaching a limit when the reaction becomes pseudo-first-order with respect to $[R]_0$.

Species to be Measured.   The method of Roberts and Regan can only be used if the concentration of some species (reagent or product—or a parameter proportional to one of those concentrations) can be measured.   The logarithmic-extrapolation method or the method of proportional equations can only be used if the total concentration of some species can be measured.   These are relatively unimportant considerations, but in some instances could eliminate one or two of the potential methods at the outset.

Number of Analyses.   If only a few analyses are to be made, the logarithmic-extrapolation method has a distinct advantage over the other two methods, because the rate constants of the individual species need not be determined before the method can be used.

Rigidity of Control of Reaction Conditions.   The logarithmic-extrapolation method has the advantage over the other two methods with respect to control of reaction conditions, because the rate constants need not be known.   It is necessary to control conditions strictly during any single determination (a complete kinetic run), but it is not necessary to reproduce these conditions exactly from one analysis to the next, as is the case with the other two methods.   For the same reason, the logarithmic-extrapolation method is more applicable if varying amounts of a catalyst are to be present in the system.

Ease of Analysis.   Once the rate constants for the system under study have been determined, the method of Roberts and Regan and the method of proportional equations are about equal in ease of operation and are considerably easier to use than the logarithmic-extrapolation method.   The latter requires a prior determination of $([A]_0 + [B]_0)$ and numerous determinations during the kinetic run; and the reaction must be rather slow so that enough points can be taken to plot a kinetic curve.   The method of Roberts and Regan requires a prior determination of $([A]_0 + [B]_0)$, but only one subsequent point is needed.   Another advantage is that, after the reaction is completed, a check determination can be made by adding another aliquot of reagent because the concentrations of the reactants are still in large excess over that of the reagent.   As an example, the analysis of carbonyls by the graphical-extrapolation method required the use of second-order kinetic conditions at 0°C to slow down the reactions sufficiently.   However, with the Roberts and Regan method, complete duplicate analyses were obtained in less than 10 min using the same system (except that different concentrations were used).   The method of proportional equations is just as simple as the method of Roberts and Regan and does not require a prior determination of $([A]_0 + [B]_0)$.   It does, however, require two points to be obtained.

The nonextrapolation methods are also much easier to adapt to automated analysis than is the logarithmic-extrapolation method.

Kinetic Complications.   In later stages, many reactions are complicated by side reactions, reversibility, equilibrium, complex kinetics, etc.   The logarithmic-extrapolation method can be seriously affected by these phenomena, thus limiting even further the useful k_A/k_B and $[A]_0/[B]_0$ ranges, to the point where the method might not be applicable.   Even worse, if the analyst is not aware of these complications, erroneous data might be obtained.   The method of proportional equations is also affected by these phenomena, but to a lesser extent in some cases because measurements can be made before complications arise.   The method of Roberts and Regan handles these situations best because only a negligible quantity of A and B reacts. There is no appreciable accumulation of product, and interference caused by side reactions will therefore be at a minimum.   Reactions that normally become complex in the latter stages will remain pseudo-first-order throughout.

More Than Two Components. All three of the methods are alleged to be applicable to systems of three components or more! The logarithmic-extrapolation method would require tremendous rate differences to handle such a system, but in theory it could be done. The method of proportional equations should handle this somewhat more easily but also would require a greater rate difference than in the two-component case, and one more determination. The method of Roberts and Regan could only be applied to three-component systems if another determination such as density, refractive index, etc., could be made. Needless to say, experimental error will significantly increase if these methods are used to analyze three-component systems; at this stage, it is difficult to envisage using them for the simultaneous determination of four components.

Accuracy. An error-analysis study of the method of proportional equations results in the conclusion that if t_2 is any time, even t_∞, the optimum short time is always before A has reacted to completion. Thus, the method of proportional equations is inherently more accurate than the logarithmic-extrapolation method if the data points can be determined with the same amount of error in both methods. It can be argued that the logarithmic-extrapolation method avoids this by averaging the experimental data with the best straight line. However, is this line, if drawn by visual inspection, really the best straight line? Unless the data are weighted correctly (weighting varies as the reaction proceeds), the answer is no. Also, it is the author's experience that it is difficult to decide how to draw this line by visual inspection of the data. The construction of the line might well be the greatest error in the method. Furthermore, by taking duplicate measurements (still at a great saving in time) the method of proportional equations can be made even more accurate.

A theoretical comparison of the accuracy of the above two methods with that of Roberts and Regan has not been made. Some experimental studies have shown that comparable accuracies are obtained with the method of Roberts and Regan and that of logarithmic extrapolation. Perhaps the best guide to comparing the various methods lies in the many published experiments in which these methods have been employed: in these, the various methods were applied to suitable systems, producing results with comparable accuracies.

18.7 INSTRUMENTATION

The accuracy and precision of the experimental measurement is, of course, important to both kinetic-based and equilibrium-based analytical methods. However, a few special factors—instrumental and experimental—are of critical importance in kinetic-based techniques; these are discussed below. The block diagram of a typical rate-measuring system is shown in Figure 18.9.

Instrument Stability

High-frequency noise in an instrument used to measure reaction rates can generally be eliminated or minimized by simple electronic filtering, since the frequency of the noise is usually very high compared to the rate of change of the signal. However, low-frequency noise or drift, which comes mainly from the reaction monitor and

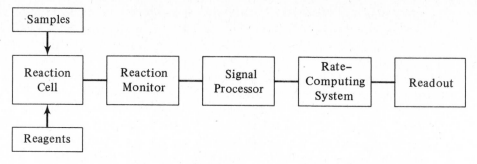

FIGURE 18.9. *Schematic diagram of typical rate-measuring instrument. Adapted from J. S. Mattson, H. B. Mark, Jr., and H. C. MacDonald, Jr., eds.,* Spectroscopy and Kinetics, *vol. 3, New York: Marcel Dekker, 1973, by permission of the publisher.*

which varies at about the same rate as the reaction rate itself, presents a much more difficult problem. In this case, it is necessary to design the instrument in such a way as to eliminate these sources of drift, because there is no way of electronically separating the reaction signal from the random drift once the data reach the rate-computation system.

Light-Source Stabilization. The effect of light-source variations can be minimized by several methods. In most conventional spectrophotometers, a double-beam system can partially cancel fluctuations by comparing reference and sample beam intensities. However, since instruments employed for kinetic methods are not often called upon for spectral scanning, most designers have discarded the double-beam approach and have developed less expensive electronic stabilization techniques for light-source regulation.

The simplest technique for stabilizing the light source against short-term fluctuations is to regulate the AC line voltage, since line-voltage fluctuations can cause changes in light intensity comparable to those caused by the measured reaction-rate. Circuits that regulate the lamp power-supply voltage or current have also been used. However, this regulation is not sufficient; a more elaborate electronic regulator has been designed that compensates for changes in light-bulb resistance and is, thus, superior to circuits that regulate only the applied voltage or the applied current.

Light-intensity variations can result from heat flow around the light bulb itself; the use of baffling to eliminate convection currents across the optical path has been reported to give satisfactory results. Such a stabilized-light-source spectrophotometer was reported to have drift stability of better than 0.003 absorbance units (AU) per hour, a noise level that produced a rate error of less than 0.001 AU per minute, and a photometric accuracy of 0.01 AU at 1.0 AU and 0.001 AU near zero absorbance.

One disadvantage of such control systems is that they control the electrical input to the lamp rather than the actual lamp intensity. Several systems have been described using optical-feedback techniques to directly control the lamp intensity. Usually in these techniques the lamp intensity is monitored with a second photodetector, and a signal from this detector is fed back to the lamp power-supply.

Detector Noise and Drift. Transducers for modern spectrophotometric systems are usually vacuum phototubes or photomultiplier tubes. Noise and drift from the transducer can be quite troublesome in kinetic methods, and special care is normally taken to ensure low-noise operation.

There is some controversy about which detector provides the highest signal-to-noise ratio—the phototube or the photomultiplier. If comparisons are made at the same light level, the photomultiplier is capable of a higher signal-to-noise ratio, because its internal amplification is so high (often about 10^6) that the Johnson noise* of the load resistor is insignificant. When a phototube, on the other hand, is used at low light-levels, Johnson noise becomes the limiting factor and external amplification does not help. If comparisons are made at the same anode current, however, the phototube has the higher signal-to-noise ratio because the light level has to be much higher to obtain an equivalent output current. Thus, in systems where the operator can control the light level, such as with absorption spectrophotometers, it is recommended that intense light-sources be used with a phototube detector. As is true in any measurement, if the input signal can be made high enough that little or no amplification is needed, higher signal-to-noise ratios can be obtained than with amplification. For systems where the light level cannot be controlled, such as in emission spectroscopy, or where the light level is very low, the photomultiplier will give superior results.

Another important consideration in detectors is power-supply stability. For phototubes, regulation is not critical because the current-versus-voltage characteristic is essentially flat in the usual operating region. For photomultipliers, however, the gain is highly dependent on the power-supply voltage. As a rule of thumb, the power-supply stability should be at least an order of magnitude better than the desired stability in gain.

Temperature Control

The rate of chemical reaction is considerably more sensitive to temperature variation than is the position of equilibrium (provided the formation constant is very large and the reaction can be considered "quantitative"). Thus, temperature control is critical in reaction-rate methods.

Two factors in temperature control must be considered. The accuracy of temperature control in the jacket of the reaction cell is the initial consideration, of course. However, since chemical reactions are either exothermic or endothermic, it has been shown that rapid temperature exchange and equilibration of the reaction solution with the cell jacket is also an extremely important consideration in obtaining good data.

Rise-Time of the Instrument

As mentioned above, high-frequency noise can often be eliminated by simple electronic filtering. However, caution is necessary and the investigator should be very familiar with the actual effective rise-time of the measuring instrument over all

---

* Johnson or thermal noise is produced by random thermal motion in resistive circuit elements.

operating ranges. Obviously, a fixed time-constant cannot be applicable over a large range of initial concentrations, since the reaction rate at any time is a function of initial concentration. Thus, it is necessary to quantitatively evaluate the rise-time of the instrument under all conditions of damping employed and to compare those results with the maximum reaction-rates measured under each setting of the filter time-constant.

Linearity of Transducer Response

Most transducers converting chemical concentration into an electrical signal have a nonlinear response; for example, electrode potential and optical transmission are not directly proportional to concentration. In general, this nonlinearity is easily and simply corrected in equilibrium analytical measurements. However, it is considerably more difficult to instrumentally correct the response-versus-concentration function in reaction-rate methods, and often the correction itself can introduce significant errors in the analytical results. For example, the simple nonlinear feedback elements employed in log-response operational-amplifier circuits are not sufficiently accurate in transforming transmittance into absorbance to be used for many analytical purposes.

As mentioned earlier, the variable-time approach can be used advantageously in the case of nonlinear response, since the measured reaction-rate in this procedure is linearly proportional to the initial concentration of the species of interest in spite of the fact that the actual transducer response is not proportional to concentration. This is because the time required to reach a fixed concentration level is the parameter measured and, thus, linearity of the overall response-versus-concentration curve is not necessary. The point here is that in some cases the instrument and not the chemical reaction can dictate the method used.

Data-Acquisition Considerations

Most reaction-rate methods utilize only a small number of actual data points (from one to about four) in the calculation of the initial concentrations. Clearly this approach throws away a considerable amount of data that could be used advantageously. Recent studies have examined parameters affecting the accuracy of mixture analysis by pseudo-first-order reaction methods, and have shown that continuous data-utilization is superior in several cases. In the early development of reaction-rate methods, the procedures used chemical reactions that were not suitable for the continuous automatic measurement of reaction-rate curves. Also, calculations at that time attempted to limit the number of data points taken and to predetermine the optimum times, concentrations, and so on for taking this minimal amount of data. However, recent advances in electronic circuitry and computer technology have had a tremendous influence on the design of kinetic-analysis instrumentation. These advances have also strongly influenced differential-rate methods in both principles and approach. Several groups have designed instruments with built-in computation systems allowing continuous analysis of the reaction-rate curve over the entire reaction; in these instruments, data are processed using both ensemble-averaging and smoothing routines in real time. Experimental results and detailed error-analysis have shown conclusively that this approach to data acquisition, reduction, and display leads to much greater accuracy and precision in the analytical results. In fact, good results can be obtained from fast differential-rate analyses in which the usual finite or minimal data-point methods fail completely.

Automation of Operations

It is obvious that automated control of solution mixing, measurement sequences, and so on, will minimize the time-measurement errors arising from manual solution

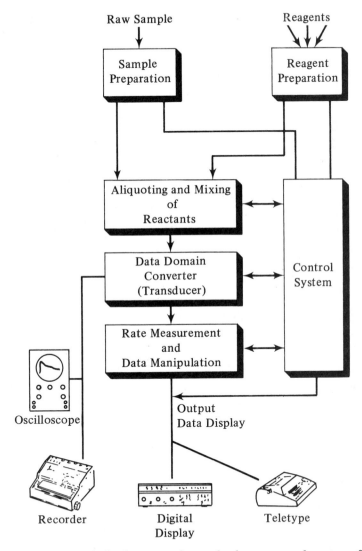

FIGURE 18.10. *Block diagram of completely automated system for reaction-rate methods. From H. V. Malmstadt, E. A. Cordos, and C. J. Delaney,* Anal. Chem., *44*(12), 26A (1972), *by permission of the senior author and the publisher. Copyright © 1972 by the American Chemical Society.*

handling and measurement control and, hence, will increase the accuracy of a given reaction-rate procedure.

As the expense of high-speed digital computers decreases, the applications of these small computers as built-in (on-line) units in chemical instrumentation for data reduction, system control, data acquisition, and experimental optimization in "real time" have increased sharply. Systems have been described in which the computer not only handles the data acquisition and sample manipulation, but actively takes part in all stages of the experiment by examining the data in real time and making decisions to optimize the experimental parameters and variables while the experiment is running. This is probably the most important single improvement in kinetic-based analysis; it will greatly expand both the routine and the specialized applications of the technique.

The block diagram for a completely computer-automated rate-measurement system is presented in Figure 18.10. By preliminary treatments (e.g., dissolution, dilution, filtration, ion exchange), the sample and reagent solutions are prepared as required for the specific procedure being used. Predetermined volumes of sample and reagents are then introduced, mixed, and transported to the reaction cell. The control and rate-measurement systems can be hardwired for specific applications, or they can be incorporated in a minicomputer-interfaced system that can provide, through software, much versatility in control of the measurement sequence and the processing and read-out of data. Read-out is visually displayed with digital lights or printed out on a serial teletype or a high-speed parallel printer. When desired, a servo recorder or storage oscilloscope can display the parameter-versus-time and rate curves. Totally automated units can analyze as many as 1000 samples per hour.

18.8 THE REACTION MECHANISM

In most equilibrium-based analytical methods, the success or failure of a determination is not affected by the reaction mechanism, provided that the reaction is either quantitative or the measured parameter at equilibrium is linearly proportional to the initial concentration of the species of interest. This is not the case in reaction-rate methods. Any development of a kinetic method should include, if possible, a complete study of the reaction mechanisms involved in the procedure. (Unfortunately, some reactions, such as catalytic reactions, are so complicated that complete elucidation of the mechanism is impossible.) It should also include a detailed study of the effects of typical sample-matrix components, which can act as catalysts, induce side-reactions, alter the activity of the reactants, and so on. The rates and rate constants for chemical reactions are very sensitive to low concentrations of such "spectator" species; hence, samples containing the same true initial composition of the species of interest but coming from different sources can very often give quite different apparent concentrations. Unless the experimenter is aware of the total reaction mechanism and of all possible factors that can affect either the activation energy or the reaction path, erroneous analytical results can be obtained. A detailed investigation of the simultaneous, in situ, analysis of binary amine mixtures illustrates this point. (Most systems, by the way, are less error-prone than this one.) The rate constants for the reaction of many individual organic amines with methyl iodide in acetone solvent had an ideal range and differentiation of absolute values when the reactions were conducted under pseudo-first-order conditions with respect to the methyl iodide. The Roberts and Regan data-reduction method was used along with a simple and accurate data-acquisition system employing a continuously recording conductivity instrument; almost ideal analytical results should have been attained. However, most binary mixtures gave very poor results when analyzed by this procedure.

A careful examination of the reaction mechanism of the system revealed numerous unexpected sources of error. First, it was found that the acetone used as a solvent undergoes a Schiff-base reaction with some primary amines at a rate comparable to that of the methylation reaction of the method. This results in the variation of the composite rate-constant, K^*, during the course of the reaction of mixtures

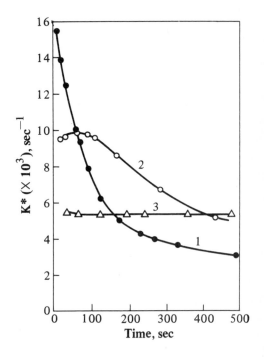

FIGURE 18.11. *Variation of K^* for n-butylamine-tributylamine mixture (71.2% n-butylamine) as a function of time, for three different solvent systems. Curve 1: 100% acetone. Curve 2: 89% acetone–11% water. Curve 3: 70% DMSO–30% n-propyl alcohol. From R. A. Grienke and H. B. Mark, Jr., Anal. Chem., 38, 1001 (1966), by permission of the publisher. Copyright © 1966 by the American Chemical Society.*

containing such primary amines, as shown in Curve 1 of Figure 18.11. As the calculation of initial concentration from K^* by the method of Roberts and Regan requires K^* to remain constant over the total reaction-time, serious errors are introduced by this side-reaction. As added water would suppress the Schiff-base reaction, acetone-water mixtures were then used as the solvent systems. Although this improved the results obtained for several amine mixtures, those containing high-molecular-weight amines still gave poor results. For example, K^* is not constant over the whole reaction for n-butylamine-tributylamine mixtures (see Curve 2 of Fig. 18.11). In this case the addition of water results in the formation of small suspended micelles of amine in the solution, which alters the reaction rates. Thus, it was necessary to use a less basic solvent system, DMSO–n-propyl alcohol, which has no significant tendency to react with primary amines and in which most amines are soluble. Curve 3 of Figure 18.11 shows that K^* for the n-butyl-amine-tribultylamine mixture is then constant and, thus, accurate initial concentrations are obtained.

However, certain amine mixtures, generally those containing methylamine, still gave poor analyses. It was found that such mixtures are slightly hygroscopic and samples often contain traces of water. This trace water acts as a catalyst in the methylation reaction. Thus, the rate constants obtained from the reactions of standard dry amine solutions and used in calculating the initial concentrations of unknown mixtures containing traces of water were not valid for the unknown mixture reactions. The addition of water to the solvent system (10% or more) swamped out these variations of rate constants in unknown amine mixtures; recall, however, that adding water can result in solubility complications for some amines. This investigation also revealed that a synergistic effect, probably caused by changes in the activity of the amines by the build-up of product, resulted in a variation of K^* during the reaction when the amine-mixture concentration was high. Other sources of error arose from the reaction of the reagent methyl iodide with its solvent during storage, and loss of measurement sensitivity when conducting impurities were present in the unknown.

The point here is that no simple general procedure for this method can be given that is universally applicable to all types of amine mixtures. This is probably true in general for any procedure employing a kinetic-based method. Thus, in using any such method, it is necessary to have investigated the chemistry of the reactions used so as to anticipate errors resulting from the chemical nature and composition of the samples.

SELECTED BIBLIOGRAPHY

CROUCH, S. R., in J. S. Mattson, H. B. Mark, Jr., and H. C. MacDonald, Jr., eds., *Computers in Chemistry and Instrumentation*, vol. 3, chap. 3. New York: Marcel Dekker, 1972. *The sections on the mathematical basis of kinetic methods were condensed from this chapter. It is an excellent source for instrumental and computerization consideration in rate measurement.*

GRIENKE, R. A., and MARK, H. B., JR., "Kinetic Aspects of Analytical Chemistry," *Anal. Chem.*, *46*, 413R (1974).

GUILBAULT, G. G. *Enzymatic Methods of Analysis.* Oxford: Pergamon, 1970.

MALMSTADT, H. V.; CORDOS, E. A.; and DELANEY, C. J., "Automated Reaction-Rate Methods," *Anal. Chem.*, *44*(12), 26A (1972).

MALMSTADT, H. V.; DELANEY, C. J.; and CORDOS, E. A., "Instruments for Rate Determination," *Anal. Chem.*, *44*(12), 79A (1972).

MARK, H. B., JR.; RECHNITZ, G. A.; and GREINKE, R. A. *Kinetics in Analytical Chemistry.* New York: Wiley-Interscience, 1968. *Much of the sections on methods of the analysis of mixtures was condensed from this source.*

PARDUE, H. L., in C. N. Reilley and F. W. McLafferty, eds., *Advances in Analytical Chemistry and Instrumentation*, vol. 7, pp 141–200. New York: Wiley-Interscience, 1968. *Instrumental considerations in rate measurement.*

SANTINI, R. E.; MILANO, M. J.; and PARDUE, H. L., "Rapid Scanning Spectroscopy: Prelude to a New Era in Analytical Spectroscopy," *Anal. Chem.*, *45*, 915A (1973).

YATSIMIRSKII, K. B. *Kinetic Methods of Analysis.* Oxford: Pergamon, 1966.

PROBLEMS

1. The conversion of γ-hydroxyvaleric acid to γ-valerolactone is an acid-catalyzed reaction. The reaction can be followed by taking aliquots of the reaction mixture and titrating with standardized base. The following data were obtained for the reaction, run at 25°C with 0.025 M HCl as catalyst:

Time, min	% Converted	Time, min	% Converted
48	17.3	238	61.3
76	25.7	289	68.1
124	38.9	∞	100
204	55.6		

(a) Ascertain that the overall reaction is first order (plot the appropriate graph). (b) Determine the rate constant for the reaction from the slope of the plot and from the appropriate equation for first-order kinetics using the second, fourth, and sixth points. (c) If the first-order rate constant determined above is equal to $k_2[H^+]$, where k_2 is the second-order rate constant for the forward reaction, calculate k_2. (d) How long would it require to obtain a 40% yield of the product at 25°C in 0.075 M HCl? A 90% yield?

2. The alkaline hydrolysis of an ester is a bimolecular second-order reaction. Walker [*Proc. Roy. Soc.*, *A78*, 157 (1906)] obtained the following data at 25°C for the reaction

$$CH_3COOCH_3 + OH^- = CH_3COO^- + CH_3OH$$

The initial concentrations of sodium hydroxide and methyl acetate were both 0.0100 M.

Time, min	Amount Converted, mM	Time, min	Amount Converted, mM
3	2.60	10	5.36
4	3.17	12	5.84
5	3.66	15	6.37
6	4.11	18	6.81
7	4.50	21	7.12
8	4.81	25	7.46

Prove that the data satisfy the second-order equation $[1/[A] - 1/[A]_0 = kt]$ by plotting the appropriate graph, and determine the rate constant for the reaction.

3. At 298°C azomethane decomposes according to

$$CH_3NNCH_3 \longrightarrow C_2H_6 + N_2$$

The first-order rate constant for the reaction is 2.50×10^{-4} sec^{-1}. Determine the partial pressures of the reactant and products after 30 min if the initial azomethane pressure is 200 torr.

4. The acid-catalyzed inversion of sucrose can be monitored by measuring the angle of rotation α of plane-polarized light with time, since the rotation shifts from dextro in sucrose to levo in invert sugar. The following data were obtained on sucrose inversion at 30°C in 2.5 M formic acid.

For an initial sucrose concentration of 0.44 M:

t, hours	α	t, hours	α
0	57.90°	40	3.40°
4	48.50°	52	−2.95°
8	40.50°	85	−11.25°
15	28.90°	∞	−15.45°
27	13.50°		

For an initial sucrose concentration of 0.167 M:

t, hours	α	t, hours	α
0	22.10°	45	0.35°
5	17.85°	73	−3.20°
10	14.15°	94	−4.30°
20	8.65°	133	−5.10°
30	4.50°	∞	−5.50°

Determine the first-order rate constant at 30°C for each concentration. Does the constant vary with the sucrose concentration? Does it depend on the concentration unit chosen?

5. Kinetic data were obtained for the reaction of benzene diazonium chloride with water:

$$C_6H_5N_2Cl + H_2O$$
$$= C_6H_5OH + N_2 + HCl$$

Time, min	HCl Generated, mM	Time, min	HCl Generated, mM
0	0	180	7.07
90	3.49	206	7.78
120	5.09	231	8.42
147	6.04	258	9.13
152	6.20		

The original solution was aqueous 27.37 mM $C_6H_5N_2Cl$ (25°C). Determine the order and the rate constant for the reaction, and calculate the time required for 90% and 99% reaction.

6. The reaction between methyl iodide and thiosulfate

$$CH_3I + S_2O_3^{2-} = CH_3S_2O_3^- + I^-$$

is followed by withdrawing 10.00-ml aliquots from the reaction mixture and quickly titrating the thiosulfate remaining with 0.0101 N iodine.

Time, min	Volume I_2 Solution, ml	Time, min	Volume I_2 Solution, ml
0	35.35	35.0	20.3
4.75	30.5	55.0	18.6
10.0	27.0	∞	17.1
20.0	23.2		

Determine the order and rate constant of the reaction.

7. The following exchange reaction occurs at the presence of strong acid

$$[Co(NH_3)_5H_2^{18}O]^{3+} + H_2O \rightleftarrows$$
$$[Co(NH_3)_5H_2O]^{3+} + H_2^{18}O$$

If the mole fraction of ^{18}O in the complex is initially 0.006649, after 25.1 hours is 0.004366, and at equilibrium is 0.002192, calculate the first-order rate constant for the reaction and the half-life of the cobalt complex in aqueous solution.

8. For the enzymatic conversion of fumarate to L-malate at pH 7, the Michaelis constant is 4.0×10^{-6} M and the maximum reaction rate is 1.3×10^3 [E] sec^{-1}, where [E] is the total molar concentration of the enzyme. For the reverse reaction the Michaelis constant and maximum reaction rate are 10×10^{-6} M and 0.80×10^3 [E] sec^{-1}, respectively. Calculate the equilibrium constant for the reaction.

9. Explain clearly the difference between thermodynamic- and kinetic-based analytical techniques.

10. Are kinetic methods of analysis commonly used? If so, in what applications?

11. What advantages do kinetic-based techniques have? What disadvantages?

12. Discuss the special instrumentation requirements encountered in kinetic-based methods.

13. What are the *derivative* and the *integral* approaches to kinetic analysis? Compare their applicability and their advantages (or disadvantages).

19

Radiochemical Methods of Analysis

Wᴵʟʟᴵᴀᴍ D. Eʜᴍᴀɴɴ
Moʀᴛᴇᴢᴀ Jᴀɴɢʜoʀʙᴀɴᴵ

Radiochemical methods of analysis employ radioactivity, with or without chemical manipulations, to obtain qualitative or quantitative information about the composition of materials. This information may concern the nature and quantity of elements or the specific chemical form of the component of interest. For example, qualitative and quantitative determinations of elements present in river waters can be readily accomplished; on the other hand, radiochemical methods can be used to determine the quantity of vitamin B_{12} (which contains an atom of cobalt) in a mixture of similar organic compounds. The fundamental difference between this method of analysis and all others is that, in this method, one either induces radioactivity in the sample or adds a radioactive substance to the sample.

Radiochemical methods of analysis are used in a wide range of analytical applications. Not only can these methods be used to obtain information regarding the nature and quantities of substances present in materials of interest, but radioactive elements can also be employed as tracers to study various physicochemical processes. Radioactive substances can be used to follow the movement of elements or of specific compounds in soils and plants, the absorption of elements in the body, and the self-diffusion of lead atoms in metallic lead, among other applications. Although these tracer applications are of great practical value, the present chapter will be concerned only with applying radioactivity to determining the presence and quantity of elements and compounds in various materials—that is, the use of radioactivity in chemical analysis.

19.1 FUNDAMENTALS OF RADIOACTIVITY

In this section, we will discuss only those fundamental aspects of radioactivity directly relevant to radiochemical analysis. For a more detailed treatment, the references given at the end of the chapter should be consulted.

All atomic nuclei are made up of protons and neutrons (known collectively as *nucleons*); the only exception is the lightest hydrogen nucleus, which consists of a single proton. The *atomic number* (Z) of an atom is the number of protons present in its nucleus (also the number of electrons in the neutral atom). The sum of protons (Z) and neutrons (N) in a nucleus is referred to as the *mass number* (A). The mass number should not be confused with the atomic or nuclidic mass, which is the mass of the atom relative to that of a ^{12}C atom (which is, by definition, exactly 12.000 . . . *atomic mass units*, amu).

All atoms whose nuclei contain the same number of protons (and are thus atoms of the same element) have virtually the same chemical properties, because these properties are determined by the structure of the orbital-electron cloud. But, atoms of the same element may have a different number of neutrons and, therefore, a different mass-number. Atoms having the same Z and a different A are referred to as *isotopes*. In nature, with few exceptions, the abundance of each isotope is in a fixed ratio to that of the other isotopes of the same element; the relative abundance of any isotope (usually expressed in units of atom percent) is called its *isotopic abundance*. Each element has two types of isotopes: (1) *stable isotopes*, and (2) *radioactive isotopes*. Stable isotopes are those whose nuclei have not been observed to undergo spontaneous radioactive disintegration. The nuclei of radioactive isotopes, on the other hand, undergo spontaneous disintegration and eventually become stable isotopes of some element. Radioactive isotopes disintegrate by emitting *electromagnetic radiation* (x- or gamma rays),* by emitting *elementary particles* (α, β, n, p, or e^-), or by undergoing *fission* (breaking up into smaller nuclei). These isotopes are either *artificial* (manmade, such as ^{60}Co) or *natural* (such as ^{40}K).

Whether or not a given isotope is stable depends on the particular number of protons and neutrons present in its nucleus and on the state of excitation of the nucleus. If one plots the atomic numbers of all stable isotopes as a function of the number of neutrons present in their nuclei, one obtains the graph shown in Figure 19.1. In order to form stable light elements, approximately equal numbers of neutrons and protons are required; however, for the heavier elements, considerably more neutrons are needed. This deviation from $Z/N = 1$ occurs because protons are charged particles and repel each other according to Coulomb's law. Since the nucleus is held together by strong, short-range binding forces between nucleons, additional forces are needed to dilute the increased Coulombic repulsion forces.

Nuclei that do not fall on this curve are unstable and disintegrate, emitting the appropriate particles or radiation until the final product nuclei are on the curve. If the unstable *nuclide*† is on the proton-rich side of the curve, it disintegrates by emitting a *positron*,‡ or by a related process known as *electron capture*. The *daughter* nuclide will then have one less proton and one more neutron than the *parent* nuclide. If, on the other hand, the radionuclide is on the neutron-rich side of the curve, it

---

* X-rays are electromagnetic radiations resulting from an orbital-electron rearrangement in the atom, whereas gamma-rays are emitted directly by the nucleus. Only their point of origin distinguishes one from the other.

† Nuclide is a general term referring to a nucleus containing Z protons and N neutrons; if the nuclide is radioactive, it is called a radionuclide.

‡ A positron is a particle having the mass of an electron, but a unit positive charge. Its symbol is β^+.

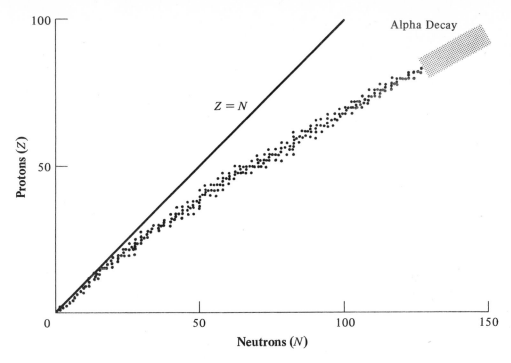

FIGURE 19.1. *The line of beta stability. Each point corresponds to a stable isotope.*

emits a *negatron** and the daughter nuclide will contain one less neutron and one more proton than the parent nuclide. For heavy nuclides, emission of an *alpha particle* (the nucleus of an ordinary helium atom) is also very common. The daughter product of an alpha decay contains two protons and two neutrons less than does the parent nuclide.

Rates of Disintegration

Not all radionuclides disintegrate at the same rate. The disintegration of any radionuclide is a first-order process and follows Equation 19.1:

$$-\frac{dN}{dt} = \lambda N \tag{19.1}$$

where N = the number of radioactive atoms of a specific radionuclide present at time t

λ = the *nuclear-decay constant* in $\sec^{-1}$

The left-hand side of Equation 19.1, dN/dt, is the number of disintegrations taking place per unit time. Each radionuclide has its own characteristic nuclear-decay constant. The minus sign indicates that the decay results in a decrease in N. Equation 19.1 indicates that the rate of decay of any radionuclide is directly proportional

---

* A negatron is an ordinary negative electron emitted from the nucleus. Its symbol is β^-. It is also often called a *β-ray* or a *β-particle*.

to the number of those atoms present at that time. One can use this equation to calculate N, the number of radioactive atoms present at any time t, by separating variables and integrating to give

$$N = N_0 e^{-\lambda(t-t_0)} \qquad (19.2)$$

N_0 is the number of radioactive atoms present at time t_0, which is the reference point in time. For convenience, t_0 is generally taken to be zero time, in which case Equation 19.2 simplifies to

$$N = N_0 e^{-\lambda t} \qquad (19.3)$$

Equation 19.3 states that if, at time $t = 0$, there are N_0 radioactive atoms having a nuclear-decay constant λ, then at any later time t there will be N radioactive atoms remaining, and $(N_0 - N)$ radioactive atoms will have undergone radioactive decay during the time t.

A convenient measure of how fast a radionuclide disintegrates is the *half-life* (H) of the radionuclide. This parameter is defined as the length of time required for one-half of a statistically large number of radioactive atoms to undergo radioactive decay. Thus, if there are N_0 radioactive atoms at time $t = 0$, one half-life later there will be $N_0/2$ radioactive atoms of the original radionuclide remaining. From Equation 19.3, it can be shown that the relationship between the half-life and the decay constant of a radionuclide is

$$H = \frac{0.693}{\lambda} \qquad (19.4)$$

Since each radionuclide has its own characteristic decay-constant, its half-life has a definite value. Half-lives of radionuclides vary over a very large range. For instance, one radioactive isotope of boron has a half-life of about 3×10^{-19} sec, whereas the half-life of naturally occurring bismuth is greater than 2×10^{18} years.

From a knowledge of the half-life of any radionuclide, one can accurately predict the relative amount of that nuclide at any time later than or prior to some reference time. This fact is extensively employed in determining the ages of materials by methods of radioactive dating. More importantly, as far as this chapter is concerned, Equation 19.1 can be used to determine the amount of radioactive material present at any given time in a sample. If the sample contained a single radionuclide, its amount could be measured by simply measuring the absolute activity of the sample with an appropriate detection system (see Sec. 19.3). Combining Equations 19.1 and 19.3,

$$A = -\frac{dN}{dt} = \lambda N_0 e^{-\lambda t} \qquad (19.5)$$

One can measure A, the *absolute activity*,* experimentally and then calculate N_0, given knowledge of the decay constant λ and the decay time t.

---

* Activity is the measure of the number of specific particles or radiations emitted per unit time (commonly, per second). In contrast, the absolute activity (A) of a given radionuclide in units of disintegrations per second (dps) or disintegrations per minute (dpm) is the total number of disintegrations taking place per unit time without regard to the distribution of emitted particles or radiations. For example, one could measure either the positron or the negatron activity from a ^{64}Cu source (a radionuclide that decays by both modes) or the absolute activity of the source, which is independent of the mode of decay. The fraction of decays occurring by either path is described by the *branching ratio*.

If the sample contains more than one radionuclide, the method of activity measurement can still be used with the following modifications. The total (gross) activity of a sample containing several independently decaying radionuclides is

$$A_{tot} = \lambda_1 N_1 + \lambda_2 N_2 + \cdots$$

or

$$A_{tot} = \lambda_1 (N_0)_1 e^{-\lambda_1 t} + \lambda_2 (N_0)_2 e^{-\lambda_2 t} + \cdots \qquad (19.6)$$

Inspection of Equation 19.6 shows that, if one knows the nature of the radionuclides present in the sample, one should be able to calculate their abundances [$(N_0)_1$, $(N_0)_2$, and so on], by making the appropriate number of activity measurements as a function of time.

For example, if the sample contains only two independent radionuclides, two independent measurements will permit application of the two following simultaneous equations with two unknowns, $(N_0)_1$ and $(N_0)_2$:

$$(A_{tot})_{t_1} = \lambda_1 (N_0)_1 e^{-\lambda_1 t_1} + \lambda_2 (N_0)_2 e^{-\lambda_2 t_1} \qquad (19.7)$$

$$(A_{tot})_{t_2} = \lambda_1 (N_0)_1 e^{-\lambda_1 t_2} + \lambda_2 (N_0)_2 e^{-\lambda_2 t_2} \qquad (19.8)$$

In general, it should be possible to calculate the individual abundances of all radioisotopes present in the sample by making the appropriate number of activity measurements, provided that two conditions are met: (1) the half-lives of the sample constituents are sufficiently different, and (2) the half-lives are such that at least one of the components has significantly changed its activity during the time interval between consecutive measurements.

A general method for distinguishing among the radioactive constituents in a sample is to plot the logarithm of total observed activity as a function of time. First, consider a single-component system. Taking the logarithm of Equation 19.5 yields

$$\log\left(-\frac{dN}{dt}\right) = \log(\lambda N_0) - 0.43\,\lambda t \qquad (19.9)$$

Therefore, if $\log\left(-\dfrac{dN}{dt}\right)$ is plotted as a function of time, one obtains a straight line whose slope is a measure of the half-life of the radionuclide and whose intercept at $t = 0$ is a measure of N_0. In practice, one plots the observed activity on the logarithmic ordinate of semilog graph paper as a function of time, which is plotted on the linear abscissa. If there were more than one radioactive component present in the sample, the observed activity at any time would be the sum of the activities of all components. A plot of total activity on semilog graph paper as a function of time would then appear as a curve. However, if the half-lives of the components are sufficiently different and if the time of experiment is long compared with at least one of the half-lives involved, one can graphically resolve this composite curve into its component straight lines. By extrapolating these straight lines to $t = 0$, one can then calculate the abundance of each of the radionuclides. Figure 19.2 shows such a plot for a two-component system.

Normally, the experiment is conducted for a sufficient length of time that all but the longest-lived component have decayed essentially completely, and the longest-lived component, therefore, produces a straight-line plot. One then fits the best

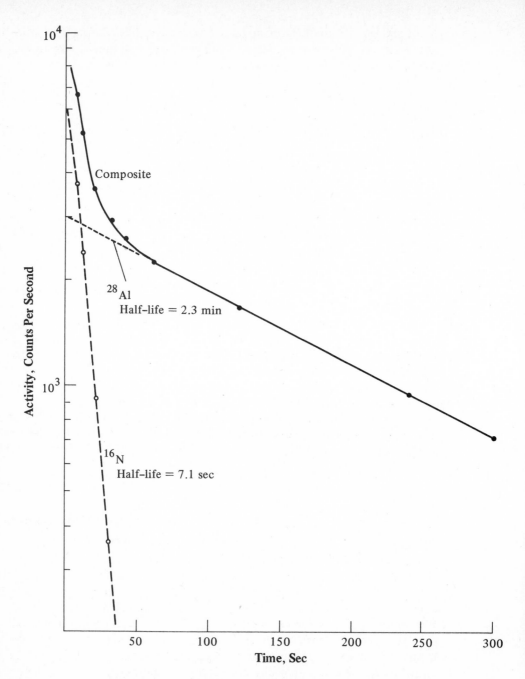

FIGURE 19.2. *Two-component decay curve for* ^{28}Al *and* ^{16}N.

straight line to this linear portion (computer line-fitting routines are commonly used) and extrapolates it to the origin. Point-by-point subtraction of this fitted straight line from this composite curve leaves another composite curve with one less member than the original one and whose end portion is also a straight line. Repetition of this *stripping* technique will give all component straight lines, from which one can calculate the quantities $(N_0)_1$, $(N_0)_2$, etc. Ordinarily, the stripping technique is applied to mixtures of three or fewer components.

In general, the great advantage of the decay curve and stripping method over the method of direct calculation using simultaneous equations is that these plots often reveal the presence of unsuspected contaminant radionuclides in the sample. In addition, a large number of points are used to characterize each straight line in the decay curve and stripping method. Therefore, the effect of random errors associated with single determinations is lessened. The advantage of the method of simultaneous equations lies in the simplicity of the experiment and subsequent mathematical manipulations, but the method assumes a priori knowledge of all sample components.

For the resolution of a decay curve of a two-component system whose half-lives are not greatly different, another simple method is often used. Writing Equation 19.6 for a two-component system and multiplying both sides by $e^{\lambda_1 t}$,

$$A_{\text{tot}}(e^{\lambda_1 t}) = \lambda_1(N_0)_1 + \lambda_2(N_0)_2 e^{(\lambda_1 - \lambda_2)t} \tag{19.10}$$

If one plots $A_{\text{tot}}e^{\lambda_1 t}$ as a function of $e^{(\lambda_1 - \lambda_2)t}$, a straight line is obtained whose intercept and slope may be used to directly calculate $(N_0)_1$ and $(N_0)_2$.

19.2 NUCLEAR REACTIONS AND TYPES OF RADIOACTIVE DECAY

By convention, a nuclide is specified as $^A_Z X$, where X is the chemical symbol for the element, the superscript A denotes the mass number, and the subscript Z the atomic number of the nuclide. When particles or radiations interact with a nucleus, nuclear reactions occur. For example, a neutron may interact with the nucleus of the nuclide $^{27}_{13}\text{Al}$ according to

$$^{27}_{13}\text{Al} + ^1_0\text{n} \longrightarrow ^{28}_{13}\text{Al} + Q \tag{19.11}$$

This equation states that a neutron is added to the nucleus of $^{27}_{13}\text{Al}$ to produce the nuclide $^{28}_{13}\text{Al}$ and the *energy Q*, which appears largely as gamma radiation.

Q may be calculated in MeV as follows:

$$Q = 931\left[\sum_{i=1}^{n} m_{r_i} - \sum_{i=1}^{k} m_{p_i}\right] \tag{19.12}$$

where m_{r_i} = the mass of reactant r_i in amu
          m_{p_i} = the mass of product p_i in amu

The constant 931 is the proportionality constant between mass in units of amu and energy in units of million electron volts (MeV). If the value of Q is positive, energy is produced and the reaction will proceed spontaneously; such a reaction is said to be *exoergic*. If Q is negative, energy is required for the reaction to proceed and the reaction is said to be *endoergic*. The energy required to initiate endoergic reactions is often supplied in the form of kinetic energy of the incident particle. The energy released in exoergic reactions may be in the form of electromagnetic radiation (called gamma radiation), or in the form of kinetic energy given to emitted particles.

An abbreviated form is usually used for writing nuclear reactions. The reaction given in Equation 19.11 can be written as

$$^{27}_{13}\text{Al}(n, \gamma)^{28}_{13}\text{Al} \qquad (19.13)$$

This is understood to mean that a neutron is absorbed by a nucleus of $^{27}_{13}\text{Al}$ and gamma radiation is emitted, resulting in the formation of a product nucleus $^{28}_{13}\text{Al}$. The product nucleus of a nuclear reaction can be either stable or radioactive. If the product nuclide is radioactive, it will eventually decay to a different nuclide. The most common modes of decay are emission of alpha particles, beta particles, and gamma rays; other particles or radiations can also be emitted in radioactive decay, but they are of little analytical utility and will not be discussed here. Radioactive decay may involve a single-step transformation or may proceed through a series of steps. An example of the former is

$$^{28}_{13}\text{Al} \longrightarrow {}^{28}_{14}\text{Si} + \beta^- \qquad (19.14)$$

The nuclide $^{28}_{14}\text{Si}$ is stable with respect to further nuclear decay. The latter type of decay scheme is exemplified by

$$^{47}_{20}\text{Ca} \longrightarrow {}^{47}_{21}\text{Sc} + \beta^-$$
$$\downarrow \qquad\qquad (19.15)$$
$$^{47}_{22}\text{Ti} + \beta^-$$

The final product nuclide, $^{47}_{22}\text{Ti}$, is stable.

Beta Decay

There are three forms of beta decay. One is called *negatron* (β^-) emission. Negatrons are ordinary electrons that are emitted from nuclei as the result of a nuclear transformation. Negatron decay is illustrated by the symbolic equation

$$^A_Z\text{X} \longrightarrow {}_{Z+1}^A\text{Y} + \beta^- + \bar{\nu} \qquad (19.16)$$

where $\bar{\nu}$ is an antineutrino, an elusive particle of no practical analytical interest. The daughter nuclide Y formed by this transformation may initially exist in an excited state or in its ground state. If negatron emission results in an excited daughter state, deexcitation usually follows promptly, with the emission of one or several gamma rays. The radionuclides ^{3}H (tritium) and ^{14}C are examples of pure negatron emitters that decay directly to the ground state of their daughters without the emission of gamma radiation. Many other negatron emitters do have accompanying gamma radiations which may be detected in preference to measuring the short-ranged negatrons, which may be absorbed within the sample.

The second beta-decay process is *positron* (β^+) emission. Positron decay is illustrated by the symbolic equation

$$^A_Z\text{X} \longrightarrow {}_{Z-1}^A\text{Y} + \beta^+ + \nu \qquad (19.17)$$

where ν is a *neutrino*—again of no analytical utility. The radionuclides $^{22}_{11}\text{Na}$ and $^{65}_{30}\text{Zn}$ are examples of positron emitters commonly used in radioanalytical work. Again, the daughter nuclide may be formed in an excited state or in its ground state. Hence, gamma radiation may also accompany this mode of decay.

The third beta-decay process is electron capture. In this process, the nucleus captures an orbital electron (usually a K-electron), which creates an orbital vacancy. This vacancy is then filled by electrons from higher energy levels. The energy difference between the electronic energy levels involved is released in the form of x-rays or by the emission of low energy *Auger* or *secondary electrons* (see Chap. 15) from higher electronic-energy orbitals. The symbolic equation for this process is similar to that for positron decay, but no positrons are emitted from the nucleus. Gamma radiation may also accompany this type of beta decay. The x-rays emitted in electron-capture decay are sometimes useful for analytical determinations. An example of a radionuclide decaying by electron capture is

$$^7_4\text{Be} + e^- \longrightarrow {}^7_3\text{Li} + \text{x-rays} + \nu \qquad (19.18)$$

The energy distribution of beta particles emitted in negatron or positron decay is continuous (Fig. 19.3). The maximum energy associated with the distribution is called E_{max} and is characteristic of the particular nuclear transformation. At energies less than this, part of the energy resides in the neutrino or antineutrino emitted with the beta particle; the sum of the two energies is equal to the characteristic maximum energy.

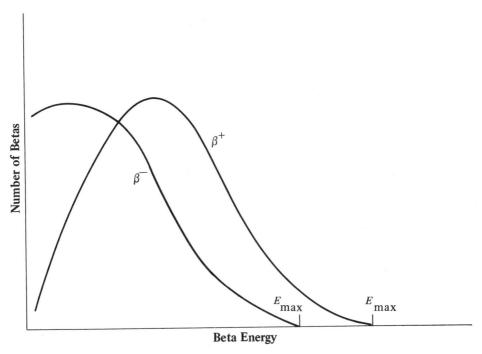

FIGURE 19.3. *Spectra of negatrons and positrons emitted during beta decay. E_{max} corresponds to the total energy of the transition.*

Beta particles generally have a short range in matter. For instance, beta particles from a transformation having $E_{max} = 1.0$ MeV are completely stopped by a 1.5 mm thickness of aluminum foil. From an analytical point of view, this is a very important observation. When counting beta rays, sample thickness becomes an extremely important parameter and must either be controlled accurately (all samples must have equal thicknesses), or appropriate corrections must be applied.

Negatrons commonly interact with matter in three ways: excitation, ionization, and bremsstrahlung. As negatrons pass through matter, they may interact with a bound electron and either eject the electron, forming an *ion pair* between the ejected electron and the ionized atom, or simply raise the electron to one of its excited levels. The incident negatron may lose part or all of its energy in each collision. On the other hand, high-energy beta particles may strike the target nucleus itself; the sudden deceleration in the strong electric field surrounding the nucleus generates an "electromagnetic shock wave," called *bremsstrahlung*, carrying away part of the kinetic energy of the electron.

Interactions of positrons with matter are similar to those encountered with negatrons. However, after dissipating most of its energy, the positron undergoes a process known as *annihilation*. The positron interacts with an electron in the vicinity of an atom and the masses of both particles are converted to energy according to Einstein's equation $E = mc^2$. Two gamma-ray photons, each having an energy equal to 0.511 MeV, are produced simultaneously. The detection of 0.511-MeV gamma rays usually indicates that a sample contains a positron-emitting radionuclide.

Alpha Decay

This type of decay is common among nuclei with high atomic number. Alpha decay is illustrated by

$$\ce{^{A}_{Z}X} \longrightarrow \ce{^{A-4}_{Z-2}Y} + \ce{^{4}_{2}He} \tag{19.19}$$

An example of a radionuclide decaying by alpha emission is $\ce{^{210}_{84}Po}$.

The emitted alpha particles have discrete energies. In passing through matter, they interact chiefly with electrons, dissociating molecules and exciting or ionizing molecules and atoms. The range of alpha particles in matter is much shorter than that of beta particles of similar energies. For example, a beam of 1.0-MeV alpha particles is stopped completely by a 3–4 μm thickness of aluminum foil (compared to about 1.5 mm for beta particles). This difference in penetrability is due to the lower velocity and greater charge of the alpha particle as compared to the beta particle. As in the case of beta decay, gamma radiation may accompany alpha decay, if the immediate product nuclide is formed in an excited state.

Electromagnetic Radiation

Electromagnetic radiation (photons) emitted from the nucleus is called gamma radiation. This radiation has neither charge nor mass, although its energy can be converted to an equivalent mass using the energy-mass equation ($E = mc^2$). Since gamma rays carry only energy, the emitting nuclide does not change in mass number or atomic number, thus preserving its chemical identity. Gamma rays emitted from any radionuclide have discrete energies characteristic of the different nuclear-energy states of that nuclide. Therefore, they can be used to "fingerprint" the materials from which they are emitted. The technique used to measure the numbers and energies of gamma rays emitted by radionuclides is called *gamma-ray spectrometry*.

The interaction of gamma radiation with matter is much more complex than the interaction of charged particles. There are three modes of interaction; the extent of each depends on the nature of the material and the energy of the radiation. In the first mode, called the *photoelectric effect*, the incoming gamma ray intersects with one of the orbital electrons in an absorber atom, ejecting that electron. The electron carries away kinetic energy equal to the energy of the gamma ray less the binding energy of the electron to the absorber atom. The ejected electron may then interact with other electrons, causing secondary ionization. The important characteristic of this process is the fact that essentially all of the energy of the gamma ray is given up in a single primary interaction. This process is most important for gamma rays of low energy (up to 1 MeV) and target materials with high atomic number.

The second process of gamma-ray interaction is called *Compton scattering*. In this process, the incoming gamma ray interacts with either a bound or free electron, losing only part of its energy in the encounter. If an electron is ejected from a bound state, its kinetic energy will be equal to the energy given up by the gamma ray less the binding energy of the electron. In this process, any one gamma ray may interact with many electrons. Of course, a gamma ray that has lost only part of its energy by this process may then undergo a photoelectric interaction, or simply escape from the absorber or detector.

The third process of gamma-ray interaction is *pair production*. This process occurs only when gamma rays have an energy equal to or greater than 1.02 MeV. In this process, the gamma-ray photon interacts with the absorber to produce an electron-positron pair. This is the reverse of the positron annihilation process discussed earlier. The reason for the minimum energy requirement is that 1.02 MeV is the energy equivalent of the two electron masses that must be created. The excess energy of the gamma ray ($E_\gamma - 1.02$ MeV) largely appears as kinetic energy given to the positron and the electron. The two particles may then interact further with other atomic electrons, causing secondary ionization.

Electromagnetic radiation penetrates much deeper into matter than do charged particles. Attenuation of gamma rays in matter follows an exponential law, similar to the Beer-Lambert law for absorption of visible light. To decrease the intensity of a 1.0-MeV parallel beam of gamma rays to one-half its original value requires a 4-cm thickness of aluminum (compared with 3–4 μm for alpha and 1.5 mm for beta radiation). In general, light materials are very ineffective for stopping gamma rays. Common shielding materials used are lead and high-density concrete.

19.3 DETECTION OF NUCLEAR RADIATION

In order to detect nuclear radiation, one ordinarily uses a transducer capable of converting the energy of the radiation into an electrical signal, usually a voltage pulse. Depending on the nature of the application, a satisfactory transducer must meet one or both of the following criteria: (1) there must be strict proportionality (preferably one-to-one) between the number of photons or particles interacting with the detector and the number of voltage pulses generated; and (2) there should be a strictly known relationship (preferably linear) between the energy that the radiation dissipates in the detector and the amplitude of the voltage pulse (called *pulse height*, PH) generated by the transducer.

Three types of radiation detectors are in common use: the *gas-ionization* detector, the *scintillation* detector, and the *solid-state* (or *semiconductor*) detector. Generally, the type used depends on the specific application. Gas-ionization detectors are commonly used for inexpensive detection of charged particles, scintillation detectors for beta- and gamma-ray detection, and solid-state detectors for x-ray and gamma-ray detection. The operation and properties of these detectors will be briefly described.

Gas-Ionization Detectors

A gas-ionization detector consists of two electrodes at different potentials and a (nonconducting) gas between them. The radiation produces ion pairs in the gas; the ions are then collected by the electrodes, yielding a voltage pulse which is measured. Figure 19.4 shows a typical cylindrical detector together with its associated measurement system. The detector proper is made of a cylindrical conducting material with an electrically isolated wire located on the central axis of the cylinder. A very thin window made of mylar, aluminum, or beryllium separates the radioactive source from the main volume of the detector (or the source can be placed directly inside the chamber). The chamber can either be permanently filled with some appropriate gas (e.g., 90% Ar + 10% CH_4), or a continuous flow of the gas can be sent through the chamber.

The detector operates as follows: as long as there is no ionizing radiation present, the filler gas acts as a very large resistor (R_2) and allows virtually no current

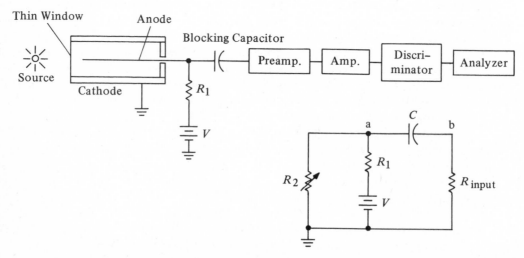

FIGURE 19.4. *A gas-ionization detector system. Top: Block diagram illustrating system components. Bottom: A simplified electrical analogue.*

to pass through the tube. The voltage appearing at point a is then equal to the bias voltage V of the battery or regulated power supply. Capacitor C acts to block this voltage from reaching point b. Therefore, the voltage seen by the input of the amplifier (R_{input}) is zero. Now, assume that a single ionizing particle enters the detector volume and produces a number of ion pairs. Since there is an electrostatic potential between the two electrodes, the positive ions are attracted towards the cathode and the electrons towards the anode. The electrons that reach the anode pass through the external circuit (made of R_1 and V), while an equal number of electrons flow from the negative terminal of the battery to the cathode to neutralize the positive ions that reach the cathode. This is analogous to a sudden drop in resistance of the filler gas (R_2 of Fig. 19.4). Thus, the voltage at point a will suddenly drop from V to v.

$$v = V \frac{R_2}{R_1 + R_2} \qquad (19.20)$$

R_2, the effective resistance of the filler gas, depends on the number of ion pairs produced. The overall effect is a sudden change in voltage at point a in the form of a sharp spike. This spike appears at the input of the preamplifier as a negative voltage pulse. The amplitude of this spike is the pulse height (PH).

Three types of ionization detectors, differing by the magnitude of the bias voltage V, are generally recognized: *ion chambers*, *proportional counters*, and *Geiger-Müller counters*. Each of these is best suited for a specific application. A plot of PH as a function of bias voltage has the general features shown in Figure 19.5. (It is important to note at this stage that PH is proportional to the number of ion pairs actually reaching the electrodes and not necessarily to how many were produced inside the detector, since some ion pairs may combine on their way and not reach the electrode—a phenomenon called ion recombination.)

Depending on their mode of production, two types of ion pairs are recognized: primary ion-pairs and secondary ion-pairs. The former are ion pairs produced from the direct interaction of radiation with the filler gas, whereas the latter are those produced by the energetic electrons of the primary ion pairs. The number of primary ion-pairs produced per incoming particle depends on the amount of energy dissipated inside the detector volume. If all of the energy of the incoming particle is dissipated inside the detector, the number of primary ion-pairs will then be directly proportional to the energy of the incoming radiation. The number of secondary ion-pairs produced depends on the kinetic energy of each primary electron and on the voltage applied to the detector.

To understand the curve in Figure 19.5, assume that a single particle of radiation enters the detector volume, dissipating all of its energy and producing 1000 primary ion-pairs. If the voltage applied is smaller than V_1, only a fraction of these primary ion-pairs will reach the electrodes. The remainder will undergo ion recombination. The higher the applied voltage (for $V < V_1$), the larger the number of primary ion-pairs reaching the electrodes and the larger the PH. This region of the curve is of limited practical value. For voltages between V_1 and V_2, the kinetic energy of the primary ion-pairs is sufficient for almost all of them to reach the electrodes, but is not enough to produce secondary ion-pairs. In this region PH is independent of applied voltage, but is directly proportional to the energy dissipated inside

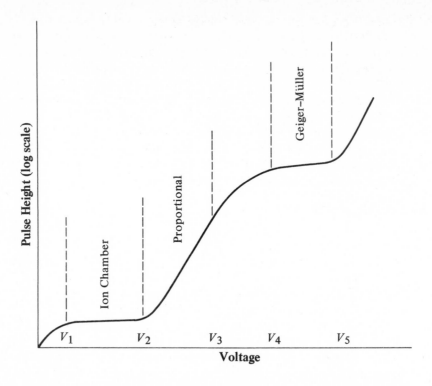

FIGURE 19.5. *Pulse height (PH) as a function of applied bias voltage for a gas-ionization detector.*

the detector. This is the region used for ion-chamber detectors. Since there are no secondary ion-pairs produced, PH is extremely small (the voltage pulse would be approximately 0.001 μV).

If the applied voltage is increased beyond V_2, the primary electrons will be subject to a relatively large electrostatic field and will acquire enough kinetic energy to, in turn, ionize the filler-gas atoms, producing secondary ion-pairs. In the region between V_2 and V_3, the total number of ion pairs reaching the electrodes, and thus PH, is proportional to both the applied voltage and the energy dissipated in the detector. This region is called the *proportional region* and is extensively used for measuring alpha and beta radiation. One important feature of this region is that PH is generally in the range of 1–100 mV and, therefore, is relatively easy to measure. Also, since PH is proportional to the energy dissipated in the detector, not only can the number of incoming particles per unit time be measured, but also their energies. Another very important feature of proportional counters is that of *detector dead-time*— only a short time (a few microseconds) passes between the entry of radiation and the time when all ion pairs are collected at the electrodes and current stops flowing. Therefore, radioactive sources with fairly high disintegration rates can be measured without correcting for detector dead-time losses.

When the applied voltage exceeds V_3, the electrostatic field becomes so large that a chain reaction results from the interaction of any ionizing particle, resulting in loss of proportionality between energy dissipated and PH. This proportionality is lost first gradually (region between V_3 and V_4) and then completely ($V_4 < V < V_5$) —the detector discharges throughout its entire volume. For the region between V_4 and V_5, PH becomes independent of the energy dissipated in the detector by the incoming particle, but may increase slightly with increasing applied voltage. This is called the *Geiger-Müller* region, and detectors operating in this region are referred to as *GM counters*. These counters produce large voltage pulses (a fraction of a volt to a few volts) and require little external amplification. Therefore, GM counting systems are often inexpensive. The basic limitations of GM counters are their large dead-time (a few hundred μsec per pulse) and their lack of energy discrimination. These counters are widely used for portable radiation monitors and for counting gross beta-activity in tracer experiments.

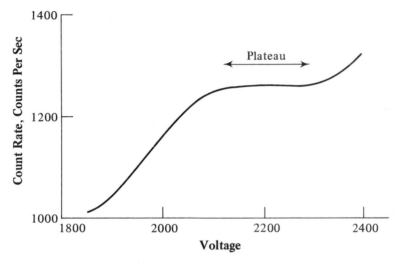

FIGURE 19.6. *The voltage plateau for a neutron proportional counter. Proper operating voltage is at the midpoint of the plateau.*

At voltages greater than V_5, the filler gas itself begins to ionize because of the large voltages involved, and produces a continuous discharge whether or not there is any ionizing radiation present. When using either proportional or GM counters, it is important to realize that the magnitude of the bias voltage may affect the observed count rate. Therefore, before using the counter, one must establish the proper bias voltage by counting an essentially constant-activity source with different bias voltages (Fig. 19.6). The proper operating voltage is that corresponding to the midpoint of the plateau. With a proportional counter, different plateaus are obtained for alpha and beta particles and, hence, discrimination is possible.

Scintillation Detectors

It was pointed out earlier that interaction of radiation with matter can result in the production of ion pairs. The electron from the ion pair can in turn produce secondary ionization, which is important in gas-ionization detectors. These secondary electrons can also electronically excite the atoms in the detection medium, which in turn can emit light quanta. *Fluors* or *phosphors* are materials in which such a sequence of events occurs. The number of light quanta emitted is proportional to the energy of the radiation absorbed, so these materials can be used as radiation detectors permitting energy discrimination. Detectors of this type are called *scintillation detectors*. Typical materials used as scintillators are thallium-doped NaI crystals, anthracene crystals, and certain organic compounds such as *p*-terphenyl dissolved in organic solvents. NaI(Tl) crystals are particularly efficient for gamma-ray detection because they contain a high-Z material (iodine) and have a relatively high density.

Liquid scintillators (organic scintillators dissolved in an appropriate solvent) are generally used for detecting beta particles. They are particularly useful for low-energy beta emitters such as ^{3}H or ^{14}C; these are used widely as tracers in biochemistry and organic chemistry. The sample is commonly dissolved in the solvent along with the scintillator. Special counters are required because the pulses generated by tritium, ^{3}H, are of nearly the same amplitude as the background pulses from thermionic emission in the photomultiplier detector at room temperature; therefore, the photomultiplier and amplifier electronics are cooled to $-10°C$.

A scintillation detector generally consists of a fluor placed in close contact with a photomultiplier tube. The flashes of light emitted from the fluor enter the photomultiplier, generating a large current pulse from each primary scintillation event. The current pulse is then converted to a voltage pulse, which is amplified and analyzed. The amplitude of this pulse is the PH, and is proportional to the energy originally deposited in the fluor by the radiation.

As discussed previously, gamma rays have discrete, well defined energies. Each incoming gamma ray interacts with the detector material by one or more of the three processes discussed before, leaving part or all of its energy inside the detector. Since each gamma ray (of the same energy) may deposit a different fraction of its initial energy, the output voltage pulses will not have identical PHs, although the PH distribution will be characteristic.

If the material of interest emits gamma rays having more than one characteristic energy, the PH distribution (gamma-ray spectrum) will be quite complex. In order to analyze such a spectrum, a multi-channel analyzer (MCA) is used with the scintillation detector. The MCA receives the voltage pulses, classifies each pulse according to its PH, and stores all the pulses of equal PH in the same memory location (channel). For example, a 400-channel analyzer can be calibrated to store a 10-V pulse in channel 400 and a 5-V pulse in channel 200. Any gamma ray giving rise to a PH of 7.5 V will be stored in channel 300, since the relationship between pulse height (gamma-ray energy) and channel number for a MCA is (generally) linear.

If one places a monoenergetic source of gamma radiation in front of a NaI(Tl) detector and uses a MCA to analyze the PH distribution of the detector, a spectrum similar to that in Figure 19.7 is obtained. Note that the total number of counts registered in each channel during the entire counting time is plotted as a function of channel number (which is proportional to energy). The actual gamma-ray spectrum is a continuum (the *Compton continuum*) with a peak (the *full-energy peak*), even if the source emits only gamma rays with a single energy. The Compton continuum, starting from low energies and ending at the point CE, is caused by incomplete de-

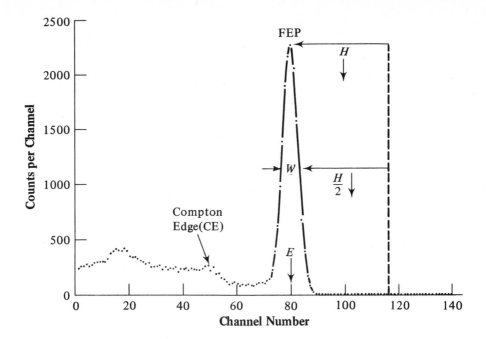

FIGURE 19.7. *Gamma-ray spectrum of a* ^{137}Cs *source, using a* $4'' \times 4''$ *NaI(Tl) scintillation-detector. The energy resolution of the detector is measured by the width (W) of the full-energy peak (FEP) at one-half the maximum height (H/2) of the FEP.*

position of the gamma-ray energy following a Compton interaction with the detector crystal. The edge of the Compton continuum is called the *Compton edge* (CE) and corresponds to the maximum energy that a gamma ray can transfer to an electron following a Compton interaction. The degraded gamma-ray produced in the Compton interaction may either escape the crystal or undergo further interaction. If all the energy of the primary gamma ray is eventually deposited in the crystal, the event is recorded in the *full-energy peak* (FEP), together with the events from photoelectric-effect interactions. If the degraded gamma ray escapes the crystal, the event is recorded in the Compton continuum.

For analytical purposes, the most important feature of the spectrum is the FEP. This peak includes all primary gamma-ray interactions that occur by the photoelectric effect, as well as those interactions caused by Compton scattering and pair production in which the energies of the secondary radiations or particles are completely dissipated in the detector crystal. Although the gamma-ray energy is well defined, the FEP always has a certain width that is a function of both the type of detector and the energy of the FEP. The energy corresponding to the channel at the center of the FEP is essentially the energy of the primary gamma ray that interacted with the crystal. The area under this peak is related to the *activity* of the source at the beginning of the counting time (t_o) by

$$\text{FEP area} = \xi \int_0^{t_o} A_0 e^{-\lambda t} \, dt = \frac{\xi A_0}{\lambda} (1 - e^{-\lambda t_o}) \qquad \textbf{(19.21)}$$

where ξ is the overall efficiency of the counting system and includes factors for the counting geometry and FEP detection probability; it is a constant for any fixed experimental set-up. A_0 is the activity of the specific gamma-ray emitted by the radioactive source at $t_c = 0$.

The width (W) of the FEP at the point corresponding to one-half its height (Fig. 19.7) is called the *full width at half maximum* (FWHM). The ratio of W to E_γ (both in units of energy) expressed in percent is called the *resolution* (R) of the detector:

$$R = \frac{W}{E_\gamma} 100\% \tag{19.22}$$

For a typical NaI(Tl) detector, R is about 8% for the 1.332-MeV FEP of ^{60}Co; for the newer Ge(Li) semiconductor detectors, R may be as low as 0.2% for ^{60}Co.

If a source emits gamma rays with different energies, a composite spectrum results. Figure 19.8 shows a composite spectrum for $^{54}_{25}$Mn, $^{60}_{27}$Co, and $^{137}_{55}$Cs. In any quantitative analysis using composite gamma-ray spectra, one needs to measure the area under each FEP. To do this, one must first select the portion of the FEP that lies above the Compton background from higher-energy peaks. This is commonly done by locating the left channel (C_1) just before the FEP appears to rise above the background and the right channel (C_2) at the point where the FEP disappears into

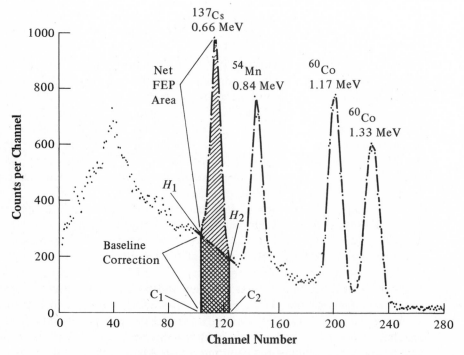

FIGURE 19.8. *A composite gamma-ray spectrum of ^{137}Cs, ^{54}Mn, and ^{60}Co. The net area of the full-energy peak (FEP), as obtained by baseline subtraction, is proportional to the activity of the radionuclide.*

the background. (This selection is sometimes difficult because of statistical variations, especially if the FEP of interest is small compared to the underlying Compton background.) One then calculates the net area of the FEP by subtracting from the total area the average background count per channel multiplied by the number of channels:

$$\text{Net area (counts)} = \left(\begin{matrix}\text{Total area} \\ C_1 \rightarrow C_2\end{matrix}\right) - \left(\frac{H_1 + H_2}{2}\right)(C_2 - C_1 + 1) \quad \textbf{(19.23)}$$

It is often necessary to determine the statistical error involved in this calculation, following the procedures given in Section 19.5. If the background count distributions around C_1 and C_2 appear to be horizontal, it is often advisable to take averages of several channels preceding the FEP and several channels following the FEP in order to obtain a more representative baseline correction. There are several more sophisticated methods of baseline correction, but their discussion is beyond the scope of this chapter.

Solid-State or Semiconductor Detectors (SSD)

A SSD operates on the same principle as a gas-ionization detector, but using a solid semiconductor instead of a filler gas. A SSD is a block of some semiconductor material (commonly Ge or Si) into which has been incorporated a minute quantity of a Group IIIA element such as gallium (Fig. 19.9). The doped block, having a lower

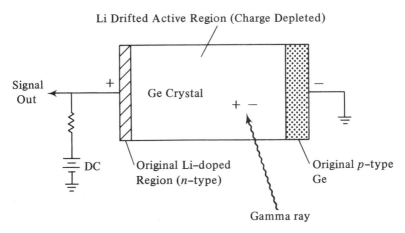

FIGURE 19.9. *Schematic diagram of a Ge(Li) detector.*

density of free electrons than the pure semiconductor, is called a p-type semiconductor. (An n-type semiconductor has a higher density of free electrons than the pure semiconductor.) A very thin layer (a few μm) of Li is then diffused into one surface of the block. If a reverse bias is applied between the p-side ($-$ bias) and the lithium side ($+$ bias) of the block, it will develop a *charge-depleted region*. This region has a very high effective resistance; by cooling the block to the temperature of liquid nitrogen, the current flow is decreased even further. The depletion region comprises the effective volume of the detector.

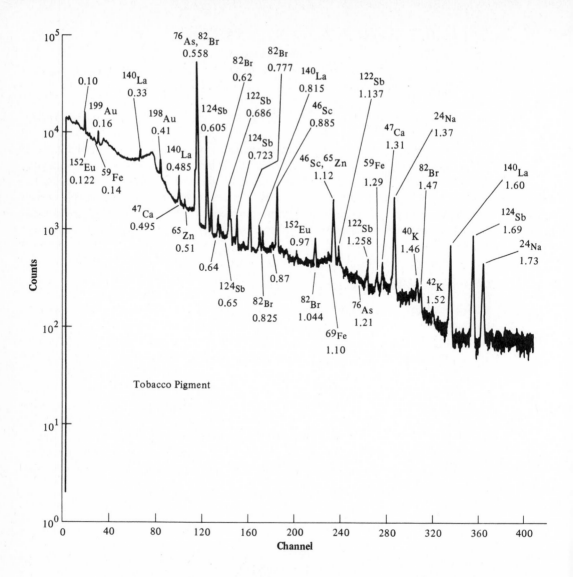

FIGURE 19.10. *A high-resolution gamma-ray spectrum obtained with a 35-cm³ Ge(Li) detector and a reactor-irradiated tobacco extract. Note that the number of counts is on a logarithmic scale.*

If a gamma ray enters the depletion region of the detector, it may interact and form an ion-electron pair, which may in turn cause secondary ionization on their way to the lithium side of the detector (the positive electrode). These electrons charge up the detector (the two electrodes of the detector separated by its dielectric form a capacitor) and produce a voltage pulse across the electrodes. The magnitude of this pulse is

$$V = \frac{Q}{C} \tag{19.24}$$

where Q = the total charge collected on the electrodes
C = the detector capacitance

This voltage pulse is very small (of the order of microvolts) and is amplified by a very sensitive preamplifier before it can be processed by conventional amplifiers and MCA's.

The two important parameters characterizing gamma-ray detectors are *resolution* and *efficiency*. The resolution of a detector measures its capability to separate (resolve) adjacent gamma rays and becomes very important when unwanted gamma rays are present near the FEP of interest. Efficiency, on the other hand, measures only the fraction of the incoming gamma rays of any given energy that contribute to the corresponding FEP. Ideally, the detector has as good a resolution (low R) and as large an efficiency (ξ) as possible. However, with present-day gamma-ray detectors these two properties are conflicting—detectors with high efficiency have poor resolving power and vice versa. Therefore, the type of detector chosen depends on the requirements of the analysis. For example, if a sample contains many gamma-emitting radionuclides, one must select a detector with good resolution and accept its lower inherent efficiency. On the other hand, if one is analyzing a region of the spectrum where there are no spectral interferences and the sample has a low activity, one would choose a detector having a high efficiency.

The fundamental advantage of a SSD over a scintillation detector is its superior resolution. The efficiency of a Ge(Li) SSD is often expressed relative to that of a $3'' \times 3''$ NaI(Tl) scintillation detector for a point source of ^{60}Co 1.332-MeV gamma rays at a distance of 25 cm from the detectors. Measured in this way, a typical Ge(Li) detector efficiency is only 10 percent. Therefore, although the resolution may be improved by a factor of 40, the efficiency is decreased by a factor of 10. The superior energy-resolution of a Ge(Li) detector is well illustrated by the spectrum in Figure 19.10. This spectrum was obtained by counting a reactor-irradiated extract from tobacco with a Ge(Li) detector. Gamma-ray peaks from at least a dozen elements can be distinguished.

19.4   NEUTRON ACTIVATION ANALYSIS

Radiochemical methods of analysis can be grouped according to whether one measures radioactivity present in the sample or employs some means of introducing radioactivity into an otherwise nonradioactive sample in order to analyze for some component. An example of the first type is the determination of radioactive ^{40}K in rock samples. The second type is exemplified by using labeled KI^*O_3 (I^* denoting a radioisotope of iodine) to determine the concentration of SO_2 in air by the radio-release method. This chapter will deal with the use of radioactivity to analyze otherwise nonradioactive substances.

Radiochemical methods discussed in this chapter are further divided into two general categories. Consider first those methods that induce radioactivity in the components of the sample to be analyzed. In all such methods, the sample is bombarded with nuclear radiations or particles (neutrons, protons, gamma rays, etc.) and the radiations emitted from the sample are measured, either simultaneously or subsequently. This general class of radiochemical methods is referred to as *activation analysis.* If the sample is bombarded with neutrons, the method is called *neutron activation analysis* (NAA), whereas if the sample is bombarded with gamma rays, the method is called *photon activation analysis.* Although the principles of the various forms of activation analysis are the same, the experimental capabilities and limitations of the method differ widely for different types of bombarding particles or radiation. Neutron activation analysis is currently the most widely employed technique and is the activation method that will be discussed in this chapter.

Principles of Neutron Activation Analysis

This method involves bombarding the sample with neutrons and measuring the radioactivity induced in the sample (commonly using gamma-ray spectrometry). In order to understand the principles of neutron activation analysis, some pertinent properties of neutrons and their interactions with matter will first be discussed.

Neutrons are nuclear particles with unit mass-number and neutral charge; they are commonly produced as a result of nuclear reactions or nuclear fission, and interact with matter almost exclusively by collisions with nuclei. A neutron interacts with the nucleus of an atom in several ways. It can undergo *elastic scattering*, whereby the neutron collides with the target nucleus and is scattered (similar to a moving billiard ball striking another (stationary) ball). Depending on the size of the target nucleus and the angle of collision, a varying amount of the kinetic energy of the neutron is lost in adding kinetic energy to the target nucleus. If the target nucleus has a low mass (hydrogen, deuterium, carbon, etc.), a considerable fraction of the energy of the incident neutron may be lost in the collision. This is why low-mass materials (H_2O, D_2O, etc.) are used to reduce the kinetic energy of fast neutrons produced by fission in nuclear reactors—a process known as *thermalization.*

A neutron also undergoes *inelastic scattering* with a target nucleus. In this case, the neutron scatters off the nucleus of a target atom, transfers part of its kinetic energy, and excites the nucleus to one of its higher energy levels. The target nucleus can then dissipate this excess energy by emitting electromagnetic radiation.

The third type of neutron interaction, the *capture reaction*, is the most important one for activation analysis. The incoming neutron is absorbed (captured) by the target nucleus, forming a new nuclide with the same atomic number as the parent nuclide, but one unit higher in mass number. An amount of energy equal to the binding energy of the neutron in that nucleus plus the kinetic energy of the incoming neutron is then available to raise the product nucleus to an excited state. The binding energy differs for different nuclides; but, for the most stable nuclides of intermediate mass, it is about 8 MeV/nucleon. Thus, even if the captured neutron had almost zero kinetic energy, the excess energy of the compound nucleus is about 8 MeV.

There are two ways in which the compound nucleus can release this excess energy: (1) it may radiate gamma rays, or (2) it may emit one or more nuclear particles (neutrons, protons, or alpha particles). Which of these two processes predominates depends on the total excitation energy of the compound nucleus. If sufficient energy is available, more than one reaction can take place.

In order to determine whether a given nuclear reaction can occur, the energy balance for the complete reaction must be calculated. If the overall reaction produces energy (Q is positive), the reaction proceeds spontaneously. Consider the nuclear reaction

$$^{27}_{13}\text{Al} + ^{1}_{0}\text{n} \longrightarrow ^{28}_{13}\text{Al} + Q \tag{19.25}$$

Using Equation 19.12,

$$\sum m_r = 26.981535 + 1.008665 = 27.990200 \text{ amu}$$

$$\sum m_p = 27.981908 = 27.981908 \text{ amu}$$

$$Q = 931 (27.990200 - 27.981908) = +7.7 \text{ MeV}$$

The positive value of Q indicates that the reaction will proceed with neutrons having nearly zero kinetic energy ("thermal" neutrons have an energy of approximately 0.04 eV).

For the following reaction

$$^{27}_{13}\text{Al} + ^{1}_{0}\text{n} \longrightarrow ^{26}_{13}\text{Al} + 2\,^{1}_{0}\text{n} + Q \tag{19.26}$$

$Q = -13.1$ MeV. Since the value of Q is negative, this reaction cannot take place without the input of energy. The needed energy must be supplied by the kinetic energy of the incoming neutron. The minimum amount of kinetic energy that the incoming neutron must provide for the above reaction is somewhat more than the calculated 13.1 MeV, because part of the kinetic energy of the incoming neutron is merely transferred to the target nucleus ($^{27}_{13}\text{Al}$) to produce a moving product nucleus, according to the principle of conservation of momentum. The *laboratory threshold energy*, E_T, required to initiate the reaction may be calculated by means of

$$E_T = Q\left(\frac{m_a + m_n}{m_a}\right) \tag{19.27}$$

where m_a = the mass of the target nuclide
m_n = the mass of the neutron

Therefore,

$$E_T = -13.1\left(\frac{26.981535 + 1.008665}{26.981535}\right) = -13.5 \text{ MeV}$$

For the above reaction to occur, the incoming neutron must have at least 13.5 MeV kinetic energy.

Now consider the slightly more complicated case

$$^{27}_{13}\text{Al} + ^{1}_{0}\text{n} \longrightarrow ^{27}_{12}\text{Mg} + ^{1}_{1}\text{p} + Q \tag{19.28}$$

where $Q = -1.8$ MeV and $E_T = -1.9$ MeV. E_T is the minimum energy required for the reaction; but, once the proton is created, it has a low probability of leaving the nucleus because it is a charged particle. In order to increase the probability of leaving the nucleus, it must have enough energy to overcome the *coulombic barrier*. For the case of the emission of a neutron there is no coulombic barrier and, therefore, once the neutron is created it can leave the nucleus. The minimum kinetic energy that a charged particle must have in order to overcome the coulombic barrier and leave the nucleus is determined by the following equation:

$$E_c = -1.44 \frac{Z_a Z_b}{r_s} \qquad (19.29)$$

where E_c = the coulombic barrier energy in MeV
  Z_a = the atomic number of the product nuclide
  Z_b = the atomic number of the emitted particle
  $r_s = r_a + r_b$
  r_a = the radius of the product nucleus
  r_b = the radius of the emitted particle

The various radii are calculated using the empirical equation

$$r \approx 1.5 \, A^{1/3} \qquad (19.30)$$

where A = the mass number
  r = radius in Fermis (1 Fermi = 10^{-13} cm)

In this example,

$$E_c = -1.44 \left(\frac{12(1)}{1.5(27^{1/3} + 1^{1/3})} \right) = -2.9 \text{ MeV}$$

Therefore, at least 1.9 MeV is needed to create the proton and an additional 2.9 MeV for it to overcome the coulomb barrier. For the above reaction to take place with high probability, the incident neutron must have a minimum kinetic energy of $1.9 + 2.9 = 4.8$ MeV. Endoergic reactions are also called *threshold reactions*.

The probability that a nuclear reaction will occur is measured by a quantity called the *reaction cross-section*. The most common unit of cross-section is the *barn* (1 barn = 1×10^{-24} cm²). If the energetics are favorable for more than one reaction, then each reaction has a specific reaction cross-section and proceeds independently of other reactions.

The rate at which a nuclear reaction proceeds depends on three parameters: the number of target atoms present, the reaction cross-section, and the number of neutrons incident per unit area of the target material per unit time. This relationship is expressed by

$$R = N\phi\sigma \qquad (19.31)$$

where R = the reaction rate in sec^{-1}
  N = the number of target nuclei present
  ϕ = the neutron flux density in n/(cm²-sec)
  σ = the reaction cross-section in cm²

The magnitude of the reaction cross-section depends on the nature of the target nuclide and on the energy of the incident neutrons. With thermal (low energy) neutrons, (n, γ) reactions generally have large cross-sections, although there are some exceptions. Threshold reactions, of course, cannot take place with thermal neutrons to any appreciable extent.

Sources of Neutrons

Three sources of neutrons are commonly used in activation analysis.

Nuclear Reactors. A nuclear reactor generates neutrons by the process of *fission*. Although the actual workings of nuclear reactors are quite complicated, the principles, for the present purpose, can be understood by considering a $^{235}_{92}U$-fueled nuclear reactor. Upon capturing a neutron, a $^{235}_{92}U$ nucleus breaks up into several lighter nuclei and produces more neutrons:

$$^{235}_{92}U + ^{1}_{0}n \longrightarrow ^{A_1}_{Z_1}X + ^{A_2}_{Z_2}X' + k\,^{1}_{0}n + Q \qquad (19.32)$$

where

$$A_1 + A_2 + k = 236$$
$$Z_1 + Z_2 = 92$$

The *average* value of k is 2.5. The fact that each nucleus of $^{235}_{92}U$ produces more neutrons than it requires for fission is responsible for the copious production of neutrons by nuclear reactors.

The fission neutrons produced in nuclear reactors have a continuous kinetic-energy spectrum, mostly in the range of 1–10 MeV. Since (n, γ) reactions are of more widespread analytical use, fission neutrons must be slowed to thermal energies by passing them through H_2O, D_2O, or graphite, which act as *moderators*. Depending on the type of nuclear reactor and the irradiation position in the reactor, the neutron spectrum may vary widely. Therefore, both (n, γ) and threshold reactions can occur in samples placed in nuclear reactors. Threshold reactions may produce interferences, of which the experimenter should be aware.

Isotopic Sources of Neutrons. Nuclear reactors are the only sources of copious quantities of neutrons. A typical research reactor might have a useful flux density of 10^{11}–10^{13} n/(cm²-sec). However, moderate flux densities of neutrons can be obtained from isotopic sources of neutrons at relatively low cost and with minimal space and maintenance requirements.

Isotopic neutron sources are of two general types. The first is a manmade radionuclide that undergoes spontaneous fission and produces neutrons. $^{252}_{98}Cf$ is a radionuclide commonly used for this purpose; a 1-mg $^{252}_{98}Cf$ source will produce 2.34×10^9 n/sec. The neutron spectrum of this source is similar to that of reactor neutrons, and therefore, for practical applications, the source is placed in a moderator or "thermalizer." The useful thermal-neutron flux density available in a typical facility is about 3×10^7 n/(cm²-sec).

The second type of isotopic neutron source consists of a radionuclide emitting intense alpha or gamma radiation, mixed with the element beryllium; one of the following reactions takes place:

$$^{9}_{4}Be + ^{4}_{2}He \longrightarrow ^{12}_{6}C + ^{1}_{0}n \qquad (19.33)$$

$$^{9}_{4}Be + \gamma \longrightarrow 2\,^{4}_{2}He + ^{1}_{0}n \qquad (19.34)$$

These neutrons also have a "fast," continuous spectral distribution and are usually slowed (moderated) by placing the source in a hydrogen-rich medium, such as water or paraffin.

Accelerators. The accelerator most commonly used for the production of neutrons is the Cockcroft-Walton neutron generator. A schematic diagram of this generator is given in Figure 19.11. Deuterium molecules are ionized in the ion-source bottle, accelerated in an electrostatic field of 100–200 kV, and focussed on a target containing tritium ($^3_1$H). The following nuclear reaction takes place:

$$^3_1\text{H} + {}^2_1\text{H} \longrightarrow {}^4_2\text{He} + {}^1_0\text{n} + Q \tag{19.35}$$

where $Q \approx +14$ MeV. The neutrons produced are, therefore, nearly monoenergetic at 14 MeV.

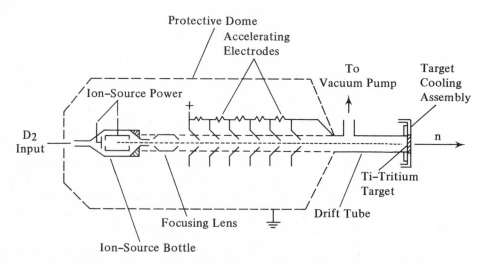

FIGURE 19.11. *Schematic diagram of a Cockcroft-Walton 14-MeV neutron generator.*

These neutrons are capable of inducing many threshold reactions. For example, consider the reaction

$$^{16}_8\text{O} + {}^1_0\text{n} \longrightarrow {}^{16}_7\text{N} + {}^1_1\text{H} + Q \tag{19.36}$$

for which $Q = -9.6$ MeV, $E_\text{T} = -10.2$ MeV, and $E_\text{c} = -1.9$ MeV. Therefore, the minimum kinetic energy of neutrons required for the above reaction must be 12.1 MeV. This method is widely used for the determination of oxygen, an element that is difficult to determine by other analytical techniques. Benchtop-sized sealed-tube neutron generators are commonly employed.

Theory of Instrumental Neutron Activation Analysis (INAA)

The procedure in INAA is as follows:

1. the sample is exposed to neutrons for a known length of time, t_i
2. it is transported to the counting station and allowed to *cool* or decay for a definite length of time, t_d
3. the gamma-ray spectrum is acquired for counting time, t_c
4. the area under the FEP of interest is calculated

This procedure is repeated for another sample (the standard) containing a known amount of the element of interest. From the weight of the element in the standard, the relative FEP areas of the sample and standard, the relative neutron fluxes used for irradiating the sample and standard, and the times involved, the amount of the element in the sample is calculated.

Assume that the weight of the element present in the unknown sample is W_u grams and that one irradiates the sample for $t_{i(u)}$ sec, allows it to decay for $t_{d(u)}$ sec, and counts the emission for $t_{c(u)}$ sec. The activity of the radionuclide of interest at the end of the irradiation is given by

$$A_u{}^0 = N\phi_u\sigma(1 - e^{-\lambda t_{i(u)}})$$

$$= 6.02 \times 10^{23} \frac{I}{M} \phi_u\sigma(1 - e^{-\lambda t_{i(u)}})W_u \qquad (19.37)$$

where $I =$ the isotopic abundance of the element
          $M =$ the atomic mass of the element
          $\phi_u =$ the neutron flux density in n/(cm²-sec)
          $N =$ the number of atoms of the specific target isotope present

Most tables list I in units of atom percent, in which case M should be the atomic mass of the element, not the mass of the individual isotope.

When acquisition of the spectrum begins, the activity will be

$$A_u = A_u{}^0 e^{-\lambda t_{d(u)}} \qquad (19.38)$$

The detector will, of course, detect only a fraction of this activity. Furthermore, only those events that register in the FEP are of interest. These factors are accounted for by the *detector photopeak efficiency* ξ. The *count rate* registered by the detection system in the FEP at the instant when counting starts is therefore given by

$$CR_u = \xi A_u{}^0 e^{-\lambda t_{d(u)}} \qquad (19.39)$$

The analyzer will integrate the count rate for the period of time, t_c. At the end of this time, *total counts* registered in the FEP, excluding any background effects, will be

$$C_u = \xi A_u{}^0 e^{-\lambda t_{d(u)}} \int_0^{t_{c(u)}} e^{-\lambda t}\, dt$$

$$= \frac{1}{\lambda} \xi A_u{}^0 e^{-\lambda t_{d(u)}}(1 - e^{-\lambda t_{c(u)}}) \qquad (19.40)$$

Combining Equations 19.37 and 19.40 results in

$$C_u = \frac{\xi}{\lambda} \frac{I}{M} \phi_u\sigma(1 - e^{-\lambda t_{i(u)}})e^{-\lambda t_{d(u)}}(1 - e^{-\lambda t_{c(u)}})W_u(6.02 \times 10^{23}) \qquad (19.41)$$

If the exact values of the parameters in the above equation were known, W_u could be calculated directly. However, because of uncertainties in the numerical values of

ξ, ϕ, and σ, it is more convenient to employ a comparative method whereby one also irradiates a sample of known content of the element of interest. Then

$$\frac{C_u}{C_s} = \frac{\xi_u \phi_u (1 - e^{-\lambda t_{i(u)}}) e^{-\lambda t_{d(u)}} (1 - e^{-\lambda t_{o(u)}}) W_u}{\xi_s \phi_s (1 - e^{-\lambda t_{i(s)}}) e^{-\lambda t_{d(s)}} (1 - e^{-\lambda t_{o(s)}}) W_s} \tag{19.42}$$

Several parameters having the same values for the sample and standard (I, M, and σ) have been canceled out. It is quite a simple matter with present-day solid-state electronics to accurately control the various times involved. If each corresponding time is the same for both the sample and standard, and if both are counted with the same detection system, then

$$W_u = \frac{C_u}{C_s} \frac{\phi_s}{\phi_u} W_s \tag{19.43}$$

Equation 19.43 is the working equation commonly used in neutron activation analysis. When employing nuclear reactors or an isotopic source, the value of ϕ_u and ϕ_s may also be the same, and a further simplification results. However, when using accelerator-generated neutrons, this is not easily done, and the values of ϕ_u and ϕ_s (or the ratio ϕ_s/ϕ_u) must be determined experimentally.

Capabilities and Limitations of Neutron Activation Analysis

This technique is a method for determining the elemental contents of substances. Its fundamental limitation is its inability to distinguish among different chemical forms or oxidation states of an element. Like most analytical methods, this technique also suffers from possible interferences and matrix effects. Three types of interferences may occur.

Type I Interferences. These arise from nuclear reactions in the other elements present in the sample that produce the same radionuclide as the one measured. For example, in determining Al in rocks by reactor irradiation employing the reaction $^{27}_{13}\text{Al}$ (n, γ) $^{28}_{13}\text{Al}$, a possible interference is $^{28}_{14}\text{Si}$ (n, p) $^{28}_{13}\text{Al}$.

Type II Interferences. These are caused by the release of secondary nuclear particles from a primary reaction. For instance, when determining nitrogen in protein products with a neutron generator, the reaction employed may be $^{14}_{7}\text{N}$ (n, 2n) $^{13}_{7}\text{N}$. If the sample is packaged in polyethylene containers, the incident neutrons may collide with the hydrogen atoms present in the container material, producing energetic protons which may in turn react with carbon in the sample according to the reaction $^{13}_{6}\text{C}$ (p, n) $^{13}_{7}\text{N}$. This type of interference is generally of limited significance, because the flux density of protons produced is much less than that of the primary neutrons.

Type III Interferences. These are caused by the inability of some detectors to resolve closely similar gamma-ray energies. For example, when determining the Al content of a material by the reaction $^{27}_{13}\text{Al}$ (n, p) $^{27}_{12}\text{Mg}$, one employs the 0.842-MeV gamma ray emitted by $^{27}_{12}\text{Mg}$. Iron, if present in the sample, will undergo the reaction $^{56}_{26}\text{Fe}$ (n, p) $^{56}_{25}\text{Mn}$, which emits 0.847-MeV gamma rays. If a NaI(Tl) detector is used to detect the 0.842-MeV gamma rays, the two gamma rays cannot be resolved. Sometimes Type III interferences involve radionuclides with half-lives different from those of the desired elements, and can be resolved by the decay-curve method discussed previously.

One of the most important advantages of INAA over many other methods of analysis is that it is essentially nondestructive. Very often a complete analysis can be performed without appreciably altering the physical or chemical nature of the sample. This is important for several reasons. First, it may be imperative to preserve the sample, such as in forensic analysis where the sample is needed as evidence in a courtroom, or in the analysis of lunar samples or works of art. Second, nondestructive analysis involves minimum sample manipulation and, therefore, a trace sample is not contaminated by reagents and containers as in conventional destructive wet-chemical techniques.

Neutron activation analysis has a high degree of sensitivity for the majority of elements. Trace-level determinations are routinely performed with reactors and can, in certain favorable cases, be performed with the other types of neutron sources. A very important advantage of neutron activation analysis over many other analytical methods is that simultaneous analyses of multi-component systems are easy to perform; many routine procedures are available to determine more than a dozen elements in a single small sample.

Practical Considerations in Neutron Activation Analysis

Figure 19.12 shows the block diagram of a complete NAA facility. As in any other analytical method, each step may introduce both random and determinate errors, degrading the overall precision and accuracy of the results. We will briefly examine each step and point out a few of the most important points that should be kept in mind.

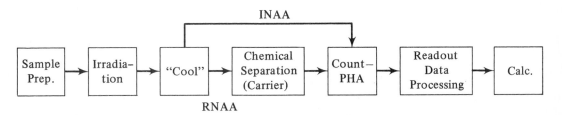

FIGURE 19.12. *Block diagram of a typical neutron-activation-analysis experiment.*

The sample may be solid, liquid, or gas, although the first two forms are most commonly used. Problems associated with sampling are the same as in any other method of analysis. Once the sample is secured, it is packaged in an appropriate container. An important point to keep in mind is that the sample and standards should be as similar as possible in matrix composition. For example, when analyzing rocks the sample is generally pulverized to a fine powder, and the standards are also preferably made from finely powdered standard rocks (such as those provided by the U.S. Geological Survey). An alternate standard could be prepared by evaporating an aliquot of a standard solution of the element on a matrix of high-purity SiO_2.

The size of the packaged samples should be as close to that of the standards as possible, so that self-absorption of the neutron flux does not introduce errors. When analyzing heterogeneous materials, complete mixing is very important. When irradiating organic materials, decomposition of the sample may occur; this is especially serious when high fluxes of neutrons are employed, since considerable heat may be generated inside the sample. The same problem occurs in the irradiation of aqueous solutions, where the build-up of pressure inside the container must be allowed for. Heat-sealed quartz vials are often used for reactor irradiations. If pressure build-ups are anticipated, the vials may be cooled to liquid-nitrogen temperatures before they are opened.

The irradiation assembly must provide the same neutron flux for both sample and standard, or appropriate correction factors must be determined. In addition to variations in the absolute magnitude of the thermal-neutron flux as a function of the position inside the nuclear reactor, the ratio of thermal-neutron and fast-neutron fluxes changes appreciably with position. This may result in serious errors caused by unwanted threshold reactions. When employing 14 MeV generators, time-dependent variations in the neutron flux may also become significant.

The optimum irradiation time is a very important factor in activation analysis. The decision is based on the specific nature of the sample and the type of information desired. Generally, two factors are considered. First, longer irradiation times increase the activity produced. However, Equation 19.37 shows that the factor $(1 - e^{-\lambda t_1})$ approaches unity as t_1 becomes large with respect to the half-life of the product radionuclide. Therefore, irradiation times in excess of 3–5 half-lives of the product desired result in little additional activity. Second, the longer the irradiation time, the greater will be the induced activities due to long-lived radionuclides that may interfere with the specific determination. (Of course, the higher the overall activity of the sample, the higher the health hazard and the more care must be used in handling it.) In general, irradiation times of approximately 3 half-lives of the product, but rarely more than one week total time, are used for conventional activation analysis.

It is often desirable to allow the irradiated specimen to decay for a period of time (cool) before counting. A suitable decay-period permits short-lived interfering activities to decay and, again, lessens the health hazard.

After the cooling period, the sample is either counted directly or some chemical manipulation is performed before counting. The first procedure is known as *instrumental neutron activation analysis* (INAA), whereas the latter is referred to as *radiochemical neutron activation analysis* (RNAA). In RNAA a stable *carrier* for the element to be determined may be added to the sample after irradiation. The carrier is equilibrated with the element in the sample (often by fusing it with Na_2O_2, or treating it with strong acid). Then the element of interest is separated along with the carrier. The chemical yield of the separation is determined from the amount of carrier recovered, and this correction is applied to the measured activity.

As mentioned earlier, in selecting the proper detector, the criteria used are detector efficiency and resolution. Where sensitivity is the overriding consideration, a NaI(Tl) detector is the detector of choice. If there are interferences, RNAA must be employed to eliminate them. In multi-element analyses of complex matrices, detector resolution becomes critical and Ge(Li) detectors should be used.

The electronic components needed for processing the detector signals have evolved into standardized modular units, and are relatively simple to select. One important factor when using multi-channel analyzers is the analyzer dead-time. Typically, a multi-channel analyzer receives a pulse, digitizes that pulse, and stores

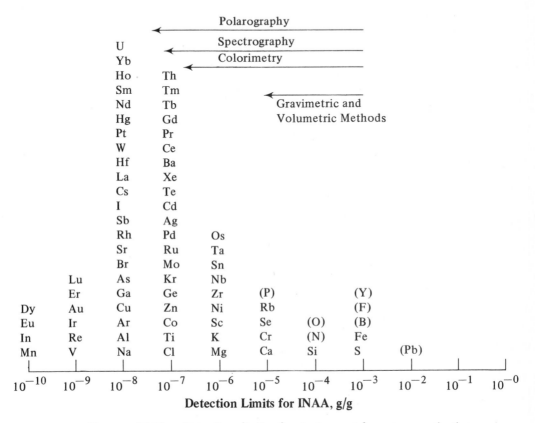

Detection Limits for INAA, g/g

FIGURE 19.13. *Detection limits for instrumental neutron activation analysis (INAA) compared to the usual sensitivity ranges for several commonly used analytical techniques. Elements listed in parentheses are determined by 14-MeV neutron activation with a flux density of 2×10^8 n/(cm²-sec) for a maximum irradiation time of 5 min, followed by NaI(Tl) gamma-ray spectrometry. Detection limits for all other elements are based on reactor irradiations of one hour or less at a flux density of 10^{13} n/(cm²-sec), followed by gamma-ray spectrometry using a 40 cm³ Ge(Li) detector. Sensitivities for many elements could be improved by several orders of magnitude by using longer irradiation times, positions of higher flux-density, or radiochemical separations. For example, Ir has been determined in rocks at levels well below 10^{-12} g/g (0.001 ppb) by long, high-flux reactor irradiations.*

it in the proper memory channel. During this time, the analyzer is *dead* to any incoming pulses. If the sample has a high activity level, this could result in an appreciable loss of counts. Most modern analyzers keep track of this *dead time* and automatically lengthen the counting time to compensate for its effect. This internal correction works best when the counting time is short compared to the half-life of the radionuclide of interest.

Figure 19.13 compares NAA with other commonly used analytical techniques. NAA, with its important advantage of high sensitivity for many elements and its inherent freedom from problems of reagent and laboratory contamination, is often the benchmark technique against which other trace-element techniques are measured. The increasing availability of inexpensive, easily housed, isotopic neutron sources and sealed-tube neutron generators can now put a "reagent bottle" of neutrons in even the most modest analytical laboratory.

Let us consider an example of an activation-analysis calculation:

> **Example 19.1.** We wish to determine the element vanadium in a 1.00 g sample of petroleum. We anticipate the vanadium content to be about 100 ppm by weight. A ^{252}Cf neutron source with a useful flux density of 2×10^7 n/(cm²-sec) is available, along with a detector system with a total FEP efficiency of 10.0% for the ^{52}V 1.43-MeV gamma ray. The 1.43-MeV gamma rays are emitted in 100% of the ^{52}V disintegrations. Calculate the number of counts that would be obtained for ^{52}V if the sample is irradiated to saturation and "cooled" for 2.00 min prior to counting for a period of 10.0 min.
>
> NUCLEAR DATA:
>
> Atomic mass of V $\quad = 50.94$ amu
> Natural abundance of ^{51}V $= 99.76\%$
> Cross section ^{51}V $\quad = 4.9$ barns
> Half-life of ^{52}V $\quad = 3.75$ min
> The nuclear reaction is ^{51}V (n, γ) ^{52}V
>
> CALCULATIONS: Combining Equations 19.37 and 19.40 and noting that if the sample is irradiated to saturation (a time long with respect to the half-life of ^{52}V) the term $(1 - e^{-\lambda t_i}) \sim 1$,
>
> $$\text{Counts} = \frac{\xi}{\lambda} \frac{W}{M} I \phi \sigma e^{-\lambda t_d}(1 - e^{-\lambda t_o})(6.02 \times 10^{23})$$
>
> $$\text{Counts} = \left(\frac{0.100}{0.693/[3.75 \text{ min } (60 \text{ sec/min})]}\right) \left(\frac{100 \times 10^{-6} \text{ g}}{50.94 \text{ g/g atom}}\right)$$
>
> $\qquad \times [6.0 \times 10^{23} \text{ atom/(g-atom)}](0.9976)[2 \times 10^7 \text{ n/(cm²-sec)}]$
> $\qquad \times (4.9 \times 10^{-24} \text{ cm}^2)(e^{-0.693(2.00 \text{ min})/3.75 \text{ min}})$
> $\qquad \times (1 - e^{-0.693(10.0 \text{ min})/3.75 \text{ min}})$
> $\qquad = 2,180$ counts recorded in counting period.

Assuming no interferences, this calculation shows that one could determine V in this sample at the 100 ppm level with a relative statistical error due to counting of less than 1% (see Sec. 19.5). Indeed, this method has been commonly employed by the petrochemical industry for the determination of vanadium in petroleum and its products.

Well over 10,000 papers dealing with activation analysis have appeared in the literature. Most of these (99%) have been published since 1955. Some of the more interesting applications have been determining potentially toxic trace elements in natural waters and environmental samples, authenticating paintings and other objects of art, and studying impurities in semiconductor materials, trace elements in plant and animal metabolism, and trace-element abundances in terrestrial rocks, meteorites, and lunar samples. In the analyses of lunar samples, more than twice as many trace-element determinations have been reported by activation analysis than by any other technique. In fact, the activation-analysis determinations on these rare samples probably exceed those by all other techniques combined.

14-MeV neutron activation analysis has been widely employed in the direct determination of oxygen in rocks and of nitrogen in food grains and explosives. Charged-particle activation analysis is useful in the analysis of thin films or coatings on metals.

Activation analysis is not without its own unique problems. However, for the determination of elements at the sub-ppm level it is certainly the technique against which other methods must be compared. Accuracy and precision of the order of a few percent are readily attainable at the nanogram level for many elements. High sensitivity, multi-element capability, and freedom from reagent and laboratory contamination problems are the major advantages offered.

19.5 METHODS INVOLVING ADDITION OF RADIONUCLIDE

The second general category of radiochemical analysis involves adding a radioactive substance to the sample, manipulating the sample by chemical or physical means, measuring the radioactivity, and ultimately calculating the amount of the component of interest. This category includes *direct and inverse isotope dilution analysis, radiochemical titrations,* and *radiorelease methods of analysis.*

Direct Isotope Dilution Analysis

In the method of activation analysis, radioactivity is induced in the sample to be analyzed. In the method of *direct isotope dilution analysis* (DIDA), a radioactive form of the component of interest is added to the sample. The component is then exhaustively purified without regard to quantitative recovery and a fraction of the pure component isolated. The amount and activity of the isolated component are measured and the quantity present in the original sample is calculated using that information.

Theory of DIDA. Consider a complex sample of W grams containing W_1 grams of the component of interest. To this sample is added W_1^* grams of a radioactive form of the component with a total activity A_1. W_2 grams of the pure component is then isolated; it contains both the active and the inactive forms and has an activity of A_2.

The *specific activity* SA_1 of the radioactive ("spike") material before it is mixed with the sample is defined as

$$SA_1 = \frac{A_1}{W_1^*} \tag{19.44}$$

and SA_2, the specific activity of the *recovered* component, as

$$SA_2 = \frac{A_2}{W_2} \tag{19.45}$$

SA_2 will remain constant regardless of how much of the pure component was isolated since it is activity per unit weight of recovered component. One can then write the following balance sheet:

	Weight of Component	*Specific Activity*
Before Mixing	W_1 (inactive form)	0
	W_1^* (active form)	SA_1
After Mixing but Before Purification	$W_1 + W_1^*$ (mixture)	SA_2
After Purification	$f(W_1 + W_1^*) = W_2$ (isolated component)	SA_2

Note that f is the fraction of the component recovered and is unknown. Also, note that the specific activity of the component of interest remains the same before and after purification. It follows that

$$W_1^* SA_1 = (W_1 + W_1^*) SA_2 \tag{19.46}$$

and solving this equation for W_1

$$W_1 = W_1^* \left(\frac{SA_1}{SA_2} - 1 \right) \tag{19.47}$$

The percentage of the component of interest in the original sample is then

$$\% \text{ Unknown} = 100 \frac{W_1^*}{W_1} \left(\frac{SA_1}{SA_2} - 1 \right) \tag{19.48}$$

Since W, W_1^*, and SA_1 are known and SA_2 can be determined experimentally, the amount of the component of interest in the original mixture can be easily calculated.

> **Example 19.2.** A dilute aqueous solution (density $= 1.000$ g/ml) is to be analyzed for its I^- content. A 50-ml aliquot of the solution is available for analysis.
>
> PROCEDURE: An aliquot of a standard solution of $^{129}_{53}I^-$ tracer is added to the 50.0 ml of solution. The standard solution added is known to contain 0.00500 mg of I^- and has an activity of 3120 counts per minute. To the resultant mixture is added an aliquot of a standard $AgNO_3$ solution sufficient to precipitate only 0.0100 mg of I^-. The precipitate obtained is then filtered and counted. Its activity is found to be 347 counts per minute.

CALCULATIONS:

$$SA_1 = \frac{3120 \text{ cpm}}{0.00500 \text{ mg}} = 6.24 \times 10^5 \text{ cpm/mg}$$

$$SA_2 = \frac{347 \text{ cpm}}{0.0100 \text{ mg}} = 3.47 \times 10^4 \text{ cpm/mg}$$

Therefore, using Equation 19.47,

$$W_{I^-} = 0.00500 \text{ mg} \left(\frac{6.24 \times 10^5 \text{ cpm/mg}}{3.47 \times 10^4 \text{ cpm/mg}} - 1 \right)$$

$$= 0.085 \text{ mg I}^-$$

and ppm $I^- = \dfrac{0.085 \text{ mg I}^- \times 10^{-3} \text{ g/mg}}{50.0 \text{ ml} \times 1.000 \text{ g/ml}} \times 10^6$

$$= 1.7 \text{ ppm}$$

In the conventional gravimetric method, it would have been necessary to quantitatively precipitate the I^- present and to weigh the precipitate (less than 0.1 mg). The only precautions in the present method are that all of the Ag^+ added should be used to precipitate AgI, and that all of the AgI be collected. If other species are precipitated (for instance, AgCl), the precipitate should be separated and purified before measuring its activity.

Advantages and Limitations of DIDA. In wet-chemical analyses, exhaustive multi-step purification procedures are often required to obtain the component in a highly pure form, and a quantitative yield is almost impossible to achieve. The main advantage of DIDA is that no quantitative separation of the component of interest is necessary. The instrumentation required is usually quite simple, since measurements of gross activity with simple counting systems are sufficient. The separated component must be in highly pure form; and once the pure component is obtained, its quantity must be accurately measured, or deduced from stoichiometric considerations. The separated component must also have a high enough level of activity to minimize statistical counting error. (This is usually not a serious limitation, since the activity of the initial labeled compound can often be adjusted to compensate for a low efficiency in the purification step.) The weight W_1^* should not be much larger than W_1, and tracer solutions of high specific activity are ordinarily used.

A very important effect, which could become either an advantage or a disadvantage, is inherent in the fundamental requirement of the method: both the active and inactive forms behave identically in the subsequent purification steps. This means either that the labeled component must be in the same chemical form as the inactive component, or that the mixture must be treated chemically to convert both forms into the same chemical compound. This situation can, of course, be of great advantage if one is trying to distinguish among different chemical forms of a given element. For instance, a solution containing both Cr^{3+} and $Cr_2O_7^{2-}$ can be analyzed for $Cr_2O_7^{2-}$ by adding $^{51}Cr_2O_7^{2-}$ tracer and excess NaOH, after which Ba^{2+} is added to precipitate $BaCrO_4$.

Inverse Isotope Dilution Analysis

In DIDA, a radioactive form of the component of interest is added to the sample and the quantity of the inactive form initially present is determined. In some instances, one may wish to determine the amount of a radioactive substance in the sample. A method similar in principle to DIDA can then be used wherein a quantity of an inactive form of the component of interest is added to the sample, the sample is purified without regard to quantitative recovery, and the amount of the recovered component and its activity are measured. From this information, the quantity of the radioactive substance initially present in the sample is calculated. This method is referred to as *inverse isotope dilution analysis* (IIDA).

Theory of IIDA. Let W_1^* and SA_1 be the weight and specific activity, respectively, of the radioactive substance initially present in the sample. W_1 grams of an inactive form of the component is added, and some fraction of the pure component, having specific activity SA_2, is recovered. Writing the balance sheet for this situation:

	Weight of Component	*Specific Activity*
Before Mixing	W_1^* (active form)	SA_1
	W_1 (inactive form)	0
After Mixing but Before Purification	$W_1 + W_1^*$ (mixture)	SA_2
After Purification	$f(W_1 + W_1^*) = W_2$ (isolated component)	SA_2

Note that f is less than unity and that SA_2 is the same before and after purification. Then

$$SA_2(W_1 + W_1^*) = SA_1(W_1^*) \tag{19.49}$$

Although SA_1 is not known, the product $SA_1(W_1^*)$ can be measured; this is the total activity of the component in the sample before any processing. Therefore,

$$SA_2(W_1 + W_1^*) = A_1 \tag{19.50}$$

and

$$W_1^* = \left(\frac{A_1}{SA_2}\right) - W_1 \tag{19.51}$$

Since $SA_2 = A_2/W_2$, where A_2 is the total activity of the recovered pure sample and W_2 is the weight of recovered sample,

$$W_1^* = \left(\frac{A_1}{A_2}\right)W_2 - W_1 \tag{19.52}$$

Advantages and Limitations of IIDA. The main advantage of this method is that one can determine the quantity of a specific radioactive component of a sample without comparing it with a known radioactive standard. The method also avoids preparing standards with the same matrix as the sample in order to assure equivalent counting efficiencies. However, the method cannot be applied if spectral interferences prevent the specific measurement of A_1. Furthermore, the method is applicable only when W_1 does not differ greatly from W_1^*. In the case of trace analysis, the method offers the advantage of not requiring a quantitative separation of the component of interest. The method of IIDA has not been applied as widely as has DIDA.

Radiometric Titrations

All titrimetric methods of analysis require some means of detecting the equivalence point. This could be an abrupt change of color (colorimetric titrations), a sudden change in the potential difference between two electrodes (potentiometric titrations), a change in current flow through two electrodes (amperometric titrations), and so on. Similarly, the radioactivity of either the titrant or the substance titrated can be employed for detecting the equivalence point. This type of analysis is called *radiometric titration*. It should be noted that the sole purpose of the radioactivity is to signal attainment of the equivalence point and that it takes no part in the titration process. The technique can be employed in all classes of titrations, provided that a phase separation can be effected.

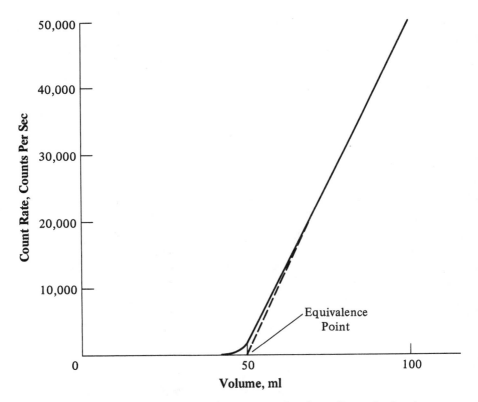

FIGURE 19.14. *Theoretical titration curve for the radiometric titration of 0.001 M Cl$^-$ with a solution of 0.001 M Ag$^+$ spiked with ^{110}Ag.*

The most straightforward application is in precipitation titrations, where the phase separation occurs spontaneously. In order to understand the method, consider the titration of 50 ml of a 0.001 M Cl$^-$ solution with a 0.001 M solution of $^{110}_{47}$Ag$^+$, with an activity of 1×10^9 dps/mol. The reaction is

$$\text{Ag}^+ + \text{Cl}^- \rightleftharpoons \text{AgCl} \downarrow \qquad (19.53)$$

with $K_{sp} = 1.82 \times 10^{-10}$. The activity of the supernatant is monitored after equilibrium has been reached following each incremental volume of added titrant. Prior to the endpoint, the supernatant has very little activity because almost all of the radioactive silver is present as precipitated AgCl. The theoretical activity of the supernatant at any point in the titration can easily be calculated from mass-action principles and the K_{sp} for silver chloride. The data for this titration are plotted in Figure 19.14. The equivalence point is the intercept of the two straight-line portions of the curve.

A typical experimental arrangement for precipitation titrations is shown in Figure 19.15. After each addition of titrant and attainment of equilibrium, an aliquot of the supernatant is drawn into the counting chamber and its activity measured. The solution is then ejected back into the titration vessel, and the next addition of titrant is made.

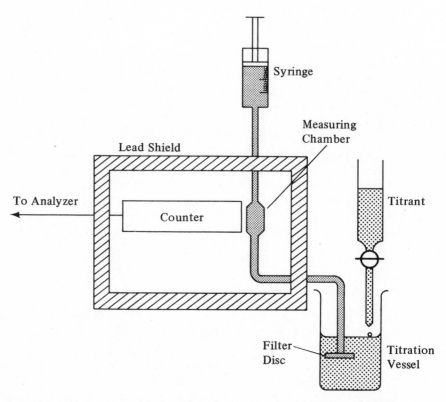

FIGURE 19.15. *A simple experimental set-up for radiometric titrations employing precipitation reactions.*

Advantages and Limitations of Radiometric Titrations. Radiometric detection of the equivalence point is a general method that does not depend on the chemical reaction employed. This contrasts with other methods of detection, which depend on specific chemical or physical transitions at the equivalence point. Amperometric titrations are applicable only to electrochemically active systems; conductometric titrations apply only to ionic solutions, and so on. In principle, any titration system in which a phase separation can be effected is amenable to radiometric detection, provided there exist suitable radioactive labels. The major limitation of the method is the requirement for phase separation. In precipitation titrations, the phase separation is automatic and the method is well suited to this class of titrations. For other classes of titrations, special phase-separation methods, such as solvent extraction, need to be applied. At the present time, the method suffers from a lack of phase-separation techniques suitable for continuous monitoring of the titration curves.

Radiorelease Methods of Analysis

This method is based on the chemical reaction of the constituent of interest with a radio-labeled reagent. The labeled component is then released either as a gas or in some readily extractable form. From a measurement of the amount of radioactivity released and the stoichiometry of the reaction, the quantity of the constituent of interest is determined. Consider the determination of SO_2 in air by this method. If air is passed through a basic solution of KI^*O_3, the following reaction takes place:

$$5\,SO_2 + 2\,KI^*O_3 + 4\,H_2O \longrightarrow K_2SO_4 + 4\,H_2SO_4 + I_2^* \qquad (19.54)$$

The solution is then acidified and the liberated I_2^* is extracted into chloroform. The chloroform phase is separated and counted for its I_2^* content. From the stoichiometry of the reaction and the quantity of liberated I_2^*, the content of SO_2 in air can be determined.

The chief advantage of this method of analysis is its sensitivity, since highly active radio-reagents are available. For instance, a micromole of I_2^* may easily have 10^7 dpm activity. However, the method is chemical in nature and suffers from all limitations inherent in the particular chemical reaction involved. In the above example, any other substance that can reduce KI^*O_3 to I_2^* will, of course, interfere with the determination (oxides of nitrogen are potential interferences). Furthermore, at trace levels quantitative extraction of the released species becomes critical.

19.6 STATISTICAL CONSIDERATIONS IN RADIOCHEMICAL ANALYSIS

In reporting the results of any analysis, two important parameters are the accuracy and the precision of the data. Accuracy is a measure of how close the reported data are to the true values. Precision, on the other hand, is only a measure of how closely one can expect to reproduce the reported data, if the experiment is repeated. Good precision does not necessarily imply accurate results. A discussion of these factors can be found in most books on quantitative analysis. However, since radioactive counting follows a different distribution law than do most other analytical manipulations, calculations of the precision of radiochemical methods require a knowledge

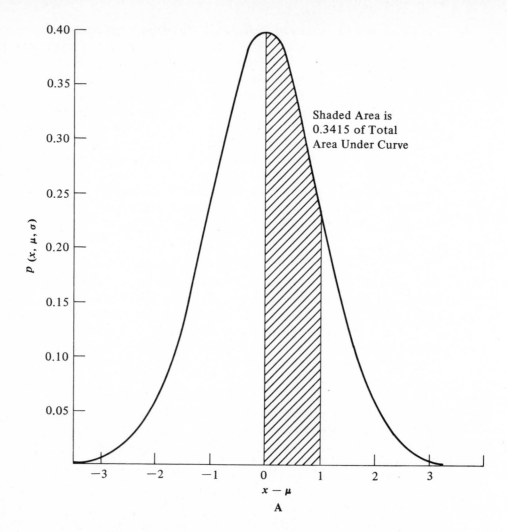

Shaded Area is
0.3415 of Total
Area Under Curve

$x - \mu$

A

FIGURE 19.16.   *Probability curves.   (A) The normal distribution curve for σ = 1.0.   (B, opposite) Poisson distribution curves for μ = 5.0 and μ = 10.0.*

of this distribution.   In this section the distribution law involved will be presented, and the calculations compared with those of most other types of analysis.

It is generally accepted that random errors arising in various analytical operations, except radioactive counting, follow a normal distribution, described by the normal distribution function (see Fig. 19.16A)

$$P_{(x,\mu,\sigma)} = \frac{1}{\sqrt{2\pi}\sigma} e^{-1/2[(x-\mu)/\sigma]^2} \qquad (19.55)$$

where μ = the true mean of the population*
          x = an individual measurement

---

* The true mean of a population is the quantity obtained if a given measurement is repeated an infinite number of times and the results averaged, assuming no determinate errors.

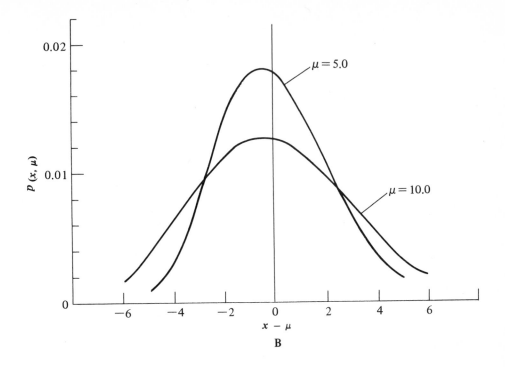

$\sigma =$ the *standard deviation* of the distribution function

$p =$ the probability of obtaining the value x in a single trial

Practically speaking, σ is a measure of the broadness of the curve in Figure 19.16A; a total of 68.3% of the entire area under the curve falls within $\pm 1\sigma$ of the value of the mean (which, in this case, is the same as the most probable value).

In practice, a finite number (n) of measurements are made, all of which would be identical were it not for the random errors involved in each measurement. From this finite (and often small) set of measurements, one estimates the most probable value of the function by averaging the experimental results. The question is: if another single measurement were made, how close would this last measurement be to the mean of the previous measurements? The answer, of course, is that this depends on the broadness of the distribution function for these measurements, as well as on the degree of confidence to be placed on the answer. For this purpose, one calculates the *standard deviation of the individual sample determination*, using

$$s_x = \sqrt{\frac{\sum (x_1 - \bar{x})^2}{n - 1}} \tag{19.56}$$

where $\bar{x} =$ the *average* or *mean* of the n individual measurements, $x_1, x_2, \ldots, x_1$

One would thus expect any other individual measurement to fall within $\mu \pm 1\,s_x$ in 68.3% of the measurements and within $\mu \pm 2\,s_x$ in 95.5% of such measurements. As can be seen, the greater the degree of confidence, the wider the range of possible values.

One can now ask, how close would one come to the first mean if one makes another set of measurements and calculates a new mean? To answer this, calculate the *standard deviation of the mean* using the following formula:

$$s_{\bar{x}} = \frac{s_x}{\sqrt{n}} \tag{19.57}$$

In contrast to most analytical operations, radioactive counting does not, in general, follow the normal distribution law. It follows the *Poisson distribution law*, an asymmetric distribution function described by

$$p(x, \mu) = \frac{\mu^x}{x!} e^{-\mu} \tag{19.58}$$

Figure 19.16B shows a typical Poisson distribution function. A very important distinction between this function and the normal distribution function is that, in order to characterize the latter, we must know both μ and σ because the broadness of the normal distribution is independent of its mean. In contrast, the Poisson distribution curve is completely characterized by its mean alone. The broadness of the distribution is a function of the mean, and is given by

$$\sigma_x = \sqrt{\mu} \tag{19.59}$$

For a finite set of measurements,

$$s_x = \sqrt{\bar{x}} \tag{19.60}$$

Thus, from only a single measurement (an estimate of the mean), the standard deviation can be estimated to be

$$s_x = \sqrt{x} \tag{19.61}$$

The standard deviation of the mean is, as before, given by Equation 19.57. As the magnitude of μ (or its estimator $\bar{x}$) increases, the portion of the Poisson distribution curve close to its mean becomes more symmetrical, and resembles more closely the normal distribution curve. Therefore, only for large values of $\bar{x}$ can one assume that the statistics of radioactive counting follow the normal distribution law, and then only as an approximation.

Propagation of Errors

Most radiochemical procedures consist of a number of measurement steps. In each step, random errors can occur which will contribute in different degrees to the uncertainty of the final result. One can therefore estimate the uncertainty of the final result, given estimates of the uncertainty of each step. Assume that two measurements or two steps with numerical values $A \pm \sigma_A$ and $B \pm \sigma_B$, yield the result $C \pm \sigma_C$. If $C = A + B$, or $C = A - B$, then

$$\sigma_C = \sqrt{\sigma_A{}^2 + \sigma_B{}^2} \tag{19.62}$$

If $C = AB$ or $C = A/B$, then

$$\sigma_C = C\sqrt{\left[\frac{\sigma_A}{A}\right]^2 + \left[\frac{\sigma_B}{B}\right]^2} \tag{19.63}$$

In combining the uncertainties, each step is assumed to have the same error distribution function, so that σ_C also has the same function. This is generally true for most analytical operations. However, when combining measurements of radioactivity with measurements such as weighing that follow the normal distribution function, one cannot always obtain a meaningful error distribution in the manner indicated above (this is analogous to adding apples to oranges!). However, if the specific Poisson distribution being considered does approximate a normal distribution, it is approximately correct to pool the standard deviations in this way. In addition, if one or more steps contribute predominantly to the uncertainty of the complete analysis, one can safely calculate error based on the uncertainty of only those steps.

SELECTED BIBLIOGRAPHY

BRAUN, T., and TÖLGYESSY, J. *Radiometric Titrations*. New York: Pergamon Press, 1967. *This book is the only authoritative book on the subject of radiometric titrations. A detailed and up-to-date account of both theoretical and experimental aspects of this subject is given.*

EHMANN, W. D. "Nondestructive Techniques in Activation Analysis," *Fortsch. Chem. Forsch.*, 14(1), 49 (1970). *This is a general article on the technique of nondestructive neutron activation analysis with major emphasis on 14-MeV neutrons. Practical aspects of this area as well as some advanced developments are discussed.*

FRIEDLANDER, G.; KENNEDY, J. W.; and MILLER, J. M. *Nuclear and Radiochemistry*, 2nd ed. New York: John Wiley and Sons, 1964. *This is a standard senior-level textbook on principles of nuclear chemistry and radiochemistry.*

HOLDEN, N. E., and WALKER, F. W. *Chart of the Nuclides, Physical Constants and Conversion Factors and Table of Equivalents*, General Electric Company, Atomic Power Equipment Department, 175 Curtner Avenue, San Jose, CA 95125. *An inexpensive ($1.00) compilation of nuclear data in a paperback format. The booklet is revised periodically. The most recent edition is dated October, 1970.*

KRUGER, P. *Principles of Activation Analysis*. New York: Wiley-Interscience, 1971. *A senior-level textbook covering various aspects of neutron activation analysis in fair depth.*

KRUGERS, J., ed. *Instrumentation in Applied Nuclear Chemistry*. New York: Plenum Press, 1973. *This is a comprehensive in-depth treatment of all aspects of nuclear instrumentation.*

LUTZ, G. J.; BORENI, R. J.; MADDOCK, R. S.; and WING, J. *Activation Analysis: A Bibliography Through 1971*. Technical Note 467. Washington, D.C.: U.S. Department of Commerce, National Bureau of Standards, 1972. *This document contains a thorough list of publications relating to activation analysis. It is periodically updated by NBS and is the most thorough source of activation analysis literature.*

MEINKE, W. W. "Is Radiochemistry the Ultimate in Trace Analysis?" *Pure Appl. Chem.*, 34, 93 (1973). *This article points out the advantages of activation analysis, as compared to other widely used methods of analysis for trace elements. Practical experience at the National Bureau of Standards is cited.*

PROBLEMS

1. A ^{252}Cf isotopic neutron-source is available that provides a flux density of 2.0×10^7 n/(cm²-sec) at the irradiation positions. The aluminum content of 1.0-gram alloy samples is to be determined by the ^{27}Al (n, γ) ^{28}Al reaction; a counting rate of at least 100 counts per minute at the start of the counting period is required for these determinations. Using the following data, calculate the minimum aluminum content that could be determined in these alloys by this technique: (1) ^{28}Al is a negatron and gamma-ray emitter that emits one 1.78-MeV gamma ray per disintegration. (2) Half-life of ^{28}Al = 2.3 min. (3) Cross-section of ^{27}Al for the (n, γ) reaction = 0.24 barns. The natural isotopic abundance of ^{27}Al is 100% and its atomic mass is 26.98. (4) The overall efficiency of the counting system is 10%, based on the 1.78-MeV gamma-ray FEP. (5) The sample is irradiated to saturation (the time of irradiation is long with respect to the half-life of ^{28}Al) and "cooled" 2 min prior to the start of counting.

2. The radionuclide $^{16}_{7}$N emits a high-energy gamma ray at 6.13 MeV. A gamma-ray spectrum of a $^{16}_{7}$N source exhibits peaks at 5.62 MeV, 5.11 MeV, and 0.511 MeV in addition to the FEP at 6.13 MeV and the usual Compton distribution. Assuming these features are not due to primary gamma rays emitted in the decay of $^{16}_{7}$N, how would you explain the existence of these three extra peaks?

3. A sample containing both Mn and Fe was irradiated with neutrons in a nuclear reactor for a period of 50 hours. The radionuclides ^{56}Mn and ^{59}Fe were formed by (n, γ) reactions on 100% natural-isotopic-abundance ^{55}Mn and 0.33% natural-isotopic-abundance ^{58}Fe. At the end of the irradiation the absolute activity ratio, ^{56}Mn activity/^{59}Fe activity, was observed to be 10^5. Using the following data, calculate the weight ratio (grams Mn/grams Fe) of the elements in the sample. (1) Cross-section for (n, γ) reactions: ^{55}Mn = 13.3 barns; ^{58}Fe = 1.2 barns. (2) Atomic masses: Mn = 54.94 amu; Fe = 55.85 amu. (3) Half-lives: ^{56}Mn = 2.57 hours; ^{59}Fe = 45 days.

4. A sample of sea water (density ≈ 1.00 g/ml) is to be analyzed for its I$^-$ content. A 5-ml aliquot is placed in an electrolytic cell, to which is added 5 ml of a mixture of 0.1 M sodium acetate and 0.1 M acetic acid as supporting electrolyte, plus 1.0 ml of a solution of K^{129}I containing 1.0 μg of iodide with a specific activity of 312,000 cpm/μg I$^-$. An identical cell containing only the supporting electrolyte plus 1.0 ml of K^{129}I is also prepared. The two cells are placed in series, and a potential of -100 mV with respect to a saturated calomel electrode is imposed on two silver electrodes acting as the anodes for each cell. After ten minutes the activity of the two anodes is measured to be 20,800 and 104,000 cpm. Assuming that the current efficiency of the two cells for deposition of I$^-$ is the same, calculate the I$^-$ concentration in the sea water in ppm.

5. A sample containing N_0 atoms of $^{38}_{17}$Cl (Half-life = 37.3 min) was received at 1200 hours for beta counting. It was placed in a liquid scintillation-counter with 100% efficiency at 1230 hrs and counted for exactly 60 min. The accumulated counts were 100,000. Calculate N_0.

6. A 50-ml solution of 1.00 mM Ag$^+$ is titrated with a 1.0 mM solution of K$_2$-^{51}CrO$_4$ (Half-life = 27.8 days) with an activity of 1.00×10^7 dps/mol. Plot the anticipated radiometric titration curve.

7. With reference to a *Chart of the Nuclides*, discuss the various neutron-activation-analysis techniques that might be used to determine Ni at the mg level. What neutron sources could be used? What nuclear reactions would be involved? What are the relative advantages and disadvantages of the various approaches to this determination?

8. Rapid analyses for Co in steel are often done by isotope dilution analysis. Assume that a 1.00-gram sample of steel is dissolved in acid and that exactly 2 ml of a "spike" solution of ^{60}Co is added to the solution. The spike solution has a concentration of 3 mg of Co/ml and a specific activity of 1.50×10^4 dpm/mg Co. Two electrodes are immersed in the solution and a small amount of Co$_2$O$_3$ plated out on the anode. The weight increase of the anode is determined to be 12.5 mg and its activity is 2500 dpm. Calculate the percent of Co in the steel sample.

9. A 2.00-min background count for a given counter yielded 3600 counts. A radioactive sample was counted for 2.00 min with the same counter and a total of 6400 counts were recorded. Calculate the background-corrected counting rate for the sample and its standard deviation, s_x. Express the counting rate in units of counts per minute.

10. Sample A, sample B, and background alone were each counted for 10 min with a given counter. The observed counting rates were 110, 205, and 44 counts per minute, respectively. Calculate the ratio of the activity of sample A to that of sample B and determine the standard deviation of this ratio.

11. Carbon-14, a β emitter with a half-life of 5720 years, is produced in the atmosphere by the reaction $^{14}N(n, p)^{14}C$, the neutrons coming from cosmic rays. The dating is based on the assumption that the amount of ^{14}C in the atmosphere (the ratio of $^{14}C/^{12}C$) remains constant over thousands of years. A living species incorporates this same ratio in all its carbon-containing molecules. When it dies, the incorporation of ^{14}C ceases, and the ^{14}C decays. The $^{14}C/^{12}C$ ratio determined from a wood sample taken from a dugout canoe at the bottom of a lake was found to be one-tenth the ratio determined from a wood sample less than 1 year old. How old is the dugout canoe?

12. One gram of pure radium emits 3.70×10^{10} disintegrations per second (1 curie). (a)

How many atoms of radium are decaying each second? (b) How long will it take before half of the radium atoms have disintegrated?

13. Radon-222, the first decay product of ^{226}Ra, is an alpha-particle emitter with a 3.82 day half-life. A sample of ^{222}Rn gas was found to have an activity of 2.22×10^6 disintegrations per minute. (a) What is its activity in microcuries? (b) What is the decay constant in sec^{-1}? (c) How many atoms of ^{222}Rn does the sample contain? (d) How many grams? (1 curie = 3.70×10^{10} dps.)

14. Sodium-24 is a beta-particle emitter with a half-life of 14.8 hours. Calculate the activity in curies of a 20-mg sample of NaCl enriched with ^{24}Na so that it contains 1 atomic percent of ^{24}Na. (1 curie = 3.70×10^{10} dps.)

15. The neutron-activation-analysis limit of detection for arsenic is listed as 2×10^{-10} g for 1-hour irradiation in a neutron flux of 10^{13} n/(cm^2 sec). Using the value of 4.3×10^{-24} cm^2 as the cross-section of the arsenic nucleus for neutron capture, calculate the disintegrations per second expected from ^{76}As after irradiation for this period of time.

16. For any given isotope, what period of neutron irradiation is required to raise the observed activity to one-half the maximum activity?

17. Derive the relationship between the average lifetime of a radioactive atom and its half-life.

20

Fractionation Processes: Solvent Extraction

Henry Freiser

Great strides have been made in the development of highly selective analytical methods. However, the analytical chemist is called upon nowadays to deal with increasingly complex samples; as a result, separation steps can be necessary even with highly selective instrumental methods such as neutron activation or atomic absorption. Furthermore, separation of a component of interest can also concentrate it, which effectively increases the sensitivity of the analytical technique ultimately used. Although separation procedures are often not, strictly speaking, instrumental techniques, they frequently comprise an integral part of an instrumental procedure, and in fact may be incorporated into an instrumental design. Because of their importance, solvent extraction and chromatographic techniques are covered in the next three chapters.

20.1 PHASE PROCESSES

One of the most powerful approaches to separations involves pairs of phases in which the component of interest transfers from one phase to the other more readily than do interfering substances. For all phase-distribution equilibria, the classical phase rule of Gibbs is applicable and useful. The phase rule

$$P + V = C + 2 \tag{20.1}$$

relates the number of independent variables (degrees of freedom) V needed to describe a system of C components with a number of phases P that can coexist in equilibrium with one another. Note that a *component* is not the same as a *chemical species*; a two-component mixture of NaCl and H_2O contains the following species: H^+, OH^-, Na^+, Cl^-, H_2O, and NaCl.

The degrees of freedom include both temperature and pressure. Hence, in systems containing only condensed phases (liquids or solids) whose properties are only slightly affected by pressure changes, the phase rule reduces to

$$P + V = C + 1 \qquad (20.2)$$

It is useful to classify phase-separation processes according to the following criteria:

1. the states of the phases involved (solid, liquid, or gas)
2. whether the phase is in bulk or spread thin as on a surface
3. the manner in which the two phases are brought into contact (batch, multi-stage, or counter-current)

Bulk and "thin" phases can be distinguished by the fact that, in the latter, the phase involved spreads out over a relatively large area. Thus, both distillation and gas-liquid chromatography (GC) are separations involving a gas and a liquid phase, but in the latter the liquid phase is spread out as a thin layer on a largely inert solid supporting material, in the form of a column. Similarly, solvent extraction and liquid-partition chromatography (either paper or column) involve two liquid phases, but, in the latter, one of the liquid phases is present as a supported thin layer. In these examples, the mode of contacting the phases can also be different. In a simple distillation process, a batch of the mixture is heated in the boiler and the distillate consists of the more volatile components. In contrast, in GC the gas mixture moves in a *counter-current* manner to the immobilized liquid layer, insuring that the increasingly depleted, mobile gas phase encounters a fresh, clean portion of the immobilized liquid phase. In counter-current processes, a component comes—or almost comes—to equilibrium between two phases many times. It is possible to carry out separations using pairs of *bulk* phases which undergo counter-current contact. Thus, fractional distillation, in which a packed distillation column and reflux head are used, involves counter-current contact.

The focus of this chapter will be the chemistry of solvent extraction and its use as a separation process, particularly altering the chemical parameters of an extraction system in order to bring about the desired separation in a single step. The following two chapters will describe in more detail the principles and applications of chromatographic processes (in which a large number of equilibrium steps occur), in contrast to the "batch" solvent extraction processes.

20.2 GENERAL PRINCIPLES AND TERMINOLOGY OF SOLVENT EXTRACTION

Solvent extraction enjoys a favored position among separation techniques because of its ease, simplicity, speed, and wide scope. Separation by extraction can usually be accomplished in a few minutes using a simple pear-shaped separatory funnel (Fig. 20.1), and is applicable both to trace-level impurities and to major constituents. Furthermore, inorganic constituents are often separated in a form suitable for direct analysis by spectrophotometric, atomic absorption, radiochemical, or other methods.

FIGURE 20.1. *Separatory funnel.*

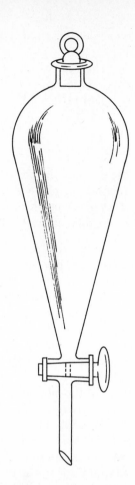

In solvent extraction, a solute of interest transfers from one solvent into a second solvent that is essentially immiscible with the first. The extent of transfer can be varied from negligible to essentially total extraction through control of the experimental conditions.

All solvent-extraction procedures can be described in terms of three aspects, or steps:

1. *The distribution of the solute*, called the extractable complex or species, *between the two immiscible solvents*. This step can be quantitatively described by Nernst's distribution law, which states that the ratio of the concentrations of a solute distributing between two essentially immiscible solvents at constant temperature is a constant, provided that the solute is not involved in chemical interactions in either solvent phase (other than solvation). That is,

$$K_D = \frac{[A]_0}{[A]} \tag{20.3}$$

where $[A]_0$ = the molar concentration of solute A in organic solvent
          $[A]$ = the concentration of solute A in aqueous solution
          K_D = the distribution constant or distribution coefficient of A

2. *Chemical interactions in the aqueous phase or formation of the extractable complex.* Inasmuch as most of the substances of interest, particularly metal ions, are not usually encountered in a form that can be directly extracted into an organic solvent, chemical transformations to produce an extractable species are of primary importance in solvent-extraction processes.

3. *Chemical interactions in the organic phase*, such as self-association or mixed-ligand-complex formation. Such chemical interactions do not invalidate the Nernst distribution law (Eqn. 20.3), but the extraction cannot be quantitatively described by that simple equation. It becomes necessary to know how each of the contributing reactions affects the extent of extraction.

The extent of extraction is described in terms of the *distribution ratio, D,* given by

$$D_A = \frac{C_{A(0)}}{C_A} \tag{20.4}$$

where $C_{A(0)}$ = the *total analytical concentration* of component A (in whatever chemical form) in the organic phase
C_A = the total analytical concentration of A in the aqueous phase

If the substance does not undergo chemical reactions in either phase, then D_A reduces to K_D.

Another important way of expressing the extent of extraction is by the *fraction extracted F*, which is

$$F_A = \frac{C_{A(0)}V_0}{C_{A(0)}V_0 + C_A V} = \frac{D_A R_V}{D_A R_V + 1} \tag{20.5}$$

where V_0 = the volume of the organic phase
V = the volume of the aqueous phase
R_V = the *phase-volume ratio,* V_0/V

The *percentage extraction* is simply 100F. The fraction remaining in the aqueous phase, G_A, is

$$G_A = \frac{1}{D_A R_V + 1} = 1 - F_A \tag{20.6}$$

Equation 20.5 shows that for a given value of D, the extent of extraction can be increased by increasing the phase-volume ratio—that is, by increasing the volume of the organic phase. Another way of increasing the fraction extracted is to extract several times using only part of the total volume of organic solvent at a step. With $D_A R_V = 10$, the fraction extracted in a single batch-extraction is about 0.90. Two extractions with $R_V/2$ increases the fraction extracted to about 0.97; three extractions with $R_V/3$ increases it to 0.99—essentially quantitative extraction.

Consider two substances, A and B, present in a solution. Initially, the concentration ratio is C_A/C_B; after extraction, the concentration ratio in the organic phase will be $C_A F_A/C_B F_B$, where F_A and F_B are the corresponding fractions extracted. The ratio F_A/F_B (the factor by which the initial concentration ratio is changed by the separation) is a measure of the *separation* of the two substances. A corollary measure of separation is G_A/G_B, the change in the ratio of concentrations remaining in the aqueous phase.

Two substances whose distribution ratios differ by a constant factor will be most effectively separated if the product $D_A D_B$ is unity. For instance, consider a pair of substances whose distribution ratios D_A and D_B are 10^3 and 10^1, respectively. If these substances were present in equal quantity, then a single extraction would remove 99.9% of the first and 90% of the second. However, if the two distribution ratios were 10^1 and 10^{-1} (again differing by a factor of 100), the respective fractions extracted would be 90% of A and 10% of B, a much more effective separation.

Classification of Extraction Systems: Organic and Inorganic

The following classification refers essentially to inorganic systems, particularly those involving metal ions. Many organic compounds, of course, are extractable without any significant chemical reaction occurring—for instance, alcohols, ethers, carboxyl compounds, and so on. Systematic changes in the extraction of such compounds by various solvents can be related to the degree of hydrogen bonding and to other, less specific, interactions of the organic compounds, as well as to their molecular weights.

Most metal salts are soluble in water but not in organic solvents, particularly hydrocarbons and chlorinated hydrocarbons. This solubility is caused by the high dielectric constant of water and by its ability to coordinate with ions, especially metal ions, so that the hydrated salt more nearly resembles the solvent. To form a metal complex that can be extracted by an organic solvent, it is necessary to replace the coordinated water around the metal ion by groups, or ligands, that will form an uncharged species compatible with the low-dielectric-constant organic solvent.

Extractable metal species can be formed in a great variety of ways. A classification system of metal extractions is therefore very useful, particularly as a guide to understanding the hundreds of different extraction systems now in use. Methods for forming an extractable species include:

1. *Simple* (monodentate) *coordination* alone, as with $GeCl_4$.

2. *Heteropoly acids*, a class of coordination complexes in which the central ion is complex rather than monatomic, as with phosphomolybdic acid, $H_3PO_3 \cdot 12MoO_3$.

3. *Chelation* (polydentate coordination) alone, as with $Al(8\text{-quinolinate})_3$.

4. *Ion-association* alone, as with $Cs^+, (C_6H_5)_4B^-$ (the comma is used to indicate association between the two ions).

Combinations of the above can be used, such as

5. *Simple coordination and ion-association*, as with $(\text{"Onium"})^+, FeCl_4^-$. "Onium" stands for one of the following cation types: hydrated hydronium ion, $(H_2O)_3H^+$, a rather labile cation requiring stabilization by solvation with an oxygen-containing solvent; a substituted ammonium ion, $R_nNH_{(4-n)}^+$, where R is an alkyl or aralkyl group and n may vary from 1 to 3; a substituted phosphonium ion R_4P^+;

stibonium ion R_4Sb^+; sulfonium ion; and other ions of this sort, including cationic dyes such as Rhodamine B.

6. *Chelation and ion-association* with either positively or negatively charged metal chelates, such as $Cu(2,9\text{-dimethyl-1,10-phenanthroline})_2{}^+,ClO_4{}^-$ or $3(n\text{-}C_4H_9NH_3{}^+),Co(\text{Nitroso-R-Salt})_3{}^{3-}$.

7. *Simple coordination and chelation*, such as in $Zn(8\text{-quinolinol}\cdot\text{pyridine})$. This category is of significance for coordinatively unsaturated metal chelates—those with a monoprotic bidentate reagent in which the coordination number of the metal is greater than twice its valence.

The above classification is used in Table 20.1; clearly, a thorough understanding of solvent extraction of metals presupposes a deep knowledge of coordination chemistry.

Methods of Extraction

Generally, one has a choice of three methods of extraction: batch extraction, continuous extraction, and counter-current extraction. The choice is generally determined by the distribution coefficient of the substance extracted and, in the case where separation is desired, by the closeness of the various distribution coefficients involved. Because of the speed and simplicity of batch extraction, this method is preferred when applicable.

Batch Extraction. When experimental conditions can be adjusted so that the fraction extracted is 0.99 or higher ($DR_V \geq 100$), then a single or batch extraction will transfer the bulk of the desired substance to the organic phase. Most analytical extractions fall into this category. The usual apparatus for a batch extraction is a separatory funnel such as the Squibb pear-shaped funnel (Fig. 20.1), although many special types of funnels have been designed [1].

Even with DR_V equal to only 10, two successive batch extractions will transfer 99% of the material to the organic phase. If one chooses as a criterion of separation that substance A be at least 99% extracted and substance B no more than 1% extracted, then, from Equation 20.5, one must have $D_A R_V > 100$ and $D_B R_V < 0.01$ for a single (batch) extraction.

Continuous Extraction. For relatively small DR_V values, even multiple batch extraction cannot conveniently or economically be used—too much organic solvent is required. Continuous extraction using volatile solvents can be carried out in an apparatus in which the solvent is distilled from an extract-collection flask, condensed, contacted with the aqueous phase, and returned to the extract collection flask in a continuous fashion.

Counter-Current Distributions. A special multiple-contact extraction is needed to effect the separation of two substances whose D values are very similar. In principle, counter-current distribution (CCD) could be carried out in a series of separatory

TABLE 20.1. *Representative Metal-Extraction Systems, with Examples*

Primary Systems

I. Simple (Monodentate) Coordination Systems
    A. Certain Halide Systems: $HgCl_2$, $GeCl_4$
    B. Certain Nitrate Systems: $(UO_2)(TBP)_2(NO_3)_2$

II. Heteropoly Acid Systems: $H_3PO_4 \cdot 12MoO_3$

III. Chelate Systems   Reactive Grouping
    A. Bidentate Chelating Agents
        1. 4-Membered Ring Systems
            a. Disubstituted dithiocarbamates: Na^+, $S{=}C{-}S^-$
               $(C_2H_5)_2NCSS^-$ or $(C_6H_5CH_2)_2NCSS^-$
            b. Xanthates: Na^+, $C_2H_5OCSS^-$
            c. Dithiophosphoric acids: diethyldithio- $S{-}P{-}S^-$
               phosphoric acid
            d. Arsenic and arsonic acids: benzenarsonic $^-O{-}As{-}O^-$
               acid
        2. 5-Membered Ring Systems
            a. *N*-Nitroso-*N*-arylhydroxylamines: Cup- $O{=}N{-}N{-}O^-$
               ferron (*N*-nitrosophenylhydroxylamine)
            b. α-Dioximes: Dimethylglyoxime $N{=}C{-}C{=}N^-$
            c. Diaryldithiocarbazones: Dithizone $N{-}N{=}C{-}S^-$
               (diphenylthiocarbazone)
            d. 8-Quinolinols: Oxine (8-quinolinol), $N{=}C{-}C{-}O^-$
               methyloxine (2-methyl-8-quinolinol)
        3. 6-Membered Ring Systems
            a. β-Diketones: Acetylacetone, TTA $O{=}C{-}C{=}C{-}O^-$
               (thenoyltrifluoroacetone), Morin,
               quinalizarin
            b. *o*-Nitrosophenols: 1-nitroso-2-naphthol $O{=}N{-}C{=}C{-}O^-$
    B. Polydentate Chelating Systems: Pyridylazo- $N{=}C{-}N{=}N{-}C{=}C{-}O^-$
       naphthol (PAN) and pyridylazoresorcinol
       (PAR)

IV. Simple Ion-Association Systems
    A. Metal in Cation
        1. Inorganic anions: Cs^+, I_3^- or Cs^+, PF_6^-
        2. Tetraphenylboride anion

Mixed Systems

V. Ion-Association and Simple Coördination Systems
    A. Metal in Cation
        1. Oxygen Solvents (alcohols, ketones, esters,
            ethers): $[(UO_2)(ROH)_6]^{2+}, 2NO_3^-$
    B. Metal in Anion (paired with "onium" ion)
        1. Halides: $FeCl_4^-$

Continued

Table 20.1. *Continued*

2. Thiocyanates: $Co(CNS)_4^{2-}$
3. Oxyanions: MnO_4^-

VI. Ion-Association and Chelation Systems
  A. Cationic Chelates
    1. Phenanthrolines and polypyridyls: Cu(I)-
      $(2,9\text{-dimethylphenanthroline})_2^+$
  B. Anionic chelates
    1. Sulfonated Chelating Agents
      a. 1-Nitroso-2-naphthol: Co(III)(nitroso
        R Salt)$_3^{3-}$
      b. 8-Quinolinol: Fe(III)(7-iodo-8-quino-
        linol-5 sulfonate)$_3^{3-}$

VII. Chelation and Simple Coordination Systems:
  $Th(TTA)_4 \cdot TBP$, $Ca(TTA) \cdot (TOPO)_2$

funnels, each containing an identical lower phase. The mixture is introduced into the upper phase in the first funnel. After equilibration, the upper phase (containing the substance of interest) is transferred to the second funnel, and a new portion of upper phase (devoid of sample) is introduced into the first funnel. After both funnels are equilibrated, the upper phase of each is moved on to the next funnel, and a fresh portion of upper phase is again added to the first funnel. This process is repeated for as many times as there are funnels, or more, collecting the upper phases as "elution fractions." With automated CCD equipment, several hundred transfers can be conveniently accomplished, which will permit the separation of two solutes whose D_A/D_B ratio is less than two.

It can be shown that the distribution ratio D of a solute in a CCD process is related to the concentration in the various separatory funnels or stages by the binomial expansion

$$(F + G)^n = 1 \tag{20.7}$$

where n is the number of stages in the CCD process and F and G are given by Equations 20.5 and 20.6.

The fraction $T_{n(r)}$ of the solute present in the rth stage for n transfers can be calculated from

$$T_{n(r)} = \frac{n!}{r!(n-r)!} \frac{(DR_V)^r}{(1 + DR_V)^n} = \frac{n!}{r!(n-r)!} F^r G^{n-r} \tag{20.8}$$

The distribution of two solutes with differing distribution ratios in the tubes after different numbers of transfers is illustrated in Figure 20.2. As the number of transfers is increased, the solute is spread through a larger number of tubes. The separating ability, however, increases with increased number of transfers. After the run is complete, each tube is analyzed for the solute. In a preparative run, the contents of the tubes containing a particular solute are combined.

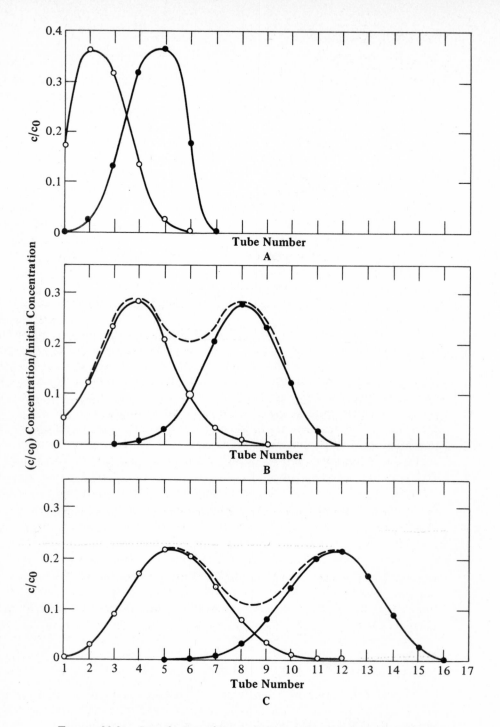

FIGURE 20.2. *Distribution of two solutes in counter-current distribution tubes after different numbers of transfers. The distribution ratio for the left peak is 7/3 and that for the right peak is 3/7. (A) After 5 transfers (n = 5); (B) After 10 transfers (n = 10); (C) After 15 transfers (n = 15). From H. Purnell,* Gas Chromatography, *New York: John Wiley, 1962, p 95, by permission of the publisher.*

20.3 EXPERIMENTAL TECHNIQUES

Selection of a particular extraction method from the large number of methods available involves considering the behavior of interfering substances that might be present, as well as that of the substance of interest. Another important factor is how the species in question is to be analytically determined after extraction. Some of the chelate systems (for instance, dithizone chelates) are strongly enough colored to provide the basis for a spectrophotometric determination. If the extract is to be aspirated into the flame of an atomic absorption apparatus, however, a dithizone solution is not as desirable as a nonbenzenoid reagent, because of its behavior in the flame.

The problem is greatly simplified by referring to the literature, from which one can choose a method on the basis of similarity or even exact matching of separation problems. One generally proceeds in a new situation by following published precedents, but a better understanding of the design of an extraction procedure can be obtained from a careful study of the *basis* of previous work.

Choice of Solvent

Solvents differ in polarity, density, and ability to participate in complex formation. Generally, it is more convenient to use a solvent denser than water when the substance of interest is being extracted and a less dense solvent when interferences are extracted away from the substance of interest. In the former case, this is because the (denser) phase containing the extracted substance of interest can be conveniently drained from a separatory funnel leaving behind the original solution; this can then be easily re-extracted if necessary. In the latter case, the (less dense) solvent containing the interferences can be left behind in the funnel. If multiple extractions are necessary to remove the interferences, however, it may be more convenient to use a solvent denser than water.

Ion-association complexes in which one of the ions is strongly solvated, such as the hydrated hydronium ion encountered in extracting chloride complexes from HCl solutions (for instance, $(H_2O)_3H^+,FeCl_4^-$), can be most effectively extracted with oxygen-containing solvents such as alcohols, esters, ketones, and ethers. Such solvents increase extractability significantly over that obtainable with hydrocarbon (or chlorinated hydrocarbon) solvents with coordinatively unsaturated chelates— that is, those in which the coordination number of the metal ion is greater than twice its oxidation state (e.g., $ZnOx_2$, where Ox refers to the 8-quinolinate (oxine) anion).

On the other hand, ion-association complexes involving quaternary ammonium, phosphonium, or arsonium ions, and coordinatively saturated chelates, can be readily extracted into hydrocarbons as well as into oxygenated solvents. In such cases, the principle of "like dissolves like," as expressed by the Hildebrand "solubility parameter" δ (defined as the heat of vaporization of one cm^3 of a liquid), offers a guide to extractability. Using this approach, the following expression can be derived:

$$2.3RT \log K_D = V_s(\delta_0 - \delta_w)(\delta_0 + \delta_w - 2\delta_s) \qquad (20.9)$$

where V_s = the molar volume of the solute
            δ_0 = the solubility parameter of the organic solvent
            δ_w = the solubility parameter of the aqueous phase
            δ_s = the solubility parameter of the distributing solute

A plot of K_D versus δ_0 is parabolic, with a maximum K_D for an organic solvent whose δ_0 matches δ_s. Simply expressed, in the absence of specific chemical interactions, a substance will be most extractable in a solvent whose δ value most closely matches its own. Thus, 8-quinolinine ($\delta = 10$) is more extractable into benzene ($\delta = 9.2$) than into CCl_4 ($\delta = 8.6$), and more into CCl_4 than into heptane ($\delta = 7.4$). The application of this principle is limited by the lack of known δ values for many extractable species.

It must not be assumed that the best solvent to use is always the one that gives the highest extractability, because a poorer solvent is often more selective for separations.

Stripping and Backwashing

Occasionally it is of advantage to remove (*strip*) the extracted solute from the organic phase into which it has been extracted as part of the analytical procedure. This is done by shaking the organic phase with a fresh portion of aqueous solution containing acids or other reagents that will decompose the extractable complex in the organic phase. The charged metal ion will then be extracted preferentially into the new aqueous solution.

The technique of *backwashing* also involves contacting the organic extract with a fresh aqueous phase. Here, the combined organic phases from multiple extraction of the original aqueous phase, which contain almost all the desired element and some of the impurities, are shaken with small portions of a fresh aqueous phase containing the same reagent concentrations initially present. Under these conditions, most of the desired element remains in the organic phase while the bulk of the impurities are back-extracted (backwashed) into the aqueous phase because of their lower distribution ratios.

Treatment of Emulsions

After shaking two immiscible liquids, a sharp phase boundary should rapidly reappear; therefore, emulsions should not be allowed to form. The tendency to form emulsions decreases with increasing interfacial tension. In liquids of relatively high mutual solubility or that contain surfactants, the interfacial tension is low and the tendency to form emulsions is correspondingly high. Low-viscosity solvents and solvents with densities significantly different from that of water are also helpful in avoiding emulsions. With systems that tend to form emulsions, repeated inversion of the two phases rather than vigorous shaking is called for. In an extreme case, using a continuous extractor rather than a separatory funnel is often successful. The tendency to form emulsions can be reduced by adding neutral salts or an anti-emulsion agent.

20.4 IMPORTANT EXPERIMENTAL VARIABLES

In addition to such important factors as the choice of organic solvent, the avoidance of emulsions, and the actual method of extraction—batch, continuous, or countercurrent—there are other important and easily controlled experimental variables. In the extraction of metals, the most important and critical of these are the pH of the aqueous solution and the use of masking agents. These two factors are often primarily responsible for the specificity (degree of separation) of an extraction method.

Chelate Extraction Systems

As seen from Table 20.1, many chelating extractants are weak acids and can be represented as HR. For a chelate extraction process

$$M^{n+} + nHR \text{ (org)} \rightleftharpoons MR_n \text{ (org)} + nH^+ \tag{20.10}$$

the distribution ratio, D_M, is given by

$$D_M = \frac{C_{M(0)}}{C_M} = \frac{[MR_n]_0}{[M^{n+}]/\alpha_M} = \frac{[MR_n]_0}{[M^{n+}]}\alpha_M \tag{20.11}$$

In this equation, $C_{M(0)} = [MR_n]_0$, since there is only one metal-containing species in the organic phase. In the aqueous phase there may be many metal-containing species in addition to M^{n+}, but these can be accounted for by using α_M, the fraction of the total metal concentration actually present as M^{n+},

$$\alpha_M = [M^{n+}]/C_M \tag{20.12}$$

The formation of the chelate MR_n is expressed by the formation constant

$$\beta_n = \frac{[MR_n]}{[M^{n+}][R^-]^n} \tag{20.13}$$

and the formation of the anion R^- from HR is quantitatively given by the acid-dissociation constant

$$K_a = \frac{[H^+][R^-]}{[HR]} \tag{20.14}$$

Incorporating these expressions as well as those for the distribution of the reagent HR and chelate MR_n (their distribution coefficients),

$$K_{D_R} = \frac{[HR]_0}{[HR]} \tag{20.15}$$

$$K_{D_C} = \frac{[MR_n]_0}{[MR_n]} = \alpha_n \text{ ?} \tag{20.16}$$

it can be seen that

$$D_M = \frac{[MR_n]_0}{[M^{n+}]}\alpha_M = \beta_n \frac{[MR_n]_0}{[MR_n]}[R^-]^n\alpha_M = \beta_n \frac{K_{D_C}K_a^n}{K_{D_R}^n}\frac{[HR]_0^n}{[H^+]^n}\alpha_M \tag{20.17}$$

The combination of constants (K_{D_C}, K_a, K_{D_R}) in Equation 20.17 is called the *overall extraction constant*, K_{ex}. Representative values of K_{ex} are listed in Table 20.2. The $pH_{1/2}$ values are explained below.

Equation 20.17 shows that the value of D_M increases with increasing concentration of the reagent in the organic phase, and decreases with increasing hydrogen-ion concentration in the aqueous phase. Control of pH is therefore important in

TABLE 20.2. *Values of Extraction Constants, K_{ex} and $pH_{1/2}$, in Selected Metal-Chelate Systems*

Metal Ion	8-Quinolinol (0.10 M in $CHCl_3$)		Dithizone (10^{-4} M in CCl_4)	
	log K_{ex}	$pH_{1/2}$	log K_{ex}	$pH_{1/2}$
Ag^+	——	6.5	7.18	-3.2
Al^{3+}	-5.22	2.87	Not extracted	
Ca^{2+}	-17.9	10.4	Not extracted	
Cd^{2+}	——	4.65	2.14	2.9
Cu^{2+}	1.77	1.51	10.53	-1.3
Fe^{3+}	4.11	1.00	Not extracted	
Pb^{2+}	-8.04	5.04	0.44	3.8
Zn^{2+}	——	3.30	2.3	2.8

chelate extractions. Inasmuch as the extractions of different metal ions with a given reagent are characterized by different extraction constants, the extraction curves (percent extracted versus pH) will be similar in shape, but displaced in pH. Figure 20.3 shows a typical set of extraction curves for various metal dithizonates. Note that, whereas the curves of all the divalent metal ions are parallel, those for Ag^+ and Tl^+ are less steep, because $n = 1$ in Equation 20.17. From the curve it can be

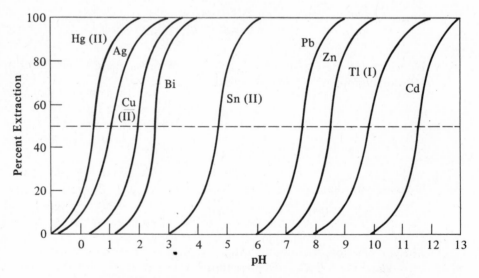

FIGURE 20.3. *Qualitative extraction curves for metal dithizonates. From G. H. Morrison and H. Freiser in C. L. Wilson and D. Wilson, eds.,* Comprehensive Analytical Chemistry, *vol. 1A, Amsterdam: Elsevier, 1959, by permission of the publisher.*

concluded that at pH = 2, Hg^{2+} is 100% extracted; Ag^+, Cu^{2+}, Bi^{3+} are fractionally extracted; and the other ions listed are not extracted at all. It would be simple to separate Hg^{2+} from Sn^{2+}, Pb^{2+}, Zn^{2+}, Tl^+, and Cd^{2+} in a mixture by extracting with dithizone at pH = 2, but difficult to separate Hg^{2+} from Ag^+, Cu^{2+}, or Bi^{3+}. Since Bi^{3+} is only 10% extracted at this pH, backwashing several times with fresh aqueous (pH = 2) portions would quantitatively remove Bi^{3+} (90% of the remaining amount each time) from the extract without appreciably affecting the extracted Hg.

One useful way to condense extraction information from curves such as in Figure 20.3 or from expressions such as Equation 20.17 is to specify the $pH_{1/2}$ value for the metal ion, obtained with a particular concentration of the reagent. The $pH_{1/2}$ is the pH value at which half the metal is extracted into the organic solvent (i.e., when $D = 1$). Thus, from Figure 20.3, the $pH_{1/2}$ values for the dithizonates are 0.3 for Hg, 1.0 for Ag, 1.9 for Cu, 2.5 for Bi, 4.7 for Sn, 7.4 for Pb, 8.5 for Zn, 9.7 for Tl, and 11.6 for Cd. For a single batch extraction, a minimum of three units difference in $pH_{1/2}$ is required to permit the quantitative separation of two metal ions; however, as mentioned above, a smaller difference suffices if backwashing is used.

Masking Agents. The factor α_M in Equation 20.17, which represents the fraction of the total metal concentration in the aqueous phase that is in the form of the simple hydrated metal ion, points to the importance of masking agents in improving the selectivity of extraction. Masking agents are competing complexing agents that form charged water-soluble complexes. Their effectiveness in preventing reaction of a metal ion with an extracting agent increases with increasing formation constant of the masking complex, increasing concentration of the masking agent, and, for the many masking agents that are bases, with increasing pH, Some representative values of α_M are listed in Table 20.3 for different masking agents.

As an illustration of masking, consider a mixture of Ag^+ and Cu^{2+} from which Ag^+ is to be selectively extracted. It can be seen from Figure 20.3 that Ag^+ can be quantitatively extracted at pH = 3; but Cu^{2+} is also appreciably extracted. In the presence of 0.1 M EDTA, the value of log $\alpha_{Cu} = -6.6$ (estimated from Table 20.3), which displaces the extraction curve of copper dithizonate to the right, increasing $pH_{1/2}$ by 3.3 units (see Eqn. 20.17). Since the value of log α_{Ag} under these conditions is about -0.2, EDTA has little effect on the extraction curve of silver dithizonate. Hence, in the presence of 0.1 M EDTA at pH = 3, Ag^+ will be selectively extracted from Cu^{2+}.

Similarly, the use of cyanide as a masking agent will permit the selective extraction of Al^{3+} by 8-quinolinol in the presence of such transition-metal ions as Cu^{2+} and Fe^{3+}, as well as Ag^+; Al^{3+} does not form a CN^- complex, whereas the other metals form strong complexes. Other examples of successful masking can be predicted with the help of Table 20.3. Masking such as this is also useful in improving the selectivity of ion-exchange separations.

Kinetics of Extraction. Kinetic factors may be important in all types of extraction, but they are most frequently observed with chelate-extraction systems. Extraction equilibrium can usually be achieved in one or two minutes of shaking because mass-transfer rates are reasonably rapid; however, the formation of an extractable complex

α_M = fraction of [total] actually present as M$^+$

TABLE 20.3. *Values of Masking Factor* ($-\log \alpha_M$ *from Eqn. 20.16) for Representative Metal Ions and Masking Agents at Various pH Values*

Metal Ion[a]	Masking Agent	pH 2	pH 5	pH 8	pH 10	
Ag$^+$	EDTA	0	0.5	3.7	5.5	10^{-6}
	NH$_3$	0	0.1	4.6	7.2	
	CN$^-$	4.7	10.7	16.7	19.0	
✓ Al^{3+}	EDTA	1.8	3.2	14.5	18.3	
	OH$^-$	0	0.4	9.3	17.3	
	F$^-$	10.0	14.5	14.5	17.3	
✓ Ca^{2+}	EDTA	0	3.2	7.1	8.9	10^{-9}
	Citrate	0	1.8	2.5	2.5	
Cd^{2+}	EDTA	1.8 4.26	7.9	12.2	14.0	
	NH$_3$	0	0	2.3	6.7	
	CN$^-$	0	0.7	10.1	14.5	
Cu^{2+}	EDTA	4.6	10.7	15.0	16.8	10^{-17}
	NH$_3$	0	0	3.6	8.2	
Fe^{3+}	EDTA	10.3	17.2	22.0	26.4	10^{-77}
	OH$^-$	0	3.7	9.7	13.7	
	F$^-$	5.7	8.9	9.8	13.7	
✓ Pb^{2+}	EDTA	4.2	10.2	14.4	16.2	10^{-17}
	OH$^-$	0	0	0.5	2.7	
	Citrate	1.0	4.2	4.2	5.3	
Zn^{2+}	EDTA	2.8	8.8	12.9	14.7	10^{-15}
	NH$_3$	0	0	0.4	0.7	
	CN$^-$	0	0	7.5	2.3	

a. Al^{3+}, Ca^{2+}, and Pb^{2+} are not masked by NH$_3$ or CN$^-$. Cu^{2+} is very strongly masked by CN$^-$, > 20. Fe^{3+} is very strongly masked by CN$^-$, but is not masked by NH$_3$.

is sometimes slow enough to affect the course of the extraction, particularly with certain metal chelates. For example, most substitution reactions of Cr^{3+} are very slow; thus, although Cr^{3+} forms stable chelates, it is rarely extracted in the usual chelate-extraction procedure. Less dramatic, but analytically useful, is the difference in the speed of formation of various metal dithizonates, which makes it possible to separate Hg^{2+} from Cu^{2+}, and Zn^{2+} from Ni^{2+}, by using shaking times of no longer than one minute.

Ion-Association Extraction Systems

As with chelate systems, ion-association extraction equilibria involve a number of reactions. An example is the extraction of Fe^{3+} from HCl solutions into ether,

$$Fe^{3+} + 4\,Cl^- \rightleftharpoons FeCl_4^- \tag{20.18}$$

$$H(H_2O)_4^+ + FeCl_4^- \rightleftharpoons H_9O_4^+, FeCl_4^- \tag{20.19}$$

$$H_9O_4^+, FeCl_4^- \rightleftharpoons H_9O_4^+, FeCl_4^-\ (ether) \tag{20.20}$$

The importance of chloride and of acid in the overall extraction is evident. About 6 M HCl is required for optimum extraction of iron. Ether, an oxygen-containing solvent, is needed to stabilize the $H_9O_4^+$ ion. If a $(C_4H_9)_4N^+$ salt is added, then the iron can be extracted out of a much less acidic solution, provided that the chloride concentration is about 6 M; and, more significantly, it would be possible to use benzene, CCl_4, or $CHCl_3$ for the extraction as well as oxygen-containing solvents.

In many ion-association extraction systems, high concentrations of electrolyte are effective in increasing the extent of extraction. The addition of such salts, referred to as *salting-out* agents, serves two purposes. The first, and more obvious, is to aid the direct formation of the complex by the mass-action effect—the formation of a chloro or nitrato complex, for instance, is promoted by increasing the concentration of Cl^- or NO_3^-. Second, as the salt concentration increases, the concentration of "free," (uncomplexed) water decreases because the ions require a certain amount of water for hydration. This decreases the solubility of the complex in the aqueous phase. Because Li^+ is more strongly hydrated than K^+, $LiNO_3$ is a much better salting-out agent than KNO_3 for nitrate extraction systems, even though equimolar solutions supply the same nitrate concentration.

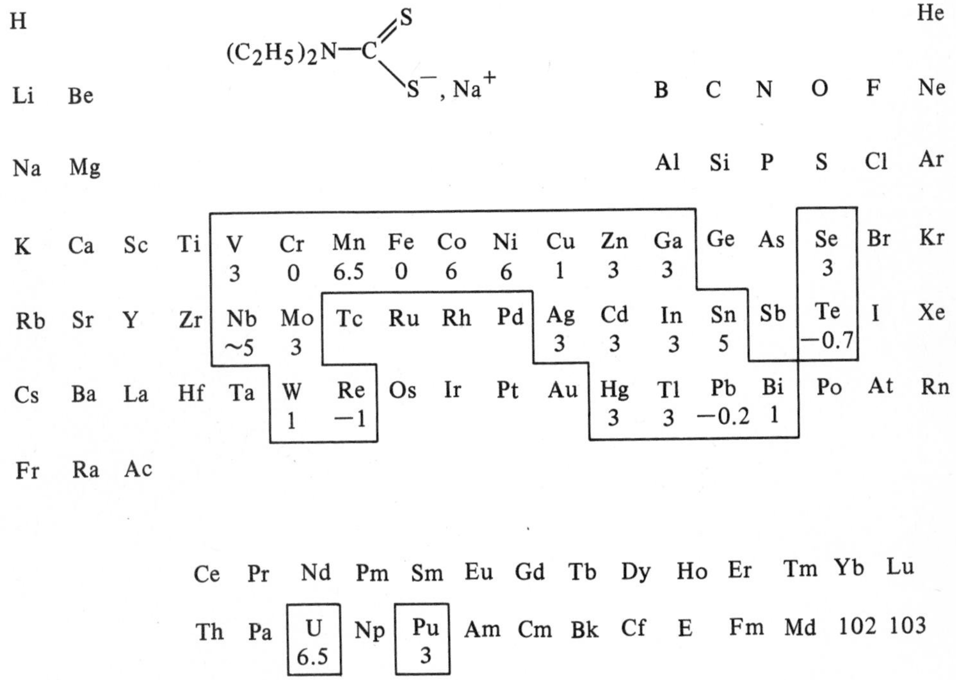

FIGURE 20.4. *Elements extractable with sodium diethyldithiocarbamate. The number under an element symbol indicates the pH value at which the element can be completely extracted. From H. Freiser and G. H. Morrison, Ann. Rev. Nucl. Sci., 9, (1959), by permission of Annual Reviews, Inc.*

20.5 METAL-EXTRACTION SYSTEMS

In this section, the applications of a few representative extractants are described in periodic array. Elements extractable as diethyldithiocarbamates are shown in Figure 20.4. The numbers under the element represent the lowest pH at which it will be extracted. Because the reagent is nonaromatic, its chelates are readily decomposed in a flame; consequently, this reagent is widely used in a separation or preconcentration step prior to atomic absorption spectrometry.

The application if dithizone is shown in Figure 20.5. Because of the highly conjugated double-bonds in the reagent molecule, the chelates are all highly colored, so that the metal ion can be determined with good sensitivity by absorption spectrophotometry once it has been extracted.

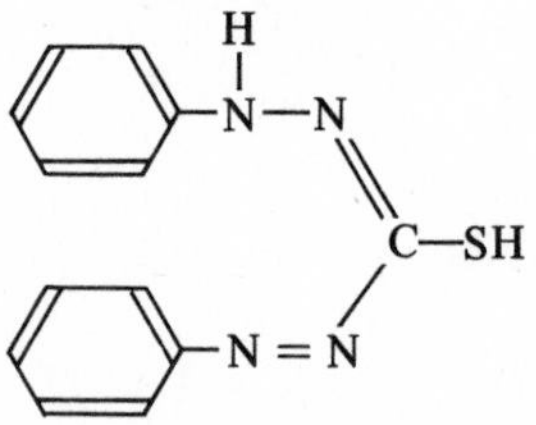

FIGURE 20.5. *Elements extractable by dithizone. The number under the element symbol indicates the pH value at which the element can be completely extracted. From H. Freiser and G. H. Morrison,* Ann. Rev. Nucl. Sci., *9, (1959), by permission of Annual Reviews, Inc.*

Extractions with 8-quinolinol (8-hydroxyquinoline, oxine) are shown in Figure 20.6. These chelates are often used in the spectrophotometric or fluorimetric determination of the element.

The conditions for extracting metal ions from hydrochloric acid solution into ethyl ether as ion-association complexes are shown in Figure 20.7.

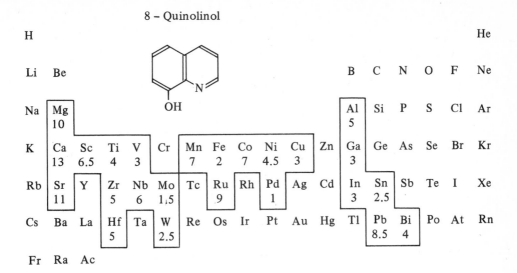

8 – Quinolinol

H																	He
Li	Be											B	C	N	O	F	Ne
Na	Mg 10											Al 5	Si	P	S	Cl	Ar
K	Ca 13	Sc 6.5	Ti 4	V 3	Cr	Mn 7	Fe 2	Co 7	Ni 4.5	Cu 3	Zn	Ga 3	Ge	As	Se	Br	Kr
Rb	Sr 11	Y	Zr 5	Nb 6	Mo 1,5	Tc	Ru 9	Rh	Pd 1	Ag	Cd	In 3	Sn 2.5	Sb	Te	I	Xe
Cs	Ba	La	Hf 5	Ta	W 2.5	Re	Os	Ir	Pt	Au	Hg	Tl	Pb 8.5	Bi 4	Po	At	Rn
Fr	Ra	Ac															

Ce 10	Pr	Nd	Pm	Sm	Eu	Gd	Tb	Dy	Ho	Er	Tm	Yb	Lu
Th 5	Pa 10	U 5	Np	Pu 4	Am	Cm	Bk	Cf	E	Fm	Md	102	103

FIGURE 20.6. *Elements extractable by 8-quinolinol. The number under the element symbol indicates the pH value at which the element can be completely extracted. From H. Freiser and G. H. Morrison,* Ann. Rev. Nucl. Sci., *9, (1959), by permission of Annual Reviews, Inc.*

Outline of Illustrative Extraction Procedures

Several specific extraction procedures are outlined below to illustrate the principles discussed in previous sections. For a working method, more detailed procedures can be found in the selected bibliography at the end of the chapter. The usual precautions peculiar to trace-element determinations (for instance, impurities and solution stability) must also be carefully observed.

Extracting Cadmium with Dithizone. It is possible to separate Cd^{2+} from Pb^{2+} or Zn^{2+} by using a highly alkaline solution during extraction; and from Ag^+, Hg^{2+}, Ni^{2+}, Co^{2+}, and Cu^{2+} by stripping the Cd^{2+} at a pH of 2 where the other dithizonates are stable.

A solution containing up to 50 μg Cd^{2+} is treated with tartrate (to avoid precipitating the hydroxide), and made basic with an excess of 25% KOH. This is now shaken with successive 5-ml portions of dithizone in $CHCl_3$ until the aqueous layer remains yellowish brown (indicating excess dithizone). The combined chloroform extracts are then shaken for two minutes with an aqueous solution buffered at pH = 2, which will strip the Cd^{2+} quantitatively. To remove small amounts of Cu^{2+} and Hg^{2+} that may accompany the Cd^{2+}, re-extract the aqueous solution (pH = 2)

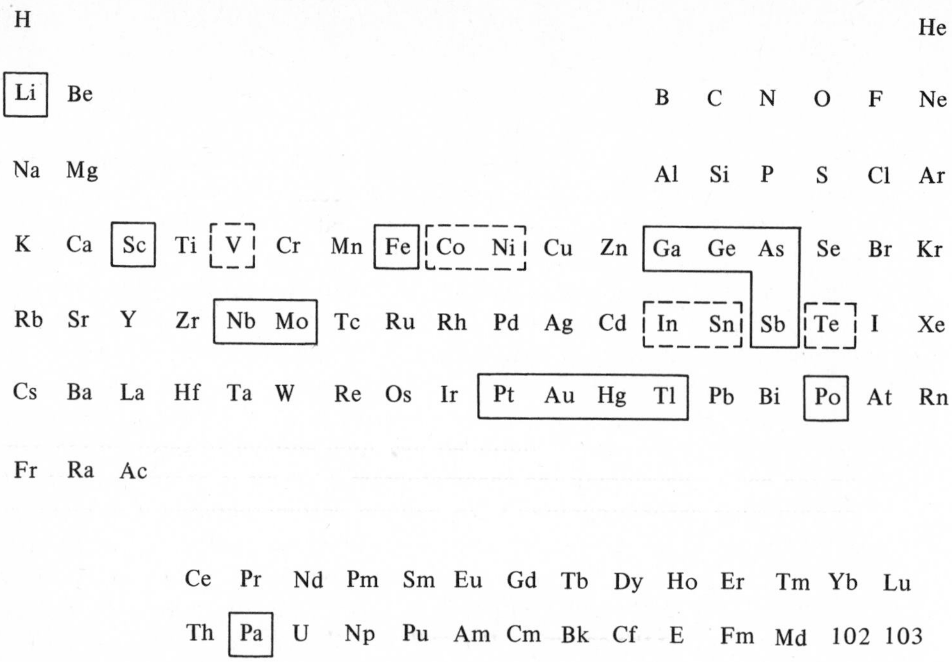

H   He

[Li] Be   B   C   N   O   F   Ne

Na   Mg   Al   Si   P   S   Cl   Ar

K   Ca [Sc] Ti [V] Cr Mn [Fe] [Co   Ni] Cu   Zn [Ga   Ge   As] Se   Br   Kr

Rb   Sr   Y   Zr [Nb Mo] Tc Ru Rh Pd Ag Cd [In   Sn] Sb [Te] I   Xe

Cs   Ba   La Hf Ta W   Re Os Ir [Pt Au Hg Tl] Pb Bi [Po] At   Rn

Fr   Ra   Ac

Ce Pr Nd Pm Sm Eu Gd Tb Dy Ho Er Tm Yb Lu

Th [Pa] U   Np Pu Am Cm Bk Cf E   Fm Md 102 103

FIGURE 20.7. *Elements extracted in chloride system. Solid blocks: appreciably extracted; broken blocks: partially extracted. From H. Freiser and G. H. Morrison,* Ann. Rev. Nucl. Sci., *9, (1959), by permission of Annual Reviews, Inc.*

with a fresh portion of dithizone in $CHCl_3$; the Cd^{2+} will remain in the aqueous solution.

Extracting Lead with Dithizone. A slightly acid solution containing up to 100 μg Pb^{2+} is treated with aqueous NH_3 and KCN prior to extraction with dithizone in $CHCl_3$. Under these conditions, no metal other than Bi^{3+} or Tl^+ interferes.

Extracting Copper with Sodium Diethyldithiocarbamate. Adjust the pH of a solution containing up to 50 μg Cu^{2+} to 4.5–5.0 with acetate buffer, add disodium EDTA followed by sodium diethyldithiocarbamate, and shake the mixture for one minute. Add butyl acetate and shake again for one minute. Backwash the butyl acetate extract with dilute H_2SO_4. There is essentially no interference.

Extracting Iron with 4,7-Diphenylphenanthroline (Bathophenanthroline). After adding $NH_2OH \cdot HCl$ to a solution containing up to 10 μg Fe to produce Fe^{2+}, adjust the pH to 4 with sodium acetate and add bathophenanthroline dissolved in ethanol. Add *n*-hexanol and shake to extract the iron. The iron complex absorbs strongly at 533 nm.

Extracting Germanium with Hydrochloric Acid. Dissolve the sample in either H_3PO_4 or HNO_3, and add concentrated HCl. The $GeCl_4$ that forms can then be extracted with portions of CCl_4. To return Ge to an aqueous phase prior to determination, the CCl_4 extract may be stripped with an ammonium oxalate and oxalic acid solution.

Liquid Chromatography

As one proceeds from a single-stage batch separation to the multi-stage counter-current distribution process, separating two components whose D values are relatively close together becomes easier. Chromatography can be viewed as a logical extension of counter-current distribution (L. C. Craig first developed CCD as a simple form of liquid chromatography) in which discrete stages or tubes are replaced by immobilized solvent supported on granules of carrier either in a two-dimensional (paper, thin-layer chromatography) or three-dimensional (column) bed. After the mixture of solutes is added to the bed, the eluant, a solvent of constant or uniformly varying composition (the latter used in *gradient elution*), is passed over or through the bed. This *elution* may be continued just long enough to separate the components on the bed—"developing the chromatogram." (This is common practice in paper or thin-layer chromatography.) In column chromatography it is more customary to continue the flow of eluant until all of the components have appeared in the eluate flowing out of the column. The distribution of solutes along the column is similar to the distribution illustrated in Figure 20.2, where tube number represents the distance along the column. Regardless of the particular chromatographic process used (that is, adsorption, partition, etc.), the separation of components is related to differences in their distribution ratios between the immobile and mobile phases. In ordinary *elution chromatography*, the eluting solvent has a low D value, so that the components move at large and varying elution volumes. On the other hand, if a component with a very high D value is part of the eluant, it will displace the solute components. In *displacement chromatography*, therefore, the solute components appear one after the other in much more tightly spaced bands than in elution chromatography. An interesting variation involves using the sample solution itself as a developing solvent. In this case, called *frontal development*, the solutes do separate in the order of their D values, but appear in the eluate as fronts rather than bands, in which the least retained solute appears first, followed by a mixture of the first solute and the next more strongly retained component and so on, until finally all of the components of the original solution appear together, as in the original solution.

The next two chapters will treat chromatography in more detail.

SELECTED BIBLIOGRAPHY

Analytical Chemistry Fundamental Reviews. The reviews published in April of even-numbered years include comprehensive surveys of newly published extraction procedures, and many references.

MORRISON, G. H., and FREISER, H. *Solvent Extraction in Analytical Chemistry.* New York: John Wiley, 1957. *A general text covering in detail the principles of solvent extraction and its application to separation and analysis.*

STARY, J. *The Solvent Extraction of Metal Chelates.* New York: Macmillan, 1964.

DYRSSEN, D.; LILJENZIN, J.-O.; and RYDBERG, J., eds. *Solvent Extraction Chemistry.* New York: Wiley-Interscience, 1967.

DEAN, J. A. *Chemical Separation Methods.* New York: Van Nostrand Reinhold, 1969.

REFERENCES

1. G. H. MORRISON and H. FREISER, *Solvent Extraction in Analytical Chemistry*, New York: John Wiley, 1957.

PROBLEMS

1. Name the categories of extractable complexes used in metal-extraction procedures and illustrate each by specific examples.

2. How does Hildebrand's theory of regular solutions apply to the role of the organic solvent in extraction processes?

3. What are masking agents? How can one tell whether a substance that masks effectively in one situation will do so in another?

4. What are ion-association complexes? Under which conditions will they form and what properties must they have to be useful in extraction?

5. What factors affect the value of an oxygen-containing solvent used in extracting ion-association complexes?

6. Relate D, the distribution ratio, to $\%E$, percent extraction as a function of R_V (the phase-volume ratio V_0/V). For what purposes is D a more (or less) appropriate criterion than $\%E$?

7. When can the ratio of D values for two substances A and B, D_A/D_B, serve as a satisfactory means of evaluating the separation of A and B? Why is D_A/D_B not used as a "separation index"?

8. What are batch, continuous, and counter-current extraction processes and when would each be used?

9. Develop an algebraic expression with which to define the influence of each of the following factors on the extraction of metal ions using chelating extractants: (a) the reagent concentration; (b) the metal-ion concentration; (c) the pH; (d) the presence (and concentration) of masking agents; (e) the nature of the organic solvent; and (f) the ionic strength of the aqueous phase.

10. What is meant by K_{ex} (extraction constant) and pH_0 (or $pH_{1/2}$), and how can each be used to calculate the D (or $\%E$) value under various conditions? How different must the K_{ex} or pH_0 values be for a pair of metals to get a separation of 100/1? Does the amount of difference depend on the valence of the metal ions? Are other characteristics relevant as well? If so, which ones? Does the efficiency of separation depend on the value of K_{ex} or on the ratio of the two constants?

11. What are the optimal conditions for using a dithizone solution in $CHCl_3$ to separate Bi(III) from a solution containing a hundredfold excess of zinc?

21

Solid and Liquid Phase Chromatography

RONALD E. MAJORS

Chromatography is the general name given to the methods by which two or more compounds in a mixture physically separate themselves by distributing themselves between two phases: (1) a *stationary phase*, which can be a solid or a liquid supported on a solid; and (2) a *mobile phase*, either a gas or a liquid, which flows continuously around the stationary phase. The separation of individual components results primarily from differences in their affinity for the stationary phase.

In *liquid chromatography* (LC) the flowing or mobile phase is a liquid, whereas in *gas chromatography* (GC) it is a gas. *Gas-solid chromatography* (GSC) is the specific term used when the stationary phase is a solid; in *gas-liquid chromatography* (GLC), the stationary phase is a liquid spread over the surface of a solid support. The present chapter is concerned with LC; the following chapter deals with GC in its various forms.

21.1 INTRODUCTION

Chromatography was discovered and named in 1906 by Michael Tswett, a Russian botanist, when he was attempting to separate colored leaf pigments by passing a solution containing them through a column packed with adsorbent chalk particles. The individual pigments passed down the column at different rates and were separated from each other. The separated pigments were easily distinguished as colored bands—hence, chroma ("color") + graphy ("writing").

The next major development was that of *liquid-liquid* (*partition*) *chromatography* (LLC) by Martin and Synge in 1941. Instead of only a solid adsorbent they used a stationary liquid phase spread over the surface of the adsorbent and immiscible with the mobile phase. The sample components partitioned themselves between the two liquid phases according to their solubilities. For this work, Martin and Synge received the Nobel prize in chemistry in 1952.

In the early days of column chromatography, reliable identification of small quantities of separated substances was difficult, so *paper chromatography* (PC) was developed. In this "planar" technique, separations are achieved on sheets of filter paper, mainly through partition. Appreciation of the full advantages of planar chromatography then led to *thin-layer chromatography* (TLC), in which separations are carried out on thin layers of adsorbent supported on plates of glass or some other rigid material. TLC gained popularity after the classic work by Stahl in 1958 standardizing the techniques and materials used. To aid or enhance the separation of ionic compounds by PC or TLC, an electric field can be applied across the paper or plate. The resulting techniques are referred to as *paper* or *thin-layer electrophoresis*, respectively.

The most recently developed chromatographic technique, gas chromatography, was first described by Martin and James in 1952 and has become the most sophisticated and widely used of all chromatographic methods, particularly for mixtures of gases or for volatile liquids and solids. Separation times of a matter of minutes have become commonplace even for very complex mixtures. The combination of high resolution, speed of analysis, and sensitive detection have made GC a routine technique used in almost every chemical laboratory.

In the last few years, interest has renewed in closed-column LC because of new instrumentation, new column packings, and a better understanding of chromatographic theory. *High-performance liquid chromatography* (HPLC) is rapidly becoming as widely used as gas chromatography and is often the preferred technique for the rapid separation of nonvolatile or thermally unstable samples.

Basic Principles of Liquid Chromatography

To illustrate the basic principles of liquid chromatography, we shall consider a hypothetical separation of a three-component sample in a closed column. The stationary phase (*packing*) consists of solid porous particles (normally small—less than 150 μm in diameter) contained inside a long narrow tube, the *column*.

Figure 21.1 demonstrates the chromatographic process. A small volume of sample solution is injected at the column inlet (Fig. 21.1A). The mobile solvent phase moves the sample through the column packing (Fig. 21.1B). The individual components undergo sorption and desorption on the packing, thereby slowing their motion in varying amounts depending on their affinity for the packing. Each component X is distributed between the stationary phase (s) and the mobile phase (m) as it passes down the column. According to

$$X_m \rightleftharpoons X_s \qquad (21.1)$$

the corresponding *distribution coefficient* for component X is given by

$$K_X = \frac{[X]_s}{[X]_m} \qquad (21.2)$$

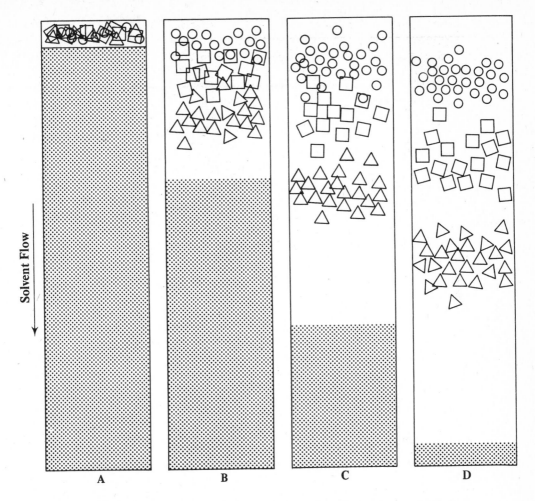

FIGURE 21.1. *Hypothetical separation of a three-component mixture: Component A:* △; *Component B:* □; *Component C:* ○. *The dotted area represents the original solvent in the column, which is being "displaced" during elution.*

A large value of K_x indicates that the component favors the stationary phase and moves slowly through the column, whereas for small values of K_x the component favors the mobile phase and moves quickly through the column.

The different speeds of the components separate them along the column (Fig. 21.1C). In elution, the separated components are moved down the entire length of the column by the mobile phase (Fig. 21.1D). If one measures the concentration of each component as it exits from the column and plots it as a function of the volume of mobile phase passed through the column, a *chromatogram* results. Individual volumes of mobile phase may be collected and the solute concentration in each measured externally (for example, spectrophotometrically), but normally the column effluent is monitored continuously by a detector that measures some physical

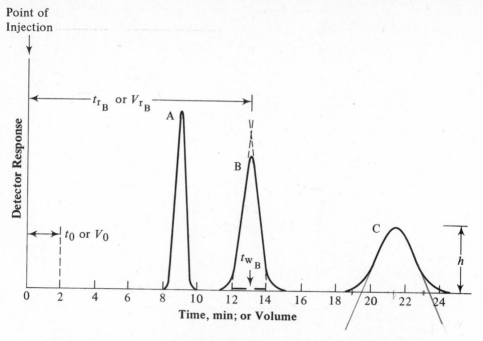

FIGURE 21.2. *Chromatogram of the three-component mixture of Figure 21.1.* t_0 = *time for solvent to traverse the column,* t_{r_B} = *retention time of substance B,* t_{w_B} = *peak basewidth of substance B, h = peak height. Units can also be given in terms of volume rather than time:* V_0, V_{r_B}, V_{w_B}, *and so forth.*

or chemical property of the solute or of the mobile phase. A chromatogram for the hypothetical three-component sample is depicted in Figure 21.2.

Types of Liquid Chromatography

Several types of LC are distinguished by their predominant mechanism of separation. The stationary phase governs the separation mode. The various modes will be briefly outlined here; each will be dealt with in somewhat greater detail in Sections 21.4 and 21.5. Since the solute molecule usually has some affinity for the stationary phase, it transfers from the mobile phase to the stationary phase, setting up the equilibrium described by Reaction 21.1. This alternating process of solute mass transfer, depicted in Figure 21.3A, eventually leads to separation.

Adsorption Chromatography. Adsorption chromatography (Fig. 21.3B), often referred to as *liquid-solid chromatography* (LSC), is based on interactions between the solute and fixed active sites on a solid adsorbent used as the stationary phase. The adsorbent may be packed in a column, spread on a plate, or impregnated into a porous paper. The adsorbent is generally an active, porous solid with a large surface area, such as silica gel, alumina, or charcoal. The active sites, such as the surface silanol groups of silica gel, generally interact with the polar functional groups of the compounds to be separated. The nonpolar (for instance, hydrocarbon) portion of a

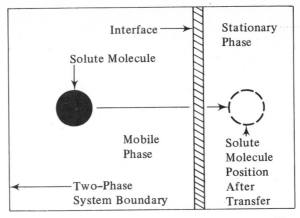

A. Transfer of Solute to a Generalized Stationary Phase

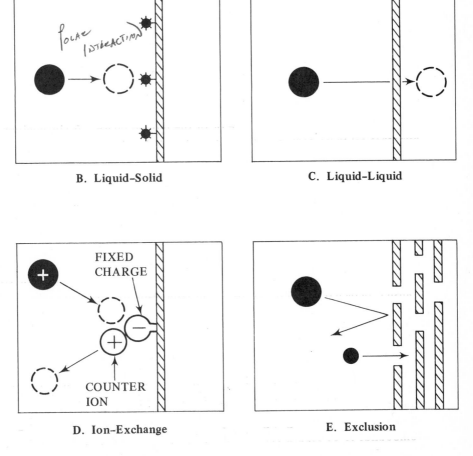

B. Liquid–Solid

C. Liquid–Liquid

D. Ion-Exchange

E. Exclusion

FIGURE 21.3. *Schematic representation of the four modes of liquid chromatography. Courtesy of Varian Associates.*

molecule has only a minor influence on the separation. Thus, LSC is well suited for separating classes of compounds (for instance, separating alcohols from aromatic hydrocarbons).

Partition Chromatography. In partition chromatography (Fig. 21.3C), also referred to as liquid-liquid chromatography, the solute molecules distribute themselves between two immiscible liquid phases, the stationary phase and the mobile phase, according to their relative solubilities. The stationary phase is uniformly spread on an inert support—a porous or nonporous particulate solid or porous paper (paper chromatography). To avoid mixing of the two phases, the two partitioning liquids must differ greatly in polarity. If the stationary liquid is polar (e.g., ethylene glycol) and the mobile phase is nonpolar (e.g., hexane), then polar components are retained more strongly; this is the usual mode of operation. On the other hand, if the stationary liquid is nonpolar (for instance, decane) and the mobile phase polar (for instance, water), polar components favor the mobile phase and elute faster. The latter technique (which has a reversed polarity) is referred to as *reverse-phase* LLC. Because of the subtle effects of solubility differences, LLC is well suited for separating homologues and isomers.

Often, the stationary phase is chemically bonded to the support material rather than mechanically applied to it. This is referred to as *bonded-phase chromatography*. The mechanism of this relatively new technique is not clear, but both partition and adsorption mechanisms may be involved.

Ion-Exchange Chromatography. Ion-exchange chromatography, depicted in Figure 21.3D, is based on the affinity of ions in solution for oppositely charged ions on the stationary phase. Ion-exchange packings consist of a porous solid phase, usually a resin, onto which ionic groups are chemically bonded. The mobile phase is usually a buffered aqueous solution containing a counter ion whose charge is opposite to that of the surface groups—that is, it has the same charge as the solute—but which is in charge equilibrium with the resin in the form of an ion pair. Competition between the solute and the counter ion for the ionic site governs chromatographic retention. Ion-exchange chromatography has found wide application in inorganic chemistry for separating metallic ions, and in biological systems for separating water-soluble ionic compounds such as proteins, nucleotides, and amino acids.

Exclusion Chromatography. The mechanism of exclusion chromatography, also referred to as *gel-permeation* or *gel-filtration chromatography*, is shown in Figure 21.3E. Here, the stationary phase should be chemically inert. Exclusion chromatography involves selectively diffusing solute molecules into and out of mobile-phase–filled pores in a three-dimensional network, which may be a gel or a porous inorganic solid. The degree of retention depends upon the size of the solvated solute relative to the size of the pore. Small molecules will permeate the smaller pores, intermediate-sized molecules will permeate only part of the pores and be excluded from others, and the very large molecules will be completely excluded. The larger molecules will travel faster through the stationary phase and elute from the column first. Thus, exclusion chromatography is especially useful in separating high-molecular-weight organic compounds and biopolymers from smaller molecules.

Uses of Liquid Chromatography

In a given chromatographic system, the volume of mobile phase at which a particular component elutes is usually constant and a characteristic of that component. Thus, the *retention volume* V_r for a chromatographic peak or spot can be used for its qualitative identification. Sometimes one or more substances may elute at the same V_r; in those cases, cross-correlation techniques may allow a more positive identification. In these techniques, a sample is run using two or more different chromatographic systems or conditions; it is unlikely, although still possible, that two substances will give the same elution behavior in more than one system. Positive identification is best accomplished by trapping the peak of interest and subjecting it to mass-spectral, infrared, NMR, or some other appropriate analysis.

Liquid chromatography can also be used for the quantitative analysis of the separated compounds. In column chromatography, the detector response is normally related to the amount of sample in the effluent. Thus, the area under a chromatographic peak is useful for quantitative analysis; in Fig. 21.2, the darkened area under peak C represents the peak area of that component. The peak height (distance h in Fig. 21.2) can also be used. In thin-layer or paper chromatography, the area of the spot is related to the amount of substance. The separated component can also be eluted from the plate or paper and measured externally by another technique (for instance, spectrophotometry).

Since many sample components are completely separated, the eluted fractions from liquid chromatography can be used for preparing pure materials in milligram to gram quantities for further use in experimentation, or for studying the molecular structure of the compounds.

21.2 THEORY RELATED TO PRACTICE

Theoretical considerations are a useful guide to the practical design and operation of the chromatographic experiment. The object of chromatography is separation— or rather, separation in a reasonable time.

Retention

In order to achieve separation, one must first have retention. Earlier, the thermodynamic distribution coefficient K_X was defined as a measure of the degree of retention for compound X. The *capacity factor* k'_X is a more practical quantity that can be determined directly from the chromatogram. It is given by

$$k'_X = \frac{\text{total moles of X in stationary phase}}{\text{total moles of X in mobile phase}} = \left(\frac{V_s}{V_m}\right)\frac{[X]_s}{[X]_m} = \left(\frac{V_s}{V_m}\right)K_X \quad (21.3)$$

where V_s = the volume of the stationary phase within the column
V_m = the volume of the mobile phase within the column

The fundamental equation for any chromatographic process, relating the *retention volume* V_r to other quantities, is

$$V_r = V_m(1 + k'_X) = V_m + V_s K_X \quad (21.4)$$

The value of V_r can be obtained from the chromatogram, since $V_r = Ft_r$, where F

is the *flow rate* (ml/min) and t_r is the peak *retention time* (Fig. 21.2). Similarly, V_m, termed the *void volume* (also *dead volume* or *interstitial volume*) is equal to Ft_0, where t_0 is the time required for solvent molecules or any other nonretained compound to traverse the column. Note that V_m is the total volume of mobile phase in the column at any given time. Substituting V_m and V_r into Equation 21.4, and rearranging, produces

$$k'_x = \frac{t_r - t_0}{t_0} \tag{21.5}$$

Example 21.1. (a) Using the hypothetical chromatogram in Figure 21.2, calculate the capacity factors of peaks B and C. (b) Assuming that 60% of the volume of a column 25 cm in length by 0.40 cm in internal diameter is occupied by solid packing particles, calculate the expected retention volume for peak C, Figure 21.2 (Hint: treat the column as a cylinder).

Solution:
(a) By Equation 21.5,

$$k'_B = \frac{t_r - t_0}{t_0} = \frac{13 - 2}{2.0}$$

$$= 5.5$$
$$k'_C = 9.8$$

(b) $V_m = 0.40\pi r^2 L$ is the fraction of column volume occupied by mobile phase, where r is the internal radius of the column and L its length.

$$V_m = (0.40)(3.14)(0.20 \text{ cm})^2(25 \text{ cm}) = 1.2_6 \text{ cm}^3$$
$$V_r = V_m(1 + k') = 1.2_6 \text{ cm}^3(1 + 9.8) = 13.6 \text{ cm}^3$$

In TLC or PC, the degree of retention for a compound is its R_f value, defined as the ratio of the distance the solute has moved to the distance the solvent front has moved. Figure 21.4 shows how one measures the R_f value; normally, the center of the solute spot is used for calculating the distance a.

Column Efficiency

Column efficiency describes the rate of band broadening as the solute travels through the column or across the plate or paper. As illustrated in Figure 21.1, all molecules do not move at the same speed. Dispersion of molecules generally results in a Gaussian profile. The center of the profile or elution band—that is, the k' value of each component—represents the average rate of travel of a solute molecule. Small deviations from the mean value are brought about by the finite rate of solute mass-transfer between the mobile and stationary phases, the different flow paths through the stationary phase caused by irregular packing in the bed, and axial (*longitudinal*) diffusion in the direction of flow.

The quantitative measure of efficiency is the number of *theoretical plates* N calculated from the chromatogram by using

$$N = 16\left(\frac{t_r}{t_w}\right)^2 \tag{21.6}$$

where t_w = the peak width measured in the same units as the retention time

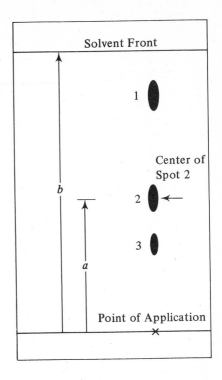

FIGURE 21.4. *Measuring the R_f value from a paper or thin-layer chromatogram. R_f for component 2 = a/b.*

The peak width is obtained from the intersection of the baseline with the tangents drawn through the inflection points on the sides of each peak. The theoretical-plate model, a carryover from distillation theory, assumes a column to be made up of a series of plates. At each plate, one equilibrium distribution of solute between the mobile phase and stationary phase occurs. Thus, the higher the value of N, the more chance there is for separation to occur (that is, the better the separating power of the column).

Another useful parameter for column efficiency is the *height equivalent to a theoretical plate*, HETP (the H value). The following simple relationship shows that H has the units of length.

$$H = \frac{L}{N} \qquad (21.7)$$

where L = the column length

Thus, a column or plate with a low H value is better than one with a high value. Values of H less than 1–3 mm are commonplace in gas chromatography and high-performance liquid chromatography.

Example 21.2. (a) From the chromatogram of Figure 21.2, determine the number of theoretical plates for peak C. (b) Assuming the same column as in Example 21.1, calculate the value of H in mm for peak C. (c) How would doubling the column length affect the peak width of peak C, keeping other parameters constant?

Solution:

(a) By Equation 21.6

$$N = 16\left(\frac{t_r}{t_w}\right)^2 = 16\left(\frac{21.5}{4.1}\right)^2 = 440 \text{ plates}$$

(b) By Equation 21.7

$$H = \frac{L}{N} = (250 \text{ mm})/440 \text{ plates} = 0.57 \text{ mm}$$

(c) By Equations 21.6 and 21.7,

$$N = 16\left(\frac{t_r}{t_w}\right)^2 \quad \text{and} \quad \frac{L}{H} = 16\left(\frac{t_r}{t_w}\right)^2$$

Therefore, $\dfrac{t_r}{t_w} \propto \sqrt{L}$.

Since $t_r \propto L$, then $t_w \propto L$, so t_w increases by $\sqrt{2} = 1.41$.

Band-Broadening Contributions to H

The development of the generalized nonequilibrium theory by Giddings and co-workers [1] has led to a more thorough understanding of the factors contributing to band spreading in chromatography and hence to the design of better chromatographic columns. In the nonequilibrium theory of chromatography, the movement of the solute through the column is treated as a random walk—that is, the progress of a molecule through the column is a succession of random stops and starts about a mean equilibrium concentration. In this dynamic nonequilibrium, represented in Figure 21.5, mass-transfer of the solute into the stationary phase results in a lag behind the equilibrium concentration (band center): when it desorbs and transfers into the mobile phase the solute moves more rapidly than the band center. Thus, dispersion in-

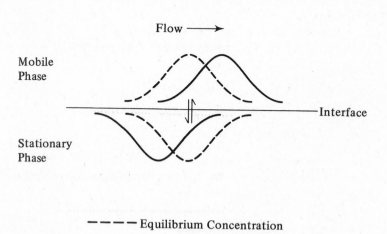

FIGURE 21.5. *Illustration of the influence of local nonequilibrium on band dispersion. Dashed lines: equilibrium concentration profile; solid lines: actual concentration profile.*

creases with the number of transfers and decreases as the velocity of the mobile phase decreases (closer approach to equilibrium).

Solute mass-transfer in the stationary phase (H_{sp}) or in the "stagnant" mobile phase contained in the pores of the column packing (H_{sm}) are a source of band broadening (Fig. 21.6). The mass-transfer rate can be increased by (a) decreasing the mean diffusion path through which the solute must pass (that is, decreasing the pore depth or the particle size); (b) increasing the rate of solute diffusion by decreasing the viscosity of the media through which it passes; (c) decreasing the thickness of the stationary phase so that the molecule can diffuse into and out of it very rapidly; or (d) lowering the k' value of the molecule so that it spends less time in the stationary phase.

Mass transfer of solute in the mobile phase (H_{mp}) also contributes to band spreading. Complex flow-patterns arise from the flow of the mobile phase through a packed bed of particles. These patterns are difficult to describe quantitatively, but this form of band dispersion is minimized by homogeneous packing of the bed with uniform particles, by small interparticle channels (less convective mixing between particles), and by the use of mobile phases of low viscosity.

Another source of band dispersion is so-called *eddy diffusion* (H_{ed}). This term arises from irregular flow through the packed particles in a column. The solute proceeds through the channels between the particles by many interconnected paths that differ in their tortuosity and degree of constriction. Because of the many possible paths, solute molecules arrive at the column exit at different times. Longitudinal molecular diffusion, H_{ld} (that is, random diffusion in and against the direction of mobile-phase flow) is minimal in liquid chromatography, although it is an important source of band broadening in gas chromatography. H_{ld} only becomes appreciable at very low flow-rates (Fig. 21.6), because the solute diffusion-coefficients in liquids are 10^5 smaller than they are in gases. Thus, these diffusional contributions to H are rarely observed.

The individual band-broadening contributions to H can be described mathematically by

$$H = \frac{1}{\left(\dfrac{1}{H_{ed}} + \dfrac{1}{H_{mp}}\right)} + H_{ld} + H_{sm} + H_{sp} \tag{21.8}$$

where $H_{ed} = C_e d_p$ (eddy diffusion)

$H_{mp} = \dfrac{C_m d_p{}^2 v}{D_m}$ (mobile-phase mass-transfer)

$H_{ld} = \dfrac{C_d D_m}{v}$ (longitudinal diffusion)

$H_{sm} = \dfrac{C_{sm} d_p{}^2 v}{D_m}$ (stagnant-to-mobile-phase mass-transfer)

$H_{sp} = \dfrac{C_s d_f{}^2 v}{D_s}$ (stationary-phase mass-transfer)

d_p = the particle diameter
D_m = the solute diffusion-coefficient in the mobile phase
D_s = the solute diffusion-coefficient in the stationary phase
v = the linear velocity of the mobile phase
d_f = the thickness of the stationary-phase film (mainly for LLC)

When the stationary phase is the same as the support or particle (as in LSC), d_t is replaced by d_p. C_e, C_m, C_d, C_{sm}, and C_s are coefficients whose characteristics are given in Reference [1].

Equation 21.8 is a slightly modified version of the Van Deemter equation, Equation 22.10, used in gas chromatography. Because of the so-called "coupling" between the A term (eddy diffusion) and the C_{liq} term of Equation 22.10, a different relationship between H and v is observed in LC than in GC. The fundamental difference between GC and LC is the great difference in sample diffusion rates in liquids and in gases: D_m is 10^4–10^6 times greater in GC. Thus, the H_{ld} contribution in LC is much smaller than in GC, whereas the H_{mp} term is larger.

A pictorial representation of the various contributions to H at different mobile-phase velocities is given in Figure 21.6. For comparison, a similar curve is presented for a typical GC column. In practice, H-versus-v relationships are determined experimentally. These curves are then used for optimizing operating conditions. For best efficiency, one prefers to use a velocity (proportional to flow rate) near the minimum of the H-versus-v plot. Although this is often done in GC, in

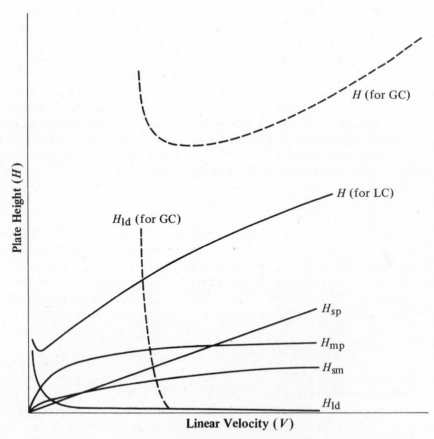

FIGURE 21.6. *Plot illustrating the flow-velocity dependence of overall plate height H and various contributions to H (Eqn. 21.8).*

LC one normally works above the minimum since the latter occurs at very low velocities and separation times would be intolerably long.

From Equation 21.8, one can deduce experimental conditions that minimize the value of H. It can be seen that H decreases with decreasing particle diameters (d_p), linear velocities (v), thickness of films of stationary phase (d_f), viscosity of the mobile phases and elevated temperatures (to increase D_m and D_s), and with uniform packing of the particles (to decrease eddy diffusion).

Care must be taken to keep additional band-broadening outside the column to a minimum. Extra-column contributions to band broadening, such as mixing or poor sample-introduction technique, will increase the H-value. Because of the slow diffusion of samples in liquid phases, extra-column volumes are more detrimental to efficiency in LC than in GC; hence, great effort should be exercised to keep those volumes between the point of injection and the top of the column to a minimum. Likewise, the volume between the column exit and the detector, and the volume of the detector itself, should be minimized. In TLC or PC, the applied spot should be kept as small as possible.

Resolution and Its Optimization

The degree of separation is referred to as *resolution, R*. Figure 21.2 and the following equation

$$R = 2 \frac{(t_{r_B} - t_{r_A})}{t_{w_A} + t_{w_B}} \tag{21.9}$$

are helpful in discussing the characteristics of chromatographic peaks that determine R. If the two components A and B of the chromatogram of Figure 21.2 are examined, resolution is determined by (a) the distance between the peak maxima and (b) the peak or bandwidths. The separation between peaks is related to the *selectivity factor α*, sometimes called relative retention, by

$$\alpha = \frac{t_{r_B} - t_0}{t_{r_A} - t_0} = \frac{k'_B}{k'_A} \tag{21.10}$$

Selectivity refers to the capability of a chromatographic system to distinguish between two components, and is a thermodynamic quantity governed by the relative solute distributions between the mobile phase and the stationary phase. Selectivity in chromatography is very difficult to predict, but one can often use possible molecular interactions between the solute and stationary phase, such as hydrogen-bonding or acid-base relationships, to roughly predict α values. As α approaches 1, separation becomes exceedingly difficult. To modify selectivity one must change the stationary phase, the mobile phase, or both.

The bandwidth is related to the efficiency of the chromatographic process, which was discussed in the previous section. Unlike selectivity, efficiency is a kinetic phenomenon and can be increased by better column design as well as by the other factors discussed previously. Figure 21.7 illustrates the influence of selectivity and efficiency on chromatographic resolution. Figure 21.7A depicts a two-component separation displaying poor resolution. By decreasing peak width (i.e., more theoretical plates), resolution can be increased without affecting selectivity (Fig. 21.7B).

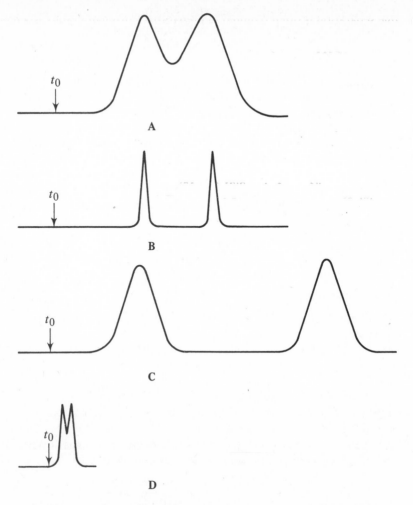

FIGURE 21.7. *Effect of selectivity, efficiency, and capacity factor on resolution. A: Poor resolution. B: Good resolution due to column efficiency. C: Good resolution due to column selectivity. D: Poor resolution due to low capacity factor despite adequate column efficiency and selectivity. Courtesy of Varian Associates.*

On the other hand, Figure 21.7C indicates that better resolution results from increasing the distance between peak maxima (that is, improving selectivity), even without increasing efficiency. Poor resolution caused by low capacity-factor (despite adequate column efficiency and selectivity) is depicted in Figure 21.7D. Better resolution can be obtained by increasing V_s (Eqn. 21.3)—for instance, by using a longer column or an adsorbent with a higher surface area.

In chromatography, a value of $R = 1$ is considered the minimum value for quantitative separation. For a two-component separation, this corresponds to a 2% contamination of each band by the other. When $R = 1.5$, the separation of the two bands is considered complete (cross-contamination less than 1%). Such a baseline separation is often required in preparative chromatography when pure substances are desired. As the value of R approaches zero, it becomes more difficult to discern separate peaks.

Example 21.3. (a) For the chromatogram shown in Figure 21.2, determine the resolution between peaks B and C. (b) Determine the value of α for the same peaks. (c) Two peaks with similar retention times generally have similar widths; for retained peaks with a width of 2 ml, what must be the difference in retention volumes to increase the resolution to 2?

Solution:

(a) $R = \dfrac{2(t_{r_C} - t_{r_B})}{t_{w_B} + t_{w_C}} = \dfrac{2(21.5 - 13)}{2.1 + 4.1} = 2.7$

(b) $\alpha = \dfrac{t_{r_C} - t_0}{t_{r_B} - t_0} = \dfrac{21.5 - 2}{13 - 2} = 1.8$

(c) $R = 2\dfrac{(t_{r_2} - t_{r_1})}{t_{w_1} + t_{w_2}} = 2\dfrac{(t_{r_2} - t_{r_1})}{2t_{w_1}} = \dfrac{t_{r_2} - t_{r_1}}{t_{w_1}}$

$2 = \dfrac{t_{r_2} - t_{r_1}}{t_{w_1}} = \dfrac{t_{r_2} - t_{r_1}}{2 \text{ ml}}$ and $t_{r_2} - t_{r_1} = 4 \text{ ml}$

An alternative equation for the resolution, which can be derived from Equation 21.10, namely

$$R = \frac{1}{4} \sqrt{N} \underbrace{\left(\frac{\alpha - 1}{\alpha}\right)}_{b} \underbrace{\left(\frac{k'}{1 + k'}\right)}_{c} \qquad (21.11)$$

a

shows that resolution is a function of three separate factors: the efficiency term a, the selectivity term b, and the capacity-factor term c (see Eqn. 22.12 in the next chapter); these parameters a, b, and c can be adjusted independently. It is evident from Equation 21.11 that R approaches zero (resolution is lost) as N or k' approach zero or as α approaches one. An increase in α, N, or k' favors better resolution, but, according to Equation 21.5, a large value of k' corresponds to a long separation time. In practice, one does not optimize all factors simultaneously, but selects a column with a high plate-number, then optimizes the k' value (usually between 2 and 5) by modifying the mobile-phase composition. If resolution is not adequate, then either N or α can be increased. If α is close to one, an increase in N may give only a modest increase in R. In that case, it is better to change α by changing the mobile phase or the stationary phase. This often time-consuming trial-and-error process of selecting and optimizing mobile and stationary phases makes the practice of chromatography something of an art.

Example 21.4. On silica gel an unretained peak, benzene, gave $V_m = 2.0$ ml, and o-diaminobenzene (ODB) and m-diaminobenzene (MDB) displayed k' values of 10 and 12, respectively. For a 100-cm column, the resolution between the isomers was 1.2. (a) Determine the length of column necessary to achieve complete baseline resolution. (b) With the new column from (a), what will be the void volume for benzene? (c) If the k' value for

MDB is increased to 18 while k' for ODB remains the same, what length of column would be necessary to resolve them to baseline? Note that in Equation 21.11, the k' value generally refers to the last eluting peak.

Solution:

(a) By Equations 21.7 and 21.11,

$$\frac{R_2}{R_1} = \frac{\sqrt{N_2}}{\sqrt{N_1}} = \frac{\sqrt{L_2}}{\sqrt{L_1}} \qquad \sqrt{L_2} = \frac{R_2\sqrt{L_1}}{R_1} = \frac{1.5\sqrt{100}}{1.2}$$

$$L_2 = 160 \text{ cm}$$

(b)
$$\frac{V_{m_2}}{V_{m_1}} = \frac{L_2}{L_1} \qquad V_{m_2} = \frac{V_{m_1}L_2}{L_1} = \frac{2.0(160)}{100} = 3.2 \text{ ml}$$

(c) By Equations 21.10 and 21.11,

$$\alpha_1 = \frac{k'_{1(MDB)}}{k'_{1(ODB)}} = \frac{12}{10} = 1.2$$

and

$$\alpha_2 = \frac{k'_{2(MDB)}}{k'_{2(ODB)}} = \frac{18}{10} = 1.8$$

$$\frac{R_2}{R_1} = \frac{\sqrt{L_2}}{\sqrt{L_1}} \frac{\left(\dfrac{\alpha_2 - 1}{\alpha_2}\right)}{\left(\dfrac{\alpha_1 - 1}{\alpha_1}\right)} \frac{\left[\dfrac{k'_{2(MDB)}}{1 + k'_{2(MDB)}}\right]}{\left[\dfrac{k'_{1(MDB)}}{1 + k'_{1(MDB)}}\right]}$$

$$\frac{1.8}{1.2} = \frac{\sqrt{L_2}}{\sqrt{100}} \frac{\left(\dfrac{1.8 - 1}{1.8}\right)}{\left(\dfrac{1.2 - 1}{1.2}\right)} \frac{\left(\dfrac{18}{1 + 18}\right)}{\left(\dfrac{12}{1 + 12}\right)}$$

$$L_2 = 30 \text{ cm}$$

Sample Capacity

The earlier discussion involving the distribution coefficient was based on the assumption that the coefficient is linear with respect to sample concentration (i.e., a linear sorption isotherm). Nonlinear isotherms, however, are sometimes encountered with the sample sizes employed in practical applications of chromatography, particularly in adsorption systems. The *sample capacity* of the stationary phase is an important consideration in practical applications. The sample capacity corresponds to the amount of sample that can be sorbed onto a particular stationary phase before overloading occurs. Exceeding the sample capacity results in unsymmetrical peak shapes, change in retention times, and loss of resolution. Sample capacity is generally expressed in milligrams of sample per gram of stationary phase. It is proportional to V_s, the volume of available stationary phase (e.g., adsorbent surface area in LSC or liquid phase loading in LLC). For porous LSC adsorbents, typical sample capacities are in the range of 2–5 mg/g. Sample capacity should not be confused with the capacity factor k' defined earlier.

The Chromatographic Compromise

The relationships among sample capacity, speed, and resolution can be represented by the triangular diagram in Figure 21.8. For a particular LC system, any one of these attributes can be improved at the expense of the other two or any two can be improved at the expense of the other one. The chromatographer must always compromise. In analytical LC, speed and resolution are the desired characteristics; sample capacity is usually unimportant, provided a detectable amount of sample is separated. In preparative LC, capacity is the main objective, provided the resolution is consistent with purity requirements; speed is usually sacrificed.

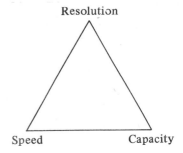

FIGURE 21.8. *Relationship of resolution, speed, and capacity. Courtesy of Varian Associates.*

21.3 APPARATUS AND TECHNIQUES OF LIQUID CHROMATOGRAPHY

Experiments in liquid chromatography can be performed with equipment ranging from simple laboratory glassware to complex and expensive automated chromatographs. The simplest technique, paper chromatography, requires a filter paper, a pipette to apply a sample, a closed jar, and the necessary solvents. On the other hand, high-performance liquid chromatography can require high-pressure pumps with electronic programmers, columns with specially prepared microparticles, and highly sensitive, flow-through, microvolume detectors.

Paper Chromatography

The basic technique is quite simple. A sheet of cellulose filter paper, such as Whatman No. 1, serves as the separation medium. For one-dimensional paper chromatography (PC), the paper is cut into strips about 5 cm wide and 20 cm long; for two-dimensional PC (below), a 20 × 20-cm sheet is commonly used. The papers come in various porosities (fine, medium, coarse); the porosity determines the rate of movement of the developing solvent. Low-porosity paper gives slow solvent movement but good resolution. Thick papers, which have increased sample capacity, are available for preparative separations.

Preparation. Prior to use, the paper strips are stored under conditions of controlled humidity. Since the predominant mechanism is partition between sorbed water and the mobile phase, the amount of water in the cellulose fibers governs its separating characteristics. The paper may also be impregnated with another stationary phase by dipping and careful drying.

The sample, dissolved in a volatile solvent, is applied to the paper as a drop or "spot" by means of a syringe or micropipette. To minimize band spreading, the spot should be restricted to about 2 mm in diameter. Sample sizes are normally 10–50 μg, and the total quantity of sample should not exceed 500 μg. Larger spots and larger sample sizes lead to poorer separations. Figure 21.9 illustrates the correct

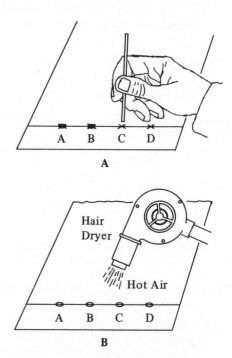

FIGURE 21.9. *Application of sample to paper in PC (or TLC). A: Applying the sample to paper. B: Drying the spots on the paper. From D. Abbott and R. S. Andrews,* An Introduction to Chromatography, *Boston: Houghton Mifflin, 1965, by permission of the publisher.*

manner of sample application. Several samples or standards can be applied as separate spots across the bottom of the paper. The solvent is removed by evaporation, often by means of a hair dryer or heat gun. If the sample is too dilute, several drops may be applied to concentrate it; the solvent should be evaporated between each application. For preparative PC, multiple spots or bands of sample are applied across the bottom of the paper. The paper is now ready to be developed.

Operation. The separation takes place inside a closed container, usually glass, as shown in Figure 21.10. Within the chamber, the paper can be supported so that the solvent flows upward (ascending PC), downward (descending PC), or horizontally. The airtight container ensures that the paper and developing solvent vapors are in equilibrium; for reproducible R_f values, the paper is usually preequilibrated with solvent vapor for 1–3 hours before development begins. For ascending PC, development begins by placing the bottom edge of the suspended paper (but not the spots) into the mobile phase, which ascends through the fibers by capillary action. In the descending method, the spotted edge of the paper strip is immersed in a trough

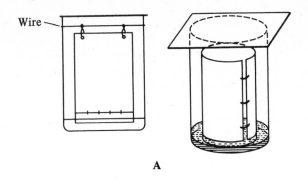

A

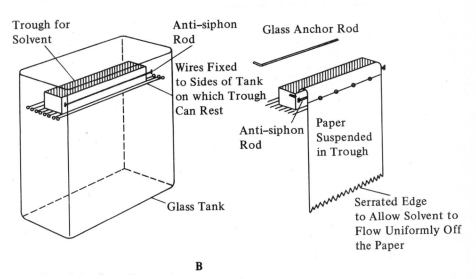

Trough for Solvent

Anti–siphon Rod

Glass Anchor Rod

Wires Fixed to Sides of Tank on which Trough Can Rest

Anti–siphon Rod

Paper Suspended in Trough

Glass Tank

Serrated Edge to Allow Solvent to Flow Uniformly Off the Paper

B

FIGURE 21.10. *Developing chambers for paper chromatography. A: Ascending development; B: Descending development. Note that similar chambers are used in TLC. From D. Abbott and R. S. Andrews,* An Introduction to Chromatography, *Boston: Houghton Mifflin, 1965, by permission of the publisher.*

near the top of the chamber, containing the solvent (Fig. 21.10A). The downward flow of solvent, caused by both capillary action and gravity, moves the solvent farther than in the ascending method. For this reason, the descending PC method is often preferred.

In ascending PC, the paper is supported by means of a clip or hook, or wrapped around a cylinder as depicted in Figure 21.10A. In descending PC, the top edge of the paper is held down by a glass rod or strip. In the horizontal (or radial) method, a circular paper is used and sample is applied in its center. After the sample dries, solvent is applied at the center and spreads out radially, carrying the sample with it. The main advantage of the radial method lies in its simplicity and its economical use of paper and solvents.

The mobile phase used for development depends on the nature of the substances to be separated. The sample should be only sparingly soluble in the solvent; if it is too soluble, distribution coefficients will strongly favor the mobile phase, components will move with the solvent front, and poor resolution will result. A single organic solvent (for example, *n*-butanol) saturated with water may serve as a mobile phase. Many popular solvents are of this type, but several useful partition solvents incorporate only small amounts of water. Very polar compounds (phenols, sugars, amino acids) will move slowly or fail to separate in these binary systems. Often, including another component in the mixtures (an acid, a base, or a complexing agent) results in a better separation of polar compounds. Organic solvent mixtures are frequently employed. One disadvantage of solvent mixtures, however, is that multi-component solvents themselves can partition along the paper, resulting in solvent "bands" which may affect component separation.

The development time should be sufficient to separate the components of interest. The rate of solvent movement depends on factors such as the porosity of the paper, the surface tension, viscosity, and volatility of the solvent, and the ambient temperature. Reasonable R_f values for good resolution are about 0.4–0.8; typical separation times for modern PC papers are in the range of 2–4 hours.

Detection. After separation, the solvent front is marked and the sheet is dried. The separated compounds are then detected in a variety of ways, chemical or physical. If they are colored, detection presents little or no problem; usually, however, the substances are colorless. In the latter case, the sheet is sprayed with or dipped in a chemical reagent to produce a colored product. There are a large variety of such visualization reagents [2] for various classes of compounds. For example, amino acids (colorless) are easily detected as a pale blue-violet product by treating the paper with a 0.2% solution of colorless ninhydrin. A number of unsaturated organic compounds fluoresce and can readily be detected under an ultraviolet lamp, and labeled (radioactive) compounds can be detected using a radiation counter.

Compounds are identified by their R_f values, as described in Section 21.2. Sometimes a reference substance, chemically similar to the sample, is run simultaneously alongside the sample and relative migration rates obtained by comparison. In this case, the R_x value defined by

$$R_x = \frac{\text{(distance moved by substance)}}{\text{(distance moved by standard substance X)}} \qquad \textbf{(21.12)}$$

is used. This procedure is especially useful in descending PC, in which the solvent is allowed to run off the bottom end of the paper to increase the migration distances.

In two-dimensional PC, a single sample is applied near one corner of the paper and the paper developed. The paper is then removed from the tank, dried, turned 90°, and developed in a second solvent. This procedure effectively increases the distance of migration, but more importantly, can separate the unresolved components, because the second solvent can have characteristics different from the first.

Thin-Layer Chromatography

Thin-layer chromatography (TLC), like paper chromatography, is performed on an open bed—a glass, aluminum, or plastic plate of dimensions not unlike those mentioned for **PC**, covered with a porous solid powder comprised of small particles about 5–40 μm in diameter. Commonly used phases include silica gel, alumina, cellulose, polyamides, and ion-exchange resins. To promote adhesion and to give better mechanical strength to the TLC plate, a binder such as calcium sulfate (5–10% by weight) is mixed with the powder.

Preparation. In preparing the plate, the powder is first usually made into a slurry with water (or other solvent) and then spread on the plate. For plate-to-plate reproducibility the layer must be very uniform. The slurry can be spread manually using a spatula or another plate, or (more reproducibly and conveniently) with a special apparatus. A "moving spreader" is shown in Figure 21.11. The cleaned plates

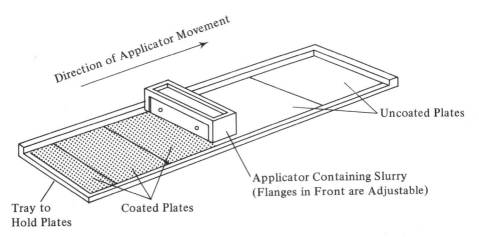

FIGURE 21.11. *Moving-spreader apparatus for preparing TLC plates. Applicator is filled with slurry.*

are held in a frame and the applicator containing the slurry is passed over them, depositing the slurry as a thin film. The thickness applied can be varied by adjusting flanges at the base of the applicator. For analytical work, the layer is 0.2–0.3 mm thick, whereas for preparative TLC, the thickness varies from 2–10 mm. After spreading, the plate is dried in air and activated by heating it at 110°C for a short period of time. Ready-made plates are available commercially; they are more expensive than homemade plates, but they are undoubtedly convenient and provide good reproducibility.

Operation. After activation, the sample application and developing procedures are carried out almost exactly as in PC. Normally, sample sizes range from 10–100 μg per spot for analytical TLC, but in preparative TLC when samples are applied as bands, up to 100 mg can be used with a 20 × 20-cm plate. Spots should be 2–5 mm in diameter. Ascending or descending development and one- or multi-dimensional techniques can be used. Because of differences in capillary action and possibly in solvent heat of adsorption, development times are usually faster in TLC than in PC. Depending on the mobile phase and the particle size of the adsorbent, a typical time is 20–30 min for a 10-cm distance, whereas for a high-porosity paper developed under similar conditions, development might take two hours. On thin layers, spots often remain compact; on filter paper, they tend to spread somewhat because of its fibrous structure. Thus, resolution is better in TLC and smaller amounts of substances can be separated and identified than in PC.

Detection. In TLC, since the supports, such as silica and alumina, are chemically more inert than paper, more strongly reactive reagents can be used to locate the separated substances. Concentrated sulfuric acid sprayed onto a silica plate makes organic substances visible as charred spots after the plate is heated in an oven. Selective color-forming reagents or iodine vapor are also used. Viewing the plate under ultraviolet radiation can reveal fluorescent substances, or an immobile fluorescent compound can be added initially to the preparation slurry. In the latter case, separated substances show up as dark spots against a fluorescing background when the plate is viewed under ultraviolet, because of their quenching effect.

R_f values are more difficult to reproduce in TLC than in PC because there are more experimental variables. R_f values are influenced by the following factors:

1. The nature of the adsorbent (its chemical nature, particle size, surface area, and binder)
2. The nature of the mobile phase (its purity, precision of mixing, moisture content, and volatility)
3. The activity of the adsorbent and its thickness and uniformity
4. The temperature of the apparatus
5. The amount of sample used
6. The vapor-pressure equilibrium between the plate and the development-chamber atmosphere

A comparison between TLC and PC for the separation of nucleotides is given in Figure 21.12. A one-dimensional development using identical conditions shows the superiority of cellulose-layer TLC over PC for separating various mixtures (a different mixture for each vertical column of spots). Note that, in the same development distance, the isomeric 2′- and 3′-nucleotides (spots 1 to 4) were only partially resolved by PC but were fully resolved by TLC, whereas spots 7 to 9 were completely resolved only by TLC. The reduced degree of spot diffusion in TLC can be readily observed. Standardization of procedure is of considerable importance. For details on TLC standardization, the reader is referred to the book by Stahl [3].

Quantitative Aspects of TLC and PC

Compared to TLC or PC, quantitation is carried out more easily in column chromatography. A good deal of care is required to obtain reproducible and accurate quantitative results in TLC or PC. It is imperative that chromatographic conditions be well standardized. Standards and samples must be applied to the paper (or plate) in spots of similar size and at similar concentrations; solvents must be prepared, the chamber brought to equilibrium, and so forth, in the same manner. The locating reagent must be applied in a reproducible way. Having obtained a developed chro-

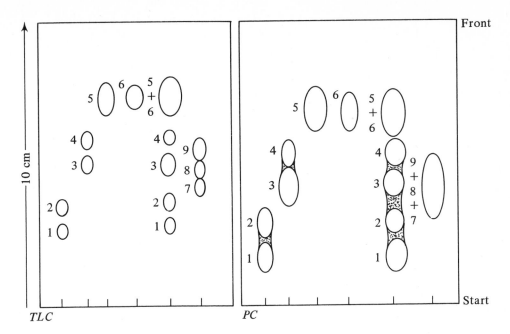

FIGURE 21.12. *Comparative TLC and PC separation of nucleotides. A: Cellulose thin-layer chromatogram—development distance, 10 cm in 91 min. B: Paper chromatogram run under identical conditions—development distance, 10 cm in 134 min; paper Schleicher and Schull 2043b. The solvent used for both was saturated ammonium sulfate/1 M sodium acetate/isopropanol (80:18:2). Each vertical column of spots corresponds to separate mixtures separated. Samples: (1) 3'-AMP; (2) 2'-AMP; (3) 3'-GMP; (4) 2'-GMP; (5) 2'- and 3'-GMP; (6) 2'- and 3'-UMP; (7) 5'-AMP; (8) 5'-ADP; (9) 5'-ATP. (A = adenosine, G = guanine, C = cytidine, M = mono-, D = di-, T = tri-, P = phosphate.)* From K. Randerath, Biochem. Biophys. Res. Comm., 6, 452 (1961–62), *by permission of Academic Press.*

matogram, the separated substance can be measured directly on the paper (or plate) or it can be removed from the paper and measured by some other means.

1. *Visual Comparison of Spots.* Samples and reference solutions containing known amounts are run on the same sheet, and the relative areas of the unknown and the standards estimated by eye.

2. *Physical Measurements of Colored Spots.* Transmission or reflectance measurements on a strip or plate are made using a spectrophotometer. Scanning photodensitometers are devices that measure spot intensity by reflectance and display the result on a recorder. Visual methods are accurate to 5–10%; scanning methods, to 3–5%.

3. *Radioactive Measurements.* For radioactive substances included in the sample, one may scan the strip with an automatic scanning device.

4. *Spot-Area Measurement.* The area of a spot is proportional to the logarithm of the amount of substance. The spot area can be determined by using transparent graph paper and counting the squares covered by the spot. Standards are run under the same conditions and a calibration curve of area versus log(standard weight applied) obtained.

5. *Spot Removal.* The spot may be removed from the paper by cutting or from a plate by scraping off the adsorbent containing the spot. The substance can be eluted or extracted from the strip or plate, and then handled as any other sample solution (e.g., measured by spectrophotometry, polarography, etc.)

Column Liquid Chromatography

Earlier, the basic principles of column chromatography were outlined. Although classical open-column LC is still a widely used technique, modern high-performance liquid chromatography (HPLC)—also called high-speed liquid chromatography (HSLC)—is quickly becoming the standard technique for column separation. There is no difference in the basic mechanism involved; only the apparatus employed and the practice of the technique are different. Relative to classical LC, the main advantages of HPLC are increased speed, resolution, and sensitivity, and its convenience for quantitative analysis.

General Considerations. When particles are packed into a column, they offer a restriction to solvent flow. The longer the column and the smaller the particles, the greater the restriction. If flow is forced through the column, it generates a back pressure. The relation of this column back pressure ΔP to the other chromatographic variables is given by

$$\Delta P = \frac{\eta L v}{\theta\, d_p^{\,2}} \tag{21.13}$$

where η = the viscosity of the mobile phase
v = the linear velocity of the mobile phase
L = the column length
d_p = the average diameter of the particles
θ = a dimensionless structural constant, ~ 600 for packed beds

If the chromatographic variables are expressed in the cgs-mks system, then ΔP has units of kg/cm^2 or of atmospheres. Often, the pressure is expressed in units of pounds-per-square-inch above gravity or psig.

High-Performance Liquid Chromatography. The difference between classical LC and HPLC can be explored by referring to Figures 21.13 and 21.14. For classical LC, large porous particles with $d_p = 100$–$250\ \mu$m (Fig. 21.13A) are packed into columns with internal diameters of 1–5 cm (Fig. 21.14A). Little pressure is required to permit slow solvent flow between these large particles. Normally, a small head of liquid in the column above the surface of the packing or, in some cases, a reservoir container connected to and placed above the column acts as the constant-pressure source. Pressure drops are of the order of 0.1–1 atmosphere. Flow rates are very

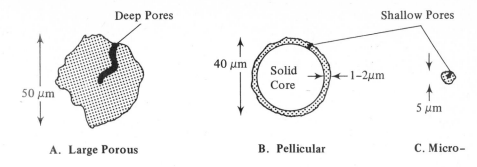

FIGURE 21.13. *Types of particles used in liquid chromatography. A: Large porous particle (d_p = 50–250 μm); B: Pellicular particle (d_p = 37–50 μm); C: Porous microparticle (d_p = 5–10 μm).*

slow (approximately 0.1 ml/min or less), and separation times very long. If attempts are made to speed up the solvent velocity, say by pumping, then, according to Equation 21.8, column efficiency (already low) and resolution will decrease because of mass-transfer limitations in the deep pores (that is, large values of H_{sm} or H_{sp}), and large interparticle channels (that is, large values of H_{ed} and H_{mp}). H-versus-v curves for such packings give steep slopes; hence the need for low flow-rates. Because of their large surface areas with high ion-exchange capacities, though, the large porous packings exhibit large sample capacities, important in preparative chromatography. Large porous packings are available at a nominal price and can be packed into columns by simple procedures.

Although an increase in column efficiency with a decrease in d_p was predicted very early in the development of column chromatography, only during the 1960s were column packings available that permitted application of the theory. These packing materials (in the range of $30 \leqslant d_p \leqslant 75\ \mu m$), when packed into narrow columns, gave rise to larger back-pressures than the classical LC columns (Fig. 21.14B). Thus, to assist in mobile-phase flow through the column, high-pressure pumps were required. This was the advent of HPLC. For analytical HPLC, flow rates of 0.5–5 ml/min became typical and pressure drops up to 300 atm were obtained. On the other hand, column efficiency was increased 10–100-fold compared to classical LC, and separation times were decreased.

These improvements were caused by the development of pellicular packings in the late 1960s. These spherical packings consist of a solid, nonporous core (usually a glass bead approximately 40 μm in diameter) and a thin, porous outer shell, as depicted in Figure 21.13B. The outer shell, normally 1–3 μm thick, may be silica gel, alumina, resin, or polyamide. Because of their dense solid cores, pellicular particles are easily packed into columns. Compared to a porous particle of equivalent diameter, stationary-phase mass-transfer in this thin shell (the value of H_{sm} and/or H_{sp} of Equation 21.8) is greatly improved. However, on account of the thin shell, V_s is significantly reduced and sample capacity is 0.05–0.1 that of the totally porous packings. Therefore, pellicular packings are less useful in preparative LC.

A decrease in d_p below 30 μm for porous particles leads to further improvements in efficiency. Ion-exchange chromatographers were among the first to recognize the advantages of using very small spherical particles—in the 10-μm range.

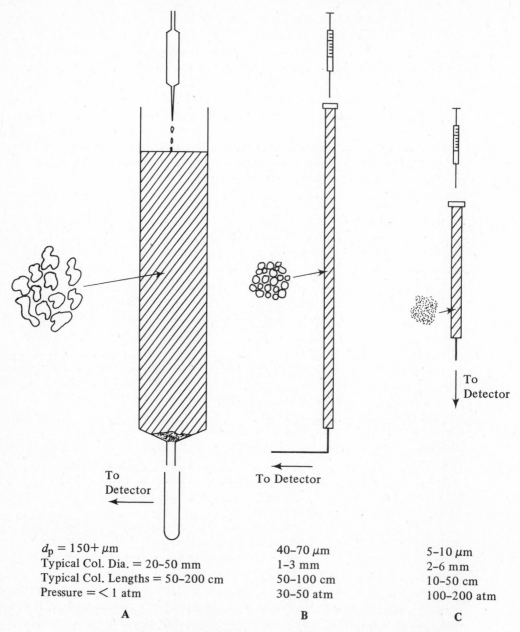

$d_p = 150+ \, \mu$m	40–70 μm	5–10 μm
Typical Col. Dia. = 20–50 mm	1–3 mm	2–6 mm
Typical Col. Lengths = 50–200 cm	50–100 cm	10–50 cm
Pressure = < 1 atm	30–50 atm	100–200 atm
A	**B**	**C**

FIGURE 21.14. *Comparison of columns used in liquid chromatography. A: Classical open column chromatography with large porous particle packings; B: HPLC with pellicular packings; C: HPLC with microparticulate packings.*

Ion-exchange resins were synthesized and then separated into narrow size-fractions by sedimentation or elutriation procedures. For the other modes of LC, commercial quantities of microparticles in narrow size-distributions, and the technology to pack them, were unavailable until the early 1970s. Through the use of air-centrifugal particle-classifiers, narrow size-distributions of adsorbents are now commercially available. In addition, high-pressure slurry-packing procedures have been developed. Microparticles in the 5–15 μm range (Fig. 21.13C) are commonly used for producing highly efficient HPLC columns. The increased efficiency (an extra factor of 10) is caused by improvements in the stationary-phase and mobile-phase mass-transfer terms of Equation 21.8. Thus, separation times and H values of 0.001–0.01 those of classical LC are obtained routinely. In addition, as their surface areas (or ion-exchange capacities) are the same as those of the large porous packings, the microparticles provide large sample capacity. Unfortunately, these microparticles are more expensive than large porous particles and require rather specialized packing techniques.

Since efficiencies for microparticulate columns are very high (optimum H values of 0.01–0.03 mm), only short columns (15–25 cm) are required for analytical HPLC, as can be seen in Figure 21.14C. The use of 5-μm particles implies greatly increased column back-pressures compared to those produced by the larger porous or pellicular particles, as suggested by Equation 21.13. However, these short columns exhibit moderate back-pressures (less than 200 atm) when used at flow rates of 1–2 ml/min with nonviscous mobile phases. But, for more difficult separations which may require tens of thousands of theoretical plates, long columns (50–100 cm) with the smallest available particles and high-pressure solvent feed are sometimes required. Likewise, according to Equation 21.13, high flow-rates or viscous mobile phases result in increased column back-pressure. In these cases, pressure drops of several hundred atmospheres may be encountered.

The overall influence of a reduction in particle size on the efficiency of a packed column is illustrated in Figure 21.15. Here curves of H-versus-v are plotted for 6.1 μm $\leqslant d_p \leqslant$ 44.7 μm for six different particle sizes of a porous silica gel. A standard test solute (N,N'-diethyl-p-aminoazobenzene) and the same mobile phase were used for all columns. Columns were packed by a high-pressure slurry technique. Note the significant decrease in H as the particle size is reduced to 6.1 μm. For comparison, an H-versus-v curve for Corasil®, a pellicular silica with an average d_p of 42.5 μm, is included. Porous silicas below 20 μm in d_p would be expected to give greater efficiency than 40-μm pellicular packings. Such H-versus-d_p relationships hold for all LC modes, including TLC.

Apparatus for Column Chromatography. A glass, metal, or plastic tube with a tapered outlet (Fig. 21.14A) is used as the column. To contain the packing, a wad of glass wool or a porous metal frit is placed at the bottom of the column, and the solid particles are poured into the top in increments until the column is full. It is important that the column be tightly packed with no voids. Although gravity can be used to force the liquid through the packed column, a pump is used for smaller diameter packings (less than 100 μm), as depicted in Figure 21.16. The sample can be injected by pipetting the sample, dissolved in a suitable solvent, onto the top of the packing. For the forced-flow systems in HPLC, an injection device—most commonly a syringe—is incorporated into the top of the column. The column temperature can be controlled by placing the column in an oven or by using a water jacket. Although glass columns are useful for low-pressure and classical open-column work, stainless-steel columns and compression-type fittings are required for high pressures (above 70 atm).

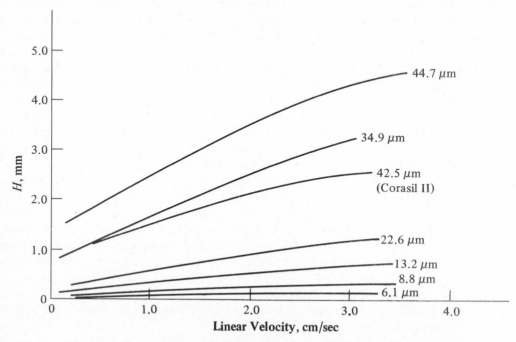

FIGURE 21.15. *Effect of velocity on plate height for porous silica gels of various particle diameters. Test solute: N,N′-diethyl-p-phenyl azoaniline (k′ = 1.2). Mobile phase: 90/9.9/0.125 parts by volume of hexane/ methylene chloride/isopropanol. Included for comparison is the same test solute run on Corasil II, a pellicular silica gel of d_p = 37–50 μm. From R. E. Majors,* J. Chromatogr. Sci., *11, 92 (1973), by permission of the publisher.*

To measure the substances eluting from the column, fractions of mobile phase can be collected and the concentration of the separated components measured externally—for example, in a spectrophotometer or using a pH meter. An automatic fraction-collector which collects a defined volume of column effluent in test tubes is sometimes employed. However, it is more convenient to employ a continuous-detection device at the exit of the column. The detector can be selective (for instance, it detects ultraviolet-absorbing or fluorescent compounds only) or universal (that is, it detects all components). In some cases, two detectors placed in series are used to gain additional information. The detector output is usually displayed on a strip-chart recorder or some other data-acquisition device. For quantitative analysis, an integrator or a minicomputer are useful to automatically measure peak areas.

The continuous detectors most often used in liquid chromatography are based on ultraviolet or visible absorption, fluorescence, and differential refractometry.

To minimize broadening of the narrow peaks often obtained in HPLC, modern detectors measure a small volume, usually 15 μl or less. A schematic of an ultraviolet detector with a flow-through cell is presented in Figure 21.17. The light source is a low-pressure mercury lamp with an intense emission line at 254 nm. The light is collimated by a quartz lens, passes through the reference and sample cells, is filtered to remove unwanted radiation, and is sensed by a dual photocell. Typically, a flow-through cell of this kind has a 1-mm diameter and 10-mm length with a 15-μl volume. The normal laws of spectrophotometry hold for these detectors—absorbance is linear with concentration. An ultraviolet detector can resolve absorbance differences as small as 0.00005 absorbance unit, equivalent to ppb detection limits in favorable cases.

FIGURE 21.16. *Block diagram of a liquid chromatograph. Courtesy of Varian Associates.*

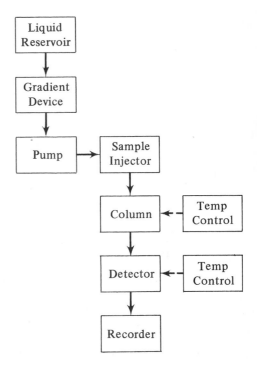

Table 21.1 classifies popular LC detectors according to several criteria for purposes of comparison. At the present time, LC detectors are generally less sensitive than GC detectors, which can detect picograms of material under good conditions. Most LC detectors provide only limited structural information. However, spectrophotometers fitted with micro flow-cells can be used to obtain a stop-flow ultraviolet- or visible-absorption spectrum of an LC peak trapped in the flow cell. On-line coupling of liquid chromatographs with mass or infrared spectrometers offers sophisticated, but indeed expensive, detection/identification methods. Such systems have been described in the literature, but are quite limited by the solvents that can be used in the chromatography step.

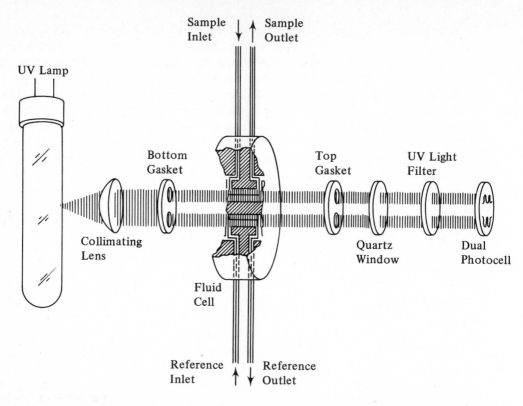

FIGURE 21.17. *Expanded optical schematic of ultraviolet detector. Courtesy of Varian Associates.*

TABLE 21.1. *Comparison of LC Detectors*

Factor	Ultraviolet (UV)	Refractive Index (RI)	Fluorescence	Electrochemical	Moving Wire/Flame Ionization
Specificity	Selective	Universal	Selective	Selective	Universal
Detection Limit	10^{-10} g/ml	10^{-7} g/ml	10^{-10} g/ml	10^{-9} g/ml	10^{-7} g/ml
Gradient Compatible	Yes	No	Yes	Yes	Yes
Major Limitations	Non-UV active solvents only	Low sensitivity, precise temperature control required	Limited dynamic range	Compound adsorption, no electroactive solvents	No salt buffers or volatile solutes

Liquid chromatography is most applicable to nonvolatile compounds such as ionic compounds or polymers, thermally unstable compounds such as explosives, and labile compounds such as many biological substances. For volatile compounds, GC is the preferred technique. However, approximately 80% of the known organic compounds are nonvolatile enough to be handled by LC. Liquid chromatography is a relatively "gentle" technique in the sense that many separations can be carried out at ambient temperature, provided the sample can be dissolved in a suitable solvent. It suffices to say that if the sample can be dissolved, it can be analyzed by LC. Sample sizes can range from nanograms to grams; the only limitation on the low end is finding a suitable detector for subnanogram quantities. As new detectors are developed, detection limits for HPLC will be lowered below the nanogram range.

Influence of the Stationary Phase in LSC

Selecting the correct chromatographic technique for a particular mixture is sometimes difficult. We will discuss those properties of the various types of stationary phases that serve to distinguish one mode of LC from another.

Adsorption or liquid-solid chromatography (LSC), the oldest chromatographic method, is the most widely used of all modes. Thin-layer or column chromatography is used by most laboratories that use liquid-chromatographic techniques, often as a screening method to select the best experimental conditions for LC. Adsorbents are porous solids with specific surface areas ranging from 50–1000 m²/g. Table 21.2 lists typical adsorbents used in several chromatographic techniques. Most adsorbents come in particle sizes to suit the needs of the various kinds of chromatography, are specially made, and can be purchased commercially. For TLC, particle sizes of 20–40 μm are frequently used, whereas for open columns the particles are larger (100–150 μm) and for HPLC they are smaller (down to 5 μm).

To illustrate the manner in which adsorbents separate compounds, consider the surface characteristics of the most widely used adsorbent, silica gel. Chromatographic-grade silica gels are prepared by reacting sodium silicate with a mineral acid, such as hydrochloric acid. Polymerization occurs and a three-dimensional array of SiO_4 tetrahedra results. This polysilicic acid, when dehydrated, forms a stable porous solid, terminated at the surface with either silanol or siloxane bonds, as illustrated in Figure 21.18. The slightly acidic silanol groups are considered to be important in separation; siloxane bonds, to have little or no influence. Silanol groups themselves are believed to have varying degrees of acidity. The most acidic ones, located on adjacent silicon atoms with intramolecular hydrogen-bonding, often lead to undesirable chromatographic effects, such as chemisorption and peak tailing. Often a polar modifier, such as water, is added to the adsorbent in order to deactivate the strongest adsorption sites.

Interactions between the adsorbent surface and the solute can vary from non-specific ones (such as dispersion or van der Waals' forces) to specific ones (electrostatic interactions involving permanent dipoles or electron-donor-acceptor interactions, such as hydrogen bonding). Retention on silica gel or alumina is governed mainly by interactions with the polar functional groups of the solute. Thus, compounds of different chemical types (e.g., hydrocarbons and alcohols) are easily separated by LSC. Weak dispersive interactions with the hydrocarbon (especially aliphatic) portion of the solute allows little or no differentiation among homologues or other mixtures differing only in the extent of aliphatic substitution. The relative positions of the functional groups in the solute molecule, and the number and spatial arrangement of surface adsorption sites, lead to a geometric specificity that makes LSC unique in

TABLE 21.2. *Adsorbents for Adsorption Chromatography*

Adsorbent	Chemical Structure	Estimated Usage (percent)	Surface Properties	Applications
Silica	$(SiO_2)_x$	80	Slightly Acid	General-Purpose Adsorbent
Alumina	$(Al_2O_3)_x$	10	Slightly Basic [a]	General-Purpose Adsorbent
Charcoal	Carbon	1	Graphitized-nonpolar Oxidized Polar (Slightly Basic)	Sample Cleanup
Florisil®	Magnesia-silica coprecipitate	2	Strongly Acidic	General-Purpose Adsorbent
Polyamides	——	3	Basic	Phenols and Aromatic Nitro Compounds
Others (clays, Kieselguhr, diatomaceous earth, Celite®, etc.)	——	5	Relatively Nonpolar	Very Polar Compounds

(handwritten margin note: (Sulfonated Polystyrene). Ion Exchange)

a. Depends on method of preparation; can also be neutral or acidic.

its ability to separate polyfunctional compounds, especially positional isomers. For instance, *cis-trans* pairs or substituted aromatic isomers can be separated. Such a separation, by HPLC, of the three isomers of nitroaniline is shown in Figure 21.19. Note that the first to elute is the *ortho* isomer, which is intramolecularly hydrogen-bonded and thus has less (intermolecular) interaction with the surface, whereas the *para-* isomer is more likely to react intermolecularly and is the most strongly retained.

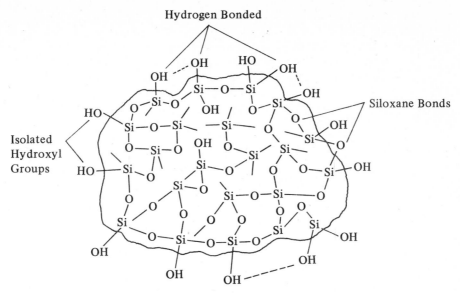

FIGURE 21.18. *Structure of silica gel depicting the various types of bonds and silanol groups present.*

Influence of the Mobile Phase in LSC

Actually, the interactions in LSC involve a competition between the solute molecules (X) and the molecules (S) of the mobile phase for the adsorption sites. This equilibrium is illustrated by

$$X_m + nS_{ads} \rightleftharpoons X_{ads} + nS_m \tag{21.14}$$

where $\quad X_m =$ the solute molecules in the mobile phase

$X_{ads} =$ the solute molecules in the adsorbed state

$S_{ads} =$ the mobile-phase molecules adsorbed on the surface site

$S_m =$ the solvent molecules in the free mobile phase

$n =$ the number of adsorbed solvent molecules displaced by the adsorption of one molecule of X

Thus, stronger adsorption of the mobile phase decreases adsorption of the solute. Solvents can be classed according to their strength of adsorption. Such a quantitative classification is referred to as an *eluotropic series*. Table 21.3 is an abbreviated eluotropic series specifically for alumina as the adsorbent, but qualitatively this series holds for other polar adsorbents as well [4].

An eluotropic series can be used to find an optimum solvent strength for a particular separation. Using a solvent of constant composition is called *isocratic elution*. If an isocratic solvent is too strong (if the k' values for the solutes are too small), a weaker solvent is substituted. On the other hand, if the initial solvent is too weak (the k' values are too large), a stronger solvent is selected. This trial-and-error approach to finding the optimum solvent can be done more rapidly by TLC than by column chromatography.

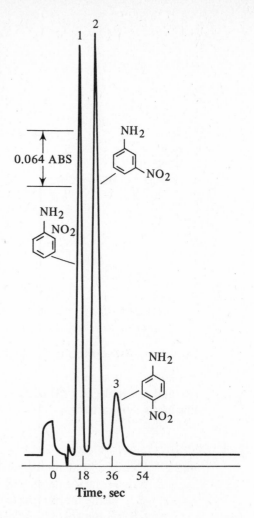

FIGURE 21.19. *LSC separation of nitro-aniline isomers on 10-μm alumina,* (1) *o-nitroaniline;* (2) *m-nitroaniline;* (3) *p-nitroaniline. Column: Micropak® Al-10. Packing: 10-μm alumina, type T. Dimensions: 15 cm × 2.4 mm. Mobile phase: 40% CH_2Cl_2 in hexane. Flow rate: 100 ml/hr. Sample size: 1 μg of each isomer. Detector: 254-nm ultraviolet absorption. From R. E. Majors,* Anal. Chem., **45,** 757 (1973), *by permission of the publisher. Copyright © 1973 by the American Chemical Society.*

Binary solvent mixtures may also be used to find an optimum value of the *solvent-strength* parameter ε^0. For example, a mixture of isoöctane ($\varepsilon^0 = 0.01$) and methylene chloride ($\varepsilon^0 = 0.42$) can be found (see Table 21.3) with an isocratic solvent strength similar to that of carbon tetrachloride ($\varepsilon^0 = 0.18$). However, the relationship between binary composition and solvent strength is not necessarily linear, owing to the solvent-solvent and preferential solvent-surface interactions. Additional selectivity in LSC can be achieved through secondary solvent effects. Such effects are produced by solvent mixtures that display equivalent values of ε^0 but that, because of various solvation interactions such as hydrogen-bonding ability, basicity, and so forth, also give rise to variations in relative retention (i.e., selectivity).

In all forms of chromatography, one must be aware of the so-called general elution problem (illustrated in Fig. 21.20) when dealing with isocratic solvent systems and multi-component samples with widely differing k' values. If a strong isocratic mobile phase is selected that will adequately elute strongly retained compounds, then the weakly retained ones will be eluted too quickly and will be poorly separated

TABLE 21.3. *Eluotropic Series for Alumina*

Solvent	Solvent-Strength Parameter (ε^0)
n-Pentane	0.00
Isoöctane	0.01
Cyclohexane	0.04
Carbon Tetrachloride	0.18
Xylene	0.26
Toluene	0.29
Benzene	0.32
Ethyl Ether	0.38
Chloroform	0.40
Methylene Chloride	0.42
Tetrahydrofuran	0.45
Acetone	0.56
Methyl Acetate	0.60
Aniline	0.62
Acetonitrile	0.65
i-Propanol, *n*-Propanol	0.82
Ethanol	0.88
Methanol	0.95
Ethylene Glycol	1.11
Acetic Acid	Large

Source: L. R. Snyder, *J. Chromatog.*, *16*, 55 (1964), by permission of the author and the North Holland Publishing Company.

(Fig. 21.20A).   Conversely, if a weak mobile phase is chosen, so that weakly retained sample components will be retained and separated, then very strongly retained solutes may not be eluted at all—or only very slowly (Fig. 21.20B)—and possibly with the peaks so broadened as to be undetectable.   No single isocratic solvent can be found that will be effective for such a mixture of components with widely varying k' values. To handle this kind of sample, the rates of band migration must be changed during the chromatographic run.

In GC, the general elution problem is solved by temperature programming and to a lesser extent by flow programming (see Chap. 22).   In LC, the most common technique is called *solvent programming* or *gradient elution*.   Here, elution is begun with a weak solvent and the solvent strength is increased with time.   The changes are made either stepwise or continuously.   The overall effect is to elute successively the more strongly retained substances and at the same time to reduce tailing.   The k' values, and hence the analysis time, can be decreased by as much as 10^6 using solvent programming.   Figure 21.20C demonstrates how solvent programming provides a solution to the general elution problem for the compounds shown.

In HPLC, since columns are reusable, the stationary phase must be returned to its initial condition at the conclusion of a solvent program so that, if necessary, another sample can be run under equivalent conditions.   This process is called *regeneration*.   Regeneration is accomplished by an instantaneous return to the initial

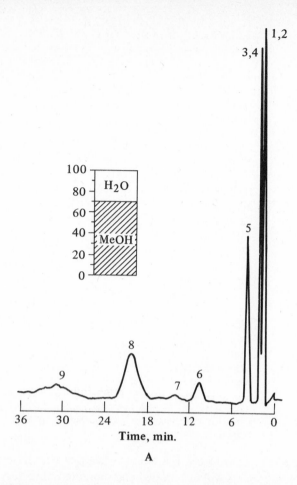

FIGURE 21.20. *Illustration of the general elution problem: separation of commercial flame retardants (brominated aromatics). Column: Perma-phase®-ODS (DuPont), 1 m × 2.4 mm. Solvent flow rate: 1 ml/min. A and B are isocratic elutions. C is a solvent-programmed run: 40% methanol in water to 100% methanol at 3%/min. Compounds: (1) Bis-phenol A; (2) Firemaster LV-723P; (3) Firemaster BP4A (Tetrabromo-bisphenol A); (4) p-Dibromobenzene; (5) 4,4'-Dibromobiphenyl; (6) Hexabromobenzene; (7) Hexabromobenzene impurity; (8) Firemaster BP-6 (Hexabromodiphenyl); (9) Firemaster BP-6 impurity (probably isomer). (Firemasters are products of the Michigan Chemical Company.) Chromatograms courtesy of Varian Associates.*

composition of the solvent, then prolonged washing to remove the stronger solvent. The time required depends on V_s, the amount of stationary phase. An alternate, and in most cases more rapid, regeneration technique is to run a "negative" solvent program to remove the stronger solvent more gradually. At the end of the negative program, the column is usually ready for another injection.

In column chromatography, solvent gradients can be formed stepwise by

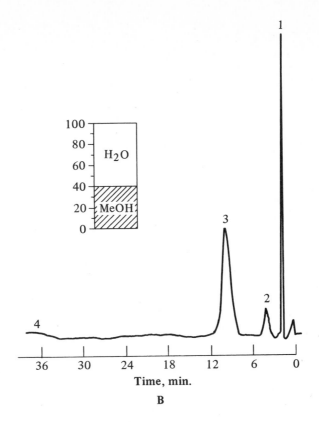

B

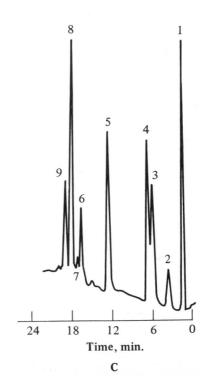

C

adding successively stronger solvents one at a time to the top of the column. A commercial apparatus is available to automatically select from two to twelve successive solvents, each at predetermined times. Continuous gradients can be formed by using a simple apparatus equipped with a magnetic stirrer (see Fig. 21.21A). The pure weaker solvent (B) is placed in the mixing flask and the stronger solvent (A) is placed in the reservoir. Solvent A is permitted to flow into the mixing flask and the mixture of A and B is delivered to the column, often by means of a reciprocating pump. Equations are available for calculating the composition of the mixture in the flask at any given time. The shape (profile) of the gradient can be varied, as shown in Figure 21.21B; both linear and nonlinear profiles are useful in LC.

Homogeneous mixing is required to provide smooth and reproducible profiles. In HPLC, gradients may be formed on the low-pressure side of the pump (analogous to the technique described above), or on the high-pressure side of the pump (depicted in Fig. 21.21C). With electronic programmers controlling the pump flows, the ratio of A to B can be varied easily and gradient profiles changed reproducibly. In addition, stepwise gradients, negative gradients, and isocratic mobile phases can be generated in the mixing chamber.

In TLC, although continuous solvent programming is feasible, it is seldom used because it is experimentally inconvenient. Stepwise development or two-dimensional TLC is used instead. More recently, programmed multiple development with the same solvent system has been introduced.

21.5 USES AND APPLICATIONS OF PARTITION CHROMATOGRAPHY

Partition or liquid-liquid chromatography is similar to solvent extraction. In fact, solvent-extraction data can be used to predict partition coefficients for LLC. The resolving power and speed of LLC are considerably greater than that of solvent extraction, however, since the equivalent of several thousand partitions takes place as the sample components move down a column. LLC is generally better suited to analytically separating complex mixtures, whereas extraction is used more for large-scale preparative separations or for separating relatively simple mixtures.

Selecting Stationary and Mobile Phases in LLC

The stationary and the mobile phases are selected so as to have little or no mutual solubility. Therefore, they generally are quite different in their solvent properties. For example, referring to Table 21.3, one might choose water as the stationary phase and pentane as the mobile phase for normal LLC. However, water does have

FIGURE 21.21. *Gradient devices used in liquid chromatography. A: Simple mixing device for gradient elution, gradient formed on low-pressure side of pump. R_1 is the flow rate of A into the flask. R_2 is the flow rate of A + B to column. B: Gradient profiles obtained from A. C: Schematic for two-pump gradient chromatograph. Gradient formed on high-pressure side of pump.*

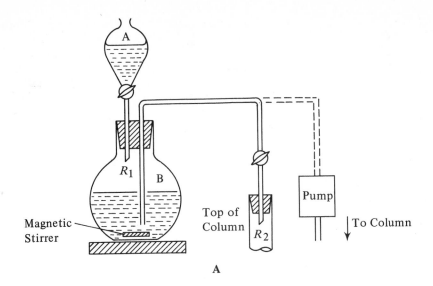

A

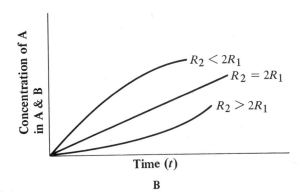

B

Total Flow (A & B) To Column

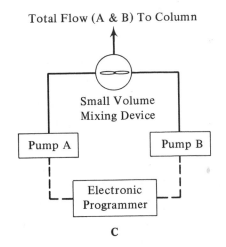

C

a finite (though very slight) solubility in pentane. If pentane, used as a mobile phase, is allowed to flow over a water-coated support long enough, it will slowly remove the water and change the nature of the separation mechanism. For this reason, the mobile phase must be presaturated with the stationary phase before it enters the column. Presaturation can be done by stirring the two phases together until equilibration takes place; but it is more conveniently done by placing a "precolumn" before the chromatographic column. The precolumn should contain a high-surface-area packing, such as silica gel, coated with a high percentage (say 30–40% by weight) of the stationary phase used in the analytical column. As the solvent passes through the highly dispersed stationary phase, the solvent becomes saturated with it and will not remove it from the analytical column.

Liquid-liquid chromatography is limited to compounds with comparatively low values of K (or k'), because the stationary phase must be a good solvent for the sample but a poor solvent for the mobile phase. In practice, increasing solvent strength in order to elute compounds with high K (or k') values will increase the solubility of the stationary phase and remove it from its support. When the solvent strength is high enough to dissolve an appreciable amount of stationary phase, presaturation is rendered difficult. Needless to say, in conventional LLC solvent programming is ruled out.

Even with its limitations, LLC is a very useful technique because it can resolve minute differences in the solubility of the solute. Many solvent pairs are available, and the choice of the proper ones allows great selectivity to be achieved. Selection of useful solvent pairs has been greatly improved by classifying solvents in terms of their ability to undergo different types of intermolecular interactions. Recently, a scheme based on the Hildebrand solubility parameter (δ) has been described [5, 6]—common chromatographic solvents are classified quantitatively in terms of parameters such as dispersion interactions, dipole interactions, and proton donor–acceptor ability. By matching the properties of the particular solute (for instance, its proton-acceptor ability) with one or more of these individual parameters, one can estimate K values and vary δ until the desired separation is obtained. The K value of a solute is related to the ratio of its concentrations (more correctly, its activities) in the two partitioning phases; selecting partitioning solvents with quite different δ values (polarity) magnifies these differences in solubility. Since the activity coefficients of members of a homologous series vary with their molecular size, members of a homologous series can be separated by LLC, whereas in LSC there is little discrimination between successive members of a homologous series.

Both PC and TLC have been carried out with coated liquid phases. The paper strip (or thin-layer plate) is impregnated with stationary phase, either neat or dissolved in a volatile solvent. In the latter case the solvent should be allowed to evaporate slowly to ensure homogeneous distribution of the stationary phase. Normal development is carried out, but some care is required to locate the separated spots since the coated liquid phase may interfere with detection.

Substances only very sparingly soluble in water are not separated by ordinary paper chromatography, since they move with the solvent front. If the paper is impregnated with silicone oil or paraffin and a highly polar solvent is used as the mobile phase, such samples are more easily separated. This technique is referred to as reverse-phase PC. In the same way, reverse-phase TLC can be carried out.

Bonded-Phase Chromatography

The limiting requirements of conventional LLC—that is, finding immiscible solvent pairs, presaturating the mobile phase to avoid removing the stationary phase, and the impossibility of using gradient elution to solve the general elution problem—have been overcome in *bonded-phase chromatography* (BPC). Although the latter is grouped here as a branch of LLC, the chromatographic behavior of bonded phases is somewhat dependent on the manner of preparation, and bonded-phase chromatography has also been classed as a form of LSC since the bonded phases may not be liquid-like, and modified adsorption may be the predominant mechanism.

Although, in principle, any number of chemical species can be bonded to the support, in practice only three general types of chemical bonding have been used with LC packings.

1. Since silica gel contains large numbers of reactive silanol groups extending from the surface, the Si–OH groups can be esterified by reaction with alcohols to yield *silicate esters*.
2. The Si–OH groups can be silanized by reaction with organochloro- or organo-alkoxysilanes.
3. Silica Si–OH groups can be converted to Si–Cl by chlorination, after which Grignard reaction, Wurtz reaction, or some other reaction typical of organo-halogen compounds yields chemically bonded species with Si–C linkages.

Because of the hydrolytic and thermal instability of the Si–O–C band, silicate esters have not proven satisfactory. Likewise, the experimental difficulty of preparing and purifying Si–C phases has discouraged their use. Therefore, most available packings for LC are of the silane (i.e., Si–O–Si–C) type. This bonded phase is stable under most conditions employed in LC and is attacked only in very basic or acidic solutions.

Siloxane phases have been prepared by reaction under anhydrous conditions to yield phases with short chain-length, or by polymerization under controlled humidity to yield polymeric phases. Polymeric phases behave like partitioning phases, whereas the short chains act like modified adsorbents. The chromatographic efficiency of polymeric phases is somewhat lower because of limitations on the mass transfer of the solute. However, both types of siloxanes can be used with solvent programming; this is a major advantage of BPC. Figure 21.20C shows a solvent-programmed separation of several brominated aromatic compounds using a water-methanol gradient and an octadecylsilane (hydrophobic) bonded phase. A conventionally-coated LLC phase could not have been used in such a solvent system; the stationary phase would have been dissolved in the mobile phase.

21.6 ION-EXCHANGE CHROMATOGRAPHY

Ion-exchange chromatography is generally applicable to ionic compounds, to ionizable compounds such as organic acids or bases, and to compounds (such as chelates or ligands) that can interact with ionic groups. Ion-exchange chromatography is carried out with stationary phases having charge-bearing functional groups. The mobile phase usually contains a counter ion, opposite in charge to the surface ionic group, in equilibrium with the resin in the form of an ion pair. The presence of a solute ion of the same ionic charge sets up an equilibrium as follows

$$\text{Cation exchange:} \quad X^+ + R^-Y^+ \rightleftharpoons Y^+ + R^-X^+ \tag{21.15}$$

$$\text{Anion exchange:} \quad X^- + R^+Y^- \rightleftharpoons Y^- + R^+X^- \tag{21.16}$$

where X = the sample ion
Y = the mobile-phase ion (counter ion)
R = the ionic site on the exchanger

Competition between the sample ion and the counter ion for the fixed ionic site is very similar to the competition between solute and solvent for adsorption sites in LSC. In fact, sometimes ion exchange is referred to as adsorption chromatography involving electrostatic interactions. However, as the nature of the stationary and mobile phases, as well as the samples handled, are quite unlike those used for LSC, we prefer to classify ion-exchange chromatography separately.

Stationary Phases

The stationary phases used in ion exchange may be naturally occurring inorganic solids such as sodium aluminosilicate and clays such as montmorillonite, or synthetic ones such as zirconium phosphate. More often, though, they are resins prepared by the copolymerization of styrene and divinylbenzene. The amount of divinylbenzene used in the synthesis controls the extent of cross-linking in the resin. High cross-linking decreases the solubility of polystyrene and improves the structural rigidity, required for high-pressure use in HPLC. However, high cross-linking also decreases the porosity required for good mass-transfer. Low-cross-linked resins have a tendency to "swell" by absorption of mobile phase. The amount of cross-linking expressed as percent of divinylbenzene varies from 2–12%, with 8% being an average value.

The ionic groups are added by chemical reaction after preparing the cross-linked resin. Cationic or anionic resins are classified as strong or weak, depending on the acidic or basic strength of the functional group. Strong cation-exchangers normally have sulfonic ($-SO_3H$) functionality (incorporated by sulfonation of the resin) whereas weak ones have carboxyl ($-COOH$) functionality. Strong anion-exchangers have tetraalkylammonium groups—for instance, $-CH_2-N(CH_3)_3{}^+Cl^-$ (incorporated by chloromethylation followed by treatment with trimethylamine)—whereas weakly basic ones might have $-NH_3{}^+Cl^-$ or $-NHR_2{}^+Cl^-$ functional groups. Resins of intermediate strength are also available.

Exchange Capacity

The number and strength of fixed ionic groups on the solid governs its exchange capacity. Since the ion-exchange capacity affects solute retention, exchangers of high capacity are most often used for separating complex mixtures, where increased retention improves resolution. The capacities of weakly acidic and basic resins show a marked dependence on pH; generally, these resins have a small range of maximum capacity, dependent on the pK of the functional group. The strongly acidic and basic resins have a much wider range of maximum capacity and are generally more widely used. Weak ion-exchangers are most often used in separating strongly basic, strongly acidic, or multi-functional ionic substances which are often firmly retained on the strong ion-exchangers; they have been used for separating such substances as proteins, peptides, and sulfonates. For porous strong resins, capacities are of the order of 3–10 meq/g. For pellicular strong resins, the capacity is much lower (5–50 μeq/g).

Influences on Distribution Coefficients and Selectivity

Ion-exchange chromatography involves more variables than other forms of chromatography. Distribution coefficients and selectivities are functions of pH, solute charge and radius, resin porosity, ionic strength and type of buffer, type of solvent, temperature, and so forth. The number of experimental variables makes ion-exchange chromatography a very versatile technique, since each may be used to effect a better separation, but a difficult one because of the time needed to optimize a separation. When using polystyrene-divinylbenzene resins, organic ions (especially aromatic ones) are sorbed both by ionic forces with exchange groups and by interactions with the resin matrix itself. For example, because of "solvent" effects of the resin matrix, phenols are more strongly retained in anion exchange than their weak ionization would suggest. <u>Even nonionic compounds can be separated on resins, probably by</u> a partition mechanism. In these cases, the presence of a buffer decreases the solubility of the compound in the mobile phase, thus increasing its affinity for the resin. This form of "salting out" chromatography is used to separate alcohols in order of increasing molecular weight.

Electrically neutral species that form a complex with ions can be separated by the exchange process. A well known example is separating sugars through the adducts formed with the borate buffer used to elute them. Ligands can be separated through their interaction with metallic ions sorbed by the resin.

Cellulose powder, chemically modified to contain ion-exchange groups, is also used in both thin-layer and column chromatography. Because of its lack of rigidity, application is limited to low-pressure columns. Sheets of modified cellulose are available for use as exchangers in paper chromatography, and ion-exchange resins and inorganic ion-exchangers have been impregnated into cellulose strips. Liquid ion-exchangers, such as trioctylamine and bis-(2-ethylhexyl)-phosphoric acid (which are immiscible with aqueous solutions) can be coated onto a support, as in LLC.

Uses of Ion-Exchange Chromatography

Ion-exchange chromatography is used most often in inorganic chemistry and in biochemistry, the latter often to deal with water-soluble polar compounds such as proteins and amino acids. Metallic ions can be separated by cation exchange using the characteristic charge-to-radius ratio of the hydrated ions. Under comparable conditions, tetravalent ions are generally retained more than monovalent ions. Within a particular series of ions carrying the same charge, there is also a range of selectivity. As a rough guide, resin affinity decreases as the radius of the hydrated ion increases.

The development of ion-exchange methods for separating lanthanides and various fission products was instrumental in the development of atomic reactors. Tables of distribution coefficients as a function of pH for almost every cation in the periodic table, and for many synthetic resins, came out of this monumental work. More recently, the extension of ion-exchange methods into the biochemical field has aided in the structural elucidation of proteins and nucleic acids. Figure 21.22 depicts the separation of amino acids, one of the most used areas of ion-exchange chromatography. The amino acids are detected as they are eluted by their reaction with ninhydrin in a postcolumn reactor. The colored product is measured in a flow-through colorimetric detector.

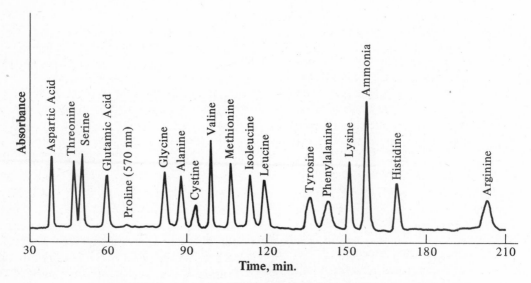

FIGURE 21.22. *Separation of amino acids by ion-exchange chromatography. Resin: Durrum® DC-1A, a sulfonated polystyrene-divinylbenzene cation exchanger of $d_p = 8 \mu m$. Ten nanomole calibration mixture. Flow rate: 70 ml/hr. From James R. Benson, Durrum Resin Report No. 5, April, 1973, Durrum Chemical Corp., by permission of Durrum Chemical Corp.*

21.7 EXCLUSION CHROMATOGRAPHY

Exclusion chromatography, also called gel chromatography, is the predominant method used for separating and characterizing substances of high molecular weight. The process is almost always carried out in a column, but it also has been performed on a thin layer. Column packing materials with pores of different (controlled) sizes are generally used. The materials can be soft gels, semirigid gels, or rigid materials. The soft and semirigid gels can change their pore sizes, depending on the solvent used as a mobile phase. The soft gels, of the polydextran or agarose type, can swell to many times their dry volume, whereas the semirigid gels of the polyvinylacetate or polystyrene type swell to 1.1–1.8 times their dry volume; the rigid materials, such as porous glass or porous silica beads, have fixed pore sizes and do not swell at all.

General Considerations

To understand how steric exclusion differs from the other forms of chromatography, refer to Equation 21.4. In this context, V_m and V_s are referred to as the *void volume* and the *total pore volume*, respectively. The distribution coefficient K_X depends on the molecular weight of the sample and on the pore size of the packing. The equilibrium established in exclusion chromatography is described by Equation 21.1; K_X is defined by Equation 21.2. In a true permeation process, assuming all pores to be accessible to a small solute molecule, $X_s = X_m$ and $K_X = 1$. If none of the pores is available to a large solute molecule (that is, it is excluded), then $X_s = 0$ and $K_X = 0$. Intermediate molecules have access to various portions of the pore volume; for them, $0 < K_X < 1$. Unlike other forms of LC, all sample molecules elute between the excluded volume V_m and the total permeation volume, V_t. Note that V_r of Equation 21.4 is then equal to V_t. If $K_X > 1$, another mechanism of sorption is present and the process is not strictly exclusion.

Selecting the pore size of the packing depends on the size of the solute molecules to be separated as well as on the overall geometric shape of the molecules. Often the samples have a wide variation of solute sizes (that is, molecular weights) and one pore size is insufficient to separate all molecular species. Some are completely excluded from the pores ($K_X = 0$) and elute as a single peak at V_m, whereas others may permeate all the pores and elute as a single peak at V_t. Others will selectively permeate part of the pores and elute at various values of V_r. A calibration curve (Fig. 21.23) is usually plotted as log(molecular weight) versus V_r. Each exclusion packing of a different average pore-size will have its own calibration curve. Note that neither the exclusion limit nor the molecular-weight range is sharply defined. Lack of precise definition occurs because the pores of the packings do not have a narrow distribution, and the distribution of the pores governs the slope of the calibration curve. If the pore distribution is wide, the curve will have a steep slope. Thus, the molecular weight operating range will be large, but the column will provide less discrimination (resolution) of species of close molecular sizes. If the pore distribution is narrow, the curve will be flatter, the molecular weight operating range smaller, but the resolution of closely-sized molecules will be increased.

Uses of Exclusion Chromatography

In exclusion chromatography, columns of different molecular weight operating ranges are used to separate components in a sample of wide molecular weight distribution. The columns are usually defined in terms of their molecular weight exclusion limits. As many as eight columns, each covering a different molecular weight range, are connected in series; each set of columns will have its own calibration curve. Calibration curves are determined by injecting standard samples of known molecular weight, and V_r is determined for each. With nonaqueous mobile phases, polystyrenes with known narrow molecular weight ranges are used; with aqueous mobile phases, soluble dextrans are employed.

To illustrate the results obtainable in steric exclusion chromatography, Figure 21.24 depicts an HPLC separation of polystyrene standards in a column packed with cross-linked polystyrene particles (average pore size 260 Å) of 10-μm d_p, using tetrahydrofuran as a mobile phase. Unlike mobile phases in other forms of chromatography, the mobile phase in exclusion chromatography serves only to dissolve the sample and transport it through the column; it does not interact with the column packing. Note that in Figure 21.24 the polymers elute in the order of decreasing molecular weight.

Calibration Curve For Exclusion Chromatography

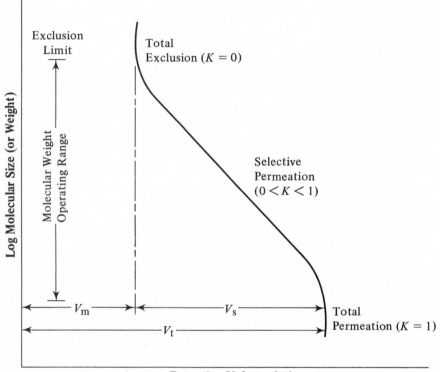

Steric Exclusion Chromatogram

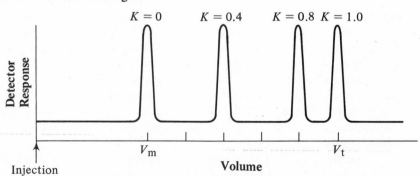

FIGURE 21.23. *Calibration curve and chromatogram for exclusion chromatography. Courtesy of Varian Associates.*

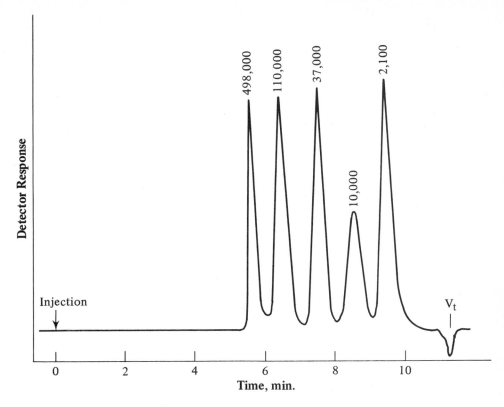

FIGURE 21.24. *High-speed exclusion chromatogram of polystyrene samples with various molecular weights. Column: Toyo Soda TSK® G 4000H8 Gel. Mobile phase: Tetrahydrofuran. Flow rate: 1.7 ml/min. Numbers on peaks represent molecular weights of fractions separated. Courtesy of Toyo Soda Manufacturing Ltd.*

Exclusion chromatography is used not only for separating sample molecules, but also (in organic chemistry) to determine the average molecular weight and the molecular weight distribution of polymers. Polymers are not separate, unique chemical entities, but are comprised of a continuous distribution of molecular weights. In these cases, the chromatogram shows a single broad peak as depicted in Figure 21.25. From such a chromatogram, the polymer chemist can obtain molecular weight and molecular weight distribution data and relate these to the physical properties of the polymeric materials (such as rigidity, tensile strength, and stability). Thus, optimum polymerization conditions can be established.

Exclusion chromatography is also widely used to separate biological compounds, which are often water soluble and of high molecular weight. Proteins, nucleic acids, enzymes, and polysaccharides are routinely examined by exclusion chromatography in aqueous solution. Most applications have been performed on soft gels of the crossed-linked polydextran variety, such as Sephadex®, in open-column chromatography. These soft gels are limited by their compressibility to low column-inlet pressures. Rigid hydrophilic gels and controlled-pore-size glasses,

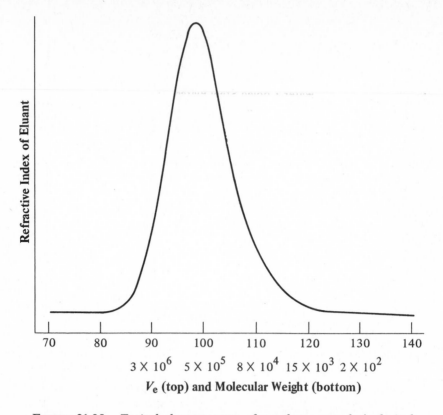

FIGURE 21.25. *Typical chromatogram of a polymer sample (polyvinyl chloride) by exclusion chromatography. From L. R. Snyder and J. J. Kirkland*, Modern Liquid Chromatography Slide Book, *Washington, D.C.: American Chemical Society*, 1973, *fig. 1.7, by permission of the publisher. Copyright © 1973 by the American Chemical Society.*

which can withstand high pressures, have recently become available and should soon be widely used in high-pressure systems.

21.8 TECHNIQUES RELATED TO LIQUID CHROMATOGRAPHY

A number of peripheral techniques closely allied to the basic chromatographic methods are worthy of mention.

Zone Electrophoresis

In electrophoresis, separation depends on the differences in the electrical properties of the components in a mixture. Although not, in principle, a chromatographic technique, electrophoresis is especially helpful in separating ionic compounds difficult to separate by paper chromatography alone. The principles of operation are depicted in Figure 21.26. Each end of a supported filter paper or cellulose-acetate strip is

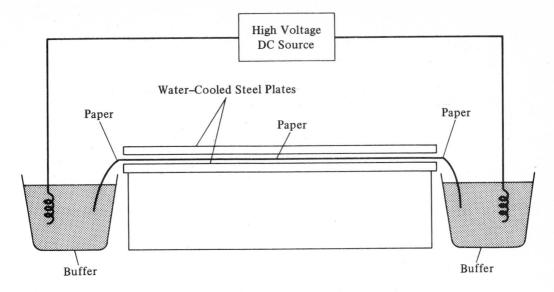

FIGURE 21.26. *Experimental setup for high-voltage electrophoresis.*

dipped into a vessel containing a buffer solution, which also acts as an electrolyte. The strip is carefully moistened with buffer solution. The sample is placed at some point on the paper strip. Then electrodes are dipped into the two vessels and connected to a high-voltage (500 V) direct-current source for a predetermined period of time, permitting a constant current to flow through the electrolyte-moistened paper. Any substance that bears an electrical charge will migrate along the paper, the direction and rate being governed by the sign and magnitude of the charge on the ion and by the mobility of the ion. The current is switched off before the substances reach the two vessels. The paper is removed, dried, and the spots or zones located in the same way as those in paper chromatograms.

The migration rate of each substance depends on several factors, such as the voltage applied, the structure and charge of the ion, and the type and pH of the buffer employed. The migration of each mixture component is independent of that of the other substances present. Since there is no solvent front, a known substance is normally used as a standard.

The primary applications of the technique are in the fields of biology and clinical chemistry, for separating amino acids and proteins. Because of the presence of acidic and basic ionic groups in amino acids, proteins, and other biological macromolecules, pH has a profound effect on migration. In acidic solution, amino acids are positively charged, whereas in basic media they are negatively charged. At a certain pH value, the net charge is zero and the amino acid exists as a zwitterion. This point is called its *isoionic* or *isoelectric point*; provided other ionic interactions are absent, there should be zero electrophoretic mobility at this point.

In some cases, compounds that bear no electrical charge themselves can be separated because they can form complexes with ions present in the buffer solution. These separations are probably based on the principle of electroosmotic buffer flow and, in that respect, are similar to separations in ordinary paper chromatography. An example is the separation of borate complexes of sugars in a sodium-borate buffer.

Voltages applied are expressed in terms of V/cm. In low-voltage electrophoresis, the applied voltage is up to about 500 V. High-voltage electrophoresis, in which voltages up to several thousand volts are used, is a technique well suited to the high-speed separation of low-molecular-weight substances; it is less suited to separating macromolecules, presumably because of their lower ionic mobilities.

In addition to filter paper and cellulose-acetate membranes, other supports can be used. Gels such as agar, starch, and polyacrylamide are supported in the form of a slab or block on a special rack. The technique is termed *gel electrophoresis*. The gels with varying pore sizes exert a slight molecular-sieve effect. In fact, specially prepared polyacrylamide-gel slabs with a continuous gradient of pore size can be used to improve resolution, since the migration of a particular macromolecule will be retarded when its pore limit is reached. *Thin-layer electrophoresis*, usually used for polar compounds such as phenols or amines, uses a thin-layer silica or alumina plate to take advantage of adsorption effects.

Two-dimensional combined techniques using electrophoresis in one direction and chromatography in the other can give better separation than either alone.

Affinity Chromatography

Affinity chromatography is a selective "filtration" technique for macromolecules utilizing highly specific, reversible biochemical reactions. A ligand with a high specificity for the component of interest is attached to a support particle, much like a chemically bonded phase. The ligand is an immobilized enzyme or an antigen, and the macromolecule of interest is an enzyme inhibitor or antibody in a complex biological sample. The immobilized enzyme (or antigen) is placed in a column and the sample introduced in a suitable buffer, the pH and ionic strength of which favors the selective interaction. Elution with the buffer removes the unwanted substances from the column, then the buffer is changed to one that reverses the enzyme-inhibitor interaction and the inhibitor is eluted. Only a small number of specific systems have been investigated thus far, but they have proved very successful. Depending on the system of interest, each ligand must be individually chemically bonded. Some intermediate packings onto which a ligand can attach are now available, and this technique should become even more useful in the future.

Desalting and Deionization

Often, isolating pure substances from biological systems requires the elimination of samples containing large amounts of inorganic salts. These can be desalted by one of several techniques. Exclusion chromatography is quite useful if the component of interest has a higher molecular weight than the salts. Most salts are of low molecular weight and, provided the correct pore-size packing is selected, are retained at the total permeation volume V_t. The higher-molecular-weight sample passes through the column and is collected before the salt elutes. This technique is commonly used for desalting proteins that have been purified by salting out.

A second technique for desalting involves the use of a hydrophobic packing, such as polystyrene-based resins like Amerlite XAD-2®. Provided the component to be collected is organic in character, the sample will pass through the column, selectively concentrating the organic species but allowing the salt to pass through unretained. Afterwards, an organic solvent is used to elute the organic compounds. Organic pollutants can be selectively concentrated from large volumes of water using this approach.

Alternatively, an ion-exchange resin can be used to adsorb ionic species, allowing uncharged organic compounds or nonelectrolytes to pass through. For example, if the contaminant is sodium chloride, a cationic resin in the hydrogen form could be used. Passing a salt sample through the column will exchange Na^+ for H^+. The hydrogen chloride can, in turn, be removed from the effluent by evaporation, or the effluent can be passed through an anion-exchange column in the OH^- form, thereby removing the Cl^- ions. Of course, this classic technique has been used for many years for deionizing water.

SELECTED BIBLIOGRAPHY

General

HEFTMANN, E. *Chromatography*, 3rd ed. New York: Van Nostrand Reinhold, 1974.

KARGER, B. L.; SNYDER, L. R.; and HORVATH, C. *An Introduction to Separation Science*. New York: John Wiley, 1973.

MORRIS, C. J. O. R., and MORRIS, P. *Separation Methods in Biochemistry*. New York: Wiley-Interscience, 1964.

MILLER, J. M. *Separation Methods in Chemical Analysis*. New York: John Wiley, 1975.

STOCK, R., and RICE, C. B. F. *Chromatographic Methods*, 3rd ed. London: Chapman and Hall, 1974.

High-Performance Liquid Chromatography

SNYDER, L. R., and KIRKLAND, J. J. *Modern Liquid Chromatography*. New York: Wiley-Interscience, 1974. *An advanced treatise on HPLC.*

BAUMANN, F., and HADDEN, N., eds. *Basic Liquid Chromatography*. Walnut Creek,

Calif.: Varian Aerograph, 1971. *A paperback coverage of practical aspects of HPLC.*

Ion Exchange

HELFFERICH, F. *Ion Exchange*. New York: McGraw-Hill, 1962.

RIEMAN, W., and WALTON, H. F. *Ion Exchange in Analytical Chemistry*. New York: Pergamon Press, 1970.

Paper and Thin-Layer Chromatography

BLOCK, R. J.; DURRUM, E. L.; and ZWEIG, G. *A Manual of Paper Chromatography and Paper Electrophoresis*, 2nd ed. New York: Academic Press, 1958.

KIRCHNER, J. G. *Thin-Layer Chromatography*. New York: Wiley-Interscience, 1976.

Electrophoresis

BIER, M., ed. *Electrophoresis*, vol. 1 (1959); vol. 2 (1967). New York: Academic Press.

SHAW, D. J. *Electrophoresis*. New York: Academic Press, 1969.

REFERENCES

1. J. C. GIDDINGS, *Dynamics of Chromatography*, part 1, *Principles and Theory*, New York: Marcel Dekker, 1965. *A complete theoretical account of chromatographic principles.*

2. I. M. HAIS and K. MACEK, *Paper Chromatography*, New York: Academic Press, 1963.

3. E. STAHL, *Thin-Layer Chromatography: A*

Laboratory Handbook, 2nd ed., Heidelberg: Springer-Verlag, 1969.

4. L. R. SNYDER, *Principles of Adsorption Chromatography*, New York: Marcel Dekker, 1968.

5. L. R. SNYDER, in J. J. Kirkland, ed., *Modern Practice of Liquid Chromatography*, New York: Wiley-Interscience, 1971.

6. R. A. KELLER, B. L. KARGER, and L. R. SNYDER, in R. Stock and S. G. Perry, eds., *Gas Chromatography 1970*, Institute of Petroleum, 1971.

PROBLEMS

1. The R_f value of a solute can be expressed as the probability of finding it in the mobile phase at any given instant, expressed as the mole fraction of a solute in the mobile phase. (a) Derive a simple equation relating the solute R_f value to its k' value. (b) From this equation, determine the k' value of estradiol, a steroid whose R_f value on a silica-gel plate was 0.3. (c) Relative to estradiol, estriol showed a selectivity factor $\alpha = 1.2$ on a silica-gel column. Would you expect the two steroids to be separated on a silica-gel thin-layer plate, assuming that spots are only distinguishable if their R_f values are at least 0.02 units apart?

2. Because of refractive-index effects, an unretained solvent used to dissolve the sample—if different from the chromatographic mobile phase—often deflects the base-line when passing through an ultraviolet detector cell. This indicates the void volume or the void time. Consider the chromatogram in Figure 21.19. (a) Determine the capacity factors for each nitroaniline isomer. (b) Determine the selectivity factor for the m- and p-substituted isomers relative to the o-nitroaniline.

3. (a) From the TLC chromatogram of Figure 21.12, determine the R_f values for 3'-GMP and 2'-GMP. (b) Using an equation similar to that derived in Problem 1 (a) above, determine the selectivity factor α between the two nucleotides.

4. In Figure 21.15, H was found to be proportional to $d_p^{1.8}$ at constant v. (a) If the average d_p of a silica gel were reduced from 20 μm (where $H = 0.3$ mm) to 2 μm, how many theoretical plates would one obtain from a 25-cm column? (b) Would this column be able to give a baseline separation between geometric isomers whose α value is 1.05 and k' value is close to 10?

5. The polystyrene peaks in Figure 21.24 were obtained by using standards with narrow molecular-weight distributions. (a) Assuming that the polystyrene with the highest molecular weight was totally excluded, construct a calibration curve like that depicted in Figure 21.23A. (b) An unknown polybutadiene gave a peak maximum $V_r = 17$ ml; determine its average molecular weight based on polystyrene. (c) Estimate the lower molecular-weight limit of the operating range (that is, the molecular weight below which no separation will occur).

6. Porous silica has a packing density of 0.55 g/ml, whereas pellicular silica, on account of its glass-bead core, has a packing density of 3.0 g/ml. Surface areas measured by nitrogen adsorption are typically 400 m²/g for porous silica and only 10 m²/g for pellicular silica. The sample capacity for a porous silica was found to be 2 mg/g. (a) For a preparative LC column of dimensions 50 cm by 0.8 cm, determine the maximum amount of sample that can be injected into the column filled with porous silica. (b) Assuming the sample capacity is proportional to the surface area, what sample size can be injected into the same column packed with pellicular silica? (c) How long would the latter column have to be to have the same sample capacity as the porous silica from (a)?

7. Linear velocity can be determined from a chromatogram by $v = L/t_0$. For a chromatograph separation, t_r for the last eluting peak is considered to be the separation time. (a) Derive an expression relating separation time to v and k'. (b) Using the equation

from (a), calculate the total separation time on a 100-cm column exhibiting an H value of 0.4 mm for the last eluting peak ($k' = 24$). The flow rate was 2 ml/min and the column void volume was determined to be 4 ml.

8. Some HPLC systems are limited to an operating pressure of 250 atm. A 100-cm column containing 40-μm particles of ion-exchange resin had a pressure drop of 10 atm at $v = 1.0$ cm/sec. The total time required for the analysis was 30 min. The column produced 300 theoretical plates, but the separation of interest required 8000 plates. The number of plates can be increased by (a) using a longer column, (b) using a lower linear velocity (i.e., flow rate), or (c) using a smaller particle size in the packing. Assuming that the relationship $H = A(v^{0.6})d_p^{1.8}$ holds for the above system (A is a constant), which of the three options would be the most advantageous to pursue, and why?

22

Gas Chromatography

CHARLES H. LOCHMÜLLER

It was noted in the previous chapter that, in 1952, A. J. P. Martin and R. L. M. Synge received the Nobel prize for the discovery of partition chromatography. In 1941, these authors had also written [1] that,

> The mobile phase need not be a liquid but may be a vapour. We show below that the efficiency of contact between the phases (theoretical plates per unit length of column) is far greater in the chromatogram than in ordinary distillation or extraction columns. Very refined separation of volatile substances should therefore be possible in a column in which a permanent gas is made to flow over a gel impregnated with a nonvolatile solvent in which the substances to be separated approximately obey Raoults' law.

Despite this clear and unequivocal prediction of gas-liquid partition chromatography, no one seized the opportunity until ten years later, when Martin and James [2] demonstrated its great potential. The growth of gas chromatography in the last quarter century has been phenomenal, and its use is now routine in many aspects of experimental chemistry, including analysis. The aim of this chapter is to give a beginning student a practical understanding and a physical model of gas chromatography, sufficient to carry out elementary experiments and to provide a basis for further reading.

Gas chromatography (GC) is one type of partition chromatography; it is similar in many ways to other techniques of this kind, such as HPLC (high-performance liquid chromatography), paper chromatography, etc. The distinguishing features are that the mobile phase is a gas and that the motion of the component bands, in the direction of "chromatographic development," involves the forced diffusion of the respective substances in their vapor phases. Many of the differences between, say, HPLC and GC are due to the physical properties of the mobile phase—for instance, its viscosity, acidity, basicity, and compressibility. The basis for differential zone-migration remains the same: two components will migrate at different rates in the same chromatographic system if their distribution constants are different. Here, the main emphasis will be on gas-liquid chromatography, but gas-solid techniques (which have some advantages) will also be mentioned.

22.1 THE THERMODYNAMICS OF GAS CHROMATOGRAPHY

Gas chromatography involves the same two types of phenomena as any chromatographic method: first, static or equilibrium processes that can be described thermodynamically; second, dynamic or flux processes (including mass-transport) that must be described kinetically. A rudimentary understanding of both statics and dynamics as they apply to gas chromatography should help the student to understand the potential and limitations of this technique and to improve his or her attack on a problem in analysis. In this section, the static aspects are considered.

Principles

The concept of retention volume in chromatography was discussed in Chapter 21. One can distinguish between the retention volume V_r (or retention time t_r) and the *adjusted retention volume* V'_r (or adjusted retention time t'_r):

$$V'_r = V_r - V_0$$

or

$$t'_r = t_r - t_0$$

(22.1)

where V_0 = the elution volume of an unretained species
            t_0 = the elution time of the species

V'_r and t'_r are also called the *elution* volume or time. The relation between t_r and V_r is

$$V_r = t_r F_c$$

(22.2)

where F_c = the adjusted flow-rate

(See Fig. 22.1 for a simple device for measuring flow rates.)

Consider a chromatographic column. When the mobile phase is a liquid, the carrier velocity (v) is not a strong function of the axial position in the column because, in general, liquids are not very compressible. Gases are, however, quite compressible and so a correction is applied to the adjusted volume V'_r to obtain the *net volume* V_n. It can be shown that the average carrier velocity in the column $\bar{v}$ is related to the outlet velocity v_0 by a correction factor j, given by

$$j = \frac{3}{2} \left[\frac{(P_i/P_0)^2 - 1}{(P_i/P_0)^3 - 1} \right]$$

(22.3)

where P_i = the inlet pressure
         P_0 = the outlet pressure

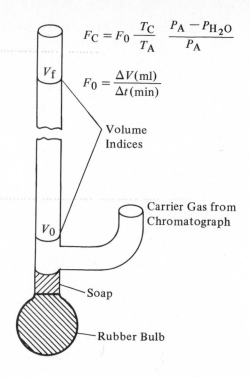

FIGURE 22.1. *A bubble-type flowmeter for volumetric flow measurements. A soap-bubble film is swept past the indices V_0 and V_f and the transit time is measured.* $\Delta V =$ *the volume of tube between V_0 and V_f; $\Delta t =$ the transit time; $F_0 =$ the volumetric flow-rate; $F_c =$ the adjusted flow rate; $T_c =$ the column temperature (K); $T_A =$ the ambient temperature (K); $P_A =$ the ambient pressure; $P_{H_2O} =$ the vapor pressure of water at the ambient temperature.*

$$F_C = F_0 \frac{T_C}{T_A} \frac{P_A - P_{H_2O}}{P_A}$$

$$F_0 = \frac{\Delta V(\text{ml})}{\Delta t(\text{min})}$$

Volume Indices

Carrier Gas from Chromatograph

Soap

Rubber Bulb

Now

$$V_n = jV'_r \qquad (22.4)$$

and $\bar{v} = jv_0$; and since v and F are related (assuming a column of constant cross-section), $\bar{F} = jF_0$. When the sample (generally a mixture of solutes) enters the column containing the stationary phase (solvent in GLC), it rapidly distributes itself between the vapor and condensed or solution phases. This is described by a distribution coefficient K, given by

$$K = \frac{c_s}{c_m} = \left(\frac{n_s}{V_s}\right)\left(\frac{V_m}{n_m}\right) \qquad (22.5)$$

where $c =$ the concentration of the solute in a phase (*stationary* or *mobile*)
$n =$ the number of moles of solute in a phase
$V =$ the total volume of a phase in the column

In conventional gas chromatographic experiments (i.e., at low pressures and with inert carrier gases such as helium), nonideal behavior of the solute in the gas phase contributes to only about 1–3% of the observed distribution coefficient.

The net retention volume increases or decreases with increasing or decreasing mass of stationary phase W_s, and the specific retention volume V_g is defined as

$$V_g = \frac{V_n}{W_s} \frac{273}{T_c} \qquad (22.6)$$

The factor $\frac{273}{T_c}$ corrects V_g to the reference temperature of 273 K. It can be shown that, for ideal behavior, the specific retention volume is given by

$$V_g = \frac{273R}{\gamma_\infty P^0 MW_s} \tag{22.7}$$

where R = the gas constant
           γ_∞ = the activity coefficient of the solute at infinite dilution in the stationary phase
           P^0 = the saturation vapor pressure of pure solute at a given temperature
           MW_s = the molecular weight of the stationary-phase material

VOLATILE .

Thus, the specific retention volume depends on only two factors in a given solvent (MW_s is assumed constant): the saturation vapor pressure of the solute P^0 and the activity coefficient γ_∞ of the solute.

Influence of Temperature and Volatility on Retention

Consider the practical significance of the above result. First, other things being equal, the greater P^0 is, the smaller V_g will be (Eqn. 22.7), and the shorter the retention time will be (Eqn. 22.2). P^0 increases with increasing temperature; thus, retention time decreases as the temperature is increased. One can also shorten retention times by converting the solutes of interest into more volatile derivatives, thus increasing P^0. For example, amino acids converted to the volatile ester-amides have smaller overall retention times than the amino acids themselves.

$$H_2N-\overset{\overset{\displaystyle R}{|}}{C}-\underset{\underset{\displaystyle O}{\|}}{C}-OH \longrightarrow H-\overset{\overset{\displaystyle R}{|}}{\underset{\underset{\displaystyle O=C}{|}}{N}}-\overset{\overset{\displaystyle O}{\|}}{C}-OR'$$
$$\underset{\displaystyle CF_3}{|}$$

The CF_3-amide is more volatile than the CH_3-analogue owing to the greater electronegativity of fluorine: the tendency for the $>C=O$ group to accept hydrogen bonds is lessened.

The Separation Factor

Separation of several substances occurs when the respective values of either K or V_g are different. A measure of this difference is the selectivity factor (or separation factor) α (see Eqn. 21.10). For two substances indicated by subscripts 1 and 2:

$$\alpha = \frac{V_{g2}}{V_{g1}} \qquad \alpha = \frac{t_{r_B} - t_o}{t_{r_A} - t_o} \tag{22.8}$$

For instance, if solute 1 is a hydrocarbon and solute 2 an alcohol, a polar stationary phase such as the polyethylene glycols or the polar silicones (Table 22.1) will increase the retention of the alcohol because of the strong specific interactions involving the –OH group. This is an example of stationary-phase selectivity.

    Extreme selectivity is required for the direct chromatographic resolution of

TABLE 22.1. *A Tabulation of Commercial Stationary Phases and Their Skeletal Structures*

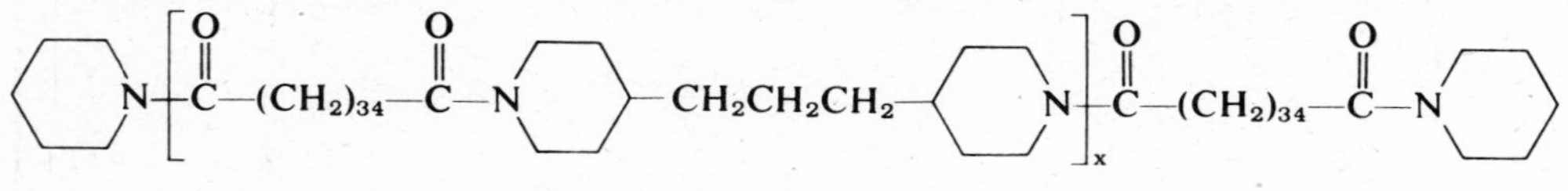

POLY-A 103 (polyamide)

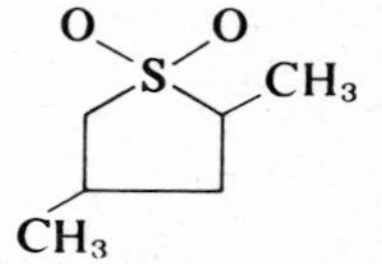

Dimethylsulfolane

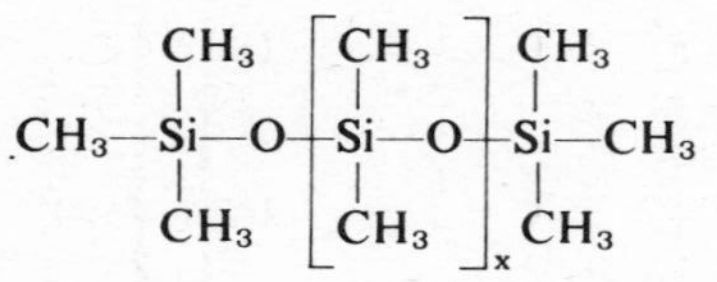

OV-101

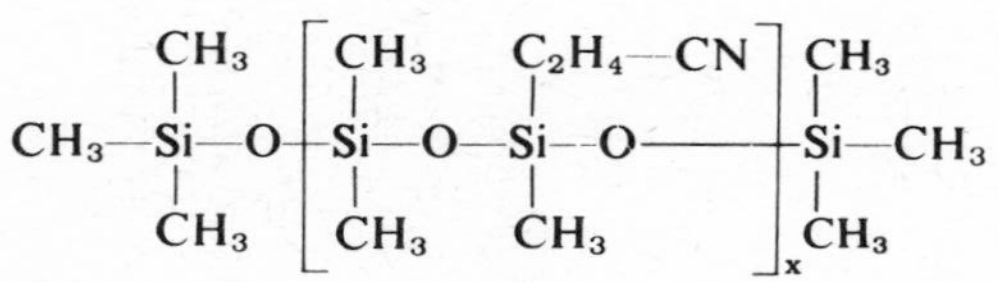

Silicone GE XE-60

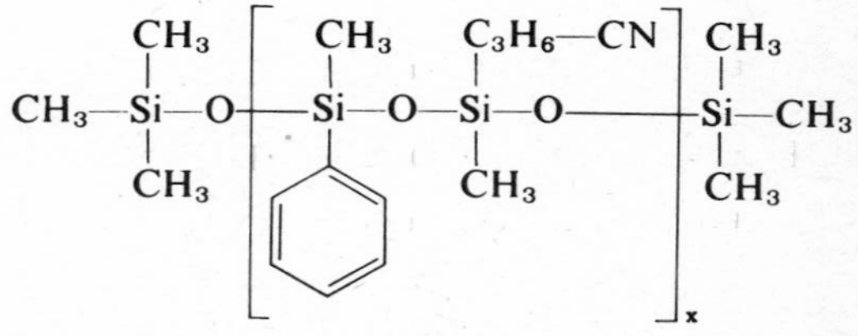

OV-225

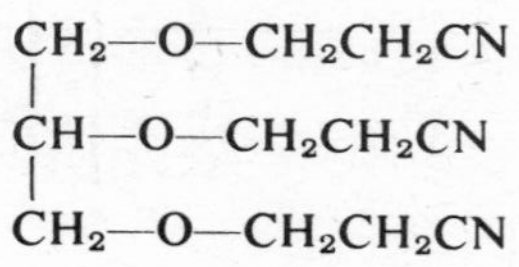

1,2,3-Tris(2-cyanoethoxy)propane

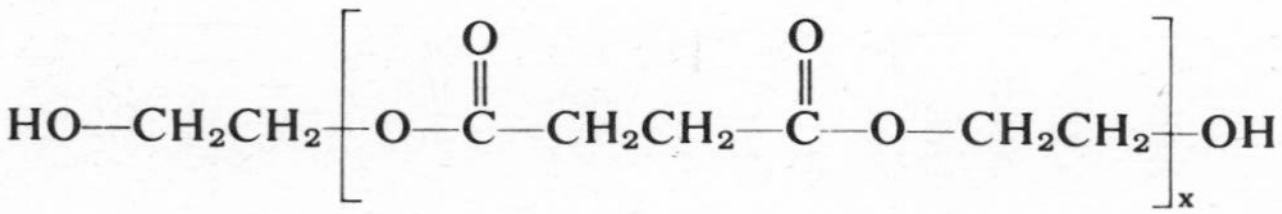

HI-EFF-2B (ethylene glycol succinate)

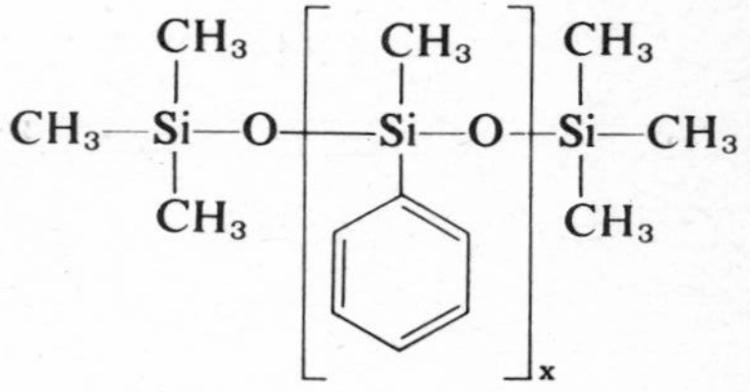

OV-17

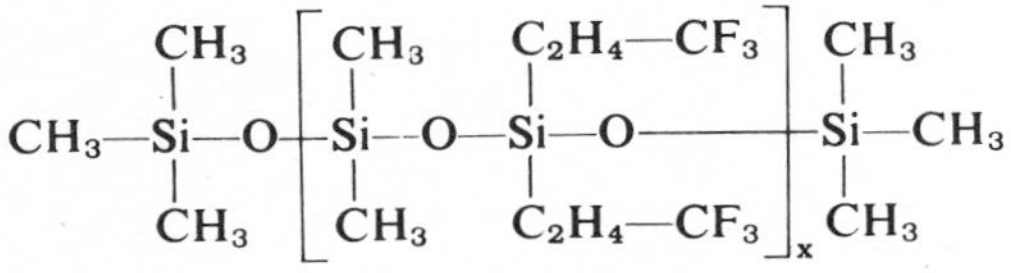

CH$_2$OCH$_2$CH$_2$CN
|
NCCH$_2$CH$_2$OCH$_2$—C—CH$_2$OCH$_2$CH$_2$CN
|
CH$_2$OCH$_2$CH$_2$CN

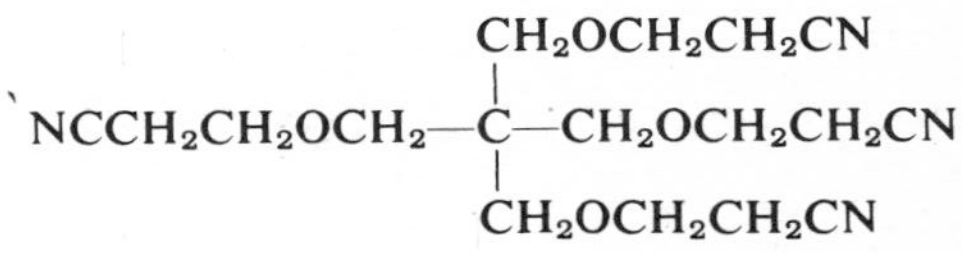

Tetracyanoethylated Pentaerythritol

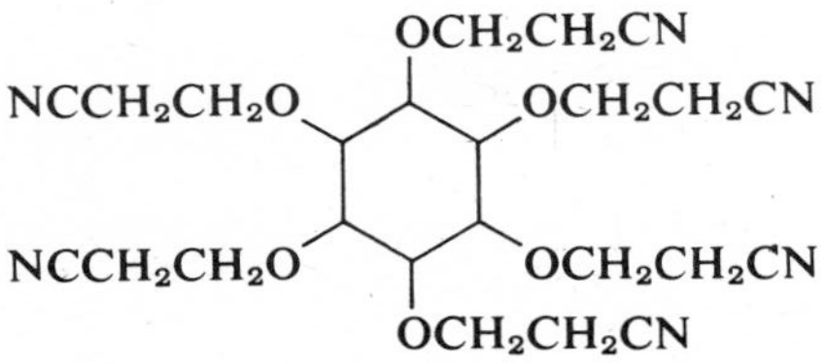

SILAR-5CP

POLY-I 110

HO—(CH$_2$—CH$_2$—O)$_x$—H

Carbowaxes

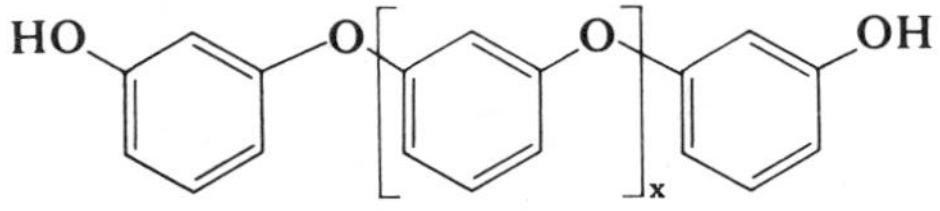

Polysev (polyphenyl ether)

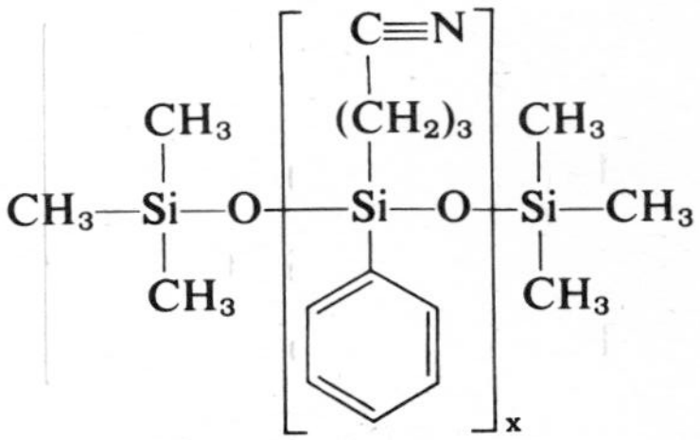

OV-210

CYCLO-N [1,2,3,4,5,6-hexakis(2-cyanoethoxy)cyclohexane]

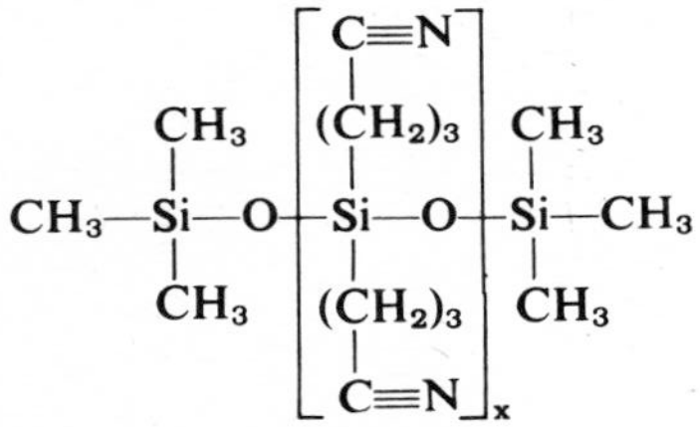

SILAR-10C

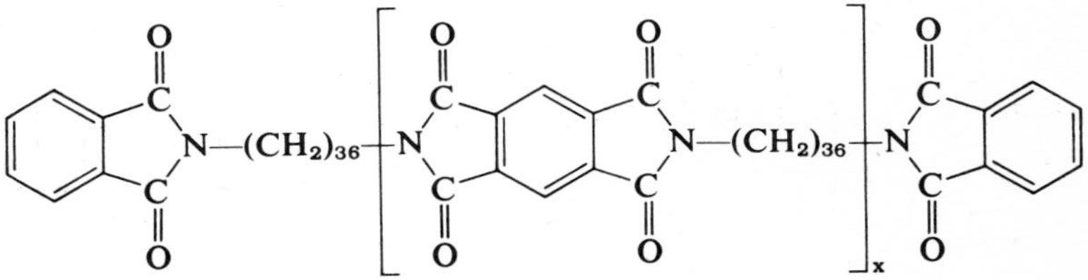

Source: Courtesy of Applied Science Laboratories, State College, Pennsylvania, Catalog 17 (1974), p 12.

enantiomers. Such molecules differ only in their "handedness"; stationary phases must be designed to take advantage of this single distinguishing property. The enantiomers of amino acids are resolved as their ester-N-trifluoro-acetamides by using the stationary phase N-trifluoroacetyl-L,L-valylvaline cyclohexyl ester. There the separation mechanism involves the formation of transient diastereomeric complexes of R–S and S–S configuration.

At an intermediate level of selectivity, adding certain metal ions, especially Ag$^+$, to a stationary phase significantly increases the retention of alkenes and the α values for geometrical (*cis-trans*) isomers. The mechanism probably involves π-complexes formed between Ag$^+$ and the unsaturated C=C double bond.

To achieve good separation, α needs to be either large or small in magnitude compared to unity. Thus, one desires a large difference in P^0 (by selective derivatiza-

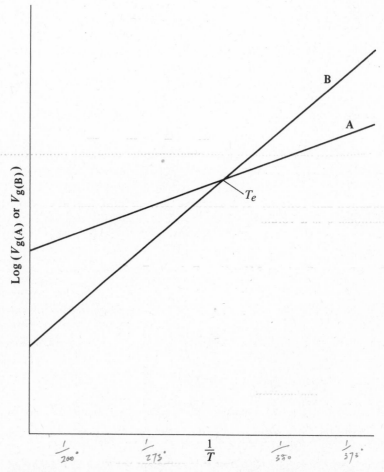

FIGURE 22.2. *A plot of log V_g for two dissimilar solutes A and B on the same stationary phase as a function of $1/T$, illustrating the possibility of resolution, no resolution, and reversal of elution order as the column temperature is varied.*

tion or varying the temperature) or a large difference in γ_∞ (Eqn. 22.7). The latter can often be achieved by invoking the rule that "like dissolves like"; but, at times, finding a suitably selective liquid stationary phase can require a great deal of experience, since there are systems whose interaction mechanisms are not known.

actuly coeff of solute.

p°
γ_∞

For dissimilar species, enthalpies of vaporization are often quite different, ΔH_v so α can depend strongly on temperature. Figure 22.2 shows that at low temperatures, A will elute before B ($\log V_g^A < \log V_g^B$) but as the temperature is increased, the difference in retention time decreases until at temperature T_e, $\log V_g^A = \log V_g^B$. At temperatures higher than T_e, B elutes before A, since now $\log V_g^A > \log V_g^B$. Such a reversal of elution order is not uncommon for dissimilar molecular species.

22.2 THE DYNAMICS OF GAS CHROMATOGRAPHY

The successful separation of two substances depends not only on the separation factor α but also on the quality of the column in terms of performance or efficiency. The latter is described in terms of the *height equivalent to a theoretical plate* (HETP) or *plate height* (H). The plate height (more precisely, the number of plates) for a given solute on the column is related to the variance σ^2 of the chromatographic zone. This total variance is the sum of many contributing factors, but three general areas of variance production can be identified: the inlet system, the column, and the detector; and

$$\sigma_{tot}^2 = \sigma_{in}^2 + \sigma_{col}^2 + \sigma_{det}^2 \tag{22.9}$$

The standard deviation σ of a chromatographic zone with (approximately) a Gaussian profile is related to the width of the zone at the inflection points. As in any error process, the square of the standard deviation (the variance) accumulates and hence Equation 22.9 follows. It is useful to keep in mind that in column-chromatographic methods, σ is a volume element and that increasing extra-column "dead volume" (for example) will increase σ_{tot}^2 and decrease the total number of plates.

Broadening Factors Affecting Column Performance

The analyst should understand the physical basis for zone broadening in gas chromatography in order to properly select the right column system for the job to be done. In the following discussion, the term σ_{col}^2 of Equation 22.9 will be expanded into separate factors, each factor adding to H. The broadening factors to be considered are:

1. Finite rate of diffusion of the solute vapor in the mobile (gas) phase along the length of the column.
2. Noninstantaneous equilibration of the solute vapor with the stationary solvent phase.
3. Factors that depend on the geometry of the column packing.

This is not a complete list, but it is sufficient for the present purpose.

It is important that the reader have a clear mental picture of an actual chromatographic column before proceeding in this section. Packed columns are similar to those discussed in Chapter 21. Open tubular columns are practically unique to GC, and the reader may wish to go forward to the section on columns first before continuing on here. These columns are open tubes coated on the inside with a film of stationary phase, the advantage being that very long columns (large numbers of theoretical plates) can be attained with a small pressure drop.

The overall plate height arising from the above factors is described by the *Van Deemter equation* as a function of carrier-gas velocity v.

$$H = A + \frac{B}{v} + (C_{\text{liq}} + C_{\text{gas}})v \qquad (22.10)$$

The A term is the eddy diffusion contribution and has the form $2\lambda d_p$, where d_p is the diameter of the particles packed in the column and λ is a geometric factor indicating how uniformly the column is packed. A represents the distance a flowing stream moves before its velocity is seriously changed by the packing; A is independent of the velocity of the gas. The B term is the longitudinal or molecular-diffusion contribution, which is a function of the diffusion coefficient D_g of the solute vapor in the carrier gas and of the time spent in the column. If a sample could be placed on the column as a zone of infinitesimal width at a time $t_0 = 0$, diffusion would cause the zone to become wider and less concentrated as time goes by, even with no flow. Diffusion is much more important in gas chromatography than in liquid chromatography (H_{liq} in Eqn. 21.8) because the diffusion coefficients of solutes are $\sim 10^5$ greater in gases than in liquids. The C terms represent the rate of mass transfer—the finite time required to establish equilibrium between the two phases. The C_{liq} term is a function of the capacity (partition) factor k' (Chap. 21), the film thickness d_f, and the interdiffusion constant D_l of the solute in the liquid stationary phase. The C_{gas} term is related to d_p^2/D_g in packed columns or r^2/D_g in open tubular columns. The C_{liq} and C_{gas} terms are often combined into a single C term, and represent the kinetic lag in attaining equilibrium between phases as well as transverse diffusion within the mobile phase itself. The B and C terms depend on the carrier gas velocity in opposite manners; B decreases with increased velocity while C increases.

The resulting equation and its components are shown in Figure 22.3. The sum curve is quasi-hyperbolic, exhibiting a minimum value of H (or *HETP*) at an optimum carrier velocity (v_{opt}); $H_{\text{min}} = A + 2\sqrt{BC}$ and $V_{\text{opt}} = \sqrt{BC}$. Equation 22.10 can be compared with Equation 21.8 for liquid chromatography. Also, as in Equation 21.6 used in liquid chromatography, $N = 16(t_r'/W)^2$ in gas chromatography.

The Van Deemter equation contains important information for the practical analyst planning to use gas chromatography. The A term suggests that the use of smaller-sized supporting particles will result in a smaller H. In practice, particles with a mesh-size of greater than 100–120 (i.e., smaller particles) are not used, since decreasing d_p increases the pressure drop in the columns.* Narrow mesh-ranges produce a more uniform packing geometry, also resulting in a smaller H. Efficiency increases with decreasing column radius, but it is difficult to pack columns less than 3 mm in inner diameter. Diffusion in the gas phase will be reduced by using carrier gases of higher molecular weight or by operating the column at increased pressure. The combined C factor suggests that the plate height depends on the partition ratio, k'

---

* Supports are usually sized by screening through standard ASTM screens. Mesh numbers refer to the number of openings per linear inch. Particles that will pass through 60 mesh, but not through 80 mesh, are referred to as 60/80 mesh.

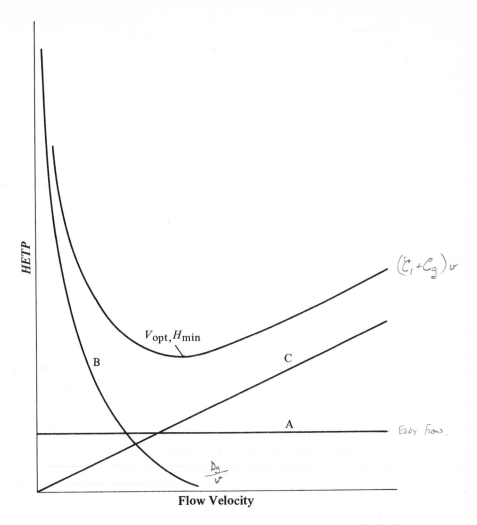

FIGURE 22.3. *A plot of HETP (height equivalent to a theoretical plate) against flow velocity, illustrating the contributions of the following factors to plate height and the position of optimum velocity for minimum HETP: (A) eddy diffusion, (B) ordinary diffusion, and (C) combined gas and liquid resistance to mass transfer.*

and therefore that the observed plate height is different for different compounds. Since small ratios between the volume of gas and the volume of liquid lead to small values of H, as much stationary phase should be used as possible. When the available surface area of the support has been covered, however, the film thickness d_f increases (and along with it H, since it is proportional to $d_f{}^2$), thus degrading column performance—an important consideration in scaling up from lightly loaded analytical columns to heavily loaded "preparative" columns. The stationary phase should not be viscous at the column temperature; high viscosity means small D_l, which increases H. A compromise must be made between capacity and sample size:

the amount of stationary phase must be large enough, and the operating temperature low enough, to produce significant retention times, but not so large or low as to broaden zones excessively by producing large mass-transfer effects.

The Resolution Factor

The separation efficiency of a particular pair of components is described by the resolution obtained, as determined by the peak-to-peak separation α and the average peak-width at the baseline V_w. A resolution factor R for substances 1 and 2 can be defined as follows:

$$R = \frac{V_{r_2} - V_{r_1}}{0.5(V_{w_1} + V_{w_2})} = \frac{V_{r_2} - V_{r_1}}{4\sigma} \tag{22.11}$$

This equation is similar to Equation 21.9. $R = 1$ corresponds to reasonably good separation, since there are 2σ units between zone centers and thus only 2% of each zone overlaps the other. At $R = 1.5$, there is a *baseline separation* with a zone overlap of less than 1%. The effective resolution also depends on the relative concentrations of the solutes.

Equation 22.11 does not show the relationship between experimental variables and the quality of a given separation. A more fundamental equation was given in the previous chapter, Equation 21.11:

$$\alpha = \frac{t_{r_B} - t_o}{t_{r_A} - t_o}$$

$$R = \left(\frac{\sqrt{N}}{4}\right)\left(\frac{\alpha - 1}{\alpha}\right)\left(\frac{k'}{1 + k'}\right) \tag{22.12}$$

This shows the relation between the number of theoretical plates N, the separation factor α, and the capacity factor k' for the second solute in determining R. The analyst is often interested in R but more often in N_{req}, the number of plates required to give a certain R value. For $R = 1$, Equation 22.12 can be rearranged to yield

$$N_{req} = 16\left(\frac{\alpha}{\alpha - 1}\right)^2\left(\frac{k' + 1}{k'}\right)^2 \tag{22.13}$$

Usually, $k' = 2$–3 is optimum. The effect of k' on resolution is important only for fast-moving peaks with packed columns where k' values range from 2–200.

The whole advantage of open tubular columns is lost if k' has a fractional value (the usual range of k' values being 0.2–20). As an example, consider the case of a vapor with $k' = 0.2$ on an open tubular column and $k' = 2$ on a packed column. The packed column would require 1/16 the number of plates to give the same resolution. Many examples of the performance of open tubular columns show capacity ratios even smaller than 0.2, so that the resolution is poorer than could be obtained on a short packed column of only a few thousand plates. Actually, it is often convenient to speak in terms of *effective* plates, N_{eff}, when comparing columns, where $N_{eff} = N(k'/1 + k)^2$. For example, open tubular columns (because of their greater length) have much larger values of N than do packed columns, but the values of N_{eff} are often comparable. In other words, the plate heights of open tubular columns are larger than those of properly prepared packed columns.

$k' = \frac{moles\ liquid}{moles\ gas}$

Optimizing Speed in Chromatographic Analysis

An analyst seeks to obtain chromatographic results in the minimum possible time, so he or she must compromise between larger k' values and shorter times of analysis. This is simple if the initial value of R is greater than 1.5, since increasing the carrier velocity will shorten the analysis without degrading the results. Since $v = 1/t_m$ and $H = L/N$ (where L = the total length of the column) then $t = [NH(1 + k')]/v$; combining this with the expression for the resolution yields a relation between analysis time and resolution,

$$t = 16R^2 \left(\frac{\alpha}{\alpha - 1} \right)^2 \left(\frac{k' + 1}{k'} \right)^3 \frac{H}{v} \qquad (22.14)$$

which indicates that if double the resolution is required (k', α, H, and v being constant), then the analysis time is increased by a factor of four. If k' is either very small or very large, then t tends toward very large values. The minimum in the expression occurs at $k' = 2$. This corresponds to a retention time for the second peak that is three times that of an unretained species (*air peak* or *methane time*).

Multiple peaks.

The value of R has a practical significance that depends on the relative concentrations of adjacent zones. For example, quantitative analysis is always possible for $R = 1.5$ regardless of relative concentrations; but for $R = 0.6$, it is difficult to detect two peaks at concentration ratios smaller than 1/8. An approach that takes into account the degree of zone overlap is that of Glueckauf [3].

22.3 GAS-CHROMATOGRAPHIC INSTRUMENTATION

Gas-chromatographic instrumentation differs very little from that used for other forms of column chromatography (see Fig. 22.4). A gas chromatograph consists of (1) a source of carrier gas, the flow rate of which can be fixed at a desired magnitude within the range provided; (2) an inlet that can be heated (25–500°C); (3) a column in a thermostatted air-bath (25–400°C); and (4) a detector suitable for vapor-phase samples. The high temperatures are needed to vaporize the solutes of interest and maintain them in the gas phase. Because the distribution coefficient depends on the temperature, the latter is controlled to between ± 0.1 and ± 0.01°C (depending on the precision desired in the measured retention times). The inlet and detector are generally maintained at a temperature approximately 10% (in °C) above that of the column (in any case, above 100°C for flame-ionization detectors, see later) to insure rapid volatilization of the sample and to prevent condensation. The temperature of the column is usually set at least 25°C higher than the boiling point of the solute. (This is not, of course, an absolute requirement, since it is only necessary that a substance have a reasonably high vapor pressure at the operating temperature.)

Columns for Gas Chromatography

The most commonly used gas-chromatographic column consists of a tube filled with solid particles of fairly uniform size; the particles are coated with the liquid stationary phase. Perhaps the most commonly used support is marine diatomite (for instance, Johns-Manville Chromosorb®). The choice of tubing material depends on the experiment. Aluminum and copper are commonly used, but may have chromatographically and catalytically active oxide films that make them undesirable for sensitive compounds (for instance, steroids); in such cases, stainless steel or glass are used (the latter is more inert, but is less conveniently manipulated).

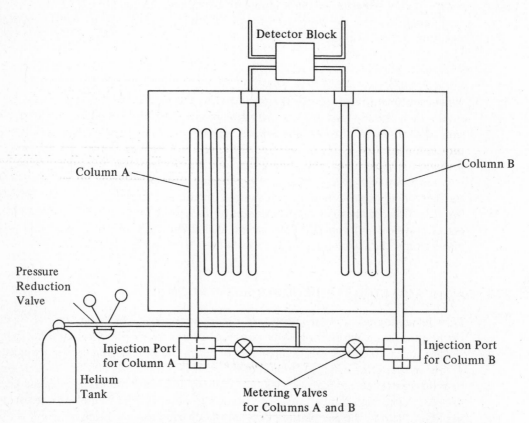

FIGURE 22.4. *Block diagram of a dual-column gas chromatograph showing essential parts. Courtesy of Gow-Mac Instrument Co., Madison, New Jersey.*

Open tubular or capillary columns consist of 50–300 m of 0.3–0.5 mm i.d. steel or glass tubing coated on the inside with a film of stationary phase. The advantage of these columns is not in plate height, which is generally larger than with well packed columns, but in the number of plates achievable with a relatively small pressure-drop. For example, if 20,000 theoretical plates is a good upper limit for packed columns, then open tubular columns can have 75,000–150,000 plates. Open tubular columns have limited capacity and, for this and other reasons, surface-coated open tubular (SCOT) columns have been introduced; these columns are internally coated with finely divided metal oxide, graphite, or alumino-silicate before the stationary phase is applied and, because of the larger surface area presented, have increased capacity.

Chromatographic Support Materials

The function of a chromatographic support is to hold the stationary phase. One useful type of support is provided by the marine diatomites, which are the skeletons of tiny unicellular algae (diatoms) and consist chiefly of amorphous hydrated silica with traces of metal-oxide impurities. This material has the advantages of high porosity and large surface-area. Some properties of a variety of diatomite supports are given in Table 22.2. Chromosorb P, for example, is prepared from one particular grade of firebrick and is a pink (hence P), calcined diatomite that is relatively hard and not easily friable. It is used mainly with solutes of low to moderate polarity (for instance, hydrocarbons). It is a relatively good adsorbent, a quality that can be an interference. If there were no liquid phase at all, the support would act as an adsorbent, and gas-solid chromatography could be carried out. The effect of placing a thin film of liquid on an active adsorbent is to moderate the gas-solid activity, but not to eliminate it. It has been shown that even 20% by weight liquid loading does not eliminate this activity. Several techniques are used to reduce the activity—for instance, acid washing, and "silanizing" the active silica sites with dimethyldichlorosilane to displace the hydrogen. The effect of these treatments on chromatograms is shown in Figure 22.5. The choice of a support for a given analysis is as important as the choice of a stationary phase; for instance, if retention is partly due to solution in the stationary phase and partly to adsorption on the support, then the retention time will vary with the size of the sample. Some compounds (such as sterols) may actually decompose on the column if a poor choice of support has been made.

Stationary Phases

The selection of the stationary phase is also important. Several guides are available in which the types of solute and of stationary phase are correlated (see Selected

TABLE 22.2. *Properties of Some Diatomite Supports*

	Chromosorb®			
Properties	A	G	P	W
Color	Pink	Oyster White	Pink	White
Type	Flux-Calcined	Flux-Calcined	Calcined	Flux-Calcined
Density, g/cm³				
(i) Loose Weight	0.40	0.47	0.38	0.18
(ii) Packed	0.48	0.58	0.47	0.24
Surface Area, m²/g	2.7	0.5	4.0	1.0
Surface Area, m²/cm³	1.3	0.29	1.88	0.29
Maximum Liquid-Phase Loading	25%	5%	30%	15%
pH	7.1	8.5	6.5	8.5
Handling Characteristics	Good	Good	Good	Slightly Friable

Source: Courtesy of Johns-Manville Corporation.

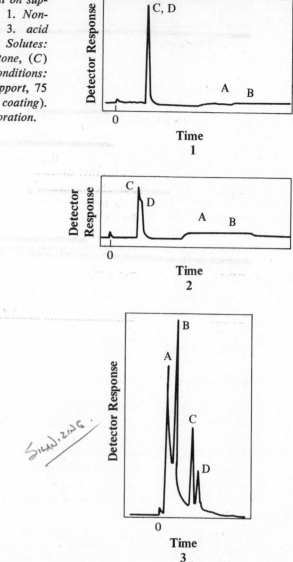

FIGURE 22.5. *Effect of treatment on support activity (Chromosorb® P).* 1. *Non-acid-washed;* 2. *acid washed;* 3. *acid washed, dimethyldichlorosilanized. Solutes: (A) ethanol, (B) methylethyl ketone, (C) benzene, (D) cyclohexane. Conditions: 6' × 1/4" column, 60/80 mesh support, 75 ml/min He flow, 100°C (no liquid coating). Courtesy of Johns-Manville Corporation.*

Bibliography). Although such information is useful, the phases listed are not necessarily the best ones; the lists merely indicate that a given stationary phase has been used with some success for a given class of compounds. The situation is complicated by the fact that about a thousand stationary phases have been reported in the literature. Many attempts have been made to glean a list of standard phases from these reported phase materials, many of which give substantially the same separations and possess unique stability. Many researchers have developed various retention-index methods to indicate the preferred phases for a given separation. Such studies involve investigating specific solute-solvent interactions fundamental to our understanding of stationary-phase selectivity. (Note particularly the recent work of Rohrschneider

TABLE 22.3. *A Proposed List of Standard Stationary Phases*

Preferred Phase	Structure	Temp Limit °C	Uses
Squalene	2,6,10,15,19,23-hexamethyl-tetracosane	150	Hydrocarbons, Gases
SE-30	Polydimethyl siloxane	350	Gases, Hydrocarbons, Aldehydes, Ketones (b.p. separ.)
OV-3	Polyphenyl methyl dimethyl siloxane	350	Alcohols, Fatty Acids, Esters, Aromatics
OV-7	Polyphenyl methyl dimethyl siloxane	350	Aromatics, Heterocyclics
DC-710	Polymethyl phenyl siloxane	300	Aromatics (similar to OV-17)
OV-22	Polyphenyl methyl diphenyl siloxane	350	Alcohols, Aromatics
QF-1	Polytrifluoropropyl methyl siloxane	250	Alcohols, Amino Acids, Steroids, Nitrogen Compounds
XE-30	Polycyanomethyl siloxane	275	Drugs, Alkaloids, Halogenated Ampds
Carbowax 20M	Polyethylene glycol	250	Alcohols, Esters, Pesticides, Essential Oils
DEG adipate	Diethylene glycol adipate	200	Fatty Acids, Esters, Pesticides
DEG succinate	Diethylene glycol succinate	200	Steroids, Amino Acids, Alcohols
TCEP	*Tris*-cyano ethoxy propane	175	Alcohols, Steroids, Pesticides

Source: Adapted from J. Leary, J. Justice, S. Tsuge, S. Lowry, and T. L. Isenhour, *J. Chromatog. Sci.*, *11*, 201 (1973), by permission of the senior author and the publisher.

and of McReynolds [4, 5].) Table 22.3 contains a list of twelve stationary phases and the compound classes that can be separated by each. The list was compiled [6] by applying the following criteria: phases should be (1) well tested, (2) readily available, (3) stable over a wide range of temperatures, and (4) cover a wide polarity range. Of the several hundred phases studied, this list is presented as a preliminary guide, but of course the infinite number of possible combinations of solutes will not always be separated using phases from this list. Squalene is a hydrocarbon; SE-30 is a methylsilicone rubber with hydrocarbon-like properties. These are selective for nonpolar species, but will also separate alcohols with different enough boiling points. Carbowax 20-M is moderately polar, and is selective for hydrogen-bonded species such as alcohols. Many synthesis laboratories do 90% of their work with SE-30 and Carbowax 20-M. As often as not, a significant difference of vapor pressure exists between starting material and product, and little selectivity is required. The result is that two phases of markedly different polarity may serve quite well.

Preparing the Column

The three most critical steps in the actual preparation of a gas-chromatographic column are: (1) coating the support, (2) packing the column, and (3) curing or conditioning after packing but before use. Highly efficient columns give lower limits of detection and shorter analysis times; a common goal, though rarely achieved, is a column with more than 3000 plates/meter.

There are some guidelines, however, by which columns with more than 2,000 plates per meter can be prepared consistently. Uniformity of particle size is achieved by using a narrow range of mesh size, by carefully removing any *fines* (particles of very small size), and by not producing more fines by rough handling in the coating and packing processes. For analytical columns of 2–3 mm i.d., 100–110 mesh size is desirable.

Coating the support can be carried out by many methods; the least desirable is using a rotary evaporator in the drying step, which tends to agitate the packing and produce fines. A reliable method is as follows:

1. Dissolve the liquid phase in a solvent in a flask. (A suitable solvent can be found in any of the suppliers' catalogs. Select one that does not boil under the vacuum to be used.)
2. Add the cooled solution to the support, swirling gently to insure wetting.
3. Stopper, and apply vacuum to remove air from the pores of the support. When no more air bubbles escape, seal the vacuum and hold for 5 min.
4. Release the vacuum, transfer the support to either a glass funnel with a coarse-porosity frit in the neck or to a fluidized-bed dryer, and immediately suck the solution off.
5. When the solution ceases to drip out, fluidize the bed of coated packing and dry with a gentle flow of hot nitrogen gas. (The packing is dry and ready for filling into the column when no odor of solvent remains.)

The coated packing is transferred, a little at a time, into the column with the aid of vacuum and gentle tapping. Electric vibrators are popular, but their use will degrade column performance by producing fines. The key factors are uniformity of the packing material and gentle tapping. To condition the packing, heat the column slowly to the upper working limit and maintain this temperature, along with a small flow of carrier gas, for several hours. This distributes the liquid evenly over the surface of the support. Many of the modern polysiloxanes do not require extensive conditioning. The most important consideration in obtaining good column performance and long life is to avoid overheating.

Column Inlets

As in liquid chromatography, the gas-chromatography sample is introduced to the column through a specially designed inlet, generally by injecting it in nanoliter amounts through a rubber septum with a microliter syringe. The inlet should be hot enough to flash evaporate the sample, and large enough in volume to allow the sample vapor to expand without blowing back through the septum. Two types of inlet are shown in Figures 22.6 and 22.7.

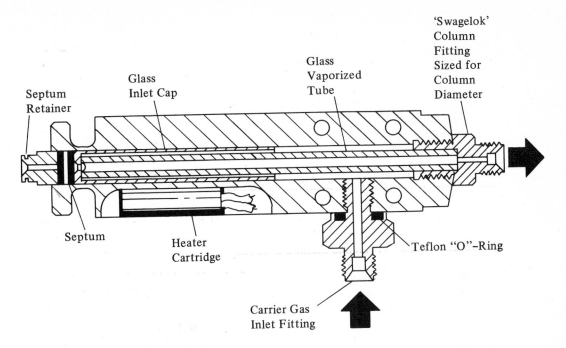

FIGURE 22.6. *Diagram of glass-lined flash-evaporation inlet. Courtesy of Hamilton Co.*

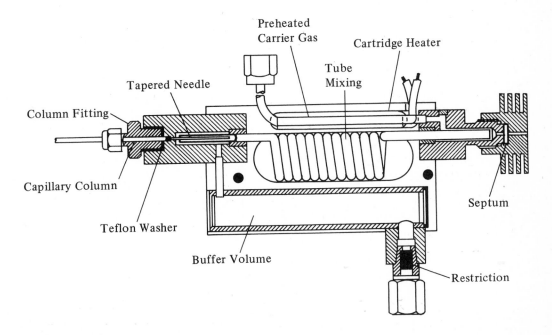

FIGURE 22.7. *Diagram of an inlet-splitter for open tubular or small-diameter packed columns. Courtesy of Hamilton Co.*

The first (most common) type is the *flash-vaporization inlet* (Fig. 22.6), an arrangement of concentric glass tubes that washes the septum area with a high-velocity, preheated carrier-gas stream, thus preventing blowback. The gas passes to the column through a 1- or 2.5-mm glass vaporizer tube heated by a cartridge heater mounted in the body of the inlet. A glass lining is preferred for samples that might decompose in an all-metal inlet. A slight modification in the position of the septum makes it possible to inject samples almost directly onto the column, for studying compounds that are too thermally labile to withstand flash evaporation.

The second type of inlet, called a *splitter* (Fig. 22.7), again uses a syringe to inject the sample. The sample is vaporized and effectively mixed with carrier gas in the mixing tube, after which the vapor passes over a tapered hollow needle. Because of the difference between the inside diameter of the mixing tube outlet and that of the tapered needle, a fraction of the total sample is introduced into the column as a narrow zone. The splitting ratio is a function of the pressure in the inlet, and can be varied. Such a sample splitter is used with capillary columns and high-resolution columns because of their relatively low capacity.

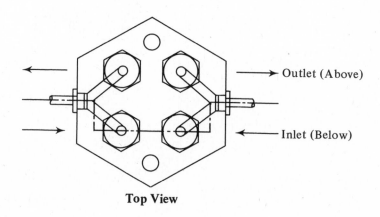

Top View

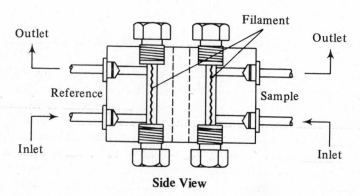

Side View

FIGURE 22.8. *Cross-section of a typical four-wire conductivity cell. Courtesy of Gow-Mac Instrument Co.*

Detectors

The three most common detectors in gas chromatography are those using thermal conductivity, flame ionization, and electron capture. The first is also the oldest; it measures heat conductivity, which is different for different gases. The second and third types respond to changes in electron currents; the electrons are produced in a flame by burning the sample, or by exposing the sample to a radioactive source.

Thermal Conductivity Detector. The thermal conductivity detector (TCD) is a simple universal detector (see Fig. 22.8) that produces a large signal requiring no amplification. The detector cell has either two or four filaments arranged in a Wheatstone bridge circuit (Fig. 22.9). In the four-filament model, two filaments in

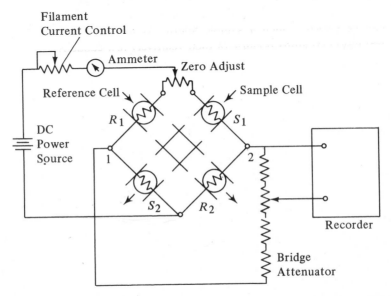

FIGURE 22.9. *Typical bridge configuration for thermal conductivity detection. Courtesy of Gow-Mac Instrument Co.*

opposite arms of the bridge are surrounded by carrier gas flowing in a reference stream, the other pair by carrier gas flowing out of the column. When the bridge is balanced, no signal appears across points 1 and 2 in Figure 22.9. Since the temperature of the filaments is proportional to the rate at which heat is transported to the cell body by the gas, and since resistance is proportional to temperature, a change in the heat conductivity of the gas will produce an output signal at points 1 and 2. Most organic vapors have low thermal conductivities (λ) compared to hydrogen or helium ($\lambda_{acetone} = 2.37 \times 10^{-5}$, $\lambda_{H_2} = 41.6 \times 10^{-5}$, $\lambda_{He} = 34.80 \times 10^{-5}$ at 0°C). For this reason, helium is widely used as a carrier gas; but if one were interested in analyzing the noble gases, nitrogen might be the carrier of choice. The TCD is reliable, simple, nondestructive, and moderately sensitive; it responds to essentially all compounds, and is widely used in preparative work. Since it is nondestructive, the solutes can be collected (for instance, in a dry ice–acetone bath) for further examination by other means, such as infrared spectroscopy. Relative responses vary widely and are frequently nonlinear with concentration, so quantitative analyses require careful calibration. The analyst is rarely justified in merely taking peak ratios as an accurate indication of relative amounts. This detector has a concentration detection limit of about 5–10×10^{-6} g/ml of eluant gas, and a dynamic (working) range of about 10^5.

Flame-Ionization Detector. The flame-ionization detector (FID) has a wide linear range and high sensitivity, and is quite reliable. It consists of a hydrogen–air flame polarized in an electrostatic field (Fig. 22.10). The flame ignites and ionizes the

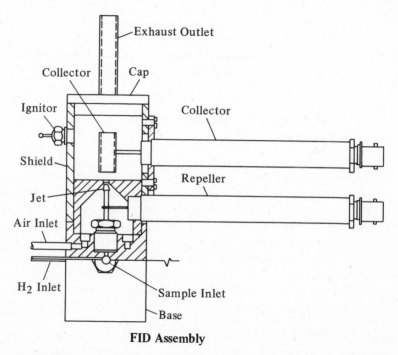

FID Assembly

FIGURE 22.10. *A flame-ionization detector. Courtesy of Gow-Mac Instrument Co.*

combustible sample components as the carrier gas passes into it, after which the ions (primarily carbon compounds) are collected at the electrodes, producing a current. The FID does not respond fully to oxygenated carbons such as carbonyls, carboxylic acids, or their sulfur analogs (for instance, cyclohexane and cyclohexanone have different response factors). However, it does not respond at all to water or to the permanent gases (N_2, O_2, CO_2, etc.), making it ideally suited for trace analysis in aqueous solutions and atmospheric samples. Response is proportional to the number of carbon atoms, but diminishes with increasing substitution by halogens, amines, hydroxyl groups or any electron-capturing species. The limit of detection is 1–$5 \times$

10^{-9} g/ml of sample gas, with a dynamic range of 10^8. Sample collection is possible if the column effluent is split into two streams.

Electron-Capture Detector. The electron-capture detector (ECD) takes advantage of the affinity of certain functional groups for free electrons (the reason for loss of sensitivity in the FID). The principle is almost identical to flow-through proportional counting of a radioactive source. The carrier gas is passed through a cell containing a beta source (e^- for nuclear decay), which ionizes the carrier gas. The source can be a Pt foil saturated with $^3H_2$, but a ^{63}Ni foil is used more frequently because of its higher temperature stability. Some typical carrier gases are He-CH$_4$, N$_2$-CH$_4$, and Ar-CH$_4$. The beta particles ionize the carrier molecules and produce electrons, which migrate to the anode (Fig. 22.11) under an applied potential of

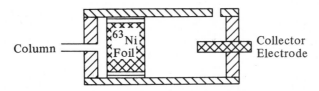

FIGURE 22.11. *A "pin-cup" design for electron-capture detection, in cross-section.*

1–100 V. An electron-capturing species eluting from the column will react with the electrons to form an ion or neutral molecule, which is swept from the cell. The net result is a reduction in the number of electrons found at steady state or a drop in the *standing current.* A "peak" in ECD detection is therefore actually a detector-current "valley," since the maximum current is found in the absence of capturing species. Response is very nonlinear, but a linear range of 0.5–1 $\times$ 10^3 can be achieved by pulsing the polarizing voltage. The pulse duration is long enough for electron collection, but not for ion collection. The limit of detection is about 1×10^{-12} g.

The major advantage of the electron-capture detector, however, is its selectivity. The ECD is insensitive to amines, alcohols, and hydrocarbons, but very sensitive to halogens, anhydrides, peroxides, ketenes, nitro groups, and so forth, with selectivity ratios of 10^5:1 being not uncommon in practice. Table 22.4 lists electron-capturing compounds and relative sensitivities. It is not uncommon for FID and ECD to be combined, displaying the response of both detectors on the same chart using a two-pen recorder. The many applications of ECD include analyzing pesticides (e.g., aldrin, dieldrin, DDT, lindane) and organometallics (e.g., lead alkyls) and tracing SF$_6$ in flue and stack gases.

Other Specific Detectors. The most elegant of the specific detectors used for gas chromatography is the mass spectrometer. (This application of mass spectrometry was discussed in Chapter 16.) Infrared spectrometry has become a practical detection method, now that rapid-scan infrared systems have made collecting samples unnecessary. In fact, part of the impetus behind developing both these techniques was the difficulty in collecting gas chromatographic fractions; vapor samples entering cold

TABLE 22.4. *Electron Absorption Coefficients of Various Compounds and Classes of Compounds for Thermal Electrons*

Electron Absorption Coefficient [a]	Compounds and Classes	Electrophores
0.01	Aliphatic Saturated, Ethenoid, Ethinoid, and Diene Hydrocarbons; Benzene; Cyclopentadiene.	None
0.01–0.1	Aliphatic Ethers and Esters; Naphthalene.	None
0.1–1.0	Aliphatic Alcohols, Ketones, Aldehydes, Amines, Nitriles; Monofluoro- and Chloro- Compounds.	$-OH$ $-NH_2$ $>CO$ $-CN$ Halogens
1.0–10	Enols; Oxalate Esters; Stilbene; Azobenzene; Acetophenone; Dichloro-, Hexafluoro-, and Mono-bromo- Compounds	$-CH{=}C{-}OH$ $-CO{-}CO-$ Halogens
10–100	Anthracene; Anhydrides; Benzaldehyde; Trichloro- Compounds; Acyl Chlorides.	$-CO{-}O{-}CO-$ Phenyl$-CO-$ Halogens
100–1,000	Azulene; Cyclooctatetrene; Cinnamaldehyde; Benzophenone; Monoiodo-, Dibromo-, Trichloro-, and Tetrachloro- Compounds; Mononitro- Compounds.	Halogens NO_2 Phenyl$-CH{=}CH{-}CO-$
1,000–10,000	Quinones; 1,2-Diketones; Fumarate Esters; Pyruvate Esters; Diiodo-, Tribromo-, Polychloro-, and Polyfluoro- Compounds; Dinitro Compounds	$-CO{-}CO-$ $-CO{-}CH{=}CH{-}CO-$ Quinone structure Halogens NO_2

Source: From J. E. Lovelock and N. L. Gregory, in N. Brenner, J. E. Callen, and M. D. Weiss, eds., *Gas Chromatography*, New York: Academic Press, 1962, by permission of the publisher.
a. Values are relative to the absorption coefficient of chlorobenzene, which is arbitrarily taken to be unity.

traps from detectors at elevated temperatures tend to form aerosol fogs that do not condense on the trap walls, but are swept out by the carrier gas instead. However, at high concentrations, enough material can be collected to run remote infrared, mass-spectral, or nuclear magnetic resonance spectra. The concentrations here are in the range of 10^{-3} g/sec, as compared to 10^{-12}–10^{-9} g/sec with the directly coupled methods.

If the detector is of the FID type, flame optical emission or absorption can also be used. Commercial detectors are available that use essentially nondispersive or filter analyzers coupled to a FID. Phosphorus, sulfur, and nitrogen are commonly detected by this method. A hollow-cathode light source makes possible the detection of many organometallic compounds by atomic absorption.

22.4 QUALITATIVE AND QUANTITATIVE ANALYSIS

Qualitative Analysis

Gas chromatographic retention times are most frequently determined from the positions of peak maxima, although the thermodynamically meaningful (and analytically preferred) value is the position of the peak center-of-gravity. Under carefully controlled conditions, values of t_r are reproducible to better than $\pm 0.1\%$; however, agreement between retention times of a standard and an unknown peak is not conclusive evidence that they arise from the same substance. To produce more conclusive evidence, the retention times can be varied by changing the operating conditions (for instance, column material, flow rate, and temperature); if the two peaks move identically, they probably represent the same material. Most analyses are carried out under isothermal conditions, but it is possible to program the temperature to change at some predictable rate (°C/min). The latter technique can be especially valuable in separating mixtures of substances with widely varying vapor pressures, but determining a suitable programming rate can be a tedious trial-and-error process. An example of temperature programming is given in Figure 22.12. By starting at a lower initial temperature, the germane (GeH_4) and arsine (AsH_3) peaks are more fully resolved, and by programming to higher temperatures, the stannane (SnH_4) and stibine (SbH_3) are eluted sooner and with less broadening.

It is a common practice for qualitative analysis to be based on measurements of t_r; this is especially true in those laboratories that run standards with each analysis. Nevertheless, t_r is not the ideal parameter for identification purposes because it is a function of temperature, flow rate, and liquid-phase volume. (Indeed, the liquid-phase volume is continuously changing with time because of evaporation; even its chemical composition can vary under the conditions of the experiment.) What is needed, then, is a parameter that is independent of all these factors. A very successful, but not perfect, solution is the Kováts index system, which relates the retention volume V_r (or the retention time t_r) of the unknown compound with that of n-hydrocarbons eluting before and after it. To each of a series of paraffins is attached an index I, given by

$$I = 100n \tag{22.15}$$

where n = the carbon number of a given paraffin

The retention index of an unknown is calculated from the relation

$$I = 100\left[\frac{\log V_n^u - \log V_n^x}{\log V_n^{x+1} - \log V_n^x}\right] + 100x \tag{22.16}$$

where x = the carbon number of the compound eluted before the unknown
V_n^u = the net retention volume of the unknown
V_n^x = the net retention volume of the hydrocarbon eluted before the unknown
V_n^{x+1} = the net retention volume of the hydrocarbon eluted after the unknown
$x + 1$ = the carbon number of the compound eluted after the unknown

(x and $x + 1$ are the bracketing hydrocarbon carbon-numbers.)

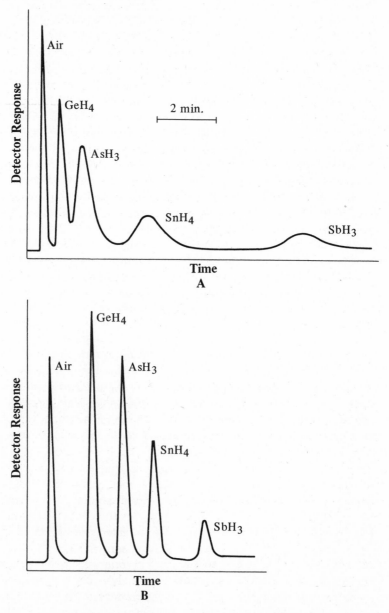

FIGURE 22.12. *Example of temperature programming to improve separations. A: Isothermal temperature, 85°C. B: Temperature programmed 8°C/min, 75°–120°C. From R. D. Kadeg and G. D. Christian,* Anal. Chim. Acta, *88, 117 (1977), by permission of the publisher.*

This method is based on a linear relation between log V_r and carbon number in a homologous series and essentially places any species on its appropriate place on the plot. The basic assumption is that variations in the retention of hydrocarbons will be reflected in the retention of all other species under isothermal conditions; hence, if the flow rate changes or if the stationary-phase volume is reduced, all observed V_r values will change, but the value of I for a given species will not. A problem arises only when the chemical composition of the phase changes with time because of polymerization or oxidation. For example, a polyglycol polymer stationary phase might change in polarity after long heating and exposure to an active catalytic support surface, so that changes in its retention of alcohols will not be mirrored by changes in its retention of paraffins. The retention of the hydrocarbons on this phase is mainly a function of vapor pressure, with almost a uniform activity coefficient contribution and no directed (that is, H-bonding) interactions, whereas the retention of alcohols depends not only on vapor-pressure differences but on directed solute-solvent interactions. A loss of H-bonding capacity will influence the retention of alcohol markedly, but may not affect that of the paraffins. Some workers use homologous series of analogous compounds—alcohols with alcohols, ketones with ketones, and so on—in an attempt to avoid this problem. The use of computers in GC is strongly encouraged, since they make the calculation of retention indices a trivial operation. Of course, just as a single t_r measurement (even with standards) does not conclusively identify a given substance, neither does a single index value. Several columns should be used and index values calculated for each as cross-references to known materials.

Quantitative Analysis

If the analyst is willing to assume that peak shape is not a function of solute concentration, he or she can carry out quantitative analyses by establishing standard curves of peak height versus concentration. The quantitative information in a gas chromatogram is found in the peak areas and not in the peak heights, since zone shape is a function of many different variables, notably injection rate. Peak areas are obtained by conventional methods, such as triangulation, mechanical or electronic integration by analog devices on the recorder, and summation in digital recorders (analog-to-digital conversion); the ease and accuracy of measurement increase in the order of the methods mentioned, as does the cost. The relative response factors for the different species are important to determine, so as to normalize the areas measured to a common base for comparison. Quantitative analysis is generally carried out with reference to standard calibration curves; in practice, an error of $\pm 2\%$ is quite reasonable. Quantitative analysis also depends on using a recording method that has the correct frequency-response for the signal observed.

22.5 APPLICATIONS OF GAS CHROMATOGRAPHY

Applications of gas chromatography are best illustrated by the actual chromatograms themselves. The examples were chosen to illustrate the utility of the technique in many areas of scientific endeavor, and because they combine many of the ideas presented in this chapter. They do not necessarily illustrate the method of choice for a given analysis.

Industrial Environmental Analysis

A good example of a gas-chromatographic analysis in the area of air quality is in the study of coke-oven emissions. By its very nature, the coke process can be expected to produce polycyclic organic matter; this is of concern because many compounds in this class are carcinogenic. Such compounds as benz[a]anthracene, benzo[a]pyrene, and benz[c]acridine are of particular importance.

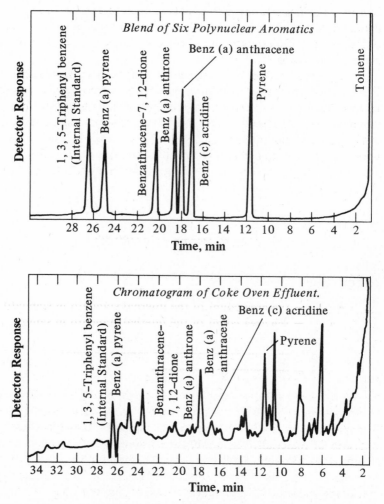

FIGURE 22.13. *Chromatograms of a standard mixture of polycyclic aromatic hydrocarbons and of a coke-furnace emission. From T. D. Searl, F. J. Cassidy, W. H. King, and R. A. Brown,* Anal. Chem., *42, 954 (1970) by permission of the senior author and the publisher. Copyright © 1970 by the American Chemical Society.*

The chromatograms shown in Figure 22.13 were obtained using a 10 ft ×
0.125 in (o.d.) column packed with 2% SE-30 on Chromosorb G. Temperature
programming was utilized (175–275°C at 4°C/min, then held for 15 min). Pertinent
fractions were trapped and analyzed remotely by ultraviolet spectrometry. Recoveries (grams found/grams present) were about 86% for benzo[a]pyrene. Actual coke-
oven samples were collected by ambient-air–filter techniques and extracted with
cyclohexane. Detection was by FID in a split-effluent stream.

Forensic Analysis for Drugs of Abuse

One of the major applications of gas chromatography is in finding legal evidence of
the presence of illicit material. Two examples are given here. The first is the analysis
of "street-quality" heroin; the second is an analysis for amphetamine and related
materials in biological fluids.

Analysis for the heroin content of illicit heroin, which is often "cut" with
quinine hydrochloride, can be accomplished directly using gas-liquid chromatography.
In this example, an internal standard (cholesterol) is added to improve both qualitative and quantitative accuracy. The chromatogram is isothermal (235°C) with a
6 ft × $\frac{1}{4}$ in column packed with 3% OV-1 on 80/100 mesh Chromosorb W. The
peak area is determined using a digital integrator. Figure 22.14 shows a typical
analysis. Heroin content is calculated by the following relations:

$$c_s = \frac{A_s}{A_{std}} \left(\frac{A_{i.s./std}}{A_{i.s./s}} \right) c_{std} \tag{22.17}$$

$$\% \text{ Heroin} = \frac{c_s}{S} (100 \%) \tag{22.18}$$

where A_s = the area count of sample
   A_{std} = the area count of standard
   $A_{i.s./std}$ = the area count of the internal standard in standard solution
   $A_{i.s./s}$ = the area count of the internal standard in sample solution
   c_{std} = the concentration of the standard
   c_s = the concentration of the sample (heroin)
   S = the weight of the sample

An analysis of amphetamine and related compounds is easily achieved in
standard solutions by derivatization to the N-trifluoroacetamide. The situation
is much different in the world of "real" samples. Biological fluids are very complex
mixtures of materials. In urine, such materials as amphetamine can be extracted,
a derivative made, and the latter analyzed without much problem; at high dilution
in blood, the problem becomes more complicated. In this example, the following
procedure yielded the highest recoveries (98%) at the 2.5×10^{-8} g/ml of blood level:
(1) extracting the substance with benzene in coated glassware, (2) scavenging
the amine with a volatile amine (diethylamine) in a HCl salt-formation step,
and (3) derivatization to the N-trifluoroacetamide. Chromatographic conditions
were similar to that of the previous example. A typical chromatogram is given in
Figure 22.15.

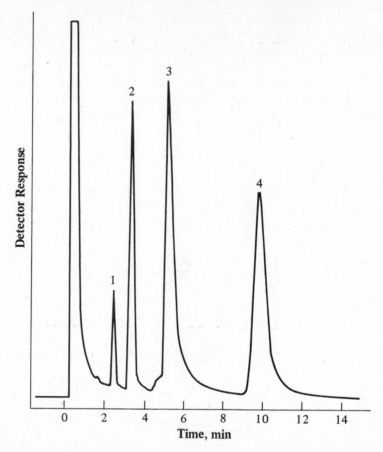

FIGURE 22.14. *Chromatogram of heroin preparation showing internal standard. Compounds: 1. Acetylcodeine or O^6-monoacetylmorphine; 2. Heroin hydrochloride; 3. Quinine hydrochloride; 4. Cholesterol internal standard. From P. De Zan and J. Fasenello,* J. Chromatogr. Sci., *10, 333 (1972), by permission of the publisher.*

Pharmacological Studies

This example of the recovery of a drug and its metabolites is important because it illustrates electron-capture detection. The drug studied is 7-chloro-1,3-dihydro-5-(2′-chlorophenyl)-2H-1,4-benzodiazepin-2-one. In this study, the intent was to recover the intact drug and to recover and identify its metabolites in blood and urine. Figure 22.16 shows a typical chromatogram of a diethyl-ether extract of blood. The detection limit for the drug was 0.002 μg/ml of blood; the very low levels of the drug

FIGURE 22.15. *A typical chromatogram of amphetamine as determined in an extract of human whole blood. A: Chromatogram. B: Calibration curve illustrating linearity, sensitivity, and recovery from whole blood. From J. E. O'Brien, W. Zazulan, V. Abbey, and O. Hinsvark,* J. Chromatogr. Sci., *10, 336 (1972), by permission of the publisher.*

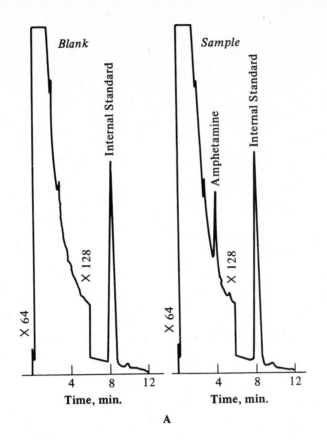

A

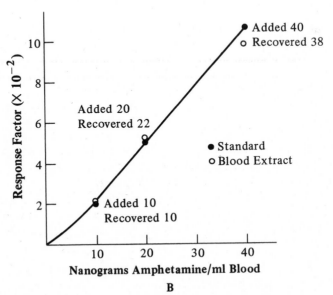

B

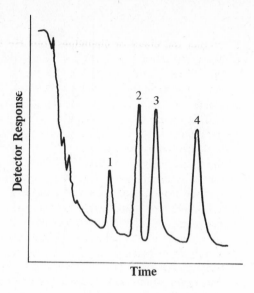

FIGURE 22.16. *Chromatogram of diethyl-
ether extract of blood showing a drug and
its metabolites. Compounds: 1. Lorazepam
(an identified metabolite); 2. Unidentified
metabolite; 3. Parent drug; 4. Reference
standard. Column: 4 ft × 4 mm borosilicate glass, 3% OV-17 stationary phase on
60/80-mesh diatomite. Argon-methane
(90:10) carrier gas. Column: Isothermal
at 240°C. Injection part, 280°C; detector,
325°C. Adapted from J. A. F. de Silva,
I. Bekersky, and C. V. Puglisi, J. Chromatogr. Sci., 11, 547 (1973), by permission
of the publisher.*

expected in human-subject studies required gas chromatography with electron-capture
detection (^{63}Ni sources) as opposed to more common spectrophotometric procedures.
The chromatogram is relatively simple, because of the selectivity of the detection
system; the ECD is essentially responding only to the chlorinated compounds. The
only metabolite positively identified was Lorazepam, the 3-hydroxy analog of the
parent drug.

SELECTED BIBLIOGRAPHY

KARGER, B. A.; SNYDER, L. R.; and HORVATH,
C. *An Introduction to Separation Science.*
New York: Wiley-Interscience, 1973. *This
text organizes the various separation techniques into a unified theme and is strongly
recommended to those whose work involves
separations.*

LITTLEWOOD, A. B. *Gas Chromatography:
Principles, Techniques and Applications,*
2nd ed. New York: Academic Press, 1970.

MCNAIR, H. M., and BONELLI, E. J. *Basic Gas
Chromatography.* Varian Aerograph, 2700
Mitchell Dr., Walnut Creek, Calif. 94598.
*A very good "first" book on practical
aspects.*

*Guide to Stationary Phases for Gas Chromatog-
raphy.* Analabs, Inc., North Haven,
Connecticut. *A correlated listing of stationary phases and solute types, updated on
a regular basis.*

REFERENCES

1. A. J. P. MARTIN and R. L. M. SYNGE,
Biochem. J., 35, 1358 (1941).

2. A. T. JAMES and A. J. P. MARTIN, *Biochem.
J. Proc., 48*, vii (1951); *Analyst, 77*, 915
(1952).

3. E. GLUECKAUF, *Trans. Faraday Soc., 51*, 34
(1955).

4. L. ROHRSCHNEIDER, *Z. Anal. Chem., 170*,
256 (1959).

5. W. O. MCREYNOLDS, *J. Chromatog. Sci., 8*,
685 (1970).

6. J. LEARY, J. JUSTICE, S. TSUGE, S. LOWRY,
and T. L. ISENHOUR, *J. Chromatog. Sci., 11*,
201 (1973).

PROBLEMS

1. Predict the effect of changing from He to N_2 carrier gas on (a) retention volume, and (b) HETP. What might be the effects of using a super-critical vapor such as CO_2?

2. Compare the following two methods of scaling up an analytical separation to preparative levels: (1) keeping column size (volume and length) constant and increasing the percent liquid loading; and (2) increasing column diameter, keeping the length and the percent liquid loading constant.

3. The following data were obtained on a nonpolar column for n-butylacetate (retention time in mm of chart paper): n-heptane, 174 mm; n-octane, 373.4 mm; n-butylacetate, 310 mm. (a) Calculate the Kováts index I for n-butylacetate. (b) Does the value of $I/100$ have any physical significance?

4. A column of support coated with an ester of low volatility is operated at 23 lb/in² and 40°C. The following results were obtained:

Compound	t_r, min
Methane + Air	1.8
Ethane	2.4
Propane	3.6
Propylene	4.3
Isobutane	5.5
Butane	7.5
Isobutylene	8.6
Trans-2-Butene	10.6
Cis-2-Butene	12.3
Isopentane	13.6
Pentane	18.2

Construct a plot of log V_r' versus carbon number, including all compounds significantly retained. What can be seen in the results?

5. Derive the expressions for optimum velocity and minimum plate-height using the simple Van Deemter expression. What are the dominant factors in each?

6. From a survey of ten articles in the literature dealing with gas-chromatographic separations, list structures of the stationary phase and the compounds separated, and your estimate of the kind of forces involved in the retention mechanism.

7. The adjusted retention times (t_R') in min for a series of compounds were determined carefully on a nonpolar column: n-pentane, 2.8; n-hexane, 5.3; n-heptane, 13.7; n-octane, 29.3; toluene, 16.5; cyclohexane, 12.4. Calculate the Kováts index for toluene and for cyclohexane.

8. Gas-reduction valves used on helium tanks in gas chromatography commonly give the pressure in units of psig (pounds per square inch above atmospheric pressure). (a) Calculate the actual inlet pressure in mm of mercury (torr) for 20, 40, 60, and 80 psig if ambient pressure is 740 mm Hg and normal atmospheric pressure (760 mm) is 14.696 psi. (b) Calculate the compressibility factor j for each of these cases.

9. Uncorrected flow rates (F_o) measured on a bubble-type flowmeter must be corrected for temperature and pressure (see Fig. 22.1). Calculate F_o for F_0 = 23.8, 40.2, and 51.9 ml/min. The ambient pressure and temperature are 750 mm Hg and 25°C; the column temperature is 110°C.

10. The following data were obtained on a 1/8" i.d. × 10' column of 15% SE-30 (by weight) on Chromosorb W. Inlet pressure = 60.0 psig; ambient pressure = 740 mm Hg; column temperature = 116°C; ambient temperature = 24°C; uncorrected He flow rate = 26.4 ml/min on a bubble-type flowmeter. A total of 1.09 g of SE-30 was contained in the column.

Compound	t_R' (min)	Peak Width, W (min)
Ether	1.78	0.31
Hexane	6.78	0.84
Ethylbenzene	18.14	1.64

For each compound, calculate (a) the adjusted retention volume, (b) the net retention volume, and (c) the specific retention volume (at 0°C). Calculate (d) the resolution between ether and hexane, and (e) between hexane and ethylbenzene.

11. The chromatographic data shown overleaf were obtained on the column used in Problem 10 with 2-μl injections of heptane.

F_0 (ml/min)	t_0 (min) "air peak"	t_r (min)	Peak Height (Chart Divisions)	Peak Width, W (min)
121.2	1.38	4.49	50.2	0.30
91.3	1.69	5.37	60.3	0.34
72.8	1.94	6.17	64.9	0.38
63.7	2.09	6.62	67.6	0.42
51.2	2.42	7.62	69.2	0.49
40.9	2.78	8.83	79.4	0.63
32.7	3.30	10.31	78.5	0.76
27.4	3.74	11.69	76.8	0.90
18.1	5.03	15.84	72.3	1.47

Ambient temperature and pressure were 25.0°C and 740-mm Hg; inlet pressure was 60.5 psig; column temperature was 109°C. For each flow rate calculate F_0, t_r', V_r', V_n, N, H, and the (triangulated) area A of the peak. Plot N and H versus F_0 and estimate the optimum flow rate. Plot the peak height and peak area versus F_0 and comment on the effect of flow rate on these.

12. What number of plates would be required to effect a separation with less than 1% contamination ($R = 1.5$) for $\alpha = 1.10$ in (a) a packed column with a capacity factor of 50; (b) a packed column with $k' = 5$; (c) an open tubular column with $k' = 2$; (d) an open tubular column with $k' = 0.5$. (e) Calculate the effective number of plates in each case. (f) What column lengths would be necessary for a good packed column of $H = 0.2$ mm and an open tubular column of $H = 10$ mm?

23

Computers in Analytical Instrumentation

S. P. PERONE
D. O. JONES

Digital instruments and digital computers have become important elements in modern analytical instrumentation, for many reasons. Together with the advances in instrumentation of the 1950s and 1960s came the need to use electronic data-processing to handle the vast amounts of raw data that could be generated. As a result of space-age technological advances, digital devices became so compact and inexpensive by the late 1960s and early 1970s that laboratory-size computers became a reality. These minicomputers could be connected to instruments to automatically acquire and process digitized data, control experimental parameters, print reports, and so forth. Because of the heavy analytical load carried by gas chromatography in industrial laboratories, chromatographs were among the first types of instruments to be computerized on a wide scale. High-resolution mass spectrometry benefited greatly from the availability of laboratory computers, because of the need to handle large quantities of data for runs lasting only a few seconds. Also, such methods as Fourier-transform nuclear magnetic resonance and infrared spectroscopy became feasible only when instruments were developed that included dedicated minicomputers.

Many other areas of analytical instrumentation have benefited greatly from computerization, and the reader is referred to review articles describing various applications in detail [1]. The objective of this chapter is to introduce the fundamental principles of on-line computer instrumentation, focusing attention on the characteristics of digital devices important for interfacing laboratory instruments to digital computers. These fundamentals include a consideration of number systems, digital logic, digital devices, analog/digital translation devices, sampling of raw data, interface design, and on-line computer operations. After the principles of inter-facing devices and their components have been presented, the design of interface devices for some specific functions will be described (Sec. 23.4).

23.1 THE DIGITAL COMPUTER

Figure 23.1 provides a block diagram of the essential components of a typical digital-computer configuration. The *memory* is a component capable of storing many thousands of binary-coded (digital) packets of information. Each packet is com-

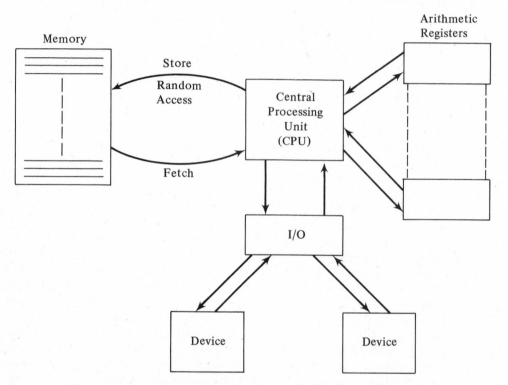

FIGURE 23.1. *Typical digital computer configuration. From S. P. Perone*, J. Chromatogr. Sci., 7, 714 (1969) *by permission of the publisher.*

posed of n binary digits (*bits*) and is called a *word* of information. Each of these n-bit words has an *address* associated with it, and the information contained within can be fetched or stored by specifying the address. The internal memory is usually either a semiconductor memory or a magnetic-ferrite-core memory [2]. Three types of information are stored in memory: *data, instruction,* or *address.* The speed with which information is fetched or stored in memory is the *memory cycle time* and is usually about 1 μsec for core memory.

The *central processing unit* (CPU) controls the overall operation of the computer. It is made up of electronic registers and logic circuits that execute the simple logical and arithmetic operations of which the computer is capable. When these operations are executed in appropriate sequences, the computer can accomplish complex mathematical or data-processing functions. Moreover, if one provides the appropriate electronic *interface*, these simple operations can be used to control experimental systems, acquire data, or print results on a teletype printer, line printer, oscilloscope, or other peripheral device.

The sequence of instructions to be executed by the computer is called a *program*. In actuality, the program is a set of binary-coded instructions stored in memory. The CPU fetches each instruction from memory, interprets and executes it, and then moves on to the next instruction. The CPU fetches instructions sequentially from memory, unless told to do otherwise by one of the instructions.

The *arithmetic registers* are high-speed electronic *accumulators* (ACs). That is, each is a set of n electronic two-state devices (like flip-flops—see Sec. 23.2), which can be used to accumulate intermediate results of binary arithmetic involving n-bit data. Nearly all the arithmetic and logical operations of the CPU are carried out in the arithmetic registers. Binary information can be transferred to or from memory and the arithmetic registers by the execution of appropriate instructions.

The *I/O* (input/output) *bus* allows transfer of binary-coded information between peripheral devices and the central processing unit. The number of peripheral devices that can be connected to the I/O bus is limited primarily by the sophistication of the hardware and software (programs).

A small digital computer (of the types currently being used for laboratory automation and experimental control)* has an instruction set of 50–100 different instructions. Each of these instructions corresponds to a specific binary coding which, when decoded by the CPU, results in the execution of a fairly simple arithmetic or logical step. Examples of some simple machine operations are binary addition of a datum in some memory location to the contents of an AC, the transfer of the contents of an AC to a memory location (and vice versa), rotation of the binary digits of the AC contents to the left or right, and the application of logical tests such as determining whether the AC is zero, nonzero, odd, even, positive, negative, etc. By developing programs composed of appropriate sequences of these elementary operations, the most sophisticated mathematical computations can be carried out. Since the computer can execute instructions so rapidly—about 10^6 instructions per second—it can complete complex computations with fantastic speed.

Thus, the digital computer is really a very simple-minded device, which must be told how to accomplish even the most fundamental computations but which can accomplish these operations with blinding speed. Moreover, it is a tireless machine, which is content to calculate endlessly and consistently. It is also very versatile, since it is programmable and capable of accomplishing an infinite variety of computational, logical, or control operations. Finally, it is a device that can (in fact, must) communicate in a variety of ways with the outside world. It is this characteristic that defines the computer as a general-purpose experimental device.

---

* Examples are the small desk-top laboratory computers manufactured by Data General Corp., Hewlett Packard Corp., Digital Equipment Corp., and others.

Programming the Digital Computer

The programming of a computer is usually accomplished with some sort of symbolic language; that is, readily recognized symbols are used to represent simple machine operations or groups of machine operations. Translating programs are supplied by the computer manufacturer to convert symbolic programs into the binary-coded machine-language programs. The simplest of these symbolic languages is the *assembly language*, where there is nearly a one-for-one conversion from symbolic statements to machine language. A program for translating these programs into machine language is called an *assembler*. The relationship between assembly and machine languages is shown in Figure 23.2. The figure shows that the assembly

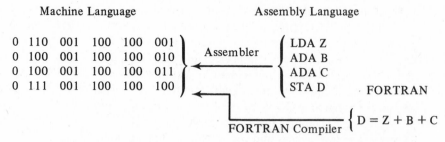

FIGURE 23.2. *Relationship of machine language to assembly language and FORTRAN. From S. P. Perone*, J. Chromatogr. Sci., 7, 714 (1969), *by permission of the publisher.*

language instructions, such as LDA Z (which may mean load the contents of memory location Z into the A register) must be translated into numerical machine language, the only language that the central processer can understand.

Because programming in assembly language can be very tedious, higher-level languages have been developed in which single statements are translated into large blocks of machine-language program segments. The translating program is called a *compiler*; one such high-level language is FORTRAN. The relationship to machine language is also shown in Figure 23.2.

Obviously, it is much simpler to prepare programs in FORTRAN than in assembly language. However, compiler-generated programs are often very inefficient in utilizing available memory space; moreover, speed of execution and synchronization of computations with outside events are relatively difficult to control with these programs. These considerations are particularly important for on-line computer applications in the laboratory; therefore, assembly-language programming must be used extensively so that the programmer can exercise the detailed control of computer operations required. Section 23.2 will deal extensively with such programming.

Off-Line Computers

The computer configuration with which most scientists are familiar is the *off-line* system (see Fig. 23.3). To use the computer in this configuration, the scientist

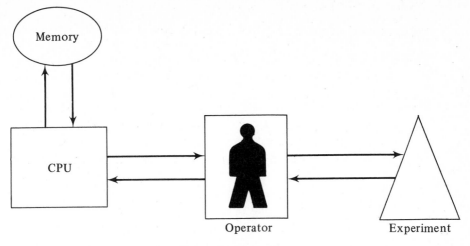

Off–line Computer System

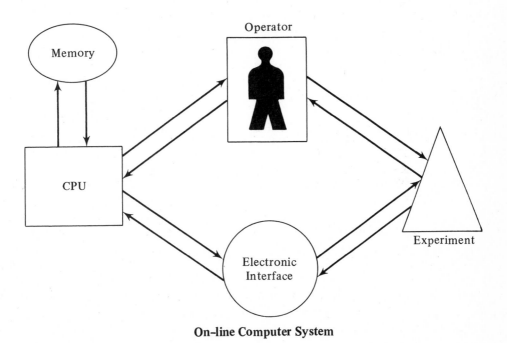

On-line Computer System

FIGURE 23.3. *Computer systems. Adapted from S. P. Perone*, J. Chem. Educ., *47*, 105 (1970) *by permission of the publisher.*

typically writes a data-processing program in FORTRAN or some other high-level computer language, runs the experiment, manually tabulates the data from the strip-chart recorder or oscilloscope trace, transfers the tabulated data to punched cards, adds the data cards to the deck of program cards, transports the combined card-deck to the computer center for processing, and then waits until the program has been executed and the results printed. Turnaround times may vary from a few minutes to a few days, depending on the capacity of the computer facility, the number of users, and the backlog and priorities of work to be processed.

On-Line Computers

For the investigator who requires very rapid or instantaneous results from his computer system, for whatever reason, the solution may be to employ an on-line computer system. The most important distinction of this configuration is that there is a *direct* line of communication between the experiment and the computer (Fig. 23.3B). The line of communication is through an electronic *interface*. (This interface includes control logic, electronic elements to provide timing and synchronization, and conversion modules, such as digitizing devices, which translate real-world data into information that the digital computer recognizes.) Data are acquired under computer control or supervision, and the program for data processing is usually held in memory to provide for very rapid completion of the computational tasks. Results can be made available to the investigator quickly by means of teletype display, line-printer, oscilloscope, or other forms of printout. In addition, the computer can be programmed to communicate directly with the experiment by controlling electronic or electromechanical devices, such as solid-state switches, relays, stepping motors, servomotors, or other devices that can be activated by changes in voltage or current.

The advantages of on-line computer operation, then, include elimination of the middle man by substituting an electronic interface, possible direct computer control of the experiment, and possible real-time interaction between the computer and the experiment. Because the computer can make computations and decisions at speeds exceeding most ordinary data-acquisition rates, it can modify the experimental conditions during the experiment. An additional advantage, of course, is that the logistic barriers of the remote computer system are eliminated.

23.2 PRINCIPLES OF DIGITAL INSTRUMENTATION

Binary and Octal Number Systems

All information handled or generated by the central processing unit (CPU) must be binary or binary-coded machine language. This includes instructions, memory addresses, and data. Thus, the small-computer user must quickly become familiar with this number system. It would be well to review here the binary number system and binary arithmetic.

The *decimal* number 369_{10}* can be broken down into $3 \times 10^2 + 6 \times 10^1 + 9 \times 10^0$. Similarly, the *binary* number (in base 2) 10101 represents $1 \times 2^4 + 0 \times 2^3 + 1 \times 2^2 + 0 \times 2^1 + 1 \times 2^0 = 21_{10}$. Large binary numbers (for instance, 101101110010101) are conveniently represented in the *octal* (base 8) system for easy

---

* 369 to the base 10.

recall or reference. The applicability of the octal system can be seen from the binary representation of the numbers 0 to 7:

000	0	011	3	110	6
001	1	100	4	111	7
010	2	101	5		

This sequence illustrates the normal binary counting sequence, which can be extended to an infinite number of binary digits (bits). It also shows the octal digits equivalent to all three-bit combinations. To convert any large binary number to octal, group binary digits in groups of three, *starting at the rightmost digit*:

$$\underset{1}{..1} \quad \underset{1}{001} \quad \underset{5}{101} \qquad = 115_8$$

$$\underset{5}{101} \quad \underset{5}{101} \quad \underset{6}{110} \quad \underset{2}{010} \quad \underset{5}{101} \quad = 55625_8$$

$$201_8 = 010 \quad 000 \quad 001$$
$$356_8 = 011 \quad 101 \quad 110$$

Counting in octal: 0, 1, 2, 3, 4, 5, 6, 7, 10, 11, 12, 13, 14, 15, 16, 17, 20, 21, 22, 23, ... 75, 76, 77, 100, 101, 102, ..., 776, 777, 1000, 1001, ..., 7776, 7777, 10000, ...

Often it is necessary to convert numbers from one base to another. The above examples illustrate the ease of converting from octal to binary and vice versa. Consider the following examples:

Decimal-to-Binary Conversion. For example, $876_{10} = ?$ in binary?

$$
\begin{array}{r}
876 \\
-512 \\
\hline
364 \\
-256 \\
\hline
108 \\
-64 \\
\hline
44 \\
-32 \\
\hline
12 \\
-8 \\
\hline
4 \\
-4 \\
\hline
0
\end{array}
$$

$512 = 2^9 = $ largest power of 2 to fit in 876_{10}

$256 = 2^8 = $ largest power of 2 to fit in 364_{10}

$64 = 2^6 = $ largest power of 2 to fit in 108_{10}

$32 = 2^5$

$8 = 2^3$

$4 = 2^2$

Thus, the binary representation of 876_{10} must include 2^9, 2^8, 2^6, 2^5, 2^3, and 2^2, so the binary number is

$$\underset{2^9}{1} \; \underset{2^8}{1} 0 \underset{2^6}{1} \; \underset{2^5}{1} 0 1 \; \underset{2^3}{1} 0 \underset{2^2}{0}$$

The octal equivalent of this binary number is 1554_8.

Digital Information

The laboratory scientist is accustomed to seeing experimental information displayed as analog data. That is, data are usually made available in a continuous signal such as given by a strip-chart recorder or oscilloscope trace. Unfortunately, the digital computer cannot handle analog information directly. The computer must have information in a digital (usually binary-coded) format.

The differences between analog and digital information are illustrated graphically in Figure 23.4. Whereas analog data are continuous with an infinite number of real values between any two points on a trace, digital data are discrete, with well defined finite limits of resolution between any two points. Thus, when digitizing an analog signal that varies between 0 and 15 V, the digital resolution will be $\pm\frac{1}{2}$ V if only 4 bits can be used to encode the digital information; that is, only 16 values (2^4) can be represented by 4 bits, allowing only 1 V increments (see Fig. 23.4). If only 2 bits are used to encode the digital information, the resolution decreases even further as there are now only four digital states possible.

It should be obvious, then, that digitizing data always results in some loss of information. This is tolerated only because it is a format change required to use the powerful data-handling features of the digital computer. However, the scientist developing and using computerized instrumentation should be aware of the problems inherent in this approach, and should learn how to take maximum advantage of digital instrumentation. To this end, digital devices, digitization methods, sampling considerations, and so forth will be discussed.

Digital Logic States

Digital logic devices are the foundation upon which digital instrumentation, including computers, interfaces, and so on, are built. They consist of a set of electronic circuits that perform simple logic operations, usually represented by the binary number system. They can be connected into more complex building blocks so as to perform the necessary logic, storage, arithmetic, interface, and timing operations required by digital instrumentation.

In the simplest case, a digital logic function can be simulated with conventional switches and a battery, the output states being indicated with a light bulb. Two such simple logic circuits are shown in Figure 23.5.

The circuit in Figure 23.5A performs the basic OR digital logic function. When both switches A and B are open, no current flows to the lamp. However, when either switch A *or* B or both are closed, current flows to light the lamp. The *output* state (whether the lamp is on or off) corresponds to the numbers of the binary

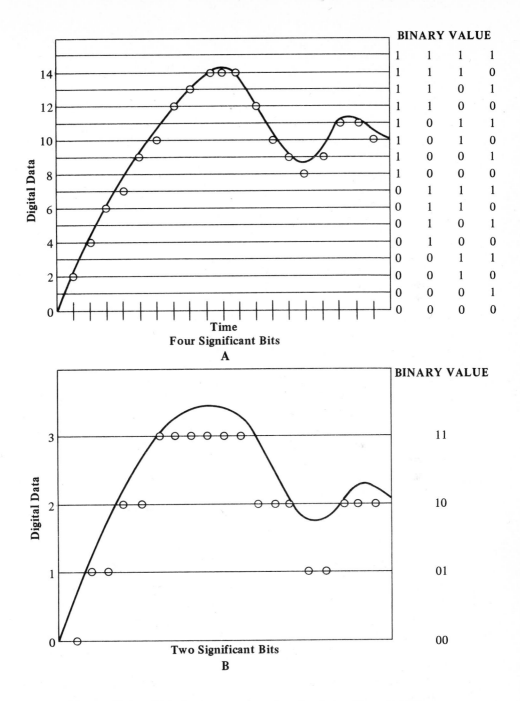

FIGURE 23.4. *Digital representation of analog data. From S. P. Perone and D. O. Jones,* Digital Computers in Scientific Instrumentation, *New York: McGraw-Hill, 1973, by permission of the publisher. Copyright © 1973 by McGraw-Hill, Inc.*

FIGURE 23.5. *Simple logic functions.*
From S. P. Perone and D. O. Jones, Digital
Computers in Scientific Instrumentation,
*New York: McGraw-Hill, 1973, by per-
mission of the publisher. Copyright ©
1973 by McGraw-Hill, Inc.*

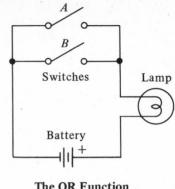

Switches   Lamp

Battery

**The OR Function
A**

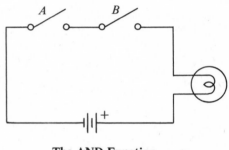

**The AND Function
B**

number system; the *on* condition is defined as the binary number 1 and the *off* condition as the binary number 0. The *input* functions or switch positions are defined
in the same manner, with the open-switch condition as a binary 0 and the closed
condition as a binary 1.

A circuit for performing another basic logic function is that in Figure 23.5B;
here, the two switches A and B are connected in series rather than in parallel, so
that both switch A *and* switch B must be closed for the lamp to light. This is a basic
digital logic circuit performing the AND function.

In Table 23.1, the operation of the circuits presented in Figure 23.5 is described
in terms of the binary number system. The output states are listed for all combinations of the input-switch conditions. If the circuits in Figure 23.5 are expanded with
more input switches, similar, but more complex, tables can be constructed. The
AND and OR circuits can also be connected together to perform more complex
logic operations. A complex logic circuit performing both AND and OR logic is
shown in Figure 23.6.

The "switch" circuits presented above are useful for defining digital logic;
they are not, however, used in modern digital computers. Modern digital logic,
available in *integrated-circuit* form, uses transistors to perform the switching opera-

TABLE 23.1. *Binary Number Representation of Logic Circuit Operation*

OR Function			AND Function		
Input Conditions		Output Condition	Input Conditions		Output Condition
Switch A	Switch B		Switch A	Switch B	
1	1	1	1	1	1
1	0	1	1	0	0
0	1	1	0	1	0
0	0	0	0	0	0

Source: S. P. Perone and D. O. Jones, *Digital Computers in Scientific Instrumentation*, New York: McGraw-Hill, 1973, by permission of the publisher. Copyright © 1973 by McGraw-Hill, Inc.

FIGURE 23.6. *Complex logic function. From S. P. Perone and D. O. Jones*, Digital Computers in Scientific Instrumentation, *New York: McGraw-Hill, 1973, by permission of the publisher. Copyright © 1973 by McGraw-Hill, Inc.*

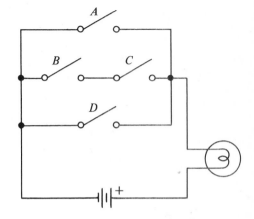

tions. Integrated circuits are miniaturized solid-state devices that may contain several complete electronic circuits; a single integrated-circuit logic package can perform extremely complex logic functions.

The logic states in integrated-circuit digital logic are usually represented by voltage levels, such as 0 and +5 V for both the inputs and outputs. For example, the basic OR logic function (Fig. 23.5) can be represented in terms of a box with two inputs and an output (Fig. 23.7). Instead of opening and closing switches as before, voltage levels are applied to the inputs and the voltage measured at the output. If

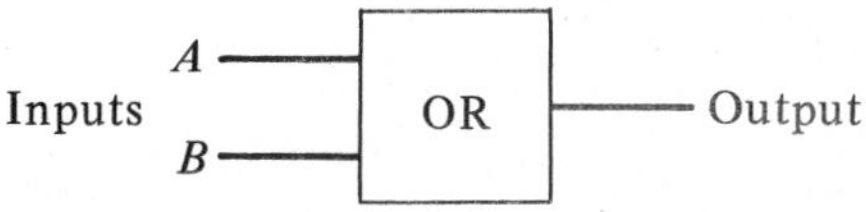

FIGURE 23.7. *Electronic logic OR function. From S. P. Perone and D. O. Jones,* Digital Computers in Scientific Instrumentation, *New York: McGraw-Hill, 1973, by permission of the publisher. Copyright © 1973 by McGraw-Hill, Inc.*

+5 V corresponds to a binary 1 and 0 V corresponds to a binary 0, the operation of the box in Figure 23.7 can be defined in the same way as the operation of the circuit in Figure 23.5A. Complex logic operations can be represented by simply connecting boxes together as in Figure 23.8, which performs the same logic function as the one represented in Figure 23.6.

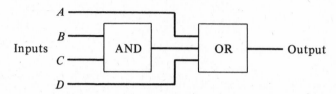

FIGURE 23.8. *Complex electronic logic function. From S. P. Perone and D. O. Jones,* Digital Computers in Scientific Instrumentation, *New York: McGraw-Hill,* 1973, *by permission of the publisher. Copyright © 1973 by McGraw-Hill, Inc.*

Often it is necessary to define the operation of a logic system in a *sentence* format. This can easily be done; for the circuits in Figures 23.6 and 23.8, the logic output is equal to a binary 1 when either A OR (B AND C) OR D is equal to a binary 1.

Simple Logic Elements: Introduction to Gates

Modern electronic digital logic comes in several microelectronic integrated-circuit forms, details of which are presented elsewhere [3]. Suffice it to say here that these different types of logic differ only in their electronic operating characteristics and requirements, not in the logic functions they perform.

The five basic logic functions are presented in Figure 23.9, along with their common symbols and "truth tables." The actual hardware electronic device used to perform a particular basic logic function is called a *gate*. The symbols in Figure 23.9 are often referred to as the *basic positive logic gate symbols*. Of these logic functions, the AND and OR gates have been considered above using switches and box diagrams. The symbols presented in the figure will, however, be used from now on.

The INVERT or NOT gate does exactly what its title suggests—it negates the input. When a binary 1 is placed on the input, the output is a binary 0. In like manner, when a binary 0 is placed on the input, the output is a binary 1. The inverter is a fundamental part of two more basic gates, the NAND and NOR gates. The term NAND is derived from AND and NOT and functionally refers to an AND gate followed by an inverter (Fig. 23.10). The logical operating characteristics of the NAND and NOR gates can be defined in the same manner as was done for the AND and OR functions previously described; the tabulations presented in Figure 23.9, commonly called *truth tables*, are by far the most commonly used road map to the operation of logic systems.

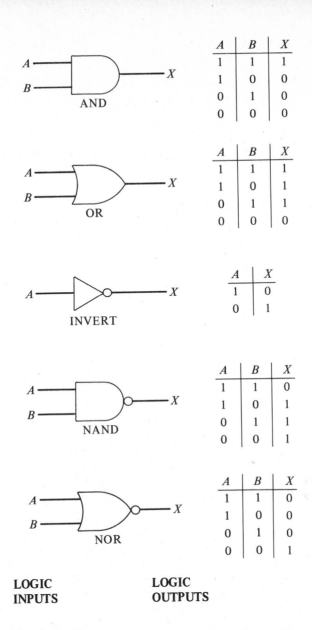

A	B	X
1	1	1
1	0	0
0	1	0
0	0	0

AND

A	B	X
1	1	1
1	0	1
0	1	1
0	0	0

OR

A	X
1	0
0	1

INVERT

A	B	X
1	1	0
1	0	1
0	1	1
0	0	1

NAND

A	B	X
1	1	0
1	0	0
0	1	0
0	0	1

NOR

LOGIC INPUTS   **LOGIC OUTPUTS**

FIGURE 23.9. *Common electronic logic symbols and truth tables. From S. P. Perone and D. O. Jones*, Digital Computers in Scientific Instrumentation, *New York: McGraw-Hill*, 1973, *by permission of the publisher. Copyright © 1973 by McGraw-Hill, Inc.*

Boolean Algebra

Boolean algebra, the algebra of logic, is a symbolic method for studying logical operations. We have previously discussed AND, OR, and NOT or INVERT functions. The Boolean algebra symbols for these functions are given in Table 23.2. The AND

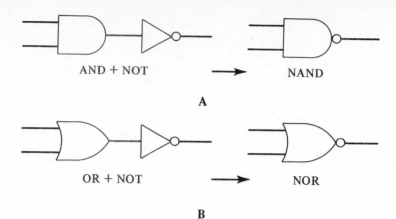

AND + NOT $\longrightarrow$ NAND

A

OR + NOT $\longrightarrow$ NOR

B

FIGURE 23.10. *Logical construction of NAND and NOR gates. From S. P. Perone and D. O. Jones,* Digital Computers in Scientific Instrumentation, *New York: McGraw-Hill, 1973, by permission of the publisher. Copyright © 1973 by McGraw-Hill, Inc.*

function can be represented by a " $\cdot$ " or by placing the variables adjacent to each other. The OR function can be represented by a " $+$." The NOT or INVERT function can be represented by a prime beside, or bar above, the variable.

A complex logic function can, of course, be written in terms of Boolean algebra. For example, $X = AB + CD + F(\bar{G} + H)$ is read, "$X = 1$ whenever A AND $B = 1$ OR C AND $D = 1$, OR $F = 1$ when $G = 0$ OR $H = 1$." Notice that $G = 0$ is a requirement rather than $G = 1$. This is because of the complement bar above it in the Boolean expression. It implies that G must be equal to 0; $\bar{G}$ is usually expressed verbally as "not G."

Many theorems and postulates have been developed for Boolean algebra and are used for designing and evaluating complex logic systems. Only one theorem, De Morgan's theorem, will be presented here; the others are presented elsewhere [4]. De Morgan's theorem is used to complement complex logic expressions such as NAND and NOR gates. A NAND gate, for instance, is equivalent to an AND gate followed by an inverter—that is, it is an *output-inverted* or *complemented* AND gate.

TABLE 23.2. *Symbols for Boolean Algebra Operations*

Function	Example	Symbol	Example
AND	$X = A$ AND B	$\cdot$	$X = A \cdot B$ or $X = AB$
OR	$X = A$ OR B	$+$	$X = A + B$
NOT	NOT A	$^-$ or $'$	$\bar{A}$ or A'

Source: S. P. Perone and D. O. Jones, *Digital Computers in Scientific Instrumentation*, New York: McGraw-Hill, 1973, by permission of the publisher. Copyright © 1973 by McGraw-Hill, Inc.

TABLE 23.3. *Complementing Boolean Expressions*

Expression	Dual	Complement
$1 \cdot A + B$	$0 + AB$	$\overline{AB}$
$\overline{A}B + C$	$\overline{A} + BC$	$A + \overline{BC}$
$A(B + C)$	$(A + B)(A + C)$	$(\overline{A} + \overline{B})(\overline{A} + \overline{C})$

Source: S. P. Perone and D. O. Jones, *Digital Computers in Scientific Instrumentation*, New York: McGraw-Hill, 1973, by permission of the publisher. Copyright © 1973 by McGraw-Hill, Inc.

Thus, a Boolean expression can be written in the following manner for a NAND gate, saying that $X = 1$ when the complement of $(A \text{ AND } B) = 1$:

$$X = (AB)' \quad \text{or} \quad X = \overline{AB} \tag{23.1}$$

This is a correct expression, but it makes constructing a complex truth-table cumbersome because it requires first constructing the AND-gate truth-table and then complementing its output column. With the use of De Morgan's theorem, the expression can be placed in a more convenient form. De Morgan's theorem states that

$$(AB)' = \overline{A} + \overline{B} \tag{23.2}$$

and

$$(A + B)' = \overline{A} \cdot \overline{B} \tag{23.3}$$

The more general implications of De Morgan's theorem can be considered after defining two new terms, a *dual* and a *literal*. To obtain the dual of a Boolean expression, one must interchange all occurrences of a " + " and a " · " and of a 1 and a 0. A literal is defined as any single *variable* within the dual expression. For example, in the expression

$$\overline{A} \cdot B + C \tag{23.4}$$

whose dual is

$$\overline{A} + B \cdot C \tag{23.5}$$

the letters $\overline{A}$, B, and C are all literals. In order to complement a Boolean expression, one must complement all literals in the dual expression. This is illustrated in Table 23.3. The application of these rules for the NAND and NOR functions leads to the statements of De Morgan's theorem presented above.

Boolean algebra is often used to interpret and generate logic diagrams. In Figure 23.11A, there are two inputs A and B; B is inverted by the upper inverter to $\overline{B}$ and A is inverted by the lower inverter to $\overline{A}$. The inputs to the upper NOR gate are then A and B. From the Boolean expression for a NOR gate (Eqn. 23.3), the output of the upper gate is $\overline{A} \cdot B$; similarly, the output of the lower NOR gate is $A \cdot \overline{B}$. These outputs become inputs to the OR gate, resulting in the output expression

$$X = A \cdot \overline{B} + \overline{A} \cdot B \tag{23.6}$$

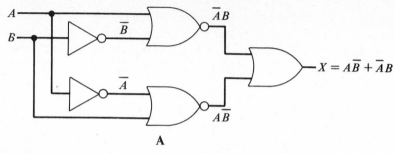

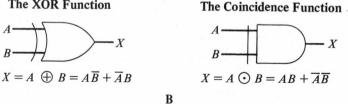

The XOR Function

$$X = A \oplus B = A\overline{B} + \overline{A}B$$

The Coincidence Function

$$X = A \odot B = AB + \overline{A}\overline{B}$$

B

FIGURE 23.11. *Exclusive OR and coincidence gates. From S. P. Perone and D. O. Jones,* Digital Computers in Scientific Instrumentation, *New York: McGraw-Hill, 1973, by permission of the publisher. Copyright © 1973 by McGraw-Hill, Inc.*

This particular function is called the *exclusive* OR function (XOR) and is the basis for binary arithmetic operations. It says that X is true if A or B, but not both, are true. It has a defining symbol "$\oplus$" and is written as

$$X = A \oplus B \equiv A \cdot \overline{B} + \overline{A} \cdot B \tag{23.7}$$

The XOR function is available in integrated-circuit form and is designated by the symbol presented in Figure 23.11B.

One more function needs to be defined, the *coincidence* function, symbolized by "$\odot$." As the name implies, this function gives a 1 output whenever both inputs are the same, either all 0's or all 1's. Its symbol is also illustrated in Figure 23.11B. The reader should construct its logic diagram using AND, OR, NAND, NOR, and INVERT gates in a manner similar to that just presented for the XOR function.

Flip-Flops

The basic device for counting and storage operations is the *flip-flop* or *bistable multivibrator*. The flip-flop, in its many forms, can be constructed from individual gates, but it is usually purchased as a single unit in integrated-circuit form.

The most basic flip-flop is called a *reset-set* or RS flip-flop. It can be constructed from two cross-coupled NAND gates, as illustrated in Figure 23.12A. It has two inputs, labeled S for set and C for clear, and two outputs, labeled Q and $\overline{Q}$. The Q output goes to a binary 1 and remains there when the S input momentarily goes from 1 to 0. In like manner, the $\overline{Q}$ output goes to a binary 1 and remains there when the C input momentarily goes from 1 to 0. Whenever Q is a 1, $\overline{Q}$ is a 0; that is, they are always complementary. As a result, the C input will also clear the Q

output to 0. The RS flip-flop will remain in whatever state it has been set or cleared to until its states are changed by applying negative-going pulses (pulses dropping from 1 to 0) to one or the other of the inputs. It is thus a bistable device with two stable states that can be used for binary data storage.

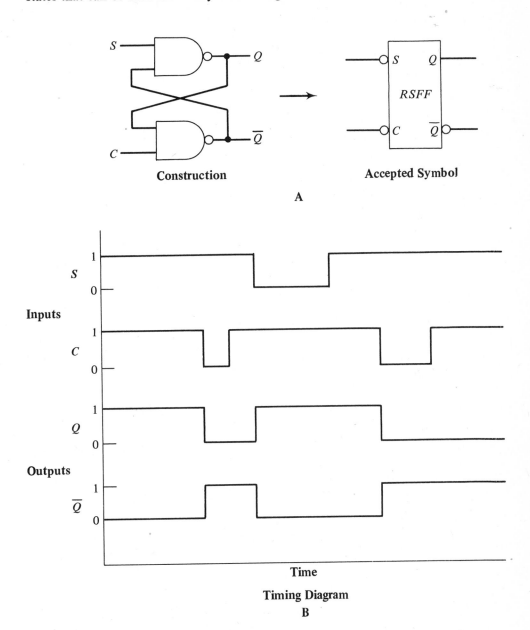

Construction   Accepted Symbol

A

Timing Diagram

B

FIGURE 23.12. *The Reset-Set (RS) flip-flop. From S. P. Perone and D. O. Jones*, Digital Computers in Scientific Instrumentation, *New York: McGraw-Hill, 1973, by permission of the publisher. Copyright © 1973 by McGraw-Hill, Inc.*

TABLE 23.4. *RS Flip-Flop Truth Table*

| | Inputs | | t_n | t_{n+1} |
Case	S	C	Q	Q
1	1	0	X	0
2	0	1	X	1
3	1	1	X	NC
4	0	0	X	U

Source: S. P. Perone and D. O. Jones, *Digital Computers in Scientific Instrumentation*, New York: McGraw-Hill, 1973, by permission of the publisher. Copyright © 1973 by McGraw-Hill, Inc. Note: NC means the output is unchanged from its previous state; U means the output is undefined and may go to either state. X means that the inputs at t_n can be in any state.

A truth table for the operation of the RS flip-flop is presented in Table 23.4. This is a somewhat different kind of table than before, in that it has time as a variable: t_n is the time before the specified input conditions have been imposed, and t_{n+1} is the time after they have been imposed. Since Q and $\bar{Q}$ always complement each other, only Q is given in the table. NC means that the output is unchanged from its previous state. U means that the output is undefined and may go to either state. X means that the inputs at t_n can be in any state.

The RS flip-flop is commonly used for control and storage operations in cases where two input signals occur. One signal is used to set its output and allow storage of a binary 1; the other input is used to clear its output and store a binary 0. Notice in Table 23.4 that when $S = C = 0$, the output is undefined. When using the RS flip-flop as a storage element with two data inputs that always complement each other, this condition offers no hindrance to its use. However, for other operations, such as counting, where only one data input signal is provided, the RS flip-flop cannot be used directly.

A timing chart for the RS flip-flop is presented in Figure 23.12B. Notice that the Q output is initially set at 1 and remains so until the C input goes to a binary 0. Q then changes to 0 and remains there until it is again set to 1 by the S input. $\bar{Q}$ is then cleared back to 0. Notice that the $\bar{Q}$ output always complements the Q output state. Timing charts are useful for defining the dynamic operation of logic devices. Often they are used in place of, as well as with, truth tables.

A more versatile flip-flop than the RS type is called a *clocked flip-flop* (Fig. 23.13), which can be used for counting operations. The clocked flip-flop has direct set S_D and direct clear C_D inputs that operate in the same manner as the S and C inputs of the RS flip-flop. (This is commonly called *asynchronous* operation, since no timing requirements are made.) For asynchronous operation, the same truth table as presented in Table 23.4 can be used, by substituting S_D and C_D for S and C. The clocked flip-flop has, however, another mode of operation called the *synchronous* mode. In the synchronous mode, information is entered into the flip-flop through

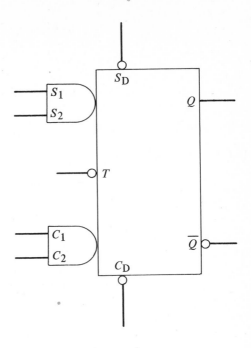

FIGURE 23.13. *The clocked flip-flop.*
From S. P. Perone and D. O. Jones, Digital
Computers in Scientific Instrumentation,
New York: McGraw-Hill, 1973, by per-
mission of the publisher. Copyright ©
1973 *by McGraw-Hill, Inc.*

the AND-gated S and C inputs (S_1, S_2 and C_1, C_2). The flip-flop does not change state, however, until a transition occurs at the *clock* or T *input*. The truth table for the synchronous mode of operation is presented in Table 23.5. Again X indicates that an input can be in either logical state. In the truth table, t_n refers to the input conditions prior to a timing pulse, and t_{n+1} refers to the time after a timing pulse has been applied to the T input. Notice, however, that there is still an undefined state. It occurs when all gated synchronous inputs are 1. As a result, the clocked

TABLE 23.5. *Clocked Flip-Flop Truth Table*

Case	t_n				t_{n+1}
	S_1	S_2	C_1	C_2	Q
1	0	X	0	X	NC
2	X	0	X	0	NC
3	X	0	0	X	NC
4	0	X	X	0	NC
5	0	X	1	1	0
6	X	0	1	1	0
7	1	1	0	X	1
8	1	1	X	0	1
9	1	1	1	1	U

Source: S. P. Perone and D. O. Jones, *Digital Computers in Scientific Instrumentation*, New York: McGraw-Hill, 1973, by permission of the publisher. Copyright © 1973 by McGraw-Hill, Inc.

flip-flop still cannot be used for counting in this mode. If, however, S_1 is connected to $\bar{Q}$, C_2 is connected to Q, and S_2 and C_1 are connected to a binary 1, as shown in Figure 23.14A, a different condition exists. Since either Q or $\bar{Q}$ must always equal 0 and since Q is connected to C_2 and $\bar{Q}$ is connected to S_1, a condition where all gated inputs equal 1 can never be generated. As a result, there will never be an undefined output state. If a pulse train is applied to the T input, the flip-flop will change state on each negative-going pulse. This is called *JK operation*; a truth table is presented in Table 23.6. Since the S_1 and C_2 inputs are connected to the outputs,

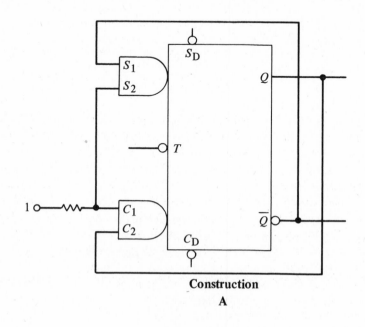

Construction

A

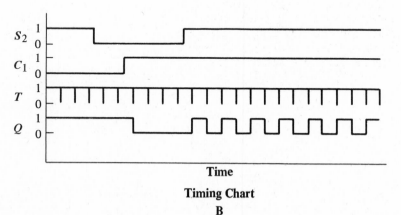

Time

Timing Chart

B

FIGURE 23.14. *JK operation of a clocked flip-flop. From S. P. Perone and D. O. Jones*, Digital Computers in Scientific Instrumentation, *New York: McGraw-Hill, 1973, by permission of the publisher. Copyright © 1973 by McGraw-Hill, Inc.*

TABLE 23.6. *JK Flip-Flop Truth Table*

t_n		t_{n+1}
S_2	C_1	Q
0	0	NC
1	0	1
0	1	0
1	1	$\bar{Q}_n$ (complements)

Source: S. P. Perone and D. O. Jones, *Digital Computers in Scientific Instrumentation*, New York: McGraw-Hill, 1973, by permission of the publisher. Copyright © 1973 by McGraw-Hill, Inc.

they are not listed in the table. The timing chart is shown in Figure 23.14B; notice that when S_2 and C_1 are 1, the Q output changes from 0 to 1 on every other input pulse, dividing the frequency in half. This flip-flop will serve for counting functions.

Normally, one would not have to connect a clocked flip-flop into the JK mode since many integrated-circuit JK flip-flops are available (see Fig. 23.15). Notice that the gated S and C inputs are renamed J and K. The connections from J and K to $\bar{Q}$ and Q are made internally and usually do not appear on the diagram.

In addition to the RS, clocked, and JK flip-flops, there are others developed for many varied applications of input gating, including capacitor coupling for AC-only operation.

Each of the above types of flip-flops come in the *master-slave* configuration,

FIGURE 23.15. *The JK flip-flop. From S. P. Perone and D. O. Jones,* Digital Computers in Scientific Instrumentation, *New York: McGraw-Hill, 1973, by permission of the publisher. Copyright © 1973 by McGraw-Hill, Inc.*

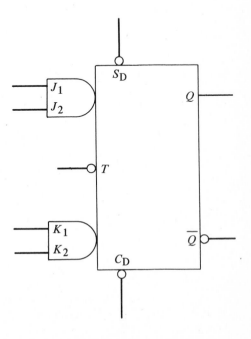

developed to overcome the timing requirements of the flip-flops already discussed. When one actually uses clocked flip-flops such as the JK units described above, one problem is that, because of the feedback required by JK operation (Fig. 23.14A), the output from a given clock pulse and set of input parameters can change the *input* information during the life of the clock pulse, thus undoing the intended result. Very critical timing requirements are often needed to ensure that the flip-flop does not settle in the wrong state. This involves very careful synchronization of clock pulses and input information, and selecting the proper clock-pulse duty cycle.

A master-slave flip-flop is actually two flip-flops in one, with a master flip-flop that feeds data to a slave flip-flop. A JK master-slave flip-flop and clock-input waveform are presented in Figure 23.16. In this figure, the various internal gates and connections are presented for the sake of illustration. In actual practice, the symbols for master-slave flip-flops are not distinguished from those already presented; almost all clocked flip-flops available in integrated-circuit form are of the master-

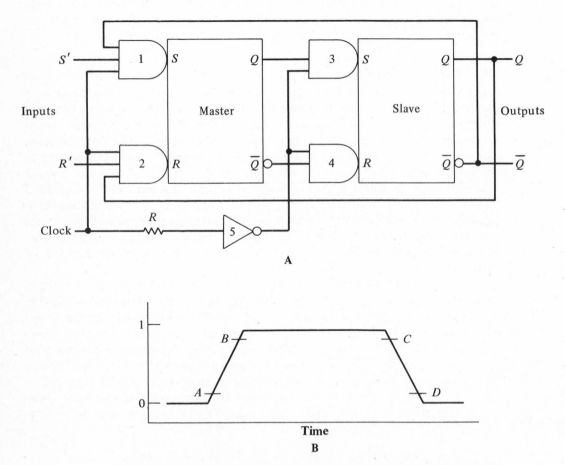

FIGURE 23.16. *The JK master-slave flip-flop. From S. P. Perone and D. O. Jones*, Digital Computers in Scientific Instrumentation, *New York: McGraw-Hill*, 1973, *by permission of the publisher. Copyright* © 1973 *by McGraw-Hill, Inc.*

slave type. All the counter and register circuits presented in the pages that follow were designed with master-slave flip-flops, so that when we say RS, clock, and JR, we mean an RS master-slave flip-flop, a clocked master-slave flip-flop, and so on.

Referring to Figure 23.16A, notice that both the master and the slave are gated RS flip-flops. The clock-pulse waveform presented in Figure 23.16B has four points on it, labeled A, B, C, and D. The master-slave JK flip-flop operates as follows: As the clock pulse goes positive from 0 to 1 past point A, the slave input gates 3 and 4 become disabled, isolating the slave from the master. The state of the master prior to A is stored on the slave outputs. As the clock pulse passes point B, input gates 1 and 2 of the master are enabled, allowing data to be transferred in through the S and R inputs. As the clock passes C, gates 1 and 2 are disabled, isolating S' and R' from the master. As the clock pulse falls past D, inverter 5 enables gates 3 and 4, allowing data transfer from the master to the slave. Notice that with master-slave operation, the outputs of the slave do not change until the clock pulse is completed, so that changes in the slave outputs cannot reach the master inputs during a clock pulse. Master-slave flip-flop configurations thus have much less critical timing requirements and much better immunity from noise.

Data-Storage Latches

One simple data-storage device is called a data *latch*, often used to temporarily store binary information. A data latch can be built either with RS or with synchronous flip-flops; the one shown in Figure 23.17A is constructed from RS flip-flops. When the timing-pulse (TP) input is high (a binary 1), the outputs of all the input OR gates are high, and no information from the data inputs D_0 and D_1 can be transferred to the latch. However, when the TP input is a binary 0, the data inputs can transfer information to the flip-flops. For example, if a binary 1 is presented at D_0, the S input of FFA will be a binary 0, which will set Q to a binary 1. (Notice that the C input will be a binary 1.) As a result, when TP is low, the Q outputs will follow the D inputs, whereas when TP is high, the Q outputs will not change regardless of what conditions occur at the D inputs. Data is thus stored in binary form until the TP input again goes momentarily to 0.

A data latch can be built using JK flip-flops, clocked flip-flops, and all varieties of synchronous master-slave flip-flops (see Figure 23.17B). The clocked flip-flop data-latch operates in much the same way as the RS flip-flop data-latch; the TP line must undergo a negative-going 1 to 0 transition each time data is transferred. However, the clocked flip-flop data-latch will operate only in a synchronous manner (that is, each time a negative-going clock pulse is present), in contrast to the RS flip-flop data-latch, in which the outputs will follow the inputs whenever the TP input is 0.

Latches can, of course, be constructed for any number of data bits. Integrated-circuit data latches are commonly available in 4-bit, 8-bit, and larger configurations.

Shift Registers

Shift registers, like data latches, are often used for data storage, but they are much more versatile. They can acquire and output data in both serial and parallel modes and also move data within the register while it is being stored.

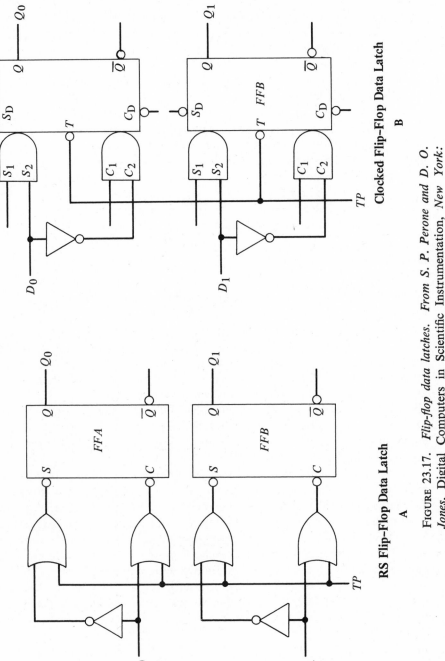

RS Flip-Flop Data Latch

A

Clocked Flip-Flop Data Latch

B

FIGURE 23.17. *Flip-flop data latches. From S. P. Perone and D. O. Jones, Digital Computers in Scientific Instrumentation, New York: McGraw-Hill, 1973, by permission of the publisher. Copyright © 1973 by McGraw-Hill, Inc.*

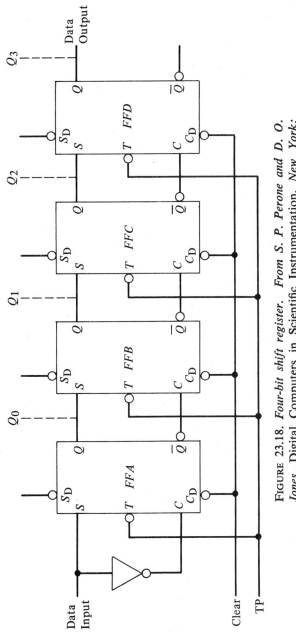

FIGURE 23.18. *Four-bit shift register. From S. P. Perone and D. O. Jones*, Digital Computers in Scientific Instrumentation, *New York: McGraw-Hill, 1973, by permission of the publisher. Copyright © 1973 by McGraw-Hill, Inc.*

The simplest shift-register is the *serial* I/O type, shown in Figure 23.18 (omitting the dashed-line outputs). The 4-bit register presented is constructed from master-slave clocked flip-flops. (It can also be constructed from JK flip-flops in exactly the same manner; but it cannot be constructed from RS flip-flops.) Notice that a shorthand notation, with the AND gate symbols omitted, is used for the clocked flip-flops.

The operation of the register is quite simple. The C_D inputs are all tied together to provide a common "clear" line, allowing all of the flip-flops to have their Q outputs set to 0 simultaneously. (A common "set" line could also be used.) The first-stage inputs to FFA are connected in exactly the same manner as for the synchronous data-latch previously presented. Successive stages have their outputs and inputs connected together to allow data to be transferred from one to the other in a serial manner. If, after the register is cleared, a binary 1 is presented at the data input and the clock-pulse changes from 1 to 0 on the TP input line, then the binary 1 will appear on the output of FFA. Notice that the binary 1 is now applied to the S input of FFB. The next clock-pulse will transfer the binary 1 to the output of FFB, presenting it at the input of FFC. Thus, data present at the data input will appear at the output of FFD four clock-pulses later. An n-clock-pulse data-delay can be generated by using n flip-flops.

In some applications, digital data is received in serial form, but is needed in parallel for the computer or data-acquisition system. A serial-to-parallel converter can be built by waiting through enough clock pulses to fill the serial I/O shift-register with data, then reading the outputs of each flip-flop in the register simultaneously. This is a *serial-input parallel-output* shift-register and is the configuration in Figure 23.18 with the dashed (parallel) outputs—Q_0 through Q_3—included.

Asynchronous Counters

Often one needs counters in an interface to divide down the clock frequencies and to count such events as the number of data points taken and the number of times data exceed a predetermined threshold. The flip-flop used in modern integrated-circuit counters is the master-slave JK flip-flop. It is used to construct two basic types of counters, asynchronous and synchronous, that will count up or down in a variety of counting schemes.

The simplest counter is the *asynchronous* binary up-counter, in which the Q output of each flip-flop is connected to the T (count) input of the next. The one presented in Figure 23.19 (with its timing chart) counts from 0 to 15 and resets. Initially, all flip-flops in the counter are cleared to 0. When the first negative-going transition or clock-pulse is presented at the count input, the output of FFA (Q_0) changes state from 0 to 1. When the second clock pulse occurs, it again changes the output state of FFA, returning it from 1 to 0. This negative-going output, fed into the count input of FFB, causes FFB (Q_1) to change state from a binary 0 to a binary 1. Two clock pulses later, FFB changes state back to 0, causing FFC to change state to 1; four clock pulses after that, FFC causes FFD to change state to 1, and so on. Any number of flip-flops can be connected in this way to count to larger numbers, the output of each flip-flop corresponding to a power of 2—$Q_0 = 2^0$, $Q_1 = 2^1$, $Q_2 = 2^2$, and so on. The asynchronous counter is often called a *ripple counter*

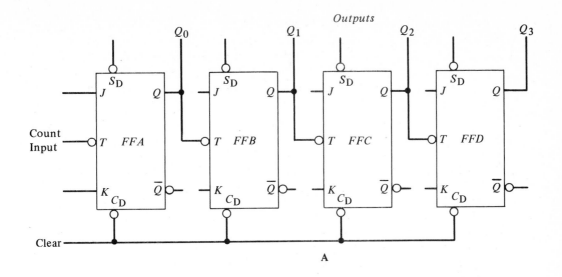

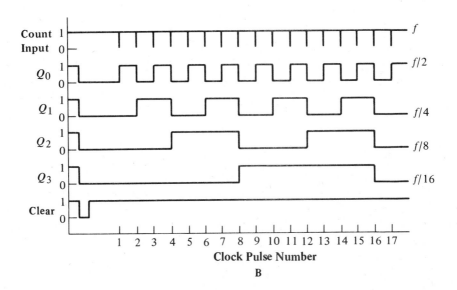

FIGURE 23.19. *Asynchronous binary counter. From S. P. Perone and D. O. Jones,* Digital Computers in Scientific Instrumentation, *New York: McGraw-Hill, 1973, by permission of the publisher. Copyright © 1973 by McGraw-Hill, Inc.*

because of the way counts ripple through or are passed along from flip-flop to flip-flop. From the timing chart, one can see that binary frequency division occurs, with $Q_0 = f/2$, $Q_1 = f/4$, $Q_3 = f/16$. This is then a convenient way to divide down clock frequencies in binary orders of magnitude. Notice also that the binary number output of the counter can be read from the timing chart after any given number of clock pulses has occurred. Consider the case after 10 clock-pulses. Reading down from the top of the chart at clock pulse number 10, $Q_0 = 0$, $Q_1 = 1$, $Q_2 = 0$, and $Q_3 = 1$; $1010_2 = 10_{10}$.

In addition to an asynchronous binary up-counter, an asynchronous binary down-counter can also be designed. A 4-bit counter will count down from 15 to 0.

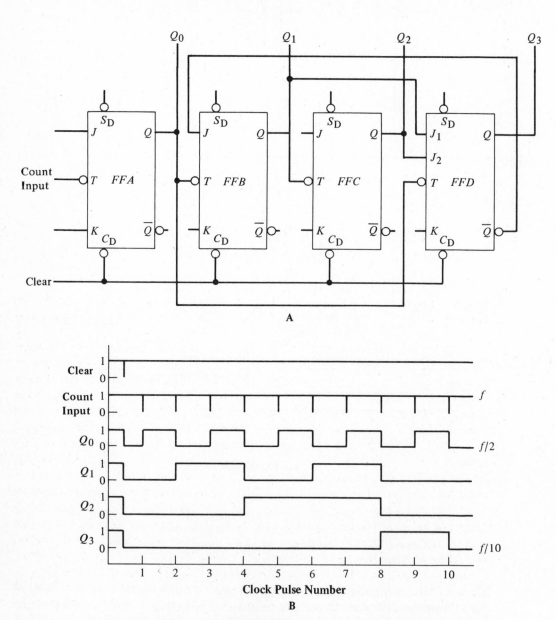

FIGURE 23.20. *Asynchronous decade counter. From S. P. Perone and D. O. Jones,* Digital Computers in Scientific Instrumentation, *New York: McGraw-Hill, 1973, by permission of the publisher. Copyright © 1973 by McGraw-Hill, Inc.*

TABLE 23.7. *Binary Coded Decimal (BCD) Number System*

Decade	BCD
0	0000
1	0001
2	0010
3	0011
4	0100
5	0101
6	0110
7	0111
8	1000
9	1001

Source: S. P. Perone and D. O. Jones, *Digital Computers in Scientific Instrumentation,* New York: McGraw-Hill, 1973, by permission of the publisher. Copyright © 1973 by McGraw-Hill, Inc.

This is accomplished by disconnecting each T input in the up-counter from the corresponding Q output and connecting it to the corresponding $\bar{Q}$ output, and setting all the flip-flops in the counter to 1.

Since we are accustomed to thinking in terms of the decimal (base 10) number system, decade counters are often used in interface systems. They not only count in powers of 10 but can be used to divide clock frequencies in decade rather than binary steps. The *decade counter* presented in Figure 23.20, along with its timing chart, follows the count sequence presented in Table 23.7. The BCD (*Binary Coded Decimal*) number system is a binary representation of the decimal number system.

Notice that the timing chart is the same as the binary up-counter timing-chart in Figure 23.19B up through clock-pulse number 8. From there on, however, it differs. The chief requirement for the operation of the decade counter is that it must reset to 0 after a count of 9_{10} or 1001_2. This requires some additional connections over those needed for the binary counter. Notice in Figure 23.20 that the $\bar{Q}$ output of FFD is connected to the J input of FFB. This allows FFB to change state only when the $\bar{Q}$ output of FFD = 1. This occurs for counts 0 to 7. However, for counts 8, 9, and above, FFB is disabled. Notice also that FFD has two J inputs, J_1 and J_2. They allow FFD to change state from 0 to 1 (Q output) only when $Q_1 = 1$, $Q_2 = 1$, and Q_0 goes from 1 to 0. These conditions are only present at a count of 7 and allow the count of 8 to occur. The count transition from 9 to 0 (clock-pulse number 10 in Fig. 23.20B) occurs in the following way: For a count of 9, FFB is disabled because of the connection from $\bar{Q}$ of FFD to its J input. It cannot change from the $Q_1 = 0$ state it is in. Inputs J_1 and J_2 of FFD are also 0. Any 1-to-0 timing signal will thus set Q_3 back to 0. This can be verified by reviewing the JK flip-flop truth-table presented in Table 23.6. Clock-pulse 10 toggles Q_0 of FFA from 1 to 0. Q_0 is connected to the T input of *FFD*, causing its Q output also to go from 1 to 0. The counter thus resets to 0 on clock-pulse 10.

Synchronous Counters

Unlike asynchronous counters, in which the output change of one flip-flop is applied to the clock input and thus changes the state of a succeeding flip-flop, *synchronous-counter* flip-flop outputs set up the J and K inputs of succeeding flip-flops so that a common clock-signal can cause the proper count sequence to occur.

A synchronous binary up-counter is illustrated in Figure 23.21A. Compare this counter with the asynchronous binary up-counter in Figure 23.19. Notice that the synchronous counter requires external gating whereas the asynchronous counter does not; this is because the count sequence is generated by the external gates which set up the J and K inputs of each flip-flop. The timing chart in Figure 23.19B for the asynchronous binary counter can also be used for the synchronous counter.

The operation of the synchronous binary counter is quite simple. If one starts with all flip-flops set to 0, the first pulse applied to the count input will change the state only of FFA. This is because the J and K inputs of all other flip-flops are at a logical 0, which disables the count input to those flip-flops. On each succeeding clock-pulse, FFA will change state. When the second clock-pulse is applied to the clock input, FFB changes state, with the Q output going to a logical 1. This occurs because its J and K inputs, which are connected to the Q output of FFA, were at a logical 1 after the first clock-pulse. Notice now that the Q output of FFA is at a logical 0, that of FFB is at a logical 1, and those of FFC and FFD are both at a logical 0. On the third clock-pulse, FFA changes state. It is now, along with FFB, at a logical 1. Since the outputs of FFA and FFB are connected to the J and K inputs of FFC through AND gate G_1, FFC now has both inputs at a logical 1. This means that the next clock-pulse will change the state of FFC. And, in fact, on the fourth clock-pulse FFA changes from 1 to 0, FFB changes from 1 to 0, and FFC changes from 0 to 1, giving a binary count of 4. In a like manner, when FFA, FFB, and FFC are all at a logical 1, FFD will change state. This occurs at a count of 8. The reader should work through the complete count-sequence from 0 to 15 in binary for the synchronous binary up-counter.

A synchronous *decade* up-counter is shown in Figure 23.21B; it should be compared to the asynchronous decade counter in Figure 23.20. (The timing chart in Figure 23.20B applies equally well to both counters.) Notice again that the synchronous counter involves more complex external gating. The operation of the synchronous decade up-counter is the same as for the binary synchronous counter, if one remembers that a flip-flop will only change state when it receives a clock pulse and when either or both of the J and K inputs are a logical 1. The reader should work through the operation of the synchronous decade counter, paying especially careful attention to what occurs between the counts of 9 and 10.

The question arises, why one would use the more complex synchronous counters rather than the simple asynchronous counters? One important reason is that in asynchronous counters the various count sequences must ripple from one flip-flop to the next. This means that an incoming count on the first flip-flop, which will

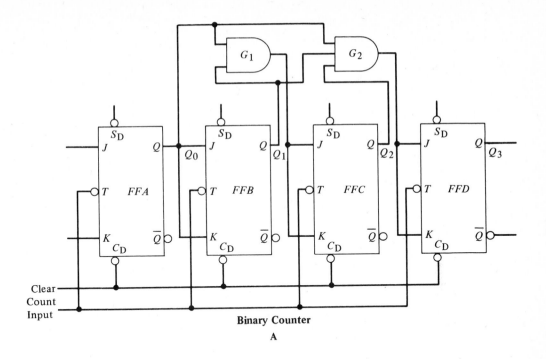

Binary Counter

A

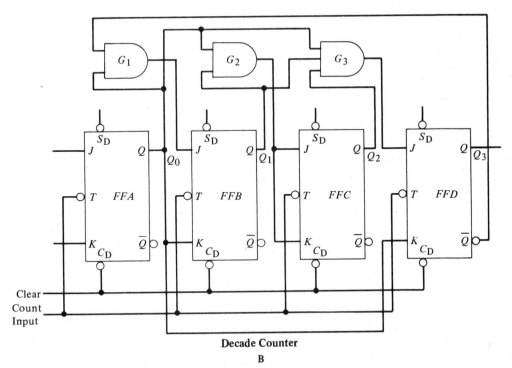

Decade Counter

B

FIGURE 23.21. *Synchronous counters. From S. P. Perone and D. O. Jones,* Digital Computers in Scientific Instrumentation, *New York: McGraw-Hill, 1973, by permission of the publisher. Copyright © 1973 by McGraw-Hill, Inc.*

eventually change the state of a flip-flop farther down the line, must pass through all intermediate flip-flops. This operation takes a fairly long period of time and is equal to the sum of the *signal-propagation delay-times* of each succeeding flip-flop. The maximum count-rate possible with asynchronous counters is determined, then, not only by the signal-propagation delay of an individual flip-flop, but by the total propagation delay of all the flip-flops in sequence. In synchronous counting systems, since the count sequences do not have to ripple down all the flip-flops, the propagation delay for a given counter is usually no more than that for one flip-flop and one gate. Therefore, synchronous counters can operate at much higher speeds. However, as the number of stages increases in synchronous counters, so does the number of inputs to the gates used between counter stages; in fact, in a synchronous binary up-counter of 15 stages, an input gate with 14 inputs is required at the last stage. One way around this problem is to use semisynchronous operation. In this mode of operation, flip-flops are run synchronously in units of perhaps eight or nine stages, and then these units are connected together asynchronously. When semisynchronous operation is used in decade counters, each decade is made up of four internally synchronous individual stages and is connected to another decade asynchronously. This decreases the cost and complexity of the counter while still allowing high-speed operation—though its speed is still not as high as that of a totally synchronous system.

23.3 INTERFACING DEVICES

A computer is considered on-line to an experimental system when there is direct electronic communication between the experiment and the computer and, perhaps, between the computer and the experiment. Figure 23.22 illustrates the various functions required for such communication. These functions are carried out by:

1. *Translation and transmission elements.* These include analog and digital hardware to convert or otherwise handle the electronic information exchanged between experiment and computer. Typical elements include analog-to-digital converters, digital-to-analog converters, voltage amplifiers, current-to-voltage converters, signal conditioners, sample-and-hold amplifiers, multiplexers, and so on.

2. *Timing, Control, and Logic Elements.* These include such hardware as digital clocks, logic gates, flip-flops, counters, one-shots, Schmitt triggers, analog switches, level converters, and so on.

3. *Appropriate Software to Drive the Interface Hardware.* The I/O programs are necessary and important parts of the interface. Software provides the necessary controls needed to operate the electronic elements in the interface.

Timing Devices

Figure 23.23 illustrates the most important experimental interface function, the generation of a stable time base. The *time-base generator*, or *digital clock*, is generally a combination of two elements: (1) a crystal-controlled, stable, fixed-frequency *oscillator* that emits a pulse train of very accurately known frequency, and (2) a *counter* or *scaler* logic section used to divide this frequency and thus generate a variety of output frequencies. The output frequency can be incrementally changed through the use of counters and can be controlled by enabling (starting) or disabling (stopping) the counter system. In subsequent discussions, the clock will be represented by the block diagram in Figure 23.23B, which shows only an enable/disable input and a series of outputs.

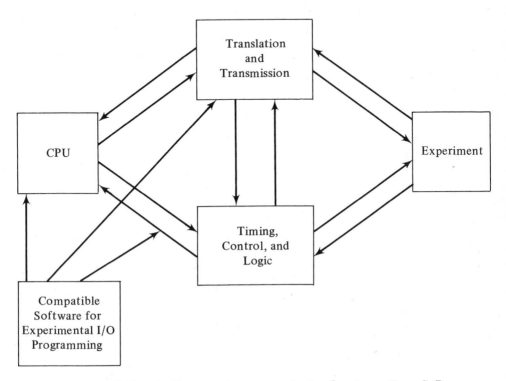

FIGURE 23.22. *On-line computer communication functions. From S. P. Perone and D. O. Jones*, Digital Computers in Scientific Instrumentation, *New York: McGraw-Hill*, 1973, *by permission of the publisher. Copyright © 1973 by McGraw-Hill, Inc.*

Adjustable time-delays, accurately known and reproducible, are often required in an interface system. The *monostable multivibrator* or *one-shot* is often used for generating these delays. (The diagram in Figure 23.24 is that of a gated one-shot; the series of gates allow logic to be performed at the input of the device.) The one-shot remains in a stable state until a trigger pulse is applied to the input; then the output changes state for a period of time called the *pulse width* (PW), which depends on the value of the resistance-capacitance (*RC*) timing network employed in the circuit. Generally, the one-shot device has a provision for attaching different resistances and capacitances. Delay times can generally be varied over wide ranges, from nanoseconds to many seconds or even minutes. Many integrated-circuit one-shots are commercially available.

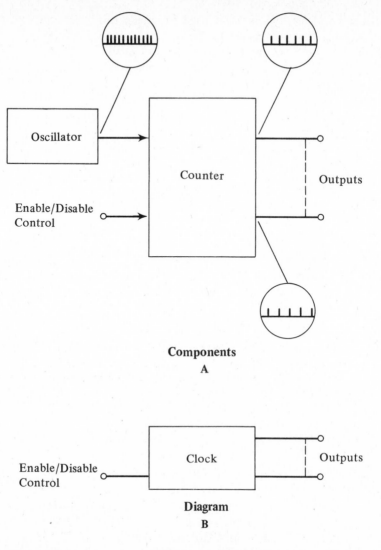

Components
A

Diagram
B

FIGURE 23.23. *Interface time-base generator. From S. P. Perone and D. O. Jones*, Digital Computers in Scientific Instrumentation, *New York: McGraw-Hill*, 1973, *by permission of the publisher. Copyright* © 1973 *by McGraw-Hill, Inc.*

Translation Elements

Digital-to-Analog Conversion. A *digital-to-analog converter* (DAC) is used to change digital numerical information into a continuously variable analog output. DACs are often used as control devices in chemical experiments. For example, in a fast-sweep polarographic experiment, a DAC can be used to provide control voltages and ramp functions for the electrochemical cell. Because the computer can generate numbers in any sequence, nonlinear ramps can be generated, allowing very precise control over the cell.

A basic DAC application is illustrated in Figure 23.25. The DAC takes a

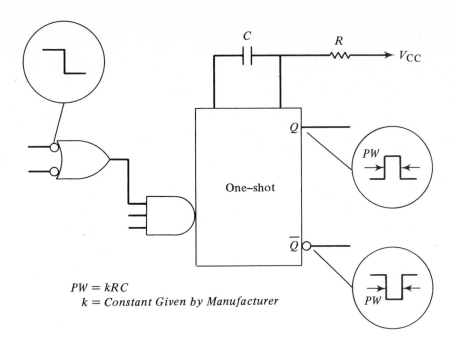

$PW = kRC$
$k = Constant\ Given\ by\ Manufacturer$

FIGURE 23.24. *Monostable multivibrator or one-shot. From S. P. Perone and D. O. Jones,* Digital Computers in Scientific Instrumentation, *New York: McGraw-Hill, 1973, by permission of the publisher. Copyright © 1973 by McGraw-Hill, Inc.*

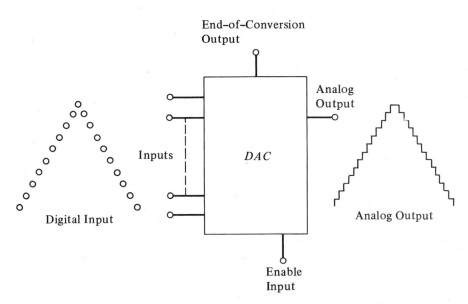

FIGURE 23.25. *Digital-to-analog conversion. From S. P. Perone and D. O. Jones,* Digital Computers in Scientific Instrumentation, *New York: McGraw-Hill, 1973, by permission of the publisher. Copyright © 1973 by McGraw-Hill, Inc.*

digital input and converts it to an analog output—a series of voltage steps. The minimum magnitude of a step is a function of the dynamic range and resolution of the converter; for example, if the converter has a 10-V output maximum and a resolution of 1 part in 1,024 (10 bits), the minimum voltage-step on the output will be about 10 mV. Notice in Figure 23.25 that there are digital inputs and an analog output, an *enable* input at which a conversion can be started, and an *end-of-conversion* output which indicates when a conversion is complete. The actual conversion from digital numbers to an analog output is accomplished within the converter by a series of resistors and switches called a *ladder network* and is discussed in detail elsewhere [5].

Voltage Comparators and Schmitt Triggers. The *voltage comparator* is an analog device with two inputs and an output. It is generally used to compare one voltage

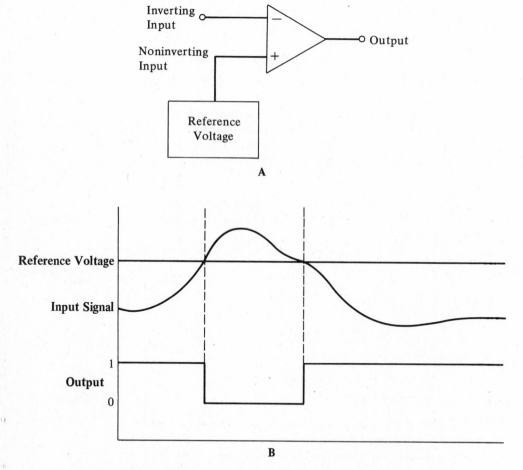

FIGURE 23.26. *Voltage comparator. From S. P. Perone and D. O. Jones,* Digital Computers in Scientific Instrumentation, *New York: McGraw-Hill, 1973, by permission of the publisher. Copyright © 1973 by McGraw-Hill, Inc.*

with another and to indicate which is larger. A voltage comparator and its resulting waveforms are shown in Figure 23.26. Notice that there are both a reference voltage and an input signal. The comparator compares the input signal with the reference voltage. When the input signal rises above the magnitude of the reference voltage, the comparator output changes state from 1 to 0; when the input signal falls below the reference voltage, the output changes back from 0 to 1.

A device somewhat similar to a comparator is the *Schmitt trigger*; Figure 23.27 shows its input, output, and upper and lower threshold terminals and also its typical waveform. The two reference levels V_{t+} and V_{t-} are the upper and lower thresholds. When the input signal goes above the *upper* threshold, the output changes from 1 to 0. However, when it goes below the upper threshold again, the output signal does not change back until it has gone below the *lower* threshold.

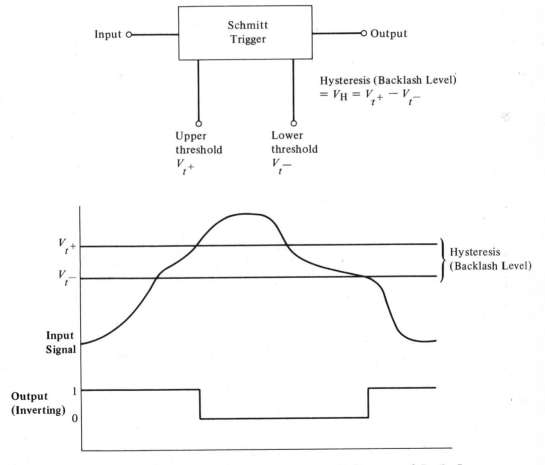

FIGURE 23.27. *Schmitt trigger. From S. P. Perone and D. O. Jones,* Digital Computers in Scientific Instrumentation, *New York: McGraw-Hill, 1973, by permission of the publisher. Copyright © 1973 by McGraw-Hill, Inc.*

The difference between the upper threshold and lower threshold is commonly called the *hysteresis* or *backlash level* of the Schmitt trigger; it provides noise immunity for the device.

In Figure 23.28, both Schmitt trigger and comparator outputs are given for a noisy input signal. Notice that, as the signal oscillates above and below the comparator reference-voltage, its output also oscillates. However, since the magnitude of the noise is less than the hysteresis of the Schmitt trigger, the output of the latter has no noise spikes. The trigger can extract control signals from noisy input signals, provided that the proper hysteresis level is selected. It is often used to convert digital signals of one voltage level to another level.

The lack of hysteresis in the comparator makes it more susceptible to noisy environments; it also makes it a more accurate switch.

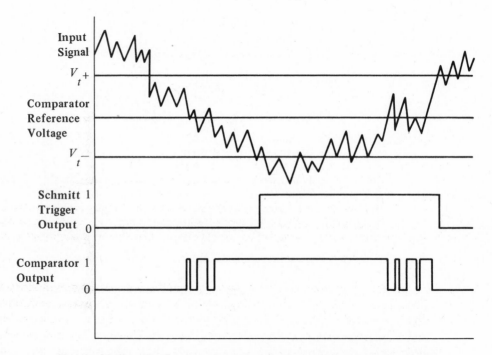

FIGURE 23.28. *Comparison of Schmitt trigger and voltage comparator for noisy signals. Source: S. P. Perone and D. O. Jones,* Digital Computers in Scientific Instrumentation, *New York: McGraw-Hill, 1973, by permission of the publisher. Copyright © 1973 by McGraw-Hill, Inc.*

Analog Multiplexers. When one has several signals that must be connected to the input of one ADC, a common device used is the *analog-signal multiplexer* (Fig. 23.29). With it, several input signals can be sequentially switched to one output. Often, the input signals will come from the output of sample-and-hold or track-and-hold amplifiers. Analog-signal multiplexers are a series of electronic switches with digital control inputs to allow a computer or interface to control this operation.

Analog Switches. Analog switches can generally be divided into three categories: mechanical, electromechanical, and electronic. Common toggle, slide, and rotary switches are examples of mechanical types; their contacts are opened or closed manually. Electromechanical switches are usually relays of one sort or another in which an electromagnetic coil is energized to open or close the contacts. The contacts are either dry or coated with mercury; mercury-wetted contacts usually exhibit somewhat better switching characteristics.

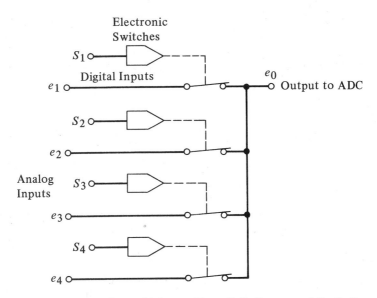

FIGURE 23.29. *Analog multiplexer. From S. P. Perone and D. O. Jones,* Digital Computers in Scientific Instrumentation, *New York: McGraw-Hill, 1973, by permission of the publisher. Copyright © 1973 by McGraw-Hill, Inc.*

Electromechanical analog switches exhibit some very desirable characteristics. They have essentially zero resistance when the contacts are closed and infinite resistance when they are open. They can handle a range of many orders of magnitude of voltage and current of either polarity. They also have, as might be expected, some undesirable characteristics. First, the contacts bounce whenever they are opened or closed. This can result in noise that must be filtered out. Mercury-wetted contacts can lessen bounce noise, but do not eliminate it. Second, electromechanical switches are rather slow in switching; the faster ones take 1 msec or so to open or close.

Electronic analog switches are usually constructed from *junction field-effect transistors* (JFETs) or *metal oxide–silicon field-effect transistors* (MOSFETs). FETs used as switches are usually activated by transistor driving circuits that open or close them. A typical FET analog switch might be closed when a logical 0 is applied. FET switches have advantages over electromechanical switches in one principal area— speed. They are orders of magnitude faster than electromechanical switches, with turn-on or turn-off times of less than 1 μsec. Since they have no contacts, they do not exhibit contact bounce noise, but they can, if not correctly designed into a circuit, generate electronic switching spikes.

Electronic analog switches also have some shortcomings. They have finite on and off resistances. JFETs usually have the smaller on or closed resistance, some types as low as 1 Ω or so. MOSFETs, on the other hand, have the higher off or open resistance, typically of the order of 10^{16} Ω. In other words, FET switches are not ideal switches, but rather electronically variable resistors.

FET switches are restricted to certain ranges of voltage and current, and have polarity restrictions. Common voltage-levels are of the order of 10 V or so, but some specialized units go as high as 100 V. Maximum currents are often no greater than 100 mA but may be greater. FET switches usually do not work well for signal levels less than a few millivolts because of a small inherent voltage drop in the transistors, which may vary with operating conditions.

Generally speaking, one should use electromechanical analog switches for low-level or high-level signals that can be switched in more than 1 msec or so, and electronic analog switches for moderate signal-levels with switching times less than 1 μsec or so. Both electromechanical and electronic types are available that can be driven directly from integrated-circuit digital logic.

Analog-to-Digital Conversion. A typical *analog-to-digital converter* (ADC) is illustrated in Figure 23.30. It consists of an analog input, digital outputs, a start-conversion input, and an end-of-conversion output. The ADC changes an analog or continuous voltage from an experimental system into a series of discrete digital values so that a computer can be presented with digital data in a format that it can handle. The most common output format is a binary digital representation of the analog input. There are many types of ADCs, some fast and some slow—some that require high-level voltage inputs in the range of from one to several volts, and some that require low-level voltage, current, or resistance inputs. In this section, several types of fast converters will be discussed.

1. *Counter Converters.* Probably the simplest ADC is the *counter converter* (Fig. 23.31A). It is usually a fast, high-level converter with a conversion time of less than 1 msec, thus capable of providing more than 1000 data-points per second. Basically, it consists of a comparator, a clock or pulse generator, a counter, and a DAC. When an analog input signal is presented to one input of the comparator and a start-of-conversion signal is presented to the counter, the counter resets to 0 and starts counting up, and presents a digital input to the DAC. The DAC in turn provides a corresponding analog output voltage to the other input of the comparator. When the counter output number reaches a magnitude that provides a voltage to the comparator (through the DAC) equal in magnitude to the analog input signal, the comparator changes state, turning off the clock and stopping the counter. The digital output representation of the analog input is read in parallel from the counter outputs. A status or end-of-conversion signal can be obtained from the output of the comparator as it changes state upon completion of a conversion. The counter converter is simple and inexpensive. The conversion time is proportional to the magnitude of the input voltage. That is, since the counter always starts counting from 0, the larger the analog input voltage, the longer it will take for the counter to count up to the value where the DAC output applied to the comparator is equal to the analog input voltage.

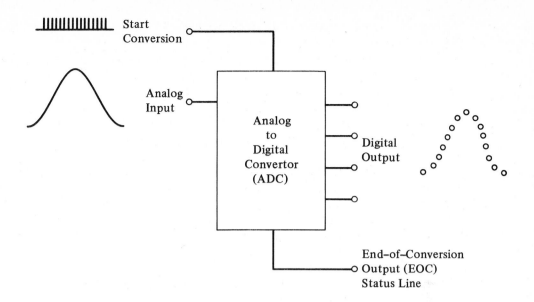

FIGURE 23.30. *Analog-to-digital conversion. From S. P. Perone and D. O. Jones*, Digital Computers in Scientific Instrumentation, *New York: McGraw-Hill*, 1973, *by permission of the publisher. Copyright* © 1973 *by McGraw-Hill, Inc.*

2. *Continuous Converters.* The *continuous converter* in Figure 23.31B is very similar to the counter converter. The main differences are that the counter used can count both up and down, that the comparator, instead of turning off the clock, controls the counting direction of the counter, and that the counter counts all the time. When the comparator senses that the output of the DAC exceeds the analog input voltage, it reverses the counting direction from up to down; likewise, when the DAC output falls below the analog input voltage, the counting direction is reversed from down to up. The up-down counter tracks the analog input voltage if it is not changing faster than the counter can follow. When a new signal is applied to the analog input, the continuous converter locks onto it and follows it. Digital outputs can be read at intervals from the output of the counter. After it locks on to a signal, the continuous converter is extremely fast.

3. *Successive-Approximation Converters.* The 4-bit *successive-approximation* ADC shown in Figure 23.32 differs from both the counter and the continuous converters in that, in place of a counter, it has a pattern generator. It consists of a comparator, a DAC, a buffer-register data-latch in which the digital output is stored, the pattern generator, and some control logic. Its operation is most easily understood with reference to Figure 23.33. The analog voltage is approximated by testing one bit at a time, beginning with the most significant (highest power of two) bit and ending with the least significant bit. All the possible number combinations generated by the pattern generator are presented for a 4-bit successive-approximation ADC. Notice that a 4-bit conversion always takes four steps to complete, so that a successive-approximation converter has a fixed conversion time.

Important Features of ADCs. In selecting high-level ADCs, several criteria are important, including:

1. the input-voltage range
2. the output format
3. the resolution of the output
4. the logic voltage-levels of the output
5. the conversion speed
6. the control signals needed
7. the power-supply requirements

Input voltages generally range from 1–10 V full scale. They may be positive, negative, or bipolar.

The most commonly used ADC output format is the binary number system, because it is directly compatible with many digital computers. Other codes, usually binary coded decimal, are sometimes used. In addition, bipolar input-converters such as the ± 1 V or ± 10 V units can have different forms of binary coding to account for the dual polarity.

The resolution and dynamic range of the converter output are determined by the number of data bits available. Common binary converters have 8-, 10-, 12-, or more output bit configurations, giving resolutions of 1 part in 256, 1024, 4096, or greater, respectively. Converters using BCD output configurations often have three or four decimal digits represented, giving resolutions in the range of 10^3–10^4. Higher-resolution converters are available if required.

By far the most common output voltage levels for logic circuits and ADCs are 0 and $+5$ V, the common integrated-circuit levels for diode-transistor (DTL) and transistor-transistor (TTL) logic [3]. Other different logic voltage-levels, including 0 and $+12$ V and 0 and -3 V, are also used. The logic voltage levels should, of course, be compatible with those used in the computer or data system. If they are not, some sort of voltage-level conversion will be necessary.

Conversion time is the time required, after a start signal, for a conversion to be completed. It determines the maximum data-rate of a given converter. High converter data-rates range from 10 kHz to about 10 MHz.

Control signals for fast ADC units usually consist of a start command and an end-of-conversion or status signal. Other control signals are possible. In units with output storage-buffers, controls may be available to load or store in the buffer.

Power-supply requirements, although they may seem trivial, are in fact very important. The presence or absence of an internal reference voltage is a good example of this. The output and stability of the general power supply are also important. ADC units with built-in voltage regulators have much less severe power-supply requirements than those with no internal regulation.

FIGURE 23.31. *Counter and continuous analog-to-digital converters. From S. P. Perone and D. O. Jones*, Digital Computers in Scientific Instrumentation, *New York: McGraw-Hill, 1973, by permission of the publisher. Copyright © 1973 by McGraw-Hill, Inc.*

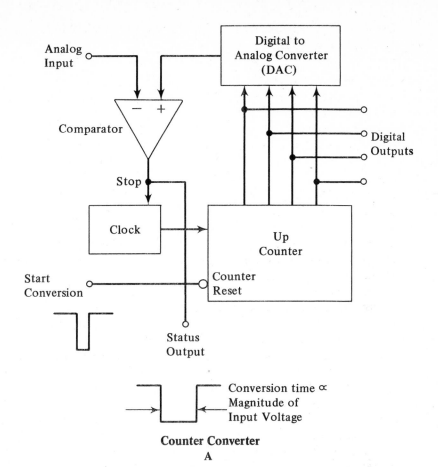

Counter Converter

A

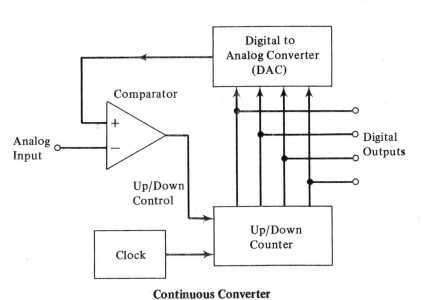

Continuous Converter

B

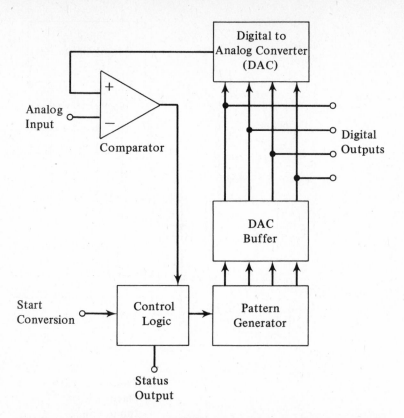

FIGURE 23.32. *Successive-approximation analog-to-digital converter.* *From S. P. Perone and D. O. Jones,* Digital Computers in Scientific Instrumentation, *New York: McGraw-Hill, 1973, by permission of the publisher. Copyright © 1973 by McGraw-Hill, Inc.*

Analog Sampling

A useful interface device is the *track-and-hold* amplifier. Although in practice one would generally buy a ready-built track-and-hold system, it is useful here to review its operation. A track-and-hold amplifier is shown in Figure 23.34, together with its response curves and timing chart. An incoming signal is fed to the capacitor when the electronic switch is closed. In this mode, the output of the amplifier will continually follow the input signal. When the electronic switch is opened and isolates the input signal from the capacitor, the output remains at the voltage last seen by the input capacitor. This is illustrated in Figure 23.34B, where, each time the digital control signal goes to a logical 1, the electronic switch opens and the magnitude of the voltage at that time remains (is stored) on the capacitor. Notice that the output waveform consists of a series of levels stored on the capacitor and read from the amplifier output.

Track-and-hold amplifiers are used to store incoming signals briefly for an ADC, particularly when several signals have to be stored simultaneously and then

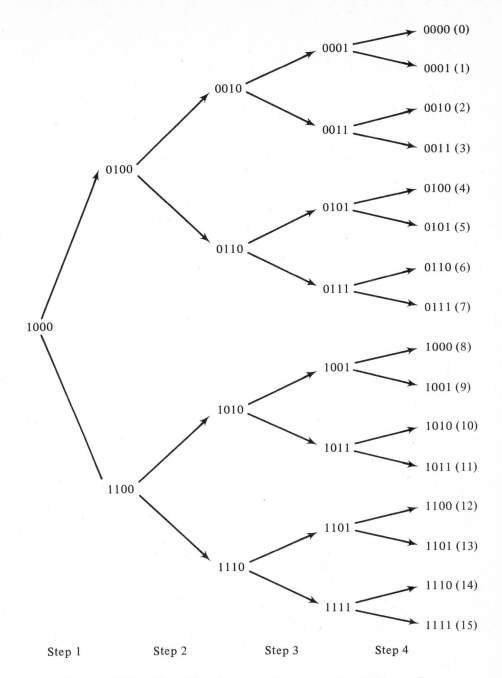

Step 1   Step 2   Step 3   Step 4

FIGURE 23.33. *Successive-approximation conversion pattern. From S. P. Perone and D. O. Jones*, Digital Computers in Scientific Instrumentation, *New York: McGraw-Hill*, 1973, *by permission of the publisher. Copyright © 1973 by McGraw-Hill, Inc.*

be sequentially switched into the input of the converter. It is also useful when converting extremely short transient signals. In effect, the track-and-hold amplifier reduces the aperture time (the actual time during which data is taken) of the **ADC** to the aperture time of the amplifier switch—a condensation of at least two orders of magnitude, usually. (See further discussion below.)

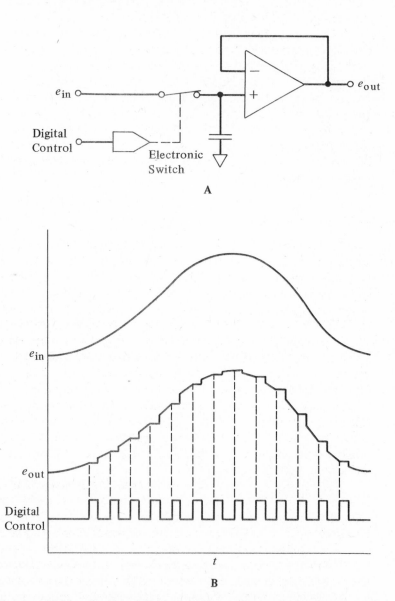

FIGURE 23.34. *Track-and-hold amplifier. From S. P. Perone and D. O. Jones,* Digital Computers in Scientific Instrumentation, *New York: McGraw-Hill, 1973, by permission of the publisher. Copyright © 1973 by McGraw-Hill, Inc.*

23.4 PRINCIPLES OF DATA ACQUISITION

Using the analog and digital devices described above, one can design the on-line communication link, or interface, between the digital computer and the experimental system. Several fundamental considerations must be kept in mind: How does the particular computer use, recognize, and interpret information from the outside world? How does the computer transmit information? What are the computer machine-language instructions available for input/output (I/O) functions?

One fundamental principle that should be emphasized here is that the computer communicates with the outside world by recognizing incoming binary voltage level changes at particular terminals at particular times, and producing other such changes at other (outgoing) terminals. Thus, the interface design is reduced to the problem of monitoring and interpreting voltage-level changes produced by the computer and ensuring that voltage-level changes produced by the experiment are detected and properly interpreted by the computer. Thus, interface design can be completed only if both the I/O hardware and software of the computer are well understood. The experimenter must also know the availability and characteristics of the hardware interface components described above.

Program-Controlled Data Acquisition

Two kinds of data-acquisition approaches can be defined. One is to operate the data-acquisition programming under *interrupt control*. That is, the computer is operated in a mode where data-acquisition devices are serviced upon demand. The other approach is called *program-controlled* data acquisition. This approach involves programming the computer to look for service requests from specific devices and to wait for these requests if necessary. The latter approach will be discussed here.

Perhaps the best way to discuss program-controlled data acquisition is to consider a specific problem. Consider the case in which an experiment of a transient nature is to be conducted and data acquired during the lifetime of the experiment— for example, monitoring the gaseous products of an explosion. The computer is to initiate the explosion and to simultaneously initiate data acquisition at a constant rate of 10 kHz. When a specified total number of data has been taken, the computer is to terminate data acquisition and reset the experimental instrumentation to the original conditions. Each data point is to be taken in from the ADC and stored in memory for later processing.

A schematic diagram of the computerized data-acquisition system is given in Figure 23.35. The computer initiates the data-acquisition cycle by executing a COMMAND instruction; this terminal goes to a "1" state and is connected to the ENABLE input of a 10-kHz clock, the output of which enables a 10-bit ADC every 0.1 msec. Simultaneous with enabling the clock and the data-acquisition process, the COMMAND output initiates the experiment. The experimental output is continuously available at the input to the ADC. Every time a conversion is completed, the ADC sets a STATUS flip-flop. When that flag goes to a 1 state, the computer determines that a conversion has been completed and that the digitized datum has been inserted into the input buffer-register.

Under program-controlled data acquisition, the computer will be programmed

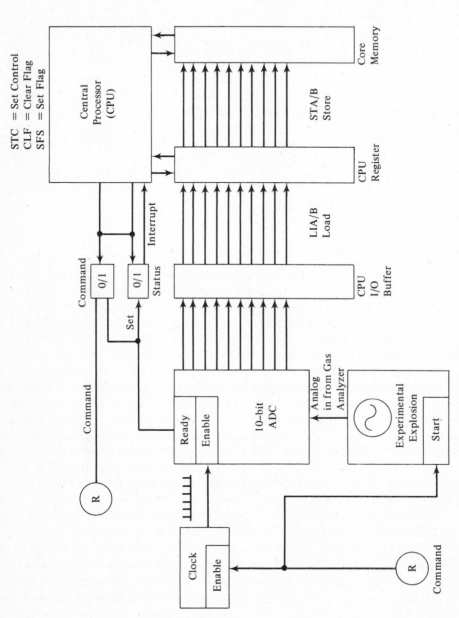

STC = Set Control
CLF = Clear Flag
SFS = Set Flag

Central Processor (CPU)

Command

0/1

0/1

Status

Set

Interrupt

Command

R

Core Memory

STA/B Store

CPU Register

LIA/B Load

CPU I/O Buffer

Ready

Enable

10-bit ADC

Analog in from Gas Analyzer

Experimental Explosion

Start

Clock

Enable

Command

R

FIGURE 23.35. *Program-controlled data-acquisition system. From S. P. Perone and D. O. Jones, Digital Computers in Scientific Instrumentation, New York: McGraw-Hill, 1973, by permission of the publisher. Copyright © 1973 by McGraw-Hill, Inc.*

to test the STATUS bit to determine when each conversion has been completed. When the computer gets a "true" answer in querying this flip-flop, it goes to a data-input routine that loads the contents of the buffer register into a CPU register, clears the STATUS bit, and then stores the datum in core memory. This routine must keep track of the total number of data taken and handle sequential storage of data in a specified block of memory. When the specified total number of data has been taken, the computer terminates the data acquisition by clearing the COMMAND bit. This disables the clock and resets the experimental instrumentation to the initial conditions.

Timing and Synchronization in Data Acquisition

Although the need for synchronization between data-acquisition operations and experimental events should be obvious, the importance of this has not been illustrated. Figure 23.36 describes what can happen when a synchronization error occurs.

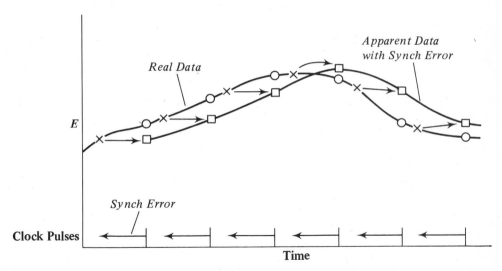

FIGURE 23.36. *Data-acquisition timing and synchronization error. From S. P. Perone and D. O. Jones,* Digital Computers in Scientific Instrumentation, *New York: McGraw-Hill, 1973, by permission of the publisher. Copyright © 1973 by McGraw-Hill, Inc.*

The trace representing the real data which starts at time zero (t_0) is presumably sampled by the data-acquisition system at time points indicated by the clock pulses on the x-axis. Because the clock can generate pulses at an accurately known frequency f, the time between pulses, $1/f$, is precisely known. The program generally will assume that the first clock-pulse is seen at exactly the fundamental time-interval $1/f$ after t_0. However, this will only be true if data acquisition has been synchronized exactly with the start of the experiment. If they are not synchronized, the first clock-pulse can come anywhere during that first time-interval. If the first clock-pulse occurs early, as shown in Figure 23.36, and the program is not aware of the synchronization error, then the program will assume that the first datum obtained really corresponds to the time assigned to the first clock-pulse on the diagram. Thus, the data points taken at the xs on the real data-trace are effectively displaced along the time axis to the points indicated by the squares on the diagram, and the digitized waveform seen by the computer has the appearance of having been translated on the time axis. For experiments where the data density is great, an error of this sort may be insignificant; however, for most experiments, this type of error causes severe difficulties in data processing. (An example of such an experiment is one involving ensemble signal-averaging, described below.)

Generally, a crystal oscillator is used for precise timing. However, this type of clock provides a continuously available pulse-train at a fixed frequency. Thus, there is no way to determine when a given clock-pulse occurs in real time. The uncertainty can be minimized if one selects a clock with a very high frequency and scales this down to the desired frequency range (see Fig. 23.23). The countdown logic can be initialized, enabled, or disabled. Thus, the output of the scaler provides a pulse train in which the uncertainty in the duration of the first time interval is no greater than the time interval $1/f_0$ of the crystal oscillator. For example, if the basic clock rate f_0 is scaled by a factor of 100, then the uncertainty in the initial scaled time-interval will be no greater than 1 percent.

The scaled clock is most valuable for establishing a time base for experiments that cannot be started at a precisely known moment by external control. If the start of a spontaneously initiated experiment can be detected electronically, this signal can be used to enable the scaler logic of the clock. Thus, a time base precisely synchronized with the experiment is obtained.

If the exact frequency of a free-running clock is to be used for data-acquisition timing, synchronization can be achieved by simple gating. This is demonstrated in Figure 23.37. The output of the free-running clock is brought to one input of an AND gate. The other input can be enabled by the command output of the computer or some other source. When this input of the AND gate is triggered, clock pulses get through the gate and are seen at the output. The first clock pulse that gets through the AND gate is used to initiate data acquisition and simultaneously start the experiment. Subsequent pulses are seen at exact multiples of the fundamental time interval $1/f_0$ of the free-running clock. Thus, data acquisition is exactly synchronized with the start of the experiment because the first available clock pulse was used to initiate the experiment. Note that this synchronization approach can be used only if the experiment can be initiated externally; for an experiment that initiates spontaneously, the alternative approach of enabling scaler logic on a high-frequency clock should be used. The scaled clock is the most generally applicable timing method and is the type implied in most illustrations here. The laboratory-computer user should be keenly aware of the synchronization limits and capabilities of the time-base generator (clock) used in his system.

Ensemble-Averaging Application

A good example of many of the principles discussed in previous sections, and a useful application of the digital computer for enhancing experimental measurements, is

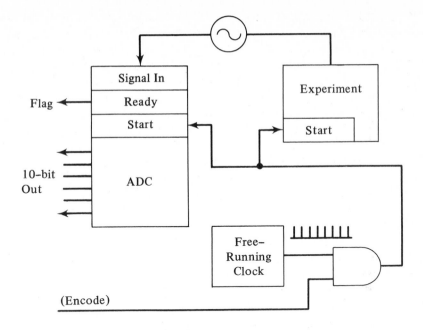

FIGURE 23.37. *Synchronization of experimental time-base generator. From S. P. Perone and D. O. Jones,* Digital Computers in Scientific Instrumentation, *New York: McGraw-Hill, 1973, by permission of the publisher. Copyright © 1973 by McGraw-Hill, Inc.*

the technique of *ensemble signal-averaging*. This technique can be applied in cases in which experimental data are obtained with large amounts of superimposed background noise. Although many approaches can be taken to handle instrumental problems leading to noisy data, it is not always possible to eliminate noise. (For example, standard noise-elimination procedures are inadequate in cases where the source of the noise is not in the electronics but is an inherent part of the experimental system.) When the frequency of the noise is similar to the frequency of the fundamental waveform of interest, conventional filtering techniques are not adequate. In such cases, some sort of signal-averaging approach must be used in order to extract the fundamental signal from the noise. However, two conditions must be met: (1) the signal must be repeatable, and (2) the noise must be random and not synchronized with the experimental output.

The ensemble signal-averaging approach involves running the experiment many times while acquiring the digitized waveform each time, and then summing the repetitive waveforms. When many such experimental outputs have been summed in this coherent fashion, the random noise-fluctuations in the individual waveforms will begin to cancel. The signal-to-noise ratio, in fact, should increase in proportion to the square root of the number of averaging cycles. This approach is illustrated in Figure 23.38.

It is extremely important in an ensemble-averaging experiment that the experimental output be synchronized exactly with the data-acquisition process. If any

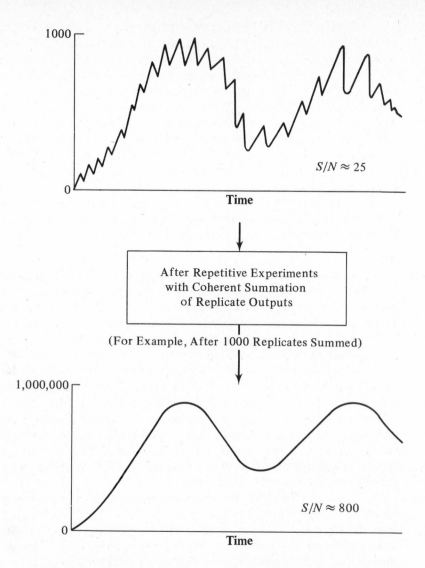

FIGURE 23.38. *Ensemble signal averaging. In this example, the signal-to-noise ratio increases from about 25 to about 800 with averaging. From S. P. Perone and D. O. Jones,* Digital Computers in Scientific Instrumentation, *New York: McGraw-Hill, 1973, by permission of the publisher. Copyright © 1973 by McGraw-Hill, Inc.*

significant fluctuation in synchronization with the time base occurs, the extracted fundamental waveform will be distorted.

Sampling of Experimental Data

Using Track-and-Hold Amplifiers. The tracking capabilities of even a high-speed ADC are relatively limited. To substantially improve the tracking features of a data-acquisition system, a track-and-hold (T/H) amplifier should precede the ADC.

During each hold period, the voltage output of the track-and-hold amplifier remains constant so that digitization may take place (see Fig. 23.34B). The digital output of the ADC will reflect the voltage level at the specific time corresponding to the beginning of each hold period, despite the fact that the conversion is completed at some later time. Thus, the T/H amplifier allows waveform sampling with time-base precision independent of the conversion rate of the ADC. The uncertainty in the timing of the sampling (the aperture time) depends on the switch-opening time and is a characteristic of the T/H amplifier. T/H amplifiers are available commercially with aperture times of the order of 10–100 nsec. Other important characteristics include *response* and *settling* times, which refer to the amplifier's ability to follow rapidly changing signals. These features actually limit the overall acquisition or sampling rate. Sampling intervals (the time from the end of one hold-period to the beginning of the next) of the order of one to several microseconds can be attained with currently available devices.

Sampling Frequency. The sampling frequency selected for data acquisition obviously should be related to the bandwidth of the sampled waveform. From information theory, the criterion for adequate sampling is that the minimum sampling frequency (*Nyquist frequency*) must be twice the bandwidth of the sampled waveform. Thus, for a 100-Hz signal, the sampling frequency must be at least 200 Hz to retain the information inherent in the waveform.

This criterion is strictly applicable in such applications as the sampling of interferograms for Fourier-transform analysis. However, sampling frequencies considerably greater than the Nyquist frequency should be used to allow faithful reproduction of the signal for straightforward data-processing algorithms. A rule-of-thumb criterion is that the sampling frequency should be at least 10 times the bandwidth of the waveform. (Of course, the previously discussed limits imposed by ADC or T/H aperture-times or amplifier response place an effective upper limit on sampling frequencies with a specific resolution.)

Oversampling of an experimental signal can cause problems, mainly because of excessive memory requirements; on the other hand, undersampling can cause even more serious problems. One of these is producing signal artifacts by *aliasing*. This phenomenon occurs when sampling frequencies lower than the Nyquist frequency are used. Figure 23.39 illustrates how a 3-kHz sine wave can be aliased to a 1-kHz signal or a 158-Hz signal by using sampling frequencies of 4 kHz and 3.16 kHz, respectively.

Multiplexing. It is sometimes necessary to sample more than one experimental waveform simultaneously during a single experiment. To accomplish this, an analog multiplexer can be used, the configurational and sampling considerations of which will be discussed here.

The primary characteristic of an analog multiplexer is that it can accommodate multiple analog inputs, any one of which can be sampled through a single output channel. The selection of the input channel to be transmitted to the digitization hardware can be accomplished by a binary-coded command from the computer or by generating an appropriate external sequencing code. The critical characteristic is the time required to switch between input channels. With solid-state analog switches, the sequential selection of analog inputs can proceed with time intervals of the order of a few microseconds or less between channels.

The reader should recognize immediately that the analog multiplexer need not provide the slow step in an overall data-acquisition process. Indeed, the slower processes will be associated with the data-acquisition hardware and software that follow the analog multiplexer. Another point is that it is impossible for the multiplexer to sample independent waveforms in a truly simultaneous fashion. Some finite time-interval must exist between samplings of different channels. The manner in which this problem is handled will depend on the need for acquiring truly simultaneous data from the different channels.

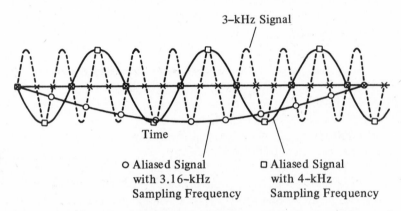

FIGURE 23.39. *Aliased signal phenomenon.* *From S. P. Perone and D. O. Jones,* Digital Computers in Scientific Instrumentation, *New York: McGraw-Hill, 1973, by permission of the publisher. Copyright © 1973 by McGraw-Hill, Inc.*

Figure 23.40 illustrates two alternative configurations for multiplexing analog signals from four independent sources. In Figure 23.40A, the multiplexer is followed by a T/H amplifier and ADC. This configuration is used if there is no need to achieve simultaneous sampling of the four input-channels. Moreover, if the total time required to complete data acquisition from the four channels is small compared to the time interval between samplings, this configuration can be used. For example, if an overall data-acquisition frequency of 10 Hz is employed for all four channels and the total sampling time per channel is 100 μsec, the maximum *skew* of the sample data will be 300 μsec. That is, the fourth channel will be sampled 300 μsec after the first channel. This amount of skew is negligible compared to the 100-msec time interval between samplings.

For the case in which simultaneous sampling is required and the time required to sequentially sample each of the input channels is long compared to the overall data-acquisition time base, the configuration shown in Figure 23.40B is recommended. In this case, each analog signal is funneled through a T/H amplifier. Because all the T/H amplifiers can be gated to the *hold* mode simultaneously, the time required to sample all channels through the multiplexer will be inconsequential, provided that it does not exceed the overall data-acquisition time-base interval. Another consideration is the *droop* specification on the T/H amplifier. That is, the T/H amplifier must be capable of holding the analog signal without significant decay until the particular channel is sampled and the digitization complete.

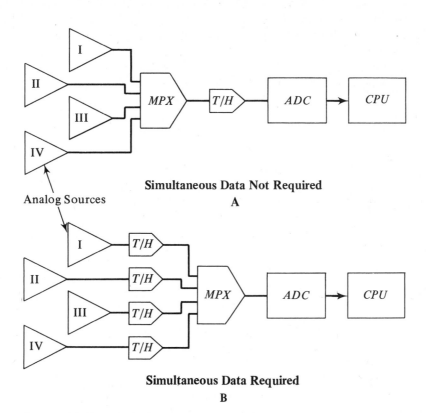

FIGURE 23.40. *Multiplexed data-acquisition system. From S. P. Perone and D. O. Jones*, Digital Computers in Scientific Instrumentation, *New York: McGraw-Hill, 1973, by permission of the publisher. Copyright © 1973 by McGraw-Hill, Inc.*

SELECTED BIBLIOGRAPHY

HOESCHELE, D. F., Jr. *Analog-To-Digital/Digital-To-Analog Conversion Techniques.* New York: Wiley, 1968.

MALMSTADT, H. V., and ENKE, C. G. *Digital Electronics for Scientists.* New York: Benjamin, 1969.

PERONE, S. P., and JONES, D. O. *Digital Computers in Scientific Instrumentation.* New York: McGraw-Hill, 1973.

WILKINS, C. L.; KLOPFENSTEIN, C. E.; ISEN-

HOUR, T. L.; and JURS, P. C.; with J. S. EVANS and R. C. WILLIAMS. *Introduction to Computer Programming for Chemists, BASIC Version.* Boston: Allyn and Bacon, 1975.

WILKINS, C. L.; PERONE, S. P.; KLOPFENSTEIN, C. E.; WILLIAMS, R. C.; and JONES, D. E. *Digital Electronics and Laboratory Computer Experiments.* New York: Plenum Press, 1975.

REFERENCES

1. S. P. PERONE and D. O. JONES, *Digital Computers in Scientific Instrumentation*, New York: McGraw-Hill, 1973, chap. 12 and references therein.

2. L. NASHELSKY, *Digital Computer Theory*, New York: Wiley-Interscience, 1966, p 238.

3. S. P. PERONE and D. O. JONES, *Digital Computers in Scientific Instrumentation*, New York: McGraw-Hill, 1973, chaps. 7 and 8, and app. B.

4. S. P. PERONE and D. O. JONES, *Digital Computers in Scientific Instrumentation*, New York: McGraw-Hill, 1973, app. C.

5. S. P. PERONE and D. O. JONES, *Digital Computers in Scientific Instrumentation*, New York: McGraw-Hill, 1973, chap. 8.

PROBLEMS

1. Convert the following decimal numbers to binary: (a) 5 (b) 52 (c) 387 (d) 10652

2. Convert the following binary numbers to decimal: (a) 1101 (b) 1000101 (c) 1010-1010 (d) 10000100001

3. Convert the following decimal numbers to octal: (a) 5 (b) 52 (c) 387 (d) 10652

4. Convert the following octal numbers to binary: (a) 5 (b) 52 (c) 307 (d) 10652

5. Convert the following binary numbers to octal: (a) 111 (b) 1101100 (c) 10101-110110 (d) 1000000101

6. Convert the following octal numbers to decimal: (a) 36 (b) 652 (c) 21237 (d) 4142437

7. Construct the four basic logic functions— AND ($X = A \cdot B$), OR ($X = A + B$), NAND ($X = \overline{A \cdot B}$), and NOR ($X = \overline{A + B}$) —using only NAND gates.

8. Construct the four basic logic functions in Problem 7 using only NOR gates.

9. Construct a truth table for $X = A \cdot B + C$.

10. Construct a truth table for $X = A \cdot \bar{B} \cdot \bar{C}$.

11. A commercial analog-to-digital converter is available in three models with 8-, 10-, and 12-bit resolution. Each model has four externally selectable full-scale input-voltage ranges: 0 to +5 V, 0 to +10 V, −5 to +5 V, −10 to +10 V. What is the theoretical resolution in mV for each case?

12. Design a divide-by-seven circuit using RS flip-flops.

13. Design a divide-by-25 circuit using JK flip-flops.

14. Define the following terms as used in relation to computers: (a) bit (b) word (c) address (d) memory cycle time (e) interface (f) assembly language (g) machine language

15. The following are common abbreviations— what do they mean? (a) CPU (b) BCD (c) I/O (d) DAC (e) FET (f) MOSFET

16. What functions are performed by the following gates? (a) AND (b) OR (c) NOT (d) NAND

17. What is meant by an *on-line* computer? What are the important implications of using a computer in this manner?

24

Automation in Analytical Chemistry

KENNETH S. FLETCHER III
NELSON L. ALPERT

Automated instruments are classed as *continuous* or *discrete* (*batch*), depending on the nature of their operation. A continuous instrument senses some physical or chemical property by directly observing the sample, yielding an output that is a smooth (continuous) function of time. A discrete instrument works upon a batch-loaded sample and supplies information only after each batch. Each derives its operating principles from conventional analytical procedures, and must include provision for continuous unattended operation: receiving samples, performing selective chemical analyses under uncontrolled environmental conditions, and communicating with monitoring or control equipment.

A clear distinction should be made between *automatic* and *automated* devices [1]. Automatic devices cause required acts to be performed at given points in an operation without human intervention. For instance, an *automatic titrator* records a titration curve or simply stops a titration at an endpoint by mechanical or electrical means (such as a relay) instead of manually. Automated devices, on the other hand, replace human manipulative effort by mechanical and instrumental devices regulated by *feedback of information*; so, the apparatus is self-monitoring or self-balancing. An *automated titrator* may be intended to maintain a sample at some preselected (set point) state—for example, at pH = 8. To do this, the pH of the solution is sensed and compared to a set point of pH = 8, and acid or base is added continuously so as to keep the sample pH at the set point. This type of automated titrator is called a *pH-stat* [2].

In the past, automated instruments were not well accepted because of their limited capability and reliability. However, because of the increased complexity and number of clinical, industrial, and other types of samples requiring analysis, classical (nonautomated) techniques, as well as automated techniques, have been improved in capability and reliability. Well established instruments such as infra-red analyzers, gas chromatographs, ion-selective electrode systems, and automatic wet-chemical analyzers can now measure quite complex species and mixtures. Reliability has also increased, because the maturity of solid-state electronics has brought easier data-handling and equipment maintenance along with it.

This chapter presents some basic considerations encountered in automating analytical instruments and illustrates some of the important interactions between the instrument and the system of which it is a part. The first part of the chapter will deal with general concepts and some automated industrial applications in which continuous monitoring and feedback control is important. The second part will deal with the approaches used in the clinical laboratory, where literally billions of tests are performed annually using automatic instruments.

24.1 INSTRUMENTAL PARAMETERS FOR AUTOMATED INSTRUMENTS

Several instrumental parameters need to be evaluated when unattended operation is proposed for a particular instrument. The definitions that follow have been accepted by the Scientific Apparatus Makers Association (SAMA) [3], and endorsed by the Instrument Society of America (ISA).

Sensitivity

Sensitivity is specified by the relationship between concentration and instrument output and hence by the slope of the instrument-response curve. Sensitivity also specifies the minimum detectable change in concentration, governed by the signal-to-noise ratio of the instrument. Sensitivity is generally defined as the concentration required to give a signal equal to twice the root-mean-square of the baseline noise. The ISA has recommended that this second definition be denoted by the term *dead band*, which is the range over which an input to an instrument can be varied without detectable response. A change in the slope of the instrument-response curve will generally result in a change in the level of detectable response—that is, the signal-to-noise ratio.

Inconspicuous instrumental, environmental, or chemical effects often cause a loss of instrument response. In atomic emission spectroscopy, for example, sensitivity is affected by such instrumental factors as flame temperature, aspiration rate, and slit width. In amperometric measurements, diffusion currents vary with temperature, and a significant loss in sensitivity may occur with a drop in sample temperature. In ion-selective electrode measurements, sensitivity may be affected by chemical effects, such as changes in ionic strength or pH.

Accuracy

Accuracy indicates how close a measured value is to an accepted standard or true value. Statements of accuracy should be a percentage of the upper-range value of the reading, or (preferably) an absolute number of measured units. In each case, accuracy is measured in terms of the largest *error* occurring when the device is used under described operating conditions.

Reproducibility

Reproducibility, or precision, differs from accuracy. A poorly calibrated instrument may be inaccurate, but these inaccurate results may nonetheless be reproduced well. Although an automated instrument used primarily as a monitor may require high accuracy (and hence precision), an instrument used for control purposes may only need high reproducibility. The first kind of instrument is used, for instance, in cost control or in clinical testing where accuracy is paramount; the second kind is used in process control, where a particular factor is to be held at a stable set point. There are various measures of precision. One of the most common is the *standard deviation s*, given by

$$s = \sqrt{\frac{\sum (\bar{X} - X_i)^2}{N - 1}} \tag{24.1}$$

where $\bar{X}$ = the mean of the individual measurements X_i
N = the number of measurements

Defining objectives in terms of accuracy, reproducibility, and sensitivity is only part of the task. The effect of ambient environmental factors, such as temperature, pressure, humidity, and supply-voltage stability, must also be evaluated. A common problem leading to loss of accuracy and sensitivity in real-world applications is the build-up of deposits on measurement transducers, such as electrodes, which then have to be periodically cleaned, either manually or automatically.

Selectivity

The selectivity of the chemical transducer is its ability to discriminate between the species of interest and possible interferences. Since commercially available instruments are designed for the largest possible number of applications, the instrument may not operate optimally in a particular situation. Therefore, both the measuring method and the chemical system being measured should be thoroughly understood.

Range and Span

Range is defined as the interval over which a quantity is measured. The *span* is simply the width of the range, the difference between the upper- and lower-range values. Consider the following example. For a typical pH-meter, 0 mV corresponds to pH 7, and (at 30°C) each unit change in pH produces a change in potential of approximately 60 mV. In Figure 24.1A, pH is measured over the range pH 7 to 9 (0 to +120 mV); the span is 2 pH-units (120 mV) and the zero is normal. If one wishes to measure pH over the range pH 8 to 10 (Fig. 24.1B), the 2-pH span is maintained, but the zero is suppressed and the millivolt range becomes +60 to +180 mV. The official glossary of the Instrument Society of America [3] defines a suppressed-zero range as one in which the zero value of the measured variable is smaller than the lower-range value. Likewise, an elevated-zero range is one in which the zero value of the measured variable is greater than the lower-range value; in Figure 24.1C,

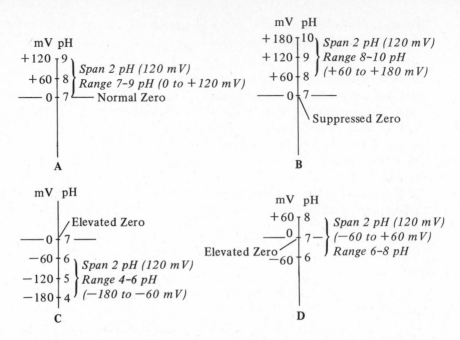

FIGURE 24.1. *Illustrative relationship between range, span, elevated-zero and suppressed-zero. Courtesy of the Foxboro Company.*

the pH range is pH 4 to 6 (-60 to -180 mV), and the span is again 2 pH-units. Note in Figure 24.1D that, if the zero value falls between the upper- and lower-range values, there is again an elevated zero.

Since a change in span requires a change in the per unit response of the instrument, it requires a change in gain; likewise, since a change in range requires a change in the zero point of the instrument, it requires a change in bias.

The dynamic (working) range of an automatic or automated instrumental technique must obviously fit the working range of concentrations to which it is being applied. In a continuous or automatic titration, for example, the dynamic range and span are governed by the sample size (the volume of the sample and the concentration of desired species in it), the size of the buret, and the concentration of the titrant. The presence of a second titratable species (interference) in the system reduces the usable span by the amount of the second species, since the titration will measure both species.

For cases in which the amount of the interference is known to be constant, a blank correction (zero elevation) may be possible if a small enough portion of the span is consumed. Unfortunately, since the concentrations of most interferences are subject to the same variations as those of the species of interest, one is usually left with three possible alternatives:

1. Find a method more selective for the species of interest
2. Find a selective measurement for the interfering species and use it to correct the primary measurement signal
3. Use chemical conditioning to remove the interference from the sample

Speed of Response

In electronic instruments, there is always some lag between the physical change being measured and the recorded signal. Speed of response is usually defined as the time required for the instrument to reach a specified percentage of the total change observed. It may be stated in terms of *rise time*, the time required for an instrument output to change from, say, 10% of the ultimate value to 90%. Another measure is the *time constant*, defined as the time required for the response to build from 0% to 63% $(100 - 100/e)$ of the ultimate value when a step-function signal is received at the detector. Approximately four time-constants are required to reach 98% of the final value; this is called the *response time*. Increasing the amplification of a system increases its noise in proportion to the square root of the amplification. This will require a larger response time to damp out the fluctuations, and so the response-time should be increased in proportion to the square root of the amplification. If the amplification is increased ten-fold, for example, the response time should be increased about three-fold. In a scanning instrument, the scan rate should be correspondingly reduced.

Dead-Time

Dead-time is often of great importance in automated systems. This is defined as the time interval, after alteration of the parameter being measured, during which no change in the parameter is observed at the detector. It can be minimized by placing transducers properly, keeping the sample lines short, and using high flow rates. It is never entirely absent. Batch-sampling analyzers introduce additional dead-time, since delay invariably exists between the time at which a sample is taken and that at which a signal is generated. The response of a gas chromatograph in an automated process-control analyzer is a good illustration of this type of delay, since the elution time of the species in the column is dead-time. In automatic batch-samplers (not used for automated process-control), times between sample injections can be much shorter than the dead-time so that after the first sample is detected, data output for subsequent samples is obtained in rapid succession.

24.2 SAMPLE CONDITIONING

Sample conditioning is the physical or chemical change needed to render samples suitable for measurement. Ignoring this basic requirement has caused many serious problems for automated instruments, particularly those designed for unattended operation.

From the physical point of view, the most important considerations are temperature, pressure, and sample cleanness. Suspended solids in liquid samples and dust in gas samples often interfere with transducers in continuous-sampling instruments and with the volumetric sampling techniques used in batch-sampling instruments. Automated systems that filter out solids should be amenable to automatic cleaning. In continuous instruments, data output must be interrupted while the filters are cleaned; in batch-sampling systems, filters can be cleaned during the dead-time after a sample has been injected for analysis.

Often the physical state of the sample (gas, liquid, or solid) is dictated by the physical principle upon which the measurement is based, and a phase conversion may be required. Some instruments (for example, gas chromatographs and infrared analyzers) utilize either gas or liquid samples; the appropriate phase may be chosen to optimize any of the instrumental parameters discussed earlier. If the measurement is temperature sensitive and the sample temperature may vary, temperature compensation or temperature control must be provided. Temperature compensation is usually supplied as part of the measuring system; the sample temperature is continuously monitored and the measurement signal electrically corrected to offset the temperature effects. When temperature control is required, a batch sample or a sample side-stream is used, and the sample temperature is adjusted prior to measurement. This procedure adds dead-time to the measurement because the sample has to be in the temperature converter long enough to come to thermal equilibrium.

The sample pressure (in a gas, for instance) may vary widely; it is often restricted by the mechanical constraints of the transducer. If a pressure drop is required in the measurement, phase changes or degassing (in liquids) may also occur and interfere severely with the measurement.

Chemical sample conditioning or reagent addition is often more difficult to apply on a practical scale than is physical conditioning, but can be invaluable in optimizing instrumental parameters. In many cases, it makes otherwise-impossible measurements feasible. Three types of reagent addition are utilized. In the first, the sample is diluted to lower the concentration of the species to be analyzed into the dynamic range of the measuring instrument. In the second, reagent addition converts a species for which no useful measurement technique exists into one amenable to measurement. In the third, reagent addition is used to suppress the effect of interfering species and thus render the measurement more selective.

The quantity of reagent added may not be critical. Frequently, only a moderate excess of reagent is required and, therefore, a 10–50% accuracy in this quantity suffices. The practical requirement in flowing systems is to maintain a constant ratio between the reagent flow and the sample flow. A simple system for accom-

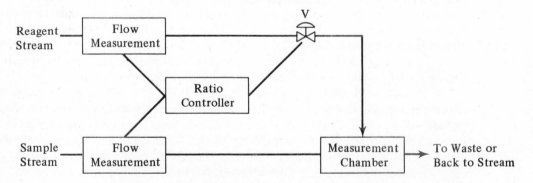

FIGURE 24.2. *Reagent addition system. The ratio controller compares reagent flow to sample flow and maintains a preset ratio by operating control valve V on the reagent stream. The streams are then mixed in (or before) the measurement chamber where the desired analytical measurement is performed. Courtesy of the Foxboro Company.*

plishing this is shown in Figure 24.2. In this system, the ratio controller maintains a flow of reagent to the sample stream at a level proportional to sample flow. This proportion is important in maintaining chemical stoichiometry as well as a known, constant dilution at the measurement point.

24.3 AUTOMATED PROCESS-CONTROL

The successful implementation of automated instruments in routine monitoring functions has led to their increased use in automated process-control. Process control is accomplished by means of the *control loop*, which contains at least three parts:

1. An instrument that senses the value of the variable being regulated
2. A controller that compares the measured variable to a reference value (set point) and produces an output proportional to the difference
3. A final operator (controlled by the output of the controller) that actuates some mechanism to reduce the difference

The two basic types of control loops applied to automated systems are termed *feedback* and *feedforward*, and are shown in Figure 24.3. The fundamental difference between these two types lies in the position of the measuring instrument. In feedback control, the measurement is performed either within or at the output of the process, and deviation from the set point causes an operation at the process input. Thus, an error must occur before corrective action can be initiated. In feedforward control, measurement is made at the input to the process, and any deviation from the set point is fed forward to initiate corrective action prior to occurrence of the error. Thus, feedforward systems are theoretically capable of perfect control.

Since a control loop is a dynamic system, its efficiency is governed by the response time of the entire system [4], which includes that of the measuring instrument, the controller, the final operator, and the process itself. Two time-response characteristics of the process are important in selecting the proper control strategy— the *dead-time* and the *resistance-capacitance* (*RC*) *time-constant*. Dead-time was discussed above; an example is the time required to initiate many polymerization reactions. The *RC* time-constant results from the ability of the process to absorb a change in input without an immediate proportionate change in output.

Process capacitance represents the ability of a process to store energy or material. An electrical capacitor, for instance, stores a quantity of electric charge determined by the potential difference. Capacitance represents the change in a quantity per unit change in a reference variable; the units depend on the particular type of system being considered. Thus, the capacitance of electrical systems is in coul/V (farads), of liquid systems is in m^3/m, of thermal systems is in cal/deg, and of pressure systems is in lbs/psi.

Resistance represents the opposition to flow of energy or material into (or out of) a process. The rate of charge flow through a conductor is determined by the applied potential difference; electrical resistance to charge flow is measured in ohms [V/(coul-sec)]. The volumetric flow-rate (m^3/sec) from a liquid-level system with a

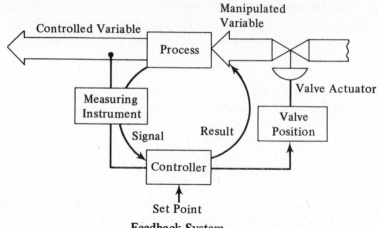

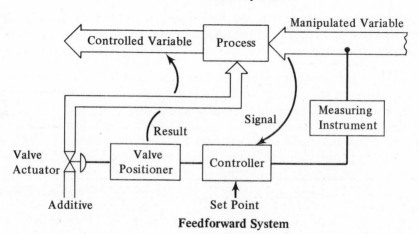

FIGURE 24.3. *Feedback and feedforward control systems. In feedback control, a measuring instrument obtains information at the output of a process, the signal obtained is compared to a set point, and the difference (or result) is applied to a final actuator. The result is ultimately detected by the measuring instrument and closed-loop control results. In feedforward control a measuring instrument obtains information at the input of a process, the signal obtained is again compared to a set point, but now the result is applied to an actuator that controls another input to the process. The result is not detected by the measuring instrument and open-loop control results. Courtesy of the Foxboro Company.*

fixed head (m) has the resistance units $\dot{m}/(m^3\text{-sec})$. Similarly, the resistance of thermal systems is expressed in $°C/(cal\text{-sec})$, and of pressure systems in psi/(lbs-sec).

The chemical composition of a process can also introduce RC time-constants. The presence of undissolved solid reactants, for example, represents chemical capacitance, and the rate of dissolution of sparingly soluble reactants represents resistance.

Modes of Process Control

Automated process control can utilize any of several modes of control, the choice being dictated by the dynamic characteristics of the process. Several of these methods are discussed below.

Two-Position Control. The simplest case is two-position (on-off) control. Here, any deviation of the measured value from a set point drives the final control-operator to either a full-on or full-off position. This forces the measured value back and forth across the set point, and the measurement signal cycles about this point. The amplitude and frequency of this cycle depend on the response characteristics of the process. As the process dead-time becomes small, the frequency of the cycle becomes high; likewise, as the process capacitance becomes high, the amplitude of the cycle becomes small. This mode of control is used only for processes in which this cycling effect can be tolerated; it is most successful with those having large capacitance.

Proportional Control. As the capacitance of the process decreases, on-off control leads to increasing amplitude of oscillation. In proportional control, a continuous linear relation between the value of the measured quantity and the position of the

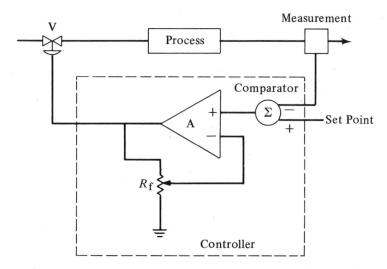

FIGURE 24.4. *The proportional controller. The feedback resistor R_f determines the gain or proportional band of the proportional controller. The symbol V means a valve, and A is an amplifier. Courtesy of the Foxboro Company.*

final control operator is established. This control scheme is shown schematically in Figure 24.4. The *proportional band* is determined by the amount of feedback around the amplifier (the value of R_f in Fig. 24.4). The proportional band is inversely proportional to the gain and is expressed as a percentage of the measurement span; it is defined as the change in the property measured that will cause the control operator to move between the fully open and fully closed positions. A narrow proportional band gives a full swing of control-operator position for a small change in the measured value, whereas a wide proportional band requires a large deviation from the set point for a full swing.

The proportional band (PB) is related to the gain by

$$\text{Gain} = \frac{100}{\% \text{ PB}} \tag{24.2}$$

Controller gain is given by the ratio of change in output to change in input.

$$\text{Gain} = \frac{\Delta \text{ output}}{\Delta \text{ input}} = \frac{\text{output}}{e} \tag{24.3}$$

where $\quad e = $ the error between set point and measurement

A bias adjustment is usually included to allow the controller output to be set at 50% of span when the measurement equals the set point. Thus,

$$\text{Output} = \frac{100}{\% \text{ PB}} e + b \tag{24.4}$$

The bias b is equal to the output when the error is zero. From Equation 24.4, it is clear that proportional action is not capable of perfect control since, after a load upset, the controller output cannot track the error as e approaches zero. The difference between the resulting measured value and the set point is called *offset*, Δe. This is shown schematically in Figure 24.5.

Under this new operating condition,

$$\text{Gain} = \frac{\text{output}}{\Delta e} \tag{24.5}$$

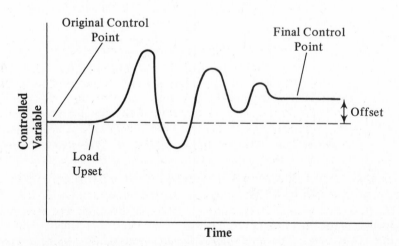

FIGURE 24.5. *Proportional control action. After a load upset, the controlled variable deviates from the set point. The new control-point may then differ from the set point by the offset. Courtesy of the Foxboro Company.*

and from Equation 24.2,

$$\Delta e = \frac{\% \, PB}{100} \, (\text{output}) \tag{24.6}$$

Equation 24.6 shows that the offset is directly related to the proportional band. In the limit as % PB approaches zero (gain approaches infinity), the offset approaches zero. Pure proportional action is therefore adequate for processes that require proportional bands no wider than a few percent—that is, to easily controlled processes in which load changes are moderate.

Proportional-Plus-Integral Control. Addition of integral action to proportional action is necessary for processes requiring wide proportional bands. In integral control, the time integral of the offset is fed back, thereby forcing the deviation to zero. This control scheme is shown in Figure 24.6. At balance, the error signal is zero and

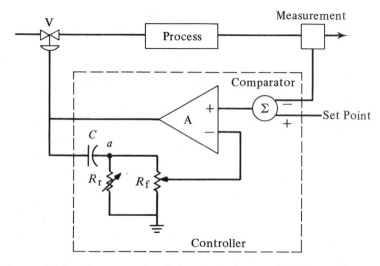

FIGURE 24.6. *The proportional-plus-integral controller. Integral action is accomplished by the series capacitor C in the feedback loop. The presence of offset causes this capacitor to charge at a rate that depends on $R_r C$, where R_r is the reset resistor. This forces the output to change in such a manner as to drive the offset to zero at a rate determined by the adjustment of the reset resistor. Courtesy of the Foxboro Company.*

point *a* is maintained at ground potential. If an offset is present, a voltage develops across the capacitor, which charges at a rate proportional to $R_r C$. This signal is fed back to the control operator to eliminate the offset and thus return point *a* to ground potential.

The response equation for the proportional-plus-integral controller may be written

$$\text{Output} = \frac{100}{\% \, PB} \left(e + \frac{1}{R_r C} \int \Delta e \, dt \right) + b \tag{24.7}$$

The time constant of the controller $R_r C$ is called *reset time* and is the time interval in which the controller output changes by an amount equal to the input change or deviation. Note that, when the offset returns to zero, Equation 24.7 reduces to that describing pure proportional control, Equation 24.4.

Proportional-plus-integral control is the most generally useful control mode and therefore the one usually applied to automated process-control. Its major limitation is in processes with large dead-time and capacitance; if reset time is faster than process dead-time, the controller-response changes are faster than the process, and cycling results. In these cases, derivative control is beneficial.

Proportional-Plus-Derivative Control. Here, derivative action is added to proportional controllers for processes with large capacitance and appreciable dead-time. Control action is now proportional to the rate of change (the time derivative) of the error signal. The response equation is written as

$$\text{Output} = \frac{100}{\% \, \text{PB}} \left(e + t_{\text{D}} \frac{de}{dt} \right) + b \tag{24.8}$$

where t_{D} = the *derivative-action time*

Derivative-action time is defined as the amount of lead, in seconds, that the derivative action advances the effect of pure proportional action. Figure 24.7 illustrates a proportional-plus-derivative controller.

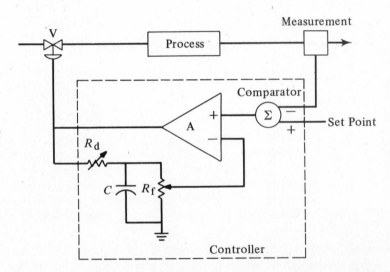

FIGURE 24.7. *The proportional-plus-derivative controller. Derivative action is accomplished by a shunt capacitor C across R_f. When deviation from the setpoint is rapid, the low reactance of the capacitor causes less negative feedback—hence, greater amplifier gain. The derivative time resistor R_d allows adjustment of the magnitude of derivative control action to a given rate of change of the error signal. Courtesy of the Foxboro Company.*

Derivative action is accomplished by placing a capacitor across the gain resistor. This capacitor has low reactance and reduces the feedback when the error signal is changing. Thus, a rapidly changing input-signal increases the controller gain, producing a larger corrective output. When the time rate of change of the error signal becomes zero, derivative action ceases and Equation 24.8 reduces to that for pure proportional control. Note that derivative action is anticipatory since, if the rate of change of a load upset on the process is rapid, the controller can take large corrective action even though the magnitude of the load change is small, thus overcoming the inertia of the process.

The Controller

An example of a typical commercial controller is shown in Figure 24.8. The Foxboro SPEC 200 PID Controller and Display provides proportional-plus-integral (PI) or proportional-plus-integral-plus-derivative (PID) control. The set-point dial on the

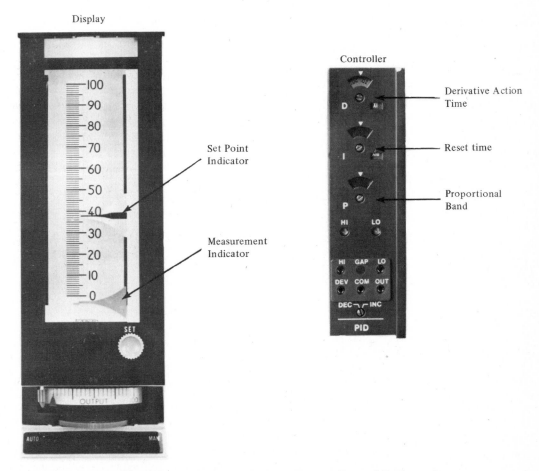

FIGURE 24.8. *The Foxboro SPEC 200 controller and display. Courtesy of the Foxboro Company.*

display unit places the set point at any level between 0 and 100% of the measurement range. A second pointer indicates the actual measurement value on the same scale. Additionally, an output meter indicates the percent of output being applied to the final control-operator. The control unit holds the adjustments for setting proportional band (R_f in Figure 24.4), reset time (R_r in Fig. 24.6), and derivative-action time (R_d in Fig. 24.7). Process controllers are also manufactured by Minneapolis Honeywell Co., General Electric Co., Leeds & Northrup Co., and others.

Discrete Instruments

Automatic instruments with discrete (batch) sample handling and analysis have special problems when used for automated process-control. These instruments consist of a sampling system, an analyzer, and a memory device that maintains the

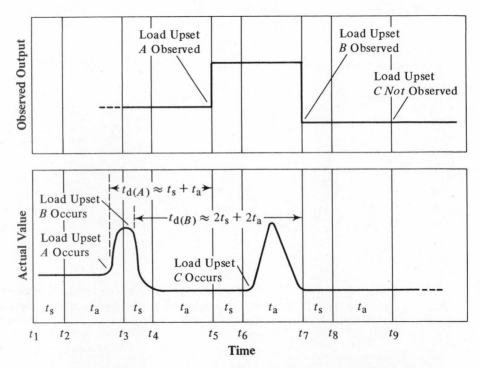

FIGURE 24.9. *Output response behavior of discrete instruments.* t_s = *sampling dead-time* = $t_2 - t_1 = t_4 - t_3 = \cdots$; t_a = *analytical dead-time* = $t_3 - t_2 = t_5 - t_4 = \cdots$; $t_s + t_a < t_d < 2t_s + 2t_a$, *where* t_d *is the total measurement dead-time. Courtesy of the Foxboro Company.*

output at a fixed level until the next signal appears (a trend output). Their output-response behavior is shown in Figure 24.9.

Two sources of dead-time are obvious. *Sampling dead-time* t_s is the time elapsed between the instant the sample is taken and the instant it enters the analyzer.

This is shortened by using short sample-lines and high flow rates. *Analytical dead-time* t_a is the time elapsed between the instant the sample enters the analyzer and the instant a new output-value is displayed.

The total measurement dead-time is not constant. In the best case, a load upset that occurs just prior to sampling (load upset A in Fig. 24.9) may be detected with the least possible dead-time—that is, $t_{d(A)} \approx t_s + t_a$. In the worst case (load upset B in Fig. 24.9) a load upset occurs just after a sampling instant, and its detection is delayed for about twice the interval observed above—that is, $t_{d(B)} \approx 2t_s + 2t_a$. Finally, a load upset that occurs entirely within an analyzer interval t_a may be completely missed (load upset C in Fig. 24.9).

Whereas derivative action is of great value in the control of continuous processes with dead-time, it is useless for batch instruments because the instrument output changes in steps. This local high rate of change produces pulsing of the manipulated variable, the effect of which cannot be seen because of the measurement dead-time.

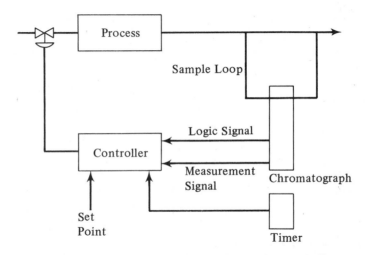

FIGURE 24.10. *The sampling controller. The sampling controller accepts a logic signal from a discrete analyzer (the chromatograph) and applies corrective action for a control interval established by a timer. Courtesy of the Foxboro Company.*

A *sampling controller* using proportional-plus-integral action is most generally useful with discrete-sampling instruments. This is illustrated for a process using a gas chromatograph in Figure 24.10. A logic signal starts a timer that allows the controller to operate for only a fraction of the analytical dead-time. After this control interval, the error signal is removed, the controller output is held, and further corrective action is prevented until the next control-interval. The time the controller waits before applying further corrective action is the total dead-time, t_d. The major limitation of this system is that it is impossible to synchronize sampling instants with changes in the variable being controlled.

24.4 AUTOMATED INSTRUMENTS IN PROCESS-CONTROL SYSTEMS

The chemical instrumentation discussed in the preceding chapters of this text can all be utilized in automated systems. The choice is largely dictated by economics and the applicability of the instrument to the proposed problem. Three groups of instruments have been widely automated: spectrometers, electrochemical instruments, and chromatographs. Some of the many techniques commonly used and a few others are listed in Table 24.1. A review of all the instruments used in automated control systems cannot be given in the space allotted here. Additional reading is found in the bibliography at the end of this chapter.

Spectroscopy

Ultraviolet-visible absorption spectrophotometry, an inherently precise and accurate measurement, is most often applied to such gaseous materials as Cl_2 (for which no other convenient method is available), SO_2, NO_2, O_3, and Hg (vapor). An interesting automated instrument in this category measures low concentrations of mercury in water streams and industrial atmospheres [5]. Mercury in any chemical form is reacted with suitable reagents to give the elemental material, the Hg is stripped with clean air as vapor, and the absorbance of the vapor is measured at the 253.7-nm resonance wavelength obtained from a Hg-vapor lamp. A pyrolysis system is used to give additional specificity when other ultraviolet absorbing materials are present. This type of instrument is capable of accurately measuring mercury at the parts-per-billion level.

TABLE 24.1. *Analytical Techniques Commonly Used in Automated Systems*

1. Spectroscopy

    A. Ultraviolet, Visible, Infrared Absorption
    B. Turbidimetry
    C. Emission Spectrometry
    D. Refractometry
    E. Chemiluminescence Measurements

2. Chromatography

    A. Gas-Liquid
    B. Liquid-Liquid

3. Electrochemistry

    A. Potentiometry
    B. Voltammetry
    C. Coulometry
    D. Conductivity
    E. Amperometry
    F. Dielectric-Constant Measurements

Applying absorption spectroscopy to liquid samples suffers from two important limitations. The spectra of two or more components may overlap, causing poor selectivity. Broad shoulders may appear on the sides of the more important absorption peaks, causing difficulty in discriminating between the components in a mixture. These problems may sometimes be avoided by using the optimum wavelength of the component sought and perhaps blank subtraction techniques (see Chaps. 6 and 7). Another approach is to use a double wavelength technique. Here one wavelength is used at which the component of interest absorbs and another at which it does not. This can compensate for the presence of an interfering substance, an indistinct shoulder on the side of a band, or even for the effects of scattering and dirty cell windows.

A second limitation of this technique arises from the high absorption and scattering of high-molecular-weight solutes and solvents between 200 and 800 nm. This causes marked loss in sensitivity and restricts the use of this technique in important applications, such as measuring high-molecular-weight polymers, colloids, or proteins. To overcome this problem, a high-intensity tungsten source is used along with low-noise photomultiplier tubes having large windows, and the sample is placed close to the detector to minimize scattering losses. Most liquid samples are measured for organic materials, such as aromatics, diolefins, ketones, and aldehydes.

This type of instrument is widely applied to measurements other than chemical composition, such as film thickness, turbidity, color, and optical rotation. The DuPont Company manufactures a versatile instrument, in modular form, that is used for all of these measurements. The same company also produces automated systems designed specifically for SO_2, NO_x, and H_2S/SO_2 ratio, all of which are useful in stack-gas pollution control. Other manufacturers are Beckman Instruments, ITT Barton Co., and GEC-Elliot Ltd. (Hallikainen Instruments).

Gas Chromatography

The chromatograph is a discrete instrument, since it operates as a batch-sampling device (see Chaps. 21 and 22) requiring that one take samples, inject them into the chromatograph, and record the chromatograms. A *process gas chromatograph* (PGC), therefore, requires an automatic sampling valve. Suitable ceramic sampling valves, electrically or pneumatically actuated, have been developed using linear and rotary sliding seals. These valves can add identical samples to the column for millions of cycles. Both liquid and gas sampling valves are available, as well as several detectors, such as thermal-conductivity and flame-ionization detectors, by which this technique can be applied over a range of concentrations from trace ppm to present levels.

Because of the complexity of many industrial fluids, the recent trend has been toward use of the PGC as a single or two-component dedicated device. In addition, *column switching* and *backflushing* techniques are essential to PGCs. Column switching allows chromatogram development using different columns during each analysis, thereby enhancing the separation of the desired components and allowing for rejection (often at an early stage of analysis) of unwanted components. Backflushing is useful for eliminating components with long elution-times. In one case, the flow of carrier gas through the column is reversed after the last component to be measured has been eluted. The slow components emerge from the beginning of the column in a single band since they leave the column at the same relative rates at which they entered. Thus, they may be used to form a composite peak on the chromatogram for "total heavies," or vented, as desired.

The operation of the chromatograph makes data utilization difficult, for two reasons. First, much effort is needed to extract information from the complex chromatographic display. Automated procedures for doing this usually employ a time-base generator that selects a predetermined portion of the chromatogram for integration. When this *window* includes only the peak of interest, the answer can be automatically presented at periodic intervals. However, the position of this window relies on the fixed time-interval between sample injection and component retention time. Since retention time is affected by column loading, temperature, and flow rate, these factors must be rigorously controlled. In one PGC system, this problem was eliminated (or at least minimized) by using programming techniques tied to a chromatogram time-base rather than an absolute time-base [6].

Second, the application of chromatography to dynamic systems is limited by the time interval between analyses. This is particularly serious when chromatography is used in automated control systems. A significant solution may be *correlation chromatography* [7]. Here, samples are repeatedly injected into the column using a predetermined switching sequence (a pseudo-random chain code), and the chromatographic output is mathematically related (correlated) with the input using a digital computer. This results in an average of the several chromatograms taken over the period of the chain code. Since many more analyses are obtained per unit time, the chromatogram is continuously updated, and the output, though still delayed by the analysis dead-time, is more nearly continuous.

Chromatography is perhaps one of the most widely applied automated instruments in process analysis, particularly in the nonaqueous chemical and petrochemical industries [8]. In petroleum refining, for example, the crude petroleum, containing hundreds of chemicals from methane to asphalt, is converted to salable cuts by distillation. Further processing by catalytic reforming, distillation, and chemical reaction yields materials used for fuels, lubricants, petrochemical feedstock, and other applications.

An illustration of the use of chromatography in this industry is in the control of distillation towers. Distillation uses the difference in composition between a liquid and the vapor formed from that liquid as the basis for separation. The efficiency of the process is affected by temperature, pressure, feed composition, and feed flow-rate. Chromatography is used to monitor the composition of the feed-stock and to apply feedforward control of the heat input (temperature) to the tower, or to monitor and control the composition of the product. In this latter case, the chromatograph output is simply compared with a set point, and the controller (using feedback) manipulates the temperature, pressure, or feed flow-rate by activating the appropriate final operator. Both types of distillation control are widely employed in petroleum refining.

In the petrochemical industries, hundreds of materials are produced using catalytic reforming, isomerization, and polymerization. Tower-distillation monitoring and control using the PGC is of great importance here also. Other specific applications include (1) monitoring the purity of monomers used in manufacturing such polymers as vinyl chloride, vinyl acetate, polyethylene, and styrene; and (2) monitoring chlorinated hydrocarbons produced by chlorination and oxychlorination reactions—chlorinated solvents, weedkillers, pesticides, and many intermediates that are polymerized directly into plastics. Additional applications of PGC are found in the pharmaceutical and food industries and, to a more limited extent, in analyzing furnace flue-gas for combustion control.

Electrochemical Instruments

Several types of electrochemical techniques have been used in automated systems (see Table 24.1). At first glance, their use in instrument systems appears straight-forward, since each transducer converts chemical information directly into an electrical signal. Unfortunately, few applications are found for those methods involving net current flow (e.g., amperometry) because the rate of mass transfer (and hence the current) depends on the sample flow-rate, which may vary, and on how clean the electrode surface is. This discussion will therefore be restricted to potentiometry, a zero-current technique.

The glass electrode used for measuring pH is one of the most successful examples of potentiometry in automated instruments. Modern glass electrodes are highly reliable; they give selective, sensitive, and stable response to acidity over a very wide range of pH and have been widely applied in industrial monitoring and control.

Using ion-selective electrodes in automated systems has several advantages. In general, many wide-range electrodes are available for several types of ions, and in many cases they provide the only practical method for determining ionic activities in solution [9]. They generally exhibit fast response and can be used continuously with small samples, and with many types of samples with no pretreatment (colored solutions, slurries, etc.).

The general acceptance of ion-selective electrodes in automated instruments, however, has been somewhat limited; this can be attributed to the fact that accuracy is strongly affected by chemical and environmental effects. Since these electrodes measure activity rather than concentration, factors such as ionic strength, complex formation, and pH need to be carefully controlled. In addition, few of these electrodes are perfectly selective for the ion of interest, and the presence of interfering ions must be considered before every application. The accuracy attainable may further suffer from temperature variations. For a monovalent ion, the Nernst equation shows that a change in temperature of 1°C causes a change in potential of 0.2 mV for a 0.1 M solution of the ion of interest, and a 1 mV change for a 10^{-5} M solution of the same ion. Electrode accuracy may suffer from drift because of pressure changes, flow changes, or electrode poisoning; the relative concentration error is 3.9% per mV uncertainty in measurement for a monovalent ion. When high accuracy is required, all of the factors must be carefully controlled. A side stream and flow-through cell allowing temperature control, flow control, adjustment of pH, and reagent addition to eliminate interfering ions may be required. An example of a flow-through cell that contains pH and reference electrodes, temperature compensator, and ultrasonic cleaner is shown in Figure 24.11.

Ultrasonic electrode cleaning has contributed significantly to the use of

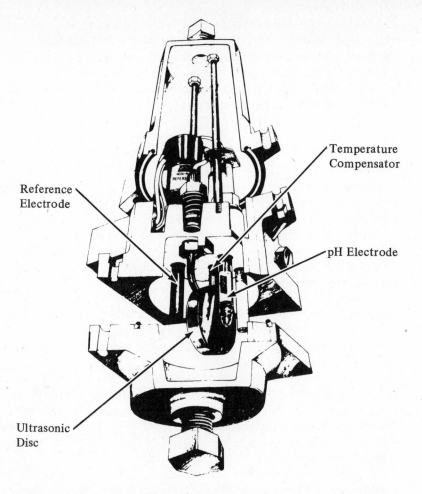

Reference
Electrode

Temperature
Compensator

pH Electrode

Ultrasonic
Disc

FIGURE 24.11. *The Foxboro Model 85A pIon Electrode Assembly.
Courtesy of the Foxboro Company.*

potentiometry in automated instruments. For example, during sugar refining, the raw washed sugar liquor is treated with phosphoric acid. Subsequently, lime is added to neutralize the acid; this quickly coats the pH electrodes, increasing the response time and finally snuffing the response entirely. Ultrasonic cleaning eliminates these problems and results in a substantially improved automated instrument in terms of reduced maintenance, increased reliability, and more efficient process control.

Some important automated instruments based on ion-selective electrodes measure sodium in boiler feedwaters, fluoride in public water-supplies, and water hardness (Ca^{2+} and Mg^{2+}) in water-conditioning systems. The sulfide electrode is extensively used in the paper industry for monitoring and control of sulfidity in paper pulping liquors (for instance, the Kraft process), for waste-treatment control of excess sulfide using a process that oxidizes sulfide with air, and for monitoring the level of sulfide being discharged from the plants. Other applications include the use of the cyanide electrode for measuring free and total cyanide in metal-plating baths, the use of the silver electrode for measuring silver ion in photographic emulsions and spent fixing solutions, and many others.

In some processes, potentiometry is used for controlling ionic species for which electrodes are not available. For example, the production of chlorine and caustic soda using mercury electrolysis cells results in wastes containing toxic levels of mercury. This waste is treated by precipitating the mercury as insoluble mercurous sulfide using sodium bisulfide, and then filtering the precipitate. Both pH and S^{2-} concentration should be controlled for efficient operation. At high pH, HgS forms soluble polysulfides; at low pH, sulfide is tied up as HS^- and H_2S. The waste liquor is therefore controlled at a pH near 7.0, and sulfide is added in a controlled manner to maintain a small residual level of about 1 ppm as H_2S. In this way the very small residual concentration of mercury ion remaining in solution (governed by the common-ion effect and the solubility product of HgS) is effectively removed by means controlled by the sulfide electrode.

When the chemical composition of a stream is to be controlled using potentiometry, a significant problem is encountered because of the logarithmic relationship between the measured potential and the concentration of the species of interest. Consider a pH-control loop (a pH measurement, reagent valve, and controller); for a neutralization reaction, the gain of the pH measurement is the incremental change in pH caused by a particular quantity of added reagent. This is the slope of the titration curve; since it is inversely related to the buffer capacity of the system, it may vary over three or four orders of magnitude. It is apparent that the gain will be affected by the pH set point selected and by the type of acids or bases (that is, strong or weak) in the system. Since efficient control requires that the total gain of the loop be less than one, the extreme range of gain resulting from the potentiometric measurement must be accommodated by the other two elements in the loop. Valves are available having 50:1 rangeability which may be sequenced to achieve nearly 2500:1 rangeability, and controllers are available having complementary logarithmic control functions.

In the future, additional electrodes with improved selectivity should become available, and their use with automated instruments for process control and in biomedical applications will undoubtedly increase. The recent introduction of the microprocessor will undoubtedly have a significant impact on the sophistication of automated instruments. This device is a small, but complex, collection of integrated circuits which will perform arithmetic and logical operations according to programmed input instructions, exactly as the central processor of a full-sized computer does. When incorporated into automated instruments, microprocessors will provide versatile and economical means for performing complex timing and sequencing operations, data manipulations, and computations, thereby producing "intelligent instruments." An example of such an approach is the Princeton Applied Research Model 374 microprocessor-controlled Polarographic Analyzer.

Many other types of instruments have been utilized in addition to those described here. The reader is referred to the bibliography for references to this material.

Billions of tests are run annually in clinical chemistry laboratories; automation has therefore played a large role there. In the preceding sections, automated process-control systems were described. The first part of the present section describes the needs of the clinical chemistry laboratory as they relate to automation. The remainder will be devoted primarily to how clinical instruments are automated and which instrumental methods are most commonly used. Selected instruments will be described.

Automation Needs in Clinical Chemistry

The most significant factor that distinguishes the needs of the clinical laboratory from those of others is that the test results can directly affect the well-being and even the survival of a human being. Some of the factors influencing the design of clinical laboratory instruments are discussed below.

The Clinical Laboratory Environment. The task of the clinical chemist is to perform chemical analyses for diagnostic purposes. The concepts described in the first part of this chapter can be applied because of the common theme of automation for chemical analysis; however, the automation requirements in the clinical laboratory significantly differ from those in either process control or industrial analytical chemistry.

1. The sample is a natural biological material. It is not synthesized, and it cannot be controlled. Automation may control the testing process to some degree, but the sample itself cannot be—except perhaps for automatically rejecting a sample that is too small or has been damaged—for instance, hemolyzed (cells ruptured).

2. The most common clinical sample, blood, is probably one of the most complex substances a chemist is called upon to analyze. He or she is expected to determine the concentrations of a few specific components out of thousands present without interference from any of the other components. This selectivity requirement is usually called *specificity* by clinical chemists.

3. In interpreting the results, the clinical chemist must be aware that the components to be measured may be affected by the recent history of the patient—ingestion of food or drugs (prescribed or not), physical exertion, and the degree of physical trauma or psychological reaction to the circumstances under which the sample is obtained. This exacerbates the problem of specificity and makes the interpretation of results critically dependent on skilled judgment, which must be applied both by responsible personnel in the laboratory and by the physician requesting the analysis.

4. Partly because of the complexity of the sample and problems relating to specificity, few standards are available. An expanding number of pertinent Standard Reference Materials is becoming available from the National Bureau of Standards. Even when available, cost dictates that these be used only to calibrate other reference materials. The latter include so-called "standards" purchased from reagent suppliers and control samples that are frequently derived from a carefully stored pool of blood samples. The precision of results can be assured by good instruments,

properly selected methods, and meticulous protocol; it can be assessed by measuring replicate samples. Accuracy, however, is much more difficult to attain.

There are several strong motives for high accuracy:

1. To insure the diagnostic value of the test results
2. To monitor the progress of a patient under therapy
3. To follow the state of health of an individual, even though the tests may have been performed at different times and perhaps in different laboratories.

It is significant that, although "normal ranges" are developed statistically, these vary widely with sex, age, geographical and ethnic differences, and other factors. The situation is further complicated by the fact that the "normal range" for some components may have wide limits in the statistical population, but narrow limits in each individual biological system. Small deviations from the normal value will then indicate illness. A notable example of this is the concentration of calcium in serum, which is maintained constant to within about 1% by a healthy body, although the "normal" range for the adult population spans $\pm 13\%$.

Automation in the clinical laboratory has been spurred by the steady rise in the number of tests, an annual growth rate of about 10%. As mentioned before, about two billion tests a year are performed in clinical chemistry laboratories in the United States. This could not be physically accomplished without some automation.

A prime objective of automation is to eliminate the need for human intervention in a process. Although this may be applied literally in, for example, process control, the clinical laboratory environment described above requires more constraints. Skilled human judgment is essential for monitoring the viability of the sample and the validity and significance of the results. Therefore, automation is aimed at aiding the clinical analyst in the exercise of these skills.

Clinical Chemistry Tests. The diversity of tests that the clinical chemistry laboratory may be called upon to perform is continually expanding. Very few older tests are displaced by the newer ones developed. A reasonably sized laboratory will be prepared to perform over 60 different tests routinely, and a regional reference laboratory will offer between 200 and 300. However, many of the latter are performed infrequently and do not justify automation. Table 24.2 lists the tests that have been commonly automated.

One indication of the general level of performance achieved in clinical chemistry laboratories is the fact that control samples show a relative standard deviation of between one and three percent. Extenuating circumstances, such as a required solvent-extraction procedure, may lead to relative deviations greater than 10%. Although automation may result in improved precision, the degree attained depends on the skills and motivation of the operator and on the general quality control prevalent in the laboratory.

Automation in the Clinical Laboratory

The first automation in clinical chemistry laboratories was applied primarily to sample handling and processing in the late 1950s. This emphasis can be attributed both to the quantity of specimens and to the state of technology.

TABLE 24.2. *Blood Tests Commonly Automated*

Acid Phosphatase	Glucose
Albumin	Iodine—Protein Bound
Alcohol	Iron
Alanine Transaminase	Lactic Acid
Alkaline Phosphatase	Lactic Dehydrogenase
Aspartate Transaminase	Lithium
Bilirubin—Direct	Oxygen
Bilirubin—Total	pH
Calcium	Phosphate—Inorganic
Carbon Dioxide	Potassium
Chloride	Protein—Total
Cholesterol	Sodium
Creatine Phosphokinase	Triglycerides
Creatinine	Urea Nitrogen
Free Fatty Acids	Uric Acid

Sampling Automation. In the terminology given in the first part of the chapter, instruments that emulate manual sample handling and processing without the use of control loops are *automatic* (mechanized), but not automated. Among the automatic functions are:

1. Sample pickup (from a container such as a small cup)
2. Sample dispensing
3. Dilution
4. Deproteinization
5. Reagent addition
6. Incubation
7. Insertion of the reacted sample into the detection system

It is interesting to note that, when blood is the sample, almost all of the automatic instruments require the use of serum or plasma; none automate the separation of the serum or plasma from the whole blood.*

It is customary to refer to instruments lacking the automatic functions on the above list as *manual* instruments. If these incorporate extensive electronic data-processing, they are called *semiautomatic*.

Discrete and Continuous-Flow Sampling. In the clinical laboratory, the terms *discrete* and *continuous flow* are applied somewhat differently than in process control. In discrete sampling, each sample undergoes a reaction measured in a cuvette not shared

---

* Serum is the clear portion of blood remaining after the blood is allowed to clot and the clot containing the red cells and fibrin is separated out by centrifuging. Plasma is identical to serum except that it still contains fibrinogen, which is normally converted to the insoluble protein fibrinogen to form the clot. Plasma is obtained by adding an anticoagulating agent to prevent the clotting reaction, and then centrifuging out the red cells.

by other reactants. In continuous flow sampling, successive samples pass into the same length of tubing, reagents are added and reactions occur, and finally they flow continuously into a cuvette for detection. In order to isolate successive samples, one or more air bubbles are pumped into the flow line between samples.

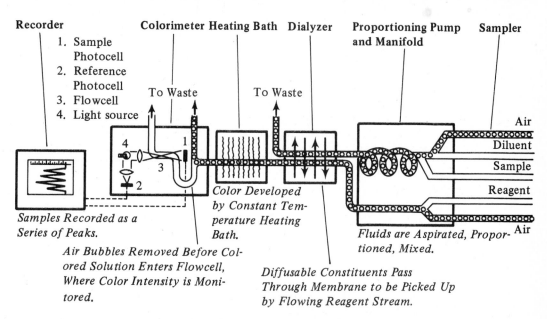

Typical Single-Channel Flow Schematic

FIGURE 24.12. *Single-channel AutoAnalyzer®. Courtesy of Technicon Instruments Corporation.*

Since successive samples must be kept isolated from each other in order to avoid cross-contamination, discrete sampling is the natural method for automatic clinical sample processing. Surprisingly, the first successful automation of clinical sampling was a flow-sampling system, the AutoAnalyzer®, marketed in 1957 by Technicon Instruments Corporation. A single-channel AutoAnalyzer is illustrated in Figure 24.12. A successful discrete-sampling instrument was not introduced until almost a decade later; as a result, Technicon has dominated the field of clinical chemistry automation. Only since the late 1960s have discrete sampling instruments begun to play a significant role in automated clinical chemistry.

Instrument Categories. Automatic chemical analyzers are classified by function as follows:

1. *Multi-channel.* These instruments analyze each sample for many different components—in parallel for a discrete analyzer, and sequentially for a continuous-flow analyzer.

2. *Batch.* Batch instruments analyze each sample for a single component at a time, but can be readily changed to analyze other components one at a time. These are also called *single-channel analyzers.*

3. *Parallel Fast.* Parallel-fast analyzers are a special variation of batch analyzers, based on the use of a centrifuge. They are sometimes called *centrifugal fast analyzers.* The principle is illustrated in Figure 24.13. A central, removable

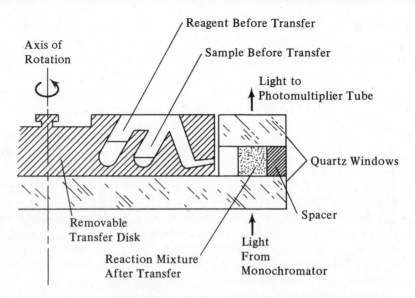

FIGURE 24.13. *Cross-section of sample disc and centrifugal-analyzer section of parallel-fast analyzer. From R. C. Coleman, W. D. Schultz, M. T. Kelly, and J. A. Dean,* Amer. Lab., *3*(7), 26 (1971), *by permission of International Scientific Communications, Inc.*

disc has radial slots, with two or more wells molded into each slot. An automatic pipette dispenses microsamples into the outer well and reagents into the inner wells of each slot. The disc is placed in a centrifuge rotor with the slots oriented in line with cuvettes around the outer circumference of the rotor. When the rotor spins, the reagents simultaneously wash all of the samples into the cuvettes, which rotate sequentially under a fixed photometer. The transmittance of each cell is read using an oscilloscope monitor, and the data are tabulated by a dedicated computer. The oscilloscope, like a strip-chart recorder, records the transmittance as a function of time as the different cells pass between the light source and the photomultiplier detector. Unlike a strip-chart recorder, however, the oscilloscope can expand the time scale so that transmittance changes over milliseconds or less can be seen. Hence, the transmittance is zero between cells and then increases as each cell passes through the measuring zone. The transmittance is usually read when the rotor speed is about 600 rpm. The sweep rate of the oscilloscope is keyed to the rotation rate to synchronize the readout to each cell. The system can be programmed to take readings over a period of time, say a minute, to obtain a kinetic curve for rate-limited reactions (for instance, enzyme reactions). The computer handles the data processing.

4. *Dedicated.* A dedicated instrument analyzes for only a specified component or a limited number of diagnostically related components; generally, it is not adaptable to other applications.

More examples of the above classes of analyzers will be given below.

The Impact of Modern Electronics

In the 1970s, modern electronics has led clinical automation in a completely new direction. The impact has been both on the instruments with automatic sample-handling and on the manual instruments. Some of the newer instruments are truly automated, as well as automatic. Most of the advantages of modern electronics derive from applications of microelectronic digital circuitry crammed into a remarkably small space—a boon to overcrowded laboratories.

Data Readout. Prior to this technological change, manual instruments, such as colorimeter/spectrophotometers, had meter read-outs with a linear transmittance (energy) scale and, in some cases, a nonlinear (logarithmic) absorbance scale, which in principle saved one computational step in deriving results in concentration units. The read-out of automatic instruments was generally a strip-chart recorder, which traced a series of peaks for the successive samples. In some cases, the chart had a nonlinear concentration scale, which was often shaded or otherwise marked to indicate "normal" physiological ranges. To use these features the deflection had to be calibrated with a sample of known concentration.

The most evident characteristic of modern automatic clinical instruments is the digital display of data. Most have illuminated numerical displays; an instrument that performs more than one determination simultaneously may have several. For example, a digital flame photometer commonly has two displays for the simultaneous read-out of Na and K, whereas a blood gas analyzer may have three, for pH and for the partial pressures of CO_2 and O_2.

Other types of data read-out include printer-listers, hard copy print-out with formatting, and (in some cases) data storage for later retrieval—on tape cassettes, for instance.

Data Processing. The above are superficial benefits of modern electronics. Of even greater value is the electronic processing of the raw data. A read-out directly proportional to concentration can easily be produced, although this requires a logarithmic conversion for colorimetric or spectrophotometric systems. If the instrument is calibrated with a standard of known concentration, the read-out can also be made directly in reportable units. This is a major time saver and, in addition, reduces errors in numerical manipulation and transcription.

As a further refinement, the electronics system can determine how long to wait before the readout signal is acceptably stable, and then lock the displayed result until the operator has recorded it and is ready to initiate the next reading. This type of automation is common to otherwise "manual" instruments. Other niceties are also available, such as automatic integration or averaging of the signal, automatic correction for nonlinear working curves, and automatic blank-subtraction, all of which save time and minimize the chance for human error.

One of the most valuable applications of electronic data-processing is in enzyme assays. Kinetic measurements of enzyme activity in which the rate of reaction is monitored (usually using UV measurement) are more specific than endpoint colorimetric methods, in which the development of color in a coupled reaction is measured after a fixed time. Modern systems continuously or intermittently monitor the growth in concentration of the reaction product or the decrease in concentration of one of the reactants (the substrate). From the rate of change in concentration or the average change in concentration over several fixed time-intervals, the circuitry calculates the activity in reportable units. Other ramifications of these systems will be discussed below.

Some modern clinical instruments are dedicated either to endpoint colorimetric or to kinetic determinations; others allow selection of either mode. Some program the electronic data-processing for the desired mode by means of a punched-card or other coded system that comes with the prepackaged reagents specifically made for this type of instrument. A design objective of this last type of system is to minimize the training needed by the operator.

Data Evaluation. In addition to data processing, electronic systems are being applied to evaluate the data as a further aid to the operator. For example, in an enzyme assay the system will evaluate the linearity of the reaction, which bears on the expected validity of the end result. Also, for samples of very high activity, the substrate may be prematurely exhausted. The electronics are often designed to warn of this dangerous possibility in which a low-level extraneous reaction may persist, yielding an erroneous reading of low activity for a serious case of high activity. Such samples may then yield useful answers by running a second aliquot at a much higher dilution.

In addition, the instrument may be programmed with the range of normal values so that the display will automatically *flag* abnormals. The flag may be an asterisk, or an *H* for high and an *L* for low. Before releasing the data to the requesting physician, flagged results in particular must be evaluated by the laboratory director to determine if the abnormality results from the patient, the instrument, or the reagent. This type of flagging is also helpful to the physician. Some laboratories have extended the principle of flagging by programming their own in-house computer systems to display a statistically likely diagnosis based on the out-of-normal-range data. This is an aid to the physician, who bases his diagnosis on his examination and on the patient's history, as well as on the test results.

Another type of data evaluation performed on some automatic instruments is statistical analysis of a series of data, computing such functions as standard deviation and coefficient of variation.

Instrument Monitoring. In addition to monitoring and evaluating data, circuitry may be arranged to monitor itself and other functions of the instrument. Among the variables that may be monitored are amplifier range, temperature, source operation, speed, reagent supplies, and waste level. The built-in electronics may also diagnose malperformance or dysfunction of the instrument.

A further useful feature is the automatic control and sequencing of multiple functions of the instrument by the built-in electronics, which are effectively a dedicated microcomputer. In some cases a closed loop is involved, so that certain functions are truly automated. For example, an instrument involved in enzyme determinations will monitor the temperature of the reaction cuvette and correct the assayed activity for deviations from the nominal temperature. Also, after initial calibration, an instrument may compare subsequent standards or control samples with the initial value and automatically correct for calibration drift, as well as alerting the operator to excessive drift.

Overview. The above description of automation as applied to clinical instruments leads to an interesting conclusion. Some of the current instruments that do not automate sample handling or processing, and which are referred to as manual or semiautomatic, may be more effective in saving skilled labor and time and reducing human error than some of the automatic instruments of the 1950s and 1960s.

For reference, a spectrophotometer/colorimeter with direct concentration readout costs on the order of $2000; a digital Na/K flame photometer with an automatic sample-diluter, about $4000; a flexible, computer-controlled, single-channel analyzer under $25,000; a computer-based parallel-fast analyzer, about $50,000; and a multi-channel analyzer from about $80,000 to well over $200,000.

Automatic Instrumental Methods

Because the majority of tests in the clinical chemistry laboratory are colorimetrically based, the greatest effort toward automation has been with colorimetric methods. As previously discussed, most of the automation classifies as automatic rather than automated.

A natural extension, because of similar sample-processing, is the use of a fluorimeter in place of the colorimeter. On the data-handling side, the fluorimeter usually provides a signal inherently linear with concentration, which avoids logarithmic conversion.

Enzyme Assays. More recently, the automatic colorimetric systems have been extended to provide kinetic enzyme determinations (or determinations of enzyme substrates). This required several key changes in the colorimetric systems:

1. Although sample processing is similar, temperature is a far more critical factor, since enzyme activity changes at a rate of about 7% per °C. Therefore, temperature equilibrium and constancy in the reaction cuvette are critical. Temperature control to within ± 0.1°C is commonly specified.

2. The detection system must be sensitive at 340 nm, where many enzyme

activity assays are performed. This generally requires sources, filters, gratings and detectors different from those used in colorimeters.

3. There are no recognized enzyme standards or reference materials. The accepted basis for measurement is the rate of reduction of the substrate, commonly nicotinamide adenine dinucleotide (NAD) for many reactions. The reduced form, NADH, absorbs at 340 nm, and the rate of change of this absorbance is measured in an enzyme-activity assay. The absorptivity (a in Beer's law) is known for NADH; from this and the rate of change of absorbance per unit time, the activity of the enzyme can be calculated in micromoles of substrate converted per minute. This is referred to as an *International Unit* (IU), expressing the activity as IU/liter. Therefore, an accurate, absolute absorbance scale must be established in each case in order to make a valid assay.

4. Many enzyme reactions require the measurement of high absorbance values (in the range of 1.0–1.6), in contrast to colorimetry, for which most measurements are made at absorbances no higher than 0.7. This distinction requires a more stable photometer with an increased linearity range.

5. Many reactions, particularly for samples of lower activity, cause very small changes in absorbance during a reasonable observation period. Therefore, the photometer must have high sensitivity and low noise. Some instruments have sensitivity in the range of 10^{-4} absorbance units.

Atomic Emission Spectroscopy. Another commonly automated spectroscopic method is atomic emission spectroscopy (flame photometry). Because sample processing is less elaborate—usually only a dilution—atomic emission spectroscopy was the first to be adapted to the modern methods of data read-out and processing. Instruments were available in 1964 that gave simultaneous numerical read-out of the concentrations of Na and K in directly reportable units.

Electrochemical Methods. The prime candidates for electrochemical automated methods are blood analyzers which measure pH, P_{CO_2}, and P_{O_2}. These are, by the nature of the data, "stat" instruments frequently employed in emergencies. (The term "stat" is applied to a test demanding immediate measurement and expeditious reporting of the result to the attending physician.) The pH is measured potentiometrically by means of the conventional glass electrode, P_{CO_2} is measured with a pH electrode covered with a plastic membrane that is permeable to CO_2, and P_{O_2} is measured amperometrically with a polarographic oxygen electrode (Pt wire covered with an O_2-permeable membrane). Blood gas determinations have depended heavily on the skill of the analyst, which held back the growth in demand. However, as instrumentation improved in the early part of this decade, the test volume grew accordingly. By 1974, the degree of automation of blood gas analyzers rivaled that of other automatic clinical analyzers.

Electrochemical analyzers based on the amperometric measurement of oxygen are used to measure the rate of oxidase enzyme reactions. For example, the substrate glucose is determined by measuring the rate of oxygen consumption in the presence of glucose oxidase. Results are obtained in less than a minute. Similarly, urea is determined enzymatically by measuring the rate of conductance change during urea hydrolysis in the presence of urease.

Radiochemical Methods. Radiochemical techniques are relatively new in the clinical chemistry laboratory; they are now being applied to radioimmunoassays and to determinations involving competitive protein binding, both sometimes called radio-receptor assays. Consequently, the range of automation is limited at this writing to taking radiation counts on a large number of samples—several hundred—with a sequential printout of the counts produced by each sample in a fixed length of time or of the time needed to accumulate a preset number of counts. These tests are labor intensive; new products introduced in 1975, however, are now increasing the level of automation.

Selected Automatic and Automated Clinical Chemistry Analyzers

This section will review selected examples in each of the categories of automation discussed above.

Multi-channel Analyzers. The first widely adopted multi-channel system was the SMA 12/60® (*s*equential *m*ultiple *a*nalyzer) introduced by Technicon in 1967. Built on the continuous-flow principle, it is similar in operation to the single-channel analyzer shown in Figure 24.12, but with the sample split into 12 channels. This generates 12 results sequentially on each sample at the rate of 60 samples, calibrators, and controls per hour. The 12/60 helped to establish the role of the screening battery or "profile" in diagnostic medicine.

The next generation of this product is the computer-controlled Technicon SMAC® which became available in 1974. This has 20 channels and generates results on 150 samples, calibrators, and controls per hour. The operator interacts with the system through a keyboard and an oscilloscope display. The effective rate on actual samples averages 90–100 samples per hour, after taking into account calibrators, controls, and samples that must be rerun because of out-of-range or questionable results. The rate of about 2000 diagnostically significant results per hour from the 20 channels is achieved only after following a start-up protocol taking about 90 min. Two operators are required for the care, feeding and operation of the system.

SMAC offers significant advances over its predecessors besides productivity. Less sample is consumed (about 700 μl), as well as smaller reagent volumes. The system utilizes more modern chemical methods, including kinetic assays and ion-selective electrodes for Na and K. Although the nature of continuous-flow systems precludes the selection of particular channels for a given sample, the computer system can suppress unwanted results and can automatically print out any unrequested test result that is out of the normal range.

Other multi-channel analyzers on the market are discrete sampling systems that feature test selection for each sample. The earlier generation Hycel Mark X and Mark 17 does this with a push-button panel, whereas a dedicated computer does it on the Ortho AcuChem Microanalyzer ("Basic") and the Coulter Chemistry System. All of these systems offer various combinations and degrees of the features discussed above, with 10–18 channels and nominal production rates of 40–60 samples per hour. The Hycel M, shown for the first time in 1975, displays the next step forward in flexibility and productivity because of the computer-based design.

An entirely different multi-channel analyzer, designed for a different application, is the DuPont Automatic Clinical Analyzer (ACA). This is pointed toward generating good answers whether or not the operator is highly skilled. It is well suited for automating the off-hours stat-testing in larger hospitals and for providing a wide selection of assays for smaller laboratories. Without such a system, the small laboratories would find it difficult to maintain personnel skilled in such a wide selection of assays.

The operator of the ACA loads the sample into a well in a rigid header that fits on a track. Hanging from this header is a form on which the operator may enter sample and patient ID information that is reproduced automatically with the test results. Then the operator loads a reagent pack for each test requested on that sample, placing each on the track just in front of the sample header. After separate aliquots of the sample are automatically dispensed into these packs, each enters the main body of the instrument, where the pack also serves as a purification column, as a mixing and reaction chamber, and finally as the test cuvette in the filter photometer. The operator need only prepare and dispense the serum, record ID data, and select the appropriate reagent packs. The expense of skilled labor is traded off for slow speed and the cost of reagent packs. The testing rate averages about one result every 55 sec.

Batch Analyzers. The American Monitor Programachem® 1040 does one test at a time on up to 89 samples at up to 15 results per minute. A prepunched program card automatically sets virtually all of the system variables for each method on insertion into the instrument card-reader. A second-generation instrument, the KDA, was shown in 1975. This provides an integrated system from request slip to report form, with a design heavily dependent on the dedicated minicomputer. Another feature offered is "graphics," which allows an oscilloscopic display of calibration curves, kinetic reaction-curves, quality-control points, etc.

On a much smaller scale, the Gilford 3500 is a computer-directed analyzer. For a given test, the operator must manually set the spectrophotometer wavelength and zero, as well as install the required reagents and set the required aspiration and dispensing volumes and locations. A magnetic program-card operates the system, including a dialogue on the printer, which guides the operator through the required setup and reminds him to key in the values of standards. The printed record includes all key operating data, results in reportable units, and flags where appropriate.

Parallel-Fast Analyzers. There are three commercial versions of centrifugal analyzers, which differ in such details as: (1) the number of samples accommodated on the rotor (15–30); (2) the means of setting variables for a run (manual or preprogrammed on paper tape or tape cassette); (3) the automating of such steps as the wash at the end of a run; and (4) the degree of sophistication in data generation, result listing, automatic evaluation of reaction linearity, flagging, collation of results from several runs, and so on.

In these analyzers, only one determination can be made for each sample during a given run. However, determinations are made in a matter of seconds after samples and reagents are loaded, and only microliter quantities of sample and reagents are required for each determination. Procedures can be changed simply by changing the reagents in the rotor and changing the wavelength setting.

Dedicated Analyzers. A wide choice of such systems, with varying degrees of automation, are available for clinical applications. One of the most prevalent is an atomic-emission spectrometer that generates both Na and K concentrations simultaneously on separate readouts a matter of seconds after a sample is aspirated. Automatic dilutors are commonly built in. Auto samplers and printers are generally available as optional attachments. Some of these systems are readily converted to Li assays when needed.

Beckman makes electrochemically based semiautomatic Glucose and Blood Urea Nitrogen (BUN) Analyzers. They "walk the operator" through the manually initiated steps required. The same company makes a combination Glucose/BUN Analyzer, the System I, which is more highly automated.

Another type of widely used dedicated system is the blood-gas analyzer. These are electrochemical instruments that measure pH, P_{CO_2} and P_{O_2} in whole blood, either simultaneously or sequentially. The recent, more automatic systems operate completely "hands off" after the sample is aspirated. Because the measurements are generally made under stat circumstances, these newer systems periodically recalibrate themselves while on "standby," so that a sample can be run as soon as it arrives in the laboratory.

The growing impact of ion-selective electrodes is evident in the proliferation of dedicated analyzers dependent on ISEs. For example, Technicon markets a Photovolt instrument, the Stat/Ion, which measures Na, K, Cl, and optionally CO_2; and Orion has offered an ionized-calcium analyzer and introduced a sodium/potassium analyzer, all using ion-selective electrodes.

SELECTED BIBLIOGRAPHY

Books

CLEVETT, K. J. *Handbook of Process Stream Analysis.* New York: Halsted Press, 1973. *An up-to-date handbook which describes many types of process analyzers.*

HOUSER, E. A. *Principles of Sample Handling and Sample Systems Design for Process Analysis.* Pittsburgh: Instrument Society of America, 1972. *Contains good information on the design of sample-handling systems.*

SHINSKEY, F. G. *pH and pIon Control in Process and Waste Streams.* New York: John Wiley and Sons, 1973. *Provides an excellent description of the application of potentiometry in process control.*

SHINSKEY, F. G. *Process Control Systems.* New York: McGraw-Hill, Inc., 1967. *All aspects of process control are covered.*

SMITH, D. E., and ZIMMERLI, F. H. *Electrochemical Methods of Process Analysis.* Pittsburgh: Instrument Society of America, 1972. *A good compilation of the electrochemical instrumentation available for use in industrial applications.*

Clinical Chemistry

ALPERT, N. L. *Clinical Instrument Reports.* Philadelphia: North American, 1975.

HICKS, R.; SCHENKIN, J. R.; and STEINRAUF, M. *Laboratory Instrumentation.* New York: Harper and Row, 1974.

LEE, L. W. *Elementary Principles of Laboratory Instruments*, 3rd ed. St. Louis, Mo.: C. V. Mosby, 1974.

WHITE, W. L.; ERICKSON, M. M.; and STEVENS, S. C. *Practical Automation for the Clinical Laboratory*, 2nd ed. St. Louis, Mo.: C. V. Mosby, 1972.

Articles

BOWERS, G. N., Jr. "Analytical Problems in Biomedical Research and Clinical Chemistry," in W. W. Meinke and J. K. Taylor, eds., *Analytical Chemistry: Key to Progress in National Problems*, chap. 3, National Bureau of Standards Special Publication 351. Washington, D.C.: U.S. Government Printing Office, 1972.

HOLLOWELL, C. D. and McLAUGHLIN, R. D.

"Instrumentation for Air Pollution Monitoring," *Environ. Sci. Tech.*, 7, 1011 (1973).

LIGHT, T. S. "Industrial Analysis and Control with Ion Selective Electrodes," in R. A. Durst, ed., *Ion Selective Electrodes*, chap. 10, National Bureau of Standards Special Publication 314. Washington, D.C.: U.S Government Printing Office, 1969.

Process Measurement and Control Terminology, SAMA Standard PMC20-2-1970, Scientific Apparatus Makers Association, 370 Lexington Ave., New York, New York, Pub. No. 219.

SOULE, L. M. "Basic Concepts of Industrial Process Control," *Chem. Eng.* Sept. 22, 1969.

SOULE, L. M. "Basic Control Modes," *Chem. Eng.*, Oct. 20, 1969.

REFERENCES

1. IUPAC Information Bulletin No. 26, International Union of Pure and Applied Chemistry, Oxford, England.

2. R. G. BATES, *Determination of pH: Theory and Practice*, New York: John Wiley and Sons, 1964, pp 382–83.

3. SAMA Standard PMC-20-1-1973, Scientific Apparatus Makers Association, 370 Lexington Ave., New York, N.Y.

4. F. G. SHINSKEY, *Process Control Systems*, New York: McGraw-Hill, 1967, chap. 1.

5. R. J. REYNOLDS and E. L. PIERSON, *Amer. Lab.*, 3(8), 27 (1971).

6. R. ANNINO, *J. Chromatogr. Sci.*, 8, 288 (1970).

7. R. ANNINO and L. E. BULLOCK, *Anal. Chem.*, 45, 1221 (1973).

8. R. VILLALOBOS, *Anal. Chem.*, 47(11), 983A (1975).

9. R. A. DURST, *Amer. Sci.*, 59, 353 (1971).

APPENDIX A

Units, Symbols, and Prefixes

Units in the text correspond to those in common usage. Many are gradually being replaced by the Système International (SI) or International System of Units. These recommended units, their symbols, and prefixes indicating multiples and fractions of units, are listed here.

SI Units

Quantity	Name	Symbol
Length	meter	m
Mass	kilogram	kg
Time	second	s
Electric Current	ampere	A
Thermodynamic Temperature	kelvin	K
Luminous Intensity	candela	cd
Amount of Substance	mole	mol
Plane Angle	radian	rad
Solid Angle	steradian	sr

Other Units in Use with SI

Quantity	Name	Symbol	Value in SI Unit
Time	minute	min	$1 \text{ min} = 60 \text{ s}$
	hour	h	$1 \text{ h} = 3600 \text{ s}$
	day	d	$1 \text{ d} = 86{,}400 \text{ s}$
Volume	liter	L	$1 \text{ L} = 1 \text{ dm}^3 = 10^{-3} \text{ m}^3$

SI Derived Units

Quantity	Name	Symbol	Units	Special Multiples
Frequency	hertz	Hz	s^{-1}	——
Force	newton	N	$kg \cdot m \cdot s^{-2}$	10^{-5} N = 1 dyne (dyn)
Pressure [a]	pascal	Pa	$kg \cdot m^{-1} \cdot s^{-2} =$ $N \cdot m^{-2}$	10^5 Pa = 1 bar
Power, Radiant Flux	watt	W	$kg \cdot m^2 \cdot s^{-3} = J \cdot s^{-1}$	——
Electric Charge, Quantity of Electricity	coulomb	C	$A \cdot s$	——
Electric Potential, Potential Difference, Electromotive Force	volt	V	$kg \cdot m^2 \cdot s^{-3} \cdot A^{-1}$	——
Electric Resistance	ohm	Ω	$kg \cdot m^2 \cdot s^{-3} \cdot A^{-2}$	——
Electrical Capacitance	farad	F	$A^2 \cdot s^4 \cdot kg^{-1} \cdot m^{-2}$	——
Conductance	siemens	S	$kg^{-1} \cdot m^{-2} \cdot s^3 \cdot A^2 =$ Ω^{-1}	——
Energy, Work, Quantity of Heat [b]	joule	J	$kg \cdot m^2 \cdot s^{-2} = V \cdot C$	10^{-7} J = 1 erg
Magnetic Flux	weber	Wb	$kg \cdot m^2 \cdot s^{-2} \cdot A^{-1}$	10^{-8} Wb = 1 maxwell (Mx)
Inductance	henry	H	$kg \cdot m^2 \cdot s^{-2} \cdot A^{-2}$	——
Magnetic Flux Density	tesla	T	$kg \cdot s^{-2} \cdot A^{-1}$	10^{-4} T = 1 gauss (G)
Luminous Flux	lumen	lm	$cd \cdot sr$	——
Illumination	lux	lx	$cd \cdot sr \cdot m^{-2}$	——

a. 101,325 Pa = 1 atmosphere (atm) = 760 millimeters of mercury (mm Hg)
   133.322 Pa = 1 torr = 1 millimeter of mercury (mm Hg)
b. 3.6×10^6 J = 1 kilowatt-hour (kWh)
   1055.056 J = 1 British thermal unit (BTU)
   4.184 J = 1 thermochemical calorie (cal_{th})

Prefixes Indicating Multiples and Fractions of Units

Multiple	Prefix	Symbol	Fraction	Prefix	Symbol
10^{18}	exa	E	10^{-1}	deci	d
10^{15}	peta	P	10^{-2}	centi	c
10^{12}	tera	T	10^{-3}	milli	m
10^9	giga	G	10^{-6}	micro	μ
10^6	mega	M	10^{-9}	nano	n
10^3	kilo	k	10^{-12}	pico	p
10^2	hecto	h	10^{-15}	femto	f
10	deka	da	10^{-18}	atto	a
			10^{-21}	flato	ϕ

APPENDIX B

Selected Fundamental Physical Constants

Numbers in parentheses refer to standard-deviation uncertainties in the last digit, computed on the basis of internal consistency.

Quantity	Symbol	Value	Error (ppm)	Decimal and Units SI	Decimal and Units cgs
Velocity of Light	c	2.9979250(10)	0.33	10^8 m·s^{-1}	10^{10} cm·s^{-1}
Electron Charge	e	1.6021917(70)	4.4	10^{-19} C	10^{-20} emu
		4.803250(21)	4.4	——	10^{-10} esu
Planck's Constant	h	6.626196(50)	7.6	10^{-34} J·s	10^{-27} erg·s
	$\hbar = \dfrac{h}{2\pi}$	1.0545919(80)	7.6	10^{-34} J·s	10^{-27} erg·s
Electron Volt	eV	1.60210	——	10^{-19} J	10^{-12} erg
		3.827	——	——	10^{-20} cal
Avogadro's Number	N	6.022169(40)	6.6	10^{26} kmol^{-1}	10^{23} mol^{-1}
Atomic Mass Unit	amu	1.660531(11)	6.6	10^{-27} kg	10^{-24} g
Proton Mass	M_p	1.672614(11)	6.6	10^{-27} kg	10^{-24} g
	M_p^*	1.00727661(8)	0.08	amu	amu
Electron Mass	m_e	9.109558(54)	6.0	10^{-31} kg	10^{-28} g
	m_e^*	5.485930(34)	6.2	10^{-4} amu	10^{-4} amu
Neutron Mass	M_n	1.674920(11)	6.6	10^{-27} kg	10^{-24} kg
	M_n^*	1.00866520(10)	0.10	amu	amu
Faraday Constant	F	9.648670(54)	5.5	10^7 C·kmol^{-1}	10^3 esu·mol^{-1}
		2.892599(16)	5.5	——	10^{14} esu·mol^{-1}
Gas Constant	R	1.9872	——		cal·K^{-1}·mol^{-1}
		8.3143	——	J·K^{-1}·mol^{-1}	10^7 erg·K^{-1}·mol^{-1}
		8.2054	——		10^{-2} l·atm·K^{-1}·mol^{-1}
Rydberg Constant	R_∞	1.09737312(11)	0.10	10^7 m^{-1}	10^5 cm^{-1}
Bohr Magneton	μ_B	9.274096(65)	7.0	10^{-24} J·T^{-1}	10^{-21} erg·G^{-1}
Boltzmann Constant	k	1.380622(59)	43	10^{-23} J·K^{-1}	10^{-16} erg·K^{-1}
Stefan-Boltzmann Constant	σ	5.66961(96)	170	10^{-8} W·m^{-2}·K^{-4}	10^{-5} erg·s^{-1}·cm^{-2}·K^{-4}

Source: Adapted in part from "Reference Guide to Optical Energy Measurements," Princeton Applied Research Corp., 1974, by permission of the publisher.

APPENDIX C

Answers to Selected Problems

Chapter 2

1. $\Delta a_1/a_1 = 3.89\%$ per mV uncertainty

3. (a) 0.03 M; (b) 0.05 M; (c) 0.3 M; (d) 0.006 M

4. (a) $f_{Mg^{2+}} = 0.70, f_{Cl^-} = 0.91$; (b) $f_{Mg^{2+}} = 0.56, f_{K^+} = f_{Cl^-} = 0.86$; (c) $f_{Mg^{2+}} = 0.22, f_{K^+} = f_{Cl^-} = 0.69$

5. (a) pH = 4.41, (b) pH = 10.70

6. $+0.622$ V versus SHE, $+0.377$ V versus SCE

7. -0.951 V

8. 160.0 g/eq

10. 7.5% Hint: Change ppm to the corresponding *molar* units.

11. $3 \times 10^{-7}, 1.2 \times 10^{-6}, 1.6 \times 10^{-6}, 7 \times 10^{-5}$, and 3.3×10^{-4} M; for a 10% interference level, the concentrations can be an order of magnitude higher.

12. 0.08%

13. 0.68 μgI/ml

14. $10^{\Delta E/S} = 10^{nF(E_2 - E_1)/2.303RT} = k_{1j}\left(\dfrac{a_1}{a_1}\right) + 1$

15. $k_{1j} = k_{I^-, Br^-} = 0.0015$; liquid junction potentials are constant—that is, $E_{constant}$ is constant—and $a_{Br^-}/a_{I^-} = c_{Br^-}/c_{I^-}$

16. The average of the two volumes used for ΔE (first derivative plot) or $\Delta^2 E$ (second derivative plot) is graphed on the volume axis, resulting in an estimation of 47.95 ml at the first-derivative endpoint, and 47.935 ml at the second-derivative endpoint.

17. k_{1j} for $Zn^{2+} = 50$, for $Pb^{2+} = 20$, for $Mg^{2+} = 0.01$, for $H^+ = 1000$, for $Na^+ = 0.003$, for $K^+ = 0.001$.

Chapter 3

8. (a) 3.58 (b) 8.7×10^{-6} cm^2/sec

9. 3.3 mm^2

10. 0.156 mM; 5.0 ppm

11. 2×10^{-5} M

12. 102 min

13. (a) $n = 2$ (b) See problem 12. Electrolyze for a known (long!) time and monitor the decrease in concentration. Using special cells that contain solution volumes as small as 1 ml or less, such experiments have been carried out in conveniently short times.

14. (a) L-shaped: $Ag \rightarrow Ag^+ + e^-$ (anode) and $Ag^+ + e^- \rightarrow Ag$ (cathode) prior to endpoint; no reactions after endpoint.
    (b) V-shaped: same reactions as above prior to endpoint; $Ag + Cl^- \rightarrow AgCl + e^-$ (anode) and $2H^+ + 2e^- \rightarrow H_2$ or $2H_2O + 2e^- \rightarrow H_2 + 2OH^-$ (cathode) after endpoint.

Chapter 4

1. $+1.632$ V versus SHE

2. 27,900 sec

3. 0.1116%

4. 96.485 mA

5. 4.6 ppm

6. 0.0537 g Cu.   Theoretical value = 0.1742 cm^3/coul

7. 3.25 μm

8. +0.202 V versus SCE

9. 7.705 mg

Chapter 5

1. 1.0×10^{-5}, 3.0×10^{-5}, 1.5×10^{-4} N

2. 890 ppm

3. (a) 25 cm^{-1}, solution resistances will vary between 73 and 86 ohm.
   (b) 100,000 micromhos (midpoint equivalent to 100 ohm).

4. 110 to 1130 ohm, or 9100 to 885 μmho

5. (a) $\Lambda = 6.73$ (b) $\alpha = 0.0176$ (c) $K_a = 6.3 \times 10^{-6}$

6. 2037 ohm

7. 0.0175 N

9. $\kappa_{AgCl} = 1.81 \times 10^{-6}$ ohm^{-1} cm^{-1}; $K_{sp,AgCl} = 1.71 \times 10^{-10}$ M^2

10. 2.4% hydrocarbon in glycol; 1.5% glycol in hydrocarbon

Chapter 7

1. 588.997 nm; 5.08960×10^{14} Hz

2. -4.9 eV, 253 nm

3. 5×10^{-10} M

4. 2.4×10^4

5. 3.7×10^{-5} M p-nitroaniline; 8.9×10^{-5} M o-nitroaniline

6. p$K_a = 6.4$

7. (a) 2.1×10^{-2} l/(g-cm)   (b) 3.16×10^4 l/(mole-cm)   (c) 0.03 mg X in 25.0 ml   (d) 1.2 ppm X

8. 0.260% Cu

9. 0.533% Mn

10. 2×10^6

11. 122

12. (a) 1:1;   (b) 2.8×10^5

13. There is probably an impurity in the "blank" which absorbs at the analytical wavelength. The impurity appears to be present at constant concentration since subtraction of the "blank" absorbance from all values results in a linear plot with zero intercept.

14. (a) 8.87 mM (b) 6.44 mM (c) 7.67

Chapter 8

1. (a) 0.7–2.5 μm; 2.5–50 μm; 50–1000 μm
   (b) 14,285–4000 cm^{-1}; 4000–200 cm^{-1}; 200–10 cm^{-1}

2. (a) 14,285 cm^{-1};   (b) 0.7 μm;   (c) 1.76 eV

3. (a) 1.76–0.49 eV;   (b) 0.49–0.02 eV;   (c) 0.02–0.001 eV

4. 2144.5 cm^{-1}; 0.265 eV; 6.11×10^3 cal/mole

5. *J. Chem. Phys.*, 47, 4325 (1967); 49, 2344 (1968); *Spectrochim. Acta*, 21, 1505 (1965).

6. $A = 0.30$

7. (a) Far infrared   (b) Medium infrared, Near infrared (overtone)

8. Medium and Far infrared

9. AgCl windows in a demountable cell; experiment with spacers

10. $\varepsilon = 40$ l/(mole-cm)

11. 2740, 4110 cm^{-1}

12. 2110, 1790 cm^{-1}

13. (a) 1190, 1680, 2060 cm^{-1};   (b) About 7.5×10^5 dyne/cm, since it is midway between a single and a double carbon-carbon bond; 1460 cm^{-1};   (c) ~ 1650 cm^{-1} for C=C; ~ 2160 cm^{-1} for C≡C; about 1470 cm^{-1} in benzene.

14.

$\bar{\nu}$	4880 Å	5145 Å	5682 Å	6471 Å
3374 cm^{-1}	5842	6226	7030	8278
3287 cm^{-1}	5812	6192	6987	8219
1974 cm^{-1}	5400	5727	6400	7419
729 cm^{-1}	5060	5345	5928	6791
612 cm^{-1}	5030	5312	5887	6738

15. $\rho = 0.75$ (depolarized), 0.074 (polarized), 0.016 (polarized), 0.78 (depolarized)

16. 4880 Å : 5145 Å : 5682 Å : 6471 Å = 3.09 : 2.50 : 1.68 : 1.00

Chapter 9

8. 84 ppm

9. 2.82; 1.83 μg/ml

10. (a) 30:1 (b) The cuvette and monochromators must transmit the same fraction of light at all wavelengths concerned.

11. In phosphorescence, an electron in an excited singlet state crosses over to a triplet state by intersystem crossing—a "forbidden transition" that occurs with some probability if the energy of the lowest vibrational level of the triplet state is lower than that of the excited singlet state. From here it can radiationally return to the singlet ground state. The emitted photon is phosphorescence, and it is of longer wavelength than a fluorescence wavelength produced by the same singlet state. Because the probability of triplet-singlet transitions is low, the lifetime of the triplet state is relatively long. Measurements are made at liquid nitrogen temperatures to minimize collisional deactivation during the relatively long lifetime of the triplet state.

Chapter 10

17. 0.34 ppm

18. 7.1 ppm

20. (a) 37.0 $\pm$ 1.0% Ba by weight (about 2.7% relative standard deviation). (b) Since the "pure" compound should be 32.12% Ba by weight, and the analytical result is about five standard deviations removed, it is highly unlikely that the preparation is 100% pure. Most probably, there is an excess of a barium salt in the crystalline compound.

21. (b) 25% added methanol, since this produces a 48% enhancement in the A/c ratio with only a 25% dilution factor. (c) $2.65 \times 10^{-5} M$; $1.78 \times 10^{-5} M$ (in the original aqueous solution) with 25% added methanol.

22. The enhancing effect of the potassium is due to the suppression of sodium ionization in the flame as potassium adds electrons to the flame. The result is a greater population of sodium atoms available for thermal excitation.

Chapter 11

6. Mg, Zn, Cu, Th, Zr, Mn, Ca, Si, Al (a Mg alloy)

7. 0.04 μg/ml

8. $\sigma = \pm 0.26$, r.s.d. = $\pm 5.8\%$

10. Fraction ionized at 2500 K is 1.24×10^{-9}; at 5000 K is 1.11×10^{-3}

11. 0.13% Si, 1.4% Na

Chapter 12

1. (a) $+0.86$ ppm (0.86 ppm downfield) (b) 293.6 Hz

2. A, e; B, f; C, c; D, d; E, b; F, a.

3. Acetone: singlet, 2.11 ppm. Methylethyl ketone: singlet, 2.05 ppm (area 3); quartet, 2.40 ppm (area 2); triplet, 0.99 ppm (area 3).

4. Propane: triplet, 0.99 ppm (area 6); multiplet, 1.29 ppm (area 2). 1-Nitropropane: triplet, 1.01 ppm (area 3); multiplet, 2.00 ppm (area 2); triplet, 4.31 ppm (area 2).

5. (a) 26,572 radians/gauss-sec (4,258 Hz/gauss) (b) 100 MHz (c) 20 MHz

7. (a) 3.55 ppm (b) 3.66 ppm (c) 438 Hz

8. Hindered rotation; therefore essentially two different environments for the methyls.

11. Benzene:toluene $\doteq$ 2:1.

12. C_3H_7Cl = 2-chloropropane; $C_7H_{16}O_3$ = $(CH_3CH_2O)_3CH$; C_7H_7ClO = 1-chloro-4-methoxybenzene; C_9H_9ClO =

$$para\text{-isomer of } CH_3CH_2\overset{\overset{\displaystyle O}{\|}}{C}\text{–}C_6H_4\text{–Cl}$$

C_9H_{10} = C_6H_5–$CH_2CH{=}CH_2$

13. $CH_2Cl(CO)CHClCH_2COOH$

14. A = $HCFCl$–$CFCl_2$
B = $HCCl_2$–CF_2Cl

Chapter 13

1. 3198, 7825, and 11908 gauss for $g = 2.100$; 3377, 8262, and 12573 gauss for $g = 1.989$

2. ΔH = 43, 105, and 160 gauss for $g_1 = 1.964$, $g_2 = 1.989$; ΔH = 11, 27, and 41 gauss for $g_1 = 2.080$, $g_2 = 2.073$

3. 0.314, 0.767, and 1.168 cm^{-1}/molecule

T (K)	$\nu = 9.4$	23 GHz	35 GHz
4	1.26×10^{-5}	1.03×10^{-12}	5.76×10^{-19}
20	1.05×10^{-1}	4.01×10^{-3}	2.25×10^{-4}
77	5.57×10^{-1}	2.38×10^{-1}	1.13×10^{-1}
298	8.60×10^{-1}	6.90×10^{-1}	5.69×10^{-1}

5. Two equivalent Fs, 2 sets of 2 equivalent Hs: 27 lines

Two equivalent Fs, 3 sets of Hs in 2:1:1 ratio: 36 lines

Two equivalent Fs, one set of 4 equivalent Hs: 15 lines

6. 5 lines

7. Twelve lines for the Cu compound; 24 lines for the V compound.

Chapter 14

11. $d_1 = 2.51$ Å, $d_2 = 2.22$ Å, $d_3 = 2.85$ Å. CuFeO$_2$ has d values of 2.51 Å, 2.23 Å, and 2.85 Å of relative intensities 100:39:25; NaCS$_3$ had d values of 2.52 Å, 2.22 Å, and 2.84 Å with relative intensities of 100:18:15. Hence, the substance appears to be CuFeO$_2$.

12. $2\theta = 34.34°$

13. $S_1 = 68.8$ mm, $S_2 = 45.2$ mm, $S_3 = 79.6$ mm

14. $\lambda = 2.287$ Å. This corresponds to the Kα line of chromium.

15. $\lambda = 0.248$ Å

16. $T = 0.633$

Chapter 15

1. O $2s$, 25 eV; Si $2p$, 100 eV; Si $2s$, 155 eV; C $1s$, 285 eV; Ag $3d$, 370 and 375 eV; O $1s$, 530 eV.

2. P $2p$, 135 eV; S $2p$, 165 eV; C $1s$, 285 eV; N $1s$, 400 eV; O $1s$, 530 eV; F $1s$, 690 eV

3. Binding energy for Fe $2p_{3/2}$ photoelectron = 714 eV in Fe$_2$O$_3$; 717 eV in FeF$_2$; 710 eV in Fe. From Table 15.1, the "nominal" $2p_{3/2}$ binding energies for Mn, Fe, and Co are 641, 710, and 779 eV, respectively.

4. See C. A. Evans, Jr., *Anal. Chem.*, *47*(9), 819A, 855A (1975).

5. (a and b) In a close-packed arrangement, one silver atom would occupy *about* 7.4×10^{-16} cm^2 of the surface area of a (flat) silicon substrate. For 0.001 monolayer, this would correspond to about 1.1×10^{10} atoms or 1.9×10^{-12} g of Ag. (c) 1.2×10^{-3} g/cm^3; 520 ppm

6. (a) 1153 eV (b) 920 eV

7. C $1s$ in CH$_4$, CO, and CO$_2$; O $1s$ in CO$_2$, CO.

8. The peaks are probably due to aluminum $2p$ photoelectrons: the peak at lower binding energy to Al^0, that at higher energy to Al^{3+}. Aluminum metal is known to quickly form a thin protective skin of Al$_2$O$_3$. Even the short exposure to air after abrasion allowed some Al$_2$O$_3$ to form; a full week's exposure allowed a thicker skin to form, although the oxide skin must still be less than about 15 Å thick, as photoelectrons from the underlying Al^0 are still seen.

9. 83%, 68%, 30% MoO$_2$

Chapter 16

1. $H = 1052$ gauss, $r = 29.05$ cm

2. $H = 2975$ gauss, $r = 29.88$ cm

3. Voltage should be reduced to 1765 V to just observe $m/e = 850$ at highest magnetic field.

4. Chamber: $+1765$ V; exit slit: ground; repellers: 1775 V; filament: 1715 V; target: 1845 V

5. Exact mass $= 220.1679$; formula $= $ C$_{11}$H$_{22}$O$_4$

6. CO$^+$/C$_2$H$_4$$^+$: $R = 770$; C$_{20}$H$_{40}$$^+$/C$_{19}H_{36}$$^+$: $R = 7700$

7. C$_2$H$_2$$^+$: 6.70×10^{-6} sec; C$_6H_5$$^+$: 1.15×10^{-5} sec; C$_6H_6$$^+$: 1.16×10^{-5} sec

8. 3.1×10^{-3} sec

9. 153 kHz

10. C$_6$H$_6$: 6.6%, 0.22%; C$_2$H$_4$O$_2$: 2.2%, 0.41%; C$_2$H$_8$N$_2$: 2.9%, 0.02%; C$_3$H$_7$Cl: 3.3%, 33%, 1.09%; C$_4$H$_4$S: 5.2%, 4.5%; C$_{16}$H$_{34}$: 17.6%, 1.5%

12. % d_3 = 90; % d_2 = 6; % d_1 = 4

13. Chlorobenzene

14. *sec*-Butylamine

15. Perbromic acid (HBrO$_4$)

16. #1: 3-methyl-2-pentanone; #2: 2-methyl-3-pentanone

17. Propylphenyl ether

18. $R = \dfrac{M}{\Delta M} = \dfrac{32}{2(15.994914) - 31.972074}$
$= 1800$

19. Mother ion = CH$_3$O$^+$ (m = 31); daughter ion = CHO$^+$ (m = 29)

20. (A) (a) C$_2$H$_5$O$^+$ → H$_3$O$^+$ + C$_2$H$_2$, m^* = 8.02
(b) C$_2$H$_5$O$^+$ → CHO$^+$ + CH$_4$, m^* = 18.69
(B) H$_3$COCH$_2$Y, since a rearrangement is necessary to facilitate elimination of C$_2$H$_2$.

21. m/e = 114: molecular (parent) ion
m/e = 99: 114–15 (loss of CH$_3$)
m/e = 71: 114–43 (loss of propyl)
m/e = 57: C$_4$H$_9$$^+$ (*t*-butyl ion)
m/e = 43: C$_3$H$_7$$^+$ (*i*-propyl ion)
2,2,4-trimethylpentane spectrum is in column (a)

22. *t*-butyl amine; C$_4$H$_{11}$N

23. Since m/e for P is an even number, there must be 0 or an even number of nitrogens (eliminating C$_4$H$_8$NO and C$_5$H$_{12}$N). Among the remaining, C$_5$H$_{10}$O gives the best correspondence.

24. Order of appearance = CO, N$_2$, C$_2$H$_4$; the order of increasing exact nuclidic masses.

Chapter 17

5. 2

6. CaC$_2$O$_4 \cdot$H$_2$O $\xrightarrow{100-250°}$
CaC$_2$O$_4$ + H$_2$O   (− 6.2 mg)

CaC$_2$O$_4$ $\xrightarrow{360-500°}$
CaCO$_3$ + CO   (− 9.6 mg)

CaCO$_3$ $\xrightarrow{620-860°}$
CaO + CO$_2$ (− 15.0 mg)

BaC$_2$O$_4 \cdot$H$_2$O $\xrightarrow{100-250°}$
BaC$_2$O$_4$ + H$_2$O   (− 3.7 mg)

BaC$_2$O$_4$ $\xrightarrow{360-500°}$
BaCO$_3$ + CO   (− 5.7 mg)

BaCO$_3$ $\xrightarrow{\sim1000°}$ BaO + CO$_2$ (− 9.0 mg)

8. From the *Merck Index*, 1952:
(1) Endotherm at ~133°C melting of urea, (2) Endo- or exotherm at ~150°C formation of biuret, (3) Endo- or exotherm at ~150°C formation of cyanuric acid, (4) Endotherm at ~190°C melting of biuret

9. Let R be the minimum rate of reaction observable via DTA or TG. Then $R = k_f$[Reactants]^x − k_r[Products]^y. Also, consider the Arrhenius equation $R = Ae^{-E_a/RT}$ which predicts a two-fold increase in rate for each 10°C rise in temperature.
(a) If product is present, $R' < R$ from the rate expression above, and temperature must be increased to get back to R.
(b) If reactant is present, the second term is zero and $R'' > R$. To decrease R'' to R, the temperature must be decreased.
(c) Since $R = k$[Reactants]$^x = Ae^{-E_a/RT}$ then x ln[Reactants] = $-E_a/RT$ + ln A
A plot of ln[Reactants] versus $-1/T$ will yield x, the kinetic coefficient, which is often (but not always) the same as the stoichiometric coefficient.

13. Area = 79.8 cm^2.

14. C_p = 151.8 cal/°C; R_H = 15.20 ohms. Since heater leads and heater contribute to R_H and V_H, the V_H will be too high and the C_p will be too high.

16. ΔH_{ion} = + 3.2 kcal/mole

17. K$_{stab}$ = 4.99 × 10^3; ΔG = −5.1 × 10^3, ΔH = −10.0 kcal; ΔS = − 16 cal/(mol-°C)

20. Assume C_p = 50.0 cal/°C (solution close to pure H$_2$O). ΔT_{TRISH^+} = 0.019°C; ΔT_{TRIS} = 0.115°C.

21. This appears to be a simple solid-state phase transition, and may be related to a structural change in the compound.

22. By comparing the weights obtained at 400° and 700°C, the amount of NO$_3$ lost by AgNO$_3$ is found. Therefore, the weight of Ag may be calculated. Since only Ag and CuO are present at 700°, the amount of CuO is easily found by difference. Hence, the weights of residual Ag and Cu above 950° can be calculated.

Chapter 18

1. (a) A plot of $\log(c_{t=\infty} - c_t)$ versus time is a straight line. (b) From slope, $k = 6.67 \times 10^{-5}$ sec^{-1}. From the 2nd, 4th, and 6th points, $k = 6.62$, 6.71, and 6.65×10^{-5} sec^{-1}. (c) $k_2 = 2.65 \times 10^3$ l/(mole-sec).

2. A plot of $1/c_a$ versus t is a straight line of slope k and intercept $1/c_a°$; $k = 0.196$ l/(mole-sec).

3. Azomethane = 128 torr; N_2 and C_2H_6 = 72 torr each.

4. $k = 9.29 \times 10^{-6}$ sec^{-1} at both 0.44 M and 0.167 M sucrose.

5. First order, $k = 2.60 \times 10^{-5}$ sec^{-1}; $t_{90\%} = 24.5$ hour, $t_{99\%} = 49.2$ hour.

6. Second order, 3.27×10^{-2} l/(mole-sec)

7. 7.94×10^{-6} sec^{-1}; $t_{1/2} = 24.3$ hr

8. 4.1

Chapter 19

1. 286 ppm Al

2. (a) The 5.62-MeV peak is due to the pair production interaction of the primary 6.13-MeV gamma ray with the crystal and the loss of *one* 0.511 position annihilation photon from the crystal without interaction. This is the "1st escape peak." (b) The 5.11-MeV peak is due to loss of *both* 0.511-MeV annihilation photons resulting from a pair production event in the crystal. This is the "2nd escape peak." (c) The 0.511-MeV peak is due to pair production interaction of the 6.13 MeV primary gamma ray in the *surroundings and shielding* of the detector. The 0.511-MeV position annihilation photons generated in the surrounding materials then intersect the crystal, yielding the observed 0.511-MeV peak.

3. 0.926 g Mn/g Fe

4. 0.8 ppm I$^-$

5. $N_0 = 2.60 \times 10^5$

7. Possible reactions:
(a) $^{64}_{28}$Ni (n, γ) $^{65}_{28}$Ni

$^{65}_{28}$Ni $\xrightarrow{\text{2.55 hr}}$

β^- and γ (1.48 MeV, etc.)

(b) $^{58}_{28}$Ni (n, γ) $^{59}_{28}$Ni

$^{59}_{28}$Ni $\xrightarrow[8 \times 10^4 \text{ years}]{\text{EC}}$ $^{59}_{27}$Co

(c) $^{62}_{28}$Ni (n, γ) $^{63}_{28}$Ni

$^{63}_{28}$Ni $\xrightarrow{\text{92 years}}$ β^- (no γ)

(d) $^{58}_{28}$Ni (n, p) $^{58}_{27}$Co

$^{58}_{27}$Co $\xrightarrow{\text{71.4 days}}$ β^+ and several γs

8. 31.4% Co

9. Net Rate = 1400 ± 50 counts/min

10. Ratio $A/B = 0.41 \pm 0.03$

11. 1.9×10^4 years

12. (a) 3.70×10^{10} atoms   (b) 1600 years

13. (a) 1.00 microcurie   (b) 2.10×10^{-6} sec^{-1} (c) 1.76×10^{10} atoms   (d) 6.49×10^{-12} g

14. 725 curies

15. 1.77 disintegrations per second

16. one half-life

17. Average lifetime of an atom = Σ (individual atomic lifetimes)/(total number of atoms) = 1.443 H.

Chapter 21

1. (a) $R_f = 1/(1 + k')$ (b) $k' = 2.3$ (c) Yes, $\Delta R_f = 0.03$

2. (a) k' for *o*-, *m*-, and *p*-nitroaniline = 1, 2, and 3.5 respectively.
(b) α for *m*- and *p*-nitroaniline = 2.0, 3.5

3. (a) R_f for 3'- and 2'-GMP = 0.50 and 0.58.
(b) $\alpha = 1.4$

4. (a) 53,000   (b) Yes, $R = 2.7$

5. (b) Molecular weight = 3.2×10^3
(c) about 1000

6. (a) 27.6 mg   (b) 3.8 mg   (c) 360 cm

7. (a) $t_r = NH(1 + k')/v$ (b) $t_r = 50$ min

8. (a) $L_2 = 26.7$, $L_1 = 26.7$ m; pressure drop = 267 atm   (b) $t_{r_2} = t_{r_1}/0.004 = 7500$ min
(c) $d_{p_2} = 8$ μm, pressure drop = 250 atm. Option (c) is best.

Chapter 22

3. (a) $I = 776$ (b) Only that *n*-butylacetate behaves in this system as if it were a hydrocarbon of 7.75 carbon-number. Structural information is better derived from the index increment ΔI ($I_{\text{polar}} - I_{\text{nonpolar}}$).

7. Toluene, 724; cyclohexane, 690.

8. (a) 1770, 2810, 3840, 4880 mm Hg (b) $j =$ 0.558, 0.374, 0.280, 0.223

9. 29.6, 50.0, 64.6 ml/min

10. (a) $V'_r = 59.6, 226.8, 606.9$ ml (b) $V_n =$ 16.7, 63.5, 170.0 ml (c) $V_g = 10.7, 40.9,$ 109.5 ml (d) 8.7, 9.2

12. (a) 4500 (b) 6300 (c) 9800 (d) 39000 (e) 4400 (f) 0.9, 1.3, 98, and 390 m

Chapter 23

1. (a) 101 (b) 110100 (c) 110000011 (d) 10100110011100

2. (a) 13 (b) 69 (c) 170 (d) 1057

3. (a) 5 (b) 64 (c) 603 (d) 24634

4. (a) 101 (b) 101010 (c) 11000111 (d) 1000110101010

5. (a) 7 (b) 154 (c) 2566 (d) 1005

6. (a) 30 (b) 426 (c) 8863 (d) 1099039

7.

9.

A	B	C	$X = A \cdot B + C$
0	0	0	0
0	0	1	1
0	1	0	0
0	1	1	1
1	0	0	0
1	0	1	1
1	1	0	1
1	1	1	1

10.

A	B	C	$X = A \cdot \bar{B} \cdot \bar{C}$
0	0	0	0
0	0	1	0
0	1	0	0
0	1	1	0
1	0	0	1
1	0	1	0
1	1	0	0
1	1	1	0

11. 8-bit: 20, 40, 40, 80 mV. 10-bit: 5, 10, 10, 20 mV. 12-bit: 1, 2, 2, 5 mV.

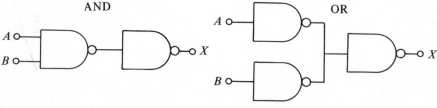

AND   OR

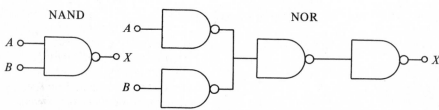

NAND   NOR

8.

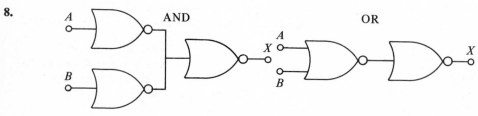

AND   OR

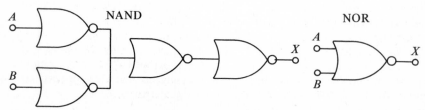

NAND   NOR

Index

AB quartet in NMR, 342
Absolute activity, 562
Absolute potential, 14
Absorption cells, long path, 194
Absorption coefficient, 262
Absorption edge, 388
Absorptivity, 158, 169
AC arc, 302
ACA. *See* Automatic Clinical Analyzer
Accumulators, 713
Accuracy, 768
Acetylsalicylic acid, fluorometric determination
    of, 244, 248, 249
Acid-base titrations, by conductance, 121
Acid error, 26
Acids, volatile derivatives for mass
    spectrometry, 446
Activation analysis, 529. *See also* Neutron
    activation analysis
Activation energies, determination of by DTA,
    504
Activation overpotential, 95
Activation polarization, 7
Activity coefficient, calculation of, 16
  effect on electrode potential, 16
Activity of radionuclides, 562
ADC. *See* Analog-to-digital converters
Adsorption chromatography. *See* Liquid-solid
    chromatography
Adsorption currents, 55, 57
Affinity chromatography, 674
Alcohols, separation of by ion-exchange
    chromatography, 667

Alkali metals, flames for, 273
Alkaline error, 26
Alkenes, separation of by gas chromatography,
    684
Allylic coupling, 350
Alpha decay, 568
Alpha particles, 561
  detection of, 570, 572
  for x-ray generation, 408
  interaction of with matter, 568
  range of in matter, 568
Aluminum, fluorometric determination of, 246
Amino acids, separation of by gas
    chromatography, 684
  separation of by ion-exchange
    chromatography, 668
  separation of by zone electrophoresis, 673
Ammonia in water, potentiometric
    determination of, 40
Amperometric titration, with one polarized
    electrode, 85
  with two polarized electrodes, 87
Amphetamine, determination of by GC, 705
  fluorometric determination of, 243
Amphiprotic solvents, 43
amu. *See* Atomic mass units
Analog multiplexer, 748, 763
Analog sampling, 754
Analog switches, 749
Analog-to-digital converters, 750
  criteria for, 752
Analyzing crystals, properties of, 392
AND gates, 722

811

Curve resolvers, 195
Cyanogen bands, 305
Czerny-Turner spectrometer, 299

DAC, 744
Data acquisition, principles of, 757
    program-controlled, 757
    sampling frequency in, 763
    timing and synchronization in, 759
Data latch, 733
Dating, by carbon-14, 603
    by mass spectrometry, 474
    by radioactivity, 562
DC Arc, 302
    plasma-jet, 303
    precision of, 317
    temperature of, 305
De Morgan's theorem, 724
Dead band, 768
Dead-stop titration, 88
Dead-time, 771
    of detectors, 572
Dead volume. *See* Void volume
Debye-Hückel Limiting Law, 16
Decade counter, 739
Decay constant. *See* Nuclear decay constant
Decimal-to-binary conversion, 717
Dedicated analyzers in clinical chemistry, 799
Dedicated instruments, 793
Degenerate, 341
Deionized water, preparation of, 675
Delves microcup, 287
Depolarization ratio, 204
Depolarized electrode, 6
Depolarizer, 6, 96
Derivative-action time, 778
Derivative rate methods, 533, 536
Derivative spectrophotometers, 187
Desalting of proteins, 674
Detectors, UV-visible, 186
Deuterium lamp, 185
Diatomite supports, properties of, 691
DIE. *See* Direct-injection enthalpimetry
Dielectric constants, table of, 136
Differential reaction rate methods, 540, 541
Differential scanning calorimetry, 487, 505
    advantage of, 506
    application of, 509
    calculations in, 509
    experimental considerations in, 508
    heating rates in, 507

instrumentation for, 506
    sample size in, 507
    sensitivity of, 507
Differential spectrometry, infrared, 223
Differential spectrophotometry, 196
Differential thermal analysis, 487, 496
    applications of, 505
    calculations in, 503
    diluents for, 502
    experimental considerations in, 499
    instrumentation for, 496
    peak-area measurement in, 504
    peak areas in, 501
    processes observed by, 498
    reference materials for, 502
    theory of, 499
    variables of, 502
Diffraction grating, 148
    dispersion of, 149
    order of, 149
    resolving power of, 149
Diffuse reflectance, 192
Diffusion, 8
Diffusion coefficient, 8, 9
Diffusion-current constant, 91
Diffusion currents, 57
Diffusion layer, 8
Digestion mixture, 286
Digital clock, 742
Digital computers, block diagram of, 712
    speed of, 713
Digital logic functions, AND, 720
    OR, 718, 720
Digital logic states, 718
Digital-to-analog converter, 744
Diluents for DTA, 502
Diode array, 285, 291
Dipolar broadening, 330
Direct-injection enthalpimetry, 488, 509. *See also* Thermometric titrations
    applications of, 517
    instrumentation for, 510
Direct-injection enthalpimetry curve, 514
Direct isotope-dilution analysis, 591
Direct-line fluorescence, 289
Direct readers, 299
Direct-reading spectrometers, 299
Discrete instruments, 780
    in clinical chemistry, 790
Dispersion, 148
    of grating, 149

Flash photolysis, 531
Flip-flop, 726
 clocked, 728
 clocked, truth table for, 729
 JK, truth table for, 731
 master-slave, 731
 reset-set, 726
 RS, truth table for, 728
Flow-proportional detectors for x-rays, 393
Fluorometric analysis, advantages and
  limitations of, 252
Fluorescence, analysis of mixtures by, 247, 249
 and structure, 243, 244
 definition of, 229
 emission, 231
 emission spectrum, 229
 excitation spectrum, 230
 in chromatography, 250
 intensity of, 233
 of inorganic compounds, 245
 of organic compounds, 243, 244
 requirements for, 243
 theory of, 230
 x-ray spectroscopy. *See* X-ray fluorescence
  spectroscopy
 x-rays, 390
Fluoride in natural water, potentiometric
  determination of, 38
Fluors, 574
Forbidden transitions, 158
Formal potential, 16
Formation constant, 615
FORTRAN, 714
Four-spin systems in NMR, 344
Fourier spectrometers, 189
Fourier spectrometry, 210
Fourier transform NMR spectroscopy, 353
Fourier transform spectra, 353
Franck-Condon principle, 158
Free energy, 488
Free induction decay, 353
Free radicals, detection of, 367
Fremy's radical, 367
Frequency factor, 528
Frequency-sweep decoupling, 347
Frontal chromatography, 623
Fructose, determination of in presence of
  glucose, 528
Full-energy peak, 574
Functional group analysis by IR, 224
Functional groups in NMR, 337

Furnace atomic absorption, direct analysis of
  solids by, 285
Furnace atomizers, 276
 detection limits for, 277

g-factor, 368
g-value, 369
 of free electron, 368
Gain, 776
Galvanic cell, 12
Gamma radiation, 565, 568
Gamma-ray spectrometry, 569
Gamma-ray spectrum, 575
 of mixtures, 576
 resolution of, 576
Gamma rays, 560
 detection of, 570
 interaction of with matter, 569
 range of in matter, 569
 shielding material for, 569
Gas analyzer, IR, 224
Gas chromatography, 625
 accuracy of, 703
 adjusted retention volume in, 679
 applications of, 703
 broadening factors in, 685
 coating of supports for, 694
 column preparation for, 694
 coulometric detector for, 107
 desired plates per meter in, 694
 detectors for, 697
 distribution coefficient in, 680
 dynamics of, 685
 effective plates in, 688
 flash-vaporization inlet for, 696
 HETP in, 633
 in automated systems, 783
 number of theoretical plates in, 686
 number of theoretical plates required for, 688
 optimizing speed of, 689
 optimum capacity factor in, 688
 optimum carrier velocity for, 686
 proposed standard stationary phases for, 693
 qualitative analysis by, 701
 quantitative analysis by, 703
 reproducibility of retention times in, 701
 required temperatures for, 689
 resolution factor in, 688
 retention vs. temperature in, 681
 retention vs. volatility in, 681

Gas chromatography *continued*
separation factor in, 681
specific retention in, 680
splitter inlet for, 696
stationary phases for, 691
support materials for, 691
temperature programming in, 701
thermodynamics of, 679
typical columns for, 689
with aqueous solutions, 698
Gas chromatography-infrared spectrometry, 699
Gas chromatography-mass spectrometry, 446, 471, 472, 699
Gas-ionization detectors, 570
types of, 571
uses of, 570
Gas-liquid chromatography, 625
Gas-sensing electrodes, 36
Gas-solid chromatography, 625
Gate, 722
Gate symbols, 722
Gauss, 326, 370
GC. *See* Gas chromatography
GCMS. *See* Gas chromatography-mass spectrometry
Geiger detector, counting rate, 393
for x-rays, 393
Geiger-Müller counters, 571
dead-time of, 573
limitations of, 573
Geiger-Müller region, 573
Gel chromatography. *See* Exclusion chromatography
Gel electrophoresis, 674
Ge(Li) detector. *See* Lithium-drifted germanium detector
Germanium, solvent extraction of, 622
Gibbs-Helmholtz expression, 488
Gibbs phase rule, 604
Glass electrode. *See* pH glass electrodes, ion-selective glass electrodes
Glass filters, elemental content of, 319
Glass transparency, 236
GLC. *See* Gas-liquid chromatography
Globar, 208
Glow discharge, 297
Glow-discharge lamp, 303
Glucose, determination of in presence of fructose, 528
Glucose oxidase, selectivity of, 524
GM counters. *See* Geiger-Müller counters

Golay detector, 208
Goniometer, 385
Gradient elution, 623, 659
Gran's plot, 40
Graphite electrodes for emission spectroscopy, 304
Grating. *See* Diffration grating
Ground-state population, 261
Group frequencies, correlation chart of, 218, 219
Group frequency, 216
GSC. *See* Gas-solid chromatography

H-value. *See* Height equivalent to a theoretical plate
Hadamard spectrometers, 189
Hadamard transform spectrometry, 210, 211
Half-cell reaction, 13
Half-life, 543
of radionuclides, 562
Half-wave potential, 52
Half-width of resonance lines, 263
Hanging mercury drop electrode, 81
Heat capacity, 489
determination of by DSC, 508, 509
determination of by DTA, 505
Heat-leak modulus, 511
Heats of reaction, determination of by TT, 515, 516
Height equivalent to a theoretical plate, 633, 685
effect of flow rate on, 636
in gas chromatography, 633
in HPLC, 633
minimizing of, 637
vs. flow velocity, 687
Heisenberg uncertainty principle, 372. *See also* Uncertainty principle
Heroin, determination of by GC, 705
HETP. *See* Height equivalent to a theoretical plate
High-frequency titrations. *See* Oscillometry
High-performance liquid chromatography, 626, 653. *See also* Liquid chromatography
advantages of, 648
apparatus for, 651
column efficiency of, 649
detectors for, 652
efficiency of with microparticles, 651
flow rates in, 649
HETP in, 633

High performance *continued*
   HETP vs. particle size in, 652
   pressure drops in, 649
   sample capacity of, 649, 651
   separation times for, 651
   vs. classical chromatography, 648
High-resolution NMR, 332
High-speed liquid chromatography. *See* **High-**
     performance liquid chromatography
High-voltage electrophoresis, 674
Hildebrand solubility parameter, 613, 664
Hollow-cathode lamp, 264, 303
HPLC. *See* High-performance liquid
     chromatography
Hydrogen chloride gas, potentiometric
     determination of, 38
Hydrogen electrode, 18
Hydrogen lamp, 185
8-Hydroxyquinoline. *See* Oxine
Hyperchromic shifts, 161
Hyperfine coupling constant in ESR, 375
Hypochromic shifts, 161
Hypsochromic shifts, 161

ICP. *See* Inductively coupled plasma
Ideally polarized electrodes, 5
Ilkovic equation, 53
Indicator electrode, 3
Inductive reactance, 131
Inductively coupled plasma, 309
Inductively coupled plasma discharge, 303
Infrared cells, 211
Infrared gas analyzer, 224
Infrared radiation, requirements for absorption
     of, 201
Infrared region, far, 205
   fingerprint, 220
   functional-group, 220
   medium, 205
   near, 206
Infrared spectra, and state of **sample**, 205
   information from, 206
   qualitative interpretation of, 220, 221
Infrared spectrometers, 206
Infrared spectrometry, with gas
     chromatography, 699
Infrared spectrophotometry, differential, **223**
Infrared spectroscopy, 153
   qualitative analysis by, 222

Inner-filter effect, 234
Input/output bus, 713
Instrumental neutron activation analysis, 588
   sensitivity of, 589
Integral rate methods, fixed-time, 533
   variable-time, 533
Integrated circuits, 720
Integrators, 101
Interface, 716
Interfacing devices, 742
Interference filters, 236, 238. *See also* Optical
     filters
   for fluorometers, 236
Interferences in flame spectroscopy, 277
Interferometer, Michelson, 210, 211
Internal conversion, 231, 233
Internal standard method, in emission
     spectroscopy, 313, 316
   in flame emission, 268
   in IR spectrophotometry, 225
   in polarography, 68
Internal standards, in gas chromatography, 705
   in NMR, 355
   in x-ray fluorescence spectroscopy, 402
International system of units, 801
International unit, 796
Interstitial volume. *See* Void volume
Intersystem crossing, 231, 233
Inverse isotope dilution analysis, 594
INVERT gates, 722
I/O bus, 713
Ion-association extraction systems, 618
Ion-association in solvent extraction, 608
Ion-chamber detectors, 571
Ion-cyclotron resonance spectroscopy, 458
Ion exchange, for collecting groups of elements,
     399
   for x-ray analysis, 399
Ion-exchange chromatography, 630
   cross-linking values in, 666
   distribution coefficient parameters in, 667
   exchange capacity in, 666
   salting-out in, 667
   selectivity parameters in, 667
   stationary phases for, 666
   strong anion-exchangers for, 666
   strong cation-exchangers for, 666
   uses of, 665, 667
   weak anion-exchangers for, 666
   weak cation-exchangers for, 666

Span, 769
Spark discharge, 303, 306
  sensitivity of, 307
Spark source, 449
Spark-source mass spectrometer, 477
  advantages of, 449
Specific activity, 592
Specific conductances, 113, 114
Specific heat, 509
Specific resistance, 112
Specificity in clinical chemistry, 788
Spectral bandwidth, 171
Spectral interferences, 278
  in inductively coupled plasma, 309
Spectral lines, broadening of, 263
Spectral slit width, 151, 171
  in IR, 223
Spectrochemical buffer, 305
Spectrofluorometer, 229, 234, 240
  corrected, 242
  uncorrected, 241
Spectrogram, 299
Spectrograph, 145, 297, 299
Spectrometer, 297
  derivative, 187
  double-beam, 186
  light-source stabilization in, 550
  rapid-scan, 189
  reflectance, 192
  single-beam, 186
Spectrometry, definition of, 139
Spectrophosphorimeter, 229
Spectrophotometer, 145, 184
  components of, 184
Spectrophotometric analysis of mixtures, 177
Spectrophotometric applications, 177
Spectrophotometry, 154
  differential, 196
  nomenclature of, 158, 159
  precision, 196
Spectroscopic methods, classification of, 142
Spectroscopic splitting factor, 368
Spectroscopy, 145
  definition of, 139
  in automated systems, 782
Specular reflectance, 192
Spex master plate, 314
Spin decoupling, 347
Spin degeneracy, 368
Spin labels for ESR, 380

Spin-lattice relaxation, 330, 372
Spin quantum number, 326
Spin relaxation, 372
Spin-spin coupling, 339
  and structure, 348
Spin-spin multiplets, 340
Spin-spin relaxation, 330, 372
Spin system, 340
  conventions for naming, 340
Stallwood jet, 305
Standard additions. *See* Method of standard
  additions
Standard addition method. *See* Method of
  standard additions
Standard deviation, 599, 769
Standard hydrogen electrode, 14
Standard potential, 14
Stat instrument, 796
Statistical weights, 260
Statistics in radiochemical methods, 597
Stepwise fluorescence, 289
Stereochemistry, ESCA studies of, 434
Steric effects in ultraviolet absorption, 166
Stokes frequencies, 202
Stopped flow method, 529
Stripping analysis. *See also* Voltammetry
  in coulometry, 102
Stripping techniques in radiochemical counting,
  565
Successive-approximation converters, 751
Sugar groups, volatile derivations for mass
  spectrometry, 446
Sugars, separation of by ion-exchange
  chromatography, 667
  separation of by zone electrophoresis, 674
Sulfhydryl groups, amperometric determination
  of, 89
Sulfur, GC detection of, 700
Sulfur dioxide in air, determination of by con-
  ductance, 130
  Raman spectroscopy of, 225
Sulfur in fuel, determination of by x-ray
  absorption, 411
Superhyperfine splitting in ESR, 378
Supporting electrolyte in polarography, 51
Surface analysis, by LEED, 435
  by mass spectrometry, 479
Surface area of catalysts, determination of by
  ESR spectroscopy, 381
Surface catalysis, ESCA study of, 439

Surface-coated open tubular column, 690
Surfaces, reflectance spectroscopy of, 193
Synchronous counters, 740
    advantages of, 742
Systèm Internationale, 801

Temperature programming in GC, 701
Term symbols, 261
Tetramethylsilane, 332
TG. See Thermal gravimetry
Thalamid electrode, 21
Thallium, fluorescence of, 245
Thallium amalgam/thallous-chloride electrode, 21
Theoretical plates, number of, 632
Thermal conductivity detector, 697
    carrier gas for, 697
    sensitivity of, 698
Thermal detector, 208
Thermal gravimetry, experimental considerations in, 492
Thermal neutrons, 582
    energy of, 581
Thermal noise, 551
Thermally assisted fluorescence, 289
Thermistor, 513
    output voltage of, 513
Thermobalances, 490
Thermocouple, 152, 208
    output voltage of, 513
Thermodynamic measurements by mass spectrometry, 474
Thermodynamic relationships, 488
Thermogravimetric curves, 489
Thermogravimetry, 487, 489
    applications of, 495
    calculations for, 495
    instrumentation for, 490
    temperature resolution in, 494
    theory of, 492
Thermometric titration curve, 513
Thermometric titrations, 488, 509
    advantage of, 518
    applications of, 517
    calculations of, 515
    experimental considerations in, 513
    instrumentation for, 510
    of mixtures, 518
    reaction types measured in, 518

required temperature change in, 511
sample size in, 517
sensitivity of, 513
Thickness gauge, 406
Thin-layer chromatography, 626
    apparatus and techniques for, 644
    phases for, 645
    phosphorous for, 251
    quantitative, 646
    reproducibility of, 646
    resolution in, 646
    reverse-phase, 664
    R_f value variables, 646
    sensitivity of, 646
    with liquid-phase coating, 664
Thin-layer electrophoresis, 626, 674
Three-spin systems in NMR, 343
Threshold reactions. See endoergic reactions
Time-base generator, 742
Time constant, 771
    RC, 773
Time-of-flight mass spectrometer, 454
Time-of-relaxation effect, 114
Tin plate on steel, determination of by x-ray fluorescence, 406
TISAB. See Total Ionic Strength Adjustment Buffer
Titration efficiency, 103
TLC. See Thin-layer chromatography
TMS. See Tetramethylsilane
Tocopherols in oils, voltammetric determination of, 84
Total angular momentum vector, 368
Total consumption burners, 269
    aspiration rates for, 275
Total Ionic-Strength Adjustment Buffer, 38
Trace element analysis, by neutron activation analysis, 591
    by spark-source mass spectrometry, 449
Trace elements in air, emission spectroscopy determination of, 319, 320
Track-and-hold amplifier, 754
    use of, 762
Transfer function, 534
Transmittance, 158, 167
Transverse relaxation, 330
Tritium, detection of, 574
Tropylium ion, 467
Truth tables, 722, 723
Tryptophan, fluorometric determination of, 252

ELEMENT	SYMBOL	ATOMIC NUMBER	ATOMIC MASS
Actinium	Ac	89	(227)[a]
Aluminum	Al	13	26.98154
Americium	Am	95	(243)[a]
Antimony	Sb	51	121.75
Argon	Ar	18	39.948
Arsenic	As	33	74.9216
Astatine	At	85	(210)[a]
Barium	Ba	56	137.34
Berkelium	Bk	97	(247)[a]
Beryllium	Be	4	9.01218
Bismuth	Bi	83	208.9804
Boron	B	5	10.81
Bromine	Br	35	79.904
Cadmium	Cd	48	112.40
Calcium	Ca	20	40.08
Californium	Cf	98	(251)[a]
Carbon	C	6	12.011
Cerium	Ce	58	140.12
Cesium	Cs	55	132.9054
Chlorine	Cl	17	35.453
Chromium	Cr	24	51.996
Cobalt	Co	27	58.9332
Copper	Cu	29	63.546
Curium	Cm	96	(247)[a]
Dysprosium	Dy	66	162.50
Einsteinium	Es	99	(254)[a]
Erbium	Er	68	167.26
Europium	Eu	63	151.96
Fermium	Fm	100	(253)[a]
Fluorine	F	9	18.99840
Francium	Fr	87	(223)[a]
Gadolinium	Gd	64	157.25
Gallium	Ga	31	69.72
Germanium	Ge	32	72.59
Gold	Au	79	196.9665
Hafnium	Hf	72	178.49
Hahnium[b]	Ha	105	(260)[a]
Helium	He	2	4.00260
Holmium	Ho	67	164.9304
Hydrogen	H	1	1.0079
Indium	In	49	114.82
Iodine	I	53	126.9045
Iridium	Ir	77	192.22
Iron	Fe	26	55.847
Krypton	Kr	36	83.80
Kurchatovium[b]	Ku	104	(260)[a]
Lanthanum	La	57	138.9055
Lawrencium	Lr	103	(257)[a]
Lead	Pb	82	207.2
Lithium	Li	3	6.941
Lutetium	Lu	71	174.97
Magnesium	Mg	12	24.305

Atomic masses ($^{12}_{6}C = 12.00000$)